Introductory
STATISTICS

Canadian Edition

Exploring The World Through Data

Exploring the World through Data

GUIDED EXPLORATION Every chapter includes carefully crafted learning tools so that students are equipped and ready for their exploration of statistics.

LEARNING OBJECTIVES

A list of **Learning Objectives** opens each chapter, giving students a quick way of reviewing the key concepts. These are revisited at the end of the chapter, with specific questions answered in the Chapter Summary.

LEARNING OBJECTIVES

After completing this chapter, you should be able to:

1. Identify questions to consider when determining the context of a data set.
2. Distinguish between numerical and categorical variables and apply methods for coding categorical variables.
3. Find and use rates and determine when they can be more useful than counts for describing and comparing groups.
4. Distinguish between observational studies and controlled experiments.
5. Determine when it is possible to infer a cause-and-effect relationship and when it is not.
6. Explain how confounding variables prevent us from inferring causation and suggest confounding variables that are likely to occur in some situations.

Andresr/Shutterstock

Statistics is the science of learning from data. This book will teach you how to examine data so as to understand the world around you better. If you know how to sift data to find patterns, can communicate the results clearly, and understand whether you can generalize your results to other groups and contexts, you will be able to make better decisions, offer more convincing arguments, and learn things you did not know before. In a world where almost everything can be monitored and measured, the ability to make sense out of data is crucial. In fact, one prominent economist predicted that statistics would be one of the most important professions of the current decade (McKinsey Quarterly 2009). In 2013, over 2000 organizations worldwide joined in promoting the importance of statistics by celebrating that year as the International Year of Statistics.

The use of statistics to make decisions and convince others to take action is not new. Some statisticians date the current practice of statistics back to the mid-nineteenth century. One famous example occurred in 1854, when the British were fighting the Russians in the brutal Crimean War. A British newspaper had criticized the military medical facilities, and a young but well-connected nurse, Florence Nightingale, was appointed to study the situation and, if possible, improve it.

Nightingale carefully recorded the numbers of deaths, the causes of the deaths, and the times and dates of the deaths. She organized these data graphically, and these graphs enabled her to see a very important pattern: a large percentage of deaths were due to contagious diseases, and many deaths could be prevented by improving sanitary conditions. Within six months, Nightingale had reduced the death rate by half. Eventually she convinced

MARGIN NOTES

- **Details** clarify or expand upon a concept.
- **Looking Back** refers students to previously covered concepts.
- **Caution** provides warnings about common mistakes or misunderstandings.

Details

Data Are What Data Is
If you want to be grammatically correct, then the word *data* is plural. So we say "data *are*" and not "data *is*." The singular form is *datum*. However, this usage is changing over time, and some dictionaries now say that *data* can be used as both a singular and a plural noun.

Looking Back

Symmetric Distributions
Recall that symmetric distributions are those for which the left-hand side of the graph of the distribution is roughly a mirror image of the right-hand side.

Caution

Don't Just Look for Numbers!
You can't always tell whether a variable is categorical simply by looking at the data table. You must also consider what the variable represents. Sometimes, researchers code categorical variables with numerical values.

SNAPSHOTS

Snapshots quickly summarize a concept or procedure and indicate when and how it should be used.

SNAPSHOT THE DOTPLOT

WHAT IS IT? ▶	A graphical summary.
WHAT DOES IT DO? ▶	Shows a picture of the distribution of a numerical variable.
HOW DOES IT DO IT? ▶	Each observation is represented by a dot on a number line.
HOW IS IT USED? ▶	To see patterns in samples of data with variation.
WHEN IS IT USED? ▶	It is most useful for small data sets.

KEY POINT We can never draw cause-and-effect conclusions from observational studies because of potential confounding variables. A single observational study can conclude only that there is a *relationship* between the treatment variable and the outcome variable.

KEY POINTS

Key Points draw special attention to essential topics.

GUIDED EXERCISES

g **2.23 Eating Out and Jobs**   College student Jacqueline Loya asked students who had full-time jobs and students who had part-time jobs how many times they went out to eat in the last month.

Full-time: 5, 3, 4, 4, 4, 2, 1, 5, 6, 5, 6, 3, 3, 2, 4, 5, 2, 3, 7, 5, 5, 1, 4, 6, 7

Part-time: 1, 1, 5, 1, 4, 2, 2, 3, 3, 2, 3, 2, 4, 2, 1, 2, 3, 2, 1, 3, 3, 2, 4, 2, 1

Question Compare the two groups by following the steps below. Include appropriate graphics.

Step 1 ▶ Create graphs.
Make dotplots (or histograms) using the same axis with one set of data above the other, as shown in the figure.

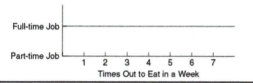

EXERCISES

A wealth of **exercises** appear at the end of each chapter, organized by section and level of difficulty. Challenging exercises are identified with a (*).

- **Guided Exercises** include step-by-stop problem-solving help at the end of the chapter.
- Exercises marked with a 🌐 have accompanying data sets available online.

EXAMPLES

Examples are abundant and they model solutions to real-world problems. Each example is tied to a **TRY THIS!** exercise, which offers practice solving a similar problem.

EXAMPLE 2 Roller Coaster Endurance

A morning radio show is sponsoring a contest in which contestants compete to win a car. About 40 contestants are put on a roller coaster, and whoever stays on it the longest wins. Suppose we make a histogram of the amount of time the contestants stay on (measured in hours or even days).

QUESTION What shape do we expect the histogram to have and why?

SOLUTION Probably most people will drop out relatively soon, but a few will last for a very long time. The last two contestants will probably stay for a very long time indeed. Therefore, we would expect the distribution to be right-skewed.

TRY THIS! Exercise 2.9

TECHTIPS

TechTips outline the steps for performing calculations using TI-83/84-Plus graphing calculators, Excel,® Minitab,® StatCrunch, and SPSS®. Whenever a new method or procedure is introduced, a 📊 refers students to the TechTips section at the end of the chapter.

TI-83/84

Resetting the Calculator (Clearing the Memory)
If you turn off the TI-83/84, it does not reset the calculator. All the previous data and choices remain. If you are having trouble and want to start over, you can reset the calculator.

1. **2nd Mem** (with the + sign)
2. **7** for **Reset**
3. **1** for **All RAM**
4. **2** for **Reset**

It will say **RAM cleared** if it has been done successfully.

SOFTWARE OUTPUT

Many examples and exercises ask the reader to interpret and critically evaluate **software output**. This builds comfort with various types of software.

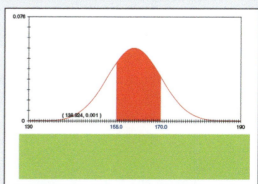

▲ FIGURE 6.16   (b) An enlarged view of the window below the N(160, 7.5) curve. The shaded area is .656296. The area to the left is given as .252493. (We usually include a 0 before the decimal point when we report or work with these values.)

Introductory STATISTICS

Canadian Edition

Exploring The World Through Data

Robert Gould
University of California
at Los Angeles

Colleen Ryan
California Lutheran
University

Jim Stallard
University of Calgary

Michelle Boué

PEARSON

Toronto

Editorial Director: Claudine O'Donnell
Acquisitions Editor: Jennifer Sutton
Marketing Manager: Euan White
Program Manager: Emily Dill
Project Manager: Sarah Gallagher
Manager of Content Development: Suzanne Schaan
Developmental Editor: Suzanne Simpson Millar
Media Editor: Nicole Mellow
Media Developer: Kelli Cadet
Production Services: Michael B. Kopf, S4Carlisle Publishing Services, Inc.
Permissions Project Manager: Kathryn O'Handley
Photo Permissions Research: Melody English
Text Permissions Research: Renae Horstman
Interior and Cover Designer: Anthony Leung
Cover Image: Borut Trdina/Getty Images

Vice-President, Cross Media and Publishing Services: Gary Bennett

Credits and acknowledgments for material borrowed from other sources and reproduced, with permission, in this textbook appear on the appropriate page within the text [or on page xxxi].

SPSS Images Reprint Courtesy of International Business Machines Corporation, © International Business Machines Corporation.

IBM, the IBM logo, ibm.com, and SPSS are trademarks or registered trademarks of International Business Machines Corporation, registered in many jurisdictions worldwide. Other product and service names might be trademarks of IBM or other companies. A current list of IBM trademarks is available on the Web at "IBM Copyright and trademark information" at www.ibm.com/legal/copytrade.shtml

1 2020

Library and Archives Canada Cataloguing in Publication
Gould, Robert, 1965-, author
    Introductory statistics : exploring the world through data / Robert Gould (University of California at Los Angeles), Colleen Ryan (California Lutheran University), Jim Stallard (University of Calgary), Michelle Boué. — Canadian edition.

Includes index.
Issued in print and electronic formats.
ISBN 978-0-13-416861-6 (loose leaf).—ISBN 978-0-321-82365-6 (bound).
ISBN 978-0-13-415447-3 (pdf).—ISBN 978-0-13-415457-2 (html)

    1. Statistics—Textbooks. I. Ryan, Colleen N. (Colleen Nooter), 1939-, author
II. Stallard, Jim, 1969-, author III. Boué, Michelle, 1968-, author IV. Title.

QA276.12.G69 2015   519.5   C2015-904826-5
                                               C2015-904827-3

978-0-13-416861-6

Dedication

To my parents and family, my friends, and my colleagues who are also friends. Without their patience and support, this would not have been possible.

—Rob

To my teachers and students, and to my family who have helped me in many different ways.

—Colleen

To my family, parents, my "Edmonton-Fam," dearest friends, and trusted colleagues. Thank you for your patience and unwavering support.

—Jim

To my mother, for her inspiring example.

—Michelle

About the Authors

Robert Gould

Robert L. Gould (Ph.D., University of California, San Diego) is a leader in the statistics education community. He has served as chair of the American Statistical Association's Committee on Teacher Enhancement, has served as chair of the ASA's Statistics Education Section, and served on a panel of co-authors for the *Guidelines for Assessment in Instruction on Statistics Education (GAISE) College Report*. As the associate director of professional development for CAUSE (Consortium for the Advancement of Undergraduate Statistics Education), Rob has worked closely with the American Mathematical Association of Two-Year Colleges (AMATYC) to provide travelling workshops and summer institutes in statistics. For over 10 years, he has served as Vice-Chair of Undergraduate Studies at the UCLA Department of Statistics, and he is Director of the UCLA Center for the Teaching of Statistics. In 2009, Rob was elected president of the Southern California Chapter of the American Statistical Association.

In his free time, Rob plays the cello, runs, and is an ardent reader of fiction.

Colleen Ryan

Colleen N. Ryan has taught statistics, chemistry, and physics to diverse community college students for decades. She taught at Oxnard College from 1975 to 2006, where she earned the Teacher of the Year Award. Colleen currently teaches statistics part-time at California Lutheran University. She often designs her own lab activities. Her passion is to discover new ways to make statistical theory practical, easy to understand, and sometimes even fun.

Colleen earned a B.A. in physics from Wellesley College, an M.A.T. in physics from Harvard University, and an M.A. in chemistry from Wellesley College. Her first exposure to statistics was with Frederick Mosteller at Harvard.

In her spare time, Colleen sings with the Oaks Camerata, has been an avid skier, and enjoys time with her family.

Jim Stallard

James B. Stallard has been teaching statistics and probability at the University of Calgary since 1996, where he currently serves as Associate Head, Teaching and Learning of the Department of Mathematics and Statistics. He has served as chair of the Statistical Education Committee of the SSC (Statistical Society of Canada) and as the President of the Statistical Education Section of the SSC. He earned a B.Sc. in statistics and economics from the University of Alberta, and a M.Sc. from the University of Calgary.

In his spare time, Jim likes to spend time with his family, play hockey, and fish the beautiful rivers that carve their way through the foothills of Southwestern Alberta.

Michelle Boué

Michelle Boué holds M.Sc. and Ph.D. degrees in Applied Mathematics from Brown University. She has over 20 years of experience teaching mathematics and statistics at different colleges and universities in Canada, the United States and Mexico, including Trent University, St. Francis Xavier University, the University of Massachusetts (Amherst), Newbury College, and the ITAM (Instituto Tecnológico Autónomo de México). In recent years, she has turned her attention to the promotion of science and mathematics education in elementary and secondary schools. She is currently a presenter for the Scientists in School organization in Ontario.

Brief Contents

Contents

Preface

About This Book

The primary focus of this text is data. We live in a data-driven economy and, more and more, in a data-centred culture. We don't choose whether we interact with data; the choice is made for us by websites that track our browsing patterns, membership cards that trace our spending habits, cars that register our driving patterns, and smartphones that record our most personal moments.

The silver lining of what some have called the Data Deluge is that we all have access to rich and valuable data relevant in many important fields: environment, civics, social sciences, economics, health care, and entertainment. This text teaches students to learn from such data and, we hope, to become cognizant of the role of the data that appear all around them. We want students to develop a data habit of mind in which, when faced with decisions, claims, or just plain curiosity, they know to reach for an appropriate data set to answer their questions. More importantly, our goal is for students to have the ability to process and objectively, as well as critically, analyze such data using the statistical tools they will acquire from their study of this text. Clearly, we've come a long way from the "mean median mode" days of rote calculation. The modern economy requires much more than knowing how to plug numbers into a formula. Today's students must know which questions can be answered by applying which statistic and how to use technology to compute such statistics from within complex data sets.

What's New in the Canadian Edition

The Canadian Edition remains true to the goals of the U.S. text: to provide students with the tools they need to make sense of the world by teaching them to collect, visualize, analyze, and interpret data. However, we have introduced a substantial number of changes that will enable us to better achieve this vision inside the Canadian classroom:

- Canadian and global data of interest to Canadian students have been incorporated throughout the text to demonstrate practical and relevant applications. The new, updated, or revised material includes over 400 exercises, nearly 100 chapter examples, and 11 completely new case studies. New content can be found involving climate change, health care, languages, Aboriginal issues, multiculturalism, sports, vaccinations, and lottery scandals, to name but a few.

- A list of Learning Objectives appears on the introductory page of each chapter. The Learning Objectives are revisited at the end of the chapter, with specific questions answered in the Chapter Summary. This new learning tool reflects the current emphasis on learning objectives and gives the student a quick way of reviewing the key concepts of the chapter.

- Chapter 5 has been substantially revised, with more examples covering conditional probability.

- Chapter 11 has been restructured and expanded, with a new section discussing the calculations required to complete an ANOVA table.

- A new section dedicated to the Kruskal-Wallis test has been added to the non-parametric tests of Chapter 13.

- Material on special topics from several chapters has been moved to MyStatLab so as to make room for new content. All online sections are indicated by an online icon 🌀, in the book's table of contents.

- IBM SPSS Statistics software ("SPSS")* has been added to the list of calculation tools covered by the text. The steps for performing calculations using **SPSS** have been added to the end of each chapter when appropriate, and some examples within the text discuss the analysis of **SPSS** output.

- **Snapshot** boxes break down key statistical concepts, quickly summarizing each concept or procedure. In this edition we have explicitly included a "When is it used?" summary in each Snapshot.

- The SI metric system of units is used throughout the text.

Approach

Our text is concept-based, as opposed to method-based. We do teach useful statistical methods, but we emphasize that applying the method is secondary to understanding the concept.

In the real world, computers do most of the heavy lifting for statisticians. We therefore adopt an approach that frees the instructor from having to teach tedious procedures and leaves more time for teaching a deeper understanding of concepts. Accordingly, we present formulas as an aid to understanding the concepts rather than as the focus of study.

We believe students need to learn how to

- determine which statistical procedures are appropriate,

- instruct the software to carry out the procedures, and

- interpret the output.

We understand that students will probably see only one type of statistical software in class. But we believe it is useful for students to compare output from several different sources, so in some examples we ask them to read output from two or more software packages.

One of the authors (Rob Gould) served on a panel of co-authors for the collegiate version of the *Guidelines and Instruction in Statistics Education* (*GAISE*). One of the Canadian authors (Jim Stallard) has served as both chair and president of various statistical education branches of the Statistical Society of Canada. In the preparation of this book, we have adopted up-to-date approaches to teaching and learning statistics endorsed by the American Statistical Association and the Statistical Society of Canada.

- We emphasize understanding over rote performance of procedures.

- We use real data whenever possible.

- We encourage the use of technology both to develop conceptual understanding and to analyze data.

- We believe strongly that students learn by doing. For this reason, the homework problems offer students both practice in basic procedures and challenges to build conceptual understanding.

Coverage

The first two-thirds of this book are concept-driven and cover exploratory data analysis and inferential statistics—fundamental concepts that every introductory statistics student should learn. The final third of the book builds on that strong conceptual foundation and is more methods-based. It presents several popular statistical methods and more fully explores methods presented earlier, such as regression and data collection.

Our ordering of topics is guided by the Cycle of Data.

Chapters 1–4: Exploratory Data Analysis. The first four chapters cover data collection and summary. Chapter 1 introduces the important topic of data collection and compares

---

*SPSS Inc. was acquired by IBM in October, 2009.

and contrasts observational studies with controlled experiments. This chapter also teaches students how to handle raw data so that the data can be uploaded to their statistical software. Chapters 2 and 3 discuss graphical and numerical summaries of single variables based on samples. We emphasize that the purpose is not just to produce a graph or a number but, instead, to explain what those graphs and numbers say about the world. Chapter 4 introduces simple linear regression and presents it as a technique for providing graphical and numerical summaries of relationships between two numerical variables.

We feel strongly that introducing regression early in the text is beneficial in building student understanding of the applicability of statistics to real-world scenarios. After completing the chapters covering data collection and summary, students have acquired the skills and sophistication they need to describe two-variable relationships and to generate informal hypotheses. Two-variable relationships provide a rich context for class discussion and allow the course to move from fabricated problems (because one-variable analyses are relatively rare in the real world) to real problems that appear frequently in everyday life. We return to regression in Chapter 14, when we discuss statistical inference in the context of regression, which requires quite a bit of machinery. We feel that it would be a shame to delay until the end of the course all the insights that regression without inference can provide.

Chapters 5–8: Inference. These chapters teach the fundamental concepts of statistical inference. The main idea is that our data mirror the real world, but imperfectly; although our estimates are uncertain, under the right conditions we can quantify our uncertainty. Verifying that these conditions exist and understanding what happens if they are not satisfied are important themes of these chapters.

Chapters 9–11: Methods. Here we return to the themes covered earlier in the text and present them in a new context by introducing additional statistical methods, such as estimating population means, analyzing categorical variables, and analyzing relations between a numerical and a categorical variable. We also introduce ANOVA as a technique for comparing means of several populations.

Chapters 12–14: Special Topics. Students who have covered all topics up to this point will have a solid foundation in statistics. These final chapters build on that foundation and offer more details, as we explore the topics of designing controlled experiments, survey sampling, additional contexts for hypothesis testing, and using regression to make inferences about a population.

In Chapter 12 we provide guidance for reading scientific literature. Even if your schedule does not allow you to cover Chapter 12, we recommend using online Section 12.3 to offer students the experience of critically examining real scientific papers.

Organization

Our preferred order of progressing through the text is reflected in the Contents, but there are some alternative pathways as well.

12- to 14-Week Semester. The first 10 chapters would provide a full, one-semester course in introductory statistics. If time remains, cover Chapter 11 as well, so that students can solidify their understanding of confidence intervals and hypothesis tests by revisiting the topics with several groups.

Proportions First. Ask two statisticians, and you will get three opinions on whether it is best to teach means or proportions first. We have come down on the side of proportions for a variety of reasons. Proportions are much easier to find in popular news media (particularly around election time), so they can be more readily tied to students' everyday lives. Also, the mathematics and statistical theory is simpler; because there's no need to provide a separate estimate for the population standard deviation, inference is based on the Normal distribution, and no further approximations (that is, the *t*-distribution) are required. Hence, we can quickly get to the heart of the matter with fewer technical diversions.

The basic problem here is how to quantify the uncertainty involved in estimating a parameter and how to quantify the probability of making incorrect decisions when posing hypotheses. We cover these ideas in detail in the context of proportions. Students can then more easily learn how these same concepts are applied in the new context of means (and any other parameter they may need to estimate).

Means First. Conversely, many people feel that there is time for only one parameter and that this parameter should be the mean. For this alternative presentation, cover Chapters 6, 7, and 9, in that order. On this path, students learn about survey sampling and the terminology of inference (population vs. sample, parameter vs. statistic) and then tackle inference for the mean, including hypothesis testing.

To minimize the coverage of proportions, you might choose to cover Chapter 6, Section 7.1 (which covers in detail the language and framework of statistical inference), and then Chapter 9. Chapters 7 and 8 develop the concepts of statistical inference more slowly than in Chapter 9, but essentially, Chapter 9 develops the same ideas in the context of the mean.

If you present Chapter 9 before Chapters 7 and 8, we recommend that you devote roughly twice as much time to Chapter 9 as you have devoted to previous chapters, because many challenging ideas are explored in this chapter. If you have already covered Chapters 7 and 8 thoroughly, Chapter 9 can be covered more quickly.

Features

We've incorporated into this book a variety of features to aid student learning and to facilitate the use of this text in any classroom.

Integrating Technology

Modern statistics is inseparable from technology. We have worked to make this textbook accessible for any classroom, regardless of the level of in-class exposure to technology, while still remaining true to the demands of the analysis. We know that students sometimes do not have access to technology when doing homework, so many exercises provide output from software and ask students to interpret and critically evaluate that given output.

Using technology is important because it enables students to handle real data, and real data sets are often large and messy. The following features are designed to guide students.

- **Tech Tips** outline steps for performing calculations using TI-83/84 graphing calculators, Excel, Minitab, StatCrunch, and SPSS. We do not want students to get stuck because they don't know how to reproduce the results we show in the book, so whenever a new method or procedure is introduced, an icon, ▦, refers students to the TechTips section at the end of the chapter. Each set of TechTips contains at least one mini-example, so that students are not only learning to use the technology but also practising data analysis and reinforcing ideas discussed in the text.

MyStatLab, which accompanies this text, includes some sections on special topics, as well as all data sets needed for examples and exercises.

Guiding Students

- After a short introduction and a list of Learning Objectives, each chapter begins by posing a real-world **Case Study**. At the end of the chapter, we show how techniques covered in the chapter helped solve the problem presented in the Case Study.

- **Margin Notes** draw attention to details that enhance student learning and reading comprehension.

  ❗ **Caution** notes provide warnings about common mistakes or misconceptions.

  👁 **Looking Back** reminders refer students to earlier coverage of a topic.

  ▦ **Details** clarify or expand on a concept.

- **Key Points** highlight essential concepts to draw special attention to them. Understanding these concepts is essential for progress.

- **Snapshots** break down key statistical concepts introduced in the chapter, quickly summarizing each concept or procedure and indicating when and how it should be used.

- An abundance of worked-out **examples** model solutions to real-world problems relevant to students' lives. Each example is tied to an end-of-chapter exercise so that students can practise solving a similar problem and test their understanding. Within the exercise sets, the icon TRY indicates which problems are tied to worked-out examples in that chapter, and the numbers of those examples are indicated.

- A **Chapter Review** concludes each chapter. In it students can find a list of important new terms, a series of specific questions and answers related to the chapter's Learning Objectives (including all important formulas), and sources for data, articles, and graphics referred to in the chapter.

Active Learning

- For each chapter we've included an activity, **Exploring Statistics**, that students are intended to do in class as a group. We have used these activities ourselves, and we have found that they greatly increase student understanding and keep students engaged in class. Detailed instructions are available for instructors in the Instructor's Edition of the text.

- All exercises are located at the end of the chapter. **Section Exercises** are designed to begin with a few basic problems that strengthen recall and assess basic knowledge, followed by mid-level exercises that ask more complex, open-ended questions. **Chapter Review Exercises** provide a comprehensive review of material covered throughout the chapter.

  The exercises emphasize good statistical practice by requiring students to verify conditions, make suitable use of graphics, find numerical values, and interpret their findings in writing. Most exercises are paired so that students can check their work on the odd-numbered exercise and then tackle the corresponding even-numbered exercise.

  Challenging exercises, identified with an asterisk (*), ask open-ended questions and sometimes require students to perform a complete statistical analysis. For exercises marked with a 🌐, accompanying data sets are available online at MyStatLab. The answers to all odd-numbered exercises appear in the back of the book. All solutions have been thoroughly revised and updated by Jim Stallard and Michelle Boué for this edition.

- Most chapters include select exercises, marked with a **g** within the exercise set, to indicate that problem-solving help is available in the **Guided Exercises** section. If students need support while doing homework they can turn to the Guided Exercises to see a step-by-step approach to solving the problem.

Acknowledgments

The Canadian authors are deeply thankful for the guidance and support of all at Pearson Canada through the writing and production process. Specifically, we would like to thank Cathleen Sullivan for giving us a chance to develop the Canadian edition of this book; to both Laura Armstrong and David Le Gallais for their leadership and guidance through the various publishing processes. Extended thanks also to our Editorial Director, Claudine O'Donnell, and our Project Manager, Sarah Gallagher, for keeping the ship steady and on course. Special thanks to Suzanne Simpson Millar, our Developmental Editor, for keeping us to task and providing the odd shove. Finally, a thank you to Michael Kopf for his guidance and patience.

We would also like to extend our sincere thanks for the suggestions and contributions made by the following reviewers:

Fouzia Baki, *McMaster University*
Guy Davis, *Lakehead University*
David Desjardins, *John Abbott College*
Alireza Fotouhi, *University of the Fraser Valley*
Paramjit Gill, *University of British Columbia Okanagan*
Taras Gula, *George Brown College*
Dorothy Levay, *Brock University*
David Medd, *Centennial College*
Margaret-Ellen Messinger, *Mount Allison University*
Dot Miners, *Brock University*

Wendi Morrison, *Sheridan College*
Bruce Newbold, *McMaster University*
Jianan Peng, *Acadia University*
Carl James Schwarz, *Simon Fraser University*
Connie Stewart, *University of New Brunswick*
Tim Swartz, *Simon Fraser University*
Xu Wang, *St. Francis Xavier University*
Sharon Wong, *Ryerson University*
Paul Wraight, *Durham College*

Supplements

Student Resources

Companion Website for this text can be accessed at www.pearsoncanada.ca/canadianstats. From there, you can download the Student Solutions Manual and Data Sets for use with this text.

Student Solutions Manual provides detailed, worked-out solutions to all odd-numbered text exercises. These downloadable PDF files are available at the textbook's Companion Website and on MyStatLab.

Data Sets, used in the textbook, have been provided in various formats for use in different applications, including Excel, Minitab, SPSS, and more. These can be accessed at the textbook's Companion Website and MyStatLab.

Study Cards for Statistics Software This series of study cards, available for Excel, Minitab, JMP, SPSS, StatCrunch, and the TI-83/84 graphing calculators, provides students with easy, step-by-step guides to the most common statistics software. These will be available free of charge through MyStatLab. You can also visit www.myPearsonStore.com for more information.

Instructor Resources

Most instructor supplements are available for download from a password-protected section of Pearson Canada's online catalogue (www.pearsoncanada.ca/highered). Navigate to your book's catalogue page to view a list of those supplements that are available. Speak to your local Pearson sales representative for details and access.

Instructor's Solutions Manual contains worked-out solutions to all the text exercises.

Computerized Test Bank. Pearson's computerized test banks allow instructors to filter and select questions to create quizzes, tests, or homework. Instructors can revise questions or add their own, and may be able to choose print or online options. These questions are also available in Microsoft Word format.

Learning Solutions Managers. Pearson's Learning Solutions Managers work with faculty and campus course designers to ensure that Pearson technology products, assessment tools, and online course materials are tailored to meet your specific needs. This highly qualified team is dedicated to helping schools take full advantage of a wide range of educational resources, by assisting in the integration of a variety of instructional materials and media formats. Your local Pearson Canada sales representative can provide you with more details on this service program.

Instructor Podcasts are brief audio podcasts from author Robert Gould that focus on the key points of each chapter, helping both new and experienced instructors prepare for

class. Available in MyStatLab or on the catalogue. (ISBN-13: 978-0-321-82423-3; ISBN-10: 0-321-82423-7).

PowerPoint® Lecture Slides, by author Michelle Boué, provide an outline to use in a lecture setting, presenting definitions, figures, Guided Exercises, Case Studies, and Snapshots from the text. These slides are available within MyStatLab or on the catalogue.

Learning Catalytics is a web-based platform for managing the interactive classroom. Learning Catalytics will generate classroom discussion and promote peer-to-peer learning with real-time analytics and can be accessed through MyStatLab.

MyStatLab™ Online Course (access code required)

MyStatLab is a course management system that delivers **proven results** in helping individual students succeed.

- MyStatLab can be successfully implemented in any environment—lab-based, hybrid, fully online, traditional—and demonstrates the quantifiable difference that integrated usage has on student retention, subsequent success, and overall achievement.

- MyStatLab's comprehensive online gradebook automatically tracks students' results on tests, quizzes, homework, and in the study plan. Instructors can use the gradebook to provide positive feedback or intervene if students have trouble. Gradebook data can be easily exported to a variety of spreadsheet programs, such as Microsoft Excel.

MyStatLab provides **engaging experiences** that personalize, stimulate, and measure learning for each student.

- **Tutorial Exercises with Multimedia Learning Aids:** The homework and practice exercises in MyStatLab align with the exercises in the textbook, and they regenerate algorithmically to give students unlimited opportunity for practice and mastery. Exercises offer immediate helpful feedback, guided solutions, sample problems, animations, videos, and eText clips for extra help at point-of-use.

- **Getting Ready for Statistics:** A library of questions now appears within each MyStatLab course to offer the developmental math topics students need for the course. These can be assigned as a prerequisite to other assignments, if desired.

  – **Data sets** from the book are provided in multiple formats.

  – **Technology Tutorial Videos.** These brief video clips walk students through common statistical procedures for Minitab, Excel, and the TI-83/84 graphing calculator.

- **Conceptual Question Library:** In addition to algorithmically regenerated questions that are aligned with your textbook, there is a library of 1000 Conceptual Questions available in the assessment manager that require students to apply their statistical understanding.

- **StatCrunch:** MyStatLab includes a web-based statistical software, StatCrunch, within the online assessment platform so that students can easily analyze data sets from exercises and the text. In addition, MyStatLab includes access to **www.StatCrunch.com,** a website where users can access more than 13,000 shared data sets, conduct online surveys, perform complex analyses using the powerful statistical software, and generate compelling reports.

- **Integration of Statistical Software:** Knowing that students often use external statistical software, we make it easy to copy our data sets, both from the ebook and the MyStatLab questions, into software such as StatCrunch, Minitab, Excel, and more. Students have access to a variety of support tools—Technology Instruction Videos, Technology Study Cards, and Manuals for select titles—to learn how to effectively use statistical software.

Pearson eText. Pearson eText gives students access to the text whenever and wherever they have online access to the Internet. eText pages look exactly like the printed text, offering powerful new functionality for students and instructors. Users can create notes, highlight text in different colours, create bookmarks, zoom, click hyperlinked words and phrases to view definitions, and view in single-page or two-page view.

And, MyStatLab comes from a **trusted partner** with educational expertise and an eye on the future.

Knowing that you are using a Pearson product means knowing that you are using quality content. That means that our eTexts are accurate, that our assessment tools work, and that our questions are error-free. And whether you are just getting started with MyStatLab, or have a question along the way, we're here to help you learn about our technologies and how to incorporate them into your course.

To learn more about how MyStatLab combines proven learning applications with powerful assessment, visit **www.mystatlab.com** or contact your Pearson representative.

MathXL® for Statistics Online Course (access code required)

MathXL is the homework and assessment engine that runs MyStatLab. (MyStatLab is MathXL plus a learning management system.) With MathXL for Statistics, instructors can:

- Create, edit, and assign online homework and tests using algorithmically generated exercises correlated at the objective level to the textbook.

- Create and assign their own online exercises and import TestGen tests for added flexibility.

- Maintain records of all student work, tracked in MathXL's online gradebook.

With MathXL for Statistics, students can:

- Take chapter tests in MathXL and receive personalized study plans and/or personalized homework assignments based on their test results.

- Use the study plan and/or the homework to link directly to tutorial exercises for the objectives they need to study.

- Access supplemental animations and video clips directly from selected exercises.

- Copy our data sets, both from the ebook and the MyStatLab questions, into software like StatCrunch, Minitab, Excel, SPSS, and more.

MathXL for Statistics is available to qualified adopters. For more information, visit **www.mathxl.com**, or contact your Pearson representative.

StatCrunch™

Powerful web-based statistical software that allows users to perform complex analyses, share data sets, and generate compelling reports of their data. The vibrant online community offers more than 13,000 data sets for students to analyze.

- **Collect.** Users can upload their own data to StatCrunch or search a large library of publicly shared data sets, spanning almost any topic of interest. Also, an online survey tool allows users to quickly collect data via web-based surveys.

- **Crunch.** A full range of numerical and graphical methods allows users to analyze and gain insights from any data set. Interactive graphics help users understand statistical concepts, and are available for export to enrich reports with visual representations of data.

- **Communicate.** Reporting options help users create a wide variety of visually appealing representations of their data.

Full access to StatCrunch is available with a MyStatLab kit, and StatCrunch is available by itself to qualified adopters. For more information, visit **www.statcrunch.com** or contact your Pearson representative.

TestGen (www.pearsoned.com/testgen)

Enables instructors to build, edit, print, and administer tests using a computerized bank of questions developed to cover all the student learning objectives of the text. TestGen is algorithmically based, and instructors can create multiple but equivalent versions of the same question or test with the click of a button. Instructors can also modify Test Bank questions or add new questions. The software and Test Bank are available for download from Pearson Education's online catalogue.

Index of Applications

Credits

Cindy-Lee Dennis, Mark H. Yudin, and Lori E. Ross, "Relation Between Place of Residence and Postpartum Depression," *Canadian Medical Association Journal*, 185(13) (2013): 1129–1135. Copyright © 2013 by Canadian Medical Association Journal.   **Page 574** From Lindsay S. Nagamatsu, Alison Chan, and Jennifer C. Davis et al., "Physical Activity Improves Verbal and Spatial Memory in Older Adults with Probable Mild Cognitive Impairment: A 6-Month Randomized Controlled Trial," *Journal of Aging Research,* 2013 (2013). Article ID 861893, 10 pages. doi:10.1155/2013/861893. Copyright © 2013 by Dr. Lindsay S. Nagamatsu. Reprinted by permission.   **Page 574** From P. Daroui et al., "Chlorhexidine–Alcohol versus Povidone–Iodine for Surgical-Site Antisepsis," *New England Journal of Medicine*, 362 (2010): 18–26.   **Page 579** From Caroline A. Crowther et al., "Effect of Treatment of Gestational Diabetes Mellitus on Pregnancy Outcomes," *New England Journal of Medicine,* 352 (2005): 2477–2486.   **Page 579** From Vesta et al., "Effect of Rotavirus Vaccination on Death from Childhood Diarrhea in Mexico," *New England Journal of Medicine,* 62 (2010): 299–305.   **Page 621** Copyright © 2015 XE Corporation.   **Page A4** From Frederick C. Mosteller, Robert E. K. Rourke, and George B. Thomas, Jr., *Probability with Statistical Applications*, 2nd ed., © 1970. Reprinted by permission of the Pearson Education, Inc. Upper Saddle River, NJ.

PHOTO CREDITS

Front Matter
Page vi (top) Robert Gould; Page vi (bottom) Colleen Ryan; Page vii (top) Wendy Stallard; Page vii (bottom) Julia McDermid Boué.

Chapter 1
Page 2 Andresr/Shutterstock; **Page 5** (top) ALCE/Fotolia (bottom) NASA; **Page 7** Sven-Olaf Fröhlich/Fotolia; **Page 9** epa european pressphoto agency b.v./Alamy; **Page 11** nexusseven/Fotolia; **Page 13** Volodymyr Krasyuk/Shutterstock; **Page 15** Peter Kim/Fotolia; **Page 18** Helder Almeida/Shutterstock; **Page 20** Coprid/Shutterstock; **Page 21** Julia Ivantsova/Shutterstock; **Page 22** Monkey Business Images/Shutterstock.

Chapter 2
Page 32 jannoon028/Shutterstock; **Page 38** Torontonian/Alamy; **Page 42** foto76/Fotolia; **Page 43** orcea david/Fotolia; **Page 45** Image Source/Getty Images; **Page 46** (top) Dean Mitchell/Getty Images (bottom) sunabesyou/Fotolia; **Page 47** RedGreen/Shutterstock; **Page 51** Michel Borges/Fotolia; **Page 52** bikeriderlondon/Shutterstock; **Page 53** Pakhnyushcha/Shutterstock; **Page 57** Ken Seet/Alamy.

Chapter 3
Page 76 Jiri Hera/Shutterstock; **Page 81** Rafa Irusta/Shutterstock; **Page 86** El Greco/Shutterstock; **Page 90** cookiesfordevo/Fotolia; **Page 92** Syda Productions/Fotolia; **Page 96** BW Folsom/Shutterstock; **Page 99** Jon Delorey; **Page 101** Natalia Bratslavsky/Fotolia; **Page 104** arka38/Shutterstock; **Page 110** (right) Pearson Education (left)Pearson Education.

Chapter 4
Page 130 FER737NG/Fotolia; **Page 135** Yamada Taro/Fotolia; **Page 146** joingate/Shutterstock; **Page 152** Creations/Shutterstock; **Page 156** Wealan Pollard/Getty Images; **Page 157** Dave Allen Photography/Shutterstock; **Page 166** MRP/Alamy.

Chapter 5
Page 192 The Seattle Times/AP Images; **Page 195** bilder/Shutterstock; **Page 198** Pearson Education; **Page 200** Pearson Education; **Page 202** Pearson Education; **Page 204** (right) stockyimages/Shutterstock (left) Noel Powell/Fotolia; **Page 212** Corbis; **Page 218** RobertNyholm/Fotolia; **Page 219** Sam Spiro/Fotolia; **Page 220** Picsfive/Shutterstock; **Page 223** Joyce Vincent/Shutterstock; **Page 228** Siri Stafford/Getty Images; **Online Page 4** Gjermund Alsos/123RF.

Chapter 6
Page 242 Elenathewise/Fotolia; **Page 245** Studiotouch/Fotolia; **Page 247** Piotr Pawinski/Fotolia; **Page 249** Alaettin YILDIRIM/Shutterstock; **Page 255** Federico Rizzato/123RF; **Page 259** Jenner/Fotolia; **Page 267** Umberto Shtanzman/Shutterstock; **Page 268** destina/Fotolia; **Page 275** Brad Calkins/123RF; **Page 276** chones/Fotolia; **Page 278** Karin Hildebrand Lau/Shutterstock.

Chapter 7
Page 298 zimmytws/Shutterstock; **Page 301** Antonio Jorge Nunes/Shutterstock; **Page 306** Orla/Shutterstock; **Page 307** Pearson Education; **Page 312** Pearson Education; **Page 314** Pashin Georgiy/Shutterstock; **Page 319** josefpittner/Fotolia; **Page 320** Seregam/Shutterstock; **Page 325** Marlo/Stockimo/Alamy; **Page 327** artisticco/Fotolia; **Page 330** Africa Studio/Fotolia.

Chapter 8
Page 344 Rick Eglinton/ZUMAPRESS/Newscom; **Page 348** Scott Maxwell/Fotolia; **Page 350** Sam Spiro/Fotolia; **Page 358** James Steidl/Shutterstock; **Page 359** Brad Calkins/123RF; **Page 361** Denis Tabler/Shutterstock; **Page 362** Piotr Marcinski/Shutterstock; **Page 367** nito/Shutterstock; **Page 369** karen roach/Shutterstock.

Introductory
STATISTICS

Canadian Edition

Exploring The World Through Data

1 Introduction to Data

Andresr/Shutterstock

LEARNING OBJECTIVES

After completing this chapter, you should be able to:

1. Identify questions to consider when determining the context of a data set.
2. Distinguish between numerical and categorical variables and apply methods for coding categorical variables.
3. Find and use rates and determine when they can be more useful than counts for describing and comparing groups.
4. Distinguish between observational studies and controlled experiments.
5. Determine when it is possible to infer a cause-and-effect relationship and when it is not.
6. Explain how confounding variables prevent us from inferring causation and suggest confounding variables that are likely to occur in some situations.

Statistics is the science of learning from data. This book will teach you how to examine data so as to understand the world around you better. If you know how to sift data to find patterns, can communicate the results clearly, and understand whether you can generalize your results to other groups and contexts, you will be able to make better decisions, offer more convincing arguments, and learn things you did not know before. In a world where almost everything can be monitored and measured, the ability to make sense out of data is crucial. In fact, one prominent economist predicted that statistics would be one of the most important professions of the current decade (*McKinsey Quarterly* 2009). In 2013, over 2000 organizations worldwide joined in promoting the importance of statistics by celebrating that year as the International Year of Statistics.

The use of statistics to make decisions and convince others to take action is not new. Some statisticians date the current practice of statistics back to the mid-nineteenth century. One famous example occurred in 1854, when the British were fighting the Russians in the brutal Crimean War. A British newspaper had criticized the military medical facilities, and a young but well-connected nurse, Florence Nightingale, was appointed to study the situation and, if possible, improve it.

Nightingale carefully recorded the numbers of deaths, the causes of the deaths, and the times and dates of the deaths. She organized these data graphically, and these graphs enabled her to see a very important pattern: a large percentage of deaths were due to contagious diseases, and many deaths could be prevented by improving sanitary conditions. Within six months, Nightingale had reduced the death rate by half. Eventually she convinced

Parliament and military authorities to completely reorganize the medical care they provided. Accordingly, she is credited with inventing modern hospital management.

In modern times, we have equally important questions to answer. Do cell phones cause brain tumours? Are alcoholic drinks healthy in moderation? Which diet works best for losing weight? What percentage of the public is concerned about job security? **Statistics**—the science

(and art!) of collecting and analyzing observations to learn about ourselves, our surroundings, and our universe—helps answer questions such as these.

Data are the building blocks of statistics. This chapter introduces some of the basic types of data and explains how we collect them, store them, and organize them. These ideas and skills will provide a basic foundation for your study of the rest of the book.

CASE STUDY

Multitasking in the Classroom

Do you bring your laptop to class, and if so, do you often multitask on your laptop during lecture time? If you do, have you ever wondered what effect multitasking has on your learning during class?

Researchers at McMaster and York universities conducted an experiment to determine the effect multitasking on a laptop has on classroom learning. They asked a group of undergraduate students to attend a university-level lecture (the experiment was repeated three times, for a total of 44 participants). Instruction sheets and seat location were assigned to students randomly. While all participants were instructed to take notes using their laptops, half of the participants were also asked to complete a list of non-lecture-related online tasks at any convenient point during the lecture. The online tasks were meant to mimic typical student browsing during class (i.e., visiting websites such as Google, YouTube, and Facebook for about 30% of class time). Students who multitasked during the lecture scored 11% lower on a comprehension test than those who did not multitask (Sana et al. 2013).

Can we conclude from this experiment that multitasking *caused* the difference in scores? After learning about the features of a well-designed experiment in this chapter, you will be in a position to judge when it is appropriate to conclude that a *cause-and-effect* relationship exists.

SECTION 1.1

What Are Data?

Two of the fundamental concepts in statistics are variation and data. To illustrate the idea of **variation,** imagine that you're making pancakes and that you're trying to make them all look the same. No matter how hard you try, they won't all be exactly the same. There will always be slight differences, say in weight, in thickness, or in shape. This is an example of variation. How can you reduce this variation? You can use a measuring cup to measure equal amounts of batter, and an egg ring to make them round. Some people even say you should use a turkey baster! Will variation still appear? It probably will, even if you need precise instruments to measure the differences.

Data are observations that you or someone else records. If in order to compare your pancakes you recorded their weight, thickness, or diameter, you would be collecting data.

Data are more than just numbers, though. David Moore, a well-known statistician, defined data as "numbers in context." By this he meant that data consist not only of the numbers we record, but also of the story behind the numbers. For example,

$$15.0, 18.5, 18.9, 24.0, 58.0, 18.0, 26.3, 22.7, 19.1$$

are just numbers. However, these numbers represent "Percentages of honey bee wintering losses in the nine beekeeping Canadian provinces over the winter 2013–2014." (A 15% loss rate is considered an acceptable percentage.) Now these numbers have a context and have thus been elevated to data (we call them **raw data** because we have not yet organized them). See how much more interesting data are than numbers?

These data were collected by the Canadian Association of Professional Apiculturists (CAPA 2014). Data on Canadian honey bee colony losses have been collected by CAPA since 2007 in an effort to help researchers understand the factors that are contributing to the dangerous decline of honey bee colonies in Canada and around the world. Given that so much of our food depends on honey bee pollination, it is imperative that scientists understand the causes of the decline so that they can stop the disappearance of the honey bees.

 KEY POINT ▸ Data are "numbers in context."

The news media regularly collect data through surveys to assess what the public thinks about an issue or a politician. Every few months, approval ratings are taken to see how people think Canada's prime minister and other politicians are doing. Politicians may say that they don't believe in polls (particularly if they don't like the outcome), but these polls often shape the behaviour of the government. This is partly because, when they are done right, polls can be an accurate gauge of what the public is thinking.

You collect data. You save pictures of events or people you want to remember. These pictures tell a story that, you hope, others can reconstruct when they flip through your picture gallery. Perhaps you save records of your spending behaviour so that you'll know how much money you have left in your account. The songs in your iTunes library are data that can tell us much about your musical tastes. Although data such as songs are not numbers, we can often use numbers to describe them. For example, iTunes will tell you the length of every track in your library as well as the number of songs in each genre or by each artist.

Data is constantly being collected about you. Every movement you make on the internet is tracked by data collectors and used by advertisers to tune their ads according to your interests. Maybe you collect points by showing your rewards card when making purchases at stores that participate in that rewards program. Your card enables the program to track your purchases so that it can alert you of offers and promotions you might be interested in—and thus encourage you to keep shopping with its sponsors.

Your school also keeps data on you. Administrators know how many classes you took, when you took them, and what grades you received. Even your car keeps data about you: how many kilometres you've driven the car and maybe the number of kilometres since your last fill-up of gas. If you are ever involved in a crash and your car is equipped with an event data recorder (most late-model cars are), then data such as your speed at the time of impact, seat belt use, and the status of the brake lights may also be recorded.

You can see that in our society, data are everywhere. That is one reason why it's important to understand how to work with and analyze data.

In this book you will study the science of data. You will learn (a little) about how data are stored and coded, and how you can organize data to see patterns that otherwise might be invisible. Most important, you'll see how data can sometimes be used to make generalizations about large groups of people or things.

Classifying and Storing Data

The first step to understanding data is to understand the different types of data you will encounter. As you've seen, data are numbers in context. But that's only part of the story; data are also recorded observations. Your photo of the Hopewell Rocks from your vacation in New Brunswick constitutes data (Figure 1.1), as do the images sent to earth from the International Space Station by Canadian astronaut and social media sensation Chris Hadfield in 2013 (Figure 1.2). You might not think of these images as numbers, but the image data are in fact large arrays of numbers representing the colour of every pixel in the image. If the picture was taken with the autofocus feature of the camera, then data were not only being collected, but they were being analyzed by the camera at the same time!

Almost always, our data sets will consist of characteristics of people or things (such as gender and weight). These characteristics are called **variables**. Variables are not "unknowns" like those you studied in algebra. We call these characteristics *variables* because they have variability: the value of a variable can change from individual to individual.

▲ **FIGURE 1.1** A photo of the Hopewell Rocks in the Bay of Fundy at low tide.

▲ **FIGURE 1.2** Canadian astronaut Chris Hadfield became a social media sensation in 2013 by chronicling life aboard the International Space Station (www.nasa.gov).

> **KEY POINT**
> Variables in statistics are different from variables in algebra. In statistics, variables record characteristics of people or things.

When we work with data, they are grouped into a collection, which we call either a **data set** or a **sample**. The word *sample* is important, because it implies that the data we see are just one part of a bigger picture. This "bigger picture" is called a **population**. Think of a population as the Data Set of Everything—it is the data set that contains all the information about everyone or everything with respect to whatever variable we are studying. Quite often, the population is really what we want to learn about, and we learn about it by studying the data in our sample. We will study methods for using data from a sample to make inferences about a population starting in Chapter 7. Such methods constitute what we call **inferential statistics**.

Many times, however, it is enough just to understand and describe the sample. For example, you might collect data from students in your class simply because you want to know about the students in your class, and not because you wish to use this information to learn about all students at your school. The methods used for describing and summarizing data sets constitute what we call **descriptive statistics**, and we will dedicate the first few chapters of this text to studying some of those methods.

Context Is Key

The context is the most important aspect of data, although it is frequently overlooked. Table 1.1 shows a few lines from a data set of singleton births in Ontario from 2002 to 2007 (Ray 2013).

To understand these data, we need to ask and answer some questions: What are the objects of interest? What variables were measured? How were they measured? What are the units of measurement? Who collected the data? How did they collect the data? Where were the data collected? Why were the data collected?

These questions can be readily answered by reading the section on data sources and methodology included in the research paper where these data are analyzed (Ray 2012). Other times we are not so lucky and must rely on very flimsy supporting documentation. If you collect the data yourself, you should be careful to record this extra supporting information. Or, if you get a chance to talk with the people who collected the data, then you should ask them these questions.

Details

More Grammar
We're using the word *sample* as a noun—it is an object, a collection of data that we study. We can also use the word *sample* as a verb; that is, to describe an action. For instance, we sampled respondents to a survey to obtain the small sample we discuss in Example 3 in the next section.

Weight (g)	Gender	Maternal Region
3335	M	British Columbia
2795	F	United States
2808	F	Ontario
3130	M	Ontario
4079	M	Poland
2490	F	Philippines

▲ **TABLE 1.1** Birth data from singleton births in Ontario (2002–2007).

- *What are the objects of interest?* By "objects of interest" we mean who or what was measured. In this case, the object of interest is a baby. Each line in the table represents a newborn singleton baby born in Ontario between 2002 and 2007. If we were to see the whole table, we would see a record of each one of the 766,688 babies included in the study.

- *What variables were measured?* For each baby, the information recorded includes the weight, the gender, and the birthplaces and ages of mother and father.

- *How were the variables measured?* Measurements on the baby were taken by the attendant/certifier (i.e., physician or midwife) at the time of the birth. Other information was provided by one of the parents.

- *What are the units of measurement?* Units of measurement are important. The same variable can have different units of measurement. For example, weight could be measured in grams, in kilograms, or in pounds. For Table 1.1,
  Weight: reported in grams
  Gender: reported as M for boys and F for girls
  Maternal Region: reported as the name of the province in which the mother was born (if mother is Canadian-born) or the name of the country in which the mother was born (if mother is from another world region)

- *Who collected the data?* The Office of the Registrar General of Ontario.

- *How did they collect the data?* Data are recorded for *all* births that occur in Ontario. The researchers included nearly all of the singleton live births in the period of interest in their study, discarding only some records because of questionable measurements. Later in the chapter you'll see that data can also be collected by drawing a random sample of subjects, or by assigning subjects to receive different treatments, as well as through other methods.

- *Where were the data collected?* The location where data were collected often gives us information about who (or what) the study is about. These data were collected in Ontario and consist of babies born in that province. In general, we should be very wary about generalizing our findings to regions other than the one where the data was collected.

- *Why were the data collected?* Sometimes, data are collected to learn about a larger population. At other times, the goals are limited to learning more about the sample itself. In this case the researchers wanted to understand the weight differences between the newborns of Canadian-born mothers and those of mothers from other regions. Ultimately, they derived ethnicity-specific percentile curves for newborns to prevent misidentifying an otherwise healthy newborn as too small or too large using conventional birth weight curves.

KEY POINT   The first time you see a data set, ask yourself these questions:

- What are the objects of interest?
- What variables were measured?
- How were the variables measured?
- What are the units of measurement?
- Who collected the data?
- How did they collect the data?
- Where were the data collected?
- Why did they collect the data?

Two Types of Variables

The variables you'll find in a data set come in two basic types, which can themselves be broken into smaller divisions, as we'll discuss later.

Numerical variables describe quantities of the objects of interest. The values will be numbers. The weight of an infant is an example of a numerical variable.

Categorical variables describe qualities of the objects of interest. These values will be categories. The gender of an infant is an example of a categorical variable. The possible values are the categories "male" and "female." Eye colour of an infant is another example; the categories might be brown, blue, green, and so on. You can often identify categorical variables because their values are *usually* words, phrases, or letters. (We say "usually" because we sometimes use numbers to represent a word or phrase. Stay tuned.)

EXAMPLE 1 Crash-Test Results

The data in Table 1.2 are an excerpt from crash-test dummy studies in which cars are crashed into a wall at 55 kilometres per hour. Each row of the data set represents the observed characteristics of a single car. This is a small sample of the database, which is available from the U.S. National Transportation Safety Administration. The *head injury* variable reflects the risk to the passengers' heads. The higher the number, the greater the risk.

Make	Model	Doors	Weight (kg)	Head Injury
Acura	Integra	2	1065	599
Chevrolet	Camaro	2	1393	733
Chevrolet	S-10 Blazer 4×4	2	1596	834
Ford	Escort	2	1035	551
Ford	Taurus	4	1084	480
Hyundai	Excel	4	990	757
Mazda	626	4	1175	846
Volkswagen	Passat	4	1356	1182
Toyota	Tercel	4	960	1138

◄ **TABLE 1.2** Crash-test results for cars.

QUESTION For each variable, state whether it is numerical or categorical.

SOLUTION The variables *make* and *model* are categorical. Their values are descriptive names. The units of *doors* are, quite simply, the number of doors. The units of *weight* are kilograms. The variables *doors* and *weight* are numerical because their values are measured quantities. The units for *head injury* are unclear; head injury is measured using some scale that the researchers developed.

TRY THIS! Exercise 1.1

Coding Categorical Data with Numbers

Sometimes categorical variables are "disguised" as numerical just because numbers have been assigned to categories. For example, the *gender* categorical variable from Table 1.1 has been coded as the *female* variable in Table 1.3. This variable has numbers for its values (0 and 1), but in fact those numbers indicate the gender of a baby. The categorical response "female" has been coded with a 1 and the categorical response "male" has been coded with a 0. By following the convention that a 1 represents an individual that belongs to the category that matches the variable's name, a reader immediately recognizes that a 1 in this case represents a female.

Weight (g)	Female
3335	0
2795	1
2808	1
3130	0
4079	0
2490	1

▲ **TABLE 1.3** Data for newborns from Table 1.1 using coding.

Men's Heights (cm)	Women's Heights (cm)
178	150
173	178
180	155
	157

▲ **TABLE 1.4** Data by groups (unstacked).

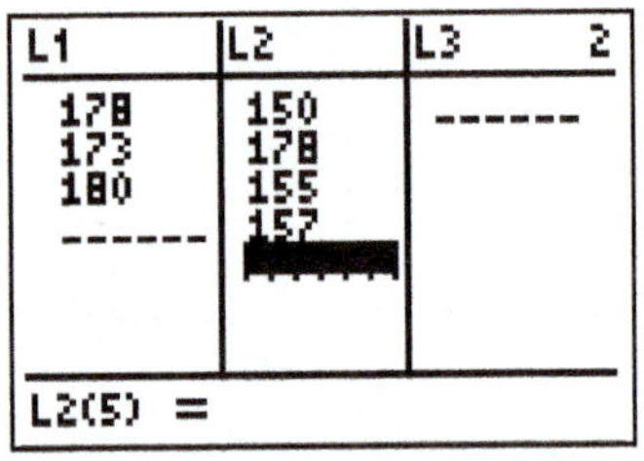

L1	L2	L3 2
178	150	------
173	178	
180	155	
------	157	

L2(5) =

▲ **FIGURE 1.3** TI-83/84 data input screen (unstacked).

Height (cm)	Gender
178	Male
173	Male
180	Male
150	Female
178	Female
155	Female
157	Female

▲ **TABLE 1.5** The same data as in Table 1.4 are shown here in stacked format.

This approach for coding categorical variables is quite common and can be very useful. However, we must remember that the numbers used for coding do not represent quantities. Arithmetic operations such as addition or averaging are not meaningful for categorical variables.

Storing Your Data

The format in which you record and store your data is very important. Computer programs will require particular formats, and by following a consistent convention, you can be confident that you'll better remember the qualities of your own data set if you need to revisit it months or even years later. Data are often stored in a spreadsheet-like format in which each row represents the individual (object or person) of interest, and each column represents a variable. All the tables we have seen so far are in this format, which is sometimes referred to as the **stacked data** format. For example, Table 1.3 displays data in stacked form, with each row representing a baby and with columns representing the variables *weight* and *female*.

When you collect your own data, the stacked format is almost always the best way to record and store your data. One reason is that it allows you to record several different variables for each subject easily. Another reason is that it is the format that most software packages will assume you are using for most analyses. (The exceptions are TI-83/84 and Excel.)

Some technologies, such as the TI calculators, require, or at least accommodate, data stored in a different format, called **unstacked data**. Unstacked data tables are also common in some books and media publications. In this format, each column represents a variable from a different group. For example, one column could represent men's heights, and another column could represent women's heights. The data set, then, is a single variable (*height*) broken into two groups. The groups are determined by a categorical variable. Table 1.4 shows an example of unstacked data, and Figure 1.3 shows the same data in TI-83/84 input format. By way of contrast, Table 1.5 shows the same data in stacked format.

The great disadvantage of the unstacked format is that it can store only two variables at a time: the variable of interest (for example, height), and a categorical variable that tells us which group the observation belongs in (for example, gender). However, most of the time, we record many variables for each observation. For example, we record a baby's weight, gender, and the mother's world region of birth. The stacked format enables us to display as many variables as we wish.

EXAMPLE 2 Olympic Moguls

The 2014 Sochi Winter Olympics were historic for Canadian athletes competing in the moguls freestyle skiing events. In the men's event, Alexandre Bilodeau (Figure 1.4) became the first Canadian man (and just the second Canadian athlete ever) to defend an individual Olympic gold medal. In the women's event, Justine and Chloé Dufour-Lapointe were the first Canadian sisters to stand together on the podium as they received their gold and silver medals. Their scores, together with those of the other nine finalists in the men's and women's final events, are shown in unstacked form in the accompanying table.

QUESTION Create a new data table that displays the data in stacked form.

Men	Women
26.31	22.44
24.71	21.66
24.34	21.49
23.35	20.66
22.80	19.43
22.16	19.37

SOLUTION At first it appears that only one numerical variable, score, is displayed. In fact, there is also a categorical variable, gender, which is used to distinguish the two groups. To stack the data, we identify the gender that is associated with each score and tabulate accordingly.

Score	Gender
26.31	M
24.71	M
24.34	M
23.35	M
22.80	M
22.16	M
22.44	F
21.66	F
21.49	F
20.66	F
19.43	F
19.37	F

TRY THIS! Exercise 1.5

> **⚠ Caution**
>
> **Look at the Data Set!**
> The fact that different people use different formats to store data means that the first step in any data investigation is to look at the data set. In most real-life situations, stacked data are the more useful format, because this format permits you to work with several variables at the same time.

▲ **FIGURE 1.4** Alexandre Bilodeau during his gold medal run at the Sochi 2014 Winter Olympics.

SECTION 1.3

Organizing Categorical Data

Once we have a data set, we next need to organize and display the data in a way that helps us see patterns. This task of organization and display is not easy, and we discuss it throughout the entire book. In this section we introduce the topic for the first time, in the context of categorical variables.

With categorical variables, we are usually concerned with knowing how often a particular category occurs in our sample. We then (usually) want to compare how often a category occurs for one group versus another (liberal/conservative, man/woman). To do these comparisons, you need to understand how to calculate percentages and other rates.

A common method for summarizing two potentially related categorical variables is to use a two-way table. **Two-way tables** show how many times each combination of categories occurs. For example, Table 1.6 is a two-way table summarizing a sample of respondents to the *Essential Facts About the Canadian Computer and Video Game Industry* survey (2014). The table shows gender and whether or not the respondent is a gamer (a respondent is a gamer if he or she has played a computer or video game in the four weeks preceding the survey). The survey included almost 4000 respondents, but we are practising on a small sample from this much larger data set.

The table tells us that six people were male and were gamers. Two people were female and were gamers. These counts are also called *frequencies*. A **frequency** is simply the number of times a value is observed in a data set.

Some books and publications present two-way tables as though they displayed the original data collected by the investigators. However, two-way tables do not consist of raw data but, rather, are summaries of data sets. For example, the data set that produced Table 1.6 is shown in Table 1.7.

> **⚠ Caution**
>
> **Two-Way Tables Summarize Categorical Variables**
> It is tempting to look at a two-way table like Table 1.6 and think that you're looking at numerical variables, because you see numbers. But the values of the variables are actually categories (gender and whether or not the subject is a gamer). The numbers you see are summaries of the data.

	Male	Female
Gamer	6	2
Non-gamer	3	4

▲ **TABLE 1.6** This two-way table shows frequencies for 15 Canadians who responded to a survey about playing video games.

Male	Gamer
1	1
1	1
1	1
1	1
1	1
1	1
1	0
1	0
1	0
0	1
0	1
0	0
0	0
0	0
0	0

▲ **TABLE 1.7** This data set is equivalent to the two-way summary shown in Table 1.6. We highlighted in red those who play video games (the gamers).

To summarize this table, we simply count how many of the males (a 1 in the Male column) are also gamers (a 1 in the Gamer column). We then count how many are male and non-gamers (a 1 in the Male column, a 0 in the Gamer column); how many are female and gamers (a 0 in the Male column, a 1 in the Gamer column); and, finally, how many are both female and non-gamers (a 0 in the Male column, a 0 in the Gamer column).

Example 3 illustrates how summarizing the data in a two-way table can make it easy to compare groups.

EXAMPLE 3 Percentages of Computer and Video Gamers

The *Essential Facts About the Canadian Computer and Video Game Industry* is a report published each year by the Entertainment Software Association of Canada. We repeat here the two-way table summarizing a small sample of respondents from the 2014 report. The participants were asked: "Have you played a computer or video game in the past four weeks?" The people who said yes are considered gamers.

	Male	Female
Gamer	6	2
Non-gamer	3	4

QUESTIONS

a. How many males are in this sample? How many females? How many people are gamers? How many are non-gamers?

b. What percentage of the sample are males? What percentage are females? What percentage are gamers? What percentage are not gamers?

c. Are the males in the sample more likely than the females in the sample to play computer or video games?

SOLUTIONS

a. We can count the males by adding the first column: $6 + 3 = 9$ males. Adding the second column gives us the number of females: $2 + 4 = 6$.

We get the number of gamers by adding the first row: $6 + 2 = 8$ people play computer or video games. Adding the second row gives us the number of non-gamers: $3 + 4 = 7$.

b. This question asks us to convert the numbers we found in part a to percentages. To do this, we first divide the numbers by 15, because there were 15 people in the sample. To convert to percentages, we multiply this proportion by 100%.

The proportion of males is $9/15 = 0.6$. The percentage is $0.6 \times 100\% = 60\%$. The percentage of females must be $100\% - 60\% = 40\%$ ($6/15 \times 100\% = 40\%$).

The proportion of gamers in this sample is $8/15 = 0.533$, or about 53%. The percentage of non-gamers is $100\% - 53\% = 47\%$. (Among all Canadians, it is estimated that about 58% of people are gamers.)

c. You might be tempted to answer this question by counting the number of males who are gamers (6 people) and comparing that to the number of females who are gamers (2 people). However, this is not a fair comparison because there are more males than females in the sample. Instead, we should look at the percentage of gamers in each group. This question should be reworded as follows:

Is the percentage of male gamers greater than the percentage of female gamers?

Because 6 out of 9 males are gamers, the percentage of males who are gamers is $(6/9) \times 100\% = 67\%$.

Because 2 out of 6 females are gamers, the percentage of females who are gamers is $(2/6) \times 100\% = 33\%$.

Therefore, females in this sample are less likely to be gamers than males. (Among all Canadians, it is estimated that about 63% of males are gamers, compared to 53% of females.)

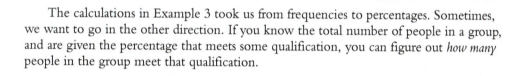

TRY THIS! Exercise 1.7

The calculations in Example 3 took us from frequencies to percentages. Sometimes, we want to go in the other direction. If you know the total number of people in a group, and are given the percentage that meets some qualification, you can figure out *how many* people in the group meet that qualification.

EXAMPLE 4 Number of Computer and Video Gamers

A statistics class has 300 students, and they are asked if they have played a computer or video game in the past four weeks. Students who say yes are considered gamers.

QUESTIONS

a. Suppose that 68% of the students are gamers. How many students is this?

b. Suppose we know that in another class, 55% of the students are gamers, and this is equal to 121 students. How many students are in the class?

SOLUTIONS

a. We need to find 68% of 300. When working with percentages, first convert the percentage to its decimal equivalent:

$$68\% \text{ of } 300 = 0.68 \times 300 = 204$$

Therefore, 204 students are gamers.

b. The question tells us that 55% of some unknown larger number (call it y) must be equal to 121.

$$0.55y = 121$$

Divide both sides by 0.55 and you get

$$y = 220$$

There are 220 students in the class, and 121 of them are gamers.

TRY THIS! Exercise 1.9

Sometimes, you may come across data summaries that are missing crucial information. To illustrate this point, let us examine data obtained from the 2010 Canada Survey of Giving, Volunteering and Participating (Statistics Canada 2012). Table 1.8 is a summary displaying the estimated number of volunteers by province (a volunteer is defined as a person aged 15 and over who did any activities without pay on behalf of a charitable group or non-profit organization, at least once in the 12 months preceding the survey).

Wow! There are many Canadians who volunteer their time, energy, and skills. Which province would you say volunteered the most? Which province volunteered the least?

Province	Volunteers
Newfoundland and Labrador	226,973
Prince Edward Island	66,745
Nova Scotia	432,915
New Brunswick	311,013
Quebec	2,447,146
Ontario	5,254,709
Manitoba	530,733
Saskatchewan	492,469
Alberta	1,665,441
British Columbia	1,913,702
Total	13,341,846

▲ **TABLE 1.8** Summary of volunteers aged 15 and over, by province.

Did you answer that Ontario was the province that volunteered the most? It does have the highest number of volunteers (5,254,709)—in fact, more than 10 times as many as Saskatchewan (492,469). So why would a newspaper print the headline "Saskatchewan again leads in volunteering" (*Southwest Booster* 2012)?

The problem with comparing the number of volunteers in each province is that the provinces vary greatly in population size. There might be more volunteers in Ontario simply because there are more people in Ontario, and not because Ontarians tend to volunteer more. One important component is missing in Table 1.8, and the lack of this component makes our analysis impossible.

Table 1.9 includes all the information we need for making comparisons. It contains the component missing from Table 1.8: the population of each province at the time of the survey. With that information, we can find the percentage of the population 15 and over that volunteered in each province. These percentages (rounded to the nearest unit) are shown in the last column of the table. For example, to calculate the percentage of volunteers in Saskatchewan, we note that there were 846,166 people aged 15 and over in the province and 492,469 of them were volunteers, so the percentage of volunteers is (492,469/846,166) × 100 = 58%. Indeed, Saskatchewan leads in volunteering.

▶ **TABLE 1.9** Summary of percentage of volunteers by province.

Province	Volunteers	Population Aged 15 and Over	Percentage of Volunteers
Newfoundland and Labrador	226,973	435,648	52
Prince Edward Island	66,745	119,829	56
Nova Scotia	432,915	804,675	54
New Brunswick	311,013	638,630	49
Quebec	2,447,146	6,667,973	37
Ontario	5,254,709	11,016,164	48
Manitoba	530,733	1,003,276	53
Saskatchewan	492,469	846,166	58
Alberta	1,665,441	3,044,682	55
British Columbia	1,913,702	3,842,775	50

Province	Injuries (per 1000 employed workers)
Newfoundland and Labrador	18.3
Prince Edward Island	11.5
Nova Scotia	15.4
New Brunswick	12.5
Quebec	18.2
Ontario	9.1
Manitoba	24.4
Saskatchewan	23.5
Alberta	11.1
British Columbia	21.5
Total	14.7

▲ **TABLE 1.10** Summary of work-related injury rates.

Sometimes we are interested in making comparisons for events that are not as common as volunteering is. For example, suppose that we want to compare work-related injuries by province. The result of dividing the number of work-related injuries by the number of employed workers in the province is so small that when we multiply by 100 to obtain a percentage, that percentage is again very small. To make the numbers easier to understand, we can multiply by 1000 instead of by 100, and report the number of injuries per 1000 employed workers instead of the percentage. The "number of events per 1000 objects" and even "per 10,000 objects" are called **rates**. As an example, Table 1.10 displays the work-related injury rates in 2010 as reported by Human Resources and Skills Development Canada (HRSDC 2012). We see that Manitoba is the province with the highest injury rate, with 24.4 injuries per 1000 employed workers.

EXAMPLE **5** Comparing Internet Use

According to data reported by the World Bank, Canada ranked 18th in the world in 2013 in terms of internet use, with a rate of 85.8 users per 100 people. In contrast, China ranked 109th in the world, with a rate of 45.8 users per 100 people (World Bank 2014).

QUESTION Why does the World Bank report internet use rates as development indicators rather than the number of internet users in each country?

SOLUTION Internet use rates take into account the fact that some countries are more populated than others. China is the most populated country in the world, so it is not surprising that it is also the country with the highest number of internet users (over half a billion users—about 18 times the total population of Canada). However, there is still plenty of room for this number to grow. By looking at the internet use rate, we see that about 54 out of every 100 persons living in China do not yet use the internet, in contrast to the 14 out of every 100 persons living in Canada who do not use the internet.

TRY THIS! Exercise 1.19

> **KEY POINT** In order for us to compare groups, the groups need to be similar. When the data consist of counts, then percentages or rates are often better for comparisons because they take into account possible differences among the sizes of the groups.

SECTION 1.4

Collecting Data to Understand Causality

Often, the most important questions in science, business, and everyday life are questions about **causality**. These are usually phrased in the form of "what if" questions. What if I take this medicine; will I get better? What if I change my Facebook profile; will my profile get more hits?

Claims about causality appear often in the media. The BBC News (2010) reported that "Happiness wards off heart disease." In British Columbia, it was reported that phytoplankton cured a man's rare form of cancer (Wilson 2005). Health food stores were inundated with requests for raspberry ketone capsules when TV personality Dr. Oz promoted them as a weight loss "miracle in a bottle" (Weeks 2012). Statements such as these are everywhere we turn these days. How do we know whether to believe these claims?

The methods we use to collect data determine the types of conclusions we can make. Only one method of data collection is suitable for making conclusions about causal relationships, but as you'll see, that doesn't stop people from making such conclusions anyway. In this section we talk about three methods commonly used to collect data for questions about causality: anecdotes, observational studies, and controlled experiments.

Most questions about causality can be understood in terms of two variables: the **treatment variable** and the **outcome variable**. (The outcome variable is also sometimes called the **response variable**, because it responds to changes in the treatment.) We are essentially asking whether changes in the treatment variable cause changes in the outcome variable. For example, the treatment variable might record whether or not a person is generally happy, and the outcome variable might record whether or not that person suffered from heart disease in a 10-year period. Or the treatment variable might record whether or not a person takes raspberry ketone capsules, and the outcome variable might record how much weight that person lost.

People who receive the treatment of interest (or have the characteristic of interest) are said to be in the **treatment group**. Those who do not receive that treatment (or do not have that characteristic) are in the **control group**, which is also called the **comparison group**.

Anecdotes

Tom Harper is a sea farmer in British Columbia who claims that marine phytoplankton cured him from lung cancer and diabetes (Wilson 2005). After his recovery, he decided to market the product. Since then, many people have shared their story about how phytoplankton has cured them of dandruff, colon cancer, melanoma, and many other conditions. Phytoplankton has even become a popular treatment given to dogs and cats.

But can phytoplankton really solve such a variety of problems? On the face of it, it seems that there's evidence that phytoplankton has cured people of illness. However, this is simply not enough evidence on the basis of which to judge whether the supplement is helpful, harmful, or without any effect at all.

These testimonials are examples of anecdotes. An **anecdote** is essentially a story that someone tells about her or his own (or a friend's or relative's) experience. Anecdotes are an important type of evidence in criminal justice because eyewitness testimony can carry a great deal of weight in a criminal investigation. However, for answering questions about groups of people with great variability or diversity, anecdotes have little value.

The primary reason why anecdotes are not useful for reaching conclusions about cause-and-effect relationships is that the most interesting things we study have so much variety that a single report can't capture such variety of experience. For example, have you ever bought something because a friend recommended it, only to find that after a few weeks it stopped working? If the object was expensive, such as a car, you might have been angry at your friend for recommending such a bad product. But how do you know whose experience was more typical, yours or your friend's? Perhaps the car is in fact a very reliable model, and chance blessed you with a lemon.

When someone claims that a product makes some kind of change, a very important question to ask is "Compared to what?" Here the claim is that taking phytoplankton supplements will make you healthier. The question to ask is "Healthier compared to what?" Compared to people who do not take the supplements? Compared to people who take medicine for their particular ailment? To answer these questions, we need to examine the health of these other groups of people who do not take phytoplankton supplements.

Anecdotes do not give us a comparison group. We might know that a group of people believe that phytoplankton made them feel better, but we don't know how these people's experiences compare to those of people who did not consume phytoplankton.

KEY POINT When someone makes a claim about causality, ask, "Compared to what?"

Another reason for not trusting anecdotal evidence is a psychological phenomenon called the *placebo effect*. People often react to the idea of a treatment rather than to the treatment itself. A **placebo** is a harmless pill (or sham procedure) that a patient believes is actually an effective treatment. Often, the patient taking the pill feels better, even though the pill actually has no effect whatsoever. In fact, a survey of Canadian physicians published in *The Canadian Journal of Psychiatry* (Raz 2011) found that about 20% of respondents had either prescribed or administered a placebo in the course of routine clinical practice. This psychological wish fulfillment—we feel better because we think we *should* be feeling better—is called the **placebo effect**.

Observational Studies

The identifying mark of an **observational study** is that the subjects in the study are put into the treatment group or the control group either by their own actions or by the decision of someone else who is not involved in the research study. For example, if we wished to study the effects on health of smoking cigarettes (as many researchers have), then our treatment group would consist of people who had chosen to smoke, and the control group would consist of those who had chosen not to smoke.

Observational studies compare the outcome variable in the treatment group with the outcome variable in the control group. Thus, if people who take raspberry ketone capsules (treatment) lose more weight than the people in the group that does not (control), then we would say that there is a **relationship** between taking raspberry ketone capsules and weight loss. If the group of happy people tend to have less heart disease than the not-happy people, we would say that there is a relationship between happiness and improved heart health.

Note that we do not conclude that raspberry ketone *caused* the weight loss. In order for us to draw this conclusion, the treatment group and the control group must be very similar in every way except that one group gets the treatment and the other one does not. For example, if we knew that the group of people taking the raspberry ketone capsules and the group that did not were alike in every way—both groups have the same overall health, are roughly the same ages, have similar exercise habits and diets, and include the same mix of genders, ethnicities, and so on—then if the raspberry ketone group loses more weight after some weeks, we would be fairly confident in concluding that the raspberry ketone supplements are the reason for the greater weight loss.

Unfortunately, in observational studies this goal of having very similar groups is *extremely* difficult to achieve. *Some* characteristic is nearly always different in one group than in the other. This means that the groups may experience different outcomes because of this different characteristic, not because of the treatment. A difference between the two groups that can explain why the outcomes were different is called a **confounding variable**.

For example, early observational studies on the effects of smoking found that a greater percentage of smokers than of nonsmokers had lung cancer. However, some scientists argued that genetics was a confounding variable (Fisher 1959). They maintained that the smokers differed genetically from the nonsmokers. This genetic difference made some people more likely to smoke and also more susceptible to lung cancer.

This was a convincing argument for many years. It not only proposed a specific difference between the groups (genetics) but also explained how that difference might come about (genetics makes some people smoke more, perhaps because it tastes better to them or because they have addictive personalities). And the argument also explained why this difference might affect the outcome (the same genetics cause lung cancer). Therefore, the skeptics said, genetics—and not smoking—might be the cause of lung cancer.

Later studies established that the skeptics were wrong about genetics. Some studies compared pairs of identical twins in which one twin smoked and the other did not. These pairs had the same genetic makeup, and still a higher percentage of the smoking twins had cancer than of the nonsmoking twins. Because the treatment and control groups had the same genetics, genetics could not explain why the groups had different cancer rates. When we compare groups in which we force one of the variables to be the same, we say that we are *controlling for* that variable. In these twin studies, the researchers controlled for genetics by comparing people with the same genetic makeup (Kaprio and Koskenvuo 1989).

A drawback of observational studies is that we can never know whether there exists a confounding variable. We can search very hard for it, but just because we don't find a confounding variable doesn't mean it isn't there. For this reason, we can never draw cause-and-effect conclusions from observational studies.

KEY POINT We can never draw cause-and-effect conclusions from observational studies because of potential confounding variables. A single observational study can conclude only that there is a *relationship* between the treatment variable and the outcome variable.

EXAMPLE 6 Does Kimchi Cause Gastric Cancer?

In a paper titled "Kimchi and Soybean Pastes Are Risk Factors of Gastric Cancer," researchers noted that gastric cancer rates were 10 times higher in Korea and Japan than in the United States and Canada (referred to in the paper more generally as North America). Koreans and Japanese also eat many times more kimchi (a heavily spiced, fermented cabbage dish) than those living in North America (Nan et al. 2005).

QUESTION On the basis of this information, can we conclude that kimchi causes gastric cancer? If yes, explain why. If no, state a potential confounding variable.

> SOLUTION No, we cannot. The treatment group consists of Japanese and Korean people, and the control group consists of North Americans. Many other factors differ between these two groups. A potential confounding variable is diet, which differs between Koreans and North Americans in many ways other than in the amount of kimchi they eat. These differences in diet may also affect cancer rates.

TRY THIS! Exercise 1.31

Controlled Experiments

In order to answer cause-and-effect questions, we need to create a treatment group and a control group that are alike in every way possible, except that one group gets a treatment and the other does not. As you've seen, this cannot be done with observational studies because of confounding variables. In a **controlled experiment**, researchers take control by assigning subjects to the control or treatment group. If this assignment is done correctly, it ensures that the two groups can be nearly alike in every relevant way except whether or not they receive the treatment under investigation.

Well-designed and well-executed controlled experiments are the only means we have for definitively answering questions about causality. However, controlled experiments are difficult to carry out (this is one reason why observational studies are often done instead). Let's look at some of the attributes of a well-designed controlled experiment.

A well-designed controlled experiment has four key features:

- The sample size must be large so that we have opportunities to observe the full range of variability in the humans (or animals or objects) we are studying.

- The subjects of the study must be assigned to the treatment and control groups at random.

- Ideally, the study should be "double-blind," as explained below.

- The study should use a placebo if possible.

These features are all essential in order to ensure that the treatment group and the control group are as similar as possible.

To understand these key design features, imagine that a friend wants to lose weight and has asked your advice about whether he should go on the Atkins diet. (See Dansinger et al. 2005 for an account of a study related to the hypothetical one described here.) The Atkins diet is fairly severe: eating bread in any form is essentially forbidden. Does this diet work? For a control group, we might compare the Atkins diet to a more traditional diet, such as that advocated by Weight Watchers. The Weight Watchers diet uses a personalized points system to restrict caloric intake and is generally considered a reliable way to lose weight. How do we know whether the Atkins diet (the treatment) works compared to the Weight Watchers diet (the control)?

Sample Size

A good controlled experiment designed to determine whether the Atkins diet works should have a large number of people participate in the study. People react to changes in their diet in a variety of ways, and the effects of a diet can vary greatly from person to person. To observe the full range of variability, you therefore need a large number of people.

The question of exactly how many people are required is difficult to answer, and most medical studies hire statisticians to determine the number of participants required. In general, the more the better, and you should be more critical of studies with very few participants. (In Chapter 7 we'll consider how to be more precise about the number of participants required for one type of study.)

Random Assignment

The next step is to assign people to the treatment and control groups such that the two groups are similar in every way possible. As we saw when we discussed observational studies, letting the participants themselves decide doesn't work, because people who choose the more severe Atkins diet over the more traditional Weight Watchers diet might differ in other important ways (such as level of motivation) that affect the outcome. Instead, a good controlled experiment uses **random assignment**. One way of doing this is to flip a coin. Heads means the participant goes into the treatment group, tails means the control group (or the other way around—as long as the researchers are consistent). In practice, the randomizing might instead be done with a computer or even with the random number generator on a calculator, but the idea is always the same: no human determines group assignment. Rather, assignment is left to chance.

If both groups have a large enough number of people, random assignment will "balance" the groups. The variation in weights, the mix of ages and genders, and the mix of most variables will be similar in both groups. Note that by "similar" we don't mean exactly the same. We don't expect both groups to have exactly the same percentage of men, for example. Except in rare cases, random variation results in slight differences in the mixes of the groups. But these differences should be small.

If you read about a controlled experiment that does not use random assignment, then there is a very real possibility that the results of the study are invalid. The technical term for what happens with nonrandomized assignment is *bias*. We say that a study exhibits **bias** when the results are influenced in one particular direction. A researcher who puts the heaviest people in one diet group, for example, is biasing the outcome. It's not always easy or possible to predict what the effects of the bias will be, but the important point is that the bias creates a confounding variable and makes it difficult, or impossible, to determine whether the treatment we're investigating really affects the outcome we're observing.

KEY POINT   Random assignment (assignment to treatment groups by a randomization procedure) helps balance the groups to minimize bias. This helps make the groups comparable.

Blinding

So far, we've recruited a large number of people and randomly assigned half to use the Atkins diet and the other half to use the Weight Watchers diet. In principle, these two groups will be very similar. However, there are still two potential differences. First, we might know who is in which group. This means that when we interact with a participant, we might consciously or unconsciously treat that person differently, depending on which group he or she belongs to. For example, if we believe strongly in the Atkins diet, we might give special advice or encouragement to people on the Atkins diet that we don't give to people on the Weight Watchers diet. If so, then we've biased the study.

To prevent this from happening, researchers should be **blind** to assignment. This means that an independent party—someone who does not regularly see the participants and who does not participate in determining the results of the study—handles the assignment to groups. The researchers do not know who is in which group until the study has ended.

Second, we must consider the participants themselves. If they know they are in the treatment group, they might behave differently than if they know they are in the control group. Perhaps they will work harder at losing weight. Or perhaps they will work less hard, because they might have a false sense of confidence in the diet. Why would we have made the Atkins diet our treatment group, they might reason, if we didn't think it was the better diet? To prevent this from happening, the participants should also not know whether they are in the treatment group or the control group.

When neither the researchers nor the participants know whether they are in the treatment or the control group, we say that the study is **double-blind**. The double-blind format helps prevent the bias that can result if one group acts differently from the other because they know they are being treated differently, or because the researchers treat the groups differently or evaluate them differently because of what the researchers expect.

Placebos

The treatment and control groups might differ in another way. People often react not just to a particular medical treatment, but also to the *idea* that they're getting medical treatment. This means that patients who receive a pill, a vaccine, or some other form of treatment often feel better even when, in truth, the treatment does absolutely nothing. Interestingly, this placebo effect also works in the other direction: if told that a certain pill might cause side effects (for example, a rash), some patients experience the side effects even though the pill they were given is just a sugar pill.

To neutralize the placebo effect, it is important that the control group receive attention similar to what the treatment group receives, so that both groups feel they are being treated the same by the researchers. In our diet study, both groups are put on a special diet, so no difference between the groups should arise from the placebo effect.

In our hypothetical study about diets, then, a placebo is not necessary, because we are comparing two diets to each other and are not interested in comparing the dieters to a group of subjects who do not go on any diet at all. However, if we were studying whether raspberry ketone capsules work for weight loss, then we would require the control group to take a placebo capsule so that we could rule out any placebo effect and thus perform a valid comparison between treatment and control.

> **KEY POINT**
>
> The Gold Standard for Experiments:
>
> *Large sample size.* This ensures that the study captures the full range of variation within the population and allows small differences to be noticed.
>
> *Controlled and randomized.* Random assignment of subjects to treatment or control groups to minimize bias.
>
> *Double-blind.* Neither subjects nor researchers know who is in which group.
>
> *Placebo (if appropriate).* This format controls for possible differences between groups that occur simply because subjects think their treatment is effective.

EXAMPLE 7 Brain Games

Brain training video games, such as Nintendo's Brain Age, claim to improve basic intelligence skills, such as memory. A study published in the journal *Nature* investigated whether playing such games can actually boost intelligence (Owen et al. 2010). The researchers explain that 11,430 people logged onto a webpage and were randomly assigned to one of three groups. Group 1 completed six training tasks that emphasized "reasoning, planning and problem-solving." Group 2 completed games that emphasized a broader range of cognitive skills. Group 3 was a control group and didn't play any of these games; instead, members were prompted to answer "obscure" questions. At the end of six weeks, the participants were compared on several different measures of thinking skills. The results? The control group did just as well as the treatment groups.

QUESTION Which features of a well-designed controlled experiment does this study have? Which features are missing?

SOLUTION Sample size: The sample size of 11,430 is quite large. Each of the three groups will have about 3800 people.

Randomization: The authors state that patients were randomly assigned to one of the three groups.

Double-blind format: Judging on the basis of this description, there was no double-blind format. It's possible (indeed, it's likely) that the researchers did not know, while analyzing the outcome, to which treatment group individuals had been assigned. But we don't know whether *participants* were aware of the existence of the three different groups and how they differed.

Placebo: The control group participated in a "null" game, in which they simply answered questions. This activity is a type of placebo, because the participants could have thought that this null game was a brain game.

TRY THIS! Exercise 1.33

Extending the Results

In both observational studies and controlled experiments, researchers are often interested in knowing whether their findings, which are based on a single collection of people or objects, will extend to the world at large.

The researchers in Example 7 concluded that brain games are not effective, but might it just be that the games weren't effective for those people who decided to participate? Maybe if the researchers tested people in another country, for example, the findings would be different.

It is usually not possible to make generalizations to a larger group of people unless the subjects for the study are representative of the larger group. The only way to collect a sample that is representative is to collect the objects we study at random. We will discuss how to select a random sample, and why we can then make generalizations about people or objects who were not in the sample, in Chapter 7.

Selecting subjects using a random method is quite common in polls and surveys (which you'll also study in Chapter 7), but it is much less common in other types of studies. Most medical studies, for example, are not conducted on people selected randomly, so even when a cause-and-effect relationship emerges between the treatment and the response, it is impossible to say whether this relationship will hold for a larger (or different) group of people. For this reason, medical researchers often work hard to replicate their findings in diverse groups of people.

Statistics in the News

When reading in a newspaper or blog about a research study that relies on statistical analysis, you should ask yourself several questions to evaluate how much faith you can put in the conclusions reached in the study.

1. *Is this an observational study or a controlled experiment?*

   If it's an observational study, then you can't conclude that the treatment caused the observed outcome.

2. *If the study is a controlled experiment, was there a large sample size? Was randomization used to assign participants to treatment groups? Was the study double-blind? Was there a placebo?*

   See the relevant section of this chapter for a review of the importance of these attributes.

3. *Was the paper published in a peer-reviewed journal? What is the journal's reputation?*

   "Peer-reviewed" means that each paper published in the journal is rigorously evaluated by at least two anonymous researchers familiar with the field. The best journals are very careful about the quality of the research they report on. They have many checkpoints to make sure that the science is as good as it can be. (But remember, this doesn't mean the science is perfect. If you read a medical journal regularly, you'll see much debate from issue to issue about certain results.) Other journals, by contrast, sometimes allow sloppy research results, and you should be very wary of these journals.

4. *Did the study follow people for a long enough time?*

   Some treatments take a long time to work, and some illnesses take a long time to show themselves. For example, many cost-conscious people like to refill water bottles again and again with tap water. Some fear that drinking from the same plastic bottle again and again might lead to cancer. If this is true, it might take a very long time for a person to get cancer from drinking out of the same bottle day after day. So researchers who wish to determine whether drinking water from the same bottle causes cancer should watch people for a very long time.

Often it is hard to get answers to all of these questions from a newspaper article. Fortunately, you can always search for the original source online. Abstracts are readily

> **⚠ Caution**
>
> **At Random**
> The concept of randomness is used in two different ways in this section. *Random assignment* is used in a controlled experiment. Subjects are randomly assigned to treatment and control groups in order to achieve a balance between groups. This ensures that the groups are comparable to each other and that the only difference between the groups is whether or not they receive the treatment under investigation. **Random selection** occurs when researchers select subjects from some larger group via a random method. We must employ random selection if we wish to extend our results to a larger group.

available, and you can have access to full-text articles in many important journals through your college or university library.

Even when a controlled experiment is well designed, things can still go wrong. One common way in which medical studies go astray is that people don't always do what their doctor tells them to do. Thus, people randomized to the treatment group might not actually take their treatments. Or people randomized to the Atkins diet might switch to Weight Watchers diet because they don't like the food on the Atkins diet. A good research paper will report on these difficulties and will be honest about the effect on their conclusions.

EXAMPLE 8 Does City Living Raise Blood Pressure?

According to a 2010 study, higher blood pressure occurs in people who live in urban areas where particulate air pollution is high (www.sciencedaily.com 2010).

QUESTION Is this more likely to be an observational study or a controlled experiment? Why? Does this mean that moving to a more urban area will result in an increase in your blood pressure?

SOLUTION This is most likely an observational study. The treatment variable is whether or not a person lives in an urban area. We are not told that participants were randomly assigned to live in urban or nonurban areas for some period of time, and in fact it is pretty unlikely that such a study could be done. Researchers probably measured blood pressure in people who chose to live in urban or nonurban settings. Because the participants themselves chose where to live, this is an observational study.

Because this is an observational study, we cannot conclude that the *treatment* (living in urban areas) causes the *outcome* (increased blood pressure). This means that simply moving to (or away from) an urban area may not change your blood pressure. One potential confounding variable could be personality, because people who prefer the fast pace of city life might have other personality traits that increase their blood pressure.

TRY THIS! Exercise 1.39

EXAMPLE 9 Crohn's Disease

Crohn's disease is a bowel disease that causes cramping abdominal pain, fever, and fatigue. A study reported in the *New England Journal of Medicine* (Columbel et al. 2010) tested two medicines for the disease: injections of infliximab (Inflix) and oral azathioprine (Azath). The participants were randomized into three groups. All groups received an injection and a pill (some were placebos, but still a pill and an injection). One group received Inflix injections alone (with placebo pills), one received Azath pills alone (with placebo injections), and one group received both injections and pills. A good outcome was defined as the disease being in remission after 26 weeks. The accompanying table shows the numbers.

	Combination	Inflix Alone	Azath Alone
Remission	96	75	51
Not in remission	73	94	119

QUESTIONS

a. Compare the percentages in remission for the three treatments. Which treatment was the most effective and which the least effective for this sample?

b. Can we conclude that the combination treatment causes a better outcome? Why or why not?

SOLUTIONS

a. For the combination: 96/169, or 56.8%, success
   For the Inflix alone: 75/169, or 44.4%, success
   For the Azath alone: 51/170, or 30%, success

   The combination treatment was the most effective for this sample, and Azath alone was the least effective.

b. Yes, we can conclude that the combination of drugs causes a better outcome than the single drugs. The study was placebo-controlled and randomized. The sample size was reasonably large. Blinding was not mentioned, but at least, thanks to the placebos, the patients did not know what treatment they were getting.

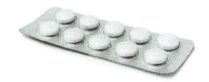

TRY THIS!   Exercise 1.41

CASE STUDY REVISITED

Did multitasking cause the difference in scores in the experiment presented at the beginning of the chapter? We can now examine the features of the experiment so that we can decide.

First of all, note that this is a controlled experiment where researchers have created a treatment group (students asked to multitask) and a control group (students not multitasking). These groups were alike in every way possible except for the multitasking condition: all students encountered the same material, taught by the same instructor, in the same room, with the same set of slides; all students had no previous knowledge of the material (as verified through a screening questionnaire); and there were no demographic differences between participants in the two groups in terms of age, gender, fluency in English, or high school grades.

Considering the key features of a well-designed experiment, here is what we find:

Sample size: The experiment included 44 students. Although this number is not very large, we can consider it large enough for a simple situation such as this one.

Randomization: Students were assigned to the treatment or control groups randomly, thus minimizing bias.

Double-blind format: The paper states that researchers graded the comprehension test blindly. In terms of students, researchers kept participants as unaware of the group they belonged to (treatment or control) as possible by having them read instructions after being seated. Unless students were looking around to see what others were doing, they would have been blind as to whether their instructions were the same as their peers' or not.

Use of placebo: This experiment does not lend itself to the use of a placebo. However, the control group also had laptops and had to take notes, so they could have thought that they were in the treatment group.

Because of these features, we can conclude that the difference in scores is caused by multitasking. If a student in a similar setting changed his or her behaviour from "multitasking" to "not multitasking," we could expect an increase in his or her level of comprehension.

EXPLORING STATISTICS

CLASS ACTIVITY

Collecting a Table of Different Kinds of Data

GOALS	MATERIALS
In this activity, you will learn about different types of data and discuss how to summarize data derived from members of the class.	A board and a marker (or a computer spreadsheet).

ACTIVITY

As a class, you will suggest possible variables that would help you describe your class to others. You will then collect data and summarize and describe these variables. How would you describe the people in your class as a group? How does your class compare to another class, maybe the class next door? Suggest variables you might collect on individuals that would help you describe your class and make comparisons. (Examples of such variables might include gender, number of credits currently taken, distance the individual lives from campus, and the like.) Be prepared to give your own values for these variables.

Some variables (such as family income, for example) might be too private; inquiring about others might be offensive to some students. You should not feel compelled to provide information that might embarrass you; try to avoid suggesting variables that you think might embarrass others. Table A shows an example of the format for the input

Gender	Age	Favourite Class	Credits	_____	_____

▲ TABLE A

BEFORE THE ACTIVITY

If someone asked you to describe the students who make up your class, which characteristics would you focus on?

AFTER THE ACTIVITY

1. Which variables that were used are numerical? Which are categorical?

2. Write a short summary of the data you collected that you think would help someone understand the composition of your class.

CHAPTER REVIEW

Summary of Learning Objectives

1. **What are some questions to consider when first examining a data set?** Ask yourself the following questions: What are the objects of interest? What variables were measured? How were they measured? What are the units of measurement? Who collected the data? How did they collect the data? Where were the data collected? Why were the data collected?

2. **What is the difference between numerical and categorical variables?** The values of numerical variables are numbers that describe quantities. The values of categorical variables are categories, usually defined by words or letters, but sometimes coded with numbers.

3. **When are percentages or rates more useful than counts for describing and comparing groups?** Since percentages and rates take into account the size of a group, they should be used when describing and comparing groups of different sizes.

4. **What is the difference between an observational study and a controlled experiment?** In a controlled experiment, researchers take control by assigning subjects to the treatment group or the control group, whereas in an observational study they do not.

5. **When is it possible to infer causality from a research study?** We cannot infer causality from an observational study. Controlled experiments, if they are well designed, allow us to draw conclusions about causality. A well-designed controlled experiment has the following attributes: large sample size; random assignment of subjects to groups; double-blind format; and a placebo (if appropriate).

6. **What is a confounding variable?** A confounding variable is an alternative explanation for the differences observed between the treatment and the control groups. We can never know if there exists a confounding variable in an observational study, which is why we cannot infer cause-and-effect relationships from observational studies.

Important Terms

Statistics, *3*
Variation, *3*
Data, *4*
Raw data, *4*
Variables, *5*
Data set, *5*
Sample, *5*
Population, *5*
Inferential statistics, *5*

Descriptive statistics, *5*
Numerical variable, *7*
Categorical variable, *7*
Stacked data, *8*
Unstacked data, *8*
Two-way table, *9*
Frequency, *9*
Rate, *12*
Causality, *13*

Treatment variable, *13*
Outcome variable
  (or response variable), *13*
Treatment group, *13*
Control group
  (or comparison group), *13*
Anecdotes, *14*
Placebo, *14*
Placebo effect, *14*

Observational study, *14*
Relationship, *14*
Confounding variable, *15*
Controlled experiment, *16*
Random assignment, *17*
Bias, *17*
Blind, *17*
Double-blind, *17*
Random selection, *19*

Sources

BBC News. February 18, 2010. http://news.bbc.co.uk (accessed May 13, 2010).

CAPA Statement on Honey Bee Wintering Losses in Canada. 2014. http://www.capabees.com/content/uploads/2013/07/2014-CAPA-Statement-on-Honey-Bee-Wintering-Losses-in-Canada.pdf (accessed Dec. 2, 2014).

Colombel, J. F., et al. 2010. Infliximab, azathioprine, or combination therapy for Crohn's disease. *New England Journal of Medicine* 362, 1383–1395.

Dansinger, M., J. Gleason, J. Griffith, H. Selker, and E. Schaefer. 2005. Comparison of the Atkins, Ornish, Weight Watchers, and Zone diets for weight loss and heart disease risk reduction: A randomized trial. *The Journal of the American Medical Association* 293(1), January 5.

Decmick, B. 2006. Koreans' kimchi adulation, with a side of skepticism. *Los Angeles Times*, May 21.

Entertainment Software Association of Canada. 2014. *Essential Facts About the Canadian Video Game Industry.* http://theesa.ca/wp-content/uploads/2014/11/ESAC-Essential-Facts-2014.pdf (accessed Dec. 2, 2014).

Fisher, R. 1959. *Smoking: The cancer controversy.* Edinburgh, UK: Oliver and Boyd.

Human Resources and Skills Development Canada. 2012. Work-related Injuries. http://www4.hrsdc.gc.ca/.3ndic.1t.4r@-eng.jsp?iid=20 (accessed Dec. 10, 2014).

Irish, P. 2012. Weight loss "miracle" supplement: Dr. Oz extols virtues of raspberry ketone. *The Toronto Star*, April 2.

Kaprio, J., and M. Koskenvuo. 1989. Twins, smoking and mortality: A 12-year prospective study of smoking-discordant twin pairs. *Social Science and Medicine* 29(9), 1083–1089.

McKinsey Quarterly. 2009. Hal Varian on how the Web challenges managers. Business Technology Office, January 2009.

Nan HongMei, et al. 2005. Kimchi and soybean pastes are risk factors of gastric cancer. *World Journal of Gastroenterology*, June 2005.

Olympic.org. 2014. http://www.olympic.org/olympic-results/sochi-2014/freestyle-skiing (accessed Dec. 11, 2014).

Owen, A., et al. 2010. Letter: Putting brain training to the test. *Nature* advance online publication, April 20, www.nature.com (accessed May 15, 2010).

Ray, J. G. 2013. Personal communication.

Ray, J. G., et al. 2012. Birth weight curves tailored to maternal world region. *Journal of Obstetrics and Gynaecology Canada* 34, 159–171.

Raz, A., et al. 2011. Placebos in clinical practice: Comparing attitudes, beliefs and patterns of use between academic psychiatrists and non-psychiatrists. *The Canadian Journal of Psychiatry* 56(4), April 2011.

Sana, F., et al. 2013. Laptop multitasking hinders classroom learning for both users and nearby peers, *Computers and Education* 62, 24–31.

Southwest Booster, April 12, 2012. http://www.swbooster.com/Living/2012-04-18/article-2958255/Saskatchewan-again-leads-in-volunteering/1 (accessed Sept. 23, 2013).

Statistics Canada. *Table 051-0001—Estimates of population, by age group and sex for July 1, Canada, provinces and territories, annual (persons unless otherwise noted),* CANSIM (database) (accessed Sept. 23, 2013).

Statistics Canada. *Table 105-0501—Health indicator profile, annual estimates, by age group and sex, Canada, provinces, territories, health regions (2012*

boundaries) and peer groups, occasional, CANSIM (database) (accessed Sept. 25, 2013).

Statistics Canada. 2012. Caring Canadians, Involved Canadians: Tables Report. http://www.statcan.gc.ca/pub/89-649-x/89-649-x2011001-eng.htm (accessed Sept. 23, 2013).

Weeks, C. 2012. Is this supplement a weight-loss miracle? *The Globe and Mail*, June 2.

Wilson, V. 2005. Man figures plankton stopped his rare cancer. *Nanaimo Daily News*, July 6.

World Bank. 2014. World Development Indicators. http://databank.worldbank.org (accessed Dec. 2, 2014).

www.sciencedaily.com. 2010. Higher blood pressure found in people living in urban areas (accessed Dec. 20, 2014).

SECTION EXERCISES

SECTION 1.2

The data in Table 1A were collected from one of the authors' statistics classes. The column heads give the variable, and each of the other rows represents a student in the class. Refer to this table for Exercises 1.1–1.4, 1.11, and 1.12.

Male	Age	Eye Colour	Shoe Size	Height (metres)	Weight (kilograms)	Number of Siblings	Credits During Fall/Winter Session	Handedness
1	20	Brown	9.5	1.80	77	1	5	Right
0	19	Blue	8	1.68	61	1	4	Right
0	42	Brown	7.5	1.60	59	3	1.5	Right
0	19	Brown	8.5	1.65	68	0	5.5	Left
1	21	Brown	11	1.78	84	5	6	Right
0	20	Hazel	5.5	1.52	48	2	3	Right
1	21	Blue	12	1.93	95	2	2.5	Right
0	21	Brown	10	1.78	64	0	3	Left
0	32	Brown	8	1.63	75	1	5	Right
1	23	Brown	7.5	1.60	66	6	2.5	Right
0	21	Brown	6.5	1.56	50	4	4.5	Right

▲ **TABLE 1A**

TRY **1.1 (Example 1)** Are the following variables, from Table 1A, numerical or categorical? Explain.

   a. Handedness

   b. Age

1.2 Are the following variables, from Table 1A, numerical or categorical? Explain.

   a. Shoe size

   b. Eye colour

1.3 Coding Explain why the variable Male, in Table 1A, is categorical, even though its values are numbers. Often, it does not make sense, or is not even possible, to add the values of a categorical variable. Does it make sense for Male? If so, what does the sum represent?

1.4 Coding Students with fewer than 3.5 credits during the Fall/Winter session are considered part-time. Create a new categorical variable that classifies each student in Table 1A as full-time (3.5 credits or more) or part-time. Call this variable Full. Report the values in a column in the same order as those in the table.

TRY **1.5 First Cigarette (Example 2)** Respondents to the 2010 Canadian Alcohol and Drug Use Monitoring Survey were asked the age (in years) at which they smoked their first cigarette and whether or not they currently smoked (either occasionally or daily). The table provides the answers from 10 respondents.

   a. Is the format of the data set stacked or unstacked?

   b. Explain the coding. What do 1 and 0 represent?

   c. If you answered "stacked" in part a, then unstack the data into two columns labelled Smoker and Nonsmoker. If you answered "unstacked," then stack the data into one column; choose an appropriate name for the stacked variable.

Age of First Cigarette	Smoker
18	0
15	1
23	0
14	1
13	1
19	0
21	0
23	1
18	0
15	0

1.6 Students' Ages The accompanying table gives ages for some of the students in two statistics classes. One class met at noon and the other at 5 p.m.

a. Is the format for the data set stacked or unstacked?

b. If you answered "stacked," then unstack the data set. If you answered "unstacked," then stack and code the data set.

5 p.m.	Noon
31	24
34	18
46	21
47	20
50	20

SECTION 1.3

TRY 1.7 Changing Answers (Example 3) On a multiple-choice exam, if you think you have made a mistake, is it better to stick with your first choice, or to erase and change your answer? One of the authors instructed her students to change the answer if the second answer they got seemed better than the first (Change!). Her colleague told his students that their first answer was usually the best and they should avoid changing answers (Don't Change!). After both classes had taken several multiple-choice exams, the exams were studied to see whether answers were erased and replaced with different answers. The results are shown in the accompanying table.

a. What is the percentage of answers that were changed for the students who were told not to change their answers?

b. What is the percentage of answers that were changed for the students who were told to change their answers?

c. Compare the answers to parts a and b, and state whether you think the instruction had any effect on whether students changed their answers.

		Instruction	
		Don't Change!	Change!
Behaviour	Changed	189	124
	Unchanged	29,428	14,389

1.8 Changing Answers Read the information in Exercise 1.7. The table summarizes the outcomes based on the instructions given by the teacher.

a. For the teacher who said Don't Change!, what percentage of the changes were from wrong to right? What percentage of the changes were from right to wrong? Did the results of the changes raise students' grades or lower them?

b. For the teacher who said Change!, what percentage of the changes were from wrong to right? What percentage of the changes were from right to wrong? Did the results of the changes raise students' grades or lower them?

c. On the basis of these data, what advice would you give to a student who asked you whether it's better to stick with your first hunch or to change your answer?

	Don't Change!	Change!
Wrong to right	91	86
Right to wrong	48	24
Wrong to wrong	50	14

TRY 1.9 Finding and Using Percentages (Example 4)

a. A statistics class is made up of 15 men and 23 women. What percentage of the class is male?

b. A different class has 234 students, and 64.1% of them are men. How many men are in the class?

c. A different class is made up of 40% women and has 20 women in it. What is the total number of students in the class?

1.10 Nursing Workforce

a. In 2010, there were 268,512 registered nurses (RNs) in Canada employed in nursing. Of these, 17,163 were male. What percentage of RNs employed in nursing were male?

b. Of the 268,512 RNs employed in nursing, 8.6% of them were educated internationally. How many RNs employed in nursing were educated in Canada?

c. The percentage of RNs employed in direct patient care nursing whose area of responsibility was emergency care was 7.5%, or 17,645 RNs. What is the total number of RNs employed in direct patient care nursing?

1.11 Women Find the frequency, proportion, and percentage of women in Table 1A on page 24.

1.12 Right-Handed People Find the frequency, proportion, and percentage of right-handed people in Table 1A on page 24.

1.13 Population Projection Under a medium-growth projection scenario, Statistics Canada projected that Canada will have an elderly population (65 and older) of 13,386,000 in the year 2061, representing 25.43% of the population. What is the total projected population of Canada in 2061?

1.14 Regular Medical Doctors Statistics Canada reported that in 2012 there were 25,087,068 Canadians aged 12 and over who had a regular medical doctor and that this was 85.1% of the Canadian population (in this age group). How large was the total population (in this age group) in 2012?

 1.15 Diabetes The table gives the number of people aged 12 and over who have been diagnosed with diabetes in the six provinces with the largest number of cases, as reported by the Statistics Canada 2010 Canadian Community Health Survey. It also shows the population of those provinces at that time (in that age group).

Find the number of people with diabetes per thousand residents in each province, and rank the six provinces from highest rate (rank 1) to lowest rate (rank 6). Compare these rankings (of rates) with the ranks of total number of cases. If you moved to one of these provinces and met 50 random people, in which province would you be most likely to meet at least one person with diabetes? In which province would you be least likely to meet at least one person with diabetes? *See page 30 for guidance.*

Province	Persons with Diabetes	Population Aged 12 and Over
Ontario	770,410	11,498,657
Quebec	448,122	6,894,185
British Columbia	224,775	3,943,421
Alberta	195,440	3,203,934
Nova Scotia	69,721	810,698
Manitoba	62,058	1,000,935

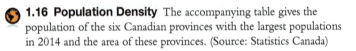 **1.16 Population Density** The accompanying table gives the population of the six Canadian provinces with the largest populations in 2014 and the area of these provinces. (Source: Statistics Canada)

Province	Population	Area (km²)
Ontario	13,678,740	1,076,395
Quebec	8,214,672	1,542,056
British Columbia	4,631,302	944,735
Alberta	4,121,692	661,848
Manitoba	1,282,043	647,797
Saskatchewan	1,125,410	651,036

a. Determine and report the rankings of the population density by dividing each population by the number of square kilometres to get the population density (in people per square kilometre). Use rank 1 for the highest density.

b. If you wanted to live in the province (of these six) with the lowest population density, which would you choose?

c. If you wanted to live in the province (of these six) with the highest population density, which would you choose?

1.17 Second-hand Smoke The estimated number of persons aged 12 and over who were exposed to second-hand smoke at home every day and the total population in that age group (in thousands) are provided in the accompanying table for several years.

Find the estimated percentage of persons exposed to second-hand smoke in each of the given years and describe the trend over time. (Source: Statistics Canada, Canadian Community Health Survey)

Year	Exposed to Second-hand Smoke (thousands)	Total Population (thousands)
2003	2148	20,264
2005	1847	20,987
2007	1600	21,621
2009	1417	22,855
2011	1268	23,055

1.18 Elderly Population The number of elderly people in Canada (age 65 or older) and the total number of people living in Canada (in millions) are reported in the accompanying table for several years. Find what percentage of the population is elderly for each year, and describe the trend of these percentages. (Source: Statistics Canada)

Year	Elderly (millions)	Total (millions)
1972	1.8	22.2
1982	2.4	25.1
1992	3.3	28.4
2002	4.0	31.4
2012	5.2	34.9

TRY★ **1.19 Course Enrolment Rates (Example 5)** Two sections of statistics are offered, the first at 8 a.m. and the second at 10 a.m. The 8 a.m. section has 25 women, and the 10 a.m. section has 15 women. A student claims this is evidence that women prefer earlier statistics classes than men do. What information is missing that might contradict this claim?

★ **1.20 Fatal Collisions** According to the 2011 Ontario Road Safety Annual Report, there were 24 people killed in motor vehicle collisions in Ottawa that year, while in Wellington County there were only 12. Can we conclude that it is safer to drive in Wellington County than it is in Ottawa? Why or why not?

SECTION 1.4

For Exercises 1.21–1.28, indicate whether the study is an observational study or a controlled experiment.

1.21 A student watched picnickers with a large cooler of soft drinks to see whether teenagers were less likely than adults to choose diet soft drinks over regular soft drinks.

1.22 The medical records of people who live near high-power lines are compared with the medical records of people who do not live near high-power lines to see whether people living near high-power lines are more likely to have cancer.

1.23 A researcher wonders whether the order in which people taste beverages influences their preference. Students are told by the researcher to drink from two unmarked cups. The researcher randomly assigns one group of students to drink Coke first and then Pepsi. The researcher assigns the other group to drink Pepsi first and then Coke. The subjects are asked whether they prefer the first or the second beverage.

1.24 Patients with Alzheimer's disease are randomly divided into two groups. One group is given a new drug, and the other is given a placebo. After six months they are given a memory test to see whether the new drug fights Alzheimer's better than a placebo.

1.25 A group of boys is randomly divided into two groups. One group watches violent cartoons for one hour, and the other group watches cartoons without violence for one hour. The boys are then observed to see how many violent actions they take in the next two hours, and the two groups are compared.

1.26 A local public school encourages, but does not require, students to wear uniforms. The principal of the school compares the grades of students at this school who wear uniforms with the grades of those who do not wear uniforms to determine whether those wearing uniforms tend to have higher grades.

1.27 A researcher was interested in the effect of exercise on academic performance in elementary school children. She went to the recess area of an elementary school and identified some students who were exercising vigorously and some who were not. The researcher then compared the grades of the exercisers with the grades of those who did not exercise.

1.28 A researcher was interested in the effect of exercise on memory. She randomly assigned half of a group of students to run up a stairway three times and the other half to rest for an equivalent amount of time. Each student was then asked to memorize a series of random digits. She compared the numbers of digits remembered for the two groups.

1.29 Effects of Tutoring on Math Grades A group of educators want to determine how effective tutoring is in raising students' grades in a math class, so they arrange free tutoring for those who want it. Then they compare final exam grades for the group that took advantage of the tutoring and the group that did not. Suppose the group participating in the tutoring tended to receive higher grades on the exam. Does that show that the tutoring worked? If not, explain why not and suggest a confounding variable.

1.30 Treating Depression A doctor who believes strongly that antidepressants work better than "talk therapy" tests depressed patients by treating half of them with antidepressants and the other half with talk therapy. After six months the patients are evaluated on a scale of 1 to 5, with 5 indicating the greatest improvement.

a. The doctor is concerned that if his most severely depressed patients do not receive the antidepressants, they will get much worse. He therefore decides that the most severe patients will be assigned to receive the antidepressants. Explain why this will affect his ability to determine which approach works best.

b. What advice would you give the doctor to improve his study?

c. The doctor asks you whether it is acceptable for him to know which treatment each patient receives and to evaluate them himself at the end of the study to rate their improvement. Explain why this practice will affect his ability to determine which approach works best.

d. What improvements to the plan in part c would you recommend?

TRY 1.31 Treating Heart Disease (Example 6) A study reported by Hannon et al. looked at people treated for heart disease and reported lower death rates for those who received a coronary bypass (CABG) compared to those who received a stent. A stent is a device to keep blood vessels open. The beginning of the abstract is given below.

> *Methods* We identified patients with multivessel disease who received drug-eluting stents or underwent CABG in New York State between October 1, 2003, and December 31, 2004, and we compared adverse outcomes (death, death or myocardial infarction, or repeat revascularization) through December 31, 2005, after adjustment for differences in baseline risk factors among the patients.

The adverse outcomes were greater with stenting. Was this an observational study or a controlled experiment? How do you know? Can we say that the use of CABG causes a better success rate? Why or why not? (Source: Hannan et al., Drug-eluting stents vs. coronary-artery bypass grafting in multivessel coronary disease, *New England Journal of Medicine* 358(4), 331–341, January 24, 2008)

1.32 Effects of Exercise on Aging In a study reported on HealthNews.com, Dr. Yonas E. Geda and colleagues analyzed data on 1324 individuals without dementia who completed a questionnaire about physical activity between 2006 and 2008 as part of the Mayo Clinic Study of Aging. The participants had an average age of 80 and were classified as having either normal cognition (1126) or mild cognitive impairment (MCI; 198). Those who reported performing moderate exercise such as yoga, aerobics, or brisk walking during midlife were 39% less likely to develop MCI, and moderate exercise later in life was associated with a 32% reduction.

Was this more likely to have been a controlled experiment or an observational study, and how do you know? Can we say that exercise reduces cognitive impairment? Why or why not?

TRY 1.33 Vitamin C Study (Example 7) A pair of college students have decided to test vitamin C to see whether it prevents colds. They recruit 500 students with a sign-up sheet, containing a numbered list. The first half of those on the sheet (Numbers 1–250) are asked to take 500 mg of vitamin C per day, and the second half are told *not* to use vitamin C. At the end of the school year, participants are asked how many colds they had. How would you improve this study, and why?

1.34 Weight Loss Study A group of overweight people are asked to participate in a weight loss program. Participants are allowed to choose whether they want to go on a vegetarian diet or follow a traditional low-calorie diet that includes some meat. Half of the people choose the vegetarian diet, and half choose to be in the control group and continue to eat meat. Suppose that there is greater weight loss in the vegetarian group.

a. Suggest a plausible confounding variable that would prevent us from concluding that the weight loss was due to the lack of meat in the diet. Explain why it is a confounding variable.

b. Explain a better way to do the experiment that is likely to remove the influence of confounding variables.

1.35 Are Optimists Healthier? In 2004, "On Health," the *Consumer Reports* medical newsletter, reported on a study of the effects of optimism on health. Researchers studied the emotional styles of 334 subjects and then squirted a cold virus in the noses of these subjects. Those who scored high on "energy, happiness, and relaxation" were significantly less likely to develop colds. Is this study evidence that you can reduce your chance of catching colds by training yourself to be more relaxed and happy? Explain your answer.

1.36 Reducing Migraines A 2004 article in *The Nutrition Reporter* stated that melatonin supplements were effective in preventing migraine headaches. The article quoted a Brazilian doctor who used melatonin for three months to treat 34 patients with a history of two to eight migraine headaches per month. Thirty-two patients completed the study, and 25 patients reported experiencing at least a 50% reduction in headaches. None of the patients had an increase in headaches. What is the major flaw in this research design that might prevent us from concluding that melatonin helps prevent migraine headaches?

1.37 Flu Vaccine The *New England Journal of Medicine* reported on a study that was done to see whether a smaller dose of the flu vaccine could be used successfully. If that were the case, then a reduced dose of the vaccine could be used in times of vaccine shortage in order to stretch vaccine supplies. In this study, the usual amount of vaccine was injected into half the patients, and the other half of the patients had only a small amount of vaccine injected. The response was measured by looking at the production of antibodies (more antibodies generally result in less risk of getting the flu). In the end, the lower dose of vaccine was just as effective as a higher dose for those under 65 years old. What more do we need to know to be able to conclude that the lower dose of vaccine was equally effective at preventing the flu for those under 65? (Source: Belshe et al., Serum antibody responses after intradermal vaccination against influenza, *New England Journal of Medicine*, 351(22): 2286–94 2004)

1.38 Effect of Confederates on Compliance A study was conducted to see whether participants would ignore a sign that said, "Elevator may stick between floors. Use the stairs." The study was done at a university dorm on the ground floor of a three-level building. Those who used the stairs were said to be compliant, and those who used the elevator were said to be noncompliant. There were three possible situations, two of which involved confederates. A confederate is a person who is secretly working with the experimenter. In the first situation, there was no confederate. In the second situation, there was a compliant confederate (one who used the stairs), and in the third situation, there was a noncompliant confederate (one who used the elevator). The subjects tended to imitate the confederates. What more do you need to know about the study to determine whether the presence or absence of a confederate causes a change in the compliance of subjects? (Source: Wogalter et al., 1987, reported in Shaffer and Merrens, 2001, *Research Stories in Introductory Psychology*. Boston: Allyn and Bacon.)

TRY 1.39 Vitamin C and Allergies (Example 8) The March 2005 issue of *The Nutrition Reporter* reported on the effects of vitamin C in breast milk on preventing allergies in infants. Researchers analyzed levels of vitamin C in the breast milk of some new mothers who had decided whether to take vitamin C during their pregnancy. The highest levels of vitamin C were associated with a 30% lower risk of allergies in the infants. Was this an observational study or a controlled experiment? On the basis of this study, can you conclude that vitamin C lowers the risk of allergies in infants? Why or why not?

1.40 Childhood Exposure to Tobacco Smoke and Emphysema A headline on the website e! Science News (esciencenews.com) in December 2009 stated, "Exposure to tobacco smoke in childhood home [is] associated with early emphysema in adulthood."

Is this likely to have been a controlled experiment or an observational study? How do you know? Is it possible to conclude, on the basis of this study, that exposure to tobacco smoke for children causes early emphysema in adulthood?

TRY 1.41 Effects of Light Exposure (Example 9) A study carried out by Baturin and colleagues looked at the effects of light on female mice. Fifty mice were randomly assigned to a regimen of 12 hours of light and 12 hours of dark (LD), while another 50 mice were assigned to 24 hours of light (LL). Researchers observed the mice for two years, beginning when the mice were two months old. Four of the LD mice and 14 of the LL mice developed tumours. The accompanying table summarizes the data. (Source: Baturin et al., The effect of light regimen and melatonin on the development of spontaneous mammary tumors in mice, *Neuroendocrinology Letters*, 2001)

	LD	LL
Tumours	4	14
No tumours	46	36

a. Determine the percentage of mice that developed tumours from each group (LL and LD). Compare them and comment.

b. Was this a controlled experiment or an observational study? How do you know?

c. Can we conclude that light for 24 hours a day causes an increase in tumours in mice? Why or why not?

1.42 Head Injury and Schizophrenia A study was conducted by researchers at the Centre for Addiction and Mental Health in Toronto to investigate whether mild head injury during childhood would be associated with the later development of schizophrenia among genetically predisposed individuals. The history of head injuries in 67 subjects with schizophrenia was compared with that of 102 of their siblings without schizophrenia. The accompanying table shows the results. (Source: Abdel Malik et al., Childhood head injury and expression of schizophrenia in multiply affected families, *Arch. Gen. Psychiatry* 60(3), 231–236, March 2003)

	Schizophrenia	No Schizophrenia
Head injury	16	12
No head injury	51	90

a. What percentage of subjects with schizophrenia reported a childhood head injury?

b. What percentage of subjects without schizophrenia reported a childhood head injury?

c. Is the percentage of subjects who reported a head injury higher among the subjects with schizophrenia or among those without schizophrenia?

d. Can you conclude that head injuries affect the development of schizophrenia? Explain.

CHAPTER REVIEW EXERCISES

1.43 Immigration and Mental Health A 2011 study was conducted in Toronto to investigate the mental health and well-being of immigrants in that city. The randomly selected participants were divided into three groups: recent immigrants (not born in Canada and had lived in Canada for 10 years or less), non-recent immigrants (not born in Canada and had lived in Canada for more than 10 years), and Canadian-born. One of the variables measured was whether or not the person had ever had a panic attack, with results summarized in the accompanying table.

	Recent Immigrants	Non-Recent Immigrants	Canadian-Born Participants
Panic attack	20	183	520
No panic attack	123	586	976
Total	143	769	1496

a. What percentage of recent immigrants has had a panic attack?

b. What percentage of non-recent immigrants has had a panic attack?

c. What percentage of Canadian-born participants has had a panic attack?

d. Which group has the highest rate of panic attacks? Does this imply that immigrant status causes panic attacks? Why or why not? If not, can you name a confounding variable?

1.44 Are Cell Phones More Dangerous Than Cigarettes? Fox News reported on a study in 2008, headed by Dr. Vini Khurana, that suggested that there is some evidence that using cell phone head sets for 10 years or more doubles the risk of brain cancer. He said that 3 billion people now use cell phones, but only 1 billion smoke and that smoking kills about 5 million each year. He concluded that cell phones are more dangerous than cigarettes, and so he suggested that people should avoid using cell phones. (Source: www.independent.co.uk)

a. Is this study more likely to be a controlled experiment or an observational study? Explain.

b. Do you think this study shows that using cell phones causes brain cancer? Also, does it show that cell phones are more dangerous than cigarettes? Why or why not?

1.45 Wild Game Consumption A study was conducted among Cree schoolchildren of the Mushkegowuk Territory First Nations in Northern Ontario. The purpose of the study was to investigate factors that influence consumption of wild game and other traditional foods. One of the factors under investigation was whether or not the child is concerned over potential environmental contaminants. The raw data on gender and concern over potential contaminants for the sample of children living in Fort Albany (one of the five communities in the study) are found in the accompanying table; c stands for concerned, n for not concerned, b for boy, and g for girl. (Source: Hlimi et al., Traditional food consumption behavior and concern with environmental contaminants among Cree schoolchildren of the Mushkegowuk Territory, *International Journal of Circumpolar Health* 71, 17344, March, 2012)

a. Make a two-way table that summarizes the data. Label the columns (across the top) Boy and Girl. Label the rows Concerned and Not Concerned.

b. Find the percentage of girls and the percentage of boys who are concerned over potential environmental contaminants.

c. Are the boys or the girls in this community more likely to be concerned over potential environmental contaminants?

Gen	Conc?	Gen	Conc?	Gen	Conc?
b	c	b	n	g	c
b	c	b	n	g	c
b	c	b	n	g	c
b	c	b	n	g	c
b	c	b	n	g	c
b	c	b	n	g	n
b	c	g	c	g	n
b	c	g	c	g	n
b	c	g	c	g	n
b	c	g	c	g	n
b	c	g	c	g	n
b	c	g	c	g	n
b	n	g	c		
b	n	g	c		

1.46 Scorpion Antivenom A study was done on children (six months to 18 years of age) who had (nonlethal) scorpion stings. Each child was randomly assigned to receive an experimental anti-venom or a placebo. Good results were no symptoms after four hours. Make a summary of the data in the form of a two-way table. Label the columns Antivenom and Placebo. Label the rows Better and Not Better. Compare the percentage better for the antivenom group and the placebo group. (Source: Boyer, Leslie et al., Antivenom for critically ill children with neurotoxicity from scorpion stings, *New England Journal of Medicine* 360(20), 2090–2098, May 14, 2009)

Antivenom	Better	Antivenom	Better
1	1	0	0
1	1	0	0
1	1	0	0
1	0	0	1
1	1	0	0
1	1	0	0
1	1	1	1
0	0		

★ **1.47 Activated Charcoal** A man posting on an internet message board claimed that his wife was sick for more than six months with many problems, including nausea, confusion, and night sweats. Doctors were unable to help her. However, when she started taking "activated charcoal," her condition began to improve. The posting on the message board also explained that his wife had possibly ingested herbicides and might have been poisoned by these "toxins."

Describe the design of a controlled experiment to determine whether activated charcoal can cure people suffering from what we will call "toxin disease," assuming that such a disease exists. Assume that you have access to 200 people suffering from this condition. Your description of your experiment should address all the major features of a controlled experiment.

★ **1.48 Allergy Experiment** A post on an internet message board reported that a person suffering from allergies took grapeseed extract and had a remarkable decrease in allergy attacks.

Describe the design of a controlled experiment to determine whether grapeseed extract can relieve the symptoms of allergy sufferers. Assume that you have access to 200 people suffering from allergies. Your description of your experiment should address all the major features of a controlled experiment.

1.49 Clinical Trials In a study of more than 2000 British patients with heart failure, patients were asked whether they would be willing to participate in a clinical trial. After 55 months, those who said they would be willing to participate were about half as likely to have died as those who were not willing to participate. Does this imply that if you have heart failure, you can increase your chance of living by being willing to participate in clinical trials? Why or why not? (Source: Clark et al., Is taking part in clinical trials good for your health? A cohort study, *European Journal of Heart Failure*, 11, 1078–1083, 2009)

1.50 Recidivism Rate In May 2010, *Time* magazine published an article about an innovative Norwegian prison, Halden Fengsel, that provides prisoners with dorm-like accommodations, flat-screen televisions, and mini-fridges. The staff does not carry guns. Within two years of release from Halden Fengsel, the rate of recidivism (being imprisoned again) is 20%. In Canada that rate is between 50% and 80%. Is this sufficient evidence to conclude that if Canada changed its prisons to be more like Halden Fengsel, the recidivism rate in Canada would go down? Explain.

1.51 Effectiveness of a Sleeping Facial An ad for a Greek yogurt sleeping facial promising long-term moisturization claims that 97% of people who used the facial saw smoother skin by morning. From just this information, can we conclude that the sleeping facial makes people's skin smoother? Why or why not?

1.52 Brief Exercise and Diabetes As part of a study, 16 young men performed high-intensity exercise that totalled only 15 minutes in a two-week period. At the end of two weeks, several (but not all) tests for diabetes, such as an insulin sensitivity test, showed improvement. Do these results indicate that brief high-intensity exercise causes an improvement in markers for diabetes? What essential component of both controlled experiments and observational studies is missing from this study? (Source: Babraj et al., Extremely short duration high intensity interval training substantially improves insulin action in young healthy males, *BMC Endocrine Disorders* 9, 3. doi: 10.1186/1472-6823-9-3, January 2009)

GUIDED EXERCISES

1.15 Diabetes The accompanying table gives the number of people aged 12 and over who have been diagnosed with diabetes in the six provinces with the largest number of cases, as reported by the Statistics Canada 2010 Canadian Community Health Survey. It also shows the population of those provinces at that time (in that age group).

Question
Find the number of people with diabetes per thousand residents in each province, and rank the six provinces from highest rate (rank 1) to lowest rate (rank 6). Compare these rankings (of rates) with the ranks of total number of cases. If you moved to one of

these provinces and met 50 random people, in which province would you be most likely to meet at least one person with diabetes? In which province would you be least likely to meet at least one person with diabetes?

Step 1 ▶ Rank the provinces by total number of persons with diabetes, and add them to the table (column 4).

Step 2 ▶ For each province, divide the number of persons with diabetes by the population, and fill in column 5.

Step 3 ▶ Multiply column 5 by 1000 and fill in column 6.

Step 4 ▶ Enter the ranks for the rates of diabetes cases per 1000 population, using 1 for the largest value and 6 for the smallest.

Step 5 ▶ Are the ranks for the rates the same as the ranks for the numbers of cases? If not, describe at least one difference.

Step 6 ▶ Finally, if you moved to one of these provinces and met 50 random people, in which province would you be most likely to meet at least one person with diabetes? In which region would you be least likely to meet at least one person with diabetes?

Province	Persons with Diabetes	Population	Rank by Cases	Diabetes/Population	Diabetes per 1000 Population	Rank by Rate
Ontario	770,410	11,498,657	1	0.067	67	2
Quebec	448,122	6,894,185	2	0.065		
British Columbia	224,775	3,943,421	3			
Alberta	195,440	3,203,934	4			
Nova Scotia	69,721	810,698	5			
Manitoba	62,058	1,000,935	6			

2 Visualizing Data

jannoon028/Shutterstock

LEARNING OBJECTIVES

After completing this chapter, you should be able to:

1. Obtain the distribution of a data set.
2. Construct appropriate graphs for numerical variables and describe the important aspects of the distribution that can be learned from them.
3. Construct appropriate graphs for categorical variables and describe the important aspects of the distribution that can be learned from them.
4. Recognize features of a graph that could be potentially misleading.

One of the major concepts of statistics is that although individual events are hard to predict, large numbers of events usually exhibit predictable patterns. The search for patterns is a key theme in science and business. An important first step in this search is to identify and visualize the key features of your data.

Using graphics to see patterns and identify important trends or features is not new. One of the earliest statistical graphs dates back to 1786, when a Scottish engineer named William Playfair published a paper examining whether there was a relationship between the price of wheat and wages. To help answer this question, Playfair produced a graph (shown in Figure 2.1) that is believed to be the first of its kind. This graph became the prototype of two of the most commonly used tools in statistics: the bar chart and the histogram.

Graphics such as these can be extraordinarily powerful ways of organizing data, detecting patterns and trends, and communicating findings. The graphs we use have changed somewhat since Playfair's day, but graphics are of fundamental importance to analyzing data. The first step in any statistical analysis is to

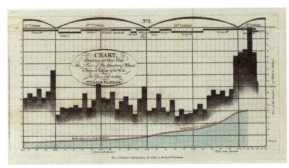

▲ **FIGURE 2.1** Playfair's chart explores a possible relationship between wages and the price of wheat. (Source: Playfair 1786)

make a picture of some kind in order to check our intuition against the data. If our intuitions are wrong, it could very well be because the world works differently than we thought. Thus, by making and examining a display of data, we gain some insight into how the world works.

In Chapter 1 we discussed some of the methods used to collect data. In this chapter we'll cover some of the basic graphics used in analyzing the data we collect. Then, in Chapter 3, we'll learn about quantifying and comparing the key features of data sets.

CASE STUDY

The Financial Benefits of Learning

Do learning and higher education levels make a difference in terms of earned income? If you are enrolled in a post-secondary institution, presumably you believe (or at least you hope) that the answer to this question is *yes*. Let us address it by examining some data.

Table 2.1 gives data on annual income before taxes (in thousands of dollars) for a small random sample of respondents to the 2009 Survey of Household Spending. Data are classified according to the highest degree, certificate, or diploma attained by the respondent: high school (the respondent attained a high school diploma or equivalent); college (the respondent attained a community college, CEGEP, or nursing school diploma); or university (the respondent attained a bachelor's degree or a university degree, certificate, or diploma above a bachelor's). What differences do you expect between the three groups? What similarities do you anticipate?

It is nearly impossible to compare the three groups without imposing some kind of organization on the data. In this chapter you will learn about several ways in which we can graphically organize groups of data like these so as to be able to make comparisons between the groups. At the end of the chapter, you'll see what the right graphical summaries can tell us about how the three levels of education compare when it comes to income.

High School					College					University				
62	65	6.4	33	29	12	39	2.3	37	17	85	31	32	90	45
25	25	45	32	10	1.7	44	85	22	220	61	38	22	51	60
32	46	31	39	15	37	41	17	0.3	24	66	48	59	76	80
10	8.8	23	24	38	31	47	49	65	37	52	50	100	190	70
10	25	4.8	73	82	33	55	110	6	37	74	78	190	31	63
23	1.1	36	14	82	130	43	50	93	1.2	55	54	62	64	110
20	22	69	56	26	29	20	21	20	38	18	100	60	26	90
22	21	47	42	15	39	60	41	26	34	55	51	47	21	77

 ▲ **TABLE 2.1** Annual income before taxes (in thousands of dollars) for a random sample of respondents to the 2009 Survey of Household Spending. Data are classified according to the highest degree, certificate, or diploma attained by the respondent.

SECTION 2.1

Visualizing Numerical Data

In order to obtain useful information from a data set, it is necessary that we organize it in some way. One simple method for organizing data is to obtain its distribution. The **distribution of a data set** (or of a sample of data) shows the pattern of "what has happened" by keeping track of the values that were observed and of their **frequencies**; that is, the number of times each of these values occurred in the data set.

Distributions are important because they capture much of the information we need in order to make comparisons between groups, examine data for errors, and learn about real-world processes. Distributions allow us to examine the variation of the data in our sample, and from this variation we can often learn more about the world.

The first step of almost every statistical investigation is to visualize the distribution of the sample. By creating an appropriate graphic, we can see patterns that might otherwise escape our notice.

For example, here are some raw data from the Canadian Football League (CFL) website. This set of data shows the total number of touchdown passes for CFL quarterbacks during the 2014 season.

Value	Frequency
28	1
22	1
17	1
16	1
15	1
14	1
11	2
8	1
6	1
5	2
4	4
2	2
1	7
0	13

▲ **TABLE 2.2** Distribution of the number of touchdown passes completed by CFL quarterbacks in 2014.

28, 17, 14, 11, 22, 16, 15, 11, 8, 4, 4, 4, 6, 5, 4, 0, 2,
2, 1, 5, 0, 0, 0, 1, 1, 0, 1, 1, 0, 0, 1, 0, 1, 0, 0, 0, 0, 0

This list includes only the values. A distribution lists the values and also the frequencies. The distribution of this sample is shown in Table 2.2.

It's hard to see patterns when the distribution is presented as a table. A picture makes it easier for us to answer questions such as "What's the typical total number of touchdown passes in 2014?" and "Is 28 touchdown passes an unusually high number?" A picture would also make it easier to compare the number of touchdown passes in 2014 to the number of touchdown passes in other seasons.

When examining distributions, we use a two-step process:

1. See it.

2. Summarize it.

In this section we explain how to visualize the distribution. In the next section, we discuss the characteristics you should look for to help you summarize it.

All the methods we use for visualizing distributions are based on the same idea: make some sort of mark that indicates how many times each value occurred in our data set. In this way, we get a picture of the distribution so that we can see at a glance which values occurred and how often.

Two very useful methods for visualizing distributions of numerical variables are dotplots and histograms. Dotplots are simpler; histograms are more commonly used and perhaps more useful.

Details

Making Dotplots

Dotplots are easy to make with pen and paper, but don't worry too much about recording values to great accuracy. The purpose of a plot like this is to help us see the overall shape of the distribution, not to record details about individual observations.

Dotplots

In constructing a **dotplot**, we simply put a dot above a number line where each value occurs. We can get a sense of frequency by seeing how high the dots stack up. Because dotplots have one dot for each observation in the data set, they are most useful for small sets of data. Figure 2.2 shows a dotplot for the number of touchdown passes completed by CFL quarterbacks in 2014.

With this simple picture, we can see more than we could from Table 2.2. We can see from this dotplot that most quarterbacks completed 4 touchdown passes or less during the season. Also, we can see that the quarterbacks who completed 28 touchdown passes

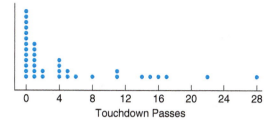

◀ **FIGURE 2.2** Dotplot of number of touchdown passes by CFL quarterbacks in 2014. Each dot represents a quarterback.

(R. Ray of the Toronto Argonauts) and 22 touchdown passes (B. Mitchell of the Calgary Stampeders, Grey Cup MVP that season) were exceptional within this group. Not only are these the largest values in this data set, but they stand apart from all the others by a considerable gap.

SNAPSHOT | THE DOTPLOT

WHAT IS IT?	▶	A graphical summary.
WHAT DOES IT DO?	▶	Shows a picture of the distribution of a numerical variable.
HOW DOES IT DO IT?	▶	Each observation is represented by a dot on a number line.
HOW IS IT USED?	▶	To see patterns in samples of data with variation.
WHEN IS IT USED?	▶	It is most useful for small data sets.

Histograms

When data sets are large, patterns in the data can be observed more clearly by first grouping observations and then constructing a **histogram**, a graph based on the grouped data. The grouping of data is done by dividing the number line into intervals of equal width and then counting the number of observations that are in each interval. Each interval is called a **bin** (also called a **class**), and the number of observations in each bin is its frequency. A histogram displays each bin as a vertical bar, with the height of each bar proportional to the frequency of the bin.

For example, with the touchdown passes in Table 2.2 we can create a series of bins that go from 0 to less than 3, from 3 to less than 6, from 6 to less than 9, and so on. Twenty-two quarterbacks completed between 0 and 3 touchdown passes (not including 3), so the first bar has a height of 22. The second bin contains six observations and consequently has a height of 6. The finished graph is shown in Figure 2.3. The histogram shows, among other things, that two quarterbacks completed between 6 and 9 touchdown passes, two completed between 9 and 12 touchdown passes, and so on.

Making a histogram requires paying attention to quite a few details. For instance, our choice of bins included a rule for what to do if an observation landed exactly on the boundary of two bins (say the observation of exactly 6). We chose to follow a common rule that always puts "boundary" observations in the bin on the right, and explicitly stated that each bin does not include the value on its right boundary. We could just as well have decided to always put boundary observations in the bin on the left, which would have resulted in a different histogram. The important point is to be consistent and to make sure that every observation belongs to one and only one bin.

▶ **FIGURE 2.3** Histogram of number of touchdown passes completed in the 2014 season by CFL quarterbacks. The first bar, for example, tells us that 22 quarterbacks completed between 0 and 3 touchdown passes (not including 3) during the season.

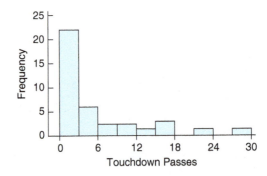

Figure 2.4 shows two more histograms of the same data. Even though they display the same data, they look very different—both from each other and from Figure 2.3. Why?

Changing the width of the bins in a histogram changes its shape. Figure 2.3 has bins with width of 3. In contrast, Figure 2.4a has much smaller bins (of length 0.5), and Figure 2.4b has wider bins (of length 10). Note that when we use small bins, we get a spiky histogram. When we use wider bins, the histogram gets less spiky. Using wide bins hides more detail. If you chose very wide bins, you would have no details at all. You would see just one big rectangle!

How large should the bins be? Too small and you see too much detail (as in Figure 2.4a). Too large and you don't see enough (as in Figure 2.4b). Most computer software will automatically make a good choice. Our software package (Minitab, in this case) automatically chose the bin width of 3 that you see in Figure 2.3. Still, if you can, you should try different sizes to see how different choices change your impression of the distribution of the data. Fortunately, most statistical software packages make it quite easy to change the bin width.

▶ **FIGURE 2.4** Two more histograms of touchdown passes, using the same data as in Figure 2.3. **(a)** This histogram has narrow bins and is spiky. **(b)** This histogram has wide bins and offers less detail.

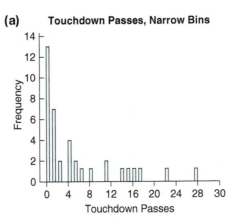

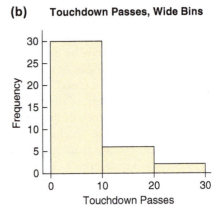

Relative Frequency Histograms

A relative frequency histogram is similar to a histogram except that the units of the vertical axis are relative frequencies instead of actual frequencies. The **relative frequency** of a bin is simply the proportion of observations that fall into that bin. So instead of reporting that the first bin had 22 observations in it, we report that the proportion of observations in the first bin was 22/38 = 0.58. We divide by 38 because there were a total of 38 observations in the data set. Figure 2.5 shows the same data as the histogram of Figure 2.3; however, Figure 2.5 reports relative frequencies, whereas Figure 2.3 reported frequencies.

Using relative frequencies does not change the shape of the graph; it just communicates different information to the viewer. Rather than answering the question "How many quarterbacks completed between 0 and 3 touchdown passes in the season?"

(22 quarterbacks), it now answers the question "What *proportion* of quarterbacks completed between 0 and 3 touchdown passes in the season? (0.58, or 58%). Relative frequency histograms are useful for making comparisons across data sets of different size.

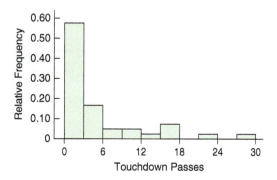

◄ **FIGURE 2.5** Relative frequency histogram of number of touchdown passes completed by CFL quarterbacks in 2014.

 SNAPSHOT   **THE HISTOGRAM**

WHAT IS IT? ►	A graphical summary for numerical data.
WHAT DOES IT DO? ►	Shows a picture of the distribution of a numerical variable.
HOW DOES IT DO IT? ►	Observations are grouped into bins, and bars are drawn to show how many observations (or what proportion of observations) lie in each bin.
HOW IS IT USED? ►	By using grouped data and smoothing over details, histograms allow us to observe overall patterns in a data set. Be aware that making the bins wider hides detail, and making the bins smaller can show too much detail. The vertical axis can display frequency, relative frequency, or percentages.
WHEN IS IT USED? ►	When there are many observations of a numerical variable.

EXAMPLE 1 Visualizing Passenger Traffic at the World's Busiest Airports

Every year, Airports Council International releases data about passenger traffic at the busiest airports in the world. Knowledge about how busy airports are can help people make informed decisions when making travel plans.

QUESTION Pearson International Airport in Toronto is Canada's busiest airport, with 36 million passengers (36,037,962 passengers, to be more precise) travelling through it in 2013. How does Pearson's passenger traffic compare to that of the other airports in the list of 50 busiest airports in the world that year?

SOLUTION One way of answering this question is to determine whether 36 million is a typical value of passenger traffic, or whether there are many airports that are busier than 36 million and, if so, how much busier these airports are. Questions such as these can be answered by considering the distribution of our data set, so our first step is to choose an appropriate graphical presentation of the distribution.

Either a dotplot or a histogram can show us the distribution. From the dotplot in Figure 2.6a, we can see that there are several airports that are about as busy as Pearson (around 36 million passengers). In fact, it seems to be a fairly common value of passenger traffic among the airports in this group.

▶ FIGURE 2.6 **(a)** A dotplot for passenger traffic (in millions of passengers) for the busiest 50 airports in the world. Each dot represents an airport, and the dot's location indicates the millions of passengers who travelled through that airport in 2013. **(b)** A histogram shows the same data as in part (a), except that the details have been smoothed by grouping the data.

(a)

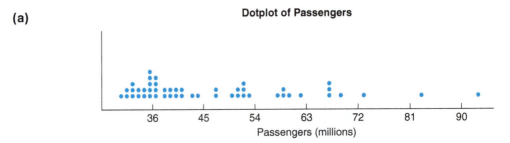

Dotplot of Passengers

(b)

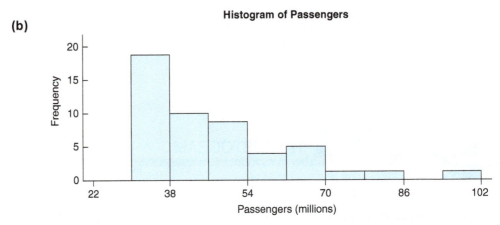

Histogram of Passengers

It is easier to make comparisons by using a histogram, as in Figure 2.6b. In this histogram, each bar has a width of 8 million passengers, and the *y*-axis tells us how many airports had passenger traffic within those limits. Pearson International Airport belongs to the first bin in the histogram, with 18 other airports in the same bin. This tells us that, among the world's 50 busiest airports, passenger traffic of about 36 million passengers is not unusual, since more than a third of these airports have about that amount of passenger traffic.

TRY THIS! Exercise 2.5

Stemplots

Stemplots, which are also called stem-and-leaf plots, are useful for visualizing numerical variables when you don't have access to technology and the data set is not large. Stemplots are also useful if you want to be able to see the actual values of the data easily.

To make a **stemplot**, divide each observation into a "stem" and a "leaf." The **leaf** is the last digit in the observation. The **stem** contains all the digits that precede the leaf. For the number 62, the 6 is the stem and the 2 is the leaf. For the number 623, 62 would be the stem and 3 would be the leaf. Note, however, that using two or more digits as the stem could easily give us a very long list of stems. In those cases, it is customary to round the quantities involved and to use as leaf the last digit before the zeroes that resulted from rounding. For example, 623 would be rounded to 620, with 6 as stem and 2 as leaf. The zeroes due to rounding would be ignored, and the units for the leaves would be indicated in the plot as tens.

We can use a stem-and-leaf plot to analyze data on some students' drinking habits. Alcohol consumption is a big problem at many colleges and universities. For this reason, a collection of college students who said that they drink alcohol were asked how many alcoholic drinks they had consumed in the past seven days. Their answers were

1, 1, 1, 1, 1, 2, 2, 2, 3, 3, 3, 3, 3, 4, 5, 5, 5, 6, 6, 6, 8, 10, 10, 15, 17, 20, 25, 30, 30, 40

For one-digit numbers, imagine a 0 at the front. The observation of 1 drink becomes 01, the observation of 2 drinks becomes 02, and so on. Then each observation is just two digits; the first digit is the stem, and the last digit is the leaf. Figure 2.7 shows a stemplot of these data.

If you rotate a stemplot 90 degrees counterclockwise, it looks not too different from a histogram. Unlike histograms, stemplots display the actual values of the data. With a histogram, you know only that the values fall somewhere within an interval.

Stemplots are often organized with the leaves in order from lowest to highest, which makes it easier to locate particular values, as in Figure 2.7. This is not necessary, but it makes the plot easier to use.

From the stemplot, we see that most students drink a moderate amount in a week but that a few drink quite a bit. Forty drinks per week is almost six per day, which qualifies as problem drinking by some clinical definitions.

Figure 2.8 shows a stemplot for the data on honey bee wintering losses that we introduced in Chapter 1 (rounded to the nearest unit). Recall that the data represent the percentage of honey bee wintering losses in the nine beekeeping Canadian provinces over the winter 2013–2014. We can see that wintering loss in all provinces except for one was above the acceptable 15% loss rate. Wintering loss in most provinces was only a few percentage points above acceptable (between 15 and 19, inclusive), but wintering loss in one province was unusually high at 58% (more on that later). Note the empty stems at 3 and 4, which show that there was no province with a wintering loss rate between 30% and 49%.

TECH

Stem	Leaves (in units)
0	111112223333345556668
1	0057
2	05
3	00
4	0

▲ **FIGURE 2.7** A stemplot for alcoholic drinks consumed by college students. Each digit on the right (the leaves) represents a student. Together, the stem and the leaf indicate the number of drinks for one student who is a drinker.

Stem	Leaves (in units)
1	58999
2	347
3	
4	
5	8

▲ **FIGURE 2.8** A stemplot for percentage of honey bee wintering losses in the nine beekeeping Canadian provinces in 2013–2014.

SNAPSHOT **THE STEMPLOT**

WHAT IS IT? ▶	A graphical summary for numerical data.
WHAT DOES IT DO? ▶	Shows a picture of the distribution of a numerical variable.
HOW DOES IT DO IT? ▶	Numbers are divided into leaves (the last digit) and stems (the preceding digits). Stems are written in a vertical column, and associated leaves are "attached," with units clearly indicated. Empty stems are kept as part of the plot.
HOW IS IT USED? ▶	The digits of the observations are rearranged in a convenient way, similar to a histogram. However, the actual observations are not lost.
WHEN IS IT USED? ▶	It is most useful when technology is not available and the data set is not large.

SECTION 2.2

Summarizing Important Features of a Numerical Distribution

When examining a distribution, pay attention to describing the shape of the distribution, the **typical value (centre)** of the distribution, and the **variability (spread)** in the distribution. The typical value is subjective, but the location of the centre of a distribution often gives us an idea of which values are typical or common for this variable. The variability is reflected in the amount of horizontal spread the distribution has.

KEY POINT When examining distributions of numerical data, pay attention to the shape, centre, and horizontal spread.

Figure 2.9 compares distributions for two groups, once again with data from the CFL website for the 2014 season. Histogram (a) shows total rushing yards and histogram (b) shows total receiving yards for the top players in each category. How do these two distributions compare?

▶ **FIGURE 2.9** Histograms of **(a)** total rushing yards and **(b)** total receiving yards for top players during the 2014 CFL season.

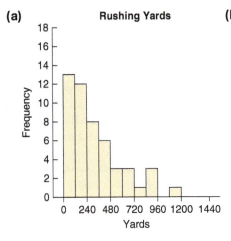 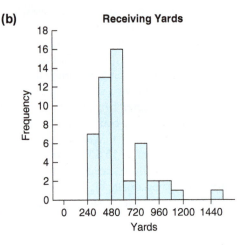

1. *Shape.* Are there interesting or unusual features about the distributions? Are the shapes very different?

2. *Centre.* What is the typical value of each distribution? Is the typical number of rushing yards different from the typical number of receiving yards?

3. *Spread.* The horizontal spread presents the variation in total number of yards for each group. How do the amounts of variation compare?

Let's consider these three aspects of a distribution one at a time.

Shape

You should look for three basic characteristics of a distribution's shape:

1. Is the distribution symmetric or skewed?

2. How many mounds appear? One? Two? None? Many?

3. Are unusually large or small values present?

Symmetric or Skewed?

A symmetric distribution is one in which the left-hand side of the graph is roughly a mirror image of the right-hand side. The idealized distributions in Figure 2.10 show two of several possibilities. Figure 2.10a is a **symmetric distribution** with one mound. (Statisticians often describe a distribution with this particular shape as a **bell-shaped distribution**. Bell-shaped distributions play a major role in statistics, as you will see throughout this book.)

Details

Vague Words

For now, we have left the three ideas of *shape*, *centre*, and *spread* deliberately vague. In Chapter 3 you'll learn ways of measuring more precisely where the centre is and how much spread exists. However, the first task in a data analysis is to examine a distribution to informally evaluate the shape, centre, and spread.

▶ **FIGURE 2.10** Sketches of **(a)** a symmetric distribution and **(b)** a right-skewed distribution.

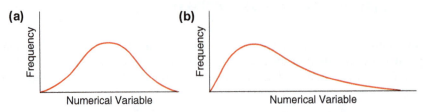

Figure 2.10b represents a nonsymmetric distribution with a skewed shape that has one mound. Note that it has a "tail" that extends out to the right (toward larger values). Because the tail goes to the right, we call it a **right-skewed distribution**. This is a typical shape for the distribution of a variable in which most values are relatively small but that also has a few very large values. If the tail goes to the left, it is a **left-skewed distribution**, where most values are relatively large but that also has a few very small values.

Figure 2.11 shows a histogram of the heights of 73 female students in a large statistics class. How would you describe the shape of this distribution? This is a real-life example of a symmetric distribution. Clearly, the distribution is not perfectly symmetric (and with a different choice of bins it would probably not appear as symmetric as it does in this histogram), but you will never see "perfect" in real-life data.

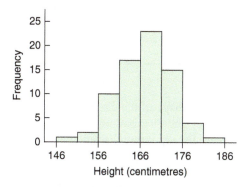

◀ **FIGURE 2.11** Histogram of heights of female students. (Source: Boué 2009)

Suppose we asked a sample of people how many hours of TV they watched in a typical week. Would you expect a histogram of these data to be symmetric? Probably not. The smallest possible value for this data set would be 0, and most people would probably cluster near a common value. However, a few people probably watch quite a bit more TV than most other people. Figure 2.12 shows the actual histogram. We've added an arrow to emphasize that the tail of this distribution points to the right; this is a right-skewed distribution.

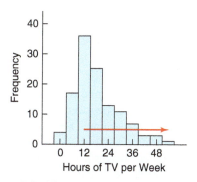

▲ **FIGURE 2.12** This data set on TV hours viewed per week is skewed to the right. (Source: Minitab Program)

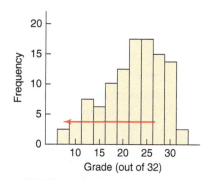

▲ **FIGURE 2.13** This data set on test scores is skewed to the left. (Source: Ryan 2006)

Figure 2.13 shows a left-skewed distribution of test scores. This is the sort of distribution that you should hope your next exam will have. Most people scored pretty high, so the few people who scored low create a tail on the left-hand side. The distribution of scores for a very difficult test, one in which most people scored very low and only a few did well, would be right-skewed.

Another circumstance in which we often see skewed distributions is when we collect data on people's income. When we graph the distribution of incomes of a large group of people, we quite often see a right-skewed distribution. You can't make less than 0 dollars per year. Most people make a moderate amount of money, but there is no upper limit to how much a person can make, and a few people in any large sample will make a very large amount of money.

Example 2 shows that you can often make an educated guess as to the shape of a distribution even without collecting data.

EXAMPLE **2** Roller Coaster Endurance

A morning radio show is sponsoring a contest in which contestants compete to win a car. About 40 contestants are put on a roller coaster, and whoever stays on it the longest wins. Suppose we make a histogram of the amount of time the contestants stay on (measured in hours or even days).

QUESTION What shape do we expect the histogram to have and why?

SOLUTION Probably most people will drop out relatively soon, but a few will last for a very long time. The last two contestants will probably stay for a very long time indeed. Therefore, we would expect the distribution to be right-skewed.

TRY THIS! Exercise 2.9

How Many Mounds?

What do you think would be the shape of the distribution of heights if we included men in our sample as well as women? The distributions of women's heights by themselves and men's heights by themselves are usually symmetric and have one mound. But because we know that men tend to be taller than women, we might expect a histogram that combines men's and women's heights to have two mounds.

The statistical term for a one-mound distribution is a **unimodal distribution**, and a two-mound distribution is called a **bimodal distribution**. Figure 2.14a shows a bimodal distribution. A **multimodal distribution** has more than two modes. The modes do not have to be the same height (in fact, they rarely are). Figure 2.14b is perhaps the more typical bimodal distribution.

◀ **FIGURE 2.14** Idealized bimodal distributions. **(a)** Modes of roughly equal height. **(b)** Modes that differ in height.

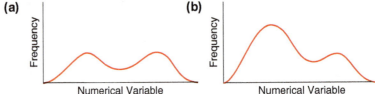

These sketches are idealizations. In real life you won't see distributions this neat. You will have to make a decision about whether a histogram is close enough to be called symmetric or whether it has one mound, two mounds, no mounds, or many mounds. The existence of multiple mounds is sometimes a sign that two very different groups have been combined into a single collection (such as combining men's heights with women's heights). When you see multimodal distributions, you may want to look back at the original data and see whether you can examine the groups separately, if separate groups exist. At the very least, whenever you see more than one mound, you should ask yourself, "Could these data be from different groups?"

EXAMPLE **3** Two Marathons, Merged

Data were collected on the finishing times of male runners for two different marathons. One marathon consisted of a small number of elite runners: the 2012 Olympic Games. The other marathon included a large number of amateur runners: a marathon in Victoria, British Columbia.

QUESTION What shape would you expect the distribution of this sample to have?

SOLUTION We expect the shape to be bimodal. The elite runners would tend to have faster finishing times, so we expect one mound on the left for the Olympic runners and another, taller mound (because there were more amateur runners) on the right. Figure 2.15 is a histogram of the data.

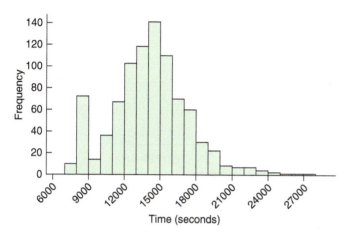

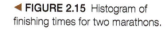

There appears to be one mound centred at about 8500 seconds (about 2.4 hours) and another centred at about 14,500 seconds (about 4 hours).

TRY THIS! Exercise 2.11

When we view a histogram, our understanding of the shape of a distribution is affected by the width of the bins. Figure 2.15 reveals the bimodality of the distribution partly because the width of the bins is such that we see the right level of detail. If we had made the bins too big, we would have gotten less detail and might not have seen the bimodal structure. Figure 2.16 shows what would happen. Experienced data analysts usually start with the bin width the computer chooses and then also examine histograms made with slightly wider and slightly narrower bins. This lets them see whether any interesting structure emerges.

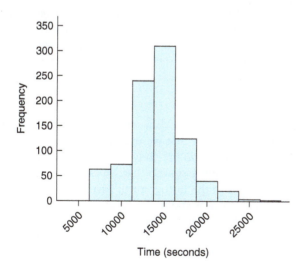

◄ **FIGURE 2.16** Another histogram of the same running times as in Figure 2.15. Here, the bins are wider and "wash out" detail, so the distribution no longer looks bimodal, even though it should.

Do Extreme Values Occur?

Sometimes when you plot the distribution of a numerical variable, you see extremely large or extremely small observations. These extreme observations are called **outliers**. For example, we asked students in one of our statistics classes to record the number of hours per week that they devoted to the course outside the classroom. Figure 2.17 shows the distribution. You can see that there are two observations that are outliers. There are only 168 hours in a week, so the two students who wrote 180 clearly made a mistake. Because we are sure that these outliers are the result of an error, we can take action by reporting them and by removing them from the data set before we analyze our data any further.

▶ **FIGURE 2.17** Histogram of hours devoted to statistics with two extreme observations. (Source: Boué 2010)

Stem	**Leaves (in units)**
1	58999
2	347
3
4
5	8

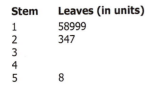

▲ **FIGURE 2.8 (repeated)**
Percentage of honey bee wintering losses in Canada, 2013–2014. The observation of 58% wintering loss is an outlier.

Outliers can result from mistakes, but very often they do not. The important thing is to make note of them when they appear and to investigate further whenever possible. For example, when examining the distribution of honey bee wintering losses in Canada, we found one province with an unusually high wintering loss rate of 58% (see Figure 2.8, which is repeated here). That observation was so unusual that, at the time of the CAPA report, the government of that province (Ontario) was conducting further analysis.

There are no precise rules for determining whether an observation is an outlier or not. Sometimes you may think an observation is an outlier, but another person might disagree, and this is fine. However, if there is no gap between the observation in question and the bulk of the histogram, then the observation probably should not be considered an outlier. Outliers are points that don't fit the pattern of the rest of the data, so if a large percentage of the observations are extreme, it might not be accurate to label them as outliers. After all, if lots of points don't fit a pattern, maybe you aren't seeing the right pattern!

KEY POINT Outliers are values so large or small that they do not fit into the pattern of the distribution. There is no precise definition of the term *outlier*. Outliers can be caused by errors, but genuine outliers are sometimes unusually interesting observations.

Centre

An important question to ask about any data set is "What is the typical value?" The typical value is the one in the centre, but we use the word *centre* here in a deliberately vague way. We might not all agree on precisely where the centre of a graph is. But the idea here is to get a rough impression so that we can make comparisons later. For example, judging on the basis of the histogram shown in Figure 2.9, the centre of the distribution of CFL rushing yards is about 300 yards. Thus we could say that the typical player in this group accumulated about 300 rushing yards in the 2014 season. In contrast, the centre of the distribution of receiving yards is about 500 yards. As you might have expected, we see that players typically accumulate less yards by rushing than by receiving passes.

If the distribution is bimodal or multimodal, it may not make sense to seek a "typical" value for a data set. If the data set combines two very different groups, then it might be more useful to find separate typical values for each group. What is the typical finishing time of the runners in Figure 2.15? There is no single typical time, because there are two distinct groups of runners. The elite group have their typical time, and the amateurs have a different typical time. However, it *does* make sense to ask about the typical test score for the student scores in Figure 2.13, because there is only one mound and only one group of students.

⚠ Caution

Multimodal Centres
Be careful about giving a single typical value for a multimodal or bimodal distribution. These distributions sometimes indicate the existence of different and diverse groups combined into the same data set. It may be better to report a different typical value for each group, if possible.

EXAMPLE 4 Typical Cost of Compulsory Undergraduate Fees

Compulsory additional fees for students (typically including athletics, student health services, and student association fees) vary from institution to institution. Figure 2.18 shows the distribution of fees for full-time undergraduate Canadian students in 2014–2015 at 105 degree-granting post-secondary institutions in Canada (i.e., universities and university-colleges).

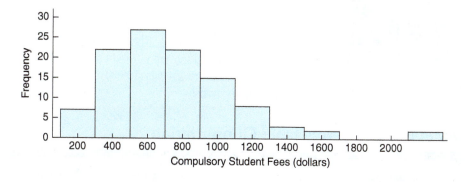

◀ **FIGURE 2.18**
Compulsory student fees for Canadian undergraduates in 2014–2015.

QUESTION What is the typical undergraduate student fee among these institutions?

SOLUTION The centre of the distribution is around $700, so we would say that the typical student fee is around $700. (Note that we are comparing fees among institutions. We cannot conclude from this that the typical student pays around $700, since we have not taken into account the number of students at each institution.)

TRY THIS! Exercise 2.13

Variability

The third important feature to consider when examining a distribution is the amount of variation in the data. If all the values of a numerical variable are the same, then the histogram (or dotplot) will be skinny. On the other hand, if there is great variety, the histogram will be spread out, thus displaying greater variability.

Here's a very simple example. Figure 2.19a shows a family of four people who are all very similar in height. Note that the histogram of these heights (Figure 2.19b) is quite skinny; in fact, it is just a single bar!

(a)

(b)

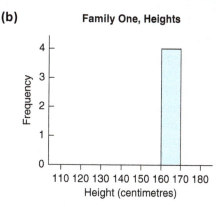

▲ **FIGURE 2.19** Family one with a small variation in height.

Figure 2.20a, on the other hand, shows a family that exhibits large variation in height. The histogram for this family (Figure 2.20b) is more spread out.

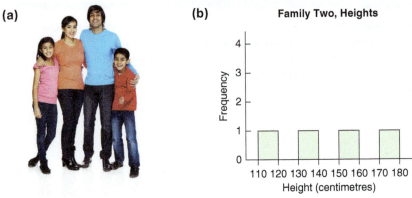

(a)

(b) **Family Two, Heights**

▲ **FIGURE 2.20** Family two with a large variation in height.

EXAMPLE 5 Daily Vegetable Consumption

Consider the histograms for daily vegetable consumption among 13-year-olds shown in Figure 2.21, according to data from the 2009/2010 Health Behaviour in School-aged Children study, a World Health Organization (WHO) collaborative cross-national study. Daily vegetable consumption was measured as the percentage of children who reported eating vegetables at least every day or more than once a day in each of the 39 countries and regions surveyed.

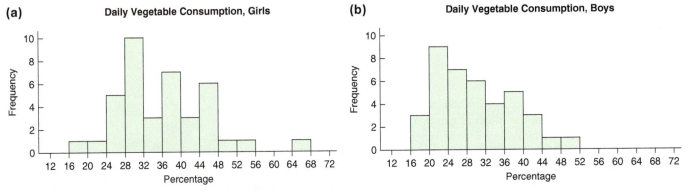

(a) **Daily Vegetable Consumption, Girls**

(b) **Daily Vegetable Consumption, Boys**

▲ **FIGURE 2.21** Histograms of daily vegetable consumption in 39 countries and regions (measured as the percentage of children who eat vegetables daily) for 13-year-old **(a)** girls and **(b)** boys.

QUESTION Do girls and boys have different variability in daily vegetable consumption? If so, which group has the greatest variability?

SOLUTION The daily vegetable consumption for girls ranges from about 16% to 68%, a difference of 52 percentage points. The daily vegetable consumption for boys ranges from 16% to 52%, a difference of 36 percentage points. We can also see that boys' observations are more clustered together than the girls' observations. Therefore, girls have more variability than boys in terms of daily vegetable consumption. Incidentally, in all countries girls were more likely than boys to eat vegetables daily. For instance, the daily vegetable consumption for 13-year-olds in Canada was 47% for girls and 40% for boys. Researchers suggest that girls eat fruits and vegetables more often because they are in general more health conscious. Understanding these gender differences is important in designing successful and targeted interventions.

TRY THIS! Exercise 2.15

Describing Distributions

When you are asked to describe a distribution or to compare two distributions, your description should include the centre of the distribution (What is the typical value?), the spread (How much variability is there?), and the shape. If the shape is bimodal, it might not be appropriate to mention the centre, and you should instead identify the approximate location of the mounds. You should also mention any unusual features, such as extreme values.

EXAMPLE **6** Body Piercings

How common are body piercings among university students? How many piercings does a student typically have? One statistics professor asked a large class of students to report (anonymously) the number of piercings they possessed.

QUESTION Describe the distribution of body piercings for students in a statistics class.

SOLUTION The first step is to "see it" by creating an appropriate graphic of the distribution of the sample. Figure 2.22 shows a histogram for these data. To summarize this distribution, we examine the shape, centre, and spread and comment on any unusual features.

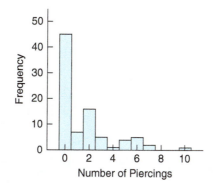

◀ FIGURE 2.22 Numbers of piercings of students in a statistics class.

The distribution of piercings is right-skewed, as we might expect, given that many people will have 0, 1, or 2 piercings, but a few people are likely to have more. The typical number of piercings (the centre of the distribution) seems to be about 1, although a majority of students have none. The number of piercings ranges from 0 to 10. An interesting feature of this distribution is that it appears to be multimodal. There are three peaks: at 0, 2, and 6, which are even numbers. This makes sense, because piercings often come in pairs. But why is there no peak at 4? (The authors do not know.) What do you think the shape of the distribution would look like if it included only the men? Only the women?

TRY THIS! Exercise 2.17

SECTION 2.3

Visualizing Variation in Categorical Variables

When visualizing data, we treat categorical variables in much the same way as numerical variables. We visualize the distribution of the categorical variable by displaying the values (categories) of the variable and the number of times each value occurs.

To illustrate, consider the data in Table 2.3, showing language(s) spoken at home for a random sample of 25 people, based on results of the 2011 Canadian Census of Population. The category "Other Only" represents people who speak only a language

Person	Language(s) Spoken at Home
1	English Only
2	French Only
3	English Only
4	Other Combination
5	English Only
6	English and French
7	French Only
8	English Only
9	Other Only
10	French Only
11	English Only
12	Other Combination
13	English Only
14	Other Combination
15	English Only
16	English Only
17	English Only
18	English Only
19	English Only
20	English Only
21	English and French
22	English Only
23	English Only
24	English Only
25	English Only

▲ **TABLE 2.3** Language(s) spoken at home for 25 people.

Language(s)	Frequency
English Only	16
French Only	3
English and French	2
Other Only	1
Other Combination	3
Total	**25**

▲ **TABLE 2.4** Summary of language(s) spoken at home.

other than English or French, while "Other Combination" represents people who speak multiple languages at home, at least one of which is not English or French.

Language(s) spoken at home is a categorical variable. Table 2.4 summarizes the distribution of this variable by showing us all the values in our sample and the frequency with which each value appears. We will now learn about the two types of graphs that are valid for this type of data: bar charts and pie charts.

Bar Charts

A **bar graph** (also called a **bar chart**) shows a bar for each observed category. The height of the bar is proportional to the frequency of that category. Figure 2.23a shows a bar graph for the languages spoken at home sample. The vertical axis measures frequency. For example, we see that the sample has 16 people who speak only English at home. We can also display the bar graph with relative frequencies, as in Figure 2.23b. The shape does not change; only the numbers on the vertical axis change.

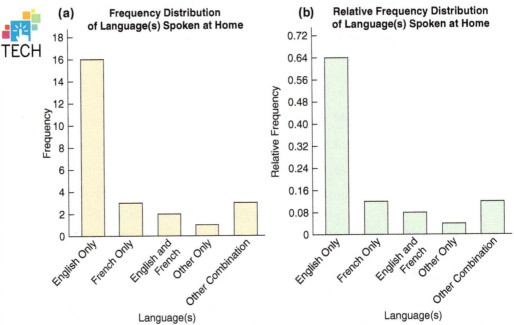

▲ **FIGURE 2.23 (a)** Bar chart showing the number of people in the sample in each language group. **(b)** The same information as shown in part (a), but with relative frequencies. People who speak only English are 0.64 (64%) of the sample.

Bar Charts vs. Histograms

Bar charts and histograms look a lot alike, but they have some very important differences.

- In a bar chart, it sometimes doesn't matter in which order you place the bars. Quite often, the categories of a categorical variable have no natural order. If they do have a natural order, you might want to sort them in that order. The categories for the *language(s) spoken at home* variable do not have a natural order, so any ordering is acceptable. For instance, Figure 2.24a shows the complete 2011 census results (33,121,175 people) with categories in the same order as in Figure 2.23. In Figure 2.24b we display the same data but with categories sorted from most frequent to least frequent. This type of graph is called a **Pareto chart**, named after the Italian economist and sociologist Vilfredo Pareto (1848–1923).

- Another difference between histograms and bar charts is that in a bar chart, it doesn't matter how wide or narrow the bars are. The widths of the bars have no meaning.

- A final important difference is that a bar chart has gaps between the bars. This indicates that it is impossible to have observations between the categories. In a histogram, a gap indicates that no values were observed in the interval represented by the gap.

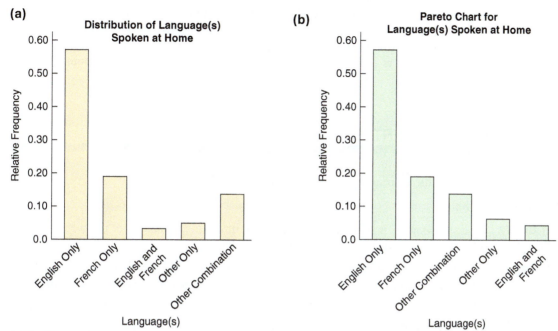

(a)

(b)

▲ FIGURE 2.24 **(a)** Bar chart for languages spoken at home—complete census data. **(b)** Pareto chart for the same data. Categories are ordered with the largest frequency on the left and arranged so that the frequencies decrease to the right.

SNAPSHOT THE BAR CHART

WHAT IS IT? ▶	A graphical summary for categorical data.
WHAT DOES IT DO? ▶	Shows a picture of the distribution of a categorical variable.
HOW DOES IT DO IT? ▶	Each category is represented by a bar. The height of the bar is proportional to the number of times that category occurs in the data set.
HOW IS IT USED? ▶	To see patterns of variation in categorical data. The categories can be presented in order of most frequent to least frequent, or they can be arranged in another meaningful order.
WHEN IS IT USED? ▶	It is appropriate for any categorical variable.

Pie Charts

Pie charts are another popular format for displaying relative frequencies of data. A **pie chart** looks, as you would expect, like a pie. The pie is sliced into several pieces, and each piece represents a category of the variable. The area of the piece is proportional to the relative frequency of that category. The largest piece in the pie in Figure 2.25 belongs to the category "English Only" and takes up 58% of the total pie.

Some software will label each slice of the pie with the percentage occupied. This isn't always necessary, however, because a primary purpose of the pie chart is to help us judge how frequently categories occur relative to one another. For example, the pie chart in Figure 2.25 shows us that "English Only" occupies a majority of the whole data set. Also, labelling each slice gets cumbersome and produces cluttered graphs if there are many categories.

Although pie charts are very common (we bet that you've seen them before), they are not commonly used by statisticians or in scientific settings. One reason for this is that the human eye has a difficult time judging how much area is taken up by the wedge-shaped slices of the pie chart. Thus, in Figure 2.25, the "French Only" slice looks only

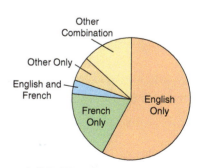

▲ FIGURE 2.25 Pie chart showing the distribution of language(s) spoken at home according to the 2011 Canadian census of population.

slightly larger than the "Other Combination" slice. But you can see from either of the bar charts in Figure 2.24 that they are actually quite different. Pie charts are also extremely difficult to use when comparing the distributions of a variable across two different groups (such as comparing the languages spoken at home at different points in time).

SNAPSHOT   THE PIE CHART

WHAT IS IT? ▶	A graphical summary for categorical data.
WHAT DOES IT DO? ▶	Shows the proportion of observations that belong to each category.
HOW DOES IT DO IT? ▶	Each category is represented by a wedge in the pie. The area of the wedge is proportional to the relative frequency of that category.
HOW IS IT USED? ▶	To understand which categories are most frequent and which are least frequent. Sometimes it is useful to label each wedge with the proportion of occurrence.
WHEN IS IT USED? ▶	Although used very frequently, statisticians do not recommend its use for graphing categorical variables.

SECTION 2.4

Summarizing Categorical Distributions

The concepts of *shape*, *centre*, and *spread* that we used to summarize numerical distributions sometimes don't make sense for categorical distributions, because we can often order the categories any way we please. The centre and shape would be different for every ordering of categories. However, we can still talk about typical outcomes and the variability in the sample.

The Mode

When describing a distribution of a categorical variable, pay attention to which category occurs most often. This value, the one with the tallest bar in the bar chart, can sometimes be considered the "typical" outcome. There might be a tie for first place, and that's okay. It just means there's not as much variability in the sample. (Read on to see what we mean by that.)

The category that occurs most often is called the **mode**. This meaning of the word *mode* is similar to its meaning when we use it with numerical variables. However, one big difference between categorical and numerical variables is that we call a categorical variable bimodal only if two categories are nearly tied for most frequent outcomes. (The two bars don't need to be exactly the same height, but they should be very close.) Similarly, a categorical variable's distribution is multimodal if more than two categories all have roughly the tallest bars. For a numerical variable, the mounds do not need to be the same height for the distribution to be multimodal.

For an example of a mode, let us consider once more the *Essential Facts About the Canadian Computer and Video Game Industry* report published by the Entertainment Software Association of Canada (ESAC). People who play video games were asked to select which of the following platforms they played video games on most frequently: (i) a cell phone, tablet computer, or other mobile device; (ii) a handheld game system; (iii) a computer; or (iv) a game console. Figure 2.26 shows the results for 2009.

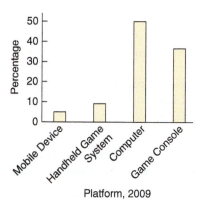

◀ **FIGURE 2.26** Percentages of respondents who played video games most frequently on a mobile device, a handheld game system, a computer, or a game console (ESAC 2009).

We see that many people (50%) played video games most frequently on a computer. The computer is the mode for this distribution. In contrast, very few people in 2009 used their cell phone or other mobile device as their most frequent platform for playing video games.

EXAMPLE 7 Platforms for Playing Video Games

The ESAC report for 2012 also included information about which platform Canadians played video games on most frequently during that year. The bar chart in Figure 2.27 shows the distribution of responses.

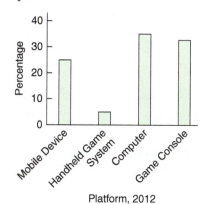

◀ **FIGURE 2.27** Percentages of respondents who play video games most frequently on a mobile device, a handheld game system, a computer, or a game console (ESAC 2012). Compare to Figure 2.26, where the data for 2009 are given.

QUESTION What is the typical response? How would you compare the responses in 2012 to those in 2009?

SOLUTION The mode is computer, which is the most frequent platform for 36% of respondents. Although the mode is the same as in 2009, the distribution of preferences has changed considerably, with a much higher percentage of people using mobile devices to play video games in 2012 than in 2009.

TRY THIS! Exercise 2.31

Variability

When thinking about the variability of a categorical distribution, it is sometimes useful to think of the word *diversity*. If the distribution has a lot of diversity (many observations in many different categories), then variability is high. If the distribution has only a little diversity (many of the observations fall into the same category), then variability is low.

For example, we can compare the responses in the ESAC report from 2009 (Figure 2.26) with the responses from 2012 (Figure 2.27). In 2009, the bar chart shows that most people preferred either computers or game consoles, with only a small percentage of players using mobile devices or handheld game systems. Although computers and game consoles were still the preferred platform for the majority of players in 2012, mobile devices were now close behind. Therefore, there was more variability and diversity in preferences in 2012 than in 2009.

EXAMPLE 8 The Inuit and Their Aboriginal Languages

Figure 2.28 shows bar charts on the ability to speak an Inuit language for Inuit aged 15 and older in two of the four regions that constitute Inuit Nunangat (the Inuit homeland, where nearly three-quarters of the Inuit population of Canada live). Figure 2.28a depicts data for Nunavut and Figure 2.28b depicts data for Nunatsiavut (in Labrador) (Aboriginal Peoples Survey 2012).

▶ FIGURE 2.28 Prevalence of ability to speak an Inuit language, Inuit population 15 and older **(a)** in Nunavut and **(b)** in Nunatsiavut.

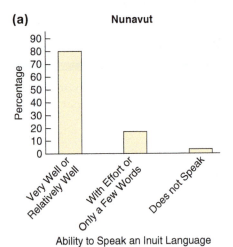

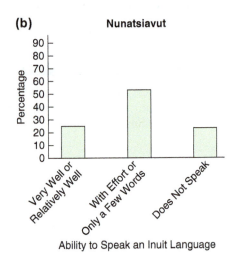

QUESTION In which region (Nunavut or Nunatsiavut) is there more variability in the ability to speak an Inuit language? Explain.

SOLUTION The first bar chart shows that in Nunavut most Inuit speak an Inuit language very well or relatively well, and only a small percentage speaks it with effort or does not speak it at all. In contrast, the majority of people in Nunatsiavut speak it with effort, while a quarter speaks it well or relatively well, and nearly a quarter does not speak it at all. Therefore, there is more variability and diversity in the ability to speak an Inuit language in Nunatsiavut than there is in Nunavut.

TRY THIS! Exercise 2.33

You might be surprised by the answer to Example 8 because the three bars in the Nunatsiavut bar chart are closer to being the same height than the ones in the Nunavut graph, so it seems as though the three categories are not as different. However, variability is not just about the heights of the bars; variability is measured by how many different categories have responses in them. The most diverse distribution for categorical data would be represented by a bar chart in which all categories had bars of exactly the same height. The least variability would be represented by one in which there was only one bar, and all the other categories were empty.

Describing Distributions of Categorical Variables

When describing a distribution of categorical data, you should mention the mode (or modes) and say something about the variability. Example 9 illustrates what we mean.

KEY POINT ⟩ When summarizing graphs of categorical data, report the mode or modes and describe the variability (diversity).

EXAMPLE 9 Causes of Death

According to Statistics Canada, about 51.3% of babies currently born in Canada are male. But among people over 100 years old, there are about seven times as many women as there are men (Statistics Canada, 2014). How does this happen? One possibility is that the percentage of boys born has changed over time. Another possibility is presented in the two bar charts in Figure 2.29. These bar charts show the numbers of deaths per 100,000 people in one year, for people aged 15–24 years, for both males and females.

QUESTION Compare the distributions depicted in Figure 2.29. Note that the categories are put into the same order on both graphs.

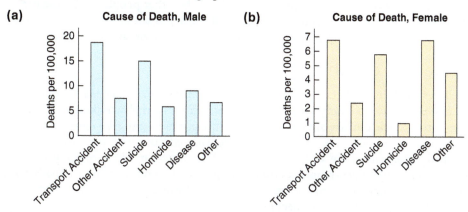

◄ FIGURE 2.29 The number of deaths per 100,000 males **(a)** and females **(b)** for people 15–24 years old in a one-year period.

SOLUTION First, note that the bar charts are not on the same scale, as you can see by comparing the values on the *y*-axes. This presentation is typical of most software and is sometimes desirable, because otherwise, one of the bar charts might have such small bars that we couldn't easily discern differences.

Although transport accidents are a mode for both groups, males show a consistently high death rate for all other causes of death, whereas females have relatively low death rates in the categories for other accident and homicide. In other words, the cause of death for females is less variable than that for males. It is also worth noting that the death rates are higher for males in every category. For example, roughly 7 out of every 100,000 females died in a transport accident in one year, while roughly 18 out of every 100,000 males died in a transport accident in the same year.

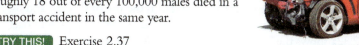

TRY THIS! Exercise 2.37

We can also make graphics that help us compare two distributions of categorical variables. When comparing two groups across a categorical variable, it is often useful to put the bars side by side, as in Figure 2.30. This graph makes it easier to compare rates of death for each cause. The much higher death rate for males is made clear.

▶ **FIGURE 2.30** Death rates of males and females, aged 15–24, graphed side by side.

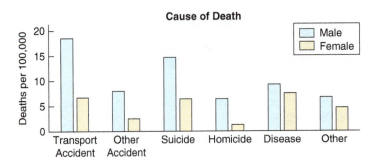

SECTION 2.5

Interpreting Graphs

The first step in every investigation of data is to make an appropriate graph. Many analyses of data begin with visualizing the distribution of a variable, and this requires that you know whether the variable is numerical or categorical. When interpreting these graphics, you should pay attention to the centre, spread, and shape.

Often, you will come across graphics produced by other people, and these can take extra care to interpret. In this section, we'll warn you about some potential pitfalls when interpreting graphs and show you some unusual visualizations of data.

Misleading Graphs

A well-designed statistical graphic can help us discover patterns and trends and can communicate these patterns clearly to others. However, our eyes can play tricks on us, and manipulative people can take advantage of this to use graphs to give false impressions.

The most common trick—one that is particularly effective with bar charts—is to change the scale of the vertical axis so that it does not start at the origin (0). Figure 2.31a shows police-reported crime rates per 100,000 population in Canada for several years, obtained from the Statistics Canada Uniform Crime Reporting Survey. The graphic indicates substantial declines in crime for all years. Note that the vertical axis starts at 5100 crimes per 100,000 population.

Because the origin starts at 5100 and not at 0, the bars are all shorter than they should be. This creates a much more dramatic apparent decline in crime. For example, the 2009 bar is more than six times higher than the 2013 bar. Does this mean that the crime rate in 2009 was more than six times higher than the crime rate in 2013? What does this chart look like if we make the bars the correct height? Figure 2.31b shows the same data, but to the correct scale. It's still clear that there has been a decline, but the decline doesn't look nearly as dramatic now, does it? Why not?

The reason is that when the origin is correctly set to 0, as in Figure 2.31b, it is clear that the crime rates have declined, but only slightly every year. For example, the actual decline from 2012 to 2013 was about 7%. This is certainly good news, especially considering the fact that the crime rate in 2013 reached its lowest level since 1969. Nevertheless, it is not as dramatically good as the first graph erroneously suggests.

A common technique for creating eye-catching graphs is the use of shading and 3-D effects that contain little or no added information, and that very often misrepresent data. For example, Figure 2.32a shows the results of a 2012 Leger Marketing survey. A sample of 1505 Canadians aged 18 or older was asked: "What is your favourite quick-service food item?" As you can see, 33% of respondents prefer pizza, so the slice representing pizza occupies 33% of the pie. However, that is not what your eyes are telling you. Because of the 3-D effect and the change in the viewing angle of the pie, the slice representing pizza occupies more than half of the visible area of the chart. Since it is the slice closest to you, we have also used a larger font. Our manipulation of the chart leaves you with the impression that respondents' preference for pizza is much larger than it is in reality.

(a)

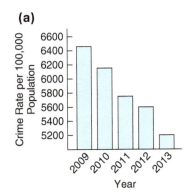

(b)

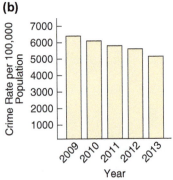

▲ **FIGURE 2.31** **(a)** This bar chart shows a consistent large decline in the crime rate from 2009 to 2013. The origin for the vertical axis begins at about 5100 and not at 0. **(b)** This bar chart reports the same data as part (a), but here the vertical axis begins at the origin (0).

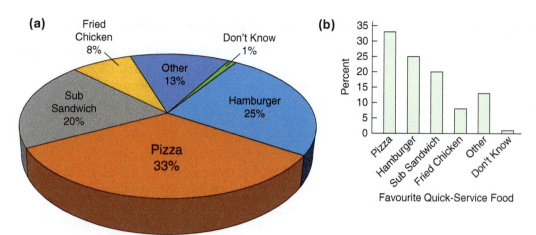

◀ FIGURE 2.32 Summary of quick-service food preferences from a 2012 survey. **(a)** The 3-D pie chart has been manipulated to exaggerate respondents' preference for pizza. **(b)** The bar chart represents the data correctly.

Figure 2.32b is a straight-forward bar graph that displays the same information as Figure 2.32a. The area of each bar is proportional to the relative frequency of the corresponding category, and so it correctly represents the data, even if it is not as eye-catching.

Other common errors found in poor graphs include the use of axes that do not keep a constant scale and the use of drawings instead of rectangular bars when creating bar graphs, just to mention a few. You must remember to be on the lookout for misleading graphs before you begin to interpret the data displayed.

Interactive Data Visualization

The internet allows for a great variety of graphical displays of data that take us beyond simple visualizations of distributions. Many statisticians, computer scientists, and designers are experimenting with new ways to visualize data. Most exciting is the rise of interactive displays. Gapminder, for example (www.gapminder.org), makes it possible to compare all UN members and other countries and territories with more than 1 million people through time by income and health. The graph animates the progress in income per capita and life expectancy from 1800 to today.

Figure 2.33 is a static version of the 2012 data. Each country is represented by a bubble, with its colour representing the region of the world in which the country is located, and its size representing the country's population. The *x*-location of the bubble represents the country's income per capita in U.S. dollars, and its *y*-location represents the country's life expectancy. (You can find Canada represented by a green bubble near the upper right-hand corner of the graph, northwest of the large green bubble representing the United States.) The graph is packed with information, but the clarity of the visual design allows us to see general trends in world income distribution easily. The interactive version allows the user to explore those trends through time, with bubbles changing size and location as time progresses.

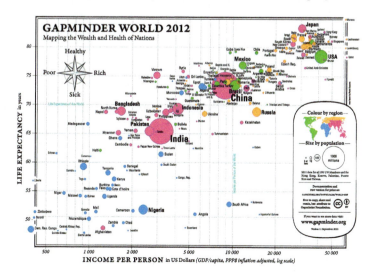

◀ FIGURE 2.33 The Gapminder World chart compares all UN members and other countries and territories with more than 1 million people, by income and health. Each country is a bubble, with its colour representing region of the world and its size representing population. (Source: www.gapminder.org)

CASE STUDY REVISITED

What difference do learning and higher education levels make in terms of annual income? The data from a random sample of respondents to the 2009 Survey of Household Spending were presented at the beginning of the chapter. The list of raw data makes it hard to see patterns, so it is very difficult to compare groups. But because annual income is a numerical variable, we can display the distributions of income as three histograms to enable us to make comparisons between people who completed different levels of education: high school, college, or university.

In Figure 2.34, histograms show annual income before taxes for respondents in each of the three groups: Figure 2.34a is for respondents who attained a high school diploma or equivalent; Figure 2.34b is for respondents who attained a community college, CEGEP, or nursing school diploma; and Figure 2.34c is for respondents who attained a bachelor's degree or a university degree, certificate, or diploma above a bachelor's. The distributions are quite different. The typical annual income for high school graduates is about $20,000 per year; for college graduates it is about $40,000 per year; and for university graduates it is about $60,000 per year. The shapes of the distributions vary as well. The distribution for high school graduates has a small right skew, but it has little variation around its typical value. The distribution for college graduates is heavily right-skewed, with a few respondents whose income is much higher than those of the rest of the sample. Finally, the distribution for university graduates is mostly symmetric, concentrated mostly around higher levels of income than the other distributions, and with only a couple of extreme high observations.

Although we have analyzed only small samples, these histograms clearly support the fact that there is a relationship between level of education and income: people with higher levels of education typically earn a higher income. According to a study by Employment and Social Development Canada (ESDC 2008), higher levels of education are also related to greater savings and assets, higher income during retirement, and lower unemployment risks, all contributing to greater financial security.

(a)

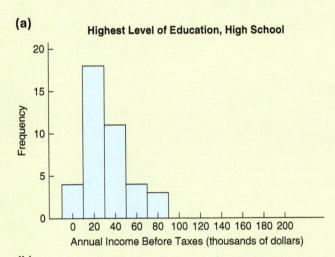

(b)

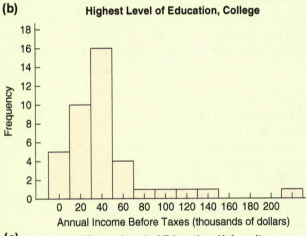

(c)

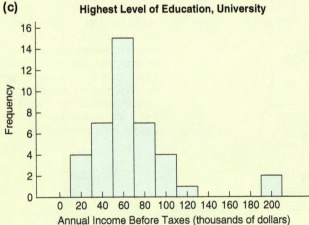

▲ **FIGURE 2.34** Histograms of annual income before taxes for respondents with different levels of education.

EXPLORING STATISTICS

CLASS ACTIVITY

Personal Distance

How much personal distance do people require when they're using an automatic teller machine?

GOALS	MATERIALS
In this activity, you will learn to make graphs of sample distributions in order to answer questions about data in comparing two groups of students.	Metre stick (or tape measure).

ACTIVITY

Work in groups of three students. Each group must have a metre stick. The first person stands (preferably in front of a wall) and imagines that she or he is at an ATM getting cash. The second student stands behind the first. The first student tells the second student how far back he or she must stand for the first student to be just barely comfortable, saying, for example, "Move back a little, now move forward just a tiny bit," and so on. When that distance is set, the third student measures the distance between the heel of the first person's right shoe to the toe of the second person's right shoe. That will be called the "personal distance."

For each student in your group, record the gender and personal distance. Your instructor will help you pool your data with the rest of the class.

Note: Be respectful of other people's personal space. Do not make physical contact with other students during this activity.

BEFORE THE ACTIVITY

1. Do you think men and women will have different personal distances? Will the larger distances be specified by the men or the women?

2. Which group will have distances that are more spread out?

3. What will be the shape of the distributions?

AFTER THE ACTIVITY

Do men and women have different personal distances? Create appropriate graphics to compare personal distances of men and women to answer this question. Then describe these differences.

CHAPTER REVIEW

Summary of Learning Objectives

1. **What is the distribution of a sample of data?** The distribution summarizes the values that were observed and the frequencies (or relative frequencies) of those values.

2. **Which graphs are appropriate for numerical variables and what important aspects of the distribution can we learn from them?** Dotplots, histograms, and stemplots are all appropriate for numerical variables. A good picture conveys information about shape (Is the distribution skewed or symmetric? Is it unimodal or multimodal?), centre (What is a typical outcome?), spread (How much variability is present?), and the presence of outliers.

3. **Which graphs are appropriate for categorical variables and what important aspects of the distribution can we learn from them?** Bar charts are the most appropriate graphs for categorical variables. Pie charts are very common, but are not recommended by statisticians. A good picture conveys information about the mode (or modes) and about variability.

4. **What are some ways in which a statistical graph can be misleading?** Be aware of axes that do not start at the origin or do not keep a constant scale, of pictures where the relative sizes of objects do not match the data, and of chart effects that do not add information to the graph.

Important Terms

Distribution of a data set, *33*
Frequency, *33*
Dotplot, *34*
Histogram, *35*
Bin/Class, *35*
Relative frequency, *36*

Stemplot (or stem-and-leaf plot), *38*
Leaf, *38*
Stem, *38*
Typical value (centre), *39*
Variability (spread), *39*

Symmetric distribution, *40*
Bell-shaped distribution, *40*
Right-skewed distribution, *41*
Left-skewed distribution, *41*
Unimodal distribution, *42*
Bimodal distribution, *42*

Multimodal distribution, *42*
Outlier, *43*
Bar graph (bar chart), *48*
Pareto chart, *48*
Pie chart, *49*
Mode (in categorical variables), *50*

Sources

Airport Traffic Report. 2013. The Port Authority of New York and New Jersey (accessed Dec. 13, 2014).

Boué, M. 2009. Unpublished data.

Boué, M. 2012. Unpublished data.

Currie, C., et al., eds. 2012. Social determinants of health and well-being among young people. Health Behaviour in School-aged Children (HBSC) study: International report from the 2009/2010 survey. Copenhagen, WHO Regional Office for Europe (Health Policy for Children and Adolescents, No. 6). http://www.hbsc.org/publications/international/

Employment and Social Development Canada (formerly Human Resources and Skills Development Canada). 2008. What difference does learning make to financial security?

Minitab 15 Statistical Software. 2007. [Computer software]. State College, PA: Minitab, Inc. (www.minitab.com)

Playfair, W. 1786. Commercial and political atlas: Representing, by copperplate charts, the progress of the commerce, revenues, expenditure, and debts of England, during the whole of the eighteenth century. London: Corry. Reprinted in H. Wainer and I. Spence (eds.), *The commercial and political atlas and statistical breviary*, New York: Cambridge University Press, 2005. http://www.math.yorku.ca/SCS/Gallery/milestone/refs.html#Playfair:1786

Ryan, C. 2006. Unpublished data.

Statistics Canada. 2014. Tuition and Living Accommodation Costs for Full-time Students at Canadian Degree-granting Institutions, 2014–2015.

Statistics Canada. 2009 Survey of Household Spending.

Statistics Canada. *Table 051-0001—Estimates of population, by age group and sex for July 1, Canada, provinces and territories, annual (persons unless otherwise noted)*, CANSIM (database) (accessed Dec. 17, 2014).

Statistics Canada. Canadian Centre for Justice Statistics. Police Reported Crime Statistics in Canada, 2009–2013.

Wallace, S. 2014. Inuit Health: Selected Findings from the 2012 Aboriginal Peoples Survey. Statistics Canada.

www.cfl.ca (accessed Dec. 12, 2014).

www.gapminder.org (accessed Dec. 20, 2014).

www.reuters.com. 2012. Canadians prefer pizza over other quick-serve items (accessed June 20, 2014).

www.runvictoriamarathon.com (accessed Dec. 14, 2014).

SECTION EXERCISES

SECTIONS 2.1 AND 2.2

2.1 Body Mass Index The dotplot shows the self-reported body mass index (BMI, in kg/m^2) of 146 randomly selected respondents to the 2010 Canadian Community Health Survey.

a. A person with a BMI of 30 kg/m^2 or more is considered obese. Report the number of obese people shown in the dotplot.

b. Report the percentage of people who qualify as obese according to their self-reported data. Compare this with the 2008 estimate obtained from measured data that 25% of Canadians are obese.

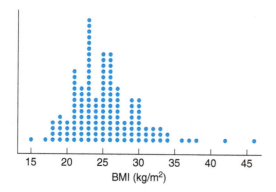

2.2 National Parks The dotplot shows the area (in thousands of km^2) of the 45 National Parks and National Park Reserves of Canada, as of December 2014. (Source: www.pc.cg.ca)

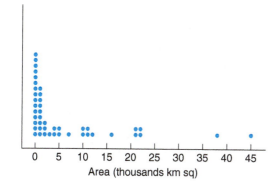

a. Report the number of National Parks that have an area larger than 5660 km^2.

b. The area of the province of Prince Edward Island is 5660 km^2. Report the percentage of National Parks that are larger than Prince Edward Island.

2.3 Ages of "Most Powerful Business People" The histogram shows frequencies for the ages of 25 people selected by *Canadian Business* magazine as "Canada's top 25 most powerful business people" in 2013. Convert this histogram to one showing relative frequencies by relabelling the vertical axis with the appropriate relative frequencies. You may just report the new labels for the vertical axis because that is the only thing that changes. (Source: www.canadianbusiness.com)

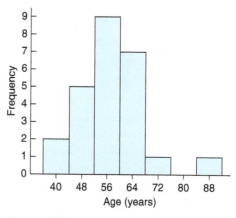

2.4 Nursing Tuition The histogram shows the distribution of tuition at 54 undergraduate nursing programs in 2011–2012, as reported by Statistics Canada. Approximately how many of these nursing programs charged $6000 or more in tuition?

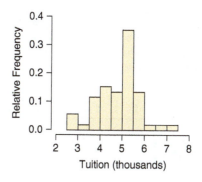

TRY 2.5 Televisions (Example 1) The histogram shows the distribution of the number of televisions in the homes of 90 community college students.

a. According to the histogram, about how many homes do not have a television?

b. How many televisions are in the homes that have the most televisions?

c. How many homes have three televisions?

d. How many homes have six or more televisions?

e. What proportion of homes have six or more televisions?

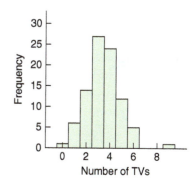

2.6 Exercise Hours The histogram shows the distribution of self-reported number of hours of exercise per week (rounded to the nearest hour) for 50 community college students. This graph uses a right-hand rule: if someone exercised for exactly 4 hours, they would be in the third bin, the bin to the right of 4.

a. According to the histogram, there are two possible values for the maximum number of hours of exercise. What are they?

b. How many people exercised 0 or 1 hour (less than 2 hours)?

c. How many people exercised 10 or more hours?

d. What proportion of people exercised 10 or more hours?

2.7 Rental Prices Have you ever wondered whether you could afford to move to another city? The dotplot shows rental prices (dollars per month) in three cities in October 2013 for units with one bedroom and one bathroom. (Source: apartmentsCanada.com)

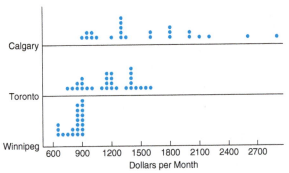

a. Centre: Which city typically has the highest rents?

b. Spread: Which city's distribution has the smallest variation?

c. Shape: Which city's distribution is the most skewed?

2.8 Rental Prices The dotplot shows rental prices (dollars per month) in three cities in October 2013 for units with one bedroom and one bathroom. (Source: apartmentsCanada.com)

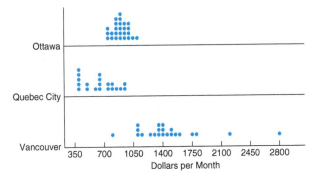

a. Centre: Which city typically has the highest rental prices?

b. Which city's distribution has the greatest variation?

c. Describe the shape of the distribution of prices in Ottawa.

TRY **2.9 CEO Compensation (Example 2)** Predict the shape of the distribution of compensation for Canada's top 100 chief executive officers (CEOs). According to data published by *The Globe and Mail*, in 2013 a typical value was about $7 million per year, but there is an outlier at $87 million. (Source: *The Globe and Mail*, June 1, 2014)

2.10 Cigarettes A physician asks all his patients to report the approximate number of cigarettes they smoke in a day. Predict the shape of the distribution of number of cigarettes smoked per day.

TRY **2.11 Armspans (Example 3)** According to the ancient Roman architect Vitruvius, a person's armspan (the distance from fingertip to fingertip with the arms stretched wide) is approximately equal to his or her height. For example, people 160 centimetres tall tend to have an armspan of 160 centimetres. Explain, then, why the distribution of armspans for a class containing roughly equal numbers of men and women might be bimodal.

* **2.12 Household Income** The distribution of income per household in Canada is bimodal. What is one possible reason for this bimodality?

TRY **2.13 Ages of "Most Powerful Business People" (Example 4)** From the histogram shown in Exercise 2.3, approximately what is a typical age of a business person in this group?

2.14 Nursing Tuition From the histogram shown in Exercise 2.4, approximately what is a typical tuition, in 2011–2012, for an undergraduate nursing program?

TRY **2.15 Commute Times (Example 5)** Use the histograms to compare the times spent commuting for community college students who drive to school in a car with the times spent by those who take the bus. Which group typically has the longer commute time? Which group has the more variable commute time?

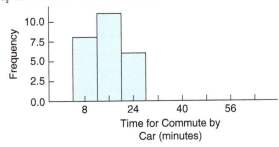

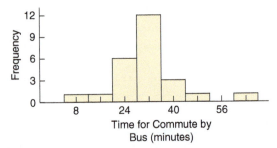

2.16 Haircuts The histograms show the distribution of the number of dollars spent on the last haircut prior to completing the survey for a sample of university female students (top) and male students (bottom).

a. Compare and describe the shape of the distributions.

b. Which group tends to spend more on haircuts?

c. Which group has more variation in dollars spent on their last haircut?

(a)

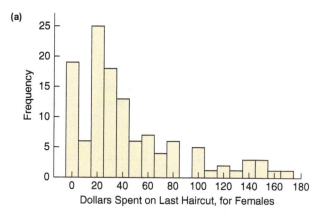

(b)

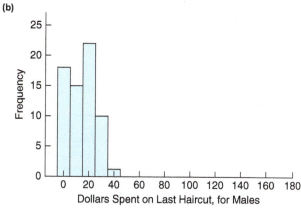

2.17 Education (Example 6) The histogram shows the distribution of data for the number of years of elementary and high school education of 20,134 respondents to the 2008 Statistics Canada General Social Survey.

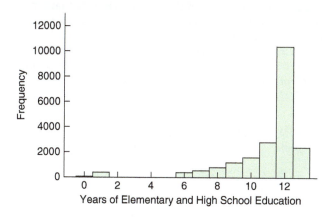

a. Describe and interpret the distribution of years of elementary and high school education.

b. Assuming that those with 12 or more years of education have earned a high school diploma, estimate how many of the people in the sample earned a high school diploma.

c. Estimate the percentage of people in the sample who earned a high school diploma.

2.18 Student–Faculty Ratios The histogram shows the distribution of student–faculty ratios (in number of students per full-time faculty member) at 130 post-secondary education institutions in Canada. (Source: CAUT Almanac 2013–2014)

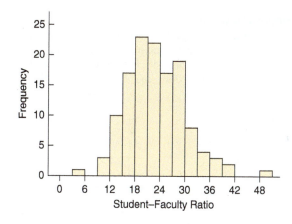

a. Describe the shape of the distribution.

b. What is the typical student–faculty ratio, approximately?

c. About how many institutions have a student–faculty ratio less than 15 students per full-time faculty member? (The histogram uses the right-hand rule.)

d. What percentage of the 130 institutions have a student–faculty ratio lower than 15 students per full-time faculty member?

* 2.19 Tobogganing Students Heathyr Francis and Colin Hoag performed an experiment in which they measured the time they took to reach the bottom of Armour Hill in Peterborough, Ontario, when tobogganing on cafeteria trays that had not been waxed and on cafeteria trays that had been waxed. Compare the distributions of time to reach the bottom of the hill for trays with and without wax.

(a)

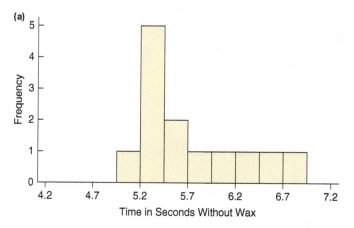

(b)

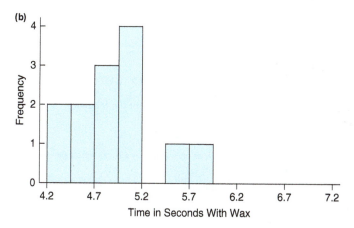

*2.20 Hours Worked Respondents to the 2008 General Social Survey who had at least one paid job were asked to report the total number of hours they usually worked in one week. (Those who said "I don't know" were not included in the data set.) Compare the distributions of hours of work for men and women.

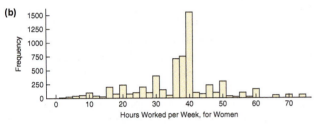

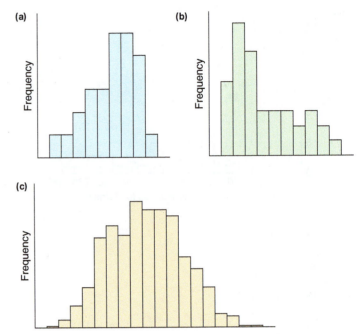

2.21 Matching Histograms Match each of the following histograms to the correct situation.

1. The age of death of a sample of 19 typical women in Canada.
2. The weekly circulation in 2012 of the 97 daily paid newspapers in Canada, according to newspaperscanada.ca.
3. The outcomes of rolling a fair die (with six sides) 5000 times.

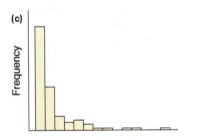

2.22 Matching Histograms Match each of the following histograms to the correct situation.

1. Test scores for students on an easy test.
2. The numbers of hours of television watched by a large, typical group of Canadians.
3. The heights of a large, typical group of adults in Canada.

g 2.23 Eating Out and Jobs College student Jacqueline Loya asked students who had full-time jobs and students who had part-time jobs how many times they went out to eat in the last month.

Write a brief comparison of the distributions of the two groups. Include appropriate graphics. *See page 70 for guidance.*

Full-time: 5, 3, 4, 4, 4, 2, 1, 5, 6, 5, 6, 3, 3, 2, 4,
5, 2, 3, 7, 5, 5, 1, 4, 6, 7
Part-time: 1, 1, 5, 1, 4, 2, 2, 3, 3, 2, 3, 2, 4,
2, 1, 2, 3, 2, 1, 3, 3, 2, 4, 2, 1

2.24 Comparing Weights of Soccer and Hockey Players The tables below show the weights (in kilograms) of men randomly sampled from the men's soccer team and from the men's hockey team at the same university in Ontario. Write a brief comparison of the distributions of weight for the two groups. Include appropriate graphics. For one approach, look at the guidance given for Exercise 2.23. (Source: oua.ca)

Soccer Players' Weights

64	61	78	70	64
89	75	64	68	73
68	77	80	77	68
80	73	66	68	84

Hockey Players' Weights

93	86	82	98	95
91	84	82	86	82
84	89	91	84	98
80	89	89	84	

2.25 Textbook Prices The table shows prices of 50 required texts at a Canadian university bookstore, rounded to the nearest dollar. Make an appropriate graph of the distribution of the data, and describe the distribution.

16	13	11	20	139	80	153	86	59	27
35	172	26	162	15	22	160	34	17	19
34	17	68	10	11	137	50	173	23	211
25	90	11	168	13	17	38	186	17	27
59	15	139	44	15	14	16	7	9	12

2.26 PAT Scores The table shows a random sample of 50 quantitative PAT (Provincial Achievement Test) scores of grade 12 students in Alberta in 2012. Make an appropriate graph of the distribution of the data, and describe the distribution.

66	42	55	79	74	55	66	95	26	74
83	51	59	51	93	62	67	55	81	59
100	55	72	83	77	74	39	81	79	59
74	57	95	93	74	79	88	39	70	51
70	75	77	57	93	75	79	100	90	42

2.27 Animal Longevity The accompanying table shows the average lifespan for some mammals in years. Graph these average lifespans and describe the distribution. What is a typical lifespan? Identify the three outliers and report their lifespans. If you were to include humans in this graph, where would the data point be? Humans average about 75 years.

2.28 Animal Gestation Periods The accompanying table also shows the gestation period (in days) for some animals. The gestation period is the length of pregnancy. Graph the gestation period and describe the distribution. If there are any outliers, identify the animal(s) and give their gestation periods. If you were to include humans in this graph, where would the data point be? The human gestation period is about 266 days.

Animal	Gestation (days)	Lifespan (years)	Animal	Gestation (days)	Lifespan (years)
Baboon	187	12	Deer	201	8
Bear, grizzly	225	25	Dog, domestic	61	12
Beaver	105	5	Elephant, African	660	35
Bison	285	15	Elephant, Asian	645	40
Camel	406	12	Elk	250	16
Cat, domestic	63	12	Fox, red	52	7
Chimp	230	20	Giraffe	457	10
Cow	284	15			

Animal	Gestation (days)	Lifespan (years)	Animal	Gestation (days)	Lifespan (years)
Goat	151	8	Rhino, black	450	15
Gorilla	258	20	Sea Lion, Cal	350	12
Hippo	238	41	Sheep	154	12
Horse	330	20	Squirrel, gray	44	10
Leopard	98	12	Tiger	105	16
Lion	100	15	Wolf, maned	63	5
Monkey, rhesus	166	15	Zebra, Grant's	365	15
Moose	240	12			
Pig, domestic	112	10			
Puma	90	12			

(Source: *The World Almanac and Book of Facts* 2013)

2.29 Matching Match each description with the correct histogram of the data.

1. Heights of students in a large statistics class that contains about equal numbers of men and women.
2. Numbers of hours of sleep the previous night in the same large statistics class.
3. Numbers of driving accidents for students in a large university in Canada.

(a)
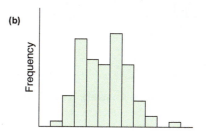

(b)
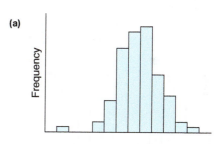

(c)
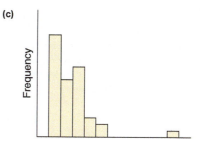

2.30 Matching Match each description with the correct histogram of the data.

1. Quantitative PAT score for 1000 grade 12 students in Alberta.

2. Weights of over 500 adults, about half of whom are men and half of whom are women.

3. Ages of all 39 students in a community college statistics class that is made up of full-time students and meets during the morning.

(a)

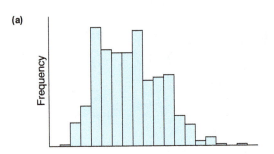

(b)

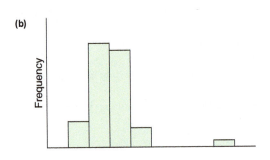

(c)

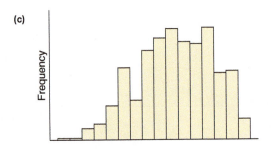

SECTIONS 2.3 AND 2.4

TRY **2.31 Changing Multiple-Choice Answers When Told *Not* to Do So (Example 7)** One of the authors wanted to determine the effect of changing answers on multiple-choice tests. She studied the tests given by another professor, who had told his students before their exams that if they had doubts about an answer they had written, they would be better off *not changing* their initial answer. The author went through the exams to look for erasures, which indicate that the first choice was changed. In these tests, there is only one correct answer for each question. Do the data support the view that students should not change their initial choice of an answer?

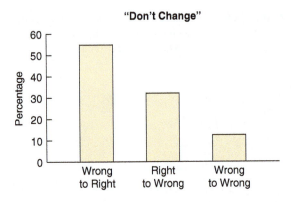

"Don't Change"

2.32 Changing Multiple-Choice Answers When Told to Do So One of the authors wanted to determine the effect of changing answers on multiple-choice tests. She had advised her students that if they had changed their minds about a previous answer, they should replace their first choice with their new choice. By looking for erasures on the exam, she was able to count the number of changed answers that went from wrong to right, from right to wrong, and from wrong to wrong. The results are shown in the bar chart.

a. Do the data support her view that it is better to replace your initial choice with the revised choice?

b. Compare this bar chart with the one in Exercise 2.31. Does changing answers generally tend to lead to higher or to lower grades?

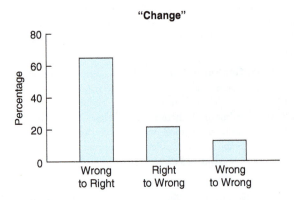

"Change"

TRY **2.33 Smartphones vs. Feature Phones (Example 8)** The figure shows smartphone market penetration in Canada as a percentage of mobile subscribers for three years. (Source: Canada Digital Future in Focus 2013 and 2014, comScore.com)

a. Report the mode for each time period. What trend do you see from 2011 to 2013?

b. In which year is there more variability in smartphone market penetration?

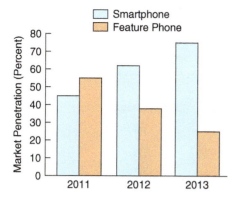

2.34 Browsers The bar chart shows the global market share of browsers according to StatCounter, a web analytics company. Write a sentence or two describing changes in the market share of these browsers from 2010 to 2014. (Source: gs.statcounter.com)

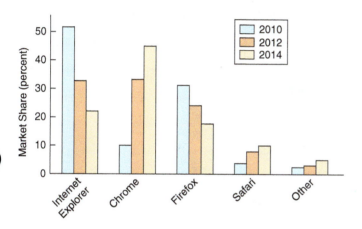

2.35 Level of Education The 2008 General Social Survey asked its respondents to report their highest level of education obtained. The results for a random sample of 950 respondents are shown (a) in a bar chart and (b) in a pie chart. (Source: Statistics Canada)

(a)

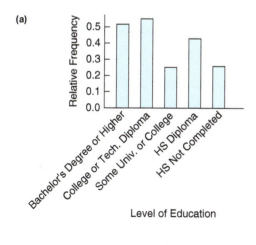

Level of Education

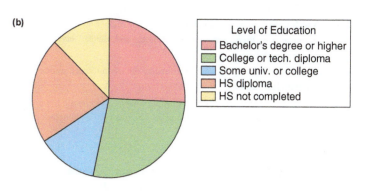

a. Which is the level of education obtained by the highest number of respondents? Is it easier to determine with the bar chart or with the pie chart? Why?

b. Which is the level of education obtained by the second largest number of respondents?

2.36 Mother's Level of Education The 2008 General Social Survey asked its respondents to report the highest level of education obtained by their mothers. The results for a random sample of 950 respondents are shown (a) in a bar graph and (b) in a pie chart. (Source: Statistics Canada)

(a)

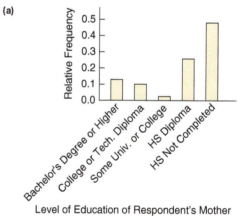

Level of Education of Respondent's Mother

(b)

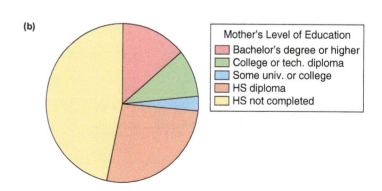

a. Which is the level of education obtained by the highest number of respondents' mothers? Is it easier to determine with the bar chart or with the pie chart? Why?

b. Which is the level of education obtained by the second largest number of respondents' mothers?

c. Compare the distribution of level of education of respondents (Exercise 2.35) with that of their mothers (the two random samples have the same 950 people).

TRY **2.37 Age by Year (Example 9)** The bar chart shows the projected percentage of people living in Canada in different age categories by year, according to Statistics Canada medium-growth projections (based on historical trends).

a. Comment on the predicted changes from 2020 through to 2040.

b. Comment on the effect this might have on the Canada Pension Plan, a government program that collects money from those currently working and gives it to retired people.

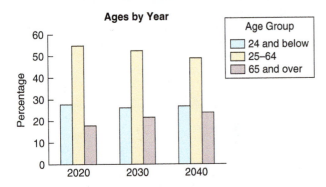

2.38 Search Engines Search engine traffic and search share in China changed considerably in a short period of time with the introduction of a new search engine in 2012: Qihoo's 360 Search. The bar chart shows market share for search engines in August of four consecutive years. (Source: CNZZ.com)

a. Which search engine had the largest market share in all four years?

b. What is the trend for Google use in China?

c. What is the trend for 360 Search?

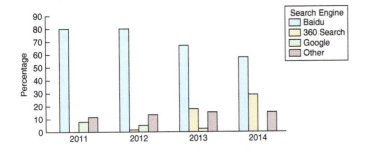

2.39 Energy Use and Home Heating The table gives information on the source of energy used for the heating equipment of a sample of 9741 Canadian households in 2011. Sketch an appropriate graph of the distribution, and comment on its important features. (Source: Statistics Canada, *Households and the Environment Survey, 2011*)

Energy Source	Percentage
Electricity	11%
Natural gas	67%
Oil	13%
Wood	6%
Propane	2%
Other	1%

2.40 Adoptions The table gives information on the top five countries from which Canadian residents and citizens adopted children in 2010. Sketch the appropriate graph of the distribution, and comment on its important features. (Source: Citizenship and Immigration Canada, RDM)

Country	Number
China	472
Haiti	172
U.S.	148
Vietnam	139
Russia	102

CHAPTER REVIEW EXERCISES

2.41 Television The table shows the first few entries for the number of hours of television viewed per week for some grade 5 students, stacked and coded, where 1 represents a girl and 0 represents a boy.

What would be appropriate graphs to compare the distributions of hours of TV watched per week for boys and girls if you had all the data? Explain.

TV	Girl
3	1
8	1
11	1
12	1
7	0
5	0
4	0

2.42 Job The table shows the job categories for some employees at a business. What type of graph(s) would be appropriate to compare the distribution of jobs for men and for women if you had all the data? Explain.

Male	Job
1	Custodial
0	Clerical
0	Managerial
1	Clerical
1	Managerial

2.43 Hormone Replacement Therapy The use of the drug Prempro, a combination of two female hormones that many women take after menopause, is called hormone replacement therapy (HRT). In July 2002, a medical article reported the results of a study that was done to determine the effects of Prempro on many diseases. (Source: Women's Writing Group, Risks and benefits of estrogen plus progestin in healthy postmenopausal women, *Journal of the American Medical Association*, 2002)

The study was placebo-controlled, randomized, and double-blind. From studies like these, it is possible to make statements about cause and effect. The figure shows comparisons of disease rates in the study.

a. For which diseases was the disease rate higher for those who took HRT? And for which diseases was the rate lower for those who took HRT?

b. Why do you suppose we compare the rate per 10,000 women (per year) rather than just reporting the numbers of women observed who get the disease?

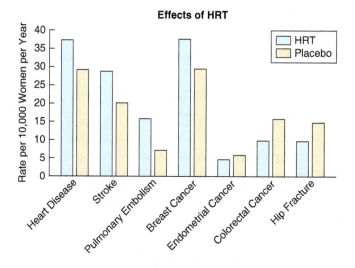

2.44 Causes of Injury The graph shows the causes of injury by age group for Canadians aged 12 or older. (Source: Statistics Canada, *Canadian Community Health Survey–Annual Component, 2009–2010 Combined*)

a. What is the most common cause of injury for all three age groups?

b. Which age group is most likely and which one is least likely to be hurt by being bumped, pushed, or bitten?

c. Which age group is most likely to be hurt by overexertion?

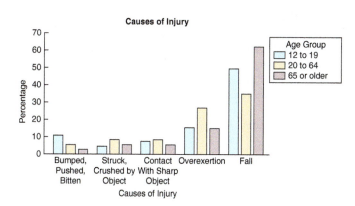

2.45 Hormone Replacement Therapy Again The bar chart shows a comparison of breast cancer rates for those who took HRT and those who took a placebo. Explain why the graph is deceptive, and indicate what could be done to make it less so.

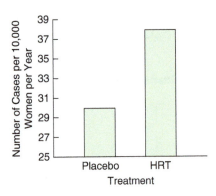

Bar Chart Rate of Breast Cancer

2.46 Holding Breath A group of students held their breath as long as possible and recorded the times in seconds. The times went from a low of 25 seconds to a high of 90 seconds, as you can see in the stemplot. Suggest improvements to the histogram below generated by Excel, assuming that what is wanted is a histogram of the data (not a bar chart).

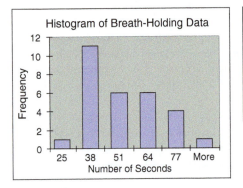

```
2   588
3   00035678
4   0033557
5   3357
6   005559
7
8
9   0
```

2.47 Gender

a. An elementary school class includes 12 girls and 8 boys. Which type of graph would be appropriate to show the distribution of gender in the class: a pie chart or a histogram?

b. In a school district, there are 45 elementary school classrooms, each containing 20 students. Which type of graph would be appropriate to show the distribution of the number of boys in the classrooms: a pie chart or a histogram?

2.48 Handedness

a. An elementary school class is made up of 3 children who are left-handed and 17 who are right-handed. The objects of study are the children, and the variable of interest is whether the child is right- or left-handed. Which type of graph would be appropriate to show the distribution of handedness in the class: a pie chart or a histogram?

b. In a school board, there are 45 elementary school classrooms, each containing 20 students. The unit of study is a classroom, and the variable is the number of right-handed students in each class. Which type of graph would be appropriate to show the distribution of the number of right-handed students in the classrooms: a pie chart or a histogram?

* 2.49 Global Temperatures The histograms show the average global temperature per year for two 33-year ranges in degrees Celsius. The range for 1880 to 1912 is on the top, and the range for 1980 to 2012 is on the bottom. Compare the two histograms for the two time periods, and explain what they show. Also estimate the difference between the centres. That is, about how much does the typical global temperature for the 1980–2012 time period differ from that for the 1880–1912 period? (Source: Goddard Institute for Space Studies, NASA, 2013)

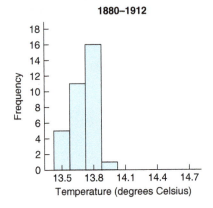

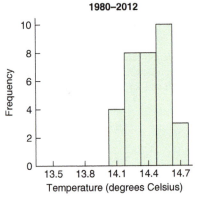

* 2.50 Composting Residential composting can reduce the amount of waste sent to landfills. Participation in composting activities varies widely between census metropolitan areas (CMAs), depending on the waste management regulations and the municipal programs available in each region. The histograms show percentages of households that composted waste in 26 CMAs in 2011. The first histogram shows the percentage of all households that composted kitchen waste, while the second histogram shows the percentage of houses with a lawn or garden that composted yard waste. Compare the two histograms. (Source: Statistics Canada, *Composting by Households in Canada, 2013*)

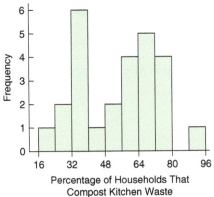

Composting Kitchen Waste

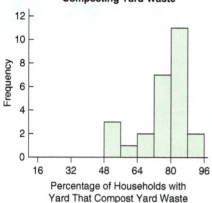

Composting Yard Waste

2.51 Create a dotplot that has at least 10 observations and is right-skewed.

2.52 Create a dotplot that has at least 10 observations and does not have skew.

* 2.53 Home Prices How do home prices compare in Vancouver's West Side (WS) and East Vancouver (EV)? Using appropriate graphics, write a few sentences comparing the distribution of home prices. The data are sampled from a real estate website, and prices are in hundreds of thousands of dollars. (Thus 10 represents $1,000,000.)

* 2.54 Anchoring Results of a survey can often be biased by the wording of questions. One source of bias is due to what is called *anchoring*. Anchoring occurs when a respondent's answers are influenced by some previously supplied starting point. To demonstrate the effect of anchoring, students in a statistics class were randomly assigned a quantity, either 10% or 65%. The students were first asked whether they thought the percentage of member states of the United Nations that are in Africa was higher or lower than that quantity, and then they were asked to estimate the correct percentage. A small excerpt of the results is shown in the table; visit the text's website for all the data. What differences do you see between the estimates of students who were supplied a starting point of 10% and of those who were supplied a starting point of 65%? Use an appropriate graphical summary, and write a comparison of the distributions. (By the way, the actual percentage is 28%.)

Starting Point	Africa Estimate
10%	8
10%	1
65%	35
10%	20

* 2.55 Canada's Top 100 Companies The 100 Canadian companies with the highest revenue for 2012 were reported by *The Globe and Mail*. First predict the shape of a histogram of the data, and explain your prediction. Then make a histogram of the data (on the text's website) and describe it.

* 2.56 Ideal Weight Thirty-nine students (26 women and 13 men) reported their ideal weight in kilograms (in most cases, not their current weight). The tables show the data.

Women					
50	50	54.5	54.5	54.5	59
52	59	54.5	68	54	61
56	57	54.5	50	54.5	41
59	54.5	50	59	61	50
48	52				

Men					
73	79.5	86	77	77	70
59	86	61	75	84	73
100					

a. Explain why the distribution of ideal weights is likely to be bimodal if men and women are both included in the sample.

b. Make a histogram combining the ideal weights of men and women. Use the default histogram provided by your software. Report the bin width and describe the distribution.

c. Vary the number of bins, and print out a second histogram. Report the bin width and describe this histogram. Compare the two histograms.

GUIDED EXERCISES

 2.23 Eating Out and Jobs   College student Jacqueline Loya asked students who had full-time jobs and students who had part-time jobs how many times they went out to eat in the last month.

Full-time: 5, 3, 4, 4, 4, 2, 1, 5, 6, 5, 6, 3, 3, 2, 4, 5, 2, 3, 7, 5, 5, 1, 4, 6, 7

Part-time: 1, 1, 5, 1, 4, 2, 2, 3, 3, 2, 3, 2, 4, 2, 1, 2, 3, 2, 1, 3, 3, 2, 4, 2, 1

Question   Compare the two groups by following the steps below. Include appropriate graphics.

Step 1 ▶ Create graphs.

Make dotplots (or histograms) using the same axis with one set of data above the other, as shown in the figure.

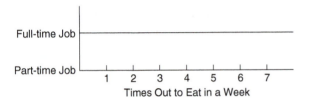

Step 2 ▶ Examine shape.

What is the shape of the data for those with part-time jobs? What is the shape of the data for those with full-time jobs?

Step 3 ▶ Examine centre.

Which group tends to go out to eat more often, those with full-time or those with part-time jobs?

Step 4 ▶ Examine variation.

Which group has a wider spread of data?

Step 5 ▶ Check for outliers.

Were there any numbers separated from the other numbers as shown in the dotplots? (In other words, were there any gaps in the dotplots?)

Step 6 ▶ Summarize.

Finally, in one or more sentences, compare the shape, centre, and variation (and mention outliers if there were any).

TECH TIPS

General Instructions for All Technology

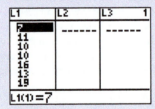

▲ **FIGURE 2A** TI-83/84 data screen.

Example A

Use the following ages to make a histogram: 7, 11, 10, 10, 16, 13, 19, 22, 42

Columns

Data sets are generally put into columns, not rows. The columns may be called variables, lists, or the like. Figure 2A shows a column of data.

TI-83/84

Resetting the Calculator (Clearing the Memory)

If you turn off the TI-83/84, it does not reset the calculator. All the previous data and choices remain. If you are having trouble and want to start over, you can reset the calculator.

1. **2nd Mem** (with the + sign)
2. **7** for **Reset**
3. **1** for **All RAM**
4. **2** for **Reset**

It will say **RAM cleared** if it has been done successfully.

Entering Data into the Lists

1. Press **STAT**, and select **EDIT** (by pressing **ENTER** when **EDIT** is highlighted).
2. If you find that there are data already in **L1** (or any list you want to use), you have three options:
   a. Clear the entire list by using the arrow keys to highlight the **L1** label and then pressing **CLEAR** and then **ENTER**. Do not press **DELETE**, because then you will no longer have an **L1**. If you delete **L1**, to get it back you can **Reset** the calculator.

b. Delete the individual entries by highlighting the top data entry, then pressing **DELETE** several times until all the data are erased. (The numbers will scroll up.)

c. Overwrite the existing data. CAUTION: Be sure to **DELETE** data in any cells not overwritten.

3. Type the numbers from the example into **L1** (List 1). After typing each number, you may press **ENTER** or use ▼ (the arrow down on the keypad). Double-check your entries before proceeding.

Histogram

1. Press **2nd**, **STATPLOT** (which is in the upper left corner of the keypad).

2. If more than the first plot is **On**, press **4** (for **PlotsOff**) and **ENTER** to turn them all off.

3. Press **2nd**, **STATPLOT**, and **1** (for **Plot1**).

4. Turn on **Plot1** by pressing **ENTER** when **On** is flashing; see Figure 2B.

▲ **FIGURE 2B** TI-83/84.

5. Use the arrows on the keypad to get to the histogram icon (highlighted in Figure 2B) and press **ENTER** to choose it. Use the down arrow to get to Xlist and press **2nd** and **1** for **L1**. The settings shown in Figure 2B will lead to a histogram of the data in List 1 (**L1**).

6. Press **ZOOM** and **9** (**ZoomStat**) to create the graph.

7. To see the numbers shown in Figure 2C, press **TRACE** (in the top row on the keypad) and move around using the group of four arrows on the keypad to see other numbers.

Figure 2C shows a histogram of the numbers in the example.

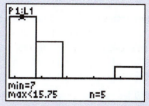

▲ **FIGURE 2C** TI-83/84 histogram.

The TI-83/84 cannot make stemplots, dotplots, or bar charts.

Downloading Numerical Data from a Computer into a TI-84

Before you can use your computer with your TI-84, you must install (on your computer) the software program TI Connect, and a driver for the calculator. You need do this only once. If you have done steps 1–3 and are ready to download the data, start with Step 4.

1. Downloading and saving the TI Connect setup program. Insert the CD that came with the TI-84 into the computer disk drive and follow the on-screen instructions. This will copy the setup file into the Downloads folder in your hard drive. (If you no longer have the CD, the programs can be downloaded free from the TI website, www.TI.com.)

2. Installing TI Connect.
Click on the globe in the lower left corner of your desktop and in the **Search** box, type **Downloads**. When you get to the **Downloads**, double click on **TIConnect** to begin the

installation. Follow the on-screen instructions. This should also create a TI Connect icon on your desktop screen.

3. Installing the calculator driver on the computer. To do this, connect the TI-84 to the computer using the USB cable that came with the calculator; then follow the on-screen instructions.
This completes the installation and the CD may now be removed from the computer.

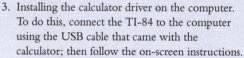

4. Double click the TI Connect icon on your desktop screen. If it doesn't exist, Click **Start**, **Programs**, **TI Tools**, and **TI-Connect**.

5. Click on **TI-Data Editor**.

6. Refer to Figure 2D.
Click on the icon for the white sheet of paper. The arrow points to it. This will give you a white column to use for the data. If you have more than one column of data, click on the piece of paper until you have the correct number of columns for your use. Figure 2D shows two columns.

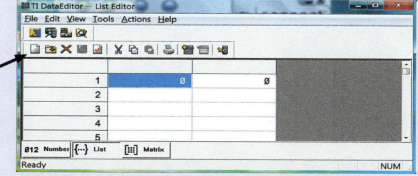

▲ **FIGURE 2D** TI data editor.

7. Copy a column or more than one column of *numerical* data from your computer. You may use Excel, Minitab, or any spreadsheet for the source of the column(s) of numbers, but do not include any labels or words. (If there are any letters or special characters in the column, they will not transfer and may show up as zeroes.) Then click on the 0 in the first cell of the column (see Figure 2D). The cell *must* become coloured (blue, as shown in the figure) before pasting. If it is not coloured, click out of the column (for example, on the grey area to the right of the column) and then click in the first cell of the first column again. When that cell is blue, paste the column(s) of numbers into the TI-84 data editor. Alternatively, you can just type numbers in the column on the data editor.

8. While your cursor is in the column you want to name, choose **File** and **Properties** from the **Data Editor**. Then refer to Figure 2E: check a list number like **L1** as shown (or if you want a name, it cannot be more than eight characters) and click **OK**. Then go back to any other column and do the same, but pick a different name, such as **L2**.

9. Connect the TI-84 to the computer with the cable and turn on the TI-84 calculator.

10. Refer to Figure 2D. To paste the column(s) of data, click **Actions, Send All Lists**.

11. When you get the **Warning**, click **Replace or Replace All** to overwrite the old data in the lists.

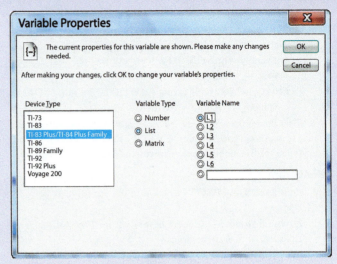

▲ **FIGURE 2E** Variable properties.

Look in your calculator lists (**STAT, EDIT**) to see the data there. If it is not there, check the cable connection, check that the TI-84 is turned on, and start again with step 6.

Caution: While the data is transferring you will not be able to use the calculator; it is thinking.

MINITAB

Entering the Data

When you open Minitab, you will see a blank spreadsheet for entering data. Type the data from the example into **C1**, column 1. Be sure your first number is put into Row 1, not above Row 1 in the label region. Be sure to enter only numbers. (If you want a label for the column, type it in the label region *above* the numbers.) You may also paste in data from the computer clipboard. Double-check your entries before proceeding.

All Minitab Graphs

After making the graph, double click on what you want to change, such as labels.

Histogram

1. Click **Graph > Histogram**.
2. Leave the default option **Simple** and click **OK**.
3. Double click **C1** (or the name for the column) and click **OK**. (Another way to get **C1** in the big box is to click **C1** and click **Select**.)
4. After obtaining the histogram, if you want different bins (intervals), double click on the *x*-axis and look for **Binning**.

Figure 2F shows a Minitab histogram of the ages.

Stemplot
Click **Graph > Stem-and-Leaf**

Dotplot
Click **Graph > Dotplot**

Bar Chart
Click **Graph > Bar Chart**

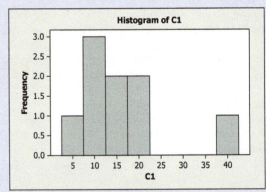

▲ **FIGURE 2F** Minitab histogram.

EXCEL

When you open Excel, you will see a blank spreadsheet for entering data. But first, click the **Data** tab (top of screen, middle); you should see **Data Analysis** just below and on the far right. If you do not see it, you will need to load the Data Analysis Toolpak (instructions below). Now click the **Add-Ins** tab; you should see the XLSTAT icon ➤ just below and on the far left. If you do not see it, you should install XLSTAT (instructions below). You will need both of these add-ins in order to perform all the statistical operations described in this textbook.

Data Analysis Toolpak

1. Click **File > Options > Add-Ins**.
2. In **Manage** Box, select **Excel Add-Ins**, and click **Go**.
3. In **Add-ins available** box, check **Analysis Toolpak**, and click **OK**.

XLSTAT

1. Close Excel.
2. Download XLSTAT from www.pearsonhighered.com/xlstat.
3. Install XLSTAT.
4. Open Excel, click **Add-Ins tab**, and click the XLSTAT icon ➤.

You need to install the Data Analysis Toolpak only once. The Data Analysis tab should be available now every time Excel is opened. For XLSTAT, however, step 4 above may need to run each time Excel is opened (if you expect to run XLSTAT routines).

Entering Data

See Figure 2G. Enter the data from the example into column A with **Ages** in cell A1. Double-check your entries before proceeding.

	A
1	Ages
2	7
3	11
4	10
5	10
6	16
7	13
8	19
9	22
10	42

▲ **FIGURE 2G** Excel data screen.

Histogram

1. Click **Add-Ins**, **XLSTAT**, **Describing data**, and **Histograms**.
2. When the box under **Data** is activated, drag your cursor over the column containing the data including the label **Ages**.
3. Click **OK** and **Continue**.

Figure 2H shows the histogram.

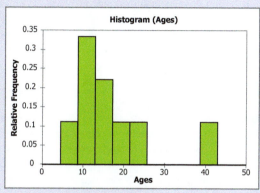

▲ **FIGURE 2H** XLSTAT histogram.

Dotplot and Stemplot

1. Click **Add-Ins**, **XLSTAT**, **Visualizing data**, and **Univariate plots**.
2. When the box under **Quantitative Data** is activated, drag your cursor over the column containing the data, including the label **Ages**.

Dotplot

3. Click **Options, Charts, Charts (1)** and select **Scattergrams** and **Horizontal**.
4. Click **OK** and **Continue**.

Stemplot

3. Click **Options, Charts, Charts (1)** and select **Stem-and-leaf plots**.
4. Click **OK** and **Continue**.

Bar Chart

After typing a summary of your data in table form (including labels), drag your cursor over the table to select it, click **Insert**, **Column** (in the **Charts** group), and select the first option.

STATCRUNCH

For Help: After logging in, click on **Help** or **Resources** and **Watch StatCrunch Video Tutorials on YouTube**.

Entering Data

1. Click **Open StatCrunch** and you will see a spreadsheet as shown in Figure 2I. There is also a Classic Version available, shown in Figure 2J. You can switch to the Classic Version by Clicking **StatCrunch > Open in Classic**. We will use the newer version throughout as it requires no plugins and it also works on mobile devices.
2. Enter the data from the example into the column labelled **var1**.
3. If you want labels on the columns, click on the variable label, such as **var1**, and backspace to remove the old label and type the new label. Double-check your entries before proceeding.

Pasting Data

1. If you want to paste data from your computer clipboard, click **Data > Load data > From paste,** which will open a screen that says **Paste/type data below**.
2. Click in the box and then paste your data.
3. Note that the program will use the first line as variable name(s) unless you uncheck that option. Click **Load data!**

Histogram

1. Click **Graph > Histogram**.
2. Under **Select Columns**, click the variable you want a histogram for.
3. Click **Compute!**
4. To copy the graph for pasting into a document for submission, click **Options** and **Copy** and then paste it into a document.

Figure 2K shows the StatCrunch histogram of the ages.

Stemplot
Click **Graph > Stem and leaf**

Dotplot
Click **Graph > Dotplot**

Bar Chart
Click **Graph > Chart > columns**

▲ **FIGURE 2I** StatCrunch data table.

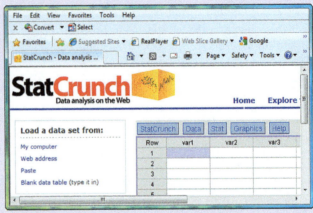

▲ **FIGURE 2J** StatCrunch data table—classic version.

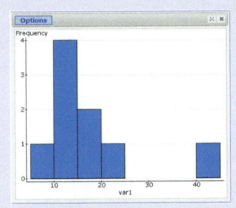

▲ **FIGURE 2K** StatCrunch histogram.

SPSS

Entering Data

1. Open SPSS and you will see a blank spreadsheet for entering data.

2. Type the data from the example into the first column, starting with Row 1. Be sure to enter only numbers. You can also paste data from the computer clipboard. Double-check your entries before proceeding.

3. If you want labels on the columns, click on the variable label, such as **var00001**, and you will see a spreadsheet containing information for variables (one per line). Change the variable name under the column Name. You can also access variable information by clicking **Variable View** at the bottom of the spreadsheet. You can return to the main screen by clicking **Data View**.

Histogram

1. Click **Analyze > Descriptive Statistics > Frequencies**.

2. Select the variable you are going to graph from the list and click on the right arrow to move it to the **Variable(s)** box.

3. Click **Charts**, and under **Chart type**, select **Histograms**.

4. Click **Continue** and then **OK**.

Figure 2L shows the SPSS histogram of the ages.

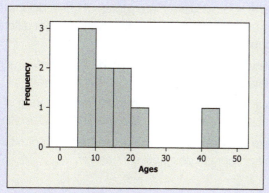

▲ **FIGURE 2L** SPSS histogram.

Stemplot

1. Click **Analyze > Descriptive Statistics > Explore**.

2. Select the variable you are going to graph from the list and click on the right arrow to move it to the **Dependent List** box.

3. Click **Plots**, and under **Descriptive**, select **Stem-and-Leaf**.

4. Click **Continue** and then **OK**.

Dotplot

1. Click **Graphs > Graphboard Template Chooser**.

2. In the **Basic** menu, select the variable you are going to graph from the list and select the **Dot Plot** template. Click **OK**.

Bar Chart

1. Click **Analyze > Descriptive Statistics > Frequencies**.

2. Select the variable you are going to graph from the list (it must be categorical) and click on the right arrow to move it to the **Variable(s)** box.

3. Click **Charts**, and under **Chart Type**, select **Bar charts**.

4. Click **Continue** and then **OK**.

3 Numerical Summaries of Centre and Variation

LEARNING OBJECTIVES

After completing this chapter, you should be able to:

1. Define and calculate the mean of a data set, recognizing when it is an appropriate measure of centre for describing a typical observation.

2. Define and calculate the median of a data set, recognizing when it is an appropriate measure of centre for describing a typical observation.

3. Define, calculate, and interpret the standard deviation of a data set.

4. Define and calculate the variance of a data set.

5. Define and calculate the z-scores of observations, and use them to compare observations from different groups.

6. Define, calculate, and interpret the interquartile range of a data set.

7. Obtain the five-number summary and the range of a data set and draw a boxplot.

8. Make comparisons between data sets in context using the appropriate descriptive measures.

Google the phrase *average Canadian* and you'll find lots of entertaining facts. For example, the average Canadian showers 7.9 minutes a day, consumes nearly 3 kilograms of peanuts and peanut butter per year, donates $216 per year to charities, and spends about $155 per year in lottery tickets. The average Canadian mom has watched her kids' favourite movie about 39 times, while the average Canadian dad has watched his kids' favourite movie only 23 times.

Whether or not these descriptions are correct, they are attempting to describe a typical Canadian. The reason for doing this is to try to understand a little better what Canadians are like, or perhaps to compare one group (Canadian moms) to another (Canadian dads).

These summaries can seem odd, because we all know that people are too complex to be summarized with a single number. Characteristics such as movie watching, money spent on lottery tickets, and length of a shower vary quite a bit from person to person. If we're describing the "typical" Canadian, shouldn't we also describe how much variation exists among Canadians? If we're making comparisons between groups, how do we do it in a way that takes into account the fact that individuals may vary considerably?

In Chapter 2, we talked about looking at graphs of distributions of data to get an intuitive, informal sense of the typical value (the centre) and the amount of variation (the spread). In this chapter, we explore ways of making these intuitive concepts more precise by looking at various quantities that represent these values of centre and spread. We will see how this step makes it much easier to compare and interpret sets of data, for both symmetric and skewed distributions. These measures are important tools that we will use throughout the text.

CASE STUDY

Health Care Waiting Times

Long waiting times are one of the most important problems facing Canada's health care system. Waiting times have been recognized in Canada as a priority area since 2004, when the First Ministers agreed to a 10-year plan to strengthen health care. Since then, significant efforts have been made to increase health care resources, aiming at improving access and shortening waiting times.

Canada is not the only country facing challenges when it comes to reducing waiting times. In fact, aside from Canada, half of the Organisation for Economic Co-operation and Development (OECD) member countries also consider long waiting times an important policy issue. So how do Canada's typical waiting times compare to those of the other OECD countries facing similar challenges?

We can answer this question, at least in part, by analyzing comparative waiting times for elective (non-emergency) procedures collected and reported by the OECD as part of the Second OECD Waiting Time Project (Siciliani et al. 2013). We will focus only on the procedures for which Canadian data are available, namely hip replacement, knee replacement, cataract surgery, and coronary artery bypass graft surgery (CABG). Table 3.1 provides median and mean waiting times for these procedures, measured in days, for countries that reported "inpatient waiting times." (Inpatient waiting time is defined as the time elapsed between the date on which a specialist adds a patient to the waiting list and the date on which the patient is admitted to an inpatient or day-case surgical unit for the procedure.) We have included data from 2011 because they contain the largest number of countries. Note that most countries reported both mean and median, some reported just the median, and the Netherlands reported only the mean.

What do the mean and the median waiting times quantify? How can we make comparisons of typical waiting times between countries using these measures? Why does the Canadian Institute for Health Information (CIHI), responsible for collecting and reporting health information in Canada, choose to report only median waiting times to capture a patient's typical experience? In this chapter you will learn about how the mean and the median capture the centre of a distribution in different ways. At the end of the chapter we will make comparisons using the most appropriate measure for these waiting time data.

Median (Mean) Inpatient Waiting Times for Common Surgical Procedures (2011)				
Country	Hip Replacement	Knee Replacement	Cataract	CABG
Australia	108	173	90	17
Canada	89	107	49	7
Finland	113 (127)	136 (149)	111 (114)	43 (58)
Netherlands	(46)	(44)	(33)	(27)
New Zealand	90 (104)	96 (112)	84 (94)	28 (37)
Portugal	87 (128)	195 (206)	49 (66)	2 (24)
UK—England	82 (90)	87 (97)	59 (66)	53 (63)
UK—Scotland	75 (90)	80 (94)	62 (70)	63 (82)

▲ TABLE 3.1 Median and mean inpatient waiting times (in days) for common surgical procedures in some OECD countries. Quantities in parentheses represent the mean.

Summaries for Symmetric Distributions

In Chapter 2 you learned how you can characterize the typical value of a distribution by the centre of the distribution, and the variability in that distribution by the horizontal spread. We left these concepts somewhat vague, but now our goal is to quantify them—to measure these concepts with numbers. However, coming up with a quantity to represent the centre or spread of a distribution is not all that straightforward. Statisticians have different ways of thinking about both centre and spread, and these different ways of thinking play different roles, depending on the context of the data.

In this chapter, the two different ways in which we will think about the concept of centre are (1) centre as the balancing point (or centre of gravity), and (2) centre as the halfway point. In this section we introduce the idea of the centre as a balancing point, most often used for symmetric distributions. Then in Section 3.3, we introduce the idea of the centre as a halfway point, a useful measure to consider when the distribution is skewed. Each of these approaches results in a different measure, and our choice also affects the method we use to measure variability.

The Centre as Balancing Point: The Mean

The most commonly used measure of centre is the mean. The **mean** of a collection of data is the arithmetic average. The mean can be thought of as the balancing point of a distribution of data, and when the distribution is symmetric, the mean closely matches our concept of the "typical value."

Visualizing the Mean

One of the most common metrics used to measure quality of education is the student–faculty ratio—the number of students enrolled divided by the number of full-time faculty members. For schools with small student–faculty ratios, we expect class sizes to be small, making it easier for students to receive individual attention. Figure 3.1 shows the distribution of student–faculty ratios (in number of students per full-time faculty member) at 130 post-secondary education institutions in Canada. We will use this distribution to explore the physical interpretation of the mean as the centre of gravity.

Looking Back

Symmetric Distributions
Recall that symmetric distributions are those for which the left-hand side of the graph of the distribution is roughly a mirror image of the right-hand side.

▶ **FIGURE 3.1** The distribution of student-faculty ratios for 130 Canadian post-secondary institutions. The mean is indicated here with a fulcrum. The mean is at the point on the dotplot that would balance if the points were placed on a teeter-totter. (Source: CAUT Almanac 2013–2014)

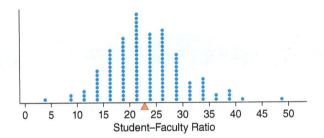

Student–Faculty Ratio

The mean student–faculty ratio among these institutions is 22.95, or about 23 students per full-time faculty member (we will discuss the calculation shortly). In the figure, it is represented by a fulcrum, indicating that it is the point where the distribution would balance if it were on a teeter-totter. Since the distribution is fairly symmetric, the balancing point is roughly in the middle of the distribution.

When the distribution is not symmetric, the balancing point will be off-centre. In such cases, the mean may not match what our intuition tells us is common or typical.

For instance, consider the distribution of yearly salaries of all National Hockey League (NHL) hockey players during the 2012–2013 season displayed in Figure 3.2. Salaries are in millions of U.S. dollars. (The highest paid player was Shea Weber of the Nashville Predators at $14 million. The first bin includes 259 players who earned

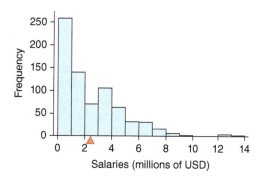

◄ **FIGURE 3.2** Salaries of NHL hockey players for the 2012–2013 season.

US$1 million or less.) Where would you place the centre of this distribution? Because the distribution is skewed to the right, the balancing point is somewhat high; the mean is at 2.4 million dollars. However, when you consider that 60% of players made less than this amount, you might not think that 2.4 million is what the "typical" player made. In other words, in this case the mean might not represent our idea of a typical salary, even for this group of famously well-paid professionals. (We will revisit this data set in Chapter 9.)

EXAMPLE **1** Math Scores

Figure 3.3 shows the distribution of mathematics achievement scores for 45 countries and education systems, as determined by the Trends in International Mathematics and Science Study (TIMSS). The scores are meant to measure the accomplishment of each system's Grade 8 students with respect to mathematical achievement. (The provinces of Alberta, Quebec, and Ontario were included in the study as individual education systems.)

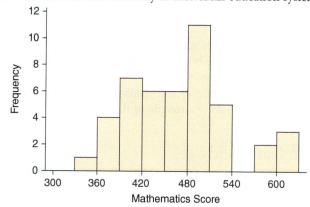

◄ **FIGURE 3.3** Distribution of international mathematics scores for 45 countries and other education systems. The scores measure the overall level of mathematical achievement of Grade 8 students in each country or education system.

QUESTION Based on the histogram, approximately what value do you think is the mean math achievement score for these countries and education systems?

SOLUTION The mean score is at the point where the histogram would balance if it were placed on a teeter-totter. For this distribution, the balancing point seems to be somewhere between 450 and 480 points.

CONCLUSION From the graph, the mean international mathematics achievement score looks to be about 465 points. This tells us that we can think of the typical country or education system as having had a score between 450 and 480 points. By the way, the three participating Canadian provinces had scores of 532 (Quebec), 512 (Ontario), and 505 (Alberta). The highest three scores were from South Korea (highest at 613), Singapore, and Chinese Taipei. Note that we are considering the average score *by country or education system*, and not by student (for that we would have to take into account the number of students in each country or education system).

TRY THIS! Exercise 3.3

The Mean in Context

As mentioned, the mean tells us the typical value in a data set with variability. We know that different countries had different math achievement scores, but typically, what is the math score of these countries? When you report the mean of a sample of data, you should not simply report the number but, rather, should report it in the context of the data so that your reader understands what you are measuring: the typical score on the international mathematics test among these education systems is between 450 and 480 points.

Knowing the typical value of one group allows us to compare this group to another group. For example, the average student–faculty ratio computed from the CAUT data for 2007 is 26.5 students per faculty member. The average for the sample that year was larger than the 2013–2014 average of 23 students per faculty member we discussed earlier.

KEY POINT   The mean of a collection of data is located at the "balancing point" of a distribution of data. The mean is one representation of the "typical" value of a variable.

Calculating the Mean

The mean is used so often in statistics that it has its own symbol: $\bar{x}$, which is pronounced "x-bar." To calculate the mean, find the (arithmetic) **average** of the numbers; that is, simply add up all the numbers and divide that sum by the number of observations. Formula 3.1 shows you how to calculate the mean, or average.

$$\text{Formula 3.1:}\quad \text{Mean} = \bar{x} = \frac{\sum x}{n}$$

The symbol $\sum$ is the Greek capital sigma, or capital S, which stands for *summation*. The x that comes after $\sum$ represents the value of a single observation. Therefore, $\sum x$ means that you should add all the values. The letter n represents the number of observations. Therefore, this equation tells us to add the values of all the observations and divide that sum by the number of observations.

The mean shown in Formula 3.1 is sometimes called the sample mean in order to make it clear that it is the mean of a sample of data.

EXAMPLE **2** Gas Buddy

According to GasBuddy.com (a website that invites people to submit prices at local gas stations), the prices of 1 litre of regular gas at the 10 service stations for which data were provided in Saskatoon (West), Saskatchewan, were as follows on one fall day in 2013 (all data in cents per litre):

111.9, 112.9, 113.9, 114.9, 116.4, 111.9, 112.9, 112.9, 114.9, 114.9

A dotplot (not shown) indicates that the distribution is fairly symmetric.

QUESTION Find the mean price of a litre of gas for these service stations. Explain what the value of the mean signifies in this context (in other words, interpret the mean).

SOLUTION Add the 10 numbers together to get 1137.5 c/L. We have 10 observations, so we divide 1137.5 c/L by 10 to get 113.75 c/L.

$$\bar{x} = \frac{111.9 + 112.9 + 113.9 + 114.9 + 116.4 + 111.9 + 112.9 + 112.9 + 114.9 + 114.9}{10}$$

$$= \frac{1137.5}{10}$$

$$= 113.75$$

CONCLUSION The typical price of 1 litre of gas at these gas stations in Saskatoon (West), Saskatchewan, was 113.75 c/L on that particular day in 2013. (Compare this with the 89.04 c/L average of January 3, 2015 for the same location!)

TRY THIS! Exercise 3.5a

Calculating the Mean Using Technology

Formula 3.1 tells you how to compute the mean if you have a small set of numbers that you can easily type into a calculator. But for large data sets, you are better off using a computer or a statistical calculator. That is true for most of the calculations in this book, in fact. For this reason, we will often just display what you would see on your computer or calculator and describe in the TechTips section the exact steps used to get the solution.

For example, the histogram in Figure 3.4 shows the distribution of the concentration of ground-level ozone in Sudbury, Ontario, at 2 p.m. for each of the 366 days of 2012, as reported by Air Quality Ontario (AQO). The units are parts per billion. Exposure to high levels of ozone can have significant effects on human health and can cause damage to many crops, garden plants, and trees, so low levels of ozone are desirable. (AQO considers air quality to be good or very good when ozone concentration is 50 ppb or below, moderate when ozone concentration is between 51 and 80 ppb, poor when ozone concentration is between 81 ppb and 149 ppb, and very poor when ozone concentration is 150 ppb or more.) Looking at the histogram, you can estimate the mean value using the fact that, since the distribution is fairly symmetric, the average will be approximately in the middle (around 33 ppb). If you were given the list of 366 values, you could find the mean using Formula 3.1. But you'll find it easier to use the pre-programmed routines of your calculator or software. Example 3 demonstrates how to do this.

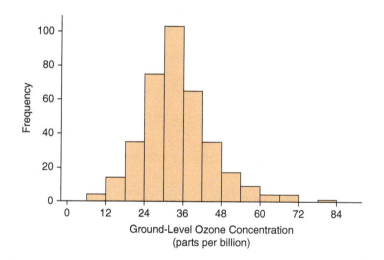

◄ **FIGURE 3.4** Ground-level ozone concentration at 2 p.m. in Sudbury, Ontario, for the 366 days of 2012. Because the distribution is fairly symmetric, the balancing point is roughly in the middle, at about 33 parts per billion.

EXAMPLE 3 Mean Ground-Level Ozone Concentration

We used five different statistical software programs to find the mean of the 366 measurements for 2012 of ground-level ozone concentration in Sudbury, Ontario. The data were uploaded into StatCrunch, Minitab, SPSS, Excel, and the TI-83/84 calculator.

QUESTION For each of the computer outputs shown in Figure 3.5, find the mean ground-level ozone concentration. Interpret the mean.

TECH

▶ **FIGURE 3.5a** StatCrunch output.

Summary statistics:

Column	n	Mean	Variance	Std. dev.	Std. err.	Median	Range	Min	Max	Q1	Q3
sudbury 2pm2012	366	33.726776	119.09227	10.91294	0.57042853	32	74	7	81	27	39

▶ **FIGURE 3.5b** Minitab output.

Descriptive Statistics: sudbury 2pm2012

```
Variable           N   N*    Mean  SE Mean   StDev  Minimum       Q1   Median
sudbury 2pm2012  366    0  33.727    0.570  10.913    7.000   27.000   32.000

Variable              Q3  Maximum
sudbury 2pm2012   39.000   81.000
```

▶ **FIGURE 3.5c** SPSS output.

Statistics

Sudbury2012

N	Valid	366
	Missing	0
Mean		33.7268
Median		32.0000
Std. Deviation		10.91294
Range		74.00
Minimum		7.00
Maximum		81.00
Percentiles	25	27.0000
	50	32.0000
	75	39.0000

▶ **FIGURE 3.5d** Excel output.

Column1	
Mean	33.72678
Standard Error	0.570429
Median	32
Mode	30
Standard Deviation	10.91294
Sample Variance	119.0923
Kurtosis	1.554002
Skewness	0.805559
Range	74
Minimum	7
Maximum	81
Sum	12344
Count	366

▶ **FIGURE 3.5e** TI-83/84 output.

```
1-Var Stats
x̄=33.72677596
Σx=12344
Σx²=459792
Sx=10.91294036
σx=10.89802178
↓n=366
```

```
1-Var Stats
↑n=366
 minX=7
 Q₁=27
 Med=32
 Q₃=39
 maxX=81
■
```

SOLUTION Statistical software packages produce a list of basic numerical summaries (called descriptive statistics) with a single command. As you can see in Figure 3.5a–d, the mean is always labelled clearly and is easy to find. If using a calculator, the mean is labelled as $\bar{x}$, as seen in the TI-83/84 output of Figure 3.5e.

CONCLUSION The outputs we obtained using technology all give us a mean of 33.7 ppb. Since the distribution is close to symmetric, we can say that a typical concentration of ground-level ozone in Sudbury, Ontario, at 2 p.m. during 2012 was about 33.7 ppb.

TRY THIS! Exercise 3.9

SNAPSHOT **THE MEAN OF A SAMPLE**

WHAT IS IT? ▶ A numerical summary.

WHAT DOES IT DO? ▶ Measures the centre of a distribution of data.

HOW DOES IT DO IT? ▶ The mean identifies the "balancing point" of the distribution, which is the arithmetic average of the values.

HOW IS IT USED? ▶ The mean represents the typical value in a set of data when the distribution is roughly symmetric.

WHEN IS IT USED? ▶ It is the most common measure of centre. Be aware that when the distribution is skewed, it might not represent what is "typical."

Measuring Variation with the Standard Deviation

The mean ground-level ozone concentration in Sudbury for 2012, 33.7 parts per billion, does not tell the whole story. Just because the mean of all observations taken is below 50 ppb (so that air quality is on average good), it does not mean that the ozone concentration in any particular day—August 17, for example—was at an adequate level. Was concentration in most days close to the mean of 33.7 ppb? Or did ozone concentration tend to be far from 33.7 ppb? Values in a data set vary, and this variation is measured informally by the horizontal spread of the distribution of data. A measure of variability, coupled with a measure of centre, helps us understand whether most observations are close to the typical value or far from it.

Visualizing the Standard Deviation

The histograms in Figure 3.6 show daily maximum temperatures in degrees Celsius recorded during 2013 in two of Canada's warmest cities. Figure 3.6a displays the distribution of data collected in Windsor, Ontario, whereas Figure 3.6b displays the distribution of data collected in Victoria, British Columbia.

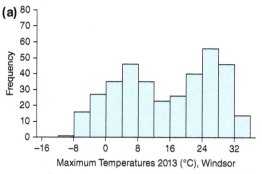
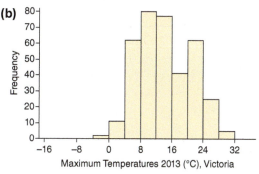

▲ **FIGURE 3.6** Distributions of daily maximum temperatures in 2013 in two cities: **(a)** Windsor, Ontario; **(b)** Victoria, British Columbia. Both cities have about the same mean temperature, although the variation in temperatures is much greater in Windsor than in Victoria.

The distributions of daily maximum temperatures in these cities are similar in several ways. Both distributions are fairly symmetric, although bimodal (one mound for the cold months and one for the warm ones). Moreover, the balancing point in both histograms is about the same (15°C for Windsor and 14°C for Victoria), so their mean daily maximum temperatures are about the same. However, note the difference in the spread of maximum temperatures.

Located in a sub-Mediterranean zone, Victoria boasts the mildest climate in Canada. Its temperate climate has earned it the nickname of "The Garden City." In 2013, many days had a maximum temperature close to the mean temperature of 14°C; rarely was it more than 14 degrees warmer or cooler than 14°C. On the other hand, despite Lake Ontario's moderating effect, Windsor sees rapid and large temperature changes between the seasons. In 2013, there were quite a few days where the high temperature in Windsor was more than 14 degrees warmer or cooler than average. The question now is, how can we measure spread so that we can quantify the differences we can see informally from the histograms?

The **standard deviation** is a number that measures how far away typical observations are from the mean. Distributions such as Victoria's temperatures have smaller standard deviations because more observations are fairly close to the mean. Distributions such as Windsor's temperatures have larger standard deviations because more observations are farther from the mean.

As you'll soon see, for many distributions, a majority of observations are within one standard deviation of the mean value.

KEY POINT The standard deviation should be thought of as the typical distance of the observations from their mean.

EXAMPLE 4 Comparing Standard Deviations from Histograms

Each of the three graphs in Figure 3.7 shows a histogram for a distribution of the same number of observations, and all the distributions have a mean value of about 3.5.

QUESTION Which distribution has the largest standard deviation, and why?

(a)

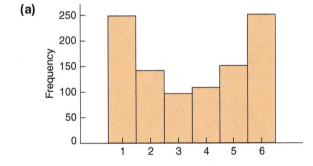

(b)

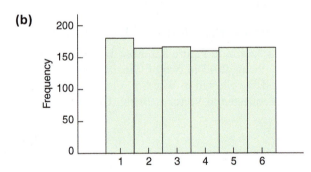

(c)

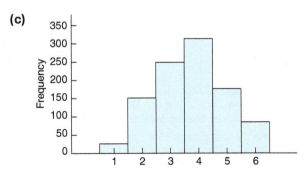

▶ **FIGURE 3.7** All three of these histograms have the same mean, but each has a different standard deviation.

SOLUTION All three groups have the same minimum and maximum values. However, the data shown in Figure 3.7a have the largest standard deviation. Why? The standard deviation measures how widely spread the points are from the mean. Note that the histogram in Figure 3.7a has the greatest number of observations farthest from the mean (at the values of 1 and 6). Figure 3.7c has the smallest standard deviation because so many of the data are near the centre, close to the mean, which we can see because the taller bars in the centre show us that there are more observations there.

CONCLUSION Figure 3.7a has the largest standard deviation, and Figure 3.7c has the smallest standard deviation.

TRY THIS! Exercise 3.13

The Standard Deviation in Context

The standard deviation is somewhat more abstract, and harder to understand, than the mean. It helps us understand how much typical values vary from the mean. For any data set, we can consider values that are within two standard deviations from the mean as typical.

For example, the 2013 maximum temperatures in Windsor (see Figure 3.6a) have a mean of 15°C and a standard deviation of 12°C. Twice the standard deviation is 24°C, which tells us that typical maximum temperatures in Windsor are within 24°C of 15°C. In other words, it is usually not colder than $15 - 24 = -9$ degrees, and not warmer than $15 + 24 = 39$ degrees. (You can see from the histogram that, in fact, all observations fall within these two values.) In contrast, maximum temperatures in Victoria (see Figure 3.6b) have a mean of 14°C and a standard deviation of 7°C, so that twice the standard deviation is only 14°C. This tells us that typical maximum temperatures in Victoria are usually not colder than $14 - 14 = 0$ degrees, and not warmer than $14 + 14 = 28$ degrees. Windsor has quite a bit more variability in temperature.

The interpretation of such typical values as those that are within two standard deviations of the mean is very general and valid for any data set. However, when a distribution is symmetric and unimodal, we can narrow down typical values to those that are within one standard deviation of the mean. In these distributions, most observations (in fact, about two-thirds of them) fall within one standard deviation of the mean.

EXAMPLE 5 Standard Deviation of Ground-Level Ozone Concentration

The mean of ground-level ozone concentration in Sudbury, Ontario, at 2 p.m. for 2012 is 33.7 ppb, with standard deviation of 10.9 ppb (see Figure 3.4).

QUESTION Find the ground-level ozone concentration one standard deviation above the mean and one standard deviation below the mean. Keeping in mind that AQO considers air quality to be good or very good when ozone concentration is 50 ppb or lower, what can we conclude about the air quality in Sudbury for most days in 2012?

SOLUTION The typical day has an ozone concentration of 33.7 ppb, and because the distribution is unimodal and (roughly) symmetric, most days have concentrations within 10.9 ppb of this value. In other words, ozone concentration at 2 p.m. on most days was between

$$33.7 - 10.9 = 22.8 \text{ ppb}$$
$$33.7 + 10.9 = 44.6 \text{ ppb}$$

CONCLUSION Since the value of 44.6 ppb (one standard deviation above the mean) is lower than 50 ppb, air quality was good or very good on most days in 2012.

As you'll soon see, the particular shape of the distribution of ozone concentration will allow us to say even more about this example. In a few pages you'll learn about the Empirical Rule, which when applied to this example says that ozone concentration for about 95% of days in 2012 should be within two standard deviations of the mean concentration.

TRY THIS! Exercise 3.15

Calculating the Standard Deviation

The formula for the standard deviation is somewhat more complicated than that for the mean, and a bit more work is necessary to calculate it. A calculator or computer is pretty much required for all but the smallest data sets. Just as the mean of a sample has its own symbol, the standard deviation of a sample of data is represented by the letter s.

$$\textbf{Formula 3.2:} \quad \text{Standard deviation} = s = \sqrt{\frac{\sum (x - \bar{x})^2}{n - 1}}$$

Think of this formula as a set of instructions. Essentially, the instructions say that we need to first calculate how far away each observation is from the mean. This distance, including the positive or negative sign, $(x - \bar{x})$, is called a **deviation**. We square these deviations so that they are all positive numbers, and then we essentially find the average. (If we had divided by n, and not $n - 1$, it would be the average. We'll discuss in Chapter 9 why we divide by $n - 1$ and not n.) Finally, we take the square root, which means that we're working with the same units as the original data, not with squared units.

EXAMPLE 6 A Litre of Gas

Consider the gas prices we examined in Example 2. Recall that the numbers represent the price of a litre of regular gas (in cents per litre) at 10 service stations in Saskatoon (West), Saskatchewan, for one day in October 2013:

111.9, 112.9, 113.9, 114.9, 116.4, 111.9, 112.9, 112.9, 114.9, 114.9

QUESTION Find the standard deviation for the prices. Explain what this value means in the context of the data.

SOLUTION We show this result two ways. The first way is by hand, which illustrates how to apply Formula 3.2. The second way uses a statistical calculator.

The first step is to find the mean. We did this earlier in Example 2, using Formula 3.1, which gave us a mean value of 113.75 cents per litre. We substitute this value for $\bar{x}$ in Formula 3.2.

Table 3.2 shows the first two steps. First we find the deviations (in column 2). Next we square each deviation (in column 3). The numbers are sorted so that you can more easily compare the differences.

The sum of the squared deviations—the sum of column 3—is 20.025. Dividing this by 9 (because $n - 1 = 10 - 1 = 9$), we get 2.225. The last step is to take the square root of this. The result is our standard deviation:

$$s = \sqrt{2.225} = 1.49164$$

x	$x - \bar{x}$	$(x - \bar{x})^2$
111.9	−1.85	3.4225
111.9	−1.85	3.4225
112.9	−0.85	0.7225
112.9	−0.85	0.7225
112.9	−0.85	0.7225
113.9	0.15	0.0225
114.9	1.15	1.3225
114.9	1.15	1.3225
114.9	1.15	1.3225
116.4	2.65	7.0225

▲ **TABLE 3.2** Deviations and squared deviations for calculating the standard deviation of gas prices.

To recap:

$$s = \sqrt{\frac{\sum(x-\bar{x})^2}{n-1}} = \sqrt{\frac{20.025}{10-1}} = \sqrt{\frac{20.025}{9}} = \sqrt{2.225}$$

$$= 1.49164, \text{ or about 1.5 cents}$$

When doing these calculations, your final result will be more accurate if you do not round any of the intermediate results. For this reason, it is far easier, and more accurate, to use a statistical calculator or statistical software to find the standard deviation. Figure 3.8 shows the standard deviation as $Sx = 1.491643389$, which coincides with the figure we obtained by hand.

CONCLUSION The standard deviation is about 1.5 cents. Therefore, at most of these gas stations, the price of a litre of gas is within 1.5 cents of 113.75 cents per litre.

TRY THIS! Exercise 3.17

TECH

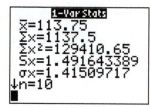

▲ **FIGURE 3.8** The standard deviation is denoted "Sx" in the TI-83/84 calculator output.

One reason why we suggest using statistical software rather than the formulas we present is that we nearly always look at data using several different numerical summaries and approaches. We nearly always begin by making a graph of the distribution. Usually the next step is to calculate a measure of the centre and then a measure of the spread. It does not make sense to have to enter the data again every time you want to examine them; it is much better to enter them once and use the functions on your calculator (or software).

SNAPSHOT   THE STANDARD DEVIATION OF A SAMPLE

WHAT IS IT? ▶	A numerical summary.
WHAT DOES IT DO? ▶	Measures the spread of a distribution.
HOW DOES IT DO IT? ▶	It measures the typical distance the data are away from the mean.
HOW IS IT USED? ▶	It tells us what values we can consider as typical (within two standard deviations of the mean in general, and within one standard deviation of the mean for symmetric, unimodal distributions).
WHEN IS IT USED? ▶	Whenever the mean is reported as a measure of centre.

Variance, a Close Relative of the Standard Deviation

Another way of measuring spread—a way that is closely related to the standard deviation—is the variance. The **variance** is simply the standard deviation squared, and it is represented symbolically by s^2.

Formula 3.3: $\text{Variance} = s^2 = \dfrac{\sum(x-\bar{x})^2}{n-1}$

In Example 5, the standard deviation of ground-level ozone concentration in Sudbury was 10.9 ppb. The variance is therefore $10.9 \times 10.9 = 118.81$ parts per billion squared. Similarly, the standard deviation for daily maximum temperatures in Victoria was about 7 degrees (see Figure 3.6b), so the variance is $7 \times 7 = 49$ degrees squared.

For most applications, the standard deviation is preferred over the variance. One reason is that the units for the variance are always squared (degrees squared in the last paragraph), which implies that the units used to measure spread are different from the units used to measure centre. The standard deviation, on the other hand, has the same units as the mean. In Chapter 11 you will see that the variance is useful for some analyses.

SECTION 3.2

What's Unusual? The Empirical Rule and z-Scores

Finding the standard deviation and the mean is a useful way to compare different samples and to compare observations from one sample with those in another sample.

The Empirical Rule

The **Empirical Rule** is a rough guideline that helps us understand how the standard deviation measures variability for the particular case when the distribution is approximately bell-shaped. In fact, the precise assumption is that the data set be a random sample from a Normal distribution, but we will have to wait until Chapter 6 to find out exactly what this means. There we will also find out how the percentages of the Empirical Rule are derived. For now, we will focus on developing some intuition regarding the standard deviation.

The Empirical Rule states that if the distribution of a data set is approximately bell-shaped (unimodal and symmetric), then

- Approximately 68% of the observations (roughly two-thirds) will be within one standard deviation of the mean.

- Approximately 95% of the observations will be within two standard deviations of the mean.

- Nearly all the observations (approximately 99.7% of them, in fact) will be within three standard deviations of the mean.

When we say that about 68% of the observations are within one standard deviation of the mean, we mean that if we count the observations that are between the mean minus one standard deviation and the mean plus one standard deviation, we will have counted about 68% of the total observations.

The Empirical Rule is illustrated in Figure 3.9 in the context of the data on ground-level ozone concentration in Sudbury, introduced in Example 3. Suppose we did not have access to the actual data and knew only that the distribution is unimodal and symmetric, that the mean ozone concentration is 33.7 ppb, and that the standard deviation is 10.9 ppb. The Empirical Rule predicts that ozone concentration for about 68% of days is between 22.8 ppb ($33.7 - 10.9 = 22.8$) and 44.6 ppb ($33.7 + 10.9 = 44.6$).

The Empirical Rule also predicts that ozone concentration in Sudbury for about 95% of days is within two standard deviations of the mean, which means that about 95% of days have ozone concentration between 11.9 and 55.5 ppb ($33.7 - (2 \times 10.9) = 11.9$ and $33.7 + (2 \times 10.9) = 55.5$). Finally, according to the Empirical Rule, nearly all days have concentrations between 1.0 and 66.4 parts per billion ($33.7 - (3 \times 10.9) = 1.0$ and $33.7 + (3 \times 10.9) = 66.4$). This is illustrated in Figure 3.9.

Details

The 68-95-99.7 Rule
To make it easier to remember the percentages appearing in the Empirical Rule, it is sometimes referred to as the 68-95-99.7 Rule.

▶ **FIGURE 3.9** The Empirical Rule predicts how many observations we will see within one standard deviation of the mean (68%), within two standard deviations of the mean (95%), and within three standard deviations of the mean (almost all).

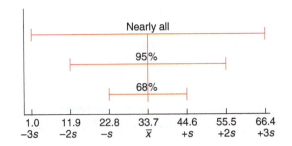

KEY POINT   In a relatively large collection of observations, if the distribution is approximately bell-shaped (unimodal and roughly symmetric), then about 68% of the observations are within one standard deviation of the mean; about 95% are within two standard deviations of the mean, and almost all observations are within three standard deviations of the mean. Not all bell-shaped distributions are the same, so your actual outcomes might differ from these values, but the Empirical Rule works well enough in a surprisingly large number of situations.

EXAMPLE 7 Comparing the Empirical Rule to Actual Ozone Concentrations

Because the distribution of ground-level ozone concentration in Sudbury, Ontario, in 2012 is roughly unimodal and symmetric, the Empirical Rule predicts that, in 2012, about 68% of days had ozone concentration between 22.8 ppb and 44.6 ppb, about 95% of days had ozone concentration between 11.9 ppb and 55.5 ppb, and nearly all days had ozone concentration between 1.0 ppb and 66.4 ppb.

QUESTION   Figure 3.10 shows the actual histograms for the distribution of ozone concentration for every day in 2012. The location of the mean is indicated, as well as the boundaries for points within one standard deviation of the mean (a), within two standard deviations of the mean (b), and within three standard deviations of the mean (c). Using these figures, compare the actual number of days that fall within each boundary to the number predicted by the Empirical Rule.

SOLUTION   From Figure 3.10a, by counting the heights of the bars between the two boundaries, we find that there are about $28 + 46 + 74 + 59 + 45 + 32 = 284$ days that actually lie between these two boundaries. (No need to count very precisely; we're

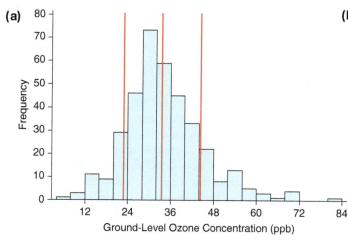

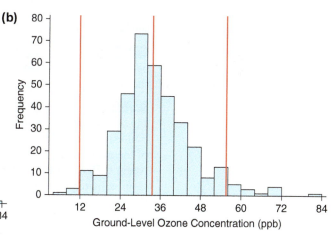

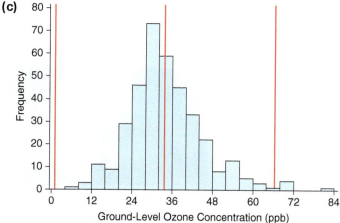

▲ FIGURE 3.10 **(a)** Boundaries are placed one standard deviation below the mean (22.8) and one standard deviation above the mean (44.6). The middle line in all three figures indicates the mean (33.7). **(b)** The Empirical Rule predicts that about 95% of observations will fall between these two boundaries (11.9 and 55.5 parts per billion). **(c)** The Empirical Rule predicts that nearly all observations will fall between these two boundaries (1.0 and 66.4 parts per billion).

after approximate numbers here.) The Empirical Rule predicts that about 68% of days, or $0.68 \times 366 = 249$ days, will fall between these two boundaries. The true number of days is slightly underestimated.

From Figure 3.10b, we count that there are about $11 + 9 + 28 + 46 + 74 + 59 + 45 + 32 + 22 + 8 + 13 = 347$ of days within two standard deviations from the mean. The Empirical Rule predicts that about 95% of days, or $0.95 \times 366 = 348$ days, will fall between these two boundaries. The Empirical Rule is pretty accurate in this case.

Finally, from Figure 3.10c, we clearly see that all but a few days (about 4 or 5) are within three standard deviations of the mean. We summarize in a table.

CONCLUSION

Interval	Empirical Rule Prediction	Actual Number
within s of mean	249	284
within $2s$ of mean	347	348
within $3s$ of mean	nearly all	all but 5

TRY THIS! Exercise 3.21

EXAMPLE **8** Thickness of Eggshells

The thickness of seabirds' eggshells is critical for successful breeding. In one of the first studies conducted since the 1970s ban of pesticides that had caused significant thinning of shells, researchers from the University of Saskatchewan measured the thickness of Common Murre eggs collected from Gull Island in Newfoundland and Labrador. They found that egg thickness measured at the "equator" (or largest circumference) of the eggs had a mean of 0.753 mm, with a standard deviation of 0.057 mm, making these the thickest eggs reported for this species.

QUESTION Assuming that the Empirical Rule holds, decide whether or not it would be unusual to find a Common Murre egg from Gull Island whose thickness measured at the equator is 0.639 mm.

SOLUTION One way of answering this question is to find out the approximate percentage of eggs that we would expect to have a thickness of 0.639 mm or less. The Empirical Rule says that about 95% of eggs will have a thickness within two standard deviations of the mean—that is, within $2 \times 0.057 = 0.114$ mm. Therefore, most eggs will be between $0.753 - 0.114 = 0.639$ mm and $0.753 + 0.114 = 0.867$ mm thick. Because only (approximately) 5% of eggs have a thickness outside this range, we know that eggs either thinner or thicker than this are rare. According to the Empirical Rule, which assumes a roughly symmetric distribution, about half of the eggs with a thickness outside this range will be thicker, and half will be thinner. Therefore, about 2.5% of Common Murre eggs from Gull Island have a thickness of 0.639 mm or less.

CONCLUSION According to the Empirical Rule, egg thickness of 0.639 mm is fairly unusual for Common Murre eggs from Gull Island. Note that your concept of "unusual" might be different from ours. The main idea is that "unusual" is rare, and in selecting two standard deviations, we chose to define egg thicknesses that occur 2.5% of the time or less as rare and therefore unusual. You might very reasonably set a different standard for what you wish to consider unusual.

TRY THIS! Exercise 3.23

z-Scores: Measuring Distance from Average

A popular question among statisticians is "How unusual is this?" (It is just as popular as "Compared to what?") Answering this question is complicated because the answer depends on the units of measurement. One hundred and fifty is a big value if we are measuring a man's weight in kilograms, but it is a small value if we are measuring his height in centimetres. Unless we know the units of measurement and the objects being measured, we can't judge whether a value is big or small.

One way around this problem is to measure the relative standing of an observation with respect to the sample rather than with respect to some absolute measure. This is done by calculating **z-scores**.

Visualizing *z*-Scores

The *z*-score of an observation is the number of standard deviations that the observation is above or below the mean. In other words, it measures a distance, but instead of measuring in centimetres or kilometres, it measures it in standard deviations. A measurement with a *z*-score of 1.0 is one standard deviation above the mean. A measurement with a *z*-score of −1.4 is 1.4 standard deviations below the mean.

Figure 3.11 shows a dotplot of the heights (in cm) of 247 adult men. The average height is 173 cm, and the standard deviation is 7 cm. Below the dotplot is a ruler that marks off how far from average each observation is measured in terms of standard deviations. The average height of 173 cm is at 0 because 173 is zero standard deviations away from the mean. The height of 187 cm is marked at 2; it has a *z*-score of 2 because it is two standard deviations above the mean ($173 + (2 \times 7) = 187$). The height of 166 cm is marked at −1; it has a *z*-score of −1 because it is one standard deviation *below* the mean ($173 - 7 = 166$). Of course, *z*-scores need not be integers, so 185 has a *z*-score of 1.71 ($173 + (1.71 \times 7) = 185$). We will see how we calculate general *z*-scores very soon.

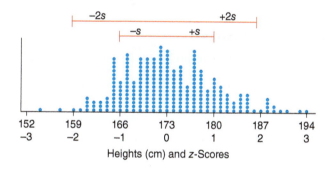

Heights (cm) and *z*-Scores

◀ **FIGURE 3.11** A dotplot of heights of 247 men marked with *z*-scores as well as heights in centimetres.

Using *z*-Scores in Context

z-Scores allow us to compare observations in one group with those in another, even if the two groups are measured in different units or under different conditions. For instance, some students might choose their math class on the basis of which professor they think is an easier grader. So if one student gets a 65 on an exam in a hard class, how do we compare his score to another student who gets a 75 in an easy class? If we converted to *z*-scores, we would know how far above (or below) the average each test score was so that we could compare these students' performances.

EXAMPLE 9 Exam Scores

Maria scored 70 out of 100 on her first statistics exam and 33 out of 45 on her second one. For the first exam, the mean was 60 and the standard deviation was 10. On the second exam, the mean was 36 and the standard deviation was 3.

QUESTION On which exam did Maria perform better when compared to the whole class?

SOLUTION Although Maria's two exams were graded on a different scale, we can use z-scores to compare her relative standing for the two exams. On the first exam, Maria is 10 points above the mean (from $70 - 60$). Because the standard deviation is 10 points, she is one standard deviation above the mean. In other words, her z-score for the first exam is 1.0.

On the second exam she is 3 points below average (from $33 - 36$). Because the standard deviation is 3 points, she is one standard deviation below the mean. In other words, her z-score is -1.0.

CONCLUSION Since Maria's z-score is higher for the first exam than for the second one, she did better on the first exam when compared to the rest of the class.

TRY THIS! Exercise 3.27

Calculating the z-Score

It's straightforward to convert to z-scores when the result is a whole number, as in the last few examples. More generally, to convert a value to its z-score, first subtract the mean. Then divide by the standard deviation. This simple recipe is summarized in Formula 3.4.

Formula 3.4: $z = \dfrac{x - \bar{x}}{s}$

Let's apply this to the data shown in Figure 3.11. What is the z-score of a man who is 185 centimetres tall? Remember that the mean height is 173 centimetres and the standard deviation is 7 centimetres. Formula 3.4 says to begin by subtracting the mean height:

$$185 - 173 = 12 \text{ centimetres}$$

Next divide by the standard deviation:

$$12/7 = 1.71 \text{ (rounded off to two decimal digits)}$$

$$z = \frac{x - \bar{x}}{s} = \frac{185 - 173}{7} = \frac{12}{7} = 1.71$$

This person has a z-score of 1.71. In other words, we would say that he is 1.71 standard deviations taller than average.

EXAMPLE 10 Daily Temperatures

The mean daily maximum temperature in Victoria, British Columbia, for the "summer" of 2013 (Victoria Day to Thanksgiving) was 22°C, and the standard deviation was 3.6 degrees. On one summer day that year, the maximum temperature was 29.8°C.

QUESTION What is the z-score for this temperature? Assuming that the Empirical Rule applies, is this temperature unusual?

SOLUTION

$$z = \frac{x - \bar{x}}{s} = \frac{29.8 - 22}{3.6} = 2.2$$

CONCLUSION This is an unusually warm day. From the Empirical Rule, we know that about 95% of temperatures have z-scores between -2 and 2. Therefore, it is unusual (though not extraordinary) to have a day as warm as or warmer than this one. (Note once again that your concept of "unusual" might be different from ours.)

TRY THIS! Exercise 3.29

THE z-SCORE

WHAT IS IT?	▶	A standardized observation.
WHAT DOES IT DO?	▶	Converts a measurement into standard units.
HOW DOES IT DO IT?	▶	By measuring how many standard deviations away a value is from the sample mean.
HOW IS IT USED?	▶	Each observation has its own z-score, so observations can be compared.
WHEN IS IT USED?	▶	When comparing observations from different groups, such as exam scores from different exams, or values measured in different units (such as centimetres and kilograms).

SECTION 3.3

Summaries for Skewed Distributions

As you saw earlier, although the mean represents the centre of a data set in one sense (the balancing point of the distribution), it does not represent what is most common or typical when the distribution is skewed. Another concept of centre, which is to think of it as being the location of the *middle* of a distribution, works better in those situations. You saw one example of this in Figure 3.2, which showed that the mean salary for NHL hockey players was higher than what a majority of players actually earned. Figure 3.12 shows another example of a strongly right-skewed distribution. This is the distribution of incomes of 933 residents of British Columbia, drawn randomly from the 2009 Survey of Household Spending. The mean income of $43,044 is marked with a triangle. However, note that the mean doesn't seem to match up very closely with what we think of as typical. The mean seems to be too high to be typical. In fact, more than half (63%) of the people in the sample earned less than this mean amount.

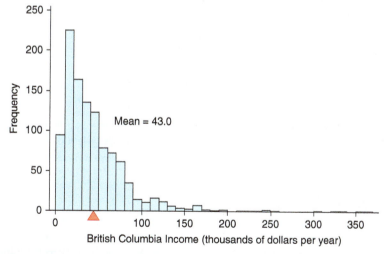

Mean = 43.0

British Columbia Income (thousands of dollars per year)

◀ **FIGURE 3.12** The distribution of annual incomes for a collection of British Columbia residents is right-skewed. Thus the mean is somewhat greater than what many people would consider a typical income. The location of the mean is shown with a triangle.

In skewed distributions, the mean can often be a poor measure of "typical." Instead of using the mean and standard deviation in these cases, we can measure the centre and spread differently.

The Centre as the Middle: The Median

The median provides an alternative way of determining a typical observation. The **median** of a sample of data is the value in the middle of the ordered data set. Because the median cuts a distribution down the middle, about 50% of observations are below it and about 50% are above it.

Visualizing the Median

Figure 3.13 shows a dotplot of the percentage of fat for each of 10 types of sliced ham sold at a grocery store. The vertical line marks the location of the median at 23.5%. Note that five observations lie below the median and five lie above it. The median cuts the distribution exactly in half. In Example 12, you'll see how the median percentage of fat in sliced turkey compares to that in sliced ham.

◀ **FIGURE 3.13** A dotplot of percentage of fat for 10 brands of sliced ham shows a median of 23.5%. This means that half the observations are below 23.5% and half are above it.

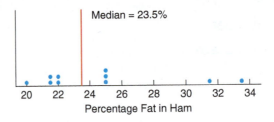

Finding the median for the distribution of incomes of the 933 British Columbia residents, shown again in Figure 3.14, is slightly more complicated because we have many more observations. The median (shown with the red vertical line) cuts the total area of the histogram in half. The median is at $34,000, and roughly 50% of the observations are below this value and about 50% are above it.

◀ **FIGURE 3.14** The distribution of incomes of British Columbia residents, with the median indicated by a vertical line. The median has about 50% of the observations above it and about 50% below it.

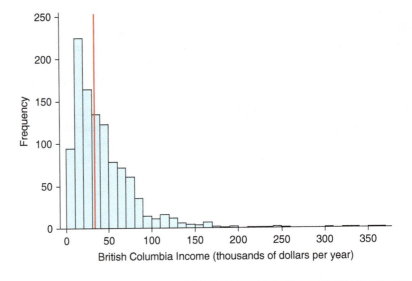

KEY POINT   The median is the value that cuts a distribution in half. In other words, one-half of the data are below the median and one-half of the data are above it. It is used to represent a typical value when the distribution of the data displays skewness.

The Median in Context

The median is used for the same purpose as the mean: to give us a typical value of a set of data. Knowing the typical value of one group helps us compare it to another. For example, as we've seen, the typical median income of this sample of British Columbia residents is $34,000. How does the typical income in British Columbia compare to the typical income in Nova Scotia? A sample of 897 Nova Scotia residents, drawn from the same 2009 Survey of Household Spending, has a median income of $31,000, which is lower than the median income in British Columbia (see Figure 3.15).

The typical person in our data set of Nova Scotia incomes makes less than the typical person in our British Columbia data set, as measured by the median. Because the median for Nova Scotia is $31,000, we know that more than half of Nova Scotia residents in the sample make less than the median British Columbia income of $34,000.

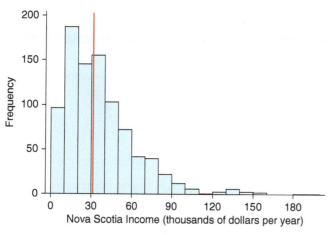

◀ **FIGURE 3.15** Distribution of incomes of a selection of Nova Scotia residents (in thousands of dollars per year). The median income is $31,000.

The median is often reported in news stories when the discussion involves variables with distributions that are skewed. For example, you may hear reports of "median housing costs" and "median salaries."

Calculating the Median

To calculate the value of the median, follow these steps:

1. Sort the data from smallest to largest.

2. If the set contains an odd number of observed values, the median is the middle observed value.

3. If the set contains an even number of observed values, the median is the average of the two middle observed values. This places the median precisely halfway between the two middle values.

EXAMPLE **11** Ten Gas Stations

The prices of a litre of regular gas (in cents per litre) at 10 Saskatoon (West) gas stations in October 2013 (see Example 2) were

111.9, 112.9, 113.9, 114.9, 116.4, 111.9, 112.9, 112.9, 114.9, 114.9

QUESTION Find the median price for a litre of gas and interpret the value.

SOLUTION First we sort the data from smallest to largest.

111.9, 111.9, 112.9, 112.9, 112.9, 113.9, 114.9, 114.9, 114.9, 116.4

Because the data set contains an even number of observations (10), the median is the average of the two middle observations, the fifth and sixth: 112.9 and 113.9.

111.9, 111.9, 112.9, 112.9, 112.9, 113.9, 114.9, 114.9, 114.9, 116.4
median

CONCLUSION The median is 113.4 cents per litre, which can be interpreted as the typical price of a litre of gas at these 10 stations. Note that, because the distribution of gas prices at these stations is roughly symmetric, there isn't a big difference between the mean (113.75 cents per litre) and the median (113.4 cents per litre). We will explore this further later on.

TRY THIS! Exercise 3.35a

Example 12 demonstrates how to find the median in a sample with an odd number of observations.

EXAMPLE **12** Percentage of Fat

Figure 3.13 showed that the median percentage of fat from the various brands of sliced ham for sale at a grocery store was 23.5%. How does this compare to the median percentage of fat for turkey? Here are the percentages of fat for the available brands of sliced turkey:

14, 10, 20, 20, 40, 20, 10, 10, 20, 50, 10

QUESTION Find the median percentage of fat and interpret the value.

SOLUTION The data are sorted and displayed below. Because we have 11 observations, the median is the middle observation, 20.

10 10 10 10 14 20 20 20 20 40 50
median

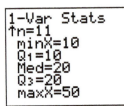

TECH

▲ FIGURE 3.16 Some TI-83/84 output for the percentage of fat in the turkey.

CONCLUSION The median is 20% fat. Thus the typical percentage of fat for these types of sliced turkey is 20%. This is (slightly) less than that for the typical sliced ham, which has 23.5% fat. Figure 3.16 provides TI-83/84 output that confirms our calculation.

TRY THIS! Exercise 3.37a

SNAPSHOT   THE MEDIAN OF A SAMPLE

WHAT IS IT? ▶	A numerical summary.
WHAT DOES IT DO? ▶	Measures the centre of a distribution.
HOW DOES IT DO IT? ▶	It is the value that has roughly the same number of observations above it and below it.
HOW IS IT USED? ▶	To measure the typical value in a data set.
WHEN IS IT USED? ▶	It is particularly useful for describing what is typical when the distribution is skewed.

Measuring Variability with the Interquartile Range

The standard deviation measures how spread out observations are with respect to the mean. But if we don't use the mean, then it doesn't make sense to use the standard deviation. When a distribution is skewed and you're using the median to measure the centre, an appropriate measure of variation is called the interquartile range. The **interquartile range (IQR)** tells us, roughly, how much space the middle 50% of the data occupy.

Visualizing the IQR

To find the IQR, we cut the distribution into four parts with roughly equal numbers of observations. The distance taken up by the middle two parts is the interquartile range.

The dotplot in Figure 3.17 shows the distribution of weights (in kilograms) for a class of introductory statistics students. The vertical lines slice the distribution into four parts so that each part has about 25% of the observations. The IQR is the distance between the first "slice" (at about 57 kg) and the third slice (at about 71 kg). This is an interval of 14 kg (71 − 57 = 14).

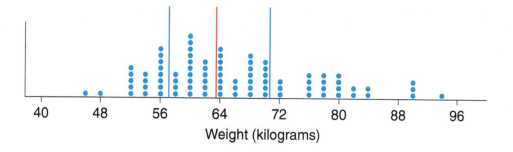

◀ **FIGURE 3.17** The distribution of weights (in kilograms) of students in a class is divided into four sections so that each section has roughly 25% of the observations. The IQR is the distance between the outer vertical lines (at 57 kg and 71 kg).

Figure 3.18 shows distributions for the same students, but this time the weights are separated by gender. The vertical lines are located so that about 25% of the data are below the leftmost line, and 25% are above the rightmost line. This means that about half of the data lie between these two boundaries. The distance between these boundaries is the IQR. You can see that the IQR for the males, about 15 kg, is much larger than the IQR for the females, which is about 8 kg. The females have less variability in their weights.

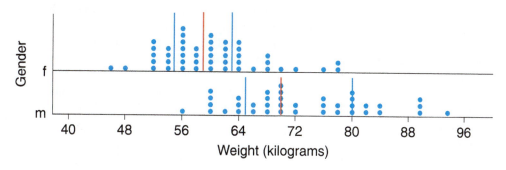

◀ **FIGURE 3.18** The dotplot of Figure 3.17 with weights separated by gender. The men have a much larger interquartile range than the women.

The IQR focuses only on the middle 50% of the data. We can change values outside of this range without affecting the IQR, as long as the relative positions of the observations inside the range do not change. For instance, Figure 3.19 shows the men's weights, but we have modified the lightest man's weight artificially to be extremely small. The IQR is still the same as in Figure 3.18.

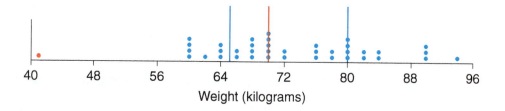

◀ **FIGURE 3.19** The men's weights are given with the lightest man's weight (in red) changed artificially to be close to 40 kg. Modifying the smallest value to be extremely small does not change the interquartile range.

The Interquartile Range in Context

The IQR for the incomes of British Columbia residents in the data set previously shown in Figure 3.14 is $39,000, as shown in Figure 3.20a. This tells us that the middle 50% of people in our data set had incomes that varied as much as $39,000. Compare this to the incomes from Nova Scotia, which have an IQR of $31,000 (Figure 3.20b). There is less variability among the Nova Scotia residents; they are more similar (at least in terms of their incomes).

An IQR of $39,000 for British Columbia residents seems like a pretty large spread. However, considered in the context of the entire distribution (see Figure 3.20a), which includes incomes as low as $0 and as large as $370,000, the IQR looks fairly small. The reason is that lots of people (half of our data set) have incomes in this fairly narrow interval.

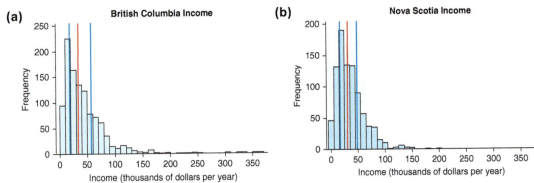

(a) British Columbia Income

(b) Nova Scotia Income

▲ **FIGURE 3.20 (a)** The distribution of incomes for residents of British Columbia. **(b)** The distribution of income for residents of Nova Scotia. In both figures, vertical bars are drawn to divide the distribution into areas with about 25% of the observations. The IQR is the distance between the outer vertical lines, and it is wider for the British Columbia incomes.

 Details

Software and Quartiles
Different software packages don't always agree with each other on the values for Q1 and Q3, and therefore they might report different values for the IQR. The reason is that several different accepted methods exist for calculating Q1 and Q3. So don't be surprised if the software on your computer gives different values from your calculator.

Calculating the Interquartile Range

Calculating the interquartile range involves two steps. First, you must determine where to "cut" the distribution. These points are called the quartiles, because they cut the distribution into quarters (fourths). The **first quartile (Q1)** has roughly one-fourth, or 25%, of the observations at or below it. The **second quartile (Q2)** has about 50% at or below it; actually, Q2 is just another name for the median. The **third quartile (Q3)** has about 75% of the observations at or below it. The second step is the easiest: to find the interquartile range, you simply find the distance between Q3 and Q1—that is, Q3 − Q1.

To find the quartiles:

- First find the median, which is also called the second quartile, Q2. The median cuts the data into two regions.

- The first quartile (Q1) is the median of the lower half of the sorted data. (Do not include the median observation in the lower half if you started with an odd number of observations.)

- The third quartile (Q3) is the median of the upper half of the sorted data. (Again, do not include the median itself if your full set of data has an odd number of observations.)

Formula 3.5:   Interquartile Range = Q3 − Q1

The next simple example will help you visualize the quartiles and IQR calculations.

EXAMPLE **13** Heights of Children

A group of eight children have the following heights (in centimetres):

122, 122, 135, 136, 137, 152, 157, 180

They are shown in Figure 3.21.

QUESTION Find the interquartile range for the distribution of the children's heights.

SOLUTION As before, we first explain how to do the calculations by hand and then show the output of technology.

First we find Q2 (the median). Note that the data are sorted and there are four observed values below the median and four observed values above the median.

Duncan	Charlie	Grant	Aidan		Sophia	Seamus	Cathy	Drew
122	122	135	136		137	152	157	180

Q2

136.5

(a)

(b)

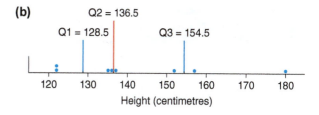

▲ **FIGURE 3.21** **(a)** Eight children sorted by height. **(b)** A dotplot of the heights of the children. The median and quartiles are marked with vertical lines. Note that two dots, or 25% of the data, appear in each of the four regions.

To find Q1, examine the numbers below the median and find the median of them, as shown.

Duncan Charlie   Grant Aidan
122   122   135   136
                  Q1
                 128.5

To find Q3, examine the numbers above the median and find the median of them.

Sophia Seamus   Cathy Drew
137   152   157   180
                  Q3
                 154.5

Together, these values are

Duncan Charlie   Grant Aidan   Sophia Seamus   Cathy Drew
122   122   135   136   137   152   157   180
           Q1   Q2   Q3
          128.5   136.5   154.5

Here's how we calculated the values:

$$Q1 = \frac{122 + 135}{2} = \frac{257}{2} = 128.5$$ (Halfway between Charlie and Grant)

$$Q2 = \frac{135 + 136}{2} = \frac{271}{2} = 135.5$$ (Halfway between Aidan and Sophia)

$$Q3 = \frac{152 + 157}{2} = \frac{309}{2} = 154.5$$ (Halfway between Seamus and Cathy)

The last step is to subtract:

$$IQR = Q3 - Q1 = 154.5 - 128.5 = 26$$

Figure 3.21b shows the location of Q1, Q2, and Q3. Note that 25% of the data (two observations) lie in each of the four regions created by the vertical lines.

Figure 3.22 shows the TI-83/84 output. The TI-83/84 does not calculate the IQR directly; you must subtract Q3 − Q1 yourself. The IQR is 154.5 − 128.5 = 26, which is the same as the IQR done by hand above.

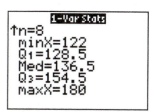

▲ **FIGURE 3.22** Some output of a TI-83/84 for eight children's heights.

CONCLUSION The interquartile range of the heights of the eight children is 26 cm.

TRY THIS! Exercise 3.39b

TECH

SNAPSHOT   THE INTERQUARTILE RANGE

WHAT IS IT? ▶	A numerical summary.
WHAT DOES IT DO? ▶	It measures the spread of the distribution of a data set.
HOW DOES IT DO IT? ▶	It computes the distance taken up by the middle half of the sorted data.
HOW IS IT USED? ▶	To measure the variability in a sample.
WHEN IS IT USED? ▶	Whenever the median is reported as a measure of centre.

Finding the Range, Another Measure of Variability

Another measure of variability is similar to the IQR but much simpler. The **range** is the distance spanned by the entire data set. It is very simple to calculate: the largest value minus the smallest value.

Formula 3.6:   Range = maximum − minimum

For the heights of the eight children (Example 13), the range is $180 - 122 =$ 58 centimetres.

The range is useful for a quick measurement of variability because it's very easy to calculate. However, because it depends on only two observations—the largest and the smallest—it is very sensitive to any peculiarities in the data. For example, if someone makes a mistake when entering the data and enters 810 cm instead of 180 cm, then the range will be very wrong. The IQR, on the other hand, depends on many observations and is therefore more reliable.

SECTION 3.4

Comparing Measures of Centre

Which should you choose, the mean (accompanied by the standard deviation) or the median (with the IQR)? These pairs of measures have different properties, so you need to choose the pair that's best for the data you're considering. Our primary goal is to choose a value that is a good representative of the typical values of the distribution. (In later chapters, you will learn about other criteria for choosing a mean or median.)

Look at the Shape First

This decision begins with a picture. The shape of the distribution will determine which measures are best for communicating the typical value and the variability in the distribution.

 EXAMPLE 14 Railway Network Lengths

Figure 3.23 shows a histogram for the total length (in thousands of kilometres) of the railway network of 134 countries. (The United States has the world's longest railway network, followed by China, India, and Russia. Canada's network is the fifth longest with 63,013 km of railway.)

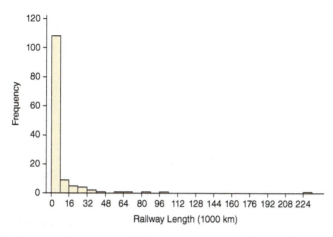

QUESTION What measures of centre and spread describe the typical railway network lengths better: the mean (8900 km) and standard deviation (24,200 km) or the median (2300 km) and interquartile range (4500 km)? (All measures have been rounded to the nearest hundred.) Interpret the appropriate measures.

SOLUTION As we can see from the histogram, the vast majority of observations (81%) fall inside the first bin, whereas the mean falls inside the second bin. The mean does not represent what is typical in the data set. The distribution of railway lengths is skewed to the right, so the median describes the typical network length better. We can then use the interquartile range as a measure of variation.

CONCLUSION The median railway network length is 2300 km, and the interquartile range is 4500 km. In other words, the typical railway network is about 2300 km long, but there is quite a bit of variability, with the middle 50% of the railway lengths differing by 4500 km.

TRY THIS! Exercise 3.47

When a distribution is right-skewed, as it is with the railway network lengths, the mean is generally larger than the median. You can see this in Figure 3.23; the right tail means the balancing point must be to the right of the median. With the same reasoning, we can see that in a left-skewed distribution, the mean is generally less than the median. In a symmetric distribution, the mean and median are approximately the same.

KEY POINT In a symmetric distribution, the mean and median will be approximately the same value. In a right-skewed distribution, the mean tends to be greater than the median, and in a left-skewed distribution, the mean tends to be less than the median.

The Effect of Outliers

Even when a distribution is mostly symmetric, the presence of one or more outliers can have a large effect on the mean. Usually, the median is a more representative measure of centre when an outlier is present.

The average height of the eight children from Example 13 was 142.6 cm. Imagine that we replace the tallest child (who is 180 cm tall) with Jamaican sprinter and six-time Olympic gold medallist Usain "Lightning" Bolt, whose height is 195 cm. Our altered data set is now

122, 122, 135, 136, 137, 152, 157, 195 centimetres

In order to keep the balance of the data, the mean has to shift to the right. The mean of this new data set is 144.5 cm, almost 2 cm higher. The median of the new data set, however, is the same: 136.5 cm, as shown in Figure 3.24.

Looking Back

Outliers
Recall from Chapter 2 that an outlier is an extremely large or small observation relative to the bulk of the data.

▶ **FIGURE 3.24** The effect of changing the tallest child's height into Usain Bolt's height. Note that the mean (shown with triangles) changes, but the median (the vertical line) stays the same.

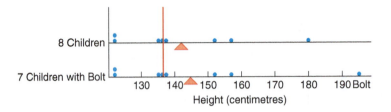

The presence of an extreme outlier explains the big difference between the two measures of centre given in Example 14 for the railway network length data. The mean (8900 km) is affected by the extremely unusual length of the United States railway, whereas the median (2300 km) is not.

When outliers are present, the median is a good choice for a measure of centre. In technical terms, we say that the median is **resistant to outliers**; it is not affected by the size of an outlier and does not change even if a particular outlier is replaced by an even more extreme value.

KEY POINT The median is resistant to outliers; it is not affected by the size of the outliers. It is therefore a good choice for a measure of the centre if the data contain outliers and you want to reduce their effect.

Many Modes: Summarizing Centre and Spread

**Looking Back**

Bimodality

Recall from Chapter 2 that a mode is a major mound in a graph (such as a histogram) of a single numerical variable. A bimodal distribution has two major mounds.

What should you do to describe the centre and spread of a distribution that is bimodal or that has several modes? Unfortunately, the answer is "It's complicated."

You learned in Chapter 2 that multiple modes in a graphical display of a distribution sometimes indicate that the data set combines different groups. For example, perhaps a data set containing heights includes both men and women. The distribution could very well be bimodal, because we're combining two groups of people who differ markedly in terms of their heights. In this case, and in many other contexts, it is more useful to separate the groups and report summary measures separately for each group. If we know which observations belong to the men and which to the women, then we can separate the data and compute the mean height for men separately from the mean height for women.

For example, Figure 3.25 shows a histogram of the finishing times of male marathon runners. The most noticeable feature of this distribution is that there appear to be two modes. When confronted with this situation, a natural question to ask is "Are two different groups of runners represented in this data set?"

▶ **FIGURE 3.25** Marathon times reported for two groups: amateur and Olympic athletes. Note the two modes. Only male runners were included.

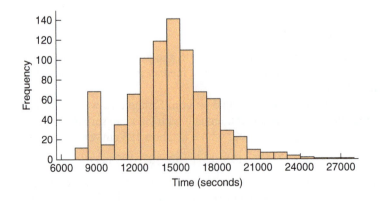

As it turns out, the answer is yes. Table 3.3 shows a few lines of the data set. From this, we see that the times belong to runners from two different events. One event was the 2012 Olympics, which includes the best marathoners in the world. The other event was an amateur marathon in Victoria, British Columbia, in 2014. The *V* in Table 3.3 means the event took place in Victoria and the *O* means it took place during the Olympics.

Figure 3.26 shows the data separately for each of these events. We could now compute measures for centre and spread separately for the Olympic and amateur events. However, you will sometimes find yourself in situations where a bimodal distribution occurs but it *does* make sense to compute a single measure of centre. We can't give you advice for what to do in all situations. Our best advice is always to ask, "Does my summary make sense?"

Time (seconds)	Event
8404	V
8829	V
7681	O
7707	O

▲ **TABLE 3.3** A few lines from the data set of marathon times for male runners.

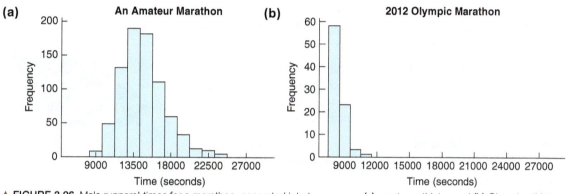

▲ **FIGURE 3.26** Male runners' times for a marathon, separated into two groups: **(a)** amateur athletes and **(b)** Olympic athletes.

Comparing Two Groups with Different-Shaped Distributions

Note that the distribution of times for the amateur runners in Figure 3.26a is fairly symmetric, which suggests we should use the mean to report the typical finishing time. But the distribution of Olympic times is right-skewed, which suggests we should compute the median. Which do you think is the better measure for comparing these two groups, the mean or the median?

When comparing two distributions, you should always use the same measures of centre and spread for both distributions. Otherwise, the comparison is not valid.

 Caution

Average
A guy comes across a statistician who is standing with one foot in a pot of boiling water and one foot frozen in a block of ice. "Isn't that painful?" the guy asks. "Maybe so," says the statistician, "but on average it feels just right." Beware of applying the mean to situations where it will not provide a "typical" measure!

EXAMPLE 15 Marathon Times, Revisited

In Figure 3.25 we lumped all of the marathon runners' finishing times into one group. But in fact, our data set had a variable that told us which time belonged to an Olympic runner and which to an amateur runner, so we could separate the data into groups. Figure 3.26 shows the same data, separated by groups.

QUESTION Typically, which group has the fastest finishing times?

SOLUTION The distribution of Olympic runners is right-skewed, so the median would be the best measure to represent a typical finishing time. Although the distribution of amateur runners is relatively symmetric, we report the median because we want to compare the typical running time of the amateurs to the typical running time of the Olympic runners. The median of the male Olympic runners is 8340 seconds (about 2.3 hours), and the

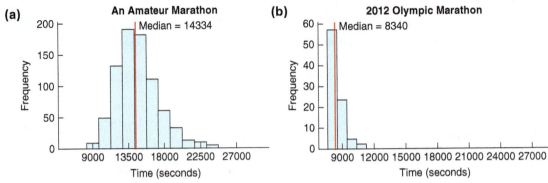

▲ **FIGURE 3.27** Men's times for a marathon, separated into two groups: **(a)** amateur athletes and **(b)** Olympic athletes. Medians are shown for each group.

> ⚠ **Caution**
>
> **Don't Get Modes from Computer Output**
> Avoid using your computer to calculate the modes. For data sets with many numerical observations, many software programs give meaningless values for the modes. For the data shown in Figure 3.27, for example, most software packages would report the location of five different modes, none of them corresponding to the high points on the graph.

median for the amateur male runners is 14,334 seconds (about 4 hours). Figure 3.27 shows the location of each group's median running time.

CONCLUSION   The typical male Olympic runner finished the marathon considerably faster: a median time of 8340 seconds (about 2.3 hours) compared to 14,334 seconds (about 4 hours) for the amateur male athletes.

TRY THIS!   Exercise 3.61

 KEY POINT   When you are comparing groups, if any one group is strongly skewed or has outliers, it is usually best to compare the medians and interquartile ranges for all groups.

Using Boxplots for Displaying Summaries

Boxplots are a useful graphical tool for visualizing a distribution, especially when comparing two or more groups of data. A boxplot shows us the distribution divided into fourths. The left edge of the box is at the first quartile (Q1) and the right edge is at the third quartile (Q3). Thus the middle 50% of the sorted observations lie inside the box. Therefore, the length of the box is proportional to the IQR.

A vertical line inside the box marks the location of the median. Horizontal lines, called whiskers, extend from the ends of the box to the smallest and largest values, or nearly so. (We'll explain soon.) Thus the entire length of the boxplot spans most, or all, of the range of the data.

Figure 3.28 compares a dotplot (with the quartiles marked with vertical lines) and a boxplot for the price of gas at stations in Saskatoon, Saskatchewan, as discussed in Examples 2 and 11.

Unlike many of the graphics used to visualize data, boxplots are relatively easy to draw by hand, assuming that you've already found the quartiles. Still, most of the time you will use software or a graphing calculator to draw the boxplot.

Most software packages produce a variation of the boxplot that helps identify observations that are extremely large or small compared to the bulk of the data. These extreme observations are called potential outliers. Potential outliers are different from the outliers we discussed in Chapter 2, because sometimes points that look extreme in a boxplot are not that extreme when shown in a histogram or dotplot. They are called *potential* outliers because you should consult a histogram or dotplot of the distribution before deciding whether the observation is too extreme to fit the pattern of the distribution. (Remember, whether or not an observation is an outlier is a subjective decision.)

Potential outliers are identified by this rule: They are observations that are a distance of more than 1.5 interquartile ranges below the first quartile (the left edge of a horizontal box) and above the third quartile (the right edge).

To allow us to see these potential outliers, the whiskers are drawn from the edge of each box to the most extreme observation that is not a potential outlier. This implies that before we can draw the whiskers, we must identify any potential outliers.

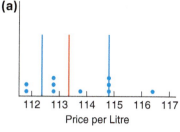

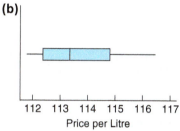

Whiskers in a boxplot extend to the most extreme values that are not potential outliers. Potential outliers are points that are more than 1.5 IQRs from the edges of the box.

Figure 3.29 is a boxplot with data for the 20 most-visited world websites in January of 2015, according to alexa.com, a company that provides commercial web traffic data. We have plotted the number of sites that are linked into each website, which is a different measure of the site's popularity. (The first lines of the data set are shown in Table 3.4.)

From the boxplot, we can see that

$$IQR = 1948 - 79 = 1869$$

$$1.5 \times IQR = 1.5 \times 1869 = 2804$$

$$\text{Right limit} = 1948 + 2804 = 4752$$

$$\text{Left limit} = 79 - 2804 = -2725$$

Any points above 4752 are the potential outliers (there cannot be any observations below −2725).

▲ **FIGURE 3.28** **(a)** A dotplot with Q1, Q2, and Q3 indicated and **(b)** a boxplot for the price of regular, unleaded gas at stations in Saskatoon, Saskatchewan.

Rank	Website	Number of Sites Linked into Website (thousands)
1	Google.com	3521
2	Facebook.com	6804
3	YouTube.com	3479
4	Yahoo.com	1197

▲ **TABLE 3.4** The most visited world websites, with the number of sites linked into each website (in thousands).

◄ **FIGURE 3.29** Boxplot of number of sites linked into the 20 most visited world websites in January 2015.

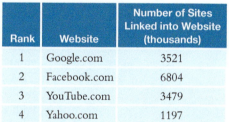

The whiskers go to the most extreme values that are not potential outliers. On the left side of the box, observations smaller than −2725 would be potential outliers. The number of sites cannot be negative, so the left whisker extends to the smallest observation, which is 14 thousand sites. This whisker is quite short because there is not a lot of variability between the smallest 25% of observations in the data set.

On the right, two values in the data set are larger than 4752 thousands. The whisker extends to the largest number of sites linked that is less than (or equal to) 4752 thousands, and the larger values are shown in Figure 3.29 with dots. They are the number of links to Facebook (ranked second in popularity) and to Twitter (ranked ninth), both unusually high.

Investigating Potential Outliers

What do you do with potential outliers? The first step is always to investigate. A potential outlier might not be an outlier at all. Or a potential outlier might tell an interesting story, or it might be the result of an error in entering data.

Figure 3.30a is a boxplot of the weights of the female students in the introductory statistics class we discussed in Section 3.3. Two students are flagged as potential outliers. However, if we examine a histogram, shown in Figure 3.30b, we see that these outliers are not really that extreme. Most people would not consider these two observations as being outliers in this distribution because they are not separated from the bulk of the distribution in the histogram.

▶ **FIGURE 3.30 (a)** Distribution of weights of female students. The boxplot indicates two potential outliers. **(b)** The histogram of weights shows that the two largest observations are not that much larger than the bulk of the data.

(a)
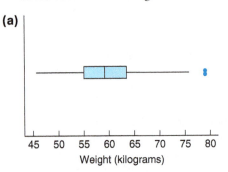

(b)
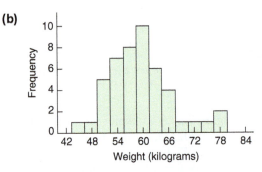

Figure 3.31 shows a boxplot and a histogram for the TIMSS science achievement scores for Grade 4 students in 57 countries and other education systems (we examined the results for Grade 8 mathematics achievement in Example 1). Two countries appear as potential outliers in the boxplot. As can be seen from the histogram, the scores are far enough from the bulk of the distribution that we can consider them real outliers. In fact, TIMSS has reservations about the reliability of the average achievement score of these two countries (Yemen and Morocco, as it turns out) because the percentage of students with achievement too low for estimation exceeded 25%. Therefore, we would have good reasons to disregard these two observations from any further analysis.

▶ **FIGURE 3.31** Distribution of international science scores for Grade 4 achievement. **(a)** The boxplot identifies two potential outliers. **(b)** The histogram confirms that these scores are indeed more extreme than the bulk of the data.

(a)
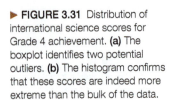

(b)
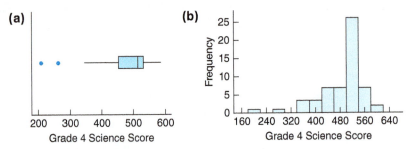

Horizontal or Vertical?

Boxplots do not have to be horizontal. Many software packages provide you with the option of making vertical boxplots. Which direction you choose is not important—pick the one that you find more readable. Figure 3.32 displays boxplots in both directions for

▶ **FIGURE 3.32 (a)** Vertical boxplot of millions of debit transactions in 19 countries. **(b)** Boxplot of the same data with horizontal orientation.

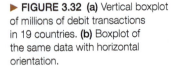

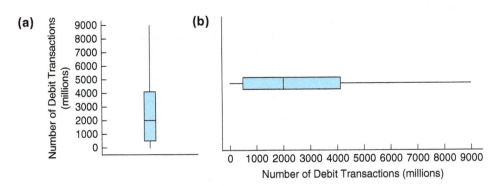

the total number of debit transactions in 2013 for 19 countries, as reported by the Bank of International Settlements. (Canada falls beyond the upper quartile, with 4519 million debit transactions in 2013.)

Using Boxplots to Compare Distributions

Boxplots are often a very effective way of comparing two or more distributions. For example, we can compare the distribution of the number of debit transactions in 2013 with the distribution of the same quantity in 2009. The side-by-side boxplots are shown in Figure 3.33. At a glance, we can see how these distributions differ and how they are similar.

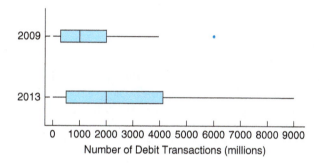

◀ FIGURE 3.33 Side-by-side boxplots for the number of debit transactions in 19 countries for two years (2009 and 2013).

Things to Watch For with Boxplots

Boxplots are best used only for unimodal distributions because they hide bimodality (or any multimodality). For example, Figure 3.34a repeats the histogram of marathon running times for two groups of male runners: amateurs and Olympians. The distribution is clearly bimodal. However, the boxplot in part (b) doesn't show us the bimodality. Boxplots can give the misleading impression that a bimodal distribution is really unimodal.

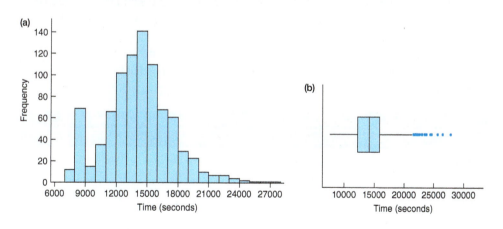

◀ FIGURE 3.34 (a) Histogram of finishing times (in seconds) for two groups of male marathon runners: Olympic athletes and amateurs. The graph is bimodal because the elite athletes tend to run faster, so there is a mode at around 8500 seconds (about 2.4 hours) and another mode at around 14,500 seconds (about 4 hours). (b) The boxplot hides this interesting feature.

Boxplots should *not* be used for very small data sets. It takes at least five numbers to make a boxplot, so if your data set has fewer than five observations, you can't make a boxplot.

Finding the Five-Number Summary

Boxplots are not really pictures of a distribution in the way that histograms are. Instead, boxplots help us visualize the location of various summarizing quantities. The boxplot is a visualization of a numerical summary called the **five-number summary**. These five numbers are

the minimum, Q1, the median, Q3, and the maximum

For example, for number of sites that link to the 20 most popular websites, the five-number summary (in thousands of sites) is

14   79   181   1948   6804

as you can see in Figure 3.29.

Note that a boxplot is not just a picture of the five-number summary. Boxplots always show the maximum and minimum values, but sometimes they also show us potential outliers.

SNAPSHOT   THE BOXPLOT

WHAT IS IT? ▶	A graphical summary.
WHAT DOES IT DO? ▶	Provides a visual display of numerical summaries of a distribution of numerical data.
HOW DOES IT DO IT? ▶	The box stretches from the first quartile to the third quartile, and a vertical line indicates the median. Whiskers extend to the largest and smallest values that are not potential outliers, and potential outliers are indicated with special marks.
HOW IS IT USED? ▶	It is easy to draw, yet it conveys information about the shape, centre, spread, and outliers of the distribution of a numerical variable.
WHEN IS IT USED? ▶	Data sets with more than five observations. Boxplots are particularly useful for comparing two or more data sets.

CASE STUDY REVISITED

How do Canada's typical waiting times for elective (non-emergency) procedures compare to those in other OECD countries where the reduction of waiting times is also a priority? Table 3.1 at the beginning of the chapter (repeated here) gave OECD data on median and mean waiting times for hip replacement, knee replacement, cataract surgery, and coronary artery bypass graft surgery (CABG). The data are measured in days, from the date on which a specialist adds a patient to the waiting list to the date on which the patient is admitted to an inpatient or day-case surgical unit for the procedure.

Median (Mean) Inpatient Waiting Times for Common Surgical Procedures (2011)				
Country	**Hip Replacement**	**Knee Replacement**	**Cataract**	**CABG**
Australia	108	173	90	17
Canada	89	107	49	7
Finland	113 (127)	136 (149)	111 (114)	43 (58)
Netherlands	(46)	(44)	(33)	(27)
New Zealand	90 (104)	96 (112)	84 (94)	28 (37)
Portugal	87 (128)	195 (206)	49 (66)	2 (24)
UK—England	82 (90)	87 (97)	59 (66)	53 (63)
UK—Scotland	75 (90)	80 (94)	62 (70)	63 (82)

▲ **TABLE 3.1 (repeated)** Median and mean inpatient waiting times (in days) for common surgical procedures in some OECD countries. Quantities in parentheses represent the mean.

Our first step is to decide which measure of centre (the mean or the median) would be most appropriate for making international comparisons of typical waiting times. Although we do not have access to histograms or to the original data, we can still predict the shape of the distributions of waiting times. We can expect the distributions to be right-skewed, since a small proportion of patients (for instance, patients who are placed on a waiting list in anticipation of the potential need for treatment) will have extremely long waiting times (Sanmartin, 2001). Therefore, the median is a more appropriate measure of centre for making comparisons of typical waiting times. (This is the reason why, in Canada, the CIHI reports median waiting times to describe a patient's typical experience.) As we can see in Table 3.1, whenever both mean and median are reported, the mean is systematically higher than the median, thus confirming that the distributions of waiting times are right-skewed.

Canada's typical waiting times in 2011 were shorter than those in Australia and Finland for all four procedures. Except for knee replacement, they were also shorter than those in New Zealand. Moreover, the typical waiting time of only one week for CABG in Canada was the second shortest among all the countries considered. However, when it comes to hip replacement, knee replacement, and cataract surgery, the comparison with the Netherlands makes it clear that there is still room for improvement. Even though we do not have the median waiting times for the Netherlands, the mean waiting times (which we expect to be higher than the median) were considerably lower than the medians in Canada.

EXPLORING STATISTICS

CLASS ACTIVITY

Does Reaction Distance Depend on Gender?

GOALS	MATERIALS
Apply the concepts introduced in this chapter to data you have collected in order to compare two groups.	A metre stick or stiff ruler for each group.

ACTIVITY

Work in groups of two or three. One person holds the metre stick vertically, with one hand near the top of the stick, so that the 0-centimetre mark is at the bottom. The other person then positions his or her thumb and index finger about 5 cm apart on opposite sides of the metre stick at the bottom. Now the first person drops the metre stick without warning, and the other person catches it. Record the location of the middle of the thumb of the catcher. This is the distance the stick travelled and is called the reaction distance, which is related to reaction time. A student who records a small distance has a fast reaction time, and a student with a larger distance has a slower reaction time. Now switch tasks. Each person should try catching the metre stick twice, and the better (shorter) distance should be reported for each person. Then record the gender of each catcher. Your instructor will collect your data and combine the class results.

BEFORE THE ACTIVITY

1. Imagine that your class has collected data and you have 25 men and 25 women. Sketch the shape of the distribution you expect to see for the men and the distribution you expect to see for the women. Explain why you chose the shape you did.

2. What do you think would be a reasonable value for the typical reaction distance for the women? Do you think it will be different from the typical reaction distance for the men?

AFTER THE ACTIVITY

1. Now that you have actual data, how do the shapes of the distributions for men and women compare to the sketches you made before you collected data?

2. What measures of centre and spread are appropriate for comparing men and women's reaction distances? Why?

3. How do the actual typical reaction distances compare to the values you predicted?

4. Using the data collected from the class, write a short paragraph (a couple of sentences) comparing the reaction distances of men and women. You should also talk about what group you could extend your findings to, and why. For example, do your findings apply to all men and women? Or do they apply only to students at your school?

CHAPTER REVIEW

Summary of Learning Objectives

1. **What is the mean, how do I calculate it, and when is it an appropriate measure of centre for describing a typical observation?** The mean is the balancing point of a distribution.

   Formula 3.1: $\text{Mean} = \bar{x} = \dfrac{\sum x}{n}$

   Although widely used, it can be influenced by extreme observations. It best describes a typical observation if the distribution is symmetric.

2. **What is the median, how do I calculate it, and when is it an appropriate measure of centre for describing a typical observation?** The median is the point that has roughly 50% observations below it and 50% above it. It is calculated by ordering the observed values from lowest to highest and selecting the middle value. It is resistant to outliers, so it is used to describe a typical observation when the distribution is skewed.

3. **What is the standard deviation, how do I calculate it, and how can I use it to decide what observations are typical?** The standard deviation measures how far away typical observations are from the mean.

   Formula 3.2: $\text{Standard deviation} = s = \sqrt{\dfrac{\sum (x - \bar{x})^2}{n - 1}}$

   In general, we can consider values that are within two standard deviations of the mean as typical. For a bell-shaped distribution, the Empirical Rule tells us that approximately 95% of observations are within two standard deviations of the mean.

4. **What is the variance and how do I calculate it?** The variance is the square of the standard deviation. It is given in squared units.

   Formula 3.3: $\text{Variance} = s^2 = \dfrac{\sum (x - \bar{x})^2}{n - 1}$

5. **What is the z-score of an observation, and how do I calculate it?** A z-score measures the number of standard deviations that an observation is above or below the mean. It is used to compare observations from different groups.

   Formula 3.4: $z = \dfrac{x - \bar{x}}{s}$

6. **What is the interquartile range, how do I calculate it, and when do I use it?** The interquartile range measures the spread of the middle 50% of observations.

   Formula 3.5: $\text{Interquartile range} = Q3 - Q1$

   It is used to measure variability when the distribution is skewed and the median is used as measure of centre.

7. **What is the five-number summary and how do I use it?** The five numbers in the five-number summary are: the minimum, Q1, the median, Q3, and the maximum. You can use the minimum and the maximum to calculate the range, a crude measure of variability.

   Formula 3.6: $\text{Range} = \text{maximum} - \text{minimum}$

   The summary is used to draw boxplots, which are an easy way to explore and compare features of distributions.

Important Terms

Mean, *78*	Empirical Rule, *88*	First quartile (Q1), *98*	Resistant to outliers, *102*
Average, *80*	z-score, *91*	Second quartile (Q2), *98*	Boxplot, *104*
Standard deviation, *84*	Median, *93*	Third quartile (Q3), *98*	Potential outlier, *105*
Deviation, *86*	Interquartile range (IQR), *96*	Range, 100	Five-number summary, *107*
Variance, *87*			

Sources

Bank for International Settlements. 2014. Statistics on payment, clearing and settlement systems in CPSS countries. http://www.bis.org/cpmi/publ/d124.pdf (accessed January 15, 2015).

Canadian Association of University Teachers. 2014. CAUT Almanac of Post-Secondary Education in Canada, 2013–2014.

Government of Canada. *Historical Climate Data.* http://climate.weather.gc.ca/index_e.html (accessed Nov. 2, 2013).

Pirie-Hay, D. W., and L. W. Bond. 2014. Thickness of Common Murre (*Uria aalge*) eggshells in Atlantic Canada. *The Canadian Field Naturalist* 128(1).

Sanmartin, C. *Toward Standard Definitions of Waiting Times.* Western Canada Waiting List Project. Final Report (2001).

Siciliani, L., V. Moran, and M. Borowitz. Measuring and comparing health care waiting times in OECD countries. OECD Health Working Papers

#67, OECD Publishing. http://dx.doi.org/10.1787/5k3w9t84b2kf-en (accessed Jan. 22, 2015).

Statistics Canada. *Table 404-0011—Railway transport survey, length of track operated, by area at end of year, annual (kilometres),* CANSIM (database) (accessed Jan. 6, 2015).

TIMSS Results 2011. https://nces.ed.gov/timss/results11.asp (accessed Oct. 29, 2013).

World Bank. http://data.worldbank.org (accessed Jan. 6, 2015).

World Fact Book. www.cia.gov/library/publications/the-world-factbook (accessed Jan. 6, 2015).

www.airqualityontario.com/history (accessed Oct. 30, 2013).

www.alexa.com/topsites (accessed Jan. 7, 2015).

SECTION EXERCISES

SECTION 3.1

3.1 Earnings A sociologist says, "Typically, men in Canada still earn more than women." What does this statement mean? (Pick the best choice.)

  a. All men make more than all women in Canada.

  b. All Canadian women's salaries are less varied than all men's salaries.

  c. The centre of the distribution of salaries for Canadian men is greater than the centre for women.

  d. The highest paid people in Canada are men.

3.2 Houses A real estate agent claims that all things being equal, houses with swimming pools tend to sell for less than those without swimming pools. What does this statement mean? (Pick the best choice.)

  a. There are fewer homes with swimming pools than without.

  b. The typical price for homes with pools is smaller than the typical price for homes without pools.

  c. There's more variability in the price of homes with pools than in the price of those without.

  d. The most expensive houses sold do not have pools.

TRY 3.3 Ages of "Most Powerful Business People" (Example 1)
The histogram shows frequencies for the ages of 25 people selected by *Canadian Business* magazine as "Canada's top 25 most powerful business people" in 2013. Based on the distribution, what is the approximate mean age of the business people in this data set? Write a sentence in context interpreting the estimated mean. The typical business person is about _____ years old. (Source: www.canadianbusiness.com)

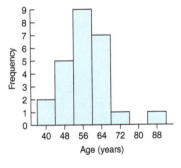

3.4 Body Mass Index The histogram shows the distribution of self-reported body mass index (BMI, in kg/m²) of 146 randomly selected respondents to the 2010 Canadian Community Health Survey. Based on the distribution, what is the approximate mean BMI of this small sample of respondents? Write a sentence in context, interpreting the estimated mean.

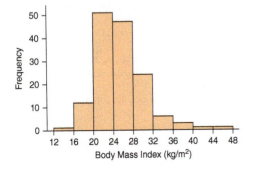

TRY 3.5 Paid Days (Example 2) This list represents the numbers of paid vacation days required by law for different countries. (Source: *2013 World Almanac and Book of Facts*)

United States	0
Australia	20
Italy	20
United Kingdom	28
Sweden	25
Canada	10

  a. Find the mean, rounding to the nearest tenth of a day. Interpret the mean in this context.

  b. Find the standard deviation, rounding to the nearest tenth of a day. Interpret the standard deviation in context.

  c. Which number of days is farthest from the mean and therefore contributes the most to the standard deviation?

3.6 Children of Prime Ministers This list represents the number of children of the first six Prime Ministers of Canada. (Source: *Dictionary of Canadian Biography*)

Sir John A. Macdonald	3
Alexander Mackenzie	3
Sir John Joseph Caldwell Abbott	8
Sir John Sparrow David Thompson	9
Sir Mackenzie Bowell	9
Sir Charles Tupper	6

  a. Find the mean number of children, rounding to the nearest tenth. Interpret the mean in this context.

  b. The mean number of children of the most recent six prime ministers (Turner to Harper) is 2.7 children. How does the mean of the first six compare to that?

  c. Which of the first prime ministers listed here had the number of children that is farthest from the mean and therefore contributes the most to the standard deviation?

  d. Find the standard deviation, rounding to the nearest tenth.

3.7 Ages of Prime Ministers When First Sworn to Office The ages of the first six prime ministers of Canada when first sworn to office were 52, 51, 70, 48, 70, and 74. (Source: Parliament of Canada, www.parl.gc.ca)

  a. Find the mean age when they were first sworn to office, rounding to the nearest tenth. The mean age of the most recent six prime ministers (Turner to Harper) is 52.7 years. Did the first six prime ministers tend to be a bit *older* or a bit *younger* than the most recent six prime ministers?

  b. Find the standard deviation of the ages when first sworn to office, rounding to the nearest tenth. The standard deviation of the most recent six prime ministers is 8.3 years. Did the ages of the first six tend to have *more* or *less* variation than the ages of the most recent six prime ministers?

3.8 Ages of Governors General When Sworn to Office
The ages of the first five Governors General of Canada who were
Canadian citizens (Massey to Schreyer) were 65, 71, 66, 60, and 43.
(Source: www.gg.ca)

   a. Find and interpret (report in context) the mean age when sworn to office of the first five Canadian Governors General of Canada, rounding
to the nearest tenth. The mean age when first sworn to office of the five
most recent Governors General (Hnatyshyn to Johnston) is 59.8. Did the
first five Canadian Governors General tend to be *older* or *younger* when
sworn to office than the most recent five Governors General?

   b. Find the standard deviation of the ages, rounding to the nearest tenth.
The standard deviation of the age of the most recent five Governors
General is 8.6 years. Did the ages of the first five Canadian Governors
General tend to have *more* or *less* variation than the ages of the most re-
cent five Governors General?

TRY 3.9 Tim Hortons Drive-Thrus (Example 3) The Minitab
output gives some numerical summaries for the number of Tim
Hortons drive-thrus within five kilometres of the centre of cities in
Alberta and Saskatchewan. (Source: www.timhortons.com)

```
Descriptive Statistics: drive-thrus

Variable      province     N    Mean  StDev  Minimum
drive-thrus   AB          16   3.625  1.962    1.000
              SK          15   2.333  2.469    0.000


Variable      province    Q1  Median     Q3  Maximum
drive-thrus   AB       7.000   2.000  3.000    5.000
              SK      10.000   1.000  2.000    3.000
```

   a. Compare the mean number of drive-thrus by completing this sentence:
The mean number of Tim Hortons drive-thrus is _____ drive-thrus
for cities in Alberta and _____ drive-thrus for cities in Saskatchewan,
showing that cities in the province of _____ tend to have more Tim
Hortons drive-thrus near the city centre.

   b. Compare the standard deviations (StDev) of the number of drive-thrus
by completing this sentence: The standard deviation of the number of
Tim Hortons drive-thrus is _____ drive-thrus for cities in Alberta and
_____ drive-thrus for cities in Saskatchewan, showing that there is
more variation in the number of drive-thrus near the city centre in the
province of _____.

   c. Does the TI-83/84 output given represent the data for Alberta or for
Saskatchewan?

```
1-Var Stats
 x̄=3.625
 Σx=58
 Σx²=268
 Sx=1.962141687
 σx=1.899835519
↓n=16
■
```

3.10 Population of Census Metropolitan Areas The
StatCrunch output shows some descriptive statistics for the
population (in thousands) of the 35 Census Metropolitan Areas
(CMAs) of Canada in 2012. The provinces are categorized by region
(Eastern and Western Canada). (Source: Statistics Canada)

Summary statistics for Population 2012 / 1000:
Group by: Region

Region	n	Mean	Variance	Std. dev.
E	26	713.11019	1718681.7	1310.985
W	9	779.73144	595054.52	771.39777

   a. Compare the means in a sentence or two. The means reported are in
thousands of people; round to the nearest thousand. See Exercise 3.9 for
one possible model of a comparison.

   b. Compare the standard deviations in a sentence or two. The standard
deviations reported are in thousands of people; round to the nearest
thousand.

 3.11 Composting The data show the percentage of households
that composted kitchen waste and those that composted yard waste
in 26 Census Metropolitan Areas in 2011. (Source: Statistics Canada.
Composting by Households in Canada)

    Kitchen: 32, 92, 47, 77, 55, 18, 65, 72, 63, 70, 72, 71,
    68, 69, 54, 32, 79, 33, 59, 59, 35, 24, 27, 34, 34, 58

    Yard: 52, 86, 67, 75, 81, 53, 85, 85, 85, 83, 86, 89, 78,
    77, 85, 82, 93, 83, 76, 76, 72, 68, 56, 55, 77, 86

   a. Compare the means in a sentence or two.

   b. Compare the standard deviations in a sentence or two.

3.12 Eating Out Student Jacqueline Loya asked a group
of 50 employed students how many times they went out to eat in
the last week. Half of the students had full-time jobs, and half had
part-time jobs.

    Full-time jobs: 5, 3, 4, 4, 4, 2, 1, 5, 6, 5, 6, 3, 3, 2, 4, 5,
    2, 3, 7, 5, 5, 1, 4, 6, 7

    Part-time jobs: 1, 1, 5, 1, 4, 2, 2, 3, 3, 2, 3, 2, 4, 2, 1, 2,
    3, 2, 1, 3, 3, 2, 4, 2, 1

   a. Compare the means in a sentence or two.

   b. Compare the standard deviations.

TRY 3.13 Rental Prices (Example 4) The histograms show rental
prices (in dollars per month) in (a) Ottawa and (b) Quebec City
in October 2013 for units with one bedroom and one bathroom.
Decide whether you think the standard deviation of rental prices in
Quebec City is larger than the standard deviation of rental prices in
Ottawa. Explain. (Source: apartmentsCanada.com)

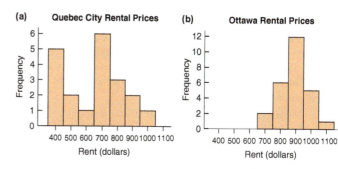

3.14 Dice The histograms contain data with a range of 1 to 6. Which group would have the larger standard deviation, group (a) or group (b)? Why?

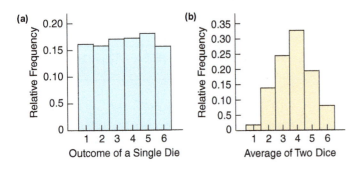

TRY 3.15 Birth Weights (Example 5) The mean birth weight for children born in Canada at full term (after 40 weeks) is 3462 grams. Suppose the standard deviation is 500 grams and the shape of the distribution is symmetric and unimodal. (Source: www.babycenter.ca)

a. According to the Empirical Rule, find the range of birth weights (in grams) that contains approximately 68% of birth weights of children born in Canada. In other words, find the weights from one standard deviation below the mean to one standard deviation above the mean.

b. Is a birth weight of 2800 grams more than one standard deviation below the mean?

3.16 Birth Length The mean birth length for children born in Canada at full term (after 40 weeks) is 52.2 cm. Suppose the standard deviation is 2.5 cm and the distribution is unimodal and symmetric. (Source: www.babycenter.ca)

a. According to the Empirical Rule, find the range of birth lengths (in cm) that contains approximately 68% of birth lengths of children born in Canada. In other words, find the lengths from one standard deviation below the mean to one standard deviation above the mean.

b. Is a birth length of 54 cm more than one standard deviation above the mean?

TRY 3.17 Children's Ages (Example 6) Mrs. Johnson's children are 2, 2, 3, and 5 years of age.

a. Find the mean of the children's current ages.

b. Without doing any calculation, indicate whether the mean age in 20 years will be larger, smaller, or about the same as the mean of the current ages. Confirm your answer and describe how adding 20 to each number affects the mean.

c. Calculate the standard deviation of their current ages.

d. Without doing any calculation, indicate whether the standard deviation of the ages in 20 years will be larger, smaller, or the same as the standard deviation of their current ages. Check your answer by calculating the standard deviation of the ages in 20 years. Explain how adding 20 to each number affects the standard deviation.

3.18 Pay Rate in Different Currencies The pay rates for three people were the following numbers of Canadian dollars per hour: 12, 14.50, and 11. In Japanese yens (at the exchange rate of 100 yens per Canadian dollar for June 2015), these pay rates are 1200, 1450, and 1100 per hour.

a. Compare the mean in Canadian dollars with the mean in yens; don't forget the units. Explain what multiplying each number in a data set by 100 does to the mean.

b. Compare the standard deviations in yens and in Canadian dollars. Explain what multiplying each number in a data set by 100 does to the standard deviation.

3.19 Olympic Races In the most recent summer Olympics, do you think the standard deviation of the running times for all men who ran the 100-metre race would be larger or smaller than the standard deviation of the running times for the men's marathon? Explain.

3.20 Weights Suppose you have a data set with the weights of all members of a high school soccer team and all members of a high school debating team. Which team do you think would have a larger standard deviation of weights? Explain.

SECTION 3.2

TRY g 3.21 Violent Crime (Example 7) In 2012, the mean rate of violent crime (per 100,000 population) in Canada's Census Metropolitan Areas (CMAs) was 1094, and the standard deviation was 288. Assume that the distribution of violent crime rates is approximately bell-shaped. *See page 124 for guidance.* (Source: Statistics Canada, Canadian Centre for Justice Statistics, Uniform Crime Reporting Survey)

a. Between what two values would you expect to find about 95% of the rates?

b. Between what two values would you expect to find about 68% of the rates?

c. If a CMA had a violent crime rate of 1383 crimes per 100,000 population, would you consider this unusual? Explain.

d. If a CMA had a violent crime rate of 380 crimes per 100,000 population, would you consider this unusual? Explain.

3.22 Drug Offences In 2012, the mean drug offence rate (per 100,000 population) in Canada's Census Metropolitan Areas (CMAs) was 285; the standard deviation was 114. Assume that the distribution of drug offence rates is approximately bell-shaped. (Source: Statistics Canada, Canadian Centre for Justice Statistics, Uniform Crime Reporting Survey)

a. Between what two values would you expect to find about 95% of the rates?

b. Between what two values would you expect to find about 68% of the rates?

c. If a CMA had a drug offence rate of 573 crimes per 100,000 population, would you consider this unusual? Explain.

d. If a CMA had a drug offence rate of 214 crimes per 100,000 population, would you consider this unusual? Explain.

TRY 3.23 Property Crime (Example 8) In 2012, the mean property crime rate (per 100,000 population) in Canada's Census Metropolitan Areas (CMAs) was 3514; the standard deviation was 892. Assume that the distribution of property crime rates is approximately bell-shaped. (Source: Statistics Canada, Canadian Centre for Justice Statistics, Uniform Crime Reporting Survey)

a. What percentage of CMAs would you expect to have property crime rates between 2622 and 4406?

b. What percentage of CMAs would you expect to have property crime rates between 1730 and 5298?

c. If someone guessed that the property crime rate in one CMA was 9000, would you agree that that number was consistent with this data set?

3.24 Breaking and Entering In 2012, the mean rate of breaking and entering offences (per 100,000 population) in Canada's Census Metropolitan Areas (CMAs) was 508; the standard deviation was 132. Assume that the distribution of breaking and entering rates is approximately bell-shaped. (Source: Statistics Canada, Canadian Centre for Justice Statistics, Uniform Crime Reporting Survey)

a. What percentage of CMAs would you expect to have breaking and entering rates between 244 and 772?

b. What percentage of CMAs would you expect to have breaking and entering rates between 376 and 640?

c. If someone guessed that the breaking and entering rate in one CMA was 104, would you agree that that number was consistent with this data set?

3.25 Heights and z-Scores The dotplot shows heights of some female students; the mean is 160 centimetres and the standard deviation is 7.5 centimetres.

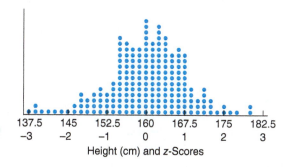

a. What is the z-score for a height of 145 centimetres?

b. What is the height of a woman with a z-score of 1?

3.26 Heights Refer to the dotplot in the previous question.

a. What is the height of a woman with a z-score of −1?

b. What is the z-score for a woman who is 175 centimetres tall?

TRY **3.27 Extreme Temperatures (Example 9)** Winnipeg's daily maximum temperature in January 2013 had a mean of −11°C and a standard deviation of 7.5°C. Kelowna's daily maximum temperature in July 2013 had a mean of 30°C and a standard deviation of 3.6°C. Assuming that both sets of temperatures have distributions that are unimodal and symmetric, which is more unusual, a day in January when the maximum temperature in Winnipeg was −30°C, or a day in July when the maximum temperature in Kelowna was 37°C?

3.28 Children's Heights Mrs. Gagnon has two children: a three-year-old boy who is 109 cm tall and a ten-year-old girl who is 145 cm tall. Three-year-old boys have a mean height of 96.5 cm and a standard deviation of 5 cm, whereas ten-year-old girls have a mean height of 138 cm and a standard deviation of 6.4 cm. Assume that the distributions of boys' and girls' heights are unimodal and symmetric. Which of Mrs. Gagnon's children is more unusually tall for his or her age and gender? Explain, showing any calculations you perform.

TRY **3.29 Low-Birth-Weight Babies (Example 10)** Babies born weighing 2500 grams or less are called low-birth-weight babies, and this condition sometimes indicates health problems for the infant. The mean birth weight for children born in Canada is about 3462 grams. The mean birth weight for babies born one month early is 2622 grams. Suppose both standard deviations are 500 grams. Also assume that the distribution of birth weights is roughly bell-shaped. (Source: www.babycenter.ca)

a. Find the standardized score (z-score), relative to all Canadian births, for a baby with a birth weight of 2500 grams.

b. Find the standardized score for a birth weight of 2500 grams for a child born one month early, using 2622 as the mean.

c. For which group is a birth weight of 2500 grams more common? Explain what that implies.

3.30 Birth Lengths Babies born after 40 weeks gestation have a mean length of 52.2 cm. Babies born one month early have a mean length of 47.4 cm. Assume that both standard deviations are 2.5 cm and the distributions are bell-shaped. (Source: www.babycenter.ca)

a. Find the standardized score (z-score), relative to all Canadian births, for a baby with a birth length of 45 cm.

b. Find the standardized score of a birth length of 45 cm for babies born one month early, using 47.4 as the mean.

c. For which group is a birth length of 45 cm more common? Explain what that means.

3.31 Exam Scores Scores for a certain exam have a mean of 70 and a standard deviation of 10. What exam score corresponds to a z-score of 1.5?

3.32 Boys' Heights Three-year-old boys in Canada have a mean height of 96.5 centimetres and a standard deviation of 5 centimetres. How tall is a three-year-old boy with a z-score of −1.0? (Source: www.kidsgrowth.com)

SECTION 3.3

3.33 Name two measures of the centre of a distribution, and state the conditions under which each is preferred for describing the typical value of a single data set.

3.34 Name two measures of the variation of a distribution, and state the conditions under which each measure is preferred for measuring the variability of a single data set.

TRY **3.35 Pixar Animated Movies (Example 11)** The 10 top-grossing Pixar animated movies for the North American box office up to January 2015 are shown in the table on the next page, in millions of dollars. (Source: boxofficemojo.com)

a. Arrange the gross income from smallest (on the left) to largest (on the right), and find the median by averaging the two middle numbers. Interpret the median in context.

b. Using the sorted data, find Q1 and Q3. Then find the interquartile range and interpret it in context.

Movie	$ Millions
Toy Story 3	415
Brave	237
Toy Story 2	246
Monsters, Inc.	256
Finding Nemo	340
The Incredibles	261
Cars	244
Monsters University	268
WALL-E	224
Up	293

 3.36 DreamWorks Animated Movies The 10 top-grossing DreamWorks animated movies for the North American box office up to January 2015 are shown in the table, in millions of dollars. (Source: www.boxofficemojo.com)

Movie	$ Millions
Shrek 2	441
Shrek the Third	323
Shrek	268
Shrek Forever After	239
How to Train Your Dragon	218
Madagascar: Europe's Most Wanted	216
Kung Fu Panda	215
Monsters vs. Aliens	198
Madagascar	194
The Croods	187

a. Find and interpret the median box office dollars for the 10 top-grossing DreamWorks animated movies.

b. Find and interpret the interquartile range for these movies.

TRY **3.37 Gas Taxes (Example 12)** The gasoline taxes in December 2013 (in cents per litre) are given for provinces in Eastern Canada, as reported by the Canadian Fuels Association. (These are provincial taxes and do not include federal taxes.)

Province	Tax
New Brunswick	28.2
Newfoundland and Labrador	31.4
Nova Scotia	32.6
Ontario	29.5
Prince Edward Island	29.0
Quebec	37.1

a. Find the median. Show the data sorted from smallest (on the left) to largest (on the right) and indicate the location of the median.

b. Indicate the locations of the first quartile (Q1) and the third quartile (Q3). Then find the interquartile range.

3.38 Gas Taxes The gasoline taxes in December 2013 (in cents per litre) are given for provinces and territories in Western and Northern Canada, as reported by the Canadian Fuels Association. (These are provincial or territorial taxes and do not include federal taxes.)

Province or Territory	Tax
Alberta	14.1
British Columbia	21.3
Manitoba	19.1
Northwest Territories	17.4
Saskatchewan	20.6
Yukon	12.3

a. Find and interpret the median gas tax for these provinces or territories. Between which two provinces or territories is the median rate?

b. Find, Q1, Q3, and the interquartile range (IQR) for these provinces or territories. Interpret the IQR.

TRY **3.39 Tim Hortons Drive-Thrus, Again (Example 13)** The following data represent the number of Tim Hortons drive-thrus within five kilometres of the centre of cities in Alberta and Saskatchewan. (Source: www.timhortons.com)

Alberta: 1, 2, 2, 2, 2, 2, 2, 3, 3, 4, 5, 5, 5, 6, 7, 7
Saskatchewan: 0, 0, 1, 1, 1, 1, 2, 2, 2, 2, 2, 3, 3, 5, 10

a. Compare the typical number of drive-thrus in the two provinces by completing this sentence: The median number of Tim Hortons drive-thrus is _____ drive-thrus for cities in Alberta and _____ drive-thrus for cities in Saskatchewan, showing that cities in the province of _____ typically have more Tim Hortons drive-thrus near the city centre.

b. Compare the interquartile ranges of the number of drive-thrus by completing this sentence: The interquartile range of the number of Tim Hortons drive-thrus is _____ for cities in Alberta and _____ for cities in Saskatchewan, showing that there is more variation in the number of drive-thrus near the city centre in the province of _____.

3.40 Eating Out, Again Student Jacqueline Loya asked 50 employed students how many times they went out to eat last week. Half of the students had full-time jobs and half had part-time jobs.

Full-time: 5, 3, 4, 4, 4, 2, 1, 5, 6, 5, 6, 3, 3, 2, 4, 5, 2, 3, 7, 5, 5, 1, 4, 6, 7

Part-time: 1, 1, 5, 1, 4, 2, 2, 3, 3, 2, 3, 2, 4, 2, 1, 2, 3, 2, 1, 3, 3, 2, 4, 2, 1

a. Using the median values, write a sentence comparing the typical numbers of times the two groups ate out. See Exercise 3.39 for one possible model.

b. Using the interquartile ranges, write a sentence comparing the variability of these two groups.

SECTION 3.4

3.41 Outliers

a. In your own words, describe to someone who knows only a little statistics how to recognize when an observation is an outlier. What action(s) should be taken with an outlier?

b. Which measure of centre (mean or median) is more resistant to outliers, and what does "resistant to outliers" mean?

3.42 Centre and Variation
When you are comparing two sets of data, and one set is strongly skewed and the other is symmetric, which measures of centre and variation should you choose for the comparison?

3.43 An Error
A dieter recorded the number of calories he consumed at lunch for one week. As you can see, a mistake was made on one entry. The calories are listed in increasing order:

331, 374, 387, 392, 405, 4200

When the error is corrected by removing the extra 0, will the median calories change? Will the mean change? Explain without doing any calculations.

3.44 Median and Average Net Worth
According to Statistics Canada, the median net worth of Canadian households was $243,800 in 2012. A report by Environics Analytics states that the average net worth of a Canadian household for that same year was $400,151. Why is there such a discrepancy between the median and the average of a Canadian household's net worth? Explain. (Sources: Statistics Canada and *Financial Post*, July 23, 2013)

3.45 Students' Ages
Here are the ages of some students in a statistics class: 17, 19, 35, 18, 18, 20, 27, 25, 41, 21, 19, 19, 45, and 19. The teacher's age is 66 and should be included as one of the ages when you do the calculations below. The figure shows a histogram of the data.

a. Describe the distribution of ages by giving the shape, the numerical value for an appropriate measure of the centre, and the numerical value for an appropriate measure of spread, as well as mentioning any outliers.

b. Make a rough sketch (or copy) of the histogram, and mark the approximate locations of the mean and of the median. Why are they not at the same location?

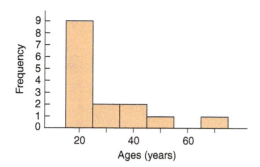

3.46 National Parks
The histogram shows the area (in thousands of km²) of the 45 National Parks and National Park Reserves of Canada. The location of the mean and the median are marked with letters. Which is the location of the mean, A or B? Explain why the mean and the median are not the same. (Source: Parks Canada, www.pc.cg.ca)

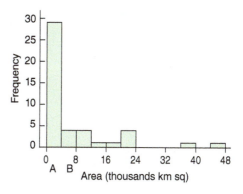

TRY 3.47 Study Hours (Example 14)
A group of 50 statistics students, 25 men and 25 women, reported the number of hours per week spent studying statistics.

a. Refer to the histograms. Which measure of centre should be compared: the means or the medians? Why?

b. Compare the distributions in context using appropriate measures. (Don't forget to mention outliers, if appropriate.) Refer to the Minitab output for the summary statistics.

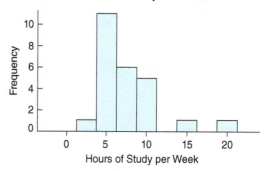

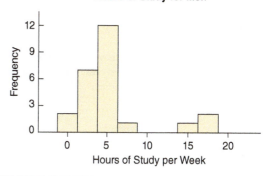

Minitab Statistics: Men, Women

Variable	N	Mean	StDev	Minimum	Q1	Median	Q3	Maximum
Men	25	5.20	4.378	1.00	2.50	4.00	5.50	17.00
Women	25	7.52	3.787	2.00	5.00	7.00	9.50	20.00

3.48 Driving Accidents
Student Sandy Hudson asked a group of students the total number of traffic accidents they had been in as drivers. The histograms are shown, and the table displays some descriptive statistics.

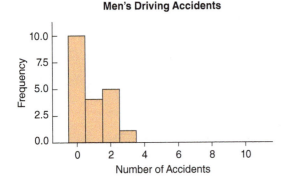

Men's Driving Accidents

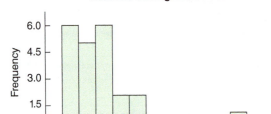

Women's Driving Accidents

Minitab Statistics: Men, Women

Variable	N	Mean	StDev	Min	Q1	Median	Q3	Max
Men	20	0.850	0.988	0.00	0.00	0.505	2.00	3.00
Women	22	1.864	2.210	0.00	0.00	1.50	2.25	10.00

a. Refer to the histograms. If we wish to compare the typical numbers of accidents for these men and women, should we compare the means or the medians? Why?

b. Write a sentence or two comparing the distributions of numbers of accidents for men and women in context.

SECTION 3.5

3.49 Life Expectancy The boxplot shows the life expectancy at birth in 2012 for countries in the world classified by continent. Assume all distributions are unimodal. (Source: *World Databank*)

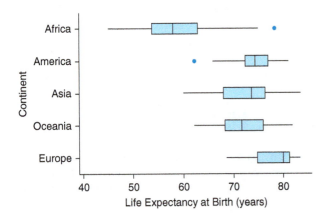

a. List the continents from lowest to highest in terms of median life expectancy at birth.

b. Which continent has the largest interquartile range?

c. Which continent has the smallest interquartile range?

d. Which region has potential outliers?

e. Why is Haiti's life expectancy of 62 years a potential outlier in America, while Afghanistan's life expectancy of 60.1 years is not a potential outlier in Asia?

3.50 Internet Users The boxplot shows the number of internet users (per 100 people) in 2012 for countries in the world classified by continent. Assume that all distributions are unimodal. (Source: *World Databank*)

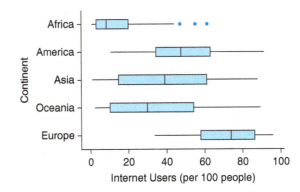

a. Compare the medians. List the regions from smallest to largest in terms of median number of internet users.

b. Which continent has the largest interquartile range?

c. Which continent has the smallest interquartile range?

3.51 City Temperatures The boxplot shows temperatures for six cities. Each city's boxplot was made from 12 temperatures: the average monthly maximum temperature over a period of years. Which city tends to be warmest? Which city has the most variation in temperatures? Compare the temperatures of the cities by interpreting the boxplots. If temperature were the only factor to consider, which city you would choose to live in, and why? (Source: currentresults.com)

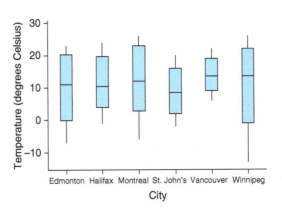

3.52 Weights of Soccer and Hockey Players The figure shows side-by-side boxplots for the weights (in kilograms) of samples from the men's soccer team and the men's hockey team at the same university in Ontario. Write a brief comparison of the distributions of weight for the two groups. (Source: oua.ca)

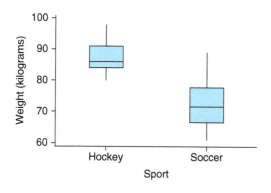

3.53 Matching Boxplots and Histograms

a. Match each of the boxplots (a, b and c) with the corresponding histogram (1, 2, or 3). Explain your reasoning.

b. For each histogram, label the shape (right-skewed, left-skewed, or symmetric) and indicate whether the mean would be larger than, smaller than, or about the same as the median.

Histogram 1

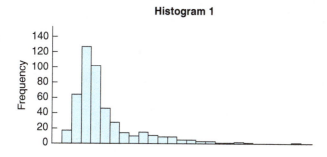

Histogram 2

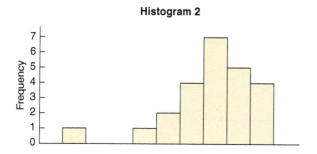

Histogram 3

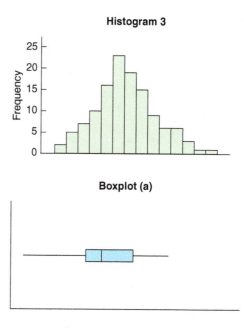

Boxplot (a)

Boxplot (b)

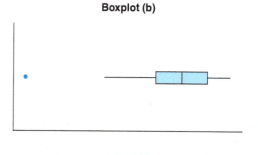

Boxplot (c)

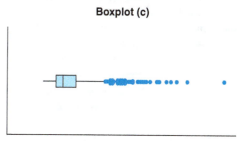

3.54 Matching Boxplots and Histograms Match each of the histograms (1, 2, and 3) with the corresponding boxplot (a, b, or c). Explain your reasoning.

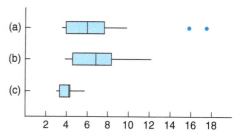

Histogram 1

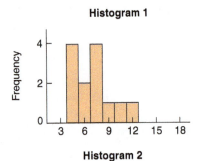

Histogram 2

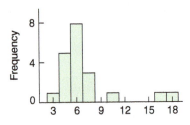

Histogram 3

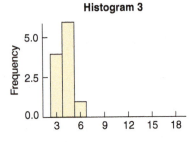

*3.55 **Driving Deaths** Have you ever wondered whether driving is more dangerous in some regions than others? You can find data on motor vehicle fatality rates (deaths per 100,000 population) in 2010 for all provinces and territories on the course website. The TI-83/84 output shows some descriptive statistics for this data set. (Source: Statistics Canada, *Canadian Vehicle Survey*)

  a. Make a boxplot of the data, and report the median and interquartile ranges. If you find potential outlier(s), identify the region(s).

  b. There are two variables involved in the calculation of the death rate for a province or territory (deaths per 100,000 population):

$$\text{Death rate} = \frac{\text{deaths}}{\text{population}} (100{,}000)$$

One way in which a province or territory can have a high death rate is to have many deaths. What is the other reason why a province or territory might have a high death rate?

```
1-Var Stats
↑n=13
 minX=4.3
 Q₁=6.1
 Med=7
 Q₃=10.4
 maxX=16
■
```

3.56 Educated Population Statistics Canada reported the percentage of the population aged 25 to 64 in each province and territory who held a bachelor's degree in 2009. Make a boxplot of the data and describe it. If there are any potential outliers, explain what they show, including the name of the province or territory.

Province or Territory	Percentage
Newfoundland and Labrador	16
Prince Edward Island	19
Nova Scotia	22
New Brunswick	19
Quebec	23
Ontario	28
Manitoba	22
Saskatchewan	20
Alberta	24
British Columbia	27
Yukon	24
Northwest Territories	24
Nunavut	12

CHAPTER REVIEW EXERCISES

3.57 Marathon Times by Gender The figure shows side-by-side boxplots of marathon times for the 2014 marathon in Victoria, British Columbia. Who tended to run faster, the men or the women? Make appropriate comparisons regarding centre and variation without reporting numbers. The men's distribution and the women's distribution were both unimodal. (Remember, smaller times mean faster runners.)

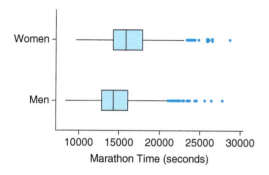

3.58 Inflation The boxplots show the 2012 annual inflation (%) as measured by the consumer price index for countries categorized by continent. (Source: The World Bank)

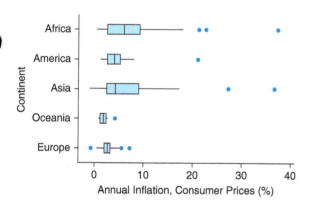

a. Compare the medians and interquartile ranges without reporting numbers. List the continents from smallest (on the left) to largest median annual inflation.

b. Explain why the medians are more appropriate for comparisons than the means.

3.59 Area The table shows the area (in thousands of km²) of Canada's provinces and territories. (Source: Statistics Canada)

a. Find the median area and interpret it (using a sentence in context).

b. Find the interquartile range (showing Q3 and Q1 in the process) to measure the variability in area.

c. What is the mean area?

d. Why is the mean so much larger than the median?

e. Why is it better to report the median, instead of the mean, as a typical measure?

Province or Territory	Area (thousands of km²)	Province or Territory	Area (thousands of km²)
Newfoundland and Labrador	405	Saskatchewan	651
Prince Edward Island	6	Alberta	662
Nova Scotia	55	British Columbia	945
New Brunswick	73	Yukon	482
Quebec	1542	Northwest Territories	1346
Ontario	1076	Nunavut	2093
Manitoba	648		

3.60 Chicken Egg Production The table shows the numbers of farms dedicated to chicken egg production in each of the provinces and territories in 2011. (Source: Statistics Canada, Census of Agriculture)

Province	Chicken Egg Farms	Province	Chicken Egg Farms
Newfoundland and Labrador	12	Manitoba	115
Prince Edward Island	7	Saskatchewan	40
Nova Scotia	57	Alberta	128
New Brunswick	33	British Columbia	708
Quebec	164	Yukon	7
Ontario	566	Northwest Territories	1
		Nunavut	0

a. Find the median.

b. Find the interquartile range (showing Q3 and Q1 in the process).

c. Find the mean number of farms dedicated to chicken egg production.

d. Why is the mean so much larger than the median?

TRY 3.61 Head Circumference (Example 15) Following are head circumferences, in centimetres, for some men and women in a statistics class.

Men: 58, 60, 62.5, 63, 59.5, 59, 60, 57, 55

Women: 63, 55, 54.5, 53.5, 53, 58.5, 56, 54.5, 55, 56, 56, 54, 56, 53, 51

Compare the circumferences of the men's and the women's heads. Start with histograms to determine shape; then compare appropriate measures of centre and spread, and mention any outliers. See page 124 for guidance.

3.62 Heights of Sons and Dads The data on the course website give the heights of 18 male students and their fathers, in centimetres.

a. Make histograms and describe the shapes of the two data sets from the histograms.

b. Fill in the following table to compare descriptive statistics.

	Mean	Median	Standard Deviation	Interquartile Range
Sons	___	___	___	___
Dads	___	___	___	___

c. Compare the heights of the sons and their dads, using the means and standard deviations.

d. Compare the heights of the sons and their dads, using the medians and interquartile ranges.

e. Which pair of descriptive statistics is more appropriate for comparing these samples: the mean and standard deviation or the median and interquartile range? Explain.

3.63 Final Exam Grades The data that follow are final exam grades for two sections of statistics students at a community college. One class met twice a week relatively late in the day; the other class met four times a week at 11 a.m. Both classes had the same instructor and covered the same content. Is there evidence that the performances of the classes differed? Answer by making appropriate plots (including side-by-side boxplots) and reporting and comparing appropriate summary statistics. Explain why you chose the summary statistics you used. Be sure to comment on the shape of the distributions, the centre, and the spread, and be sure to mention any unusual features you observe.

11 a.m. grades: 100, 100, 93, 76, 86, 72.5, 82, 63, 59.5, 53, 79.5, 67, 48, 42.5, 39

5 p.m. grades: 100, 98, 95, 91.5, 104.5, 94, 86, 84.5, 73, 92.5, 86.5, 73.5, 87, 72.5, 82, 68.5, 64.5, 90.75, 66.5

3.64 Speeding Tickets Students Diane Glover and Esmeralda Olguin asked 25 men and 25 women how many speeding tickets they had received in the last three years.

Men: 14 said they had 0 tickets, 9 said they had 1 ticket, 1 had 2 tickets, and 1 had 5 tickets.

Women: 18 said they had 0 tickets, 6 said they had 1 ticket, and 1 had 2 tickets.

Is there evidence that the men and women differed? Answer by making appropriate plots and comparing appropriate summary statistics. Be sure to comment on the shape of the distributions and to mention any unusual features you observe.

3.65 Heights The graph shows the heights for a large group of adults. Describe the distribution and explain what might cause this shape. (Source: www.amstat.org)

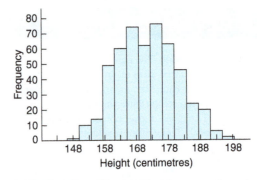

* 3.66 Marathon Times The histogram of marathon times includes data for men and women and also for both an Olympic marathon and an amateur marathon. Greater values indicate slower runners. (Sources: www.runvictoriamarathon.com and www.olympic.org)

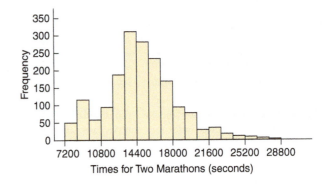

a. Describe the shape of the distribution.

b. What are two different possible reasons for the shape of the distribution?

c. Knowing that a lot more people ran in the amateur marathon than the Olympic marathon, and that there were about the same number of men and women running the amateur marathon, look at the size of the mounds and decide which of the reasons stated in part b is likely to be the explanation for the shape of the distribution. Explain.

* 3.67 Student Fees The histogram shows the distribution of compulsory additional fees for full-time undergraduate Canadian students in 2012–2013 at 106 post-secondary institutions. (Source: Statistics Canada, Tuition and Living Accommodation Costs for Full-time Students at Canadian Degree-granting Institutions, 2012–2013)

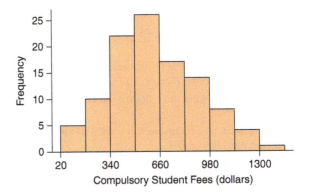

a. State an approximate value for the mean student fee.

b. Here is a proposed method for finding an approximation to the standard deviation based on a histogram: find the approximate range and divide by 6. Use this method to find an approximate standard deviation for the compulsory student fees. For comparison, the true standard deviation is 270.

c. Consider the shape of the distribution and explain why dividing the range by 6 should produce a reasonable approximation of the standard deviation.

3.68 Mortgage Payments In 2008, the Canadian Financial Capability Survey asked respondents who owned their principal residence with a mortgage how many more years they expected to make mortgage payments on that residence. The histogram contains the data from 150 randomly selected respondents.

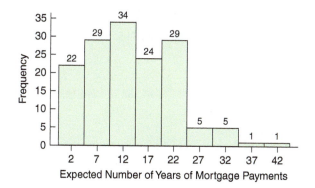

a. Approximately what is the mean number of years respondents expect to continue making mortgage payments? Explain how you chose this value.

b. What is the approximate value for the median number of years respondents expect to continue making mortgage payments? Describe how you chose this value.

c. Approximate the mean from the summarized data by completing the work below:

$$\bar{x} = \frac{22(2) + 29(7) + \ldots + 1(42)}{150}$$

d. Which is more appropriate to report for these data, the mean or the median? Why?

3.69–3.72 *Construct two sets of numbers with at least five numbers in each set (showing them as dotplots) with the following characteristics:*

* 3.69 The means are the same, but the standard deviation of one of the sets is larger than that of the other. Report the mean and both standard deviations.

* 3.70 The means are different, but the standard deviations are the same. Report both means and the standard deviation.

* 3.71 The mean of set A is larger than that of set B, but the median of set B is larger than the median of set A. Label each dotplot with its mean and median in the correct place.

* 3.72 The standard deviation of set A is larger, but the interquartile range of set B is larger. Report both standard deviations and interquartile ranges.

* 3.73 Meal Preparation Time In 2010, the General Social Survey measured the time in one day spent by respondents in meal preparation. Data on time (in minutes) spent in meal preparation and age group (15–24, 25–34, 35–44, 45–54, 55–64) can be found in the course website for a random sample of 227 respondents who spent time preparing at least one and at most three meals. (The 35% of respondents who spent 0 minutes in meal preparation and those who prepared more than 3 meals were excluded from this sample.) Write a few sentences comparing the five age groups in terms of time spent in meal preparation. Support your description with appropriate graphs.

* 3.74 Population Increase The following data were reported by the World Bank, and can be found in the course website: the country, its population in 2000, its population in 2012, and the continent in which it is located. Find the percentage population increase for each country by applying the following formula:

$$\frac{\text{pop}_{2012} - \text{pop}_{2000}}{\text{pop}_{2000}} \times 100$$

Write a few sentences comparing the distribution of percentage population increases for the five continents. Support your description with appropriate graphs.

3.75 Airline On-Time Performance Airline on-time performance is provided every year by FlyStats. The following data were recorded for 2012, and can be found in the course website: carrier, percentage of flights that arrived on time (delayed less than 15 minutes), and region (North America, Europe, Asia, or Middle East). Write a few sentences comparing airline on-time performance in the four regions. Include boxplots. (Source: www.flystats.com)

3.76 Living Accommodation Cost at Residence Data were recorded on the cost of the least expensive room at residences in 87 post-secondary institutions in Canada for the 2012–2013 academic year, and can be found in the course website. Each observation is classified by region (Quebec, Ontario, Prairies, British Columbia, Atlantic). Write a few sentences comparing living accommodation costs in the five regions. Include boxplots. (Source: Statistics Canada)

GUIDED EXERCISES

3.21 Violent Crime In 2012, the mean rate of violent crime (per 100,000 population) in Canada's Census Metropolitan Areas (CMAs) was 1094, and the standard deviation was 288. Assume that the distribution of violent crime rates is approximately bell-shaped. The Empirical Rule would apply, so that approximately 95% of observations would be within two standard deviations of the mean, and approximately 68% of observations would be within one standard deviation of the mean.

Questions

Answer these questions by following the numbered steps.

a. Between which two values would you expect to find about 95% of the violent crime rates?

b. Between which two values would you expect to find about 68% of the violent crime rates?

c. If a CMA had a violent crime rate of 1383 crimes, would you consider this unusual? Explain.

d. If a CMA had a violent crime rate of 380 crimes, would you consider this unusual? Explain.

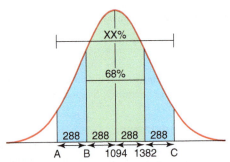

▲ **FIGURE A** The green area is 68% of the area under the curve. The green and blue areas together shade XX% of the area. The numbers without percentage signs are crime rates, with a mean of 1094 and a standard deviation of 288.

Step 1 ▶ Percentage
Reproduce Figure A, which is a sketch of the distribution of the crime rates. What percentage of data should occur within two standard deviations of the mean? Include this number in the figure, where it now says XX.

Step 2 ▶ Why 1382?
How was the number 1382, shown on the sketch, obtained?

Step 3 ▶ A, B, and C
Fill in numbers for the crime rates for areas A, B, and C.

Step 4 ▶ Boundaries for 95%
Read the answer from your graph:

a. Between which two values would you expect to find about 95% of the rates?

Step 5 ▶ Boundaries for 68%
Read the answer from your graph:

b. Between which two values would you expect to find about 68% of the violent crime rates?

Step 6 ▶ Unusual?

c. If a CMA had a violent crime rate of 1383 crimes, would you consider this unusual? Many people would consider any numbers outside your boundaries of A and C to be unusual because such values occur in 5% of the CMAs or fewer.

Step 7 ▶ Unusual?

d. If a CMA had a violent crime rate of 380 crimes, would you consider this unusual? Explain.

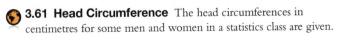

3.61 Head Circumference The head circumferences in centimetres for some men and women in a statistics class are given.

Men: 58, 60, 62.5, 63, 59.5, 59, 60, 57, 55

Women: 63, 55, 54.5, 53.5, 53, 58.5, 56, 54.5, 55, 56, 56, 54, 56, 53, 51

Question

Compare the circumferences of the men's and women's heads by following the numbered steps.

Step 1 ▶ Histograms
Make histograms of the two sets of data separately. (You may use the same horizontal axes—if you want to—so that you can see the comparison easily.)

Step 2 ▶ Shapes
Report the shapes of the two data sets.

Step 3 ▶ Measures to Compare
If either data set is skewed or has an outlier (or more than one), you should compare medians and interquartile ranges for *both* groups. If both data sets are roughly symmetric, you should compare means and standard deviations. Which measures should be compared with these two data sets?

Step 4 ▶ Compare Centres
Compare the centres (means or medians) in the following sentence: The _____ (mean or median) head circumference for the men was _____ cm, and the _____ (mean or median) head circumference for the women was _____ cm. This shows that the typical head circumference was larger for the _____.

Step 5 ▶ Compare Variations
Compare the variations in the following sentence: The _____ (standard deviation or interquartile range) for the head circumferences for the men was _____ cm, and the _____ (standard deviation or interquartile range) for the women was _____ cm. This shows that the _____ tended to have more variation, as measured by the _____ (standard deviation or interquartile range).

Step 6 ▶ Outliers
Report any outliers and state which group(s) they belong to.

Step 7 ▶ Final Comparison
Finally, in a sentence or two, make a complete comparison of head circumferences for the men and the women.

Example

Analyze the data given by finding descriptive statistics and making boxplots. The tables give calories per 100 grams for sliced ham and turkey. Table 3A shows unstacked data, and Table 3B shows stacked data. We coded the meat types with numerical values (1 for ham and 2 for turkey), but you could also use descriptive terms such as "ham" and "turkey."

Ham	Turkey
74	123
88	88
123	88
123	88
88	88
106	88
106	102
123	102
141	81
106	176
	88

▲ TABLE 3A

Cal	Meat
74	1
88	1
123	1
123	1
88	1
106	1
106	1
123	1
141	1
106	1
123	2
88	2
88	2
88	2
88	2
88	2
102	2
102	2
81	2
176	2
88	2

▲ TABLE 3B

Enter the unstacked data (Table 3A) into **L1** and **L2**.

For Descriptive Comparisons of Two Groups

Follow the steps twice, first for **L1** and then for **L2**.

Finding One-Variable Statistics

1. Press **STAT**, choose **CALC** (by using the right arrow on the keypad), and choose **1** (for **1-Var Stats**)
2. Specify **L1** (or the list containing the data) by pressing **2ND**, **1**, and **ENTER**.
3. Output: On your calculator, you will need to scroll down using the down arrow on the keypad to see all of the output.

Making Boxplots

1. Press **2ND**, **STATPLOT**, **4 (PlotsOff)**, and **ENTER** to turn the plots off. This will prevent you from seeing old plots as well as the new ones.
3. Press **2ND**, **STATPLOT**, and **1**.
4. Refer to Figure 3A. Turn on **Plot1** by pressing **ENTER** when **On** is flashing. (**Off** will no longer be highlighted.)
5. Use the arrows on the keypad to locate the boxplot in the lower left corner of the six graphs (as shown highlighted in Figure 3A), and press **ENTER**. (If you accidentally choose the other boxplot—the one in the middle—there will never be any separate marks for potential outliers.)

▲ **FIGURE 3A** TI-83/84 plot dialogue screen.

6. Use the down arrow on the keypad to get to the **XList**. Choose **L1** by pressing **2ND** and **1**.
7. Press **ZOOM** and **9** (**Zoomstat**) to make the graph.
8. Press **TRACE** and move around with the arrows on the keypad to see the numerical labels.

Making Side-by-Side Boxplots

For side-by-side boxplots, turn on a second boxplot (**Plot2**) for data in a separate list, such as **L2**. Then, when you choose **ZOOM** and **9**, you should see both boxplots. Press **TRACE** to see numbers.

Figure 3B shows side-by-side boxplots with the boxplot from the turkey data on the bottom and the boxplot for the ham data on the top.

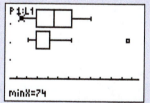

▲ **FIGURE 3B** TI-83/84 boxplots.

For Comparisons of Two Groups

Use the data from the course website or manually enter the data given. You may use unstacked data entered into two different columns (Table 3A), or you may use stacked data and use labels such as Ham and Turkey or codes such as 1 and 2 (Table 3B).

Finding Descriptive Statistics: One-Column Data or *Unstacked* Data in Two or More Columns

1. **Stat > Basic Statistics > Display Descriptive Statistics**.
2. Double click on the column(s) containing the data to put it (them) in the **Variables** box.
3. Ignore the **By variables** box.
4. (Optional) Click on **Statistics**; you can choose what you want to add, such as the interquartile range.
5. Click **OK**.

125

Finding Descriptive Statistics: *Stacked and Coded*

1. **Stat > Basic Statistics > Display Descriptive Statistics**.
2. See Figure 3C: Double click on the column(s) containing the stack of data to put it in the **Variables** box.

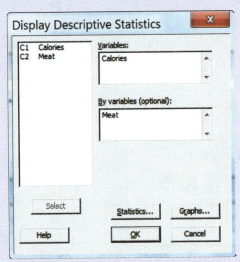

▲ **FIGURE 3C** Minitab descriptive statistics dialogue box.

3. When the **By variables** box is activated (by clicking in it), double click the column containing the categorical labels or code.
4. (Optional) Click on **Statistics**; you can choose what you want to add, such as the interquartile range. You can also make boxplots by clicking **Graphs**.
5. Click **OK**.

Making Boxplots

1. **Graph > Boxplot**.
2. For a single boxplot, choose **One Y, Simple** and click **OK**. See Figure 3D.
3. Double click the label for the column(s) containing the data and click **OK**.
4. For side-by-side boxplots
   a. If the data are unstacked, choose **Multiple Y's Simple**, shown in Figure 3D. Then double click both labels for the columns and click **OK**.
   b. If the data are stacked, choose **One Y With Groups** (the top right in Figure 3D). Then see Figure 3E and double click on the label for the stack (such as Calories) and then click in the **Categorical variables ...** box and double click the label for codes or words defining the groups such as **Meat**.
5. Labelling and transposing the boxplots. If you want to change the labelling, double click on what you want to change after the boxplot(s) are made. To change the orientation of the boxplot to horizontal, double click on the *x*-axis and select **Transpose value and category scales**.

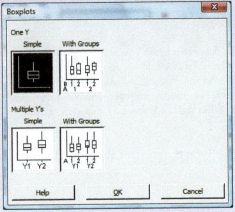

▲ **FIGURE 3D** Minitab first boxplot dialogue box.

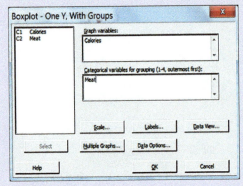

▲ **FIGURE 3E** Minitab dialogue screen for Boxplots: One Y with Groups.

Figure 3F shows Minitab boxplots of the ham and turkey data, without transposition.

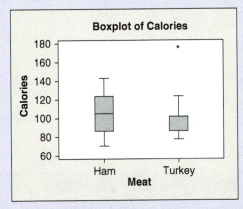

▲ **FIGURE 3F** Minitab boxplots.

EXCEL

Entering Data

Use the data from the course website or enter it manually. You may have labels in the first row such as **Ham** and **Turkey**.

Finding Descriptive Statistics

1. Click **Data, Data Analysis,** and **Descriptive Statistics**.
2. See Figure 3G: In the dialogue screen, for the **Input Range** highlight the cells containing the data (one column only) and then click **Summary Statistics**. If you include the label in the top cell, such as A1, in the **Input Range**, you need to check **Labels in First Row**. Click **OK**.

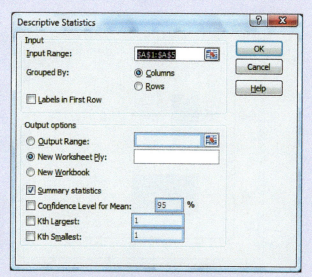

▲ **FIGURE 3G** Excel dialogue box for descriptive statistics.

Comparing Two Groups

To compare two groups, use unstacked data and do the above analysis twice. (Choosing **Output Range** and selecting appropriate cells on the same sheet makes comparisons easier.)

Boxplots (Requires XLSTAT Add-in)

1. Click **Add-ins**, **XLSTAT**, **Visualizing data**, and **Univariate plots.**
2. When the box under **Quantitative data** is activated, drag your cursor over the column containing the data, including the label at the top such as **Ham**.
3. Click **Charts.**
4. Click **Box plots, Outliers** and choose **Horizontal** (or **Vertical).**
5. Click **OK** and **Continue**. See step 6 in the side-by-side instructions.

Side-by-Side Boxplots

Use unstacked data with labels in the top row.

1. Click **Add-ins**, **XLSTAT**, **Visualizing data,** and **Univariate plots**.
2. When the box under **Quantitative data** is activated, drag your cursor over all the columns containing the unstacked data, including labels at the top such as **Ham** and **Turkey**.
3. Click **Charts**.
4. Click **Box plots, Group plots, Outliers,** and choose **Horizontal** (or **Vertical**).
5. Click **OK** and **Continue**.
6. When you see the small labels **Turkey** and **Ham**, you may drag them to where you want them and you can increase the font size.

Figure 3H shows boxplots for the ham and turkey data. The red crosses give the location of the two means.

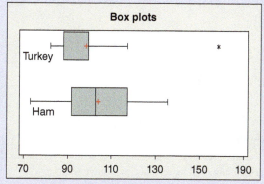

▲ **FIGURE 3H** XLSTAT boxplots.

STATCRUNCH

For Comparisons of Two Groups

Use the data from the course website or enter the data manually. You may use stacked or unstacked data. Use the data from the example.

Finding Summary Statistics (*stacked* or *unstacked* data)

1. **Stat > Summary Stats > Columns**
2. Refer to Figure 3I. If the data are stacked, put the stack (here, Calories) in the top box on the right and put the code (here, Meat) in the rectangle labelled **Group by.**

   If the data are unstacked, select both lists into the top box on the right.

3. Select the statistics you wish to compute in the rectangle labelled **Statistics.**
4. Click **Compute!** to compute the summary statistics.

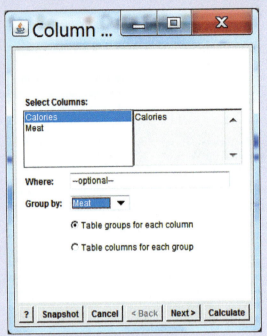

▲ **FIGURE 3I** StatCrunch dialogue screen for summary statistics.

Making Boxplots (stacked or unstacked)

1. **Graph > Boxplot**
2. *Unstacked* data: Select the columns to be displayed. A boxplot for each column will be included in a single graph.
3. *Stacked* and coded data: Refer to Figure 3J.

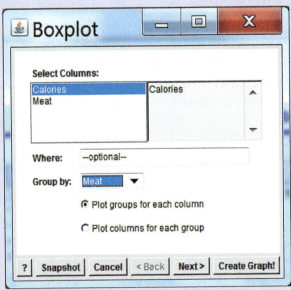

▲ **FIGURE 3J** StatCrunch dialogue screen for boxplots.

Put the one column with all the data into the top box on the right and then select the column of codes or categories to put in the **Group by** small rectangle.

4. Check **Use fences to identify outliers** to make sure that the outliers show up as separate marks. You may also check **Draw boxes horizontally** if that is what you want. You can also change the colour scheme and add titles if you wish.
5. Click **Compute!**
6. To copy your graph, click **Options** and **Copy** and paste it into a document.

Figure 3K shows boxplots of the ham and turkey data; the top box comes from the turkey data (calories per 100 grams).

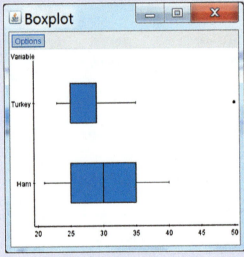

▲ **FIGURE 3K** StatCrunch boxplots.

SPSS

For Comparisons of Two Groups

Use the data from the course website or enter the data manually. You may use stacked or unstacked data.

Finding Descriptive Statistics: One-Column Data or *Unstacked* Data in Two or More Columns

1. **Analyze > Descriptive Statistics > Frequencies**.
2. Select the variable(s) you are going analyze from the list and click on the right arrow to move it (them) to the **Variable(s)** box.
3. Click **Statistics**, and check any percentile values and measures of central tendency and dispersion that you want to calculate.
4. Click **Continue** and then **OK**.

Finding Descriptive Statistics: *Stacked and Coded*

1. **Analyze > Descriptive Statistics > Explore**.
2. Select the variable you are going analyze from the list and click on the right arrow to move it to the **Dependent List** box. Select the variable that has the coding and click on the right arrow to move it to the **Factor List** box. See Figure 3L.
3. Click **Statistics**, and check **Descriptives**. Then click **Continue**.
4. Make sure **Statistics** is selected under **Display**. Click **OK**.

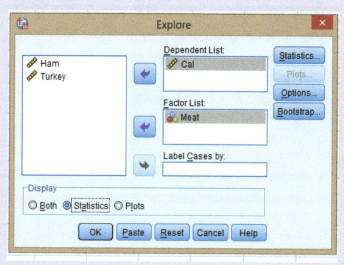

▲ **FIGURE 3L** SPSS descriptive statistics dialogue box.

Making Side-By-Side Boxplots

1. **Analyze > Descriptive Statistics > Explore**.
2. Select the variable you are going to analyze from the list and click on the right arrow to move it to the **Dependent List** box. Select the variable that has the coding and click on the right arrow to move it to the **Factor List** box. See Figure 3L. (If plotting unstacked data, select and move to the **Dependent List** all the variables that will be graphed together, leaving the **Factor List** empty. Continue to step 3.)
3. Click **Plots**, and check **Dependents together** under **Boxplots**. Then click **Continue**.
4. Make sure **Plots** is selected under **Display**. Click **OK**.

Figure 3M shows side-by-side boxplots of the ham and turkey data.

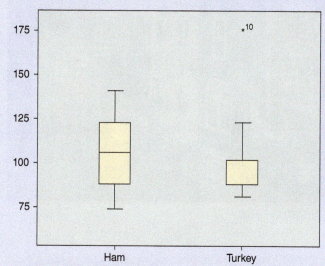

▲ **FIGURE 3M** SPSS boxplots.

4 Regression Analysis: Exploring Relationships between Variables

FER737NG/Fotolia

LEARNING OBJECTIVES

After completing this chapter, you should be able to:

1. Write a description of the relationship between two numerical variables based on a scatterplot.
2. Define, calculate, and interpret the correlation coefficient between two variables.
3. Summarize the linear relationship between two variables with a regression line.
4. Interpret the intercept and the slope of a regression line.
5. Define, calculate, and interpret the coefficient of determination.
6. Avoid errors that are common when applying regression.

The online real estate value calculator Zoopraisal (launched by Zoocasa.com) can estimate the market value of any home in Canada. You need merely type in an address. Zoopraisal estimates the value of a home even if the home has not been on the market for many years. How can this tool come up with an estimate for something that is not for sale? The answer is that Zoopraisal takes advantage of relationships between the value of a home and other easily observed variables—size of the home, selling price of nearby homes, number of bedrooms, and so on.

What role does genetics play in determining basic physical characteristics, such as height? This question fascinated nineteenth-century statistician Francis Galton (1822–1911). He examined the heights of thousands of father-son pairs to determine the nature of the relationship between these heights. If a father is 15 centimetres taller than average, how much taller than average will his son

be? How certain can we be of the answer? Will there be much variability? If there's a lot of variability, then perhaps factors other than the father's genetic material play a role in determining height.

Relationships between variables can be used to predict as yet unseen observations. You might think that estimating the value of a piece of real estate and understanding the role of genetics in determining height are unrelated. However, both take advantage of relationships between two numerical variables. They use a technique called regression, developed by Galton, to analyze the extent of such relationships.

As in previous chapters, graphs play a major role in revealing patterns in data, and graphs become even more important when we have two variables, not just one. For this reason, we'll start by using graphs to visualize relationships between two numerical variables, and then we'll talk about quantifying these relationships.

CASE STUDY

Interactive Video Game Exercise

Physical activity is essential to staying healthy. As stated by the Public Health Agency of Canada, people who are physically active are more productive, more likely to avoid illness and injury, and live longer and healthier lives.

Physical activity tends to decline steadily between high school and young adulthood. Given the appeal of television and video games in that age group, researchers have been investigating different ways in which active gaming can be used to improve physical activity in young adults.

One such study was conducted by researchers at the University of British Columbia. Fourteen low-active young males were randomly assigned to either the intervention group or the control group. The participants in the intervention group were required to exercise on a GameBike interactive video gaming system that was linked to a Sony Playstation 2 and a television monitor. The system reads the participant's speed and steering, giving the participant the opportunity to play a variety of video games. The participants in the control group were required to exercise on a standard stationary bicycle. All participants were given a recommended exercise training regime consisting of moderate-intensity exercise, three days a week for 30 minutes a day for six weeks. Despite the recommendations, all participants were allowed complete freedom to choose the exercise intensity and frequency with which they participated in training.

Researchers observed significant differences in the attendance of the interactive video game and the traditional cycling groups. They also observed a significant change in aerobic fitness in the interactive video game group, while there was no improvement in aerobic fitness in the control group. At the end of this chapter you will see what the linear relationship between attendance and improvement in aerobic fitness tells us about the possible health benefits of interactive video game exercise for young males.

SECTION 4.1

Visualizing Variability with a Scatterplot

Canada's life expectancy—the number of years a person is expected to live—ranks among the top in the world. Nevertheless, life expectancy varies greatly within Canada, reflecting the disparities in socio-economic characteristics and living habits of people in different regions. As an example, let us examine how life expectancy varies across the nation in relation to the smoking habits of the population. The primary tool for examining relationships between numerical variables such as these is the **scatterplot**. In a scatterplot, each point represents one observation. The location of the point depends on the values of the two variables. Figure 4.1 shows a scatterplot of these data, taken from the 2007 Canadian Community Health Survey. Each point represents a health region, showing us the percentage of adults who smoke and the life expectancy in that region. As you might have expected, the picture shows that health regions with the lowest life expectancies tend to have the highest rates of smoking. The point in the lower right corner represents the 10 largest communities in Nunavut.

When examining histograms (or other pictures of distributions for a single variable), we look for centre, spread, and shape. When studying scatterplots, we look for **trend** (which is like centre), **strength** (which is like spread), and **shape** (which is like, well, shape). Let's take a closer look at these characteristics.

▶ **FIGURE 4.1** A scatterplot of smoking rate and life expectancy. Each point represents a health region.

TECH

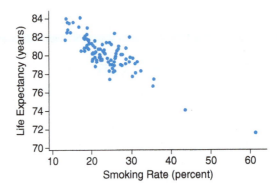

Recognizing Trend

The trend of a relationship is the general tendency of the scatterplot as you scan from left to right. Usually trends are either increasing (uphill, /) or decreasing (downhill, \), but other possibilities exist. Increasing trends are called **positive relationships** (or **positive trends**) and decreasing trends are called **negative relationships** (or **negative trends**).

Figure 4.2 shows examples of positive and negative trends. Figure 4.2a reveals a positive trend between the age of a used car and the kilometres it was driven (mileage). The positive trend matches our common sense: we expect older cars to have been driven farther, because generally, the longer a car is owned, the more kilometres it travels. Figure 4.2b shows a negative trend—the birthrate of a country against that country's literacy rate. The negative trend suggests that countries with higher literacy rates tend to have a lower rate of childbirth.

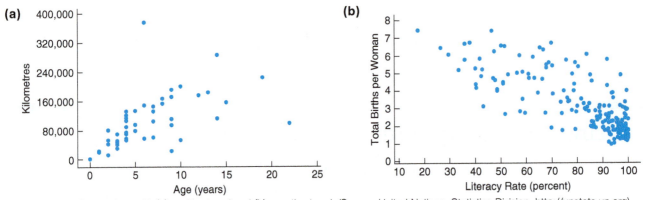

▲ **FIGURE 4.2** Scatterplots with **(a)** positive trend and **(b)** negative trend. (Source: United Nations, Statistics Division, http://unstats.un.org)

Figure 4.3a shows an example of a scatterplot with no trend. The variables plotted are age and weight of road cyclists who participated in the 2012 Olympics. Even though athletes stay fit throughout their competitive career, we might still expect that the weight of an athlete is related to his or her age, so that older athletes tend to weigh more than younger ones. At the 2012 Olympics, that was indeed the case for most sports. However, cycling (mountain bike, track, and road), basketball, rowing, and volleyball were sports that did not show such a trend. The lack of trend means that, on average, athletes in these disciplines tended to weigh the same, irrespective of their age.

Figure 4.3b shows simulated data of a relationship between two variables that cannot be easily characterized as positive or negative—for smaller x-values the trend is negative (\), and for larger x-values it is positive (/).

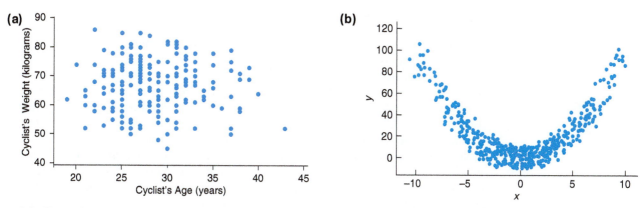

▲ **FIGURE 4.3** Scatterplots with **(a)** no trend and **(b)** a changing trend. (Sources: (a) Could you be an athlete? Olympics 2012 by age, weight and height, www.theguardian.com; (b) simulated data)

Seeing Strength of a Relationship

Weak relationships result in a large amount of scatter in the scatterplot. A large amount of scatter means that points have a great deal of spread in the vertical direction. This vertical spread makes it somewhat harder to detect a trend. Strong relationships have little vertical variation.

Figure 4.4 allows us to compare the strengths of two relationships. Figure 4.4a shows the relationship between height and weight for a sample of active adults. Figure 4.4b involves the same group of adults, but this time we examine the relationship between waist size (typically given in inches, even in Canada) and weight. Which relationship is stronger?

The relationship between waist size and weight is the stronger one (Figure 4.4b). To see this, in Figure 4.4a, consider the data for people who are 165 centimetres tall. Their weights vary anywhere from about 50 kilograms to 105 kilograms, a range of 55 kilograms. If you were using height to predict weight, you could be off by quite a bit. Compare this with the data in Figure 4.4b for people with a waist size of 30 inches. Their weights vary from about 50 kilograms to 80 kilograms, only a 30-kilogram range. The relationship between waist size and weight is stronger than that between height and weight because there is less vertical spread, so better predictions can be made. If you had to guess someone's weight, and could ask only one question before guessing, you'd do a better job if you asked about the person's waist size than about his or her height.

Labelling a trend as strong, very strong, or weak is a subjective judgment. Different statisticians might have different opinions. Later in this section, we'll see how we can measure strength with a number.

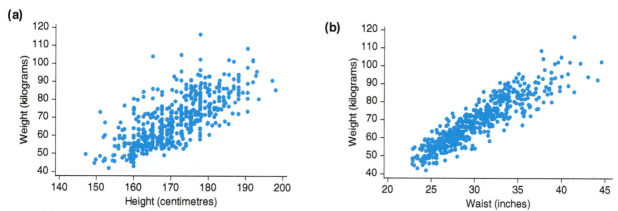

▲ **FIGURE 4.4 (a)** This graph shows a relatively weak relationship. **(b)** This graph shows a stronger relationship, because the points have less vertical spread. (Source: Heinz et al. 2003)

Identifying Shape

The simplest shape for a trend is **linear**. Fortunately, linear trends are quite common in real-life situations. Linear trends always increase (or decrease) at the same rate. They are called linear because the trend can be summarized with a straight line. Scatterplots of linear trends often resemble a football, as shown in Figure 4.4a, particularly if there is some scatter and a large number of observations. Figure 4.5 shows a linear trend from data provided in Nielsen's Global E-Commerce Report, a study aimed at understanding consumers' online shopping and purchasing intentions in 60 countries (Nielsen 2014). Each point represents one of the e-commerce categories included in the study. The variables measured are the percentage of global respondents who plan to browse for products in that category online in the next six months, and the percentage who plan to buy products in that category online in the next six months. Figure 4.5 shows that a positive, linear relationship exists between online searching and online shopping intentions: those who plan to browse online also tend to buy online, and the more they plan to browse, the more they tend to plan to buy. (Categories with low browsing and purchasing intentions include flowers, alcohol, and baby products, whereas those with high browsing and purchasing intentions include clothing and accessories, event tickets, and hotel reservations.) We've added a straight line to the scatterplot to highlight the linear trend.

► **FIGURE 4.5** A line has been inserted to emphasize the linear trend.

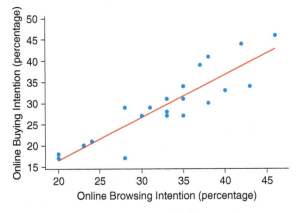

Not all trends are linear; in fact, a great variety of shapes can occur. But don't worry about that for now: all we want to do is classify trends as either linear or not linear.

Figure 4.6 shows the relationship between the Life Satisfaction Index and the income per capita (in U.S. dollars) for countries that are members of the Organisation for Economic Co-operation and Development (OECD 2013). You can see that there is a tendency for countries with a higher income per capita to have a higher Life Satisfaction Index. However, the relationship is not linear, as is made clear by the curved line superimposed on the graph.

► **FIGURE 4.6** The Life Satisfaction Index and the income per capita of countries in the OECD are related in a nonlinear way.

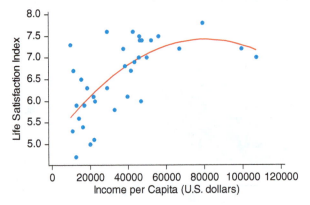

Nonlinear trends are more difficult to summarize than linear trends. This book does not cover nonlinear trends. Although our focus is on linear trends, it is very important that you first examine a scatterplot to be sure that the trend is linear. If you apply the techniques in this chapter to a nonlinear trend, you might reach disastrously incorrect conclusions!

KEY POINT When examining relationships between two variables, look for the trend, the strength of the trend, and the shape of the trend.

Writing Clear Descriptions of Relationships

Good communication skills are vital for success in general, and being able to clearly describe patterns in data is an important goal of this book. Here are some tips to help you describe relationships between two variables.

- A written description should always include (1) trend, (2) shape, and (3) strength (not necessarily in that order) and should explain what all of these mean in (4) the context of the data. You should also mention any observations that do not fit the general trend.

  Example 1 demonstrates how to write a clear, precise description of the relationship between numerical variables.

EXAMPLE 1 Age and Mileage of Used Cars

Figure 4.2a on page 132 displays the relationship between the age and number of kilometres of a sample of used cars.

QUESTION Describe the relationship.

SOLUTION The relationship between the age and number of kilometres of used cars is positive and linear. This means that older cars tend to have greater mileage. The relationship is moderately strong; some scatter is present, but not enough to hide the shape of the relationship. There is one exceptional point: one car is only about six years old but has been driven many kilometres.

TRY THIS! Exercise 4.7

The description in Example 1 is good because it mentions trend (a "positive" relationship), shape ("linear"), and strength ("moderately strong") and does so in context ("older cars tend to have greater mileage").

- It is very important that your descriptions be precise. For example, it would be wrong to say that older cars have higher kilometres. This statement is not true of every car in the data set. The one exceptional car (upper left corner of the plot) is relatively new (about six years old) but has a high number of kilometres driven (about 400,000 kilometres). Some older cars have relatively few kilometres on them. To be precise, you could say that older cars *tend* to have been driven for more kilometres. The word *tend* indicates that you are describing a trend that has variability, so the trend you describe is not true of all individuals but instead is a characteristic of the entire group.

- When writing a description of a relationship, you should also mention unusual features, such as outliers, small clusters of points, or anything else that does not seem to be part of the general pattern. Figure 4.7 includes an outlier. These data are from a group of adults who reported their weights and heights. One person clearly wrote the wrong height.

▶ **FIGURE 4.7** A fairly strong, positive relationship between height and weight for a group of adults. One person reported the wrong height.

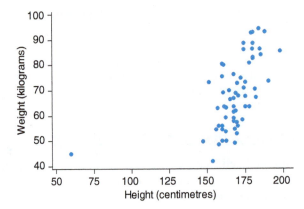

Measuring the Strength of a Relationship with Correlation

The **correlation coefficient** is a number that measures the strength of the linear relationship between two numerical variables—for example, the relationship between people's heights and weights. We can't emphasize enough that the correlation coefficient *makes sense only if the trend is linear and if both variables are numerical.*

The correlation coefficient, represented by the letter r, is a statistic whose value is always between -1 and $+1$. Both the value and the sign (positive or negative) of r have information we can use. If the value of r is close to -1 or $+1$, then the relationship is very strong; if r is close to 0, the relationship is weak. If the value of the correlation coefficient is positive, then the trend is positive; if the value is negative, the trend is negative.

Visualizing the Correlation Coefficient

Figure 4.8 on the next page presents a series of scatterplots that show relationships of gradually decreasing strength. The strongest linear relationship appears in Figure 4.8a; the points fall exactly along a line. Because the trend is positive and perfectly linear, the correlation coefficient is equal to 1.

The next scatterplot, Figure 4.8b, is slightly weaker. The points are more spread out vertically. We can see a linear trend, but the points do not fall exactly along a line. The trend is still positive, so the correlation coefficient is also positive. However, the value of the correlation coefficient is less than 1 (it is 0.98).

The remaining scatterplots show weaker and weaker linear relationships, and their correlation coefficients gradually decrease. In the last scatterplot, Figure 4.8f, there is no linear relationship between the two variables, and the correlation coefficient has a value of 0.0.

The next set of scatterplots (Figure 4.9 on page 138) starts with that same Olympic cyclists' data (having a correlation of 0.0), and the negative correlations gradually get stronger. The last figure has a correlation of -1.00.

The Correlation Coefficient in Context

The correlation between online browsing intentions and buying intentions is $r = 0.89$. If we are told, or already know, that the relationship between these variables is linear, then we know that the trend is positive and strong. The fact that the correlation is high and close to 1 means that there is little scatter in the scatterplot.

University admission offices sometimes report correlations between students' Grade 12 average marks and their first-year grades. If the relationship is linear and the correlation is high, this justifies using Grade 12 marks to make admissions decisions, because a high correlation would indicate a strong relationship between Grade 12 marks and academic

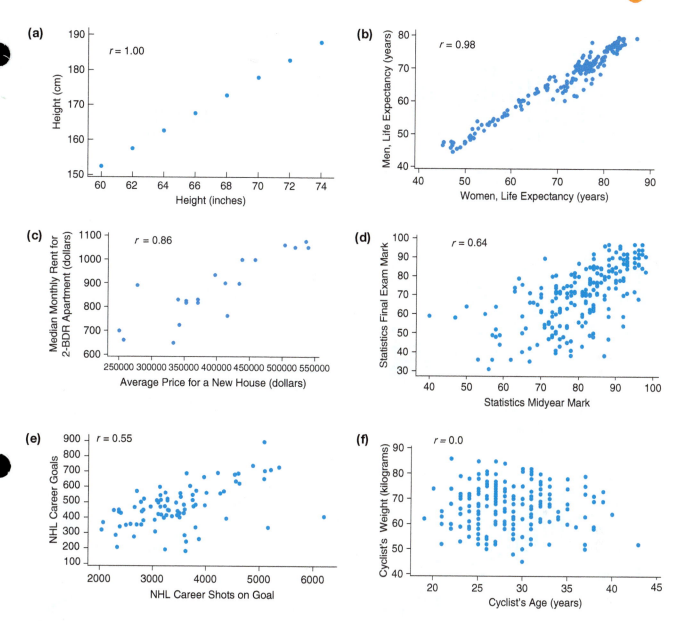

▲ **FIGURE 4.8** Scatterplots with decreasing positive correlation coefficients. (Sources: (a) simulated data; (b) World Health Organization, www.who.int; (c) Federation of Canadian Municipalities 2012; (d) Boué 2010; (e) www.nhl.com; (f) www.theguardian.com)

performance. A positive correlation means that students who have above-average Grade 12 marks tend to get above-average grades in first year. Conversely, those who have below-average Grade 12 marks tend to get below-average grades in first year. Note that we're careful to say "tend to." Certainly, some students with low Grade 12 marks do very well, and some with high Grade 12 marks struggle to pass their courses. The correlation coefficient does not tell us about individual students; it tells us about the overall trend.

More Context: Correlation Does Not Mean Causation!

Quite often, you'll hear someone use the correlation coefficient to support a claim of cause and effect. For example, one of the authors once read that a politician wanted to close liquor stores in a city because there was a positive correlation between the number of liquor stores in a neighbourhood and the amount of crime.

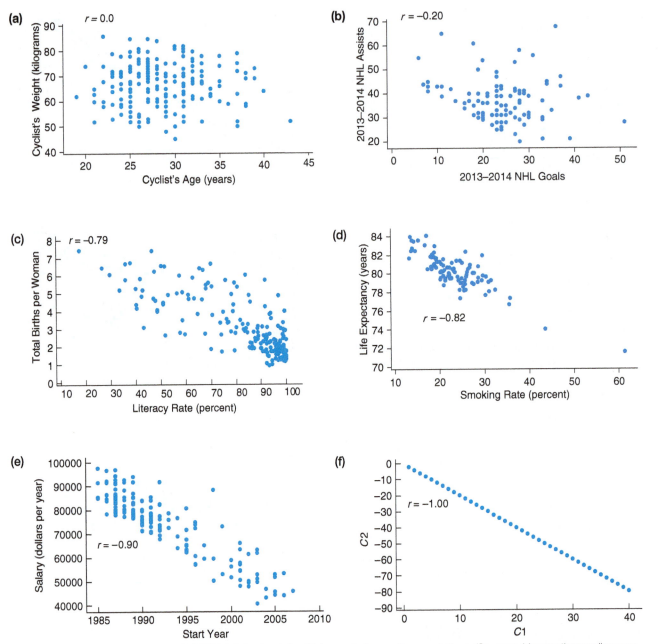

▲ **FIGURE 4.9** Scatterplots with increasingly negative correlations. (Sources: (a) www.theguardian.com; (b) www.nhl.com; (c) UN Statistics; (d) Statistics Canada. Canadian Community Health Survey; (e) Minitab Student 12 file "Salary," adjusted for inflation; (f) simulated data)

As you learned in Chapter 1, we can't form cause-and-effect conclusions from observational studies. If your data came from an observational study, it doesn't matter how strong the correlation is. Even a correlation near 1 is not enough to conclude that changing one variable (closing down liquor stores) will lead to a change in the other variable (crime rate).

A positive correlation also exists between the number of toques sold in Canada per week and the number of brush fires in Australia per week. Are brush fires in Australia caused by cold Canadians? Probably not. The correlation is likely to be the result of weather. When it is winter in Canada, people buy toques. When winter is happening in Canada, summer is happening in Australia (which is located in the southern hemisphere), and summer is brush-fire season.

What, then, can we conclude from the fact that the number of liquor stores in a neighbourhood is positively correlated with the crime rate in that neighbourhood? Only that neighbourhoods with a higher-than-average number of liquor stores typically (but not always) have a higher-than-average crime rate.

If you learn nothing else from this book, remember this: no matter how tempting, do *not* conclude that a cause-and-effect relationship between two variables exists just because there is a correlation, no matter how close to +1 or −1 that correlation might be!

> **KEY POINT** ▶ Correlation does not imply causation.

Finding the Correlation Coefficient

The correlation coefficient is a messy quantity to compute, so it is best to use technology to compute its value. Nevertheless, it is useful to know how it is computed. Without technology, we compute the value of *r* by first multiplying the *x* and *y* values for each observation together. We then add up all these products and from this we subtract $n\bar{x}\,\bar{y}$, where *n* is the number of two-variable data points you have, $\bar{x}$ is the mean of all the *x*-values, and $\bar{y}$ is the mean of all the *y*-values. A *positive* difference means that as one variable increases in value, so does the other and there is a positive linear relationship between the *x*-variable and the *y*-variable. A *negative* difference means that as one variable *increases* in value, the other variable *decreases* in value (or vice versa) and the linear relationship between the two variables is negative. If there is no relationship between the two variables, then this difference should be zero (or very close to zero). The last step is to divide this difference by the product of $n-1$, s_x, and s_y, where s_x is the standard deviation of all the *x*-values and s_y is the standard deviation of all the *y*-values.

This description for computing the correlation coefficient is summarized by the following formula:

$$\textbf{Formula 4.1: } r = \frac{\sum xy - n\,\bar{x}\,\bar{y}}{(n-1)s_x s_y}$$

The next example illustrates how to use Formula 4.1 in a calculation.

EXAMPLE 2 Heights and Weights of Six Women

Figure 4.10a shows the scatterplot for heights and weights of six women.

> **QUESTION** Using the data provided, find the correlation coefficient between height (in centimetres) and weight (in kilograms) for these six women.

Height	155	158	160	163	168	174
Weight	47	50	64	57	75	73

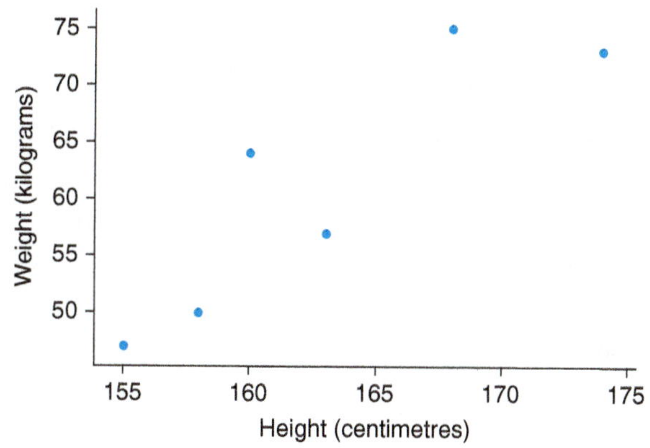

◀ **FIGURE 4.10a** Scatterplot showing heights and weights of six women.

TECH

SOLUTION Before proceeding, we verify that the condition of linearity holds. Figure 4.10a suggests that the trend's shape can be considered linear; a straight line through the data might summarize the trend, although this is hard to see with so few points.

Next, we calculate the correlation coefficient. Ordinarily, we use technology to do this, and Figure 4.10b shows the output from StatCrunch, which gives us the value $r = 0.88$.

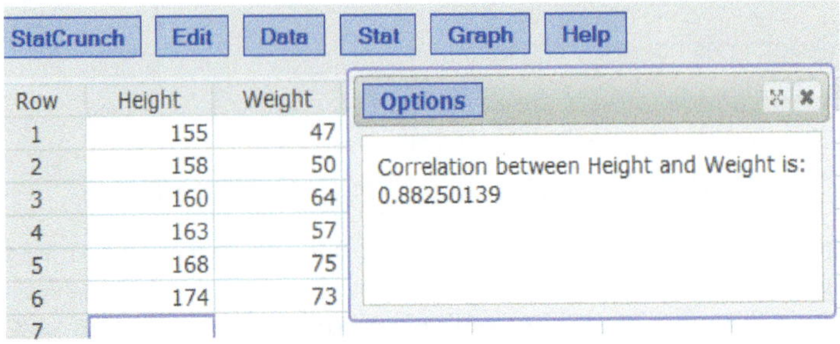

► **FIGURE 4.10b** StatCrunch, like all statistical software, lets you calculate the correlation between any two columns you choose.

| StatCrunch | Edit | Data | Stat | Graph | Help |

Row	Height	Weight	**Options**
1	155	47	
2	158	50	Correlation between Height and Weight is:
3	160	64	0.88250139
4	163	57	
5	168	75	
6	174	73	
7			

Because the sample size is small, we can confirm this output using Formula 4.1. It is helpful to go through the steps of this calculation to better understand how the correlation coefficient measures linear relationships between variables.

The first step is to multiply each of the x-values by its corresponding y-value, and then add up the products. We have.

$$\sum xy = (155 \times 47) + (158 \times 50) + (160 \times 64) + (163 \times 57) +$$
$$(168 \times 75) + (174 \times 73)$$
$$= 7285 + 7900 + 10240 + 9291 + 12600 + 12702$$
$$= 60018$$

Next we calculate average values of height and weight and then determine the standard deviation for each.

For the height: $\bar{x} = 163$ and $s_x = 6.986$

For the weight: $\bar{y} = 61$ and $s_y = 11.679$

Being reminded that there are six pairs of heights and weights ($n = 6$), we now use Formula 4.1 to find the value of the correlation coefficient. We get

$$r = \frac{\sum xy - n\,\bar{x}\,\bar{y}}{(n-1)s_x s_y}$$

$$= \frac{60018 - (6 \times 163 \times 61)}{(6-1) \times 6.986 \times 11.679}$$

$$= \frac{360}{407.95}$$

$$= 0.8825$$

The correlation between height and weight for these six women comes out to be about 0.88.

CONCLUSION The correlation coefficient for the linear association of weights and heights of these six women is $r = 0.88$. Thus, there is a strong positive correlation between height and weight for these women. Taller women tend to weigh more.

TRY THIS! Exercise 4.19a

Understanding the Correlation Coefficient

The correlation coefficient has a few features you should know about when interpreting the value of r or deciding whether you should even compute the value.

- Changing the order of the variables does not change r. Note that in the equation for r it doesn't matter which variable is called x and which is called y. In practice, this means that if the correlation between life expectancy for men and women is 0.977, then the correlation between life expectancy for women and men is also 0.977. This makes sense because the correlation measures the strength of the linear relationship between x and y, and that strength will be the same no matter which variable gets plotted on the horizontal axis and which on the vertical.

  Figure 4.11a and b have the same correlation; we've just swapped axes.

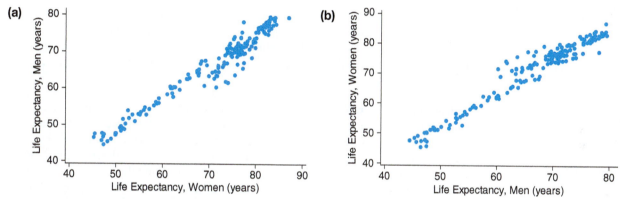

▲ **FIGURE 4.11** Scatterplots showing the relationship between men's and women's life expectancy for various countries. **(a)** Women's life expectancy is plotted on the x-axis. **(b)** Men's life expectancy is plotted on the x-axis. (Source: World Health Organization, www.who.int)

- Adding or multiplying by a constant does not affect r. The correlation between the heights and weights of the six women in Example 2 was 0.88. What would happen if all six women in the sample had been asked to wear 8-centimetre high platform heels when their heights were measured? Everyone would have been 8 centimetres taller. Would this have changed the value of r? Intuitively, you should sense that it wouldn't. Figure 4.12a shows a scatterplot of the original data, and Figure 4.12b shows the data with the women in 8-centimetre heels.

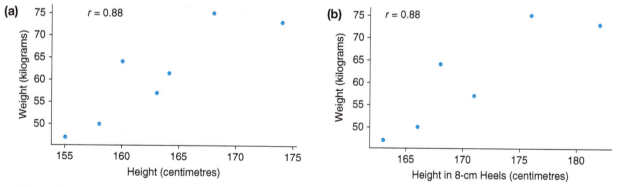

▲ **FIGURE 4.12** **(a)** A repeat of the scatterplot of height and weight for six women. **(b)** The same women in 8-cm heels. The correlation remains the same.

We haven't changed the strength of the relationship. All we've done is shift the points on the scatterplot 8 centimetres to the right. But shifting the points doesn't change the relationship between height and weight. We can verify that the correlation is unchanged by looking at the formula. Each height is increased by 8 cm, so Σxy becomes $\Sigma xy + 8\,\Sigma y$, and $n\bar{x}\bar{y}$ becomes $n\bar{x}\bar{y} + 8\,\Sigma y$. When subtracting in the numerator of Formula 4.1, the new terms cancel out and we obtain the same value for the correlation. As another example, if science found a way to add five years to the life expectancy of men in all countries in the world, the correlation between life expectancies for men and women would still be the same.

More generally, we can add a constant (a fixed value) to all of the values of one variable, or of both variables, and not affect the correlation coefficient.

For the very same reason, we can multiply either or both variables by positive constants without changing r. For example, to convert the women's heights from centimetres to metres, we divide their heights by 100. Doing this does not change how strong the relationship is; it merely changes the units we're using to measure height. Because the strength of the relationship does not change, the correlation coefficient does not change.

- The correlation coefficient is unitless. Height is measured in centimetres and weight in kilograms, but r has no units because the numerator and the denominator in Formula 4.1 have the same units, so they cancel out. This means that we will get the same value for correlation whether we measure height in centimetres, inches, or fathoms.

> ⚠ **Caution**
>
> **Correlation Coefficient and Linearity**
> A value of r close to 1 or −1 does *not* tell you that the relationship is linear. You must check visually; otherwise, your interpretation of the correlation coefficient might be wrong.

- Linear, linear, linear. We've said it before, but we'll say it again: We're talking only about linear relationships here. The correlation can be misleading if you do not have a linear relationship. Figures 4.13a through d illustrate the fact that different nonlinear patterns can have the same correlation. All of these graphs have $r = 0.817$, but the graphs have very different shapes. The take-home message is that the correlation alone does not tell us much about the shape of a graph. We must also know that the relationship is linear to make sense of the correlation.

Remember: *always* make a graph of your data. If the trend is nonlinear, the correlation (and, as you'll see in the next section, other statistics) can be very misleading.

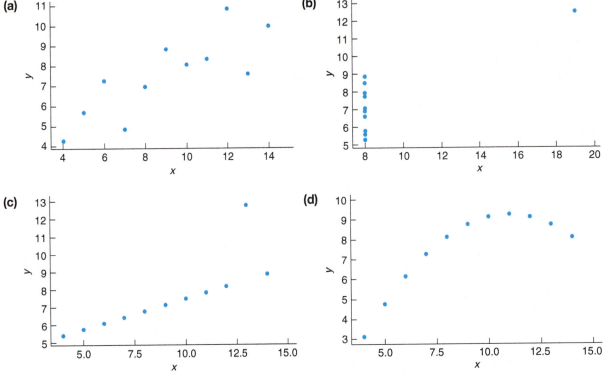

▲ **FIGURE 4.13 (a–d)** Four scatterplots with the same correlation of 0.817 have very different shapes. The correlation coefficient is meaningful only if the trend is linear. (Source: Anscombe, F. Anscombe's Quartet)

KEY POINT The correlation coefficient does not tell you whether a relationship is linear. However, if you already know that the relationship is linear, then the correlation coefficient tells you how strong the relationship is.

SNAPSHOT THE CORRELATION COEFFICIENT

WHAT IS IT? ▶	A quantity with values between -1 and 1.
WHAT DOES IT DO? ▶	Measures the strength of a linear relationship between two numerical variables.
HOW DOES IT DO IT? ▶	Through a formula that uses the sum of products of the two observations for each point, and the mean and standard deviation for each variable.
HOW IS IT USED? ▶	The sign tells us whether the trend is positive ($+$) or negative ($-$). The value tells us the strength. If the value is close to 1 or -1, then the points are tightly clustered about a line; if the value is close to 0, then there is no linear relationship.
WHEN IS IT USED? ▶	The correlation coefficient can be interpreted only when a scatterplot shows a linear relationship between the two variables.

SECTION 4.3

Modelling Linear Trends

How much more do people tend to weigh for each additional centimetre in height? How much value do cars lose each year as they age? Do NHL teams with a higher team-payroll do better through winning more points in the regular season standings? Can we predict how much space a book will take on a bookshelf just by knowing how many pages there are in the book? To answer these types of questions, it is not enough to re-mark that a trend exists. We need to measure the trend and the strength of the trend.

To measure the trend, we will summarize the relationship between two variables with a model. The model consists of an equation and a set of condi-tions that describe when the model will be appropriate. Ideally, this equation is a very concise and accurate description of the data; if so, then the model is a good fit of the data. When this happens, any understanding we gain about the model accurately applies to our understanding of the real world. If the model is a bad fit, however, then the model does not imitate "real-life" situations and should not be used.

The Regression Line

The **regression line** is a tool for making predictions about one variable based on the values of another variable. It also provides us with a useful way of summarizing a linear relationship. Recall from Chapter 3 that we could summarize a sample distribution with a mean and a standard deviation. The regression line works the same way: it reduces a linear relationship to its bare essentials and allows us to analyze a relationship without being distracted by small details.

Review: Equation of a Line

The regression line is given by an equation for a straight line. Recall from algebra that equations for straight lines contain a **y-intercept** and a **slope**. The equation for a straight line is

$$y = mx + b$$

The letter m represents the slope, which tells how steep the line is, and the letter b represents the y-intercept, which is the value of y when $x = 0$.

Statisticians write the equation of a line slightly differently and put the intercept first. For now, we will use the notation b_0 to denote the y-intercept, and b_1 to denote the slope (we will see some different notation in Chapter 14). We then write the regression line as

$$y = b_0 + b_1 x$$

We often use the names of variables in place of x and y to emphasize that the regression line is a model about two real-world variables. We will sometimes write the word *predicted* in front of the y-variable to emphasize that the line consists of predictions for the y-variable, not actual values. A few examples should make this clear.

Visualizing the Regression Line

Can we know how wide a book is on the basis of the number of pages in the book? A student took a random sample of books from his shelf, measured the width of the spine (in millimetres, mm), and recorded the number of pages. Figure 4.14 illustrates how the regression line captures the basic trend of a linear relationship between width of the book and the number of pages for this sample. The equation for this line is

Predicted Width = 6.22 + 0.0366 Pages

▶ FIGURE 4.14 The regression line summarizes the relationship between the width of the book and the number of pages for a small sample of books. (Source: Onaga, E. 2005, UCLA, Department of Statistics)

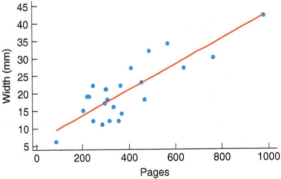

One way of comparing the performance of NHL hockey teams is through the total number of points scored during the regular season. If we consider the amount of money paid by an NHL team to its players, we might expect that teams that pay their players more tend to have better regular season performance and therefore a higher total number of points scored. Figure 4.15 shows the relationship between the total number of points scored during the regular season and the team's total payroll (in millions of dollars) for the 2011–2012 season. The relationship seems fairly linear (although weak), and the regression line can be used to predict how many regular season points a team scored, given the team's payroll. The data suggest that teams that pay their players more do tend to score more points on average.

Predicted Regular Season Points = 61.5 + 0.538 Payroll

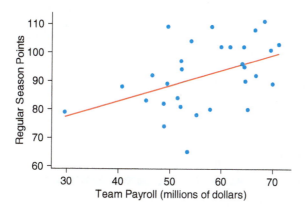

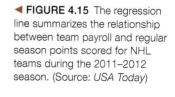

Regression in Context

Suppose you have a 10-year-old car and want to estimate how much it is worth. One of the more important uses of the regression line is to make predictions about what *y*-values can be obtained for particular *x*-values. Figure 4.16 suggests that the relationship between age and value is linear, and the regression line that summarizes this relationship is

$$\text{Predicted Value} = 20771 - 1355 \text{ Age}$$

We can use this equation to predict approximately how much a 10-year-old car is worth:

$$\text{Predicted Value} = 20771 - (1355 \times 10)$$
$$= 20771 - 13550$$
$$= 7221$$

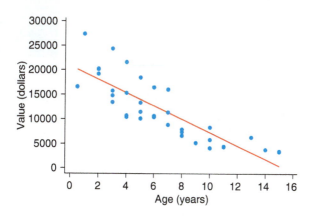

◄ FIGURE 4.16 The regression line summarizes the relationship between the value of a car, according to VMR Canada, and the car's age for a small sample of cars.

The regression line predicts that a 10-year-old car will be valued at about $7221. As we know, many factors other than age affect the value of a car, and perhaps with more information we might make a better prediction. However, if the only thing we know about a car is its age, this may be the best prediction we can get. It is also important to keep in mind that this sample is not representative of all used cars on the market in Canada.

Using the regression line to make predictions requires certain assumptions. We'll go into more detail about these assumptions later, but for now, just use common sense. This predicted value of $7221 is useful only for situations similar to those we observed in the data set. For instance, if all the cars in our data set are Toyotas, and our 10-year-old car is a Chevrolet, then the prediction is probably not useful.

EXAMPLE 3 Book Width

A college instructor with far too many books on his shelf is wondering whether he has room for one more. He has about 20 mm of space left on his shelf, and he can tell from the online bookstore that the book he wants has 598 pages. The regression line obtained from a small sample of books is

$$\text{Predicted Width} = 6.22 + 0.0366 \text{ Pages}$$

QUESTION Will the book fit on his shelf?

SOLUTION Assuming that the data used to fit this regression line are representative of all books, we would predict the width of the book corresponding to 598 pages to be

$$\text{Predicted Width} = 6.22 + (0.0366 \times 598)$$
$$= 6.22 + 21.8868$$
$$= 28.1068 \text{ mm}$$

CONCLUSION The book is predicted to be 28 mm wide. Even though the actual book width is likely to differ somewhat from 28 mm, it seems that the book will probably not fit on the shelf.

TRY THIS! Exercise 4.21

Common sense tells us that not all books with 598 pages are exactly 28 mm wide. There is a lot of variation in the width of a book for a given number of pages. In Chapter 14, we'll see how to place upper and lower limits on this predicted width so that we can take into account the uncertainty caused by the variation in books.

Finding the Regression Line

In almost every case, we'll use technology to find the regression line. However, it is important to know how the technology works, and to be able to calculate the equation when we have access only to summary statistics and not to the complete data set.

To understand how technology finds the regression line, imagine trying to draw a line through the scatterplots in Figures 4.14 through 4.16 to best capture the linear trend. We could have drawn almost any line, and some of them would have looked like pretty good summaries of the trend. What makes the regression line special? How do we find the intercept and slope of the regression line?

The regression line is chosen because it is the line that comes closest to most of the points. More precisely, the square of the vertical distances between the points and the line, on average, is bigger for any other line we might draw than for the regression

Details

Least Squares
The regression line is also called the least squares line because it is chosen so that the sum of the squares of the differences between the observed y-value, y, and the value predicted by the line, $\hat{y}$, is as small as possible. Mathematically, this means that the slope and intercept are chosen so that $\Sigma(y - \hat{y})^2$ is as small as possible.

line. Figure 4.17 shows these vertical distances with black lines. The regression line is sometimes called the "best fit" line because, in this sense, it provides the best fit to the data.

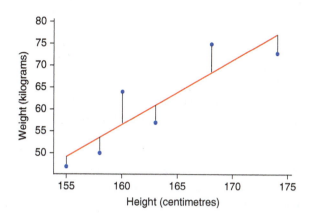

◀ **FIGURE 4.17** The "best fit" regression line, showing the vertical distance between each observation and the line. For any other line, the average of the squared distances is larger.

To find this best fit line, we need to find the slope and the intercept. The slope, b_1, of the regression line is the ratio of the standard deviations of the two variables (s_x and s_y), multiplied by the correlation coefficient:

Formula 4.2a: The slope, $b_1 = r \dfrac{s_y}{s_x}$

Once we have found the slope, we can find the intercept. Finding the intercept, b_0, requires that we first find the means of the variables, $\bar{x}$ and $\bar{y}$:

Formula 4.2b: The intercept, $b_0 = \bar{y} - b_1\bar{x}$

Now put these quantities into the equation of a line, and the regression line is given by

Formula 4.2c: The regression line, Predicted $y = b_0 + b_1x$

EXAMPLE 4 Term and Final Exam Marks

A professor wants to predict the final exam mark for students in an introductory statistics class based on their going-into-the-final-exam mark, or term mark. Figure 4.18a shows a scatterplot of the term mark and the final exam mark for a sample of 211 students. The scatterplot suggests a moderately strong, positive linear relationship: students with high term marks tend to get high final exam marks. The average term mark of this sample was 70.19 with standard deviation 13.30. The average final exam mark was 66.82 with standard deviation 16.28. The correlation between term mark and final exam mark was 0.745.

QUESTIONS

a. Find the equation of the regression line that best summarizes this relationship. Note that the x-variable is the term mark and the y-variable is the final exam mark.

b. Using the equation, find the predicted final exam mark for a student in this class with a term mark of 74%.

▶ **FIGURE 4.18a** The scatterplot suggests a moderate linear positive relationship: students with higher term marks tend to have higher final exam marks. (Source: Stallard 2013)

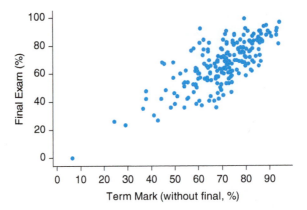

TECH

▶ **FIGURE 4.18b** StatCrunch output for the regression line to predict the final exam mark from the term mark. The structure of the output is typical for many statistical software packages.

SOLUTIONS

a. With access to the full data set on the text's companion website, we can use technology to find (and plot) the regression line. Still, when summary statistics are provided (means and standard deviations of the two variables as well as their correlation), it is not time-consuming to use Formula 4.2 to find the regression line.

Figure 4.18b shows StatCrunch output for the regression line. (StatCrunch provides quite a bit more information than we will use in this chapter.)

According to technology, the equation of the regression line is

$$\text{Predicted FinalExamMark} = 2.81 + 0.91 \text{ TermMark}$$

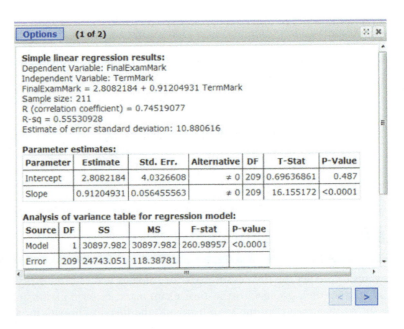

Simple linear regression results:
Dependent Variable: FinalExamMark
Independent Variable: TermMark
FinalExamMark = 2.8082184 + 0.91204931 TermMark
Sample size: 211
R (correlation coefficient) = 0.74519077
R-sq = 0.55530928
Estimate of error standard deviation: 10.880616

Parameter estimates:

Parameter	Estimate	Std. Err.	Alternative	DF	T-Stat	P-Value
Intercept	2.8082184	4.0326608	≠ 0	209	0.69636861	0.487
Slope	0.91204931	0.056455563	≠ 0	209	16.155172	<0.0001

Analysis of variance table for regression model:

Source	DF	SS	MS	F-stat	P-value
Model	1	30897.982	30897.982	260.98957	<0.0001
Error	209	24743.051	118.38781		

We now check this calculation by hand, using Formula 4.2.

We are given that

For term marks: $\bar{x} = 70.19,\ s_x = 13.30$

For final exam marks: $\bar{y} = 66.82,\ s_y = 16.28$

and $r = 0.745$

First we must find the slope:

$$b_1 = r\frac{s_y}{s_x} = 0.745 \times \frac{16.28}{13.30} = 0.912$$

Now we can use the slope to find the intercept:

$$b_0 = \bar{y} - b_1\bar{x} = 66.82 - (0.912 \times 70.19) = 66.82 - 64.01 = 2.81$$

We can then write:

Predicted FinalExamMark = 2.81 + 0.912 TermMark

b. Predicted FinalExamMark = 2.81 + 0.912 TermMark

$$\begin{aligned} &= 2.81 + (0.912 \times 74) \\ &= 2.81 + 67.488 \\ &= 70.3 \end{aligned}$$

CONCLUSION

We would expect someone with a term mark of 74% to have a final exam mark of 70.3%.

TRY THIS! Exercise 4.23

Different software packages present the intercept and slope differently. Therefore, you need to learn how to read the output of the software you are using. Example 5 shows output from several packages.

EXAMPLE 5 Technology Output for Regression

Figure 4.19 shows outputs from Minitab, StatCrunch, the TI-83/84, Excel, and SPSS for finding the regression equation in Example 4 for final exam marks and term marks.

QUESTION For each software package, explain how to find the equation of the regression line from the given output.

CONCLUSION Figure 4.19a: Minitab gives us a simple equation directly:
Final Exam Mark = 2.81 + 0.912 Term Mark.
However, the more statistically correct format would be

Predicted Final Exam Mark = 2.81 + 0.912 Term Mark

◄ **FIGURE 4.19a** Minitab output.

> **Regression Analysis: FinalExamMark versus TermMark**
>
> ```
> The regression equation is
> FinalExamMark = 2.81 + 0.912 TermMark
> ```

Figure 4.19b: StatCrunch gives the equation directly near the top, but it also lists the intercept and slope separately in the table near the bottom.

Figure 4.19c: TI-83/84 gives us the coefficients to put together. The "a" value is the intercept, and the "b" value is the slope. If the diagnostics are on (use the CATALOG button), the TI-83/84 also gives the correlation.

Figure 4.19d: Excel shows the coefficients in the column labelled "Coefficients." The intercept is in the first row, labelled "Intercept," and the slope is in the row labelled "Variable 1."

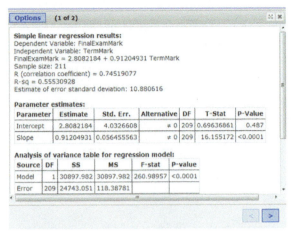

Options (1 of 2)

Simple linear regression results:
Dependent Variable: FinalExamMark
Independent Variable: TermMark
FinalExamMark = 2.8082184 + 0.91204931 TermMark
Sample size: 211
R (correlation coefficient) = 0.74519077
R-sq = 0.55530928
Estimate of error standard deviation: 10.880616

Parameter estimates:

Parameter	Estimate	Std. Err.	Alternative	DF	T-Stat	P-Value
Intercept	2.8082184	4.0326608	≠ 0	209	0.69636861	0.487
Slope	0.91204931	0.056455563	≠ 0	209	16.155172	<0.0001

Analysis of variance table for regression model:

Source	DF	SS	MS	F-stat	P-value
Model	1	30897.982	30897.982	260.98957	<0.0001
Error	209	24743.051	118.38781		

▲ **FIGURE 4.19b** StatCrunch output.

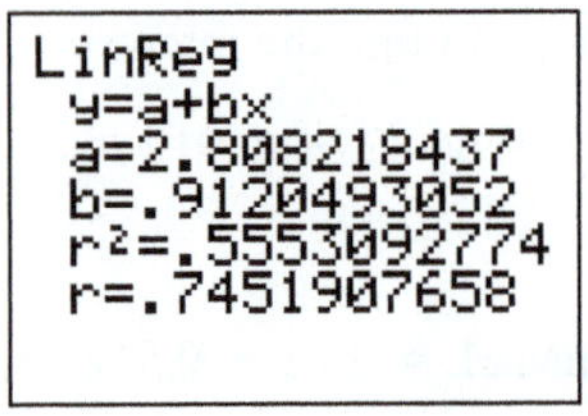

```
LinReg
y=a+bx
a=2.808218437
b=.9120493052
r²=.5553092774
r=.7451907658
```

▲ **FIGURE 4.19c** TI-83/84 output.

	Coefficients	Standard Error	t Stat	P-value	Lower 95%	Upper 95%	Lower 95.0%	Upper 95.0%
Intercept	2.80817	4.03266	0.696357	0.486979	-5.14173	10.75807	-5.14173	10.75807
Variable 1	0.91205	0.056456	16.15518	1.23E-38	0.800754	1.023345	0.800754	1.023345

▲ **FIGURE 4.19d** Excel output.

Coefficients[a]

Model		Unstandardized Coefficients B	Unstandardized Coefficients Std. Error	Standardized Coefficients Beta	t	Sig.
1	(Constant)	2.808	4.033		.696	.487
	TermMark	.912	.056	.745	16.155	.000

a. Dependent Variable: FinalExamMark

▲ **FIGURE 4.19e** SPSS output.

Figure 4.19e: SPSS shows the coefficients in the column labelled "Unstandardized Coefficients." The intercept is in the first row, labelled "(Constant)," and the slope is in the row labelled "TermMark."

TRY THIS! Exercise 4.27

Interpreting the Regression Line

An important use of the regression line is to make predictions about the value of y that we will see for a given value of x. However, the regression line provides more information than just a predicted y-value. The regression line can also tell us about the rate of change of the mean value of y with respect to x and can help us understand the underlying theory behind cause-and-effect relationships.

Choosing *x* and *y*: Order Matters

In Section 4.2, you saw that the correlation coefficient is the same no matter which variable you choose for *x* and which you choose for *y*. With regression, however, order matters.

Consider the collection of data about book widths. We used it earlier to predict the width of a book, given the number of pages. The equation of the regression line for this prediction problem (shown in Figure 4.20a) is

$$\text{Predicted Width} = 6.22 + 0.037 \text{ Pages}$$

But what if we instead wanted to predict how many *Pages* there are in a book on the basis of the width of the book?

To do this, we would switch the order of the variables, and use *Pages* as our *y*-variable and *Width* as our *x*-variable. Then the slope is calculated to be 19.6 (Figure 4.20b).

It is tempting to think that because we are flipping the graph over when we switch *x* and *y*, we can just flip the slope over to get the new slope. If this were true, then we could find the new slope simply by calculating 1/(old slope). However, that approach doesn't work. That would give us a slope of

$$\frac{1}{0.037} = 27.0, \text{ which is not the same as the correct value of 19.6.}$$

How, then, do we know which variable goes where?

We use the variable plotted on the horizontal axis to make predictions about the variable plotted on the vertical axis. For this reason, the *x*-variable is called the **explanatory variable**, the **predictor variable**, or the **independent variable**. The *y*-variable is called the **response variable**, the **predicted variable**, or the **dependent variable**. These names reflect the different roles played by the *x*- and *y*-variables in regression. Which variable is which depends on what the regression line will be used to predict.

You'll see many pairs of terms used for the *x*- and *y*-variables in regression; some are shown in Table 4.1.

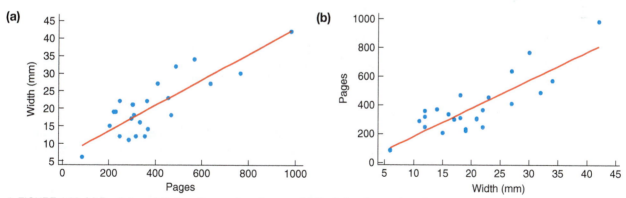

▲ FIGURE 4.20 (a) Predicting width from the number of pages. (b) Predicting the number of pages from width.

x-Variable	y-Variable
Predictor variable	Predicted variable
Explanatory variable	Response variable
Independent variable	Dependent variable

◀ TABLE 4.1 Terms used for the *x*- and *y*-variables.

EXAMPLE **6** Bedridden

It is hard to measure the height of people who are bedridden, and for many medical reasons it is often important to know a bedridden patient's height. However, it is not so difficult to measure the length of the ulna (the bone that runs from the elbow to the wrist). Data collected on non-bedridden people show a strong linear relationship between ulnar length and height.

QUESTION When making a scatterplot to predict height from ulnar length, which variable should be plotted on the *x*-axis and which on the *y*-axis?

CONCLUSION We are measuring ulnar length to predict a person's height. Therefore, ulnar length is the predictor (independent variable) and is plotted on the *x*-axis, while height is the response (dependent variable) and is plotted on the *y*-axis.

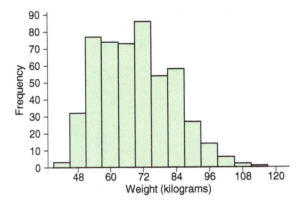

TRY THIS! Exercise 4.35

The Regression Line Is a Line of Averages

Figure 4.21 shows a histogram of the weights (in kilograms) of a sample of 507 active people. What is the typical weight?

▶ **FIGURE 4.21** A histogram of the weights of 507 active people.

One way of answering this question is to calculate the mean of the sample. The distribution of weights is a little right-skewed but not terribly so, and so the mean will probably give us a good idea of what is typical. The average weight of this group is 69.2 kilograms.

Now, we know that a relationship exists between height and weight and that shorter people tend to weigh less. If we know someone's height, then, what weight would we guess for that person? Surely not the average weight of the whole group! We can do better than that. For instance, what's the typical weight of someone 170 centimetres tall? To answer this, it makes sense to look only at the weights of those people in our sample who are about 170 centimetres tall. To make sure we have enough 170-centimetres-tall people in our sample, let's include everyone who is *approximately* 170 centimetres tall. So let's look at a slice of people whose height is between 169 centimetres and 171 centimetres. We come up with 37 people. Some of their weights are

63, 66, 53, 57, 67 . . . kilograms

Figure 4.22a shows this slice, which is centred at 170 centimetres.

The mean of these numbers is 66.3 kilograms. We put a special symbol on the plot to record this point—a triangle at the point (170, 66.3), shown in Figure 4.22b.

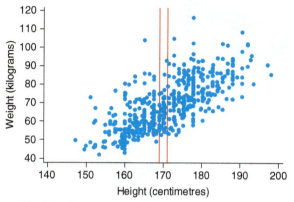

▲ **FIGURE 4.22a** Heights and weights with a slice at 170 centimetres.

▲ **FIGURE 4.22b** Heights and weights with the average at 170 centimetres, which is 66.3 kilograms.

The reason for marking this point is that if we wanted to predict the weights of those who were 170 centimetres tall, one good answer would be 66.3 kilograms.

What if we wanted to predict the weight of someone who is 178 centimetres tall? We could take a slice of the sample and look at those people who are between 177 centimetres and 179 centimetres tall. Typically, they're heavier than the people who are about 170 centimetres tall. Here are some of their weights:

83, 94, 73, 72, 60 . . . kilograms

Their mean weight is 79.3 kg. Let's put another special triangle symbol at (178, 79.3) to record this. We can continue in this fashion, and Figure 4.22c shows where the mean weights are for a few more heights.

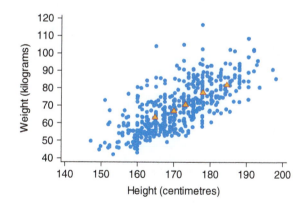

◄ **FIGURE 4.22c** Heights and weights with more means marked.

Note that the means fall (nearly) on a straight line. What could be the equation of this line? Figure 4.22d shows the regression line superimposed on the scatterplot with the means. They're nearly identical.

In fact, if we knew the distribution of all weights at every height, the means would lie exactly on the regression line. However, because we are working with only a sample of real data, the fit is only approximate.

The series of graphs in Figure 4.22 illustrates a fundamental feature of the regression line: it is a line of means. You plug in a value for x, and the regression line "predicts" the mean y-value for everyone in the population with that x-value.

▶ **FIGURE 4.22d** Heights and weights with means and a straight line.

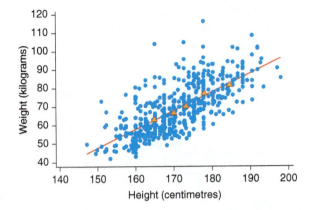

EXAMPLE 7 An Alternative to Weighing a Bear?

A bear's body mass is of interest to researchers who study bears in the field. However, weighing bears in the field is difficult, requiring a net, a heavy spring scale, and the effort of two people to suspend the animal from the scale. Chest girth, on the other hand, can be measured much more easily with a soft measuring tape. Because of this, researchers from the Ministry of National Resources wanted to determine if a black bear's mass could be predicted from its chest girth. As you can see in Figure 4.23, the scatterplot of body mass (response variable) versus chest girth (predictor) for a sample of 50 bears shows a reasonably linear relationship.

▶ **FIGURE 4.23** A scatterplot of chest girth versus body mass for a sample of 50 black bears. (Source: Obbard, M. E., 2013)

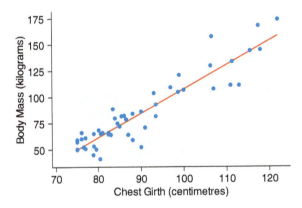

The regression line is

$$\text{Predicted Body Mass} = -125 + 2.33 \text{ Chest Girth}$$

QUESTION What is the predicted mean body mass of a black bear with chest girth of 84 centimetres?

SOLUTION We predict by estimating the mean body mass of a bear with chest girth of 84 centimetres. To do this, we substitute 84 into the regression line:

$$\text{Predicted Body Mass} = -125 + (2.33 \times 84) = 70.7 \text{ kilograms}$$

CONCLUSION We predict that the mean body mass of black bears with a chest girth of 84 centimetres is about 71 kilograms.

TRY THIS! Exercise 4.37

Interpreting the Slope

The slope tells us how to compare the mean y-values for objects that are 1 unit apart on the x-variable. For example, how different is the mean body mass of black bears whose chest girths differ by 1 centimetre? The slope in Example 7 tells us that the means differ by 2.33 kilograms. What if the bears' chest girths differ by 10 centimetres? Then the difference in mean body mass is $10 \times 2.33 = 23.3$ kilograms.

We should pay attention to whether the slope is 0 or very close to 0. When the slope is 0, we say that no (linear) relationship exists between x and y. The reason is that a 0 slope means that no matter what value of x you consider, the predicted value of y is always the same. The slope is 0 whenever the correlation coefficient is 0.

The slope is close to 0 whenever the correlation coefficient is close to 0. For example, the slope for Olympic road cyclists' ages and their weights (see Figure 4.3a) is very close to 0 ($b_1 = 0.025$).

SNAPSHOT   **THE SLOPE OF A REGRESSION LINE**

WHAT IS IT? ▶	In the regression line $y = b_0 + b_1x$, the slope is the coefficient of x, b_1.
WHAT DOES IT DO? ▶	It tells us how different the mean y-value is for observations that are 1 unit apart on the x-variable.
HOW DOES IT DO IT? ▶	The regression line tells us the average y-values for any value of x. The slope tells us how the average y-values differ for different values of x.
HOW IS IT USED? ▶	To measure the steepness and the direction of trend of the regression line. When the slope is close to 0, there is no linear relationship between the two variables.
WHEN IS IT USED? ▶	Whenever a scatterplot shows a linear trend.

EXAMPLE **8** Math and Reading EQAO Scores

Each year EQAO (Education Quality Accountability Office) publishes student achievement results for elementary schools in Ontario. To study the relationship between achievement in reading and achievement in mathematics for students in Grade 3, a regression analysis relating the percentage of students at or above provincial standard in reading with the percentage of students at or above provincial standard in mathematics resulted in the following model:

$$\text{Predicted Reading} = 32.4 + 0.548\,\text{Math}$$

This model was based on data from 61 schools belonging to the same school board.

The scatterplot in Figure 4.24 shows a linear relationship with a moderately strong positive trend.

▶ **FIGURE 4.24** The regression line shows a moderately strong positive trend between the percentage of students at or above provincial standard in reading and in mathematics.

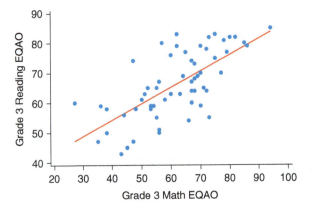

▶ **FIGURE 4.24** The regression line shows a moderately strong positive trend between the percentage of students at or above provincial standard in reading and in mathematics.

QUESTION Interpret the slope of this regression line.

SOLUTION The slope tells us that schools with 10% more students at or above provincial standard in mathematics had an average percentage of students at or above provincial standard in reading that was

$$10 \times 0.548 = 5.48 \text{ percent higher}$$

CONCLUSION Schools in this school board with 10% more students at or above provincial standard in mathematics have, on average, 5.48% more students at or above provincial standard in reading.

TRY THIS! Exercise 4.55a

Interpreting the Intercept

The intercept tells us the predicted mean y-value when the x-value is 0. Quite often, this is not terribly helpful. Sometimes it has no applicable meaning. For example, the regression line to predict weight, given someone's height, tells us that if a person is 0 centimetres tall, then his or her predicted weight is negative 200.5 kilograms!

Before interpreting the intercept, ask yourself whether it makes sense to talk about the x-variable taking on a 0 value. For example, suppose that a law school has found a regression line that predicts a student's first year average grade from the student's LSAT scaled score. You might think it makes sense to talk about getting a 0 on the LSAT score (no questions right). However, the lowest possible scaled LSAT score is 120, so it is not possible to get a score of 0. (One lesson statisticians learn early is that you must know something about the data you analyze—knowing only the numbers is not enough!)

EXAMPLE 9 Predicting Bears' Body Mass

What can we learn about the relationship between the chest girth and the body mass of a bear by looking at the intercept and slope of the regression line? The regression model is

$$\text{Predicted Body Mass} = -125 + 2.33 \text{ Chest Girth}$$

QUESTION Interpret the intercept and the slope.

CONCLUSION The intercept is not meaningful. It tells us that the mean body mass for bears with chest girth of 0 cm is negative 125 kilograms.

The slope is meaningful. The positive sign indicates that there is a positive trend: bears with larger chest girths tend to weigh more. In particular, for each additional centimetre of chest girth, a bear weighs on average 2.33 kilograms more.

TRY THIS! Exercise 4.59

 SNAPSHOT   **THE INTERCEPT OF A REGRESSION LINE**

WHAT IS IT? ▶	In the regression line $y = b_0 + b_1 x$, the intercept is the value of b_0.
WHAT DOES IT DO? ▶	It tells us the average y-value when the x-value is 0.
HOW DOES IT DO IT? ▶	The intercept is the y-value where the regression line crosses the y-axis.
HOW IS IT USED? ▶	It is always used to graph the line and to obtain predicted values. However, its value does not always have a meaningful interpretation.
WHEN IS IT USED? ▶	When a scatterplot has a linear trend. It can be interpreted only if the value of $x = 0$ makes sense for the observed data.

EXAMPLE 10 Age and Value of Cars

Figure 4.25 shows the relationship between age and VMR Canada values for a sample of cars.

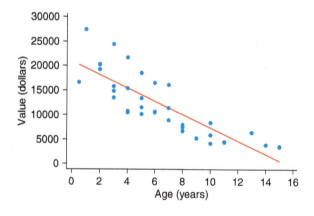

◀ **FIGURE 4.25** The age of a car and its value for a chosen sample.

The regression line is

$$\text{Predicted Value} = 20771 - 1355\ \text{Age}$$

QUESTION Interpret the slope and the intercept.

CONCLUSION The intercept estimates that the average value of a new car (0 years old) in this sample is $20,771. The slope tells us that, on average, cars lost $1355 in value per year.

TRY THIS! Exercise 4.61

Evaluating the Linear Model

Regression is a very powerful tool for understanding linear relationships between numerical variables. However, we need to be aware of several potential interpretation pitfalls so that we can avoid them. We will discuss some of them in this section. We will also discuss methods for determining just how well the regression model fits the data.

Pitfalls to Avoid

You can avoid most pitfalls by simply making a graph of your data and examining it closely before you begin interpreting your linear model. This section will offer some advice for sidestepping a few subtle complications that might arise.

Don't Fit Linear Models to Nonlinear Relationships

Regression models are useful only for linear relationships. If the relationship is not linear, a regression model can be misleading and deceiving. For this reason, before you fit a regression model, you should always make a scatterplot to verify that the relationship seems linear. Chapter 14 will provide a slightly more sophisticated (and discerning) method for checking linearity.

Figure 4.26 shows an example of a bad regression model. The relationship between the life expectancy at birth of people in a country and the country's per-person wine consumption is nonlinear. The regression model is

$$\text{Predicted Life Expectancy} = 65.4 + 2.13 \text{ Wine Consumption}$$

but it provides a poor fit. The regression model suggests that countries with middle values of wine consumption should have lower mortality rates than they actually do.

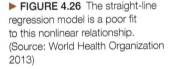

▶ **FIGURE 4.26** The straight-line regression model is a poor fit to this nonlinear relationship. (Source: World Health Organization 2013)

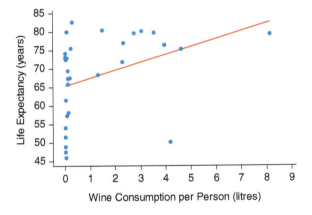

Correlation Is Not Causation

One important goal of science and business is to discover relationships between variables such that if you make a change to one variable, you know the other variable will change in a reliably predictable way. This is what is meant by "x causes y": make a change in x, and a change in y will usually follow. For example, the distance it takes to stop your car depends on how fast you were travelling when you first applied the brakes (among other things); the amount of memory an mp3 file takes on your hard drive depends on the length of the song; and the size of your phone bill depends on how many minutes you talked. In these cases, a strong causal relationship exists between two variables, and if you were to collect data and make a scatterplot, you would see a relationship between the variables.

In statistics, however, we are often faced with the reverse situation, in which we see a relationship between two variables and wonder whether there is a cause-and-effect relationship. The correlation coefficient for the linear relationship could be quite strong, but as we saw earlier, correlation does not mean cause and effect. A strong correlation or a good-fitting regression line is not evidence of a cause-and-effect relationship.

KEY POINT   A relationship between two variables is not sufficient evidence to conclude that a cause-and-effect relationship exists between the variables, no matter how strong the correlation or how well the regression line fits the data.

Be particularly careful about drawing cause-and-effect conclusions when interpreting the slope of a regression line. For example, for the EQAO Grade 3 data,

$$\text{Predicted Reading} = 32.4 + 0.548 \text{ Math}$$

Even if this regression line fits the relationship very well, it does not give us sufficient evidence to conclude that if a school were to improve its math score by 10 percentage points (so that 10% more students are at or above the provincial standard), its critical reading score will go up by about 5.5 percentage points. As you learned in Chapter 1, because these data were not collected from a controlled experiment, the presence of confounding factors could prevent you from making a causal interpretation.

When can we conclude that a relationship between two variables means a cause-and-effect relationship is present? Strictly speaking, never from an observational study and only when the data were collected from a controlled experiment. (Even in a controlled experiment, care must be taken that the experiment was designed correctly.) However, for many important questions, controlled experiments are not possible. In these cases, we can sometimes make conclusions about causality after a number of observational studies have been collected and examined, and if there is a strong theoretical explanation for why the variables should be related in a cause-and-effect fashion. For instance, it took many years of observational studies to conclude that smoking causes lung cancer, including studies that compared twins—one twin who smoked and one who did not—and numerous controlled experiments on lab animals.

Moreover, beware of the algebra trap. In algebra, you were taught to interpret the slope to mean that "as x increases by 1 unit, y goes up by b_1 units." However, quite often with data, the phrase "as x increases" doesn't make sense. When looking at the height and weight data, where x is height and y is weight, to say "x increases" means that people are growing taller! This is not accurate. It is much more accurate to interpret the slope as making comparisons between groups. For example, when comparing people of a certain height with those who are 1 centimetre taller, you can see that the taller individuals tend to weigh, on average, b_1 kilograms more.

Beware of Outliers

Recall that when calculating sample means, we were warned that outliers can have a big effect. Because the regression line is a line of means, you might think that outliers would have a big effect on the regression line. And you'd be right. You should always check a scatterplot before performing a regression analysis to be sure there are no outliers.

The graphs in Figure 4.27 illustrate this effect. Both graphs in Figure 4.27 show yearly expenditure for meals and snacks purchased from restaurants (restaurants include refreshment stands, snack bars, vending machines, mobile canteens, caterers, and coffee wagons) versus total income before taxes for a small random sample of respondents to the 2009 Survey of Household Spending. Figure 4.27a includes the complete sample of 100 respondents. The respondent with an income of $250,000 is an outlier and has a strong influence on the regression line. Figure 4.27b excludes this observation.

There is a positive linear relationship between expenditure for restaurants and income. However, compare the correlation coefficients and note how the inclusion of the

Looking Back

Outliers
You learned about outliers for one variable in Chapter 3. Outliers are values that lie a great distance from the bulk of the data. In two-variable associations, outliers are points that do not fit the trend or are far from the bulk of the data.

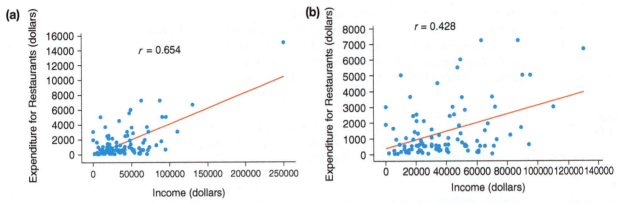

▲ **FIGURE 4.27** Expenditure for restaurants and income for a sample of people. Part **(a)** includes an outlier observation and part **(b)** does not. (Source: 2009 Survey of Household Spending)

outlier makes that relationship seem stronger than it actually is. These types of observations are called **influential points** because their presence or absence has a big effect on conclusions. When you have influential points in your data, it is good practice to try the regression and correlation with and without these points (as we did) and to comment on the difference.

Regressions of Aggregate Data

Researchers sometimes do regression analysis based on what we call **aggregate data**. Aggregate data are those for which each plotted point is from a summary of a group of individuals. For example, in a study to examine the relationship between EQAO mathematics and reading results for Grade 3 students, we might use the combined results for each of the school boards in the province rather than the scores of individual schools.

There is nothing wrong with using aggregate data, as long as you don't assume that relationships that hold for the aggregate data will also hold for the individual data. For example, Figure 4.28 shows scatterplots of 2012–2013 EQAO results for Grade 3 students in Ontario. The variables represent the percentage of students in Grade 3 at or above provincial standard in reading and in mathematics. In Figure 4.28a, each point represents the percentages at or above standard for a single school. In Figure 4.28b, each point represents the percentages at or above standard for all schools in a school board. As a consequence of the lower variability of the aggregate data, the scatterplot in Figure 4.28b seems to show a much stronger relationship between the two variables.

We can still interpret Figure 4.28b, as long as we're careful to remember that we are talking about school boards, and not about individual schools. We *can* say that a strong

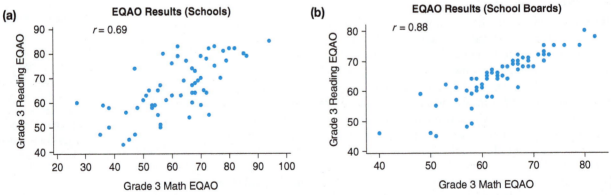

▲ **FIGURE 4.28** Reading and math percentages of students at or above provincial standard. **(a)** Percentages for schools. **(b)** Percentages for school boards.

correlation exists between a school board's percentage of students at or above provincial standard in reading and a school board's percentage of students at or above provincial standard in mathematics. We *cannot* say that there is the same correlation between a school's percentage of students at or above provincial standard in reading and a school's percentage of students at or above provincial standard in mathematics.

Don't Extrapolate!

Extrapolation means that we use the regression line to make predictions beyond the range of our data. This practice can be dangerous, because although the relationship may have a linear shape for the range we're observing, that might not be true over a larger range. This means that our predictions might be wrong outside the range of observed *x*-values.

Figure 4.29a shows a graph of height versus age for children between 2 and 9 years old from a large study. We've superimposed the regression line on the graph, and it looks like a very good fit. However, although the regression model provides a good fit for children aged 2 through 9, it fails when we use the same model to predict heights for older individuals.

The regression line of the data shown in Figure 4.29a is

$$\text{Predicted Height} = 80.6 + 6.22 \, \text{Age}$$

However, we observed only children between the ages of 2 and 9. Can we use this line to predict the height of a 20-year-old?

The regression model predicts that the mean height of 20-year-olds is 205 cm:

$$\text{Predicted Height} = 80.6 + 6.22 \, \text{Age} = 80.6 + (6.22 \times 20) = 205$$

We can see from Figure 4.29b that the regression model provides a poor fit if we include people over the age of 9. Beyond that age, the trend is no longer linear, so we get bad predictions from the model.

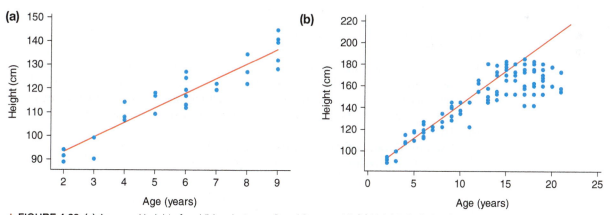

▲ **FIGURE 4.29** **(a)** Ages and heights for children between 2 and 9 years old. **(b)** Heights included for people up to age 21 years. The straight line is not valid in the upper range of ages. (Source: U.S. National Health and Nutrition Examination Survey, Centers for Disease Control)

It is often tempting to use the regression model beyond the range of data used to build the model. Don't. Unless you are very confident that the linear trend continues without change beyond the range of observed data, you must collect new data to cover the new range of values.

KEY POINT ▶ Don't extrapolate!

The Origin of the Word *Regression* (Regression Toward the Mean)

The term *regression* was coined by Francis Galton, who used the regression model to study genetic relationships. He noticed that even though taller-than-average fathers tended to have taller-than-average sons, the sons were somewhat closer to average than the fathers were. Also, shorter-than-average fathers tended to have sons who were closer to the average than their fathers. He called this phenomenon regression toward mediocrity, applying the term regression in the sense of a backward movement. Later on it came to be known as **regression toward the mean**.

You can see how regression toward the mean works by examining the formula for the slope of the regression line:

$$b_1 = r \frac{s_y}{s_x}$$

This formula tells us that fathers who are one standard deviation taller than average (s_x centimetres above average) have sons who are not one standard deviation taller than average (s_y) but are instead r times s_y centimetres taller than average. Because r is a number between -1 and 1, r times s_y is usually smaller than s_y. Thus the "rise" will be less than the "run" in terms of standard deviations.

The *Sports Illustrated* jinx is an example of regression toward the mean. According to the jinx, athletes who make the cover of *Sports Illustrated* end up having a really bad year after appearing. Some professional athletes have refused to appear on the cover of *Sports Illustrated*. (Once, the editors published a picture of a black cat in that place of honour, because no athlete would agree to grace the cover.) However, if an athlete's performance in the first year is several standard deviations above average, the second year is likely to be closer to average. This is an example of regression toward the mean. For a star athlete, closer to average can seem disastrous.

The Coefficient of Determination

If we are convinced that the relationship we are examining is linear, then the regression line provides the best numerical summary of the relationship. But how good is "best"? The correlation coefficient, which measures the strength of linear relationships, can also be used to measure how well the regression line summarizes the data.

The **coefficient of determination** is simply the correlation coefficient squared: r^2. In fact, this quantity is often called **r-squared**. When reporting r-squared, we will multiply by 100% to convert it to a percentage. Because r is always between -1 and 1, r-squared will be between 0% and 100%. A value of 100% means the relationship is perfectly linear and the regression line perfectly predicts the observations. A value of 0% means there is no linear relationship and the regression line does a horrible job.

For example, when we predicted the width of a book from the number of pages in the book, we found the correlation between these variables to be $r = 0.9202$. So the coefficient of determination is $0.9202^2 = 0.8468$, which we report as 84.7%.

What does this value of 84.7% mean? A useful interpretation of r-squared is that it measures how much of the variation in the response variable is explained by the linear relationship with the explanatory variable. For example, 84.7% of the variation in book widths was explained by the number of pages. What does this mean?

Figure 4.30 shows a scatterplot (simulated data) with a constant value for y ($y = 6240$) no matter what the x-value is. You can see that there is no variation in y, so there is also nothing to explain.

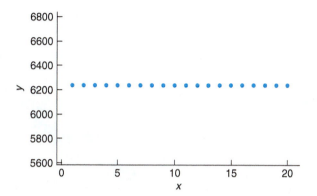

◄ **FIGURE 4.30** Because y has no variation, there is nothing to explain.

Figure 4.31 shows the height in inches and in centimetres for several people. Here, variation in the y-variable does occur. Height as measured in centimetres varies from about 150 cm to about 190 cm. However, the points are perfectly linear and have a correlation of 1.000. That means that if you are given an x-value (a person's height in inches), then you know the y-value (the person's height in centimetres) precisely. Thus all the variation in y is explained by the regression model. In this case, the coefficient of determination is 100%; all variation in y is perfectly explained by the best-fit line.

Real data are messier. Figure 4.32 shows a plot of the age and value of some cars. The regression line has been superimposed to remind us that there is, in fact, a linear trend and that the regression line does capture it. The regression model explains some of the variation in y, but as we can see, it's not perfect; plugging the value of x into the regression line gives us an imperfect prediction of what y will be. In fact, for these data, $r = -0.837$, so we've explained $(-0.837)^2 = 0.701$, or about 70.1%, of the variation in y with this regression line.

The practical implication of r-squared is that it helps determine which explanatory variable would be best for making predictions about the response variable. For example, is

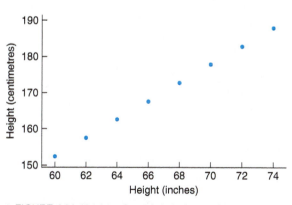

▲ **FIGURE 4.31** Heights of people in inches and in centimetres with a correlation of 1. The coefficient of determination is 100%.

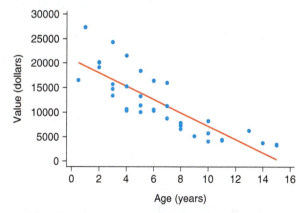

▲ **FIGURE 4.32** Age and value of cars; the correlation is -0.837, and the coefficient of determination is 70.1%.

waist size or height a better predictor of weight? We can see the answer to this question from the scatterplots in Figure 4.33, which show that the linear relationship is stronger (has less scatter) for waist size.

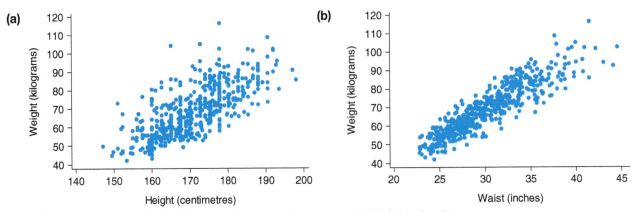

▲ **FIGURE 4.33** Scatterplots of **(a)** height vs. weight and **(b)** waist size vs. weight. Waist size has the larger coefficient of determination.

The *r*-squared for predicting weight from height is 51.4% (Figure 4.33a), and the *r*-squared for predicting weight from waist size is 81.7% (Figure 4.33b). We can explain more of the variation in these people's weights by using their waist sizes than by using their heights, and therefore, we can make better (more precise) predictions using waist size as the predictor.

KEY POINT   If the relationship is linear, the larger the coefficient of determination (*r*-squared), the smaller the variation or scatter about the regression line, and the more accurate the predictions tend to be.

 SNAPSHOT   **R-SQUARED**

WHAT IS IT? ▶	*r*-squared or coefficient of determination.
WHAT DOES IT DO? ▶	Measures how well the data fit the linear model.
HOW DOES IT DO IT? ▶	If the points are tightly clustered around the regression line, r^2 has a value near 1, or 100%. If the points are more spread out, it has a value closer to 0. If there is no linear trend, and the points are a formless blob, it has a value near 0.
HOW IS IT USED? ▶	Large values of *r*-squared tell us that predicted *y*-values are likely to be close to actual values. The coefficient of determination shows us the percentage of variation that can be explained by the regression line.
WHEN IS IT USED? ▶	When a scatterplot shows a linear relationship.

As we mentioned at the beginning of the chapter, researchers observed a significant difference in the attendance of participants who cycled using an interactive video game system and those who cycled on a regular stationary bike. There was also an improvement in the aerobic fitness of the interactive video game group, with no improvement in the control group. We will now examine the relationship that exists between these two outcomes.

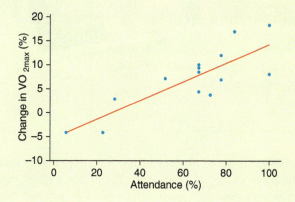

CASE STUDY REVISITED

◄ **FIGURE 4.34** The regression line summarizes the relationship between attendance of a participant and his change in VO_{2max}, a measurement of change in aerobic fitness.

The scatterplot in Figure 4.34 shows the relationship between attendance (measured as the percentage of recommended training sessions attended) and change in maximal aerobic power (VO_{2max}, an indicator of aerobic fitness) for all participants. There is a strong, positive, linear trend between attendance and change in VO_{2max}. The positive trend indicates that higher attendance rates are related to larger improvements in aerobic fitness. The regression line is

$$\text{Change in } VO_{2max} = -5.02 + 0.1935 \text{ Attendance}$$

The coefficient of determination of the regression line is $r^2 = 0.69$, meaning that 69% of the variation in change in VO_{2max} is explained by attendance.

This model allows us to conclude that the improvement in aerobic fitness for the active gaming group is related to attendance. A higher attendance rate implies a higher volume of exercise, and volume of exercise is of key importance for health benefits. By promoting high attendance levels, active gaming ultimately led to improved health in this group of young males. Although these are encouraging findings, note that we cannot generalize them to other populations (young females, for example).

EXPLORING STATISTICS

CLASS ACTIVITY

Guessing the Age of Famous People

GOALS	MATERIALS
In this activity, you will learn how to interpret the slope and intercept of a regression line, using data you collect in class.	Graph paper and a calculator or computer.

ACTIVITY

Your instructor will give you a list of names of famous people. Beside each name, write your guess of the person's age, in years. Even if you don't know the age or don't know who the person is, give your best guess. If you work in a group, your group should discuss the guessed ages and record the best guess of the group. After you've finished, your instructor will give you a list of the actual ages of these people.

To examine the relationship between the actual ages and the ages you guessed, make a scatterplot with actual age on the *x*-axis and guessed age on the *y*-axis. Use technology to find the equation for the regression line and insert the line in the graph. Calculate the correlation.

BEFORE THE ACTIVITY

1. Suppose you guessed every age correctly. What would be the equation of the regression line? What would be the correlation?

2. What correlation do you think you will actually get? Why?

3. Suppose you consistently guess that people are older than they actually are. How will the intercept of the regression line compare with your intercept in Question 1? How about the slope?

AFTER THE ACTIVITY

1. How would you describe the relationship between the ages you guessed and the actual ages?

2. Is a regression line appropriate for your data? Explain why or why not.

3. What does it mean if a point falls above your regression line? Below your line?

4. What is the intercept of your line? What is the slope? Interpret the slope and intercept. Explain what these tell you about your ability to guess the ages of these people.

CHAPTER REVIEW

Summary of Learning Objectives

1. **What are the important features of a scatterplot that need to be discussed when describing the relationship between two numerical variables?** You should discuss the trend, the strength of the trend, the shape of the trend, and any unusual observations, always in the context of the data.

2. **What is the correlation coefficient, how do I calculate it, and how can I interpret it?** The correlation coefficient is a number between -1 and 1 that measures the strength of the linear relationship between two variables.

   Formula 4.1: Correlation Coefficient $= r = \dfrac{\sum xy - n\,\bar{x}\,\bar{y}}{(n-1)s_x s_y}$

   It can only be interpreted if a scatterplot shows that the relationship between the variables is linear. In that case, the sign of r tells us whether the linear trend is positive or negative. Values of r close to -1 and 1 mean that the linear relationship is strong, whereas values close to 0 indicate that there is no linear relationship.

3. **What is a regression line and how do I obtain it?** The regression line tells us the average y-values for any value of x. First obtain the slope:

   Formula 4.2a: Slope $= b_1 = r\dfrac{s_y}{s_x}$

Then find the intercept:

Formula 4.2b: Intercept $= b_0 = \bar{y} - b_1\bar{x}$

Write the regression line:

Formula 4.2c: Predicted $y = b_0 + b_1 x$

4. **How do I interpret the slope and the intercept of the regression line?** The regression line can only be interpreted if a scatterplot shows a linear relationship. In that case, the slope tells us how different the mean y-value is for observations that are 1 unit apart on the x-variable. The intercept is the mean value of y when x is 0, but it does not always have a useful interpretation.

5. **What is the coefficient of determination, how do I calculate it, and how do I interpret it?** The coefficient of determination (or r-squared) gives us the percentage of variation in the y-variable that is explained by the regression line. When a relationship is linear, it is calculated as the correlation coefficient squared (r^2). The linear relationship is very strong if its value is close to 1, or 100%.

6. **What are some common errors to avoid when using regression?** Correlation does not imply causation: do not make cause-and-effect conclusions if the data are observational. Don't extrapolate. Beware of outliers and influential points. Beware of conclusions you make from aggregate data.

Important Terms

Scatterplot, *131*
Trend, *131*
Strength, *131*
Shape, *131*
Positive relationship
 (positive trend), *132*

Negative relationship
 (negative trend), *132*
Linear, *134*
Correlation coefficient, *136*
Regression line, *143*
Intercept, *144*

Slope, *144*
Explanatory variable, predictor
 variable, independent
 variable, *151*
Response variable, predicted variable, dependent variable, *151*

Influential point, *160*
Aggregate data, *160*
Extrapolation, *161*
Regression toward the mean, *162*
Coefficient of determination, r^2,
 r-squared, *162*

Sources

Education, Quality and Accountability Office School, Board and Provincial Results. http://www.eqao.com (accessed Nov. 21, 2013).

Heinz, G., L. Peterson, R. Johnson, and C. Kerk. 2003. Exploring relationships in body dimensions. *Journal of Statistics Education* 11(2). http://www.amstat.org/publications/jse

Hughes, N., and S. Rogers. 2012. Could you be an athlete? Olympics 2012 by age, weight and height. http://www.theguardian.com/sport/datablog/2012/aug/07/olympics-2012-athletes-age-weight-height#age (accessed Jan. 29, 2015).

Nielsen. 2014. *E-commerce: Evolution or Revolution in the Fast-moving Consumer Goods World?* Global Report. http://ir.nielsen.com/files/doc_financials/Nielsen-Global-E-commerce-Report-August-2014.pdf (accessed Jan. 30, 2015).

Obbard, M. E. 2013. Ontario Ministry of Natural Resources. Unpublished data.

OECD. 2013. *How's Life? 2013. Measuring Well-being.* OECD Publishing. http://www.oecdbetterlifeindex.org (accessed Jan. 30, 2015).

Onaga, E. 2005. Unpublished data.

Public Health Agency of Canada. Benefits of Physical Activity. http://www.phac-aspc.gc.ca/hp-ps/hl-mvs/pa-ap/02paap-eng.php (accessed Feb. 5, 2015).

Stallard, J. 2013. Unpublished data.

Statistics Canada. Canadian Community Health Survey, CANSIM Table 105-0501 (2007). Statistics Canada, Vital Statistics, CANSIM Table 102-4307 (2005–2007).

Warburton, D. E. R., et al. 2007. The health benefits of interactive video game exercise. *Applied Physiology, Nutrition, and Metabolism* 32. 655–663.

SECTION EXERCISES

SECTION 4.1

4.1 Predicting Land Value Both figures concern the assessed value of land (with homes on the land), and both use the same data set.

a. Which do you think has a stronger relationship with value of the land—the number of acres of land or the number of rooms in the homes? Why?

b. If you were trying to predict the value of a parcel of land in this area (on which there is a home), would you be able to make a better prediction by knowing the acreage or the number of rooms in the house? Explain.

(Source: Minitab File, Student 12, "Assess")

(a)

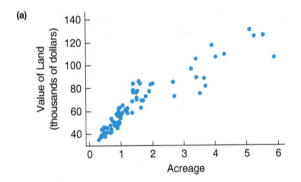

(b)

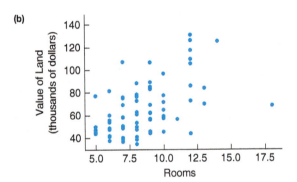

4.2 Predicting Total Value of Property Both figures concern the total assessed value of properties that include homes, and both use the same data set.

a. Which do you think has a stronger relationship with value of the property—the number of square feet in the home (shown in part (b) of the figure) or the number of fireplaces in the home (shown in part (a) of the figure)? Why?

b. If you were trying to predict the value of a property in this area (where there is a home), would you be able to make a better prediction by knowing the number of square feet or the number of fireplaces? Explain.

(a)

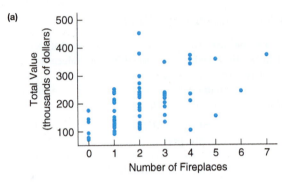

(b)

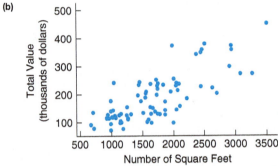

4.3 Car Value and Age of Student The figure shows the age of students and the value of their cars according to VMR Canada. Does it show an increasing trend, a decreasing trend, or very little trend? Explain.

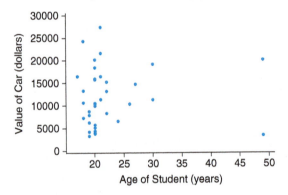

4.4 Shoe Size and Grades The figure shows a scatterplot of shoe size and grade on a statistics exam for some students. Does it show an increasing trend, a decreasing trend, or no trend? Is there a strong relationship?

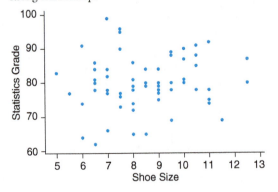

4.5 Weight Loss The scatterplot shows the actual weight and desired weight change of some students. Thus, if they weighed 70 kg and wanted to weigh 60, the desired weight change would be negative 10 kg.

Explain what you see. In particular, what does it mean that the trend is negative?

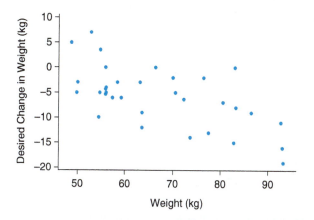

4.6 Comparing Salaries The figure shows the salary and year of first employment for some professors at a university. Explain, in context, what the negative trend shows. Who makes the most and who makes the least? (Source: Minitab, Student 12, "Salary")

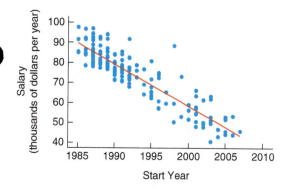

TRY 4.7 Residential and Non-Residential Building Permits (Example 1) The figure shows the residential and non-residential building permits issued in 2012, by metropolitan area. Explain what the trend shows. (Source: Canada Mortgage and Housing Corporation)

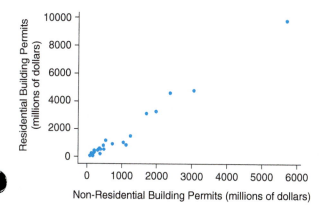

4.8 Household Income and Food Expenditure The scatterplot shows data from a random sample of respondents to the 2009 Survey of Household Spending—the annual household income and the annual household expenditure for food. Describe and interpret the trend. (Source: Statistics Canada)

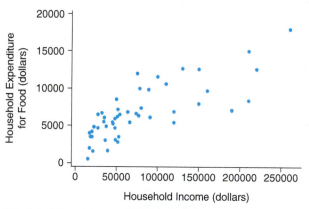

4.9 Adult Smoking and Youth Smoking The figure shows the percentage of adults who smoke and the percentage of youth aged 12 to 19 who smoke. Each point represents a province (data on youth smoking were unavailable for Prince Edward Island). Describe what you see. Is the trend positive or negative? What does that mean? (Source: Statistics Canada)

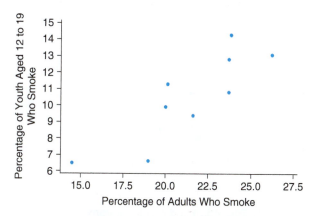

4.10 Food Expenditures and Household Size The figure shows a scatterplot of household size and yearly food expenditure for a sample of respondents to the Survey of Household Spending 2009. Describe what you see. Is the trend positive, negative, or near zero? Explain.

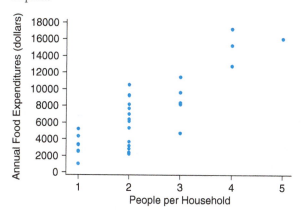

SECTION 4.2

4.11 Children's Ages and Heights The figure shows information about the ages and heights of several children. Why would it not be appropriate to find the correlation or to perform linear regression with this data set? Explain.

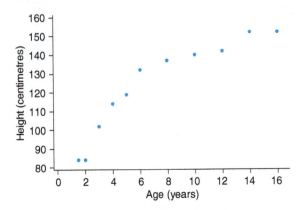

4.12 Blackjack Tips The figure shows the amount of money won by people playing blackjack and the amount of tips they gave to the dealer, in dollars.

Would it be appropriate to find a correlation for this data set? Explain.

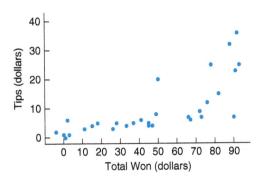

4.13 University Education and Median Income The scatterplot shows data from all provinces and territories taken from the Labour Force Survey—the percentage of the population aged 25 to 64 with university education and the median family income.

Would it be appropriate to find the correlation for this data set? Explain.

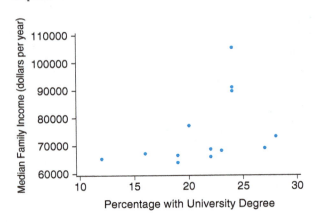

4.14 Ages of Women Who Give Birth The figure shows a scatterplot of birthrate (live births per 1000 women) and age of the mother in Canada. Would it make sense to find the correlation for this data set? Explain. According to this graph, at approximately what age is the highest fertility rate? (Source: Statistics Canada)

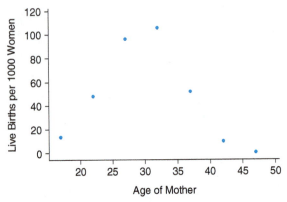

4.15 Do Older Students Get Better Grades? On the basis of the scatterplot, do you think the correlation coefficient between age and average grade in a statistics class for this figure is positive, negative, or near zero?

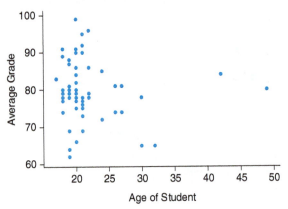

4.16 Handspans Refer to the figure. Is the correlation coefficient between the handspan of the dominant hand and that of the nondominant hand positive, negative, or near zero?

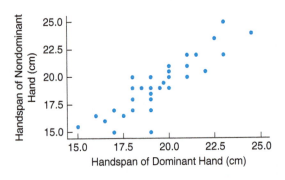

4.17 Matching Pick the letter of the graph that goes with each numerical value listed below for the correlation. Correlations:

0.767 _____

0.299 _____

−0.980 _____

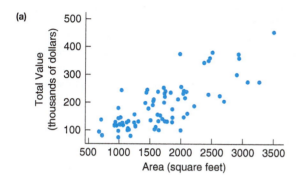

(a)

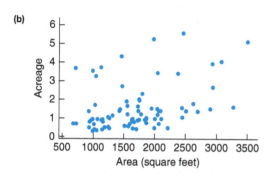

(b)

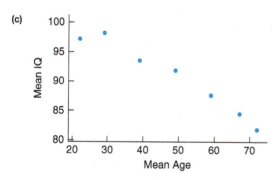

(c)

4.18 Matching Pick the letter of the graph that goes with each numerical value listed below for the correlation. Correlations:

−0.903 _____

0.374 _____

0.777 _____

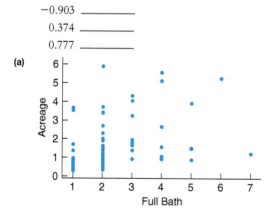

(a)

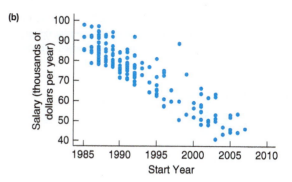

(b)

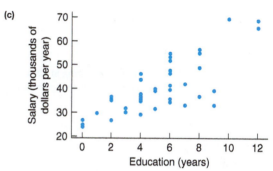

(c)

TRY **4.19 Cost of Flights (Example 2)** The table for part a shows approximate distances between selected cities and the approximate cost of flights between those cities in November 2013.

a. Calculate the correlation of the numbers shown in the table by using a computer or statistical calculator.

Cost ($)	Distance (kilometres)
230	350
250	550
290	700
250	730
290	1050
380	1300

b. The table for part b shows the same information, except that the distance was converted to miles by dividing the number of kilometres by 1.609. What happens to the correlation when numbers are multiplied by a constant (we multiplied by 1/1.609)?

Cost ($)	Distance (miles)
230	217.5
250	341.8
290	435.1
250	453.7
290	652.6
380	808.0

c. Suppose that Transport Canada adds a tax to each flight. Fifty dollars are added to every flight, no matter how long it is. The table for part c shows the new data. What happens to the correlation when a constant is added to each number?

Cost ($)	Distance (miles)
280	217.5
300	341.8
340	435.1
300	453.7
340	652.6
430	808.0

4.20 Trash The table shows the number of people living in a house and the weight of trash (in kilograms) at the curb just before trash pickup.

People	Trash (kilograms)
2	8
3	15
6	42
1	10
7	38

a. Find the correlation between these numbers by using a computer or a statistical calculator.

b. Suppose some of the weight was from the container (each container weighs 2 kilograms). Subtract 2 kilograms from each weight and find the new correlation with the number of people. What happens to the correlation when a constant is added (we added negative 2) to each number?

c. Suppose each house contained exactly twice the number of people, but the weight of the trash was the same. What happens to the correlation when numbers are multiplied by a constant?

SECTION 4.3

TRY **4.21 Are Men Paid More Than Women? (Example 3)**
The scatterplot shows the median hourly wage rate for men and women for different occupations, as reported by Statistics Canada's Labour Force Survey in October 2013. The correlation is 0.94. The regression equation is above the graph.

a. Find the rough estimate (by using the scatterplot) of median hourly pay for women in an occupation that has median pay of about 25 dollars per hour for men.

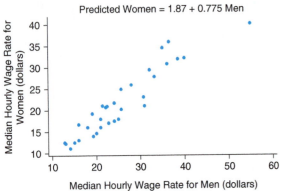

Predicted Women = 1.87 + 0.775 Men

b. Use the regression equation above the graph to get a more precise estimate of the median hourly pay for women for an occupation that has a median pay of 25 dollars per hour for men.

4.22 Number of Births and Population The figure shows the number of births and the populations (in thousands) for the 13 provinces and territories in 2012, according to Statistics Canada. The correlation is 0.996.

a. Find a rough estimate (by using the scatterplot) of the number of births in a province or territory with a population of about 4 million (4000 thousand).

b. Use the regression equation above the graph to get a more precise estimate of the number of births for a province or territory with a population of 4 million.

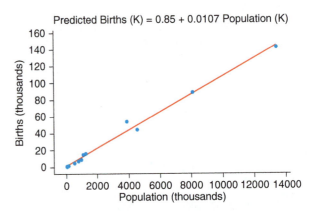

Predicted Births (K) = 0.85 + 0.0107 Population (K)

4.23–4.26 Refer to the following table for Exercises 4.23–4.26. It provides various body measurements for some university women. The height is self-reported. All measurements are in centimetres.

Head is the circumference of the head.

HandL is the length of the hand.

FootL is the length of the foot.

HandW is the width of the hand with the fingers spread wide.

Armspan is the armspan with the arms spread wide.

Ht	Head	HandL	FootL	HandW	Armspan
157.5	56.0	17.0	23.0	20.0	159.5
165	54.0	17.5	23.5	18.0	161.0
168	55.0	18.0	24.0	16.5	161.5
160	58.0	18.5	23.5	19.5	160.5
173	55.0	19.0	25.0	18.0	173.0
142	54.5	16.5	22.0	17.0	142.0
155	50.0	16.0	22.0	18.0	155.0
170	53.5	18.0	23.5	15.0	165.0
168	55.5	16.0	21.0	20.0	166.0
162.5	57.0	19.0	24.5	20.0	163.0
156	55.0	19.0	24.5	21.0	152.0

TRY 4.23 Height and Armspan for Women (Example 4)
TI-83/84 output from a linear model for predicting armspan from height (both in cm) is given in the figure. Summary statistics are also provided.

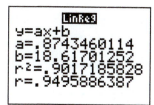

	Mean	Standard Deviation
Height, x	161.55	8.793
Armspan, y	159.86	8.097

To do parts a–c, assume that the relationship between armspan and height is linear.

a. Report the regression equation, using the words "Height" and "Armspan," not x and y, using the output given.

b. Verify the slope by using the formula $b_1 = r\dfrac{s_y}{s_x}$.

c. Verify the y-intercept using $b_0 = \bar{y} - b_1\bar{x}$.

d. Using the regression equation, predict the armspan (in cm) for someone 163 cm tall.

4.24 Hand and Foot Length for Women Refer to the data shown in the table for Exercises 4.23–4.26. Some computer output is shown in the figure. The output is for a linear model used to predict foot length from hand length.

Assume the trend is linear. Summary statistics for these data are shown below.

	Mean	Standard Deviation
Hand, x	17.682	1.168
Foot, y	23.318	1.230

```
The regression equation is
Y = 5.67 + 0.998 X
Pearson correlation of HandL and FootL = 0.948
```

a. Report the regression equation, using the words "Hand" and "Foot," not x and y.

b. Verify the slope by using the formula $b_1 = r\dfrac{s_y}{s_x}$.

c. Verify the y-intercept by using the formula $b_0 = \bar{y} - b_1\bar{x}$.

d. Using the regression equation, predict the foot length (in cm) for someone who has a hand length of 18 cm.

4.25 Hand Width and Armspan for Women Refer to the data shown in the table for Exercises 4.23–4.26. Use hand width as the predictor and armspan as the response.

a. Make a scatterplot of the data.

b. Explain why linear regression is probably not appropriate for these variables.

4.26 Head Circumference and Hand Width for Women
Refer to the data shown in the table for Exercises 4.23–4.26. Use head circumference as x and hand width as y.

a. Make a scatterplot of the data.

b. Explain why linear regression is probably not appropriate for these variables.

TRY 4.27 Height and Armspan for Men (Example 5) Measurements were made for a sample of adult men. A regression line was fit to predict the men's armspan from their height. The output from several different statistical technologies is provided. The scatterplot confirms that the relationship between armspan and height is linear.

a. Report the equation for predicting armspan from height. Use words such as armspan, not just x and y.

b. Report the slope and intercept from each technology, using all the digits given.

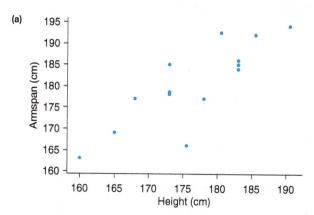

(a)

(b)
```
The regression equation is
Armspan = 13.1 + 0.948 Height
```

From Minitab

(c)
Simple linear regression results:
Dependent Variable: Armspan
Independent Variable: Height
Armspan = 13.093566 + 0.94847838 Height
Sample size: 14
R (correlation coefficient) = 0.82930308
R-sq = 0.68774361
Estimate of error standard deviation: 5.6458988

From StatCrunch

(d)

	Coefficients
Intercept	13.09357
Ht men	0.948478

From Excel

(e)
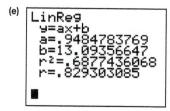

From TI-83/84

(f)

Model		B
1	(Constant)	13.094
	Height	.948
a. Dependent Variable: Armspan		

From SPSS

4.28 Hand Length and Foot Length for Men Measurements were made for a sample of adult men. Assume that the relationship between their hand length and foot length is linear. Output for predicting foot length from hand length is provided from several different statistical technologies.

   a. Report the equation for predicting foot length from hand length. Use words like foot or foot length, not just x and y.

   b. Report the slope and intercept from each technology, using all the digits given.

(a)

```
The regression equation is
FootL = 15.8 + 0.563 HandL
```

From Minitab

(b)

Simple linear regression results:

Dependent Variable: FootL
Independent Variable: HandL
FootL = 15.807631 + 0.5626551 HandL
Sample size: 17
R (correlation coefficient) = 0.404
R-sq = 0.1632489
Estimate of error standard deviation: 1.6642156

From StatCrunch

(c)
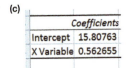

	Coefficients
Intercept	15.80763
X Variable	0.562655

From Excel

(d)
```
LinReg
y=a+bx
a=15.80763027
b=.5626550868
r²=.1632489032
r=.4040407197
```

From TI-83/84

(e)
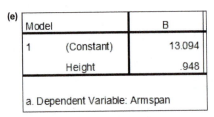

Model		B
1	(Constant)	13.094
	Height	.948
a. Dependent Variable: Armspan		

From SPSS

4.29 Height and Head Circumference for Men Explain what makes this scatterplot hard to interpret. What should have been done differently?

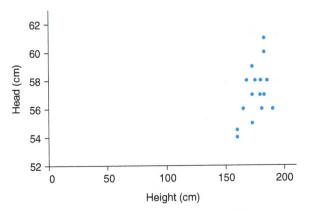

4.30 Elbow-to-Wrist and Knee-to-Ankle Measurements The scatterplot shows measurements for the distance from elbow to wrist and from knee to ankle for some male students. Explain what makes this scatterplot difficult to interpret.

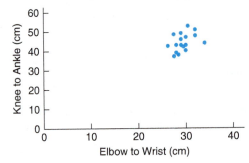

4.31 Comparing Correlation for Armspan and Height The correlation between height and armspan in a sample of adult women was found (in Exercise 4.23) to be $r = 0.950$. The correlation between armspan and height in a sample of adult men was found (in Exercise 4.27) to be $r = 0.829$. Which relationship—the relationship between height and armspan for women, or the relationship between height and armspan for men—is stronger? Explain.

*4.32 Age and Weight for Men and Women The scatterplot shows a solid blue line for predicting weight from age of men; the dotted red line is for predicting weight from age of women. The data were collected from a large statistics class.

   a. Which line is higher and what does that mean?

   b. Which line has a steeper slope and what does that mean?

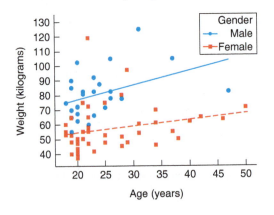

4.33 Social Insurance Number and Age The figure shows a scatterplot of the last two digits of some students' Social Insurance Numbers and their ages.

a. If a regression line were drawn on this graph, would it have a positive slope, a negative slope, or a slope near 0?

b. Give an estimate of the numerical value of the correlation between age and Social Insurance Number.

c. Explain what this graph tells us about the relation between Social Insurance Number and age.

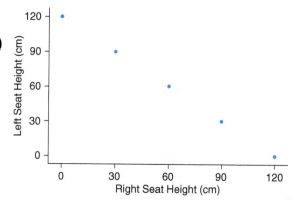

4.34 Teeter-Totter The figure shows a scatterplot of the height of the left seat of a teeter-totter and the height of the right seat of the same teeter-totter. Estimate the numerical value of the correlation and explain the reason for your estimate.

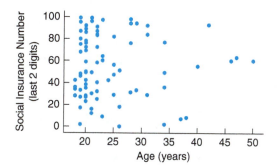

TRY 4.35 Choosing the Predictor and Response (Example 6) Pick out which variable you think should be the predictor (x) and which variable should be the response (y). Explain your choices.

a. You collect data on the number of litres of gas it takes to fill up the tank after driving a certain number of kilometres. You wish to know how many kilometres you've driven based on the number of litres it took to fill up the tank.

b. You have data on laying date and clutch size (the number of eggs in a single nesting) for a certain species of owl. You want to estimate the clutch size for eggs laid on April 2.

c. You wish to buy a belt for a friend and know only his weight. You have data on the weight and waist sizes for a large sample of adult men.

4.36 Choosing the Predictor and Response Pick out which variable you think should be the predictor (x) and which variable should be the response (y). Explain your choices.

a. Weights of nuggets of gold (in grams) and their market value over the last few days are provided, and you wish to use this to estimate the value of a gold ring that weighs 115 grams.

b. You have data collected on the amount of time since chlorine was added to the public swimming pool and the concentration of chlorine still in the pool. (Chlorine evaporates over time.) Chlorine was added to the pool at 8 a.m., and you wish to know what the concentration is now, at 3 p.m.

c. You have data on the circumference of oak trees (measured 30 cm from the ground) and their age (in years). An oak tree in the park has a circumference of 90 cm, and you wish to know approximately how old it is.

TRY 4.37 Fertility Rate and Contraceptive Prevalence Rate (Example 7) The figure shows a scatterplot with the regression line. The data are for 145 countries. The predictor is the contraceptive prevalence rate (the percentage of women who are practising, or whose partners are practising, any form of contraception). The response is the fertility rate (in number of births per woman). The data came from the World Databank.

a. Explain what the trend shows.

b. Use the regression equation to predict the fertility rate of a country with a contraceptive prevalence rate of 70%.

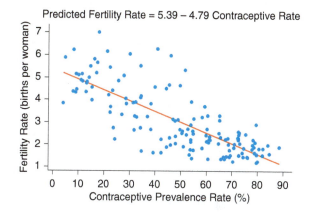

4.38 Daily Newspaper Circulation The figure shows a fitted line plot. The data represent a random sample of 30 Canadian paid daily newspapers. The predictor is the population of the newspaper's local market. The response is the newspaper's average daily circulation. (Source: www.newspaperscanada.ca)

a. Explain what the trend shows.

b. Use the regression equation to predict the circulation of the *Brandon Sun*, given that the population of Brandon is 46 thousand people.

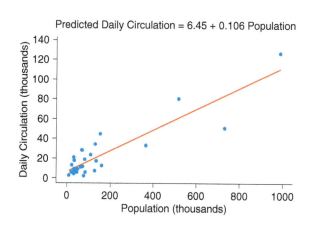

4.39 Drivers' Fatalities and Ages The figure shows a graph of the death rate in motor vehicle traffic collisions and the age of the driver. The numbers came from Transport Canada.

a. Explain what the graph tells us about drivers at different ages; state which ages show the safest drivers and which show the most dangerous drivers.

b. Explain why it would not be appropriate to use these data for linear regression.

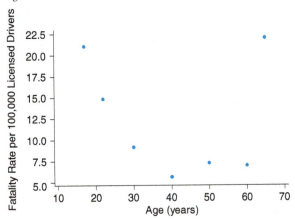

4.40 Do Women Tend to Live Longer Than Men? The figure shows life expectancy versus age for males and females in Canada (2009–2011), up to age 110. Females are represented by the blue circles and males by the red squares. These figures were reported by Statistics Canada.

a. Find your own age on the graph and estimate your life expectancy from the appropriate graph.

b. Would it make sense to find the best straight line for this graph? Why or why not?

c. Is it reasonable to predict the life expectancy for a person who is 120 from the regression line for these data? Why or why not?

d. Explain what it means that nearly all of the blue circles (for women) are above the red squares (for men). (Above the age of 100, the red squares cover the blue circles because both are in the same place.)

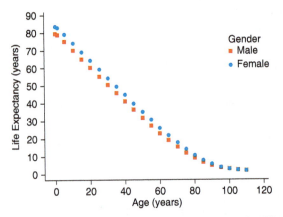

g 4.41 Does the Cost of a Flight Depend on the Distance? The table gives the round-trip fare for direct flights between Toronto and some other cities on major airlines. These were the lowest prices shown on www.ca.kayak.com on November 28, 2013. The airlines varied. (The travel dates were all the same, in mid-January.) *See page 185 for guidance.*

Round-Trip Air Fares from Toronto

City	Cost ($)	Distance (kilometres)
Montreal	227	506
Vancouver	513	3366
Halifax	374	1268
Fredericton	286	1041
Calgary	487	2716
Ottawa	227	354
Regina	454	2045
St. John's	456	2117
Winnipeg	403	1516
Quebec City	249	729
Saskatoon	465	2227
Charlottetown	399	1314
Boston	286	696
New York	250	554
Orlando	296	1688
Mexico City	602	3256
Chicago	286	703

How much would it cost, on average, to fly to Washington, D.C., which is 566 kilometres from Toronto? To answer this question, perform a complete regression analysis, including a scatterplot with a regression line.

 4.42 Travelling Abroad Canadians like to travel abroad, taking more than 30 million overnight trips in 2012. The table gives the number of nights spent (in thousands) and the amount of money spent (in millions of Canadian dollars) for the top 13 countries visited by Canadians outside North America in 2012. (Source: Statistics Canada, Tourism and the Centre for Education Statistics)

Country	Nights	Spending in Country
Cuba	8947	748
United Kingdom	10955	1,056
Dominican Republic	6704	674
France	9068	942
Italy	3897	480
Germany	3501	311
Mainland China	6445	521
Spain	2615	284
Jamaica	2189	248
Netherlands	1579	158
Hong Kong	2709	211
Republic of Ireland	2161	205
Australia	3808	329

a. Without doing any calculations, predict whether the correlation and slope will be positive or negative. Explain your prediction.

b. Make a scatterplot with the number of nights (in thousands) on the *x*-axis and the amount of money spent (in millions of dollars) on the *y*-axis. Was your prediction correct?

c. Find the numerical value of the correlation.

d. Find the value of the slope and explain what it means in context. Be careful with the units.

e. Explain why giving and interpreting the value for the intercept does not make sense in this situation.

4.43 Pumpkinseed Sunfish Characterizing the growth pattern of fish is a crucial aspect of fisheries research and management. One widely used approach is based on the linear relationship between body length and scale length established for a sample of fish of a given species and population caught at the same time of year. For instance, consider the data on body length and scale length for a sample of pumpkinseed sunfish caught in the Otonobee River in Ontario in late September. (Source: Michael Fox, Trent University, unpublished data)

Body Length (mm)	Scale Length (mm)	Body Length (mm)	Scale Length (mm)
47	0.458	109	2.063
48	0.500	122	2.500
45	0.417	116	2.458
75	1.617	125	2.708
81	1.250	135	2.958
78	1.542	133	2.771
64	1.125	135	2.917
85	1.792		

a. Make a scatterplot of the data, with scale length on the x-axis and body length on the y-axis.

b. Find the numerical value for the correlation.

c. Find the equation of the regression line and insert the line in the scatterplot, or use technology to insert the line in your plot.

d. Report the value of the slope and explain what it means in context.

e. Report the value of the intercept, known as the "body-scale intercept." This value is used by fish researchers to estimate the length of a fish at each age of its life before it was captured.

*4.44 Semesters and Credits The table shows the self-reported number of semesters completed and the number of credits completed for 15 students at a Canadian university. All credits were counted (including transfer credits), but attending summer school was not counted as a semester.

a. Make a scatterplot with the number of semesters on the x-axis and the number of credits on the y-axis. Does one point stand out as unusual? Explain why it is unusual. (Most full-time students take between 1.5 and 3 credits per semester.)

   For parts b–e, finish each part *two ways*, with and without the unusual point, and comment on the differences.

b. Find the numerical values for the correlation between semesters and credits.

c. Find the two equations for the two regression lines.

d. Insert the lines. Use technology if possible.

e. Report the slopes and intercepts of the regression lines and explain what they show. If the intercepts are not appropriate to report, explain why.

Semesters	Credits	Semesters	Credits
2	7.0	3	7.0
5	14.5	4	8.0
4	26.0	3	6.0
7	19.0	5	12.0
3	12.0	3	10.0
3	8.5	8	20.0
8	19.0	6	15.5
0	0.0		

4.45 Calories and Fat The table gives the calories and the total fat content (in grams) in a sample of Tim Hortons breakfast items. (Source: timhortons.com)

a. Do you expect the correlation between calories and fat content to be positive or negative? Why?

b. Make a scatterplot of the data.

c. Report the correlation.

d. Report the equation of the regression line and insert the line in the scatterplot, or use technology to insert the line in your plot.

e. Report the slope of the regression line and explain what it shows.

Breakfast Item	Calories	Fat (g)
Biscuit, ham, egg, cheese sandwich	400	21
Biscuit, sausage, egg, cheese sandwich	530	34
English muffin, egg, cheese sandwich	280	11
English muffin, bacon, egg, cheese sandwich	330	15
English muffin, ham, egg, cheese sandwich	300	11
English muffin, sausage, egg, cheese sandwich	430	25
Sausage, egg, cheese wrap	420	28
Bacon, egg, cheese wrap	320	18
Bagel BELT	460	15
Sausage bagel BELT	560	25
Hash brown	100	5
Oatmeal – maple	220	2.5

4.46 Calories and Fat The table gives the calories and the total fat content (in grams) in a sample of Tim Hortons donuts and cookies. (Source: timhortons.com)

a. Do you expect the correlation between calories and fat content to be positive or negative? Why?

b. Make a scatterplot of the data. Are there any unusual points?

c. Report the correlation.

d. Report the equation of the regression line and insert the line in the scatterplot, or use technology to insert the line in your plot.

e. Report the slope of the regression line and explain what it shows.

Item	Calories	Fat (g)
Sour cream glazed donut	340	17
Chocolate dip donut	210	8
Old fashion plain donut	260	19
Old fashion glazed donut	320	19
Double chocolate donut	250	10
Walnut crunch donut	360	23
Honey cruller	320	19
White chocolate macadamia nut cookie	240	12
Oatmeal raisin spice cookie	220	8
Chocolate chunk cookie	230	9
Triple chocolate cookie	250	13
Caramel chocolate pecan cookie	230	11

SECTION 4.4

4.47 Answer the questions using complete sentences.

a. What is an influential point?

b. It has been noted that people who go to church frequently tend to have lower blood pressure than people who don't go to church. Does this mean you can lower your blood pressure by going to church? Why or why not? Explain.

4.48 Answer the questions, using complete sentences.

a. What is extrapolation and why is it a bad idea in regression analysis?

b. How is the coefficient of determination related to the correlation, and what does the coefficient of determination show?

★c. When testing the IQ of a group of adults (aged 25 to 50), an investigator noticed that the correlation between IQ and age was negative. Does this show that IQ goes down as we get older? Why or why not? Explain.

4.49 If there is a positive correlation between number of years studying math and shoe size (for children), does that prove that larger shoe sizes cause more years studying math, or vice versa? Can you think of a hidden variable that might be influencing both of the other variables?

4.50 Suppose that the growth rate of children looks like a straight line if the height of a child is observed at the ages of 24 months, 28 months, 32 months, and 36 months. If you use the regression obtained from these ages and predict the height of the child at 21 years, you might find that the predicted height is 6 metres. What is wrong with the prediction and the process used?

4.51 Coefficient of Determination If the correlation between height and weight of a large group of people is 0.67, find the coefficient of determination (as a percent) and explain what it means. Assume that height is the predictor and weight is the response, and assume that the relationship between height and weight is linear.

4.52 Coefficient of Determination Does a correlation of −0.70 or +0.50 give a larger coefficient of determination? We say that the linear relationship having the larger coefficient of determination is more strongly correlated. Which of the values shows a stronger correlation?

*4.53 Decrease in Cholesterol A doctor is studying cholesterol readings in his patients. After reviewing the cholesterol readings, he calls the patients with the highest cholesterol readings (the top 5% of readings in his office) and asks them to come back to discuss cholesterol-lowering methods. When he tests these patients a second time, the average cholesterol readings tended to have gone down somewhat. Explain what statistical phenomenon might have been partly responsible for this lowering of the readings.

*4.54 Test Scores Suppose that students who scored much lower than the mean on their first statistics test were given special tutoring in the subject. Suppose that they tended to show some improvement on the next test. Explain what might cause the rise in grades other than the tutoring program itself.

TRY **4.55 Salary and Year of Employment (Example 8)** The equation for the regression line relating the salary and the year first employed is given above the figure.

a. Report the slope and explain what it means.

b. Either interpret the intercept ($4,255,000) or explain why it is not appropriate to interpret the intercept.

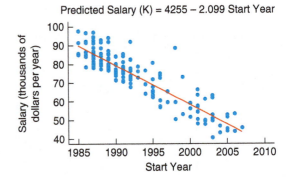

Predicted Salary (K) = 4255 − 2.099 Start Year

4.56 Fuel Consumption: Highway and City The figure shows the relationship between the fuel consumption (in litres per 100 kilometres) on the highway and in the city for some cars. (Source: Natural Resources Canada, Fuel Consumption Guide 2013)

a. Report the slope and explain what it means.

b. Either interpret the intercept (0.925) or explain why it is not appropriate to interpret the intercept.

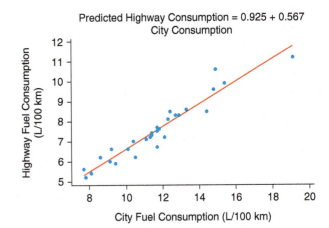

Predicted Highway Consumption = 0.925 + 0.567 City Consumption

4.57 Cost of Turkeys The table on the next page shows a list of the weights and prices of some turkeys at different supermarkets.

a. Make a scatterplot with weight on the x-axis and cost on the y-axis. If using computer statistical technology, include the regression line on your scatterplot.

b. Find the numerical value for the correlation between weight and price. Explain what the sign of the correlation shows.

c. Report the equation of the best straight line, using weight as the predictor (x) and cost as the response (y).

d. Insert the line on the scatterplot if you did not do it in part a.

e. Report the slope and intercept of the regression line and explain what they show. If the intercept is not appropriate to report, explain why.

f. Add a new point to your data: a 14-kilogram turkey that is free. Give the new value for *r* and the new regression equation. Explain what the negative correlation implies. What happened?

Weight (kilograms)	Price
5.58	$17.10
8.4	$23.87
9.13	$26.73
7.58	$19.87
7.08	$23.24
4.63	$ 9.08

4.58 Office Space and Parking Rates The figures show the average monthly parking rate downtown and the office space available (in million square feet) downtown for some of Canada's most populated cities. Comment on the difference in graphs and in the coefficient of determination between (a) the graph that included Toronto, and (b) the one that did not include Toronto. Toronto is the point with 40.1 million square feet of office space.

(a)

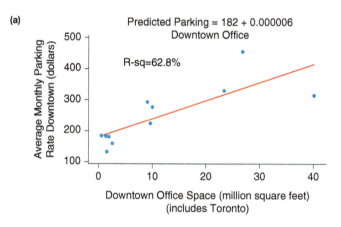

Predicted Parking = 182 + 0.000006 Downtown Office

R-sq=62.8%

Downtown Office Space (million square feet) (includes Toronto)

(b)

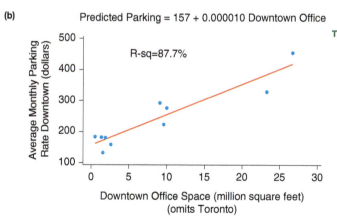

Predicted Parking = 157 + 0.000010 Downtown Office

R-sq=87.7%

Downtown Office Space (million square feet) (omits Toronto)

TRY **4.59 Teachers' Pay and Education Expenditure (Example 9)** The figure shows a scatterplot with a regression line for educators' average pay and the expenditure per student for public schooling in each province in 2008, according to Statistics Canada.

a. From the graph, is the correlation between educators' average pay and expenditure per student positive or negative?

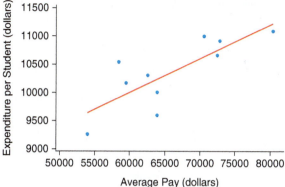

Predicted Expenditure = 6427 + 0.0596 Average Pay

Average Pay (dollars)

b. Interpret the slope.

c. Interpret the intercept or explain why it should not be interpreted.

4.60 Teachers' Pay and Student–Educator Ratios The figure shows a scatterplot with a regression line for educators' average pay and the student–educator ratio (in students per educator) for public schooling in each province in 2008, according to Statistics Canada.

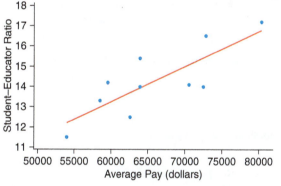

Predicted Student–Educator Ratio = 2.91 + 0.000173 Average Pay

Average Pay (dollars)

a. From the graph, is the correlation between educators' average pay and student–educator ratio positive or negative?

b. Interpret the slope.

c. Interpret the intercept or explain why it should not be interpreted.

TRY **4.61 Does Having a Job Affect Students' Grades? (Example 10)** Grades on a political science test and the number of hours of paid work in the week before the test were studied. The instructor was trying to predict the grade on a test from the hours of work. The figure shows a scatterplot and the regression line for these data.

a. By looking at the plot and the line (without doing any calculations), state whether the correlation is positive or negative and explain your prediction.

b. Interpret the slope.

c. Interpret the intercept.

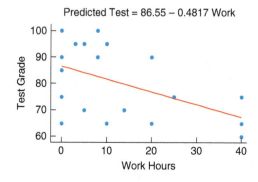

Predicted Test = 86.55 – 0.4817 Work

Work Hours

4.62 Waste Disposal and Population The figure shows a scatterplot with a regression line for amount of waste disposal (in tonnes) and population (in thousands) by province in 2010, according to Statistics Canada.

a. Is the trend positive or negative? What does that mean?

b. Calculate the correlation between waste disposal and population. (Use R-Sq from the figure and take the square root of it.)

c. Report the slope. How many additional tonnes of waste disposal are there, on average, for each additional thousand people?

d. Either report the intercept or explain why it is not appropriate to interpret it.

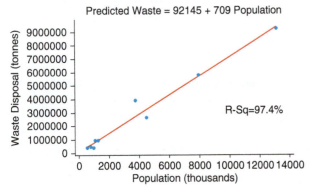

Predicted Waste = 92145 + 709 Population
R-Sq=97.4%

*4.63 Education of Fathers and Mothers The data shown in the table are the number of years of formal education of the fathers and mothers of a sample of 29 statistics students at a small community college in an area with many recent immigrants. (The means are both about 8, and the standard deviations are both about 4.6.) The scatterplot (not shown) suggests a linear trend.

Father	Mother	Father	Mother
3	3	4	7
11	13	16	13
3	4	13	3
12	12	11	10
8	16	6	6
1	2	3	2
8	8	12	14
6	4	14	12
12	8	12	12
0	10	12	13
8	12	12	18
5	5	13	8
8	8	0	0
5	5	3	5
12	6		

a. Find and report the regression equation for predicting the mother's years of education from the father's. Then find the predicted number of years for the mother if the father has 12 years of education, and find the predicted number of years for a mother if the father has 4 years of education.

b. Find and report the regression equation for predicting the father's years of education from the mother's. Then find the predicted number of years for the father if the mother has 12 years of education, and find the predicted number of years for the father if the mother has 4 years of education.

c. What phenomenon from the chapter does this demonstrate? Explain.

*4.64 Heights of Fathers and Sons The table shows some data on a sample of heights of fathers and their sons.

You may want to use the computer or a statistics calculator to verify that

$$\bar{x}_{father} = 175.85 \quad s_{father} = 7.166$$
$$\bar{y}_{son} = 175.4 \quad s_{son} = 7.003$$
$$r = 0.765$$

The scatterplot (not shown) suggests a linear trend.

a. Find and report the regression equation for predicting the son's height from the father's height. Then predict the height of a son with a father 188 centimetres tall. Also, predict the height of a son of a father who is 165 centimetres tall.

b. Find and report the regression equation for predicting the father's height from the son's height. Then predict a father's height from that of a son who is 188 centimetres tall. Also, predict a father's height from that of a son who is 165 centimetres tall.

c. What phenomenon does this show?

Father's Height (cm)	Son's Height (cm)
190.5	188
184.15	180.5
182.88	180.5
180.34	185.5
180.34	174
177.8	178
175.26	175
175.26	169
175.26	183
173.99	169
171.45	166.5
171.45	178
170.18	170
166.37	164
162.56	170

g ***4.65 Test Scores** Assume that in a political science class, the teacher gives a midterm exam and a final exam. Assume that the relationship between midterm and final scores is linear. The summary statistics have been simplified for clarity.

Midterm: Mean = 75, Standard deviation = 10

Final: Mean = 75, Standard deviation = 10

Also, $r = 0.7$ and $n = 20$.

According to the regression equation, for a student who gets a 95 on the midterm, what is the predicted final exam grade? What phenomenon from the chapter does this demonstrate? Explain. *See page 186 for guidance.*

*4.66 Test Scores Assume that in a sociology class, the teacher gives a midterm exam and a final exam. Assume that the

relationship between midterm and final scores is linear. Here are the summary statistics:

Midterm: Mean = 72, Standard deviation = 8

Final: Mean = 72, Standard deviation = 8

Also, $r = 0.75$ and $n = 28$.

a. Find and report the equation of the regression line to predict the final exam score from the midterm score.

b. For a student who gets 55 on the midterm, predict the final exam score.

c. Your answer to part b should be higher than 55. Why?

d. For a student who gets a 100 on the midterm, without doing any calculations, state whether the predicted value would be higher, lower, or the same as 100.

CHAPTER REVIEW EXERCISES

*4.67 Heights and Weights of People The table shows the height and weight of some people. The figure shows that the relationship is linear enough to proceed.

Height (inches)	Weight (pounds)
60	105
66	140
72	185
70	145
63	120

a. Calculate the correlation, and find and report the equation of the regression line, using height as the predictor and weight as the response.

b. Change the height to centimetres by multiplying each height in inches by 2.54. Find the weight in kilograms by dividing the weight in pounds by 2.205. Retain at least six digits in each number so that there will be no errors due to rounding.

c. Calculate the correlation between height in centimetres and weight in kilograms, and compare it with the correlation for the heights in inches and the weights in pounds.

d. Find the equation of the regression line for predicting weight from height, using height in cm and weight in kg. Is the equation for weight (in pounds) and height (in inches) the same or different from the equation for weight (in kg) and height (in cm)?

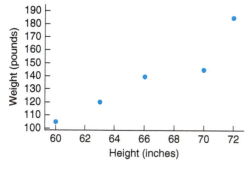

*4.68 Heights and Weights of Men The table shows the heights (in inches) and weights (in pounds) of 14 university men. The figure shows that the relationship is linear enough to proceed.

Height (inches)	Weight (pounds)	Height (inches)	Weight (pounds)
68	205	70	200
68	168	69	175
74	230	72	210
68	190	72	205
67	185	72	185
69	190	71	200
68	165	73	195

a. Find the equation for the regression line with weight (in pounds) as the response and height (in inches) as the predictor. Report the slope and intercept of the regression line and explain what they show. If the intercept is not appropriate to report, explain why.

b. Find the correlation between weight (in pounds) and height (in inches).

c. Find the coefficient of determination and interpret its value.

d. If you changed each height to centimetres by multiplying heights in inches by 2.54, what would the new correlation be? Explain.

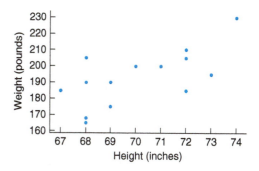

e. Find the equation with weight (in pounds) as the response and height (in cm) as the predictor, and interpret the slope.

f. Summarize what you found: Does changing units change the correlation? Does changing units change the regression equation?

4.69 House Price and Square Feet The figure gives a scatterplot, using data taken from *Peterborough This Week Best Homes* (November, 2013), of the number of square feet in some houses and their list price for sale.

a. Choose the correct correlation from these choices: +1.00, 0, −1.00, −0.84, +0.84.

b. The equation of the regression line is given above the graph. Report the slope and intercept of the regression line and explain what they show in this context. If the intercept is not appropriate to report, explain why.

c. By looking at the graph or using the equation, predict the average cost of a house that is about 2000 square feet.

d. Find the coefficient of determination from the correlation that you chose in part a and explain what it means in the context of the problem.

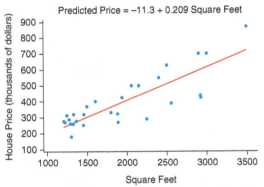

4.70 Heights and Weights of Grade 1 and 2 Students
Some statistics students recorded the heights and weights of a sample of Grade 1 and 2 students. Refer to the figure.

a. Choose the correct correlation coefficient from these choices: +1.00, 0, −1.00, −0.84, +0.84.

b. The equation is given above the graph. Report the slope and intercept of the regression line and explain what they show in this context. If the intercept is not appropriate to report, explain why.

c. By looking at the graph or using the equation of the regression line, predict the weight for a Grade 1 or 2 student who is 125 centimetres tall.

d. Find the coefficient of determination from the correlation that you chose in part a and explain what it means in the context of the problem.

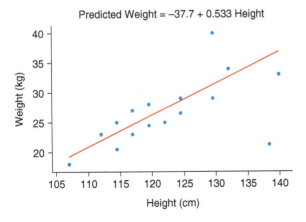

4.71 Hours of Study and of TV Viewing The number of hours of study and the number of hours of TV viewing per week were recorded for some community college students.

a. Make a scatterplot of the data, using hours of study as the predictor.

b. Describe the relationship, if any, between hours of study and hours of TV viewing.

c. Is the correlation strong and positive, strong and negative, or near zero? Do not calculate.

4.72 Salary and Age The age and salary (dollars per hour) were recorded for some students with jobs.

a. Make a scatterplot of the data, using age as the predictor.

b. Find the equation of the regression line.

c. Report the slope and intercept of the regression line and explain what they show. If the intercept is not appropriate to report, explain why not.

4.73 Age and Weight for Women The figure shows a scatterplot and regression line for the age and weight of some women in a statistics class.

a. Find the correlation by taking the positive square root of R-Sq shown on the graph and attaching the proper sign.

b. Using the equation given, find the predicted weight for a woman 35 years old.

c. Report the slope and explain what it means. This study did not follow the same people over time.

d. If it is appropriate, report the intercept and explain what it means. Otherwise, explain why it is not appropriate to report.

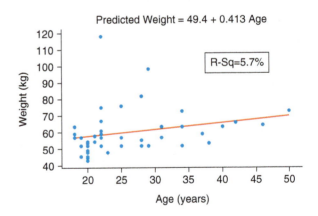

4.74 Age and Weight for Men The figure on the next page shows a scatterplot and regression line for the age and weight of some men in a statistics class.

a. Find the correlation by taking the positive square root of R-Sq shown on the graph and attaching the proper sign.

b. Using the equation given, find the predicted weight for a man 35 years old.

c. Report the slope and explain what it means. (Note that this study did not follow the same people over time.)

d. Either report the intercept and explain what it shows or explain why it should not be reported.

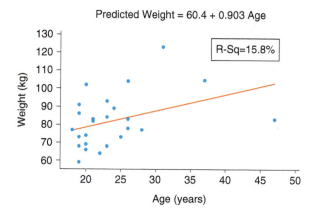

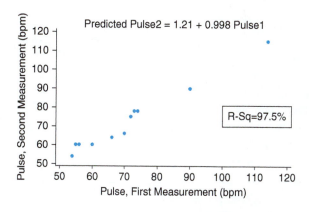

4.75 The figure shows a scatterplot of the educational level of twins. Describe the scatterplot. Explain the trend and mention any unusual points. (Source: www.stat.ucla.edu)

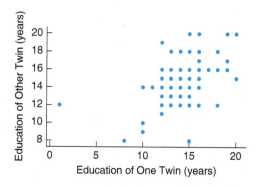

4.76 Film Opening Weekend and Total Gross The figure shows a scatterplot of the opening weekend gross and the total gross in Canada and the United States for some of the top movies of 2013. Describe what you see. Explain the trend and mention any unusual points. (Source: www.boxofficemojo.com)

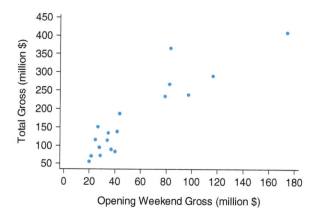

4.77 Student Pulses A group of students took their pulse (in beats per minute) and a few seconds later took their pulse again. The figure shows the results. Explain what they show.

4.78 Hours of Exercise and Hours of Studying A group of students reported the number of hours they exercised per week and the number of hours they spent studying statistics per week. The figure shows the results. Explain what they show.

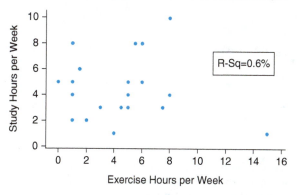

4.79 Tree Heights Loggers gathered information about some trees. The diameter is in centimetres, the height is in metres, and the volume of the wood is in cubic metres. Loggers are interested in whether they can estimate the volume of the tree given any single dimension. Which is the better predictor of volume: the diameter or the height?

4.80 Salary and Education Does education pay? The salary per year in dollars, the number of years employed (YrsEm), and the number of years of education after high school (Educ) for the employees of a company were recorded. Determine whether number of years employed or number of years of education after high school is a better predictor of salary. Explain your thinking. (Source: Minitab File)

4.81 Film Budgets and Grosses Movie studios put a lot of effort into trying to predict how much money their movies will make. One possible predictor is the amount of money spent on the production of the movie. In the table on the next page you can see the budget and the amount of money made worldwide for the 15 movies with the highest profit (as of November 2013). The budget and gross are in millions of dollars. Make a scatterplot and comment on what you see. If appropriate, find, report, and interpret the regression line. If it is not appropriate to do so, explain why. (Source: www.boxofficemojo.com)

Movie	Budget (millions of dollars)	Gross (millions of dollars)
Titanic	200	2185.7
The Lord of the Rings: The Return of the King	94	1141.4
Jurassic Park	63	1035.3
Transformers: Dark of the Moon	195	1123.8
Marvel's The Avengers	225	1514.3
The Dark Knight Rises	275	1079.3
Pirates of the Caribbean: Dead Man's Chest	225	1060.6
Iron Man 3	200	1212
Harry Potter and the Deadly Hollows Part 2	125	1328.1
Toy Story 3	200	1063.8
Avatar	425	2783.9
Skyfall	200	1108.7
Pirates of the Caribbean: On Stranger Tides	250	1043.7
Alice in Wonderland	200	1024.4
The Hobbit: An Unexpected Journey	250	1014.7

 4.82 Fuel Consumption of Cars The table gives the fuel consumption (in litres per 100 kilometres) in the city and on the highway for some of the most fuel-efficient cars of 2013, as reported by Consumer Reports. Make a scatterplot, using the city fuel consumption as the predictor. Find the equation of the regression line for predicting the litres per 100 kilometres (L/100 km) on the highway from the litres per 100 kilometres in the city. Use the equation to predict the highway fuel consumption from a city fuel consumption of 4.2 L/100 km. Also find the coefficient of determination and explain what it means.

Vehicle	City (L/100 km)	Highway (L/100 km)
Ford Focus	1.7	2.0
Nissan Leaf	1.8	2.3
Chevrolet Volt	2.3	2.5
Toyota Prius Plug-in	2.0	1.9
Toyota Prius	3.5	4.0
Lexus CT 200h	4.5	4.8
Honda Civic Hybrid	4.4	4.2
Ford Fusion Hybrid	4.0	4.1
Smart Fortwo Coupe	5.8	4.7

For Exercises 4.83–4.86 show your points in a rough scatterplot and give the coordinates of the points.

*4.83 Construct a small set of numbers with at least three points with a perfect positive correlation of 1.00.

*4.84 Construct a small set of numbers with at least three points with a perfect negative correlation of −1.00.

*4.85 Construct a set of numbers (with at least three points) with a strong negative correlation. Then add one point (an influential point) that changes the correlation to positive. Report the data and give the correlation of each set.

*4.86 Construct a set of numbers (with at least three points) with a strong positive correlation. Then add one point (an influential point) that changes the correlation to negative. Report the data and give the correlation of each set.

GUIDED EXERCISES

4.41 Does the Cost of a Flight Depend on the Distance?

The table gives the round-trip fare for direct flights between Toronto and some other cities on major airlines. These were the lowest prices shown on www.ca.kayak.com on November 28, 2013. The airlines varied. (The travel dates were all the same, in mid-January.)

How much would it cost, on average, to fly to Washington, D.C., which is 566 kilometres from Toronto? To answer this question, perform a complete regression analysis, including a scatterplot with a regression line, following the steps below.

Round-Trip Air Fares from Toronto

City	Cost ($)	Distance (kilometres)
Montreal	227	506
Vancouver	513	3366
Halifax	374	1268
Fredericton	286	1041
Calgary	487	2716
Ottawa	227	354
Regina	454	2045
St. John's	456	2117
Winnipeg	403	1516
Quebec City	249	729
Saskatoon	465	2227
Charlottetown	399	1314
Boston	286	696
New York	250	554
Orlando	296	1688
Mexico City	602	3256
Chicago	286	703

Step 1 ▶ Make a scatterplot

Be sure that distance is the *x*-variable and cost is the *y*-variable. You may want to include the regression line with your scatterplot if you have that option with your technology; refer to Step 4.

Step 2 ▶ Is the linear model appropriate?

In this case the answer is yes, because there is a linear trend. It is hard to see with so few points, but a strong curvature is not present and the cost tends to increase as the distance increases.

Step 3 ▶ Obtain the equation

When finding the regression equation, be sure that you use distance as the *x*-variable and cost as the *y*-variable. For example, if you are using the TI-83/84, the predictor (which you probably put into List 2 because the second column of numbers has the kilometres) has to be entered first and the response (in List 1) is entered second, after the comma. See the TI-83/84 figure.

Step 4 ▶ Add the regression line to the scatterplot

If your technology will make a plot with a line, do so. Refer to the TechTips, which begin on page 187, to see how to do this. If your technology will not draw the line, you can choose two *x*-values (distances), find the corresponding *y*-values (cost), plot these, and then draw the line to connect them. For example, to choose the first point on the line, choose an *x*-value such as $x = 400$ and follow these additional steps:

- **First Predicted Point**
  Pick an arbitrary small distance, such as 400 kilometres, that is still larger than the smallest distance given. Substitute it into the equation you got to find the predicted cost:

$$\text{Predicted Cost} = 195.02 + 0.113 \text{ Distance}$$
$$= 195.02 + 0.113(400)$$
$$= 195.02 + 45.2$$
$$= 240.22$$

  A predicted point is (400, 240.22), so a flight of about 400 kilometres should cost, on average, about $240.20. Put the point on the graph with a symbol you will remember.

- **Second Point**
  To get a second point, pick an arbitrary large distance, such as 3000 kilometres, that is still smaller than the largest distance given. Substitute it into the equation to find the cost and put the point on the graph using the same symbol you chose before.

- **The Line**
  The regression line will be a straight line between these two predicted points (use a ruler to make the line). Extend the line out to the edges of the data, to the left to about 300 kilometres, and to the right to about 3500 kilometres.

Step 5 ▶ Interpret the slope and intercept in context

Predicted $y = b_0 + b_1 x$
Predicted Cost $= 195.02 + 0.113$ Distance

The slope is b_1 (which is the multiplier for *Distance*), which is 0.113, and the intercept is b_0, which is the first number, $195.02.

Fill in the blanks that follow.

For the slope: For every additional kilometre, on average, the price goes up by ____ dollars.

For the intercept: A trip with zero kilometres should cost about ____ dollars. Explain why interpreting the *y*-intercept like this is questionable.

Step 6 ▶ Answer the question by using the regression equation

How much would it cost to fly to Washington, D.C., which is 566 kilometres from Toronto?

4.65 Test Scores Assume that in a political science class, the teacher gives a midterm exam and a final exam. Assume that the association between midterm and final scores is linear. The summary statistics have been simplified for clarity.

Midterm: Mean = 75,   Standard deviation = 10

Final: Mean = 75,   Standard deviation = 10

Also, $r = 0.7$ and $n = 20$.

For a student who gets 95 on the midterm, what is the predicted final exam grade? Assume that the graph is linear.

Step 1 ▶ Find the equation of the line to predict the final exam score from the midterm score: $y = b_0 + b_1 x$

a. First find the slope: $b_1 = r\left(\dfrac{s_{final}}{s_{midterm}}\right)$

b. Then find the y-intercept, b_0, from the equation

$$b_0 = \bar{y} - b_1 \bar{x}$$

c. Write out the following equation:

$$\text{Predicted } y = b_0 + b_1 x$$

However, use "Predicted Final" instead of "Predicted y" and "Midterm" in place of x.

Step 2 ▶ Use the equation to predict the final exam score for a student who gets 95 on the midterm.

Step 3 ▶ Your predicted final exam grade should be less than 95. Why?

General Instructions for All Technology

Upload data from the website, or enter data manually using two columns of equal length. Refer to TechTips in Chapter 2 for a review of entering data. Each row represents a single observation, and each column represents a variable. All technologies will use the example that follows.

Example Analyze the six points in the data table with a scatterplot, correlation, and regression. Use height (in centimetres) as the *x*-variable and weight (in kilograms) as the *y*-variable.

Height	Weight
155	47
158	50
160	64
163	57
168	77
173	73

TI-83/84

Making a Scatterplot

1. Press **2ND**, **STATPLOT** (which is the button above **2ND**), **4**, and **ENTER**, to turn off plots made previously.
2. Press **2ND**, **STATPLOT**, and **1** (for Plot1).
3. Refer to Figure 4A: Turn on **Plot1** by pressing **ENTER** when **On** is highlighted.

▲ **FIGURE 4A** TI-83/84 plot1 dialogue screen.

4. Use the arrows on the keypad to get to the scatterplot (upper left of the six plots) and press **ENTER** when the scatterplot is highlighted. Be careful with the **Xlist** and **Ylist**. To get **L1**, press **2ND** and **1**. To get **L2**, press **2ND** and **2**.
5. Press **ZOOM** and **9** (**Zoomstat**) to create the graph.
6. Press **TRACE** to see the coordinates of the points, and use the arrows on the keypad to go to other points. Your output will look like Figure 4B, but without the line.

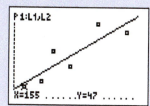

▲ **FIGURE 4B** TI-83/84 plot with line.

7. To get the output with the line in it, shown in Figure 4B: **STAT**, **CALC**, 8:LinReg(a+bx), **L1➐ L2➐ Y1** (You get the **Y1** by pressing **VARS**, **Y-VARS**, I: Function, I:**Y1**, **ENTER**.) Here **➐** represents a comma (the button above the 7).
8. Press **ZOOM** and **9**.
9. Press **TRACE** to see the numbers, and use the arrows on the keypad to get to other number.

Finding the Correlation and Regression Equation Coefficients

Before finding the correlation, you must turn the diagnostics on, as shown here.

Press **2ND**, **CATALOG**, and scroll down to **DiagnosticOn** and press **ENTER** twice. The diagnostics will stay on unless you **Reset** your calculator or change the batteries.

1. Press **STAT**, choose **CALC**, and **8** (for LinReg (a + bx)).
2. Press **2ND L1** (or whichever list is X, the predictor), press **➐** (comma: the button above the 7), press **2ND L2** (or whichever list is Y, the response), and press **ENTER**.

Figure 4C shows the output.

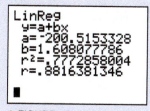

▲ **FIGURE 4C** TI-83/84 output.

MINITAB

Making a Scatterplot

1. **Graph > Scatterplot**
2. Leave the default **Simple** and click **OK**.
3. Double click the column containing the weights so that it goes under the **Y Variables**. Then double click the column containing the heights so that it goes under the **X Variables**.
4. Click **OK**. After the graph is made, you can edit the labels by clicking on them.

Finding the Correlation

1. **Stat > Basic Statistics > Correlation**
2. Double click both the predictor column and the response column (in either order).
3. Click **OK**. You will get 0.881.

Finding the Regression Equation Coefficients

1. **Stat > Regression > Regression**
2. Put in the **Response** (y) and **Predictor** (x) columns.
3. Click **OK**. You may need to scroll up to see the regression equation. It will be easier to understand if you have put in labels for the columns, such as "Height" and "Weight." You will get: Weight = −443 + 9.03 Height.

To Display the Regression Line on a Scatterplot

1. **Stat > Regression > Fitted Line Plot**
2. Double click the **Response (y)** column and then double click the **Predictor (x)** column.

3. Click **OK**. Figure 4D shows the fitted line plot.

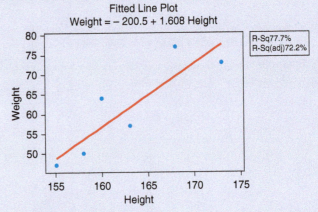

▲ **FIGURE 4D** Minitab fitted line plot.

Alternatively, you can add the regression line to an existing scatterplot by right-clicking on the scatterplot to open a graphing menu. Then select **Add > Regression Fit > Linear** (make sure **Fit intercept** is selected) and click **OK**. This instruction will add the regression line, but not the equation of the line.

EXCEL

Making a Scatterplot

1. Select (highlight) the two columns containing the data, with the predictor column to the *left* of the response column. You may include the labels at the top or not include them.
2. Click **Insert**, in **Charts** click the picture of a scatterplot, and click the upper left option shown here:

3. Click **OK**.
4. Note that the lower left corner of the chart is not at the origin, (0, 0). If you want to zoom in or out on the data by changing

the minimum value for an axis, right-click on the axis numbers, click **Format axis**, in **Axis Options** change the **Minimum** to **Fixed**, and put in the desired value. You may want to do this twice: once for the x-axis and once for the y-axis. Then click **Close**.

5. When the chart is active (click on it), **Chart Tools** are shown at the top of screen, right of centre. Click **Layout** (not **Page Layout**), then **Axis Titles**, and **Chart Title** to add appropriate labels. After the labels are added, you can click on them to change the spelling or add words. Delete the labels on the right-hand side, such as **Series 1**, if you see any.

Finding the Correlation

1. Click on **Data**, click on **Data Analysis**, select **Correlation**, and click **OK**.
2. For the **Input Range**, select (highlight) both columns of data (if you have highlighted the labels as well as the numbers, you must also click on the **Labels in first row**).
3. Click **OK**. You will get 0.881638.

   (Alternatively, just click the f_x button, for **category** choose **statistical**, select **CORREL**, click **OK**, and highlight the two columns containing the numbers, one at a time. The correlation will show up on the dialogue screen, and it will appear in the last active cell if you click **OK**.)

Finding the Coefficients of the Regression Equation

1. Click on **Data**, **Data Analysis**, **Regression**, and **OK**.
2. For the **Input Y Range**, select the column of numbers (not words) that represents the response or dependent variable. For the **Input X Range**, select the column of numbers that represents the predictor or independent variable.
3. Click **OK**.

A large summary of the model will be displayed. Look under **Coefficients** at the bottom. For the **Intercept** and the slope (next to **XVariable1**), see Figure 4E, which means the regression line is

$$y = -200.5 + 1.61x$$

	Coefficients
Intercept	−200.515
X Variable 1	1.608078

▲ FIGURE 4E Excel regression output.

To Display the Regression Line on a Scatterplot

4. After making the scatterplot, under **Chart Tools** click **Design**. In the **Chart Layouts** group, click the triangle to the right of **Quick Layout**. Choose Layout 9 (the option in the lower right portion, which shows a line in it and also fx).

   Refer to Figure 4F.

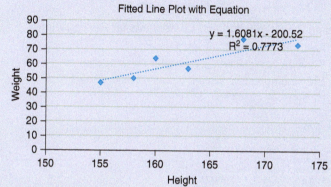

▲ FIGURE 4F Excel fitted line plot with equation.

STATCRUNCH

Making a Scatterplot

1. **Graph > Scatterplot**
2. Select an **X column** and a **Y column** for the plot.
3. Click **Compute!** to construct the plot.
4. To copy the graph, click **Options** and **Copy**.

Finding the Correlation and Coefficients for the Equation

1. **Stat > Regression > Simple Linear**
2. Select the **X variable** and **Y variable** for the regression.
3. Click **Compute!** to view the equation and numbers, which are shown in Figure 4G.

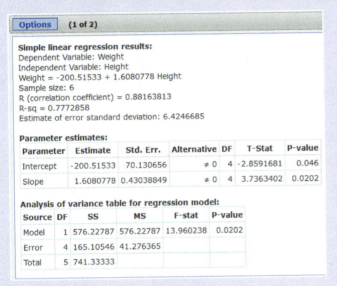

Options   (1 of 2)

Simple linear regression results:
Dependent Variable: Weight
Independent Variable: Height
Weight = -200.51533 + 1.6080778 Height
Sample size: 6
R (correlation coefficient) = 0.88163813
R-sq = 0.7772858
Estimate of error standard deviation: 6.4246685

Parameter estimates:

Parameter	Estimate	Std. Err.	Alternative	DF	T-Stat	P-value
Intercept	-200.51533	70.130656	≠ 0	4	-2.8591681	0.046
Slope	1.6080778	0.43038849	≠ 0	4	3.7363402	0.0202

Analysis of variance table for regression model:

Source	DF	SS	MS	F-stat	P-value
Model	1	576.22787	576.22787	13.960238	0.0202
Error	4	165.10546	41.276365		
Total	5	741.33333			

▲ **FIGURE 4G** StatCrunch regression output.

Plotting the Regression Line on a Scatterplot

1. The instructions for finding the coefficients for the regression equation produce the regression line as part of the output. Simply click on the right arrow at the bottom right-hand corner of the output to move to the next page. Refer to Figure 4H.

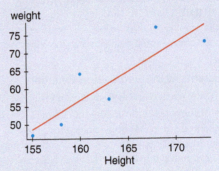

▲ **FIGURE 4H** StatCrunch fitted line plot.

SPSS

Making a Scatterplot

1. **Graphs > Legacy Dialogs > Scatter/Dot**
2. Select **Simple Scatter** and click **Define**.
3. Highlight the response or dependent variable and click on the right arrow to move it to the **Y axis** box.
4. Highlight the independent variable and click on the right arrow to move it to the **X axis** box.
5. Click **OK**.

Finding the Correlation

1. **Analyze > Correlate > Bivariate**
2. Highlight and move each variable to the **Variable** box by clicking on the right arrow.
3. Select **Pearson** and click **OK**.

Finding the Coefficients of the Regression Equation

1. **Analyze > Regression > Linear**
2. Highlight the response or dependent **variable** and click on the right arrow to move it to the **Dependent** box.
3. Highlight the independent variable and click on the right arrow to move it to the **Independent(s)** box.
4. Click **OK**.

Several tables appear as output. Look at the table of **Coefficients** at the bottom. The intercept is listed as the **(Constant)** coefficient, and the slope as the coefficient for the independent variable (in this case **Height**). See Figure 4I. Once again, the regression line is

$$y = -201 + 1.61x$$

Coefficients[a]

Model		Unstandardized Coefficients	
		B	Std. Error
1	(Constant)	-200.515	70.131
	Height	1.608	.430

a. Dependent Variable: Weight

▲ **FIGURE 4I** SPSS regression output.

Plotting the Regression Line on a Scatterplot

1. Follow the steps for making a scatterplot.
2. Double click on the scatterplot to activate the chart editor.
3. **Elements > Fit Line at Total > Close** (the default is **Linear**). See Figure 4J.

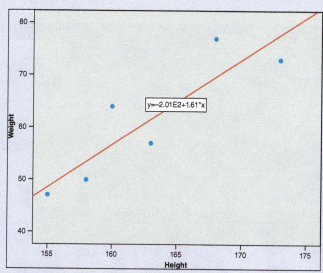

▲ **FIGURE 4J** SPSS fitted line plot with equation.

5 Modelling Variation with Probability

The Seattle Times/AP Images

LEARNING OBJECTIVES

After completing this chapter, you should be able to:

1. Distinguish between non-random and random experiments.

2. Demonstrate the meaning of probability and how to compute one through direct observation.

3. Compute probabilities of events by using the rules of probability.

4. Differentiate dependent from independent events and compute the probability of an event that depends on another.

5. Compute probabilities of independent events.

6. State the Law of Large Numbers in your own terms and explain how it can be used to compute a probability through repeated observation of a random experiment. 🌐

7. Design a random experiment simulating a real-life scenario in order to compute a probability. 🌐

In 1971, the United States was fighting the Vietnam War and drafting men to serve in the military. To determine who was chosen, government officials wrote the days of the year (January 1, January 2, and so on) on capsules. The capsules were placed in a large container and mixed up. They were then drawn out one at a time. The first date chosen was assigned the rank 1, the second date was assigned the rank 2, and so on. Men were drafted on the basis of their birthday. Those whose birthday had rank 1 were drafted first, then those whose birthday had rank 2, and so on until the officials had enough men.

Although the officials thought that this method was random, some fairly convincing evidence indicates that it was not (Starr 1997). Figure 5.1a shows boxplots with the actual ranks for each month. Figure 5.1b shows what boxplots might have looked like if the lottery had been truly random. In Figure 5.1b, each month has roughly the same rank. However, in Figure 5.1a, a few months had notably lower ranks than the other months. Bad news if you were born in December—you were more likely to be called up first.

What went wrong? The capsules, after having dates written on them, were clustered together by month as they were put into the tumbler. But the capsules weren't mixed up enough to break up these clusters. The mixing wasn't adequate to create a truly random mix.

It's not easy to generate true randomness, and humans have a hard time recognizing random events when they see them. Probability gives us a tool for understanding randomness. Probability helps us answer the question "How often does something like this happen by chance?" By answering that question, we create an important link between our data and the real world. In previous chapters, you learned how to organize, display, and summarize data to see patterns and trends. Probability is a vital tool because it gives us the ability to generalize our understanding of data to the larger world. In this chapter, we'll explore issues of randomness and probability: What is randomness? How do we measure it? And how do we use it?

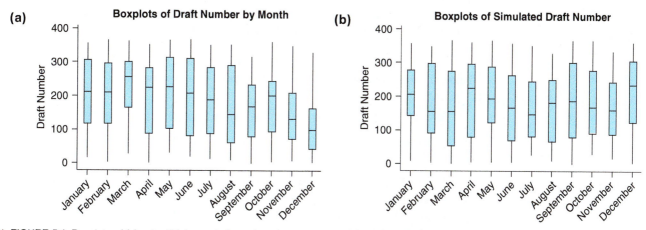

▲ FIGURE 5.1 Boxplots of **(a)** actual Vietnam draft numbers by month, and **(b)** what might have happened if the draft had really been random.

CASE STUDY

SIDS or Murder?

In November 2000, Sally Clark was convicted in England of killing her two children. Her children had died several years apart, and the initial diagnosis was sudden infant death syndrome (SIDS). SIDS is the sudden, unexplained death of an infant under one year of age. Health Canada reports that SIDS is the leading cause of death among infants between 28 days and one year in age. Although some risk factors have been identified (most are related to the mother's health during pregnancy), the cause or causes are as yet unknown.

Clark was convicted of murder on the basis of the expert testimony of Sir Roy Meadow, a prominent British physician who was an expert on SIDS. Dr. Meadow quoted a published statistic: The probability of an infant dying of SIDS is 1/8543. That is, in the U.K., one child in every 8543 dies of SIDS. Dr. Meadow concluded that the probability of two children in the same family dying of SIDS was therefore (1/8543) × (1/8543), or about 1 in 73 million. The jury agreed that this event—two children in the same family dying of SIDS—was so unlikely that they convicted Ms. Clark of murder, and she was sent to prison.

But then in 2003, Sally Clark's conviction was overturned and she was released from prison. Dr. Meadow was accused of professional misconduct. Why did Dr. Meadow multiply the two probabilities together? Why was the verdict overturned? We will answer these questions at the end of the chapter.

SECTION 5.1

What Is Randomness?

What exactly is randomness? According to the *Oxford English Dictionary, random* means "having no definite aim or purpose." You probably use the word to describe events that seem to happen for no reason. Sometimes the word is used to describe things that have no predictable pattern. However, in statistics, the word *random* has a more precise meaning, as you will see.

We can do a small experiment to compare our natural understanding of randomness with real-life randomness. We asked a student to imagine flipping a coin and to write down the resulting heads (H) and tails (T). To compare this to a real random sequence, we flipped an actual coin 20 times and recorded the results. Which of the sequences below do you think is real and which is invented by the student?

H	H	T	H	T	H	H	T	T	H	H	T	H	H	H	T	H	T	T	H
T	T	T	H	H	H	T	T	T	T	T	H	H	H	H	T	T	H	T	H

The first row of results is the one made up by the student, and the second row records the results of actually tossing a coin 20 times. Is it possible to tell by comparing the two sequences? Not always, but this time the student did something that most people would do in this situation. Most of the time the student wrote very short sequences of consecutive heads or tails, or "streaks." HH is streak of two heads. Only once did he write as many as three heads or three tails in a row. It's as if, after writing three heads in a row, he thought, "Wait! If I put a fourth, no one will believe it's random."

However, the real, truly random sequence had one streak of five tails (beginning at the seventh flip) and another streak with four heads. These long streaks are examples of the way chance creates things that look like a pattern or structure, but really are not.

You Try It

Use a computer to flip a coin 20 times for you. Go to www.socr.ucla.edu.

Click on the **Experiments** tab and select **Coin Sample Experiment** from the dropdown menu that will appear. Set *n* to be 20 (by moving the slider to the left of $n = 10$), and set *p* to be 0.50. Press the **Play** (▶) button, and count the resulting streaks. Do this a few times, and keep track of the longest streak you get each time. How long does the longest streak have to be before you think it is unusually long?

KEY POINT ▸ People are not good at identifying truly random experiments, so we need to rely on outside mechanisms such as coin flips or random number tables.

Randomness is hard to pull off without help from a computer or some other randomizing device, and even then what we end up with is not really random most of the time (more on that later). If a computer is not available to generate random numbers, another useful approach is to use a random number table. (An example is provided in Appendix A of this book.) A random number table provides a sequence of digits from 0 to 9 in a random order. Here, **random** means that no predictable pattern occurs and that no digit is more likely to appear than any other. (Of course, if you use the same table often enough, it might seem predictable to you, but to an outsider, it will not seem predictable.)

For example, if we are doing a controlled experiment, we might assign each subject in our study a random number from this table as the subjects come into our office. The odd-numbered subjects would then go into the Control group, and the even-numbered would go into the Treatment group.

To use a random number table to simulate coin flipping, we assign a number to each outcome. For example, suppose we let even numbers (0, 2, 4, 6, 8) represent tails and let odd numbers (1, 3, 5, 7, 9) represent heads. Now choose any row of the table you wish and any column. For example, we arbitrarily chose column 11 and row 30 because that's the date of the day we wrote this paragraph (November 30, or 11/30). Read off the next 20 digits, but translate them into "heads" and "tails." What's the longest streak you get?

Line						
28	31498	85304	22393	21634	34560	77404
29	93074	27086	62559	86590	18420	33290
30	90549	53094	76282	53105	45531	90061
31	11373	96871	38157	98368	39536	08079
32	52022	59093	30647	33241	16027	70336

◀ **TABLE 5.1** Lines 28–32 (indicated at the left side of the table) from the random number table in Appendix A. The red 7 in the 11th column and the 30th line, or row, is our starting point.

EXAMPLE **1** Simulating Randomness

Let's play a game. You roll a six-sided die until the first 6 appears. You win one point for every roll. You pass the die to your opponent, who also rolls until the first 6 appears. Whoever has the most points, wins.

QUESTION Simulate rolling the die until a 6 appears. Use Table 5.1, and start at the very first entry of line 28. How many rolls did it take?

SOLUTION We'll let the digits 1 through 6 represent the outcome shown on the die. We'll ignore the digits 7, 8, 9, and 0. Starting at line 28, we get these random digits:

3, 1, 4, (ignore, ignore, ignore), 5, 3, (ignore), 4, 2, 2, 3, (ignore), 3, 2, 1, 6

CONCLUSION We rolled the die 12 times before the first 6 appeared.

TRY THIS! Exercise 5.1

Computers and calculators have random number generators that come close to true randomness. For instance, the internet game you played (to simulate flipping a coin 20 times) uses a random number generator. Computer-generated random numbers are sometimes called pseudo random numbers, because what is actually generated is based on arithmetic operations on a seed value—a number that starts the random sequence. If you input the same seed number, you will always see the same sequence of pseudo-random numbers. However, it is not possible to predict what number will come next in the sequence, and in this sense the generated numbers are considered random. For most practical work (and certainly for everything we cover in this book), these pseudo–random numbers are as random as we need. (You should be aware, though, that not all statistics packages produce equally convincing sequences of random numbers.)

Less technological ways exist for generating random outcomes, such as actually flipping a coin. When you play a card game, you carefully shuffle the cards to mix them up. In the games of Mah Jong and tile rummy, players create randomness by scrambling the tiles on the tabletop. In many board games, players either roll dice or spin a spinner to determine how far they will move their game pieces. In raffles, tickets are put into a basket, the basket is spun, and then a ticket is drawn by someone who does so without looking into the basket.

Such physical randomizations must be done with care. A good con artist can flip a coin so that it always comes up heads. A child learns quickly that a gentle tap of a spinner can move the spinner to the desired number. A deck of cards needs to be shuffled at least seven times in order for the result to be considered random (as mathematician and magician Persi Diaconnis proved). Many things that we think are random might not be. This is the lesson the U.S. government learned from its flawed Vietnam draft lottery, which was described in the chapter introduction. Quite often, statisticians are employed to check whether random processes, such as the way winners are selected for lotteries, are truly random.

 **Looking Back**

Relative Frequencies
Relative frequencies, introduced in Chapter 2, are the same as proportions.

Determining Probabilities

Probability is used to measure how often random events occur. When we say, "The probability of getting heads when you flip a coin is 50%," we mean that flipping a coin results in heads about half the time (assuming that the outcome of the flips is random). This is often called the "frequentist" approach to computing a probability because it involves computing a relative frequency.

Here, the 50% probability is computed from our knowledge that if the coin is flipped an infinite number of times, half the coin-flips will show heads. It is also computed under the condition that the coin being flipped is fair. This means that each coin flip will come up heads, or tails, with the same opportunity.

Obviously we can't do anything an infinite number of times. It is not practical for us to infinitely flip a coin and then observe the percentage of these flips that come up heads. So how can we compute the probability of getting heads?

As an example, our coin has two sides. When we flip the coin once we can get one of two sides, heads or tails, with each side being determined by randomness. We *assume* that each side is equally likely to come up when we flip the coin. We don't know for a fact that it is true, but we *assume* it is true. Keep in mind that we have yet to flip the coin; we haven't yet done an experiment! We have simply reasoned on the basis of the theory that when the experiment is done, of the two possible sides that can come up, one will be heads. One out of two is 50%.

This is the "theoretical" approach to computing probabilities. It requires that we think about the experiment and imagine what can happen. From our list of "what can happen," we count how many in this list satisfy the event whose probability we are trying to compute, and then divide this by the total number of outcomes the experiment can give. This does not require us to repeat the experiment an infinite number of times and calculate a relative frequency. In theory, we assume that this relative frequency would be *equal* to the probability we have computed without running the experiment!

 KEY POINT   Probabilities are based on theory and tell us the percentage of times an event would occur if an experiment were repeated *infinitely* many times.

SECTION 5.2

Finding Probabilities

We have just seen how to use theory to find the probability of a coin coming up heads. In order to advance our ability to compute a probability, we need to take a closer look at the rules under which a probability can be computed.

Facts about Probabilities

A probability is the expected percentage of times an event will happen. Probabilities can be expressed as fractions, decimals, or percentages: 1/2, 0.5, and 50% are all used to represent the probability that a coin comes up heads. However we wish to represent a probability, we must remember that it can never be less than zero or greater than 1 (100%).

Some values have special meanings. If the probability of an event happening is 0, then that event never happens. If you purchase a lottery ticket after all the prizes have been given out, the probability is 0 that you will win one of those prizes. If the probability of an event happening is 1, then that event always happens. If you flip a coin, the probability of a coin landing heads or tails is 1.

Another useful property to remember is that the probability that an event will *not* happen is 1 minus the probability that it will happen. If there is a 0.90 chance that it will snow, then there is a $1 - 0.9 = 0.10$ chance that it will not. If there is a 1/6 chance of rolling a "1" on a die, then there is a $1 - (1/6) = 5/6$ probability that you will not get a 1.

We call such a "not event" a **complement**. The complement of the event "it snows today" is the event that it "does not snow today"; the complement of a "coin lands heads" is a "coin lands tails." The die landing and showing a "2, 3, 4, 5, or 6 on top" is the complement of the die landing and showing a "1 on top"; in other words, everything but a "1 on top."

Events are usually represented by uppercase letters: A, B, C, and so on. For example, we might let A represent the event "it snows tomorrow." Then the notation P(A) means "the probability that it will snow tomorrow." In sentence form, the notation $P(A) = 0.50$ translates into English as "The probability that it will snow tomorrow is 0.50, or 50%."

In the same way, we also represent the complement of an event in capital letter notation, with "not A" being represented as A^c. $P(A^c)$ represents "the probability that it will not snow tomorrow." $P(A^c) = 0.50$ means "the probability that it will not snow tomorrow is 0.50, or 50%."

A common misinterpretation of probability is to think that large probabilities mean that the event will certainly happen. For example, suppose your local weather reporter predicts a 90% chance of snow tomorrow. Tomorrow, however, it doesn't snow. Was the weather reporter wrong? Not necessarily. When the weather reporter says there is a 90% chance of snow, it means that on 10% of the days like tomorrow it does not snow. Thus a 90% chance of snow means that on 90% of all days just like tomorrow, it snows, but on 10% of those days it does not.

Summary of Probability Rules

Rule 1: A probability is always a number from 0 to 1 (or 0% to 100%) inclusive (which means 0 and 1 are allowed). It may be expressed as a *fraction,* a *decimal,* or a *percentage.*

In symbols, for any event A,

$$0 \leq P(A) \leq 1$$

Rule 2: The probability that an event will not occur is 1 minus the probability that the event will occur. In symbols, for any event A,

$$P(A \text{ does } not \text{ occur}) = 1 - P(A \text{ does occur})$$

or

$$P(A^c) = 1 - P(A)$$

Finding Probabilities with Equally Likely Outcomes

In some situations, all of the possible outcomes of a random experiment occur with the same chance. We call these situations "equally likely outcomes." For example, when you flip a fair coin, getting heads and getting tails are equally likely. When you roll a fair die, 1, 2, 3, 4, 5, and 6 are all equally likely.

When we are dealing with equally likely outcomes, it is sometimes helpful to create a list of "all that can happen." A list that contains all possible outcomes is called a **sample space**. We often represent the sample space with the letter S. An **event** is a collection of outcomes in the sample space that share a property. For example, the sample space S for rolling a die is the numbers 1, 2, 3, 4, 5, 6. The event "get an even number on the topside of the die" consists of all the outcomes in the sample space that share the property of the showing number being even. This can happen three different ways—the topside shows a 2, a 4, or a 6, with each topside being an even number.

When the outcomes are equally likely, the probability that a particular event will occur is just the number of outcomes that make up that event, divided by the total number of equally likely outcomes in the sample space. In other words, it is the number of outcomes producing the event divided by the number of outcomes in the sample space.

Summary of Probability Rules

Rule 3:

$$\text{Probability of A} = P(A) = \frac{\text{Number of outcomes in A}}{\text{Number of all possible outcomes}}$$

This is true *only* for equally likely outcomes.

For example, suppose 30 people are in your class, and one person will be selected at random by a raffle to win a prize. What is the probability that you will win? The sample space is the list of the names of the 30 people. The event A is the event that contains only one outcome: your name. The probability that you win is 1/30, because there is only 1 way for you to win and there are 30 different ways that this raffle can turn out. We write this using mathematical notation as follows:

$$P(\text{you win prize}) = 1/30$$

We can be even more compact:

Let A represent the event that you win the raffle. Then

$$P(A) = 1/30.$$

One consequence of Rule 3 is that the probability that *something* in the sample space will occur is 1. In symbols, $P(S) = 1$. This is because

$$P(S) = \frac{\text{Number of outcomes in S}}{\text{Number of outcomes in S}} = 1$$

EXAMPLE 2 Ten Dice in a Bowl

A bowl contains 5 red dice, 3 green dice, and 2 white dice (Figure 5.2). But assume that the dice are well mixed (unlike the image here). Close your eyes, reach into the bowl, and pick one die.

► FIGURE 5.2 Ten dice in a bowl.

QUESTION What is the probability of picking (a) a red die? (b) a green die? (c) a white die?

SOLUTIONS The bowl contains 10 dice, so we have 10 possible outcomes. All are equally likely (assuming that all the dice are equal in size, they are mixed up within the bowl, and we do not look when choosing).

a. Five dice are red, so the probability of picking a red die is 5/10, 1/2, 0.50, or 50%. That is,

$$P(\text{red die}) = 1/2, \text{ or } 50\%.$$

b. Three dice are green, so the probability of picking a green die is 3/10, or 30%. That is,

$$P(\text{green die}) = 3/10, \text{ or } 30\%.$$

c. Two dice are white, so the probability of picking a white die is 2/10, 1/5, or 20%. That is,

$$P(\text{white die}) = 1/5, \text{ or } 20\%.$$

Note that the probabilities add up to 1, or 100%, as they must.

TRY THIS! Exercise 5.11

Example 3 shows that it is important to make sure the outcomes in your sample space are equally likely.

EXAMPLE 3 Adding Two Dice

Roll two dice and add the topsides. Assume that each side of each die is equally likely to appear face up when rolled. Event A is the event that the sum of the two dice is 7.

QUESTION What is the probability of event A? In other words, find P(A).

SOLUTION This problem is harder because it takes some work to list all of the equally likely outcomes, which are shown in Table 5.2.

Die 1	1	1	1	1	1	1	2	2	2	2	2	2
Die 2	1	2	3	4	5	6	1	2	3	4	5	6

Die 1	3	3	3	3	3	3	4	4	4	4	4	4
Die 2	1	2	3	4	5	6	1	2	3	4	5	6

Die 1	5	5	5	5	5	5	6	6	6	6	6	6
Die 2	1	2	3	4	5	6	1	2	3	4	5	6

◀ **TABLE 5.2** Possible outcomes for two six-sided dice.

Table 5.2 lists 36 possible equally likely outcomes. Here are the outcomes that make up event A:

(1, 6), (2, 5), (3, 4), (4, 3), (5, 2), (6, 1)

There are six outcomes for which the dice add to 7.

CONCLUSION The probability of rolling a sum of 7 is 6/36, or 1/6.

TRY THIS! Exercise 5.15

A common mistake when solving Example 3 is double-counting outcomes when the topsides of Die 1 and Die 2 show the same number. There is one outcome when

Die 1 and Die 2 each show a 1. Similarly, there is only one outcome when Die 1 and Die 2 both show a 6. Another common mistake in this example is listing all the possible *sums* instead of listing all the equally likely outcomes of the two dice. If we made that mistake here, our list of sums would look like this:

$$2, 3, 4, 5, 6, 7, 8, 9, 10, 11, 12$$

This list has 11 sums, and only one of them is a 7, so we would incorrectly conclude that the probability of getting a sum of 7 is 1/11.

Why didn't we get the correct answer of 1/6? The reason is that the outcomes we listed—2, 3, 4, 5, 6, 7, 8, 9, 10, 11, 12—are not equally likely. For instance, we can get a sum of 2 in only one way: roll two "aces," for $1 + 1$. Similarly, we have only one way to get a 12: roll two 6's, for $6 + 6$.

However, there are six ways of getting a 7: (1, 6), (2, 5), (3, 4), (4, 3), (5, 2), and (6, 1). In other words, a sum of 7 happens more often than a sum of 2 or a sum of 12. The outcomes 2, 3, 4, 5, 6, 7, 8, 9, 10, 11, 12 are not equally likely.

Usually it is not practical to list all the outcomes in a sample space—or even just those in the event you're interested in. For example, the Lotto Max lottery involves picking seven numbers (without replacement) from 49 numbers (1 through 49). If you are wondering how many different tickets are possible (or the total number of ways to pick seven numbers from 1 through 49), the sample space has 85,900,584 different outcomes! Listing these outcomes would take forever, and is entirely unnecessary, since mathematicians have developed rules for counting the number of outcomes in complex situations such as these. These rules do not play an important role in introductory statistics, and we do not include them in this book.

Combining Events with "AND" and "OR"

As you saw in Chapter 4, we are often interested in studying more than one variable at a time. Real people, after all, often have several attributes we want to study, and we frequently want to know the relationship among these variables. The words AND and OR can be used to combine events into new, more complex events. The real people in Figure 5.3a, for example, have two attributes we decided to examine. They are either wearing a hat, or not. Also, they are either wearing glasses, or not.

In the photo, the people who are wearing hats AND glasses are raising their hands. Another way to visualize this situation is with a **Venn diagram**, as shown in Figure 5.3b. The rectangle represents the sample space, which consists of all possible outcomes if we were to select a person at random. The ovals represent events—for example, the event that someone is wearing glasses. The people who "belong" to *both* events are in the intersection of the two ovals.

(a)

(b)

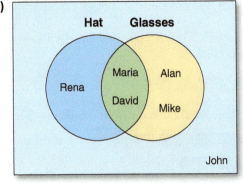

▲ **FIGURE 5.3 (a)** Raise your hand if you are wearing glasses AND a hat. **(b)** The people wearing both glasses AND a hat (Maria and David) appear in the intersection of the two circles in this Venn diagram.

The word **AND** creates a new event out of two other events. The probability that a randomly selected person in this photo is wearing a hat is 3/6, because three of the six people are wearing a hat. The probability that a randomly selected person wears glasses is 4/6. The probability that a person is wearing a hat AND glasses is 2/6, because only two people are in both groups. We could write this, mathematically, as

P(wears glasses AND wears a hat) = 2/6

KEY POINT   The word AND creates a new event out of two events A and B. The new event consists of *only* those outcomes that are in *both* event A and event B.

In most situations, you will not have a photo to rely on. A more typical situation is given in Table 5.3, which gives the frequencies of two variables for students taking an introductory statistics class, similar to this one, at a university in western Canada. The two attributes are gender and most common method of transportation used to get to class.

Gender	Transportation Method					
	Drive Alone	Carpool	Transit	Walk	Bicycle	Total
Male	19	0	25	3	0	47
Female	22	6	25	5	2	60
Total	41	6	50	8	2	107

◄ **TABLE 5.3** Gender and method of transportation of 107 students taking an introductory statistics course.

EXAMPLE 4 Gender and Method of Transportation

Suppose we select a student at random from the class of 107 students categorized in Table 5.3.

QUESTIONS

a. What is the probability that the student is female?

b. What is the probability that the student uses transit as their most common method of transportation to get to class?

c. What is the probability that the student is female AND uses transit as her most common method of transportation to get to class?

SOLUTIONS   The sample space has a total of 107 equally likely outcomes.

a. In 60 of those outcomes, the student is female. So the probability that a randomly selected student is female is 60/107, or 56.1%.

b. In 50 of those outcomes, the student has taken transit as their most common method of transportation used to get to class. So the probability that a randomly selected student uses transit as their most common method of transportation to get to class is 50/107, or 46.7%.

c. In 25 of those outcomes, the student is both female AND uses transit as the most common method of transportation used to get to class. So the probability that a randomly selected student is female and uses transit as her most common method of transportation to get to class is 25/107, or 23.4%.

TRY THIS!   Exercise 5.21

 Caution

AND
P(A AND B) will always be less than (or equal to) P(A) and also less than (or equal to) P(B). If this isn't the case, you've made a mistake!

Using "OR" to Combine Events

The people in Figure 5.4a were asked to raise their hands if they were wearing glasses OR wearing a hat. Note that people who are wearing both also have their hands raised. If we were to select one of these people at random, the probability that this person is wearing glasses OR wearing a hat would be 5/6, because we would count people who wear glasses, people who wear hats, and people who wear both glasses AND hats.

(a)

Mike Rena Maria Alan John David

(b)

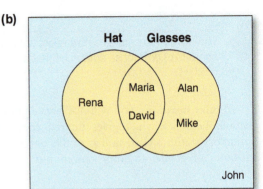

▲ **FIGURE 5.4 (a)** Raise your hand if you are wearing a hat OR glasses. This photograph illustrates the inclusive OR. **(b)** In this Venn diagram, note the yellow region for "raise your hand if you are wearing a hat OR glasses."

In a Venn diagram, OR events are represented by shading all relevant events. Here Mike, Rena, Maria, Alan, and David appear in the yellow area because each is wearing glasses OR wearing a hat. The word OR is another, yet different event that represents a combination of the two other events.

The last example illustrates a special meaning of the word OR. This word is used slightly differently in mathematics and probability than you may use it in English. In statistics and probability, we use the **inclusive OR**. For example, the people in the photo shown in Figure 5.4a were asked to raise their hands if they had a hat OR glasses. This means that the people who raise their hands have a hat only, or have glasses only, or have both hats and glasses.

 KEY POINT The word OR creates a new event out of the events A and B. This new event consists of the outcomes that are only in A, or only in B, or that are in both.

EXAMPLE 5 OR with Method of Transportation

Again, select a student at random from Table 5.3.

QUESTION What is the probability that the student drives alone OR uses transit as their most common method of transportation to get to class?

SOLUTION The event of interest occurs if the randomly chosen student either drives alone, or uses transit as their most common method of transportation to get to class. There are 107 equally likely outcomes. Of these, 41 drive as their most common method of transportation to class; 50 take transit as their most common method of transportation to class. There are then 41 + 50 = 91 students who most commonly drive OR take transit to get to class.

CONCLUSION The probability that the randomly chosen student drives alone OR uses transit as their most common method of transportation used to get to class is 91/107, or 85.0%.

TRY THIS! Exercise 5.23

EXAMPLE 6 Gender OR with Method of Transportation

Select a student at random from Table 5.3 (which is shown again in Table 5.4 below).

QUESTION What is the probability that the student is female OR uses transit as their most common method of transportation to get to class?

SOLUTION Table 5.4 gives us 107 possible outcomes. The event of interest happens if we select a student who is female, a student who most commonly uses transit as the method of transportation to get to class, or a student who is female AND uses transit as the most common method of transportation to get to class. There are 60 females, and 50 students who most commonly use transit to get to class.

But wait a minute: there are not $60 + 50 = 110$ different students who are female or use transit as the most common method of transportation; some of these students get counted twice! Those who are both female and use transit as the most common method of transportation were counted once when we looked at students who are female, and were counted again when we counted the number of students who use transit as the most common method to get to class. We can see from Table 5.4 that 25 students are both female AND use transit as the most common method of transportation used to get to class.

Gender	Drives Alone	Carpool	Transit	Walk	Bicycle	Total
Male	19	0	**25**	3	0	47
Female	**22**	**6**	**25**	**5**	**2**	60
Total	41	6	**50**	8	2	107

◄ **TABLE 5.4** Here we reprint Table 5.3, with ovals for Female and Transit added.

The numbers in the bold type represent the students that are female OR most commonly use transit as transportation to get to class. This Venn-like treatment emphasizes that one group (of 25 students) is in both categories and reminds us not to double-count them.

Another way to say this is that there are 85 distinct outcomes by adding the numbers in the ovals in the table, ensuring we do not add any of these counts more than once:

$$25 + 25 + 22 + 6 + 5 + 2 = 85$$

CONCLUSION The probability that a randomly selected student is female OR uses transit as the most common method of transportation to get to class is 85/107, or 79.4%.

TRY THIS! Exercise 5.25

Mutually Exclusive Events

Did you notice that the first example of an OR (drives alone or uses transit) was much easier than the second (female or uses transit)? In the second example, we had to be careful not to count some people twice. In the first example, this was not a problem. Why?

The answer is that in the first example, we were counting people who either drive alone OR take transit as their most common method of getting to class. No person can be in both categories—a person either most frequently drives (with no one else in the vehicle) to get to class or most often takes transit. When two events have no outcomes in common—that is, when two events cannot occur at the same time—they are called **mutually exclusive events**. The events "student drives alone" and "student takes transit" are mutually exclusive. A randomly selected student will either "most frequently drive alone" to get to class or "most frequently take transit" to get to class.

The Venn diagram in Figure 5.5 shows two mutually exclusive events. There is no intersection between these events; it is impossible for both event A AND event B to happen at once. This means that the probability that both events occur at the same time is 0.

▶ **FIGURE 5.5** In a Venn diagram, two mutually exclusive events have no overlap.

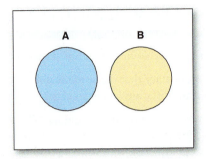

EXAMPLE 7 Mutually Exclusive Events: Gender and Method of Transportation

Imagine selecting a student at random from those represented in Table 5.4.

QUESTION Name two mutually exclusive events, and name two events that are not mutually exclusive. Remember that method of transportation is the type of transportation most commonly used by a student to get to class—the type that has the highest relative frequency for each student.

SOLUTION For mutually exclusive events, we can choose any two categories of most commonly used methods of transportation, or any two columns. One of the 107 students will fall into only one of these columns; he or she cannot fall into two columns. It is impossible for a student to "most commonly drive alone to class" and "most commonly walk to class." The events "most commonly carpool to class" and "most commonly drive alone to class" are also mutually exclusive events. If a student falls into the "most commonly carpools" column, this student is most often taking turns being a passenger/taking their turn driving with others. A student satisfying this event cannot be "driving alone" most often.

To find two events that are not mutually exclusive, find events that *can occur together*. That is, find a row and a column where the number of students satisfying both events is not zero. The events "student is male" and "most commonly drives alone" are not mutually exclusive events, as there are 19 students who are both "male" and "drive alone" most often. The probability that a randomly selected student is a male and most commonly drives alone is 19/107, or 17.8%. However, the events "student is male" and "most commonly carpools" *are mutually exclusive events* because of the 107 students, 0 are male and carpool to get to class. Guys in this class don't carpool, but girls in this class do.

TRY THIS! Exercise 5.29

Summary of Probability Rules

Rule 4: The probability that event A happens OR event B happens is

> (the probability that A happens) plus (the probability that
> B happens) minus (the probability that both A AND B happen).

If A and B are mutually exclusive events (for example A is the event that the selected student's most common method of transportation to class is driving, and B is the event that the student's most common method of transportation to class is transit), then P(A AND B) = 0. Then the rule becomes easier:

Rule 4a: If A and B are mutually exclusive events, the probability that event A happens OR event B happens is the sum of the probability that A happens and the probability that B happens.

Rule 4 in symbols:

$$\text{Always: P(A OR B)} = \text{P(A)} + \text{P(B)} - \text{P(A AND B)}$$

Rule 4a in symbols:

$$\text{Only if A and B are mutually exclusive: P(A OR B)} = \text{P(A)} + \text{P(B)}$$

EXAMPLE 8 Rolling a Six-Sided Die

Roll a fair, six-sided die.

QUESTIONS

a. Find the probability that the die shows an even number OR a number greater than 4 on top.

b. Find the probability that the die shows an even number OR the number 5 on top.

SOLUTIONS

a. We could do this in two ways. First, we note that six equally likely outcomes are possible. The even numbers are (2, 4, 6) and the numbers greater than 4 are (5, 6). Thus the event "even number OR number greater than 4" has four different ways of happening: roll a 2, 4, 5, or 6. We conclude that the probability is 4/6.

   The second approach is to use Rule 4. The probability of getting an even number is 3/6. The probability of getting a number greater than 4 is 2/6. The probability of getting both an even number AND a number greater than 4 is 1/6 (because the only way for this to happen is to roll a 6). So

$$\text{P(even OR greater than 4)} = \text{P(even)} + \text{P(greater than 4)} - \text{P(even AND greater than 4)}$$
$$= 3/6 + 2/6 - 1/6$$
$$= 4/6$$

b. $\text{P(even OR roll 5)} = \text{P(even)} + \text{P(roll 5)} - \text{P(even AND roll 5)}$

It is impossible for the die to be both even AND a 5, because 5 is an odd number. So the events "get a 5" and "get an even number" are mutually exclusive. Therefore, we get

$$\text{P(even number OR a 5)} = 3/6 + 1/6 - 0 = 4/6$$

CONCLUSIONS

a. The probability of rolling an even number OR a number greater than 4 is 4/6 (or 2/3).

b. The probability of rolling an even number OR a 5 is 4/6 (or 2/3).

TRY THIS! Exercise 5.33

Estimating Probabilities

We've seen how to find probabilities when the sample space of the experiment can be listed without too much trouble. From this list, we count the number of outcomes that make the event happen and divide by the total number of possible outcomes. But what if the experiment has a sample space that we cannot list? Maybe there are just too many possible outcomes to list. Or what if we do not know *all that can happen*, but we do know *a few outcomes that can occur*?

   In such situations, we can repeat the experiment and observe the relative frequency of the event of interest. Let us look at the game of "Craps." In this popular casino game the player throws two dice and observes the numbers showing on the topside of the dice. The player—and people around the table—are free to place bets on the various outcomes of the game: the numbers showing on the topside of the dice.

Of the many types of "bets" that can be made here, one is the *pass-line* bet. This bet is won when the two die are tossed and show topsides with numbers that add up to seven or eleven—that is, we roll a sum of seven or eleven. If the first toss of the die shows a sum of two, three, or twelve, the bet results in a loss. If the sum of the dice shows anything else—like a four—the dice are gathered and tossed again until the "anything else" occurs again (a win) or a sum of seven shows before the "anything else" comes up again (a loss).

The outcome of the pass-line bet on a game of Craps is very complex. How do we find the probability of winning in a single game of Craps? Well, we can conduct an experiment and see what happens: we play Craps a few times, each time observing whether a game gives a "winning" or a "losing" outcome. So here we go: grab a pair of dice and toss once, or "throw the bones." If the topsides of the dice sum to seven or eleven, a win occurs; if the dice sum to two, three, or twelve, a loss occurs. Otherwise, we observe a different sum that means we continue to throw the dice until we either get this same "continuing" outcome, or a sum of seven or eleven. Table 5.5 below gives the results of 10 plays of Craps.

▶ **TABLE 5.5** Results of our 10 games of Craps.

Game	1	2	3	4	5	6	7	8	9	10
Outcome	Win	Loss	Win	Win	Win	Win	Win	Win	Win	Loss

In the 10 repeated experiments, we won 8 games and lost 2. The short-term relative frequency, the percentage of games won out of these 10, is 8/10, or 80%. But this does not mean that the probability of winning is 80%. Suppose we were to play another 10 games, now winning 3. This relative frequency is 30%, which is different from 80%. *In total*, there are 11 winning games out of 20, or 55%. We can see that these short-run relative frequencies change as additional experiments are carried out. A graph of the game-by-game outcomes and the relative frequencies of wins found at each game in the series of 20 is given in Figure 5.6.

▶ **FIGURE 5.6** Running relative frequencies of wins for 20 games of Craps.

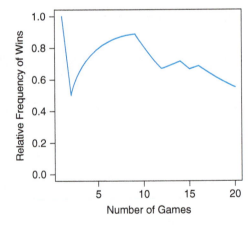

Here we are attempting to estimate the probability of winning on the pass-line bet in a game of Craps through the repeated *observation* of the experiment. Such probability estimates are themselves random and vary from experiment to experiment.

KEY POINT By keeping track of how often an event occurs in an actual set of experiments, we can estimate the probability of the event by finding its relative frequency.

Why Compute Probabilities through Observation of the Experiment?

A probability measures the proportion of the time we expect the event to occur if the experiment were repeated *infinitely many times*. That's a very long time—forever, in fact. This means it is impossible to carry out an experiment that will provide the exact value of a probability; to do so would literally take forever. But it turns out that we can use probabilities through observation of the experiment to *estimate* and to *test* assumed values of probabilities.

Why do we need to estimate the probability of an event by observing the results of a repeated experiment? Sometimes it is just too difficult to compute the probability by creating a list of all possible outcomes. Development of the mathematics of probability began in the 1600s, and we can now find exact probabilities for very complex events. But this does not mean it's easy! In many situations, an approximate value based on an experiment that allows us to estimate how often a certain event might happen if we could repeat the experiment infinitely many times is good enough. On other occasions, the event for which we need a probability may be too complex for theory, so running an experiment is the only way of approximating the probability.

Why do we need to test assumed probability values? We might not trust an assumed probability value, as it may be based on assumptions that we are not sure are true. A probability estimated by observing results of an experiment repeated many, many times can be used to verify or refute a value derived from theory, as long as the experiment is repeated in similar conditions. In fact, much of the rest of this book will develop this theme.

Through continued observation of the rolling of two dice, in the short run we would estimate the probability of winning the pass-line bet in a game of Craps to be 55%. This is based on 20 identical games. If we continued to play many games of Craps, we would find that our short-run relative frequency of 55% would start to settle around a specific value. In the long run, our relative frequency would not vary from game to game.

Simulations are experiments used to find probabilities through such observation. The investigators hope that these experiments (or simulations) act like the random situation they are investigating. A large simulation of playing a game of Craps was repeated 500 times. The running relative frequency of wins and the number of games played are shown in Figure 5.7.

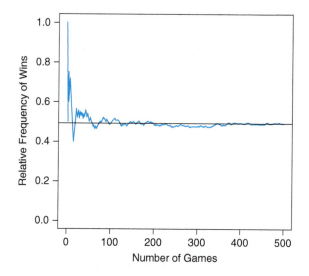

◀ **FIGURE 5.7** Running relative frequencies of wins for 500 games of Craps.

We can observe how the running relative frequency of wins varies dramatically from game to game in the short run, but after about 500 games the relative frequency of wins settles at around 50%. We then estimate the probability of winning the pass-line bet to be 50%. In fact, advanced probability methods will show that the probability of winning the pass-line bet is 49.29%! Our estimate looks pretty good.

If you do the "Let's Make a Deal" activity described at the end of this chapter, through observation of a repeated experiment you will estimate the probabilities of winning for each of the two strategies offered to contestants: always stay or always switch. These values allow you to estimate the probability of winning and allow you to test whether your own ideas about which strategy is best are correct.

In most situations, you will not have a Venn diagram to rely on as we did in Figures 5.3 and 5.4. A more typical situation is given in Table 5.6, which records the frequencies of two attributes for people in a random sample of 997 Canadian citizens who participated in a Statistics Canada survey in 2008 (we encountered a similar data set in the case study for Chapter 2, The Financial Benefits of Learning, page 33). The two attributes are highest education level and before-tax income. We would like to estimate probabilities of characteristics of interest (events) for all Canadian citizens by computing relative frequencies based on these results. The "experiment" that we are repeating here is the random selection of a Canadian citizen.

► **TABLE 5.6** Education and before-tax income of 997 Canadian residents. (Source: Survey of Labour and Income Dynamics (SLID), 2008. Statistics Canada)

Education Level	Below $25,000	$25,000 to $50,000	$50,000 to $75,000	$75,000 to $100,000	Over $100,000	Total
Less than HS	159	58	13	4	5	239
High School	129	97	36	13	7	282
Two-Year Diploma/Degree	107	117	63	21	13	321
Four-Year Diploma/Degree	36	38	37	19	25	155
Total	431	310	149	57	50	997

EXAMPLE **9** Education and Annual Income

Suppose we select a person at random from the collection of 997 people categorized in Table 5.6.

QUESTIONS

a. What is the probability that the person has an annual income that is between $75,000 and $100,000?

b. What is the probability that the person has a two-year diploma/degree or a four-year diploma/degree?

c. What is the probability that the person has an annual income that is between $75,000 and $100,000 AND has a two-year diploma/degree or a four-year diploma/degree?

d. What is the probability that the person has an annual income that is between $75,000 and $100,000 OR has a two-year diploma/degree or a four-year diploma/degree?

SOLUTIONS The sample space has a total of 997 equally likely outcomes.

a. In 57 of these outcomes, the person has an annual income that is between $75,000 and $100,000. So the probability that a randomly selected person has an annual income between $75,000 and $100,000 is 57/997, or 5.7% (approximately).

b. To have a two-year diploma/degree or a four-year diploma/degree, the person has to have either a two-year diploma/degree or a four-year diploma/degree or both, which is not possible. This happens in 321 + 155, or 476 outcomes. So the probability that the selected person has a two-year diploma/degree or a four-year diploma/degree is 476/997, or 47.4%.

c. Of the 997 possible outcomes, there are 21 + 19 = 40 where people have an annual income between $75,000 and $100,000 AND have a two-year diploma/degree or a four-year diploma/degree. So the probability that the selected person has an annual income between $75,000 and $100,000 AND a two-year diploma/degree or a four-year diploma/degree is 40/997, or 4.0%.

d. We could do this in two ways. First, we note from part (a) that 57 people have an annual income between $75,000 and $100,000. Second, we see from part (b) that 476 people have a two-year diploma/degree or a four-year diploma/degree. In total, there are 57 + 476 = 533 people who have an annual income between $75,000 and $100,000 OR have a two-year diploma/degree or a four-year diploma/degree. But we need to be careful. With these 533 people, we have double-counted those who have an annual income between $75,000 and $100,000 AND have a two-year diploma/degree or a four-year diploma/degree. We found in part (c) that 40 of these people have both attributes. We then subtract 40 from the 533 to correct our double-counting problem, and the probability that the selected person has an annual income between $75,000 and $100,000 OR a two-year diploma/degree or a four-year diploma/degree is (533 − 40)/997, or 49.4%.

The second approach is to use Rule 4. The probability that the person has an annual income between $75,000 and $100,000 is 57/997. The probability that the person has a two-year diploma/degree or a four-year diploma/degree is 476/997. The probability that the person has both attributes is 40/997. So

P($75,000 to $100,000 OR a two-year diploma/degree or a four-year diploma/degree)

= P($75,000 to $100,000) + P(a two-year diploma/degree or a four-year diploma/degree) −
P($75,000 to $100,000 OR a two-year diploma/degree or a four-year diploma/degree)

= 57/997 + 476/997 − 40/997

= 493/997, or 49.4%

TRY THIS! Exercise 5.45

EXAMPLE 10 Education and Annual Income

Again, a person from Table 5.6 is chosen at random.

QUESTION Are the events "having an annual income over $50,000" and "having an education level that is less than high school" mutually exclusive events?

SOLUTION Rule 4 says that for these events to be mutually exclusive, P(income over $50,000 AND an education level that is less than high school) = 0. The probability that the selected person has an annual income over $50,000 AND has a level of education that is less than high school is found by looking at the Less than HS row in Table 5.6 and adding the frequencies in the "$50,000 to $75,000," "$75,000 to $100,000," and "over $100,000" columns. Of the 997 people, there are 13 + 4 + 5, or 22 outcomes where a person without a high school diploma has an annual income over $50,000.

CONCLUSIONS The probability that the chosen person has an annual income greater than $50,000 AND an education level that is less than high school is 22/997, or 2.2%. This probability is quite small, but not equal to zero. Therefore, the events "having an annual income over $50,000" and "having an education level that is less than high school" are not mutually exclusive events. These events are not likely to occur together, but their simultaneous occurrence is not impossible.

TRY THIS! Exercise 5.46

SECTION 5.3

Relationships between Categorical Variables

Based on our discussion in Chapter 4, when we are faced with data on two quantitative variables, we can create a scatterplot to see if there is a relationship between variable X and variable Y. Table 5.6 shows data on two qualitative variables—a person's highest level of education and a person's pre-tax income—with the pre-tax income being classified as one of five different categories. We can't make a scatterplot of these data, but we are probably still interested in whether or not there is a relationship. Is there a relationship between a person's highest level of education and their pre-tax income classification?

Maybe the answer is obvious—and that's why you're taking post-secondary education classes. We consistently read and hear that a post-secondary education of some form will translate to higher incomes. Is this statement supported by the data appearing in Table 5.6? If so, we would expect the probability of people with an annual income between $50,000 and $75,000 to be different for those who have at least a college/technical school diploma and those whose highest level of education is high school. That is, if a person chosen from Table 5.6 has at least a college/technical school diploma, the probability that this person will have a pre-tax income of between $50,000 and $75,000 will be different from the probability that a person not having a college/technical school diploma has a pre-tax income between $50,000 and $75,000.

Conditional Probabilities

Language is important here. The probability that a person with "at least a college/technical diploma has an annual income between $50,000 and $75,000" is different from the probability that a person "has at least a college/technical diploma AND an annual income between $50,000 and $75,000." In the AND case, we're looking at everyone in the sample and wondering how many have both at least a two-year diploma/degree AND an income between $50,000 and $75,000. But when we ask for the probability that a person with at least a two-year diploma/degree has an annual income between $50,000 and $75,000, we're taking it as a *given* that the person has a two-year diploma/degree or a four-year diploma degree. We're not saying "choose someone from the whole collection." We're saying, "Just focus on those people who have at least a college/technical school diploma. What proportion of these people have an annual income between $50,000 and $75,000?"

These types of probabilities, where we focus on just one group of objects and imagine taking one from only this subgroup, are called **conditional probabilities**.

For example, Table 5.7 (which repeats Table 5.6), highlights in red the people who have at least a college/technical school diploma. Of the 997 people, there are 476 (321 + 155) who satisfy such an event. In this subgroup, there are 100 (63 + 37) people satisfying

▶ **TABLE 5.7** What is the probability that a person who has at least a college/technical school diploma has an annual income between $50,000 and $75,000? Focus on the rows shown in red and imagine randomly picking a person from these red rows.

Education Level	Below $25,000	$25,000 to $50,000	$50,000 to $75,000	$75,000 to $100,000	Over $100,000	Total
Less than HS	159	58	13	4	5	239
High School	129	97	36	13	7	282
Two-Year Diploma/Degree	107	117	63	21	13	321
Four-Year Diploma/Degree	36	38	37	19	25	155
Total	431	310	149	57	50	997

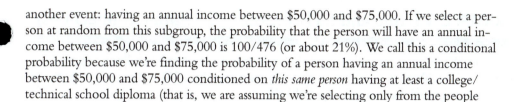

another event: having an annual income between $50,000 and $75,000. If we select a person at random from this subgroup, the probability that the person will have an annual income between $50,000 and $75,000 is 100/476 (or about 21%). We call this a conditional probability because we're finding the probability of a person having an annual income between $50,000 and $75,000 conditioned on *this same person* having at least a college/technical school diploma (that is, we are assuming we're selecting only from the people who have a minimum level of education that is a college/technical school diploma).

"Given That" vs. "AND"

Often conditional probabilities are worded with the phrase *given that*, as in "Find the probability that a randomly chosen person has an annual income between $50,000 and $75,000, given that the person has at least a two-year diploma/degree." But you might also see it phrased: "Find the probability that a randomly chosen person with at least a two-year diploma/degree has an annual income between $50,000 and $75,000." The last phrasing is more subtle, because it implies that we're supposed to assume that the person chosen has an education that is at least at the college/technical school level: we must assume we are *given that* the person has such a level of education.

Figure 5.8a shows a Venn diagram representing all the data. The green overlap region represents the event of having a two-year diploma/degree or a four-year diploma/degree as a minimum level of education AND an annual income between $50,000 and $75,000. By way of contrast, Figure 5.8b shows only those with a two-year diploma/degree as a minimum level of education; it highlights that if we wish to find the probability of one's annual income being between $50,000 and $75,000, given that a person has at least a two-year diploma/degree, we need to focus on only those who have a two-year or four-year diploma/degree.

The probability notation used to state a conditional probability might seem strange. We write

P($50,000 to $75,000 | a two-year or four-year diploma/degree) = 100/476 = 0.210

The vertical bar inside the probability parentheses is *not a division sign*. You should think of this vertical bar as code for "given that." The probability expression above reads as: "Given that a person has a two-year or four-year diploma/degree, the probability that a person has an annual income between $50,000 and $75,000 is 100/476." Statisticians sometimes think of this vertical bar as "conditioning on" and state this as "The probability that we randomly select a person with an annual income between $50,000 and $75,000 from the subgroup of people who have at least a college/technical school diploma is 100/476." Both statements are perfectly acceptable.

(a)

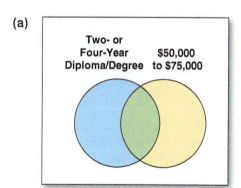

(b)

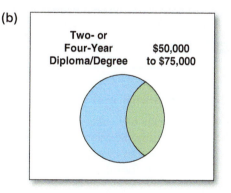

◀ **FIGURE 5.8 (a)** The probability of having a two-year or four-year diploma/degree and an annual income between $50,000 and $75,000; **(b)** the probability of having an annual income between $50,000 and $75,000 given that the person has at least a two-year diploma/degree.

KEY POINT ▶ In the study of conditional probabilities, P(A | B) means to find the probability that event A occurs, but to restrict your consideration to those outcomes of A that occur within event B. It means "the probability of A occurring, given that event B has occurred."

EXAMPLE 11 Age and STIs (Sexually Transmitted Infections)

Consider the following statements, which are based on a study of sexually transmitted infection rates (Chlamydia, gonorrhea, and infectious syphilis) of Canadians who are young (15–29 years) or who are middle-aged (40–49 years).

a. The probability that a randomly selected Canadian between the ages of 15 and 29 will have contracted one of these STIs is 0.87% (about 8.7 out of every 1000). Event A: the chosen Canadian is between the ages of 15 and 29. Event B: the chosen Canadian has had an STI.

b. The probability that a randomly selected Canadian between the ages of 40 and 49 will have contracted one of these STIs is 0.034% (about 3.4 out of every 10,000). Event A: the chosen Canadian is between the ages of 40 and 49. Event B: the chosen Canadian has had an STI.

c. The probability that a randomly selected Canadian is between the ages of 15 and 29 and has had an STI is 0.02% (about 2 out of 10,000). Event A: the chosen Canadian is between the ages of 15 and 29. Event B: the chosen Canadian has had an STI.

We wish to use this information to find the probability that a randomly selected person in Canada will be between 15 and 29 years old and has had an STI.

QUESTION For each of these three statements, determine whether the events in the question are used in a conditional probability or an AND probability. Explain. Write the statement using probability notation.

SOLUTIONS

a. This statement is asking about a conditional probability. It says that among the subgroup of Canadians aged between 15 and 29 years, 0.87% have had an STI. We are "given that" the group being sampled from comprises only Canadians 15 to 29 years old. In probability notation, this statement is P(person has had an STI | person is between 15 and 29 years of age) = 0.0087.

b. This statement is also a conditional probability. In probability notation, P(person has had an STI | person is between 40 and 49 years of age) = 0.00034.

c. This statement is different. It is asking us to assume nothing, and instead, once the person is randomly chosen from the Canadian population, to determine whether this person has these two characteristics: between the ages of 15 and 29 AND has had an STI. In probability notation, P(person has had an STI AND person is between 15 and 29 years of age) = 0.0002.

TRY THIS! Exercise 5.47

Finding Conditional Probabilities

If you are given a table like Table 5.7, you can find conditional probabilities as we did above: by isolating the group from which you are sampling. However, a formula exists that is useful for times when you do not have such complete information.

The formula for calculating conditional probabilities is

$$P(A|B) = \frac{P(A \text{ AND } B)}{P(B)}$$

To show how this formula works, suppose we draw a card from a standard deck of playing cards. When playing card games, players always try to avoid showing their cards to the other players. The reason for this is that knowledge of the other players' cards can often

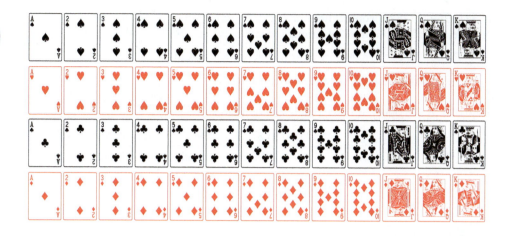

give you an advantage. Suppose you are wondering whether your opponent has the Ace of Spades. If you find out that one of the cards he holds is an ace, is this information useful?

Suppose a deck of cards is well-shuffled, and assumed to be in random order. One card is dealt face-down on the table. From Figure 5.9, we can find that the probability of this card being an ace is 4/52. If this card is an ace, we are interested only in the outcomes that produce such a given event. That is, we are concerned only with the outcomes that will give an ace. There are four outcomes in this subgroup: Ace of Hearts, Ace of Diamonds, Ace of Clubs, and Ace of Spades. If we know that the face-down card is an ace, the conditional probability that the given ace is a spade is 1/4, or 25%.

Using the formula for calculating conditional probabilities, we wish to find P(Ace of Spades | face-down cards is an ace).

$$P(\text{Ace of Spades} \mid \text{face-down card is an ace}) = \frac{P(\text{Ace of Spades AND face-down card is an ace})}{P(\text{face-down card is an ace})}$$

First let's find the probability of the *given event*, P(face-down card is an ace). We have already found this probability to be 4/52. This probability is placed in the *denominator* of the above formula. Second, we find P(Ace of Spades AND face-down cards is an ace) by counting the number of outcomes that cause both the card to be an ace—of which there are 4, and the card to be an Ace of Spades—of which there is 1. The P(Ace of Spades AND face-down card is an ace) = 1/52. This probability is then placed in the *numerator* of this formula.

$$P(\text{Ace of Spades} \mid \text{face-down cards is an ace}) = \frac{1/52}{4/52} = 1/4 = 0.25$$

You could think of this in another way. If we know the face-down card is an ace, then there are only four possible cards it could be—the Ace of Spades being one of them. So the probability that the card is the Ace of Spades given that it is an ace is 1/4.

Interestingly, if the face-down card is an ace, the probability that it is the Ace of Spades is 1/4, or 25%. Without knowing that the face-down card is an ace, this probability is 1/52, or 1.9%.

EXAMPLE **12** Education Level and Annual Income

Suppose a person is randomly chosen from those represented in Table 5.7 on page 210.

QUESTION Find the probability that a person whose highest level of education is a high school diploma has an annual income between $50,000 and $75,000.

SOLUTION We are asked to find P($50,000 to $75,000 | at most a high school diploma)—in other words, the probability that a person whose highest education level is a high school diploma will have an annual income between $50,000 and $75,000. There are 521 (239 + 282) people whose highest level of education is a high school diploma. Of these, 49 (13 + 36) have an annual income between \$50,000 and \$75,000.

P(\$50,000 to \$75,000 | at most a high school diploma) = 49/521 = 0.094

The conditional probability formula confirms this:

P(\$50,000 to \$75,000 | at most a high school diploma)

$$= \frac{P(\$50{,}000 \text{ to } \$75{,}000 \text{ AND at most a high school diploma})}{P(\text{at most a high school diploma})}$$

$$= \frac{49/997}{521/997} = 49/521 = 0.094$$

TRY THIS! Exercise 5.49

With a little algebra, we can discover that this formula can serve as another way of finding AND probabilities:

$$P(A \text{ AND } B) = P(A)P(B|A)$$

We'll make use of this formula later.

Summary of Probability Rules

Rule 5a: $P(A|B) = \dfrac{P(A \text{ AND } B)}{P(B)}$

Rule 5b: $P(A \text{ AND } B) = P(A|B) P(B)$ and also $P(A \text{ AND } B) = P(B|A) P(A)$

Both forms of Rule 5b are true, because it doesn't matter which event is called A and which is called B.

Flipping the Condition

A common mistake with conditional probabilities is thinking that $P(A|B)$ is the same as $P(B|A)$.

$$P(B|A) \neq P(A|B)$$

A second common mistake is to confuse conditional probabilities with fractions and think that $P(B|A) = 1/P(A|B)$.

$$P(B|A) \neq \frac{1}{P(A|B)}$$

Using the data in Table 5.7, we earlier computed P(\$50,000 to \$75,000 | at least a two-year diploma/degree) = 100/476 = 0.210. What if we wanted to know the probability that a randomly selected person having an annual salary between \$50,000 and \$75,000 had at least a two-year diploma/degree?

P(at least a two-year diploma/degree | \$50,000 to \$75,000) = ?

From Table 5.7, we can see that if we know the person has an annual income between \$50,000 and \$75,000, there are 149 possible outcomes. Of these 149 people, 100 (63 + 37) have a two-year or a four-year diploma/degree:

P(at least a two-year diploma/degree | \$50,000 to \$75,000) = 100/149, or about 0.671

Clearly, P(at least a two-year diploma/degree| $50,000 to $75,000), which is 0.671, does not equal P($50,000 to $75,000 | at least a two-year diploma/degree), which is 0.210.

Also, it is *not* true that P(at least a two-year diploma/degree | $50,000 to $75,000) = 1/P ($50,000 to $75,000 | at least a two-year diploma/degree) = 476/100 = 4.76, a number bigger than 1! It is impossible for a probability to be bigger than 1, so obviously,

$$P(A|B) \text{ does not equal } 1/P(B|A).$$

> **KEY POINT**
>
> $P(B|A) \neq P(A|B)$ and $P(A|B) \neq \dfrac{1}{P(B|A)}$

Independent and Dependent Events

We've seen that the probability of a person having an annual income between $50,000 and $75,000 differs depending on whether they have at least a two-year diploma/ degree or if their highest level of education is at most a high school diploma. Similarly, if we were to focus on a different income group that we randomly select from, we would notice that the probability of a person having an annual income greater than $100,000 would be different if we were to select from those having a university degree than if we were to select from those who have a college/technical school diploma. Another way of saying this is that annual income and education level are **related events**. We know they are related because the probability of falling into a certain annual income bracket will change *depending* on which educational level we condition on.

We call variables or events that are *not* related, or dependent, **independent events**. Independent variables or events play a very important role in statistics.

Two events are independent when the occurrence of one event, say A, does not affect the probability of occurrence of the other event, event B. In the conditional probability notation,

$$A \text{ and } B \text{ are independent events means } P(A|B) = P(A).$$

In other words, if the event "a person has an annual income between $50,000 and $75,000" is independent from the event "a person has at least a two-year diploma/ degree," then the probability that a person has an annual income between $50,000 and $75,000 will be the same regardless of their level of education, or

$$P(\$50,000 \text{ to } \$75,000 \mid \text{at least a two-year diploma/degree}) = 0.210 \text{ and}$$

$$P(\$50,000 \text{ to } \$75,000) = 149/997 = 0.149$$

Although these probabilities do not differ by much, they are not exactly the same. Therefore the events "a randomly chosen person has an annual income between $50,000 and $75,000" and "a randomly chosen person has at least a two-year diploma/degree" are not independent. For now we will assume that *probabilities have to be exactly the same to conclude independence*. By this, we conclude that a person's annual income and their education level are *not* independent events.

> **KEY POINT**
>
> To say that events A and B are independent means that $P(A|B) = P(A)$. In words: Knowledge that event B occurred does not change the probability of event A occurring.

It doesn't matter which event you call A and which B, so events are also independent if $P(B|A) = P(B)$.

EXAMPLE **13** Dealing a Diamond

Figure 5.9 on page 213 shows all the outcomes from a random experiment where a card is randomly chosen from a standard deck. We've already pointed out that when playing card games, players nearly always try to avoid showing their cards to the other players, since knowing the other players' cards can sometimes give you an advantage. Suppose you are wondering whether your opponent has a diamond. If you find out that one of the cards he holds is red, does this provide useful information?

QUESTION Suppose a deck of cards is shuffled and one card is dealt face-down on the table. Are the events "the card is a diamond" and "the card is red" independent?

SOLUTION To answer this, we must apply the definition of independent events and find

$$P(\text{card is a diamond})$$

and compare it to

$$P(\text{card is a diamond} \mid \text{card is red})$$

If these probabilities are different, then the events are not independent; they are related events.

First we find P(card is a diamond).

Out of a total of 52 cards, 13 are diamonds. Therefore,

$$P(\text{card is a diamond}) = 13/52, \text{ or } 1/4$$

Now suppose we know the card is red. What's the probability that a red card is a diamond? That is, find

$$P(\text{card is a diamond} \mid \text{card is red})$$

The number of equally likely possible outcomes is reduced from 52 to 26, because there are 26 red cards. You are now limited to the 26 cards in the middle two rows of Figure 5.9. There are still 13 diamonds. Therefore, the probability that the card is a diamond, given that it is red, is $13/26 = 1/2$.

$$P(\text{card is a diamond}) = 1/4$$
$$P(\text{card is a diamond} \mid \text{card is red}) = 1/2$$

These probabilities are *not* equal.

CONCLUSION The events "select a diamond" and "select a red card" are related, because P(select a diamond | card is red) is not the same as P(select a diamond). This means that if you learn, somehow, that your opponent's card is red, then you have gained some information that will be useful in deciding whether he has a diamond.

Note that we could also have compared P(card is red) to P(card is red | card is a diamond), and we would have reached the same conclusion.

TRY THIS! Exercise 5.57

EXAMPLE **14** Dealing an Ace

A playing card is dealt face-down. This time, you are interested in knowing whether your opponent holds an ace. You have discovered that his card is a diamond. Is this helpful information?

QUESTION Are the events "card is a diamond" and "card is an ace" independent?

SOLUTION Now we must find P(card is an ace) and compare it to P(card is an ace | card is a diamond).

We have found that P(card is an ace) $= 4/52 = 1/13$.

P(card is an ace | card is a diamond):
There are 13 diamonds in the deck, and only one of these 13 is an ace.
Therefore, P(card is an ace | card is a diamond) = 1/13.

We find that P(card is an ace) = 1/13 = P(card is an ace | card is a diamond).

CONCLUSION The events "card is a diamond" and "card is an ace" are independent. This means the information that your opponent's card is a diamond will not help you determine whether it is an ace.

Note that we could also compare P(card is a diamond) to P(card is a diamond | card is an ace), and we would have reached the same conclusion.

TRY THIS! Exercise 5.59

Intuition about Independence

Sometimes you can use your intuition to decide whether two events are independent. For example, flip a coin twice. You should know that P(second flip is heads) = 1/2. But what if you know that the first flip was also a head? Then you need to find

P(second flip is heads | first flip was heads)

Intuitively, we know that the coin always has a 50% chance of coming up heads. The coin doesn't know what happened earlier. Thus

P(second is heads | first is heads) = 1/2 = P(second is heads)

The two events "second flip comes up heads" and "first flip comes up heads" are independent.

Although you can sometimes feel very confident in your intuition, you should check your intuition with data whenever possible.

EXAMPLE 15 Education Level and Annual Income

Suppose a person is randomly chosen from the sample of people asked about pre-tax income and their highest level of education in Table 5.7. Is the event "person selected has an annual income between $75,000 and $100,000" independent of the event "person selected has a four-year diploma/degree"? We would think the answer to this is "no." Perhaps this is the reason why you are in post-secondary education, to improve your earning potential. But no matter, what do the data say?

QUESTION From the data in Table 5.7 on page 210, check if these two events are independent.

SOLUTION To check independence, we need to check whether P(A|B) = P(A). It doesn't matter which event we call A and which we call B, so let's check to see whether

P(person selected has annual income between $75,000 and $100,000 | person has a four-year diploma/degree) = P(person has annual income between $75,000 and $100,000)

From the table, we see there are 155 people with a four-year diploma/degree. Of these 155, 19 have an income between $75,000 and $100,000. So,

P(person selected has annual income between $75,000 and $100,000 | person has a four-year diploma/degree) = 19/155 = 0.123

P(person has annual income between $75,000 and $100,000) = 57/997 = 0.057

The two probabilities are not equal.

CONCLUSION The events are related, or not independent. If you know that the selected person has a university degree, such a person has a higher chance of having an annual income between $75,000 and $100,000 than a person whose highest level of education is unknown. These data support the idea that higher incomes appear to be dependent on a person's education level.

TRY THIS! Exercise 5.61

Sequences of Independent and Related Events

A common challenge in probability is to find probabilities for sequences of events. By sequence, we mean events that take place in a certain order. For example, a married couple plans to have two children. What's the probability that the first will be a boy and the second a girl? When dealing with sequences, it is helpful to first determine whether the events are independent or related.

If the two events are related, then our knowledge of conditional probabilities is useful, and we should use Probability Rule 5b:

$$P(A \text{ AND } B) = P(A)P(B \mid A)$$

If the events are independent, then we know $P(B \mid A) = P(B)$, and this rule simplifies to $P(A \text{ AND } B) = P(A) P(B)$. This formula is often called the **multiplication rule**.

Summary of Probability Rules

Rule 5c: Multiplication Rule. If A and B are independent events, then

$$P(A \text{ AND } B) = P(A) P(B).$$

Independent Events

When two events are independent, the multiplication rule speeds up probability calculations for events joined by AND.

Here's an example: An apparent spike in concussions as a result of "head shots" in the National Hockey League (NHL) prompted a survey of Canadians 18 years or older (Forum Research 2011). This survey found that 60% of Canadians agree that fighting should be banned from professional hockey. If we were to randomly select one Canadian, we can say that the probability that they agree with a fighting ban in professional hockey, P(ban fighting), is *estimated* to be 0.60—an estimated probability because it results from a survey. Then what is the probability that two randomly chosen Canadians will agree with a fighting ban in pro hockey? In other words, how do we find the sequence probability

P(1st ban fighting AND 2nd ban fighting)?

Notice how these two people are chosen. The random selection means that if the first agrees there should be a ban on fighting in pro hockey, this will not influence how the second person feels about fighting in pro hockey—whether or not it should be banned. These two events are then independent. Because of this, we can apply the multiplication rule:

P(1st ban fighting AND 2nd ban fighting) = P(1st ban fighting) $\times$ P(2nd ban fighting)
= 0.60 $\times$ 0.60 = 0.36

The probability that both agree to a fighting ban in professional hockey is estimated to be 36%.

The same logic can be applied to finding the probability that the first person chosen agrees with a fighting ban in pro hockey and the second person selected does not agree with a fighting ban in pro hockey:

P(1st ban fighting AND 2nd no fighting ban) = P(1st ban fighting) $\times$ P(2nd no fighting ban)
= 0.60 $\times$ (1 − 0.60) = 0.24

The probability that the first will agree with a fighting ban in pro hockey and the second will not is estimated to be 24%.

EXAMPLE **16** Three Coin Flips

Toss a fair coin three times. A fair coin is one in which each side is equally likely to land up when the coin is tossed.

QUESTION What is the probability that all three tosses are tails? What is the probability that the first toss is heads AND the next two are tails?

SOLUTION Using mathematical notation, we are trying to find P(first toss is tails AND second is tails AND third is tails). We know that these events are independent (this is theoretical knowledge; we "know" this because the coin cannot change itself on the basis of its past). This means that the probability is

P(first is tails) $\times$ P(second is tails) $\times$ P(third is tails) = 1/2 $\times$ 1/2 $\times$ 1/2 = 1/8

Also, P(first is heads AND second is tails AND third is tails) is

P(heads) $\times$ P(tails) $\times$ P(tails) = 1/2 $\times$ 1/2 $\times$ 1/2 = 1/8

CONCLUSION The probability of getting three tails is the same as that of getting first heads and then two tails: 1/8.

TRY THIS! Exercise 5.63

EXAMPLE **17** Ten Coin Flips

Suppose you toss a coin 10 times and record whether each toss lands heads or tails. Assume that each side of the coin is equally likely to land up when the coin is tossed.

QUESTION Which sequence is the more likely outcome?

Sequence A: HTHTHTHTHT

Sequence B: HHTTTHTHHH

SOLUTION Because these are independent events, the probability that sequence A happens is

$$P(H)P(T)P(H)P(T)P(H)P(T)P(H)P(T)P(H)P(T) = \frac{1}{2} \times \frac{1}{2} \times \frac{1}{2} \times \frac{1}{2} \times \frac{1}{2} \times \frac{1}{2}$$
$$\times \frac{1}{2} \times \frac{1}{2} \times \frac{1}{2} \times \frac{1}{2}$$
$$= \left(\frac{1}{2}\right)^{10} = 0.0009766$$

The probability that sequence B happens is

$$P(H)P(H)P(T)P(T)P(T)P(H)P(T)P(H)P(H)P(H) = \frac{1}{2} \times \frac{1}{2} \times \frac{1}{2} \times \frac{1}{2} \times \frac{1}{2} \times \frac{1}{2}$$
$$\times \frac{1}{2} \times \frac{1}{2} \times \frac{1}{2} \times \frac{1}{2}$$
$$= \left(\frac{1}{2}\right)^{10} = 0.0009766$$

CONCLUSION Even though sequence A looks improbable because it alternates between heads and tails, both outcomes have the same probability!

TRY THIS! Exercise 5.65

Another common probability question asks about the likelihood of "at least one" of a sequence happening a certain way.

EXAMPLE **18** Ipsos Reid Poll and "at Least One"

An Ipsos Reid poll of Canadians found that 55% of Canadian parents agree that without government support their child would not be able to attend post-secondary studies. Suppose we select three Canadian parents, with children in post-secondary studies, at random from all Canadian parents with children in post-secondary studies.

QUESTIONS

a. What is the probability that all three agree that without government support their children would not be able to attend post-secondary studies?

b. What is the probability that none of the three will agree that without government support their children would not be able to attend post-secondary studies?

c. What is the probability that at least one of the three adults agrees that without government support their children would not be able to attend post-secondary studies?

SOLUTIONS

a. We are asked to find P(first agrees AND second agrees AND third agrees). Because the parents were selected at random from the population, these are independent events. (One parent's response to "agree" won't affect the probability that the next one will agree or disagree.) Because these are independent events, this is just P(first agree) $\times$ P(second agree) $\times$ P(third agree) $= 0.55 \times 0.55 \times 0.55 = 0.1664$.

b. The probability that none agrees is trickier to determine. This event occurs if the first doesn't agree AND the second doesn't agree AND the third doesn't agree. So we need to find P(first doesn't agree AND second doesn't agree AND third doesn't agree) = P(first doesn't agree) $\times$ P(second doesn't agree) $\times$ P(third doesn't agree) = $(1 - 0.55) \times (1 - 0.55) \times (1 - 0.55) = 0.0911$.

c. The probability that at least one of the parents agrees is the probability that one agrees or two agree or all three agree. The calculation is easier if you realize that "at least one of the three agrees" is the complement of "none of the three agrees" because it includes all categories except "none."

$$P(\text{at least one agrees}) = 1 - 0.0911 = 0.9089$$

CONCLUSION The probability that all three randomly selected parents will agree that without government support their children would not be able to attend post-secondary studies is 0.1664. The probability that none would agree is 0.0911. The probability that at least one would agree is 0.9089.

TRY THIS! Exercise 5.67

Caution

False Assumptions of Independence
If your assumption that A and B are independent events is wrong, P(A AND B) can be very wrong!

Watch Out for Incorrect Assumptions of Independence

Do not use the multiplication rule if events are not independent. For example, suppose we wanted to find the probability that a randomly selected person is female AND has long hair (say, more than 15 centimetres long).

About half of the population is female, so P(selected person is female) = 0.50. Suppose that about 35% of everyone in the population has long hair; then P(selected person has long hair) $= 0.35$. If we use the multiplication rule, we would find that P(selected person has long hair AND is female) $= 0.35 \times 0.5 = 0.175$.

This relatively low probability of 17.5% makes it sound somewhat unusual to find a female with long hair. The reason is that we assumed that having long hair and being female are independent. This is a bad assumption: a woman is more likely than a man to have long hair. Thus "has long hair" and "is female" are related, not independent, events. Therefore, once we know that the chosen person is female, there is a greater chance that the person has long hair.

Related Events with "AND"

If events are not independent, then we rely on Probability Rule 5b: P(A AND B) $=$ P(A) P(B $|$ A). Of course, this assumes that we know the value of P(B $|$ A).

For example, many medical tests done today are not perfect in their detection of an illness. We often hear about a "false-positive" test result, which means that the medical test indicates someone has the illness—it comes back with a positive result—when the person does not have the illness. A "false negative" result happens when the medical test results in a "person does not have the illness" when the person does have the illness.

If a medical test is perfect, then the probability of a false positive, or P(positive result | person does not have illness) $= 0$. Also, the probability of a false negative will be zero, or P(negative result | person does have illness) $= 0$.

Let's look at mammography, which is a medical test used in breast cancer screening. The Canadian Cancer Society indicates that 11% of Canadian women will develop breast cancer during their lifetime. Also, if a woman does have breast cancer, there is a 90% chance a mammogram will return a "positive" result—or detect the tumour. Keep in mind that mammograms are *not* perfect. Even if a woman does not have a cancerous tumour, there is a probability that a mammogram will return a positive result. Let's suppose that, given that a woman does not have breast cancer, there is a 6% chance that a mammogram test will return a positive result.

What is the probability that a randomly chosen woman will be breast-cancer free and will still test positive for breast cancer? In other words, for a randomly chosen Canadian woman, we need to find

P(does not have breast cancer AND tests positive)

To summarize, we have the probabilities for a randomly selected Canadian woman:

P(has breast cancer) $= 0.11$

P(does not have breast cancer) $= 1 - 0.11 = 0.89$

P(tests positive | has breast cancer) $= 0.90$

P(tests positive | does not have breast cancer) $= 0.06$

Note that this is a sequence of events. First, the woman either has breast cancer or does not. Then she has a mammogram. The mammogram produces a result: positive (mammogram detects breast cancer) or negative (mammogram does not detect breast cancer).

According to Rule 5b,

P(A AND B) $=$ P(A) P(B $|$ A)

P(does not have breast cancer AND tests positive) $=$ P (does not have breast cancer)
P(tests positive | does not have breast cancer)

$$= 0.89 \times 0.06$$

$$= 0.0534$$

We see that roughly 5.34% of all women tested will be both breast-cancer free AND test positive for breast cancer.

Often people find it useful to visualize problems where events occur in sequence with a tree diagram. We can represent this sequence of all possible outcomes in the tree diagram shown in Figure 5.10.

► **FIGURE 5.10** Tree diagram showing probabilities for the sequence of events in which a Canadian woman either has or does not have breast cancer, and then is tested for the presence of breast cancer.

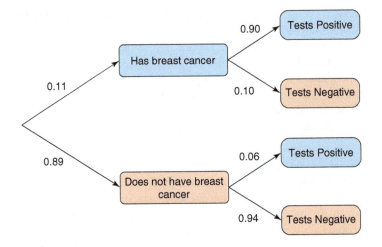

The tree diagram shows all possible outcomes after selecting a woman (who either has breast cancer or does not) and testing (the mammogram will be either positive or negative). Because the events "has breast cancer" and "positive test" are related, the probabilities of testing positive are different for the "has breast cancer" branch and the "does not have breast cancer" branch.

We want to find P(does not have breast cancer AND tests positive). We start at the root of the tree and then "climb" over the branches in order to arrive at a certain outcome (multiplying probabilities along the way), starting with "does not have breast cancer" and ending with "tests positive":

P(does not have breast cancer AND tests positive) = P(does not have breast cancer)

P(tests positive | does not have breast cancer)

= 0.89 × 0.06

= 0.0534

EXAMPLE 19 Airport Screeners

At many airports you are not allowed to take water through the security checkpoint. This means that security screeners must check for people who accidentally pack water in their bags. Suppose that 5% of people accidentally pack a bottle of water in their bags. Also suppose that if there is a bottle of water in a bag, the security screeners will catch it 95% of the time.

QUESTION What is the probability that a randomly chosen person with a backpack has a bottle of water in the backpack and security finds it?

SOLUTION We are asked to find P(packed water AND security finds the water). This is a sequence of events. First the person packs the water into the backpack. Later, security finds (or does not find) the water.

We are given

P(packs water) = 0.05

P(security finds water | water packed) = 0.95

Therefore,

P(packs water and security finds it) = P(packs water) ×

P(security finds water | water packed)

= 0.05 × 0.95

= 0.0475

The tree diagram in Figure 5.11 helps us show how to find this probability.

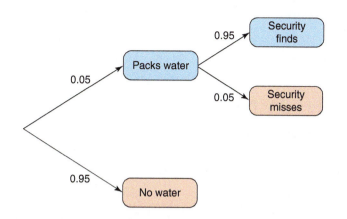

◀ **FIGURE 5.11** Tree diagram showing probabilities for the sequence of events in which a traveller either packs or does not pack water and then security either finds or does not find the water.

CONCLUSION There is about a 5% (4.75%) chance that a randomly selected traveller will both have packed water and will have the water found by security.

TRY THIS! Exercise 5.69

Adjusting Probabilities

Sometimes a sequence of events occurs where the first event in the sequence is *unknown*, but the last event in the sequence is *known*. In Example 16, if the third toss of the coin produces tails, what is the chance that the first toss was heads? Because the events are independent, we would say that P(first is tails) = 50%. In the preceding example, let's suppose that Security did not find water, does this mean that the randomly chosen person did not pack water? Or did the person pack water and the security screener not find it (which occurs 5% of the time)?

Suppose we come across a mammogram exam on a randomly chosen Canadian woman, and the result of the mammogram is positive. This test result could be correct, or it could be in error. That is, the result is positive for a woman who actually has breast cancer or the result is positive for a woman who is cancer-free—a false-positive test result. If the test result is positive, what is the probability that the woman does have breast cancer? That is,

P(has breast cancer | tests positive) = ?

We can use Rule 5a,

$$P(A|B) = \frac{P(A \text{ AND } B)}{P(B)}$$

In this formula, think of event A as "has breast cancer" and event B as "tests positive." We need to find

P(has breast cancer | tests positive) = $\dfrac{P(\text{has breast cancer AND tests positive})}{P(\text{tests positive})}$

From Figure 5.10, we can see that there are two mutually exclusive ways for the sequence of events to end with "tests positive"—one can start with "breast cancer AND test positive" and the other can start with "does not have breast cancer AND test positive":

P(tests positive) = P(has breast cancer AND tests positive)
            + P(does not have breast cancer AND tests positive)

Again, to find each of these probabilities we start at the root of the tree and crawl along each branch until we get to each of the branches that end in "tests positive":

P(has breast cancer AND tests positive) = P(has breast cancer)

P(tests positive | has breast cancer)

= 0.11 × 0.90

= 0.0990

In the same way, we find the P(does not have breast cancer AND tests positive):

P(does not have breast cancer AND tests positive) = P(does not have breast cancer)

P(tests positive | does not have breast cancer)

= 0.89 × 0.06

= 0.0534

The probability that a woman tests positive whether she has breast cancer or not, is

$$P(\text{tests positive}) = 0.0990 + 0.0534 = 0.1524, \text{ or } 15.24\%$$

The P(has breast cancer | tests positive) is the proportion of the "tests positive" subgroup that is made up of women who have breast cancer. This is then computed as:

$$P(\text{has breast cancer | tests positive}) = \frac{P(\text{has breast cancer AND tests positive})}{P(\text{tests positive})}$$

$$= \frac{0.0990}{0.0990 + 0.0534}$$

$$= \frac{0.0990}{0.1524}$$

$$= 0.6496$$

If a mammogram result is positive, the probability that the woman having this mammogram has breast cancer is 0.6496, much higher than the *initial* probability of 11%. In other words, if a mammogram result is positive, the chance that the woman having the mammogram has breast cancer is not 11%, but rather almost 65%.

This working-backwards approach is useful when we know the last event occurring in the sequence but not what event occurred at the start of the sequence. Often this is called a revision probability. Here we have revised the probability of a woman having breast cancer based on the additional information that her mammogram test is positive.

This adjustment of the initial probability of a woman having breast cancer of 11% to the woman having breast cancer given she tests positive for breast cancer being 64.96% uses what statisticians refer to as Bayes' Theorem. Thomas Bayes (1701–1761) was an ordained Presbyterian minister in England who had an interest in probability. His theorem—which can be presented in the form of a long and full-of-notation formula—is used when one of a series of *prior* events can occur. A secondary event, with a probability of occurrence that depends on which "prior event happened," then occurs. If all we know is (1) the occurrence of the secondary event, (2) the conditional probability of this secondary event's occurrence for each prior event, and (3) the probability of each prior event's occurrence, Bayes' Theorem allows us to work backwards *to find the probability of which prior event occurred, given the occurrence of the secondary event.*

In this example, there were two "prior" events: the occurrence, or non-occurrence, of breast cancer. The secondary event is that a mammogram produces a positive result. The chance of this positive result is related to "which" prior event happened. If the woman has breast cancer, the probability of a positive test result is 90%; if the woman does not have breast cancer (the second prior event), the probability of a positive test result is 6%. If all we know is that the test result is positive, we can use the idea developed by Bayes to find the probability of which prior occurred; that is, whether the positive test result belongs to a woman who has breast cancer. We found this probability, P(has breast cancer | tests positive), to be 64.96%.

To summarize, the probability that a randomly chosen woman having a mammogram has breast cancer is 11%. However, if we know she had a positive mammogram result, the probability that this woman has breast cancer is much higher: 64.96%.

Bayes' Theorem is a long formula, so it is not included here. From a tree diagram and Rule 5a, we can work through problems like this without writing out the formula.

KEY POINT   P(A|B) = P(A AND B)/P(B)

EXAMPLE 20 Method of Commuting and Time to Commute

In the months of May through September, a statistics professor will either ride his bicycle to work or drive his car, with probabilities of 0.35 and 0.65, respectively. Because of the number of traffic lights, traffic volume, and speed limits, the probability that it will take no more than five minutes to get to work is higher when he bikes compared to when he drives his car. If he rides his bike, the probability that it will take no more than five minutes is 0.80. If he drives his car, this probability is then 0.25.

QUESTION   On a randomly chosen day sometime between the beginning of May and the end of September, the time it took this statistics professor to commute to work was no more than five minutes. What is the probability that the statistics professor drove to work?

SOLUTION   We are asked to find P(drives car | no more than 5 minutes). This is a sequence of events. First the professor has to use a means of transportation. Then, the commuting time is categorized as being at most 5 minutes or more than 5 minutes. We are given

$$P(\text{rides bike}) = 0.35$$
$$P(\text{drives car}) = 0.65$$
$$P(\text{no more than 5 minutes} \mid \text{rides bike}) = 0.80$$
$$P(\text{no more than 5 minutes} \mid \text{drives car}) = 0.25$$

The tree diagram in Figure 5.12 is used to find P(drives car | no more than 5 minutes):

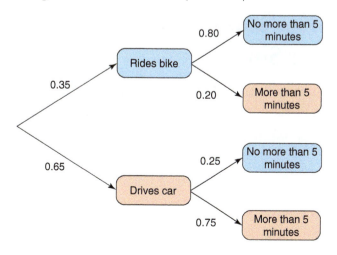

◄ **FIGURE 5.12** A tree diagram showing probabilities for the sequence of events in which the statistics professor either bikes or drives to work and then gets to work in at most 5 minutes or more than 5 minutes.

From Rule 5a,

$$P(\text{drives car} \mid \text{no more than 5 minutes}) = \frac{P(\text{drives car AND no more than 5 minutes})}{P(\text{no more than 5 minutes})}$$

From the tree diagram showing all possible outcomes, we see there are two that end with the event "no more than 5 minutes." We can find the probability of the event appearing in the denominator as

$$P(\text{no more than 5 minutes}) = P(\text{rides bike AND no more than 5 minutes})$$
$$+ P(\text{drives car AND no more than 5 minutes})$$

To find P(rides bike AND no more than 5 minutes), we start at the tree root and crawl along the "rides bike" branch and the "no more than 5 minutes" branch:

$$P(\text{rides bike AND no more than 5 minutes}) = 0.35 \times 0.80$$
$$= 0.28$$

We now find P(drives car AND no more than 5 minutes) the same way:

$$P(\text{drives car AND no more than 5 minutes}) = 0.65 \times 0.25$$
$$= 0.1625$$

$$P(\text{no more than 5 minutes}) = 0.28 + 0.1625 = 0.4425$$

$$P(\text{drives car} \mid \text{no more than 5 minutes}) = \frac{P(\text{drives car AND no more than 5 minutes})}{P(\text{no more than 5 minutes})}$$

$$= \frac{0.1625}{0.4425}$$

$$P(\text{drives car} \mid \text{no more than 5 minutes}) = 0.3672$$

CONCLUSION If it takes no more than five minutes for this statistics professor to get to work, the chance that he drove his car to work is 36.72%, which is lower than the initial probability of his driving his car, which is 65%.

TRY THIS! Exercise 5.71

SECTION 5.4

Finding Probabilities with Simulations

 Section 5.4 is available online, and can be found on MyStatLab.

CASE STUDY REVISITED

Sally Clark was convicted of murdering two children on the basis of the testimony of physician/expert Dr. Meadow. Dr. Meadow testified that the probability of two children in the same family dying of SIDS was extremely low and that, therefore, murder was a more plausible explanation. In Dr. Meadow's testimony, he assumed that the event "one baby in a family dies of SIDS" AND "a second baby in the family dies of SIDS" were independent. For this reason, he applied the multiplication rule to find the probability that two babies die of SIDS in the same family. The probability of one baby dying was 1/8543, so the probability of two independent deaths was (1/8543) × (1/8543), or about 1 in 73 million.

However, as noted in a press release by the Royal Statistical Society, these events may not be independent. "This approach (multiplying probabilities) . . . would only be valid if SIDS cases arose independently within families, an assumption that would need to be justified empirically. Not only was no such justification provided in the case, but there are very strong *intuitive* reasons for supposing that the assumption will be false. There may well be unknown genetic or environmental factors that predispose families to SIDS, so that a second case within the family becomes much more likely."

Dr. Meadow made several other errors in statistical reasoning, which are beyond the scope of this chapter but quite interesting nonetheless. For a summary and a list of supporting references, including a video by a statistician explaining the statistical errors, see http://en.wikipedia.org/wiki/Sally_Clark.

Sally Clark was released from prison but died in March 2007 of alcohol poisoning at the age of 43. Her family believes her early death was caused in part by the stress inflicted by her trial and imprisonment.

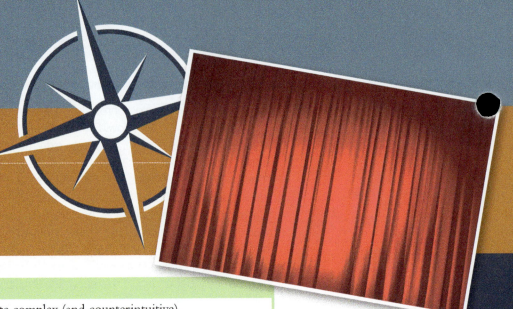

EXPLORING STATISTICS

CLASS ACTIVITY

Let's Make a Deal: Stay or Switch?

GOALS

Simulate an experiment to estimate complex (and counterintuitive) probabilities.

ACTIVITY

Curtain A	Curtain B	Curtain C

▲ FIGURE A Three curtains, and the contestant picked curtain A.

Curtain A		Curtain C

▲ FIGURE B The host, who knows there is a goat behind curtain B, reveals curtain B. Should the contestant stick with curtain A or switch to curtain C?

Curtain A		

▲ FIGURE C The contestant switched and won.

In the popular game show *Let's Make a Deal*, contestants are shown three curtains. Behind one curtain is a high-value prize, for example a car, and behind the other two are less desirable prizes, for example, goats. The contestant picks one of the three curtains. Then the host (who knows what is behind each curtain) raises another curtain to reveal a goat. The host then asks the contestant whether he or she wants to stay or switch to the other curtain before revealing what is behind the contestant's chosen curtain.

There are three possibilities: the contestant should stay; the contestant should switch; it doesn't matter whether the contestant stays or switches.

Visit the website www.grand-illusions.com/simulator/montysim.htm. Select one of the three question marks. Follow the on-screen instructions. Run through the simulation a couple of times just to get a feel for how the game is played. After this, run the simulation 1000 times with "keep" as the choice. Press start. The applet will simulate 1000 plays of *Let's Make a Deal*. Notice that the estimated probability of winning with the "keep" option will start to settle to a certain percentage.

Clear the result and repeat this, changing the "keep" option to the "change" option.

BEFORE THE ACTIVITY	Which strategy do you think will be better: staying or switching? Or does it make no difference whatsoever? Why?
AFTER THE ACTIVITY	Judging on the basis of your simulated data, what is your estimate of the probability of winning if the contestant stays? What is it if the contestant switches? Do these probabilities convince you to change your strategy? Explain.

CHAPTER REVIEW

Summary of Learning Objectives

1. **What are random experiments and how do they differ from non-random experiments?** Random experiments produce outcomes that appear to have no identifiable pattern(s). They must be generated with the help of outside mechanisms such as computer algorithms or using random number tables. Human thought and intuition can't produce randomness that is reliable.

2. **What is probability and how is it computed?** Probability is based on the concept of long-run relative frequencies: If a random experiment is repeated infinitely many times, how often does a particular event occur? To find the probability of this event, we consider how many outcomes the random experiment produces and count how many of these outcomes make the event happen. The percentage of all possible outcomes that make the event happen is the probability of the event.

3. **What probability rules can I use to compute probabilities of events?** There are five probability rules that can be used; the first four are below.

   Rule 1: A probability is always a number from 0 to 1 (or 0% to 100%), inclusive (which means 0 and 1 are allowed). It is usually expressed as a fraction, a decimal, or a percentage

   $$0 \leq P(A) \leq 1$$

   Rule 2: For any event A,

   $$P(A \text{ does } not \text{ occur}) = 1 - P(A \text{ does occur})$$

   A^c is the complement of A:

   $$P(A^c) = 1 - P(A)$$

   Rule 3: When outcomes are equally likely:

   $$P(A) = \frac{\text{Number of outcomes in A}}{\text{Number of all possible outcomes}}$$

   Rule 4a: Always: $P(A \text{ OR } B) = P(A) + P(B) - P(A \text{ AND } B)$

   Rule 4b: If A and B are mutually exclusive events, then:
   $P(A \text{ OR } B) = P(A) + P(B)$

4. **What are dependent events, and how are probabilities of dependent events computed?** Dependent events happen when the occurrence of one event (B) influences the occurrence of another event (A). To compute the probability of event A given that event B has occurred, or to find the conditional probability of A given B, we use

   Rule 5a: $P(A \mid B) = \dfrac{P(A \text{ AND } B)}{P(B)}$

   From Rule 5a, we get:

   Rule 5b: $P(A \text{ AND } B) = P(A \mid B) \, P(B)$

5. **How do independent events differ from dependent events and how is the probability of two independent events computed?** Independent events happen when the occurrence of one event (B) has no influence on the occurrence of the other event (A). They are computed with the Multiplication Rule, **Rule 5c:**

   If A and B are independent events, then $P(A \text{ AND } B) = P(A)P(B)$

   This applies for any (finite) number of events. For example,

   $P(A \text{ AND } B \text{ AND } C \text{ AND } D) = P(A)P(B)P(C)P(D)$ if A, B, C, and D are independent of each other.

6. **What is the Law of Large Numbers and how can it be used to compute a probability?** When we can't list all possible outcomes, we can observe the random experiment many times, or rely on a computer or a random number table to quickly carry out a simulation to estimate the probability of the event. The Law of Large Numbers tells us that a probability computed this way will become closer to the true probability of the event as the number of repetitions increases.

7. **How can a random experiment—a simulation study—be used to compute a probability?** A random number generator from a computer or a table can be used to imitate a real-life random experiment. The random experiment is simulated many times and a running percentage of how many times the event occurred is recorded. This percentage is used to estimate the true value of a probability through the application of the Law of Large Numbers.

Important Terms

Random, *194*	Event, *197*	Mutually exclusive events, *203*	Independent events, *215*
Probability, *196*	Venn diagram, *200*	Simulation, *207*	Multiplication rule, *218*
Complement, *197*	AND, *201*	Conditional probabilities, *210*	
Sample space, *197*	Inclusive OR, *202*	Related events, *215*	

Sources

Alberta Education. 2011. Five-Year Diploma Exam Results. http://education.alberta.ca/media/6594762/2011_5yeardipexamresults.pdf

Canadian Cancer Society. http://www.cancer.ca/canada-wide/about%20cancer/cancer%20statistics/stats%20at%20a%20glance/breast%20cancer.aspx (accessed April 2012).

Canadian College Student Survey. 2009. https://qspace.library.queensu.ca/bitstream/1974/5890/2/POKVol4_Ch7_Backgrounder.pdf

Forum Research. Strong majority of Canadians support a ban on fighting in professional hockey. https://www.forumresearch.com (accessed April 2012).

Harris/Decima poll. 2009. http://blogs.chicagotribune.com/news_columnists_ezorn/2009/08/%20; http://www.harrisdecima.com/en/downloads/pdf/news_releases/071009E.pdf

Ipsos Reid. http://www.ipsos-na.com/news-polls/pressrelease.aspx?id=5578 (accessed April 2012).

MADD. 2012. http://www.madd.ca/english/research/estimating_presence.pdf

Sexually Transmitted Diseases 37(1). 2010. Trends in age disparities between younger and middle-aged adults among reported rates of chlamydia, gonorrhea, and infectious syphilis infections in Canada: Findings from 1997 to 2007.

Starr, Norton. 1997. Nonrandom risk: The 1970 draft lottery. *Journal of Statistics Education* 5(2). Vietnam-era draft data can be found, along with supporting references, at www.amstat.org/publications/jse/datasets/draft.txt.

Statistics Canada. 2008. Survey of Labour and Income Dynamics (SLID).

Statistics Canada. 2010. Internet Use Survey. http://www.statcan.gc.ca/daily-quotidien/110525/dq110525b-eng.htm

Statistics Canada. 2014. Table 051-0001—Estimates of population, by age group and sex. http://www5.statcan.gc.ca/cansim/a26?lang=eng&retrLang=eng&id=0510001&pattern=&tabMode=dataTable&srchLan=-1&p1=-1&p2=9

Statistics Canada. 2012. The Canadian Tobacco Use Monitoring Survey. http://www.hc-sc.gc.ca/hc-ps/tobac-tabac/research-recherche/stat/_ctumsesutc_prevalence/prevalence-eng.php#wave2_10

SECTION EXERCISES

SECTION 5.1

TRY **5.1 Simulation (Example 1)** If we flip a coin 10 times, how often do we get 6 or more heads? A first step to answering this question would be to simulate 10 flips. Use the random number table in Appendix A to simulate flipping a coin 10 times. Let odd digits (1, 3, 5, 7, 9) represent heads, and let even digits (0, 2, 4, 6, 8) represent tails. Begin with the first digit in the third row.

 a. Write the sequence of 10 random digits.

 b. Write the sequence of 10 "heads" and "tails." Write H for heads and T for tails.

 c. Did you get 6 or more heads? How many heads did you get?

5.2 Simulation Suppose you are carrying out a randomized, controlled experiment to test whether guided meditation lowers blood pressure (treatment) compared to reading in a quiet room (control). Use the random number table in Appendix A to assign the first 12 subjects to treatment or control. You want each subject to have a 50% chance of being assigned to the treatment group. Let the digits 0, 1, 2, 3, 4 represent assignment to the meditation group, and let the digits 5, 6, 7, 8, 9 represent assignment to the control group. Begin with the first digit on the fourth line of the table.

 a. Write the 12 numbers, and below them write M for meditation and C for control.

 b. How many subjects were assigned to the meditation group?

 c. A research assistant wants to use the digits 0–5 to represent assignment to the meditation group and the digits 6–9 for assignment to the control group. Explain why this will not work.

5.3 A Monopoly player claims that the probability of getting a 4 when rolling a six-sided die is 1/6 because the die is equally likely to land on any of the six sides. Is the 1/6 an estimated probability or the true value of the probability? Explain.

5.4 A person was trying to figure out the probability of getting two heads when flipping two coins. He flipped two coins 10 times, and in 2 of these 10 times both coins landed heads. On the basis of this outcome, he claims that the probability of two heads is 2/10, or 20%. Is the 2/10, or 20%, an estimated probability or the true value of the probability? Explain.

5.5 A friend flips a coin 10 times and says that the probability of getting a head is 60% because he got six heads. Is the friend referring to an estimated probability or the probability's true value? Explain.

5.6 A magician claims that he has a fair coin—"fair" because both sides, heads and tails, are equally likely to land face up when the coin is flipped. He tells you that if you flip the coin three times, the probability of getting three tails is 1/8. Is this an estimated probability or the probability's true value? Explain.

SECTION 5.2

5.7 Criminal Court Judges Criminal cases are assigned to judges randomly. A list of criminal judges is given in the table. Assume that only Carolyn Blackett and Paula Skahan are women and the rest are men. If you were a criminal defence lawyer, you might be interested in whether the judge assigned to your case was a man or a woman.

 James C. Beasley

 Carolyn W. Blackett

 Lee V. Coffee

 Chris Craft

 John T. Fowlkes

 W. Otis Higgs

 James M. Lammey

 Paula L. Skahan

 W. Mark Ward

Suppose the names are put into a pot, and a clerk pulls a name out at random.

 a. List the equally likely outcomes that could occur; last names are enough.

 b. Suppose the event of interest, event A, is that a judge is a woman. List the outcomes that make up event A.

 c. What is the probability that one case will be assigned to a female judge?

 d. List the outcomes that are in the complement of event A.

5.8 Random Assignment of Professors You are to be part of a study that looks at how students attending your school are randomly assigned to different professors for Calculus I, with equal numbers of students assigned to each professor. Some professors were experienced, and some were relatively inexperienced. Suppose the names of the professors are Gibson, Bos, Kim, Lu, and Enns. Suppose Gibson and Kim are inexperienced and the others are experienced. Carrell and West have reported that students who had experienced professors in Calculus I did better in Calculus II. (Source: Scott E. Carrell and James E. West, "Does professor quality matter? Evidence from random assignment of students to professors," 2010)

 a. List the equally likely outcomes that could occur for your assignment to a professor.

 b. Suppose the event of interest, event A, is that a professor is experienced. List the outcomes that make up event A.

 c. What is the probability that you will be assigned to an experienced professor?

 d. List the outcomes in the complement of event A. Describe this complement in words.

 e. What is the probability that you will be assigned to an inexperienced professor?

5.9 Which of the following numbers could *not* be probabilities, and why?

0.5, 1.3, 0.001, 75%, 1/4, 150%, −0.5

5.10 Which of the following numbers could *not* be probabilities, and why?

$$0, \ 2/5, \ 7/4, \ 0.002, \ -10\%, \ 0.998, \ 45\%$$

TRY **5.11 Playing Cards (Example 2)** There are four suits: clubs (♣), diamonds (♦), hearts (♥), and spades (♠), and the following cards appear in each suit: ace, 2, 3, 4, 5, 6, 7, 8, 9, 10, jack, queen, king. The jack, queen, and king are called face cards because they have a drawing of a face on them. Diamonds and hearts are red, and clubs and spades are black.

If you draw 1 card randomly from a standard 52-card playing deck, what is the probability that it will be:

a. A heart?

b. A red card?

c. An ace?

d. A face card (jack, queen, or king)?

e. A three?

5.12 Playing Cards Refer to Exercise 5.11 for information about cards. If you draw 1 card randomly from a standard 52-card playing deck, what is the probability that it will be:

a. A black card?

b. A diamond?

c. A face card (jack, queen, or king)?

d. A nine?

e. A king or queen?

5.13 Guessing on Tests

a. On a true/false quiz in which you are guessing, what is the probability of guessing correctly on one question?

b. What is the probability that a guess on one true/false question will be incorrect?

5.14 Guessing on Tests On a multiple-choice test with a total of four possible options for each question,

a. What is the probability of guessing correctly on one question?

b. What is the probability that a guess on one question will be incorrect?

TRY **5.15 Four Children (Example 3)** The sample space given here shows all possible sequences for a family with four children, where B stands for boy and G stands for girl.

GGGG	GGGB	GGBB	GBBB	BBBB
	GGBG	GBGB	BGBB	
	GBGG	GBBG	BBGB	
	BGGG	BGGB	BBBG	
		BGBG		
		BBGG		

Assume that all of the 16 outcomes are equally likely. Find the probability of having the following numbers of girls out of four children: (a) exactly 0 girls, (b) exactly 1 girl, (c) exactly 2 girls, (d) exactly 3 girls, (e) exactly 4 girls.

(*Hint:* The probability of having 3 girls and a boy is 4/16, or 25%, because the second column shows that there are four ways to have 3 girls and 1 boy.)

5.16 Three Coins The sample space shows the possible sequences for flipping three fair coins or flipping one coin three times, where H stands for heads and T stands for tails.

HHH	HHT	HTT	TTT
	HTH	THT	
	THH	TTH	

Assume that all of the eight outcomes are equally likely. Find the probability of having exactly the following numbers of heads out of the three coins: (a) exactly 0 heads, (b) exactly 1 head, (c) exactly 2 heads, (d) exactly 3 heads. What do the four probabilities add up to and why?

5.17 Birthdays What is the probability that a baby will be born on a Friday OR a Saturday OR a Sunday if all the days of the week are equally likely as birthdays?

5.18 Playing Cards If *one* card is selected from a well-shuffled deck of 52 cards, what is the probability that the card will be a club OR a diamond OR a heart? What is the probability of the complement of this event? (Refer to Exercise 5.11 for information about cards.)

5.19 Political Leanings Surveys of Canadians are done frequently to measure voter preference in Canada. One extensive survey of randomly selected Canadian voters was done by Statistics Canada in 2008. This survey, summarized in the table below, asked each respondent to report their gender and the political party that most represents their political views. (LIB stands for Liberal Party, CP stands for Conservative Party, NDP stands for New Democratic Party, BLOC stands for Bloc Quebecois, GRN stands for Green Party, OTH stands for other.)

	LIB	CP	NDP	BLOC	GRN	OTH	Total
Male	213	368	151	119	54	6	911
Female	261	372	224	106	67	7	1037
Total	474	740	375	225	121	13	1948

a. If one person is chosen randomly from the group, what is the probability that the person is female?

b. If one person is chosen randomly from the group, what is the probability that the person identifies him- or herself with the NDP?

5.20 Political Leanings Refer to the table given in Exercise 5.19.

a. If one person is chosen randomly from the group of 1948, what is the probability that the person is male?

b. If one person is chosen randomly from the group of 1948, what is the probability that the person identifies him- or herself with the Conservative Party?

TRY **5.21 Political Leanings: AND (Example 4)** Refer to the table given in Exercise 5.19. Suppose we select a person at random from this collection of 1948 people. What is the probability that the person is female and identifies herself with the NDP? In other words, find P(person is female AND person is NDP).

5.22 Political Leanings: AND Refer to the table in Exercise 5.19. Suppose we select a person at random from this collection of 1948. What is the probability that the person is male and identifies himself with the Conservative Party? In other words, find P(person is male and person is CP).

TRY 5.23 Political Leanings: OR (Example 5) Select someone at random from the 1948 people in the table given in Exercise 5.19. What is the probability that the person identifies him- or herself as a Liberal or a Conservative?

5.24 Political Leanings: OR Select someone at random from the 1948 people in the table given in Exercise 5.19. What is the probability that the person is male or female?

TRY 5.25 Political Leanings: OR (Example 6) Assume that one
g person is chosen randomly from the 1948 people in the table given in Exercise 5.19. What is the probability that the person is a female or identifies as NDP? *See page 239 for guidance.*

5.26 Political Leanings: OR Assume that one person is chosen randomly from the 1948 people in the table given in Exercise 5.19. What is the probability that the person is a male or identifies with the CP?

5.27 Mutually Exclusive Suppose a person is selected at random. Label each pair of events as *mutually exclusive* or *not mutually exclusive*.

a. The person has brown eyes; the person has blue eyes.

b. The person is 50 years old; the person is a member of Parliament.

5.28 Mutually Exclusive Suppose a person is selected at random. Label each pair of events as *mutually exclusive* or *not mutually exclusive*.

a. The person is a parent; the person is a toddler.

b. The person is a woman; the person is a CEO (chief executive officer).

TRY 5.29 Political Leanings: Mutually Exclusive (Example 7) Referring to the table given in Exercise 5.19, name a pair of mutually exclusive events that could result from selecting an individual at random from this sample.

5.30 Political Leanings: Mutually Exclusive Referring to the table given in Exercise 5.19, name a pair of events that are not mutually exclusive that could result from selecting an individual at random from this sample.

5.31 "OR" In 2009 it was reported that 20% of Canadian households owned at least one dog and 23% owned at least one cat. (Source: *Canadian Veterinary Journal* 50(1), 48–52)

a. From this information, is it possible to find the percentage of households that owned at least a cat OR a dog? Why or why not?

b. The *Canadian Veterinary Journal* also reported that 13% of Canadian households had at least one dog AND at least one cat. From this information, can you find the probability that a randomly selected Canadian household will own a cat or dog? If not, explain. If so, find this probability.

5.32 "OR" Suppose you discovered that on your campus, 6% of the female students were married and 4% of the female students had at least one child.

a. From this information, is it possible to determine the percentage of female students who were married OR had a child?

b. If your answer to part a is no, what additional information would you need to answer this question?

TRY 5.33 Fair Die (Example 8) Roll a fair six-sided die.

a. What is the probability that the die shows an odd number OR a number less than 3 on top?

b. What is the probability that the die shows an odd number OR a number less than 2 on top?

5.34 Roll a Die Roll a fair six-sided die.

a. What is the probability the die shows an odd number OR a number greater than 5 on top?

b. What is the probability the die shows an odd number OR a number greater than 4 on top?

5.35 Grades Assume that the only grades possible in a history course are A, B, C, or lower than C. The probability that a randomly selected student will get an A in a certain history course is 0.18, the probability that a student will get a B in the course is 0.25, and the probability that a student will get a C in the course is 0.37.

a. What is the probability that a student will get an A OR a B?

b. What is the probability that a student will get an A OR a B OR a C?

c. What is the probability that a student will get a grade lower than a C?

5.36 Changing Multiple-Choice Answers One of the authors did a survey to determine the effect of students changing answers while taking a multiple-choice test on which there is only one correct answer for each question. Some students erase their initial choice and replace it with another. It turned out that 61% of the changes were from incorrect answers to correct and that 26% were from correct to incorrect. What percentage of changes were from incorrect to incorrect?

5.37 "AND" and "OR" Consider these categories of people, assuming that we are talking about all the people in Canada:

Category 1: People who are currently married

Category 2: People who have children

Category 3: People who are currently married OR have children

Category 4: People who are currently married AND have children

a. Which of the four categories has the most people?

b. Which category has the fewest people?

5.38 "AND" and "OR" Assume that we are talking about all students at your school.

a. Which group is larger: students who are currently taking English AND math, or students who are currently taking English?

b. Which group is larger: students who are taking English OR math, or students who are taking English?

5.39 Coin Flips Let H stand for heads and let T stand for tails in an experiment where a fair coin is flipped twice. Assume that the four outcomes listed are equally likely outcomes:

HH, HT, TH, TT

What are the probabilities of getting:

a. 0 heads?

b. Exactly 1 head?

c. Exactly 2 heads?

d. At least 1 head?

e. Not more than 2 heads?

5.40 Cubes A hat contains a number of cubes: 15 red, 10 white, 5 blue, and 20 black. One cube is chosen at random. What is the probability that it is:

a. A red cube?

b. Not a red cube?

c. A cube that is white OR black?

d. A cube that is neither white nor black?

e. What do the answers to part a and part b add up to and why?

5.41 Age Level The table gives the number of Canadian citizens (in thousands) and their age bracket in 2011, according to Statistics Canada. Each person is put into an age bracket based on their age in 2011.

If a Canadian is randomly selected, what is the probability that:

a. The person is more than 20 and at most 40 years old?

b. The person is over the age of 60?

c. The person is more than 20 and at most 40 years old OR is over the age of 60?

Age Bracket	(1000s of Canadians)
0 to 20 years	7,841
more than 20 to 40 years	9,460
more than 40 to 60 years	10,170
more than 60 to 80 years	5,634
Over the age of 80 years	1,378

5.42 Age Level Refer to the table in Exercise 5.41. If one person is randomly chosen from all the people in Canada, what is the probability that:

a. The person is not over the age of 60?

b. The person is not 20 years old or younger?

5.43 Multiple-Choice Exam An exam consists of 12 multiple-choice questions. Each of the 12 answers is either right or wrong. Suppose the probability that a student makes fewer than 3 mistakes on the exam is 0.48 and that the probability that a student makes from 3 to 8 (inclusive) mistakes is 0.30. Find the probability that a student makes:

a. More than 8 mistakes

b. 3 or more mistakes

c. At most 8 mistakes

d. Which two of these three events are complementary and why?

5.44 Driving Exam A driving exam consists of 30 multiple-choice questions. Each of the answers is either right or wrong. Suppose that the probability of making fewer than 7 mistakes is 0.23 and the probability of making from 7 to 15 mistakes is 0.41. Find the probability of making:

a. 16 or more mistakes

b. 7 or more mistakes

c. At most 15 mistakes

d. Which two of these three events are complementary? Explain.

TRY **5.45 Social Networking (Example 9)** A survey of a class of first-year business students at a university in western Canada asked each respondent for their gender and how many hours each spends per week on Facebook. The results are given in the table below.

	Less than 5 hrs	5 to < 10 hrs	10 to < 15 hrs	15 to < 20 hrs	20 hrs or More	Total
Male	29	12	3	1	3	48
Female	36	19	3	2	0	60
Total	65	31	6	3	3	108

One person is randomly chosen from this class of first-year business students.

a. What is the probability that this person is a male?

b. What is the probability that this person spends at least 20 hours a week on Facebook?

c. What is the probability that this person is male OR spends at least 20 hours a week on Facebook?

d. What is the probability that this person is female OR spends at least 20 hours a week on Facebook?

TRY **5.46 Social Networking (Example 10)** A person is randomly selected from the table in Exercise 5.45.

a. Name a pair of events that are mutually exclusive.

b. Name a pair of events that are not mutually exclusive.

SECTION 5.3

TRY **5.47 Political Leanings (Example 11)** The table summarizes the results of a survey in which each respondent was to report their gender and the political party that most represents their political views. (LIB stands for Liberal Party, CP stands for Conservative Party, NDP stands for New Democratic Party, BLOC stands for Bloc Quebecois, GRN stands for Green Party, OTH stands for other.)

	LIB	CP	NDP	BLOC	GRN	OTH	Total
Male	213	368	151	119	54	6	911
Female	261	372	224	106	67	7	1037
Total	474	740	375	225	121	13	1948

A person is selected randomly from the sample summarized in the table. We want to find the probability that a female identifies herself as NDP.

a. Which of the following probability statements represents this probability? (Choose one.)
  i. P(female | NDP)
  ii. P(NDP | female)
  iii. P(NDP AND female)

b. Calculate the probability in statements (i), (ii), and (iii) in part a.

5.48 Political Leanings Refer to the table in Exercise 5.47. A person is selected randomly from the sample summarized in the table. We want to determine the probability that the person is a male Conservative (CP).

a. Which of the following probability statements represents this probability? (Choose one.)
  i. P(male | CP)
  ii. P(CP | male)
  iii. P(male and CP)

b. Calculate the probability in statements (i), (ii), and (iii) in part a.

TRY **5.49 Political Leanings, Again (Example 12)** Refer to the table in Exercise 5.47.

a. Find the probability that a randomly chosen respondent identifies with the Liberal Party given that the respondent is a female. In other words, what percentage of women identify with the Liberal Party?

b. Find the probability that a randomly chosen respondent identifies with the Liberal Party given that the respondent is a man. In other words, what percentage of men identify with the Liberal Party?

c. Which respondents are more likely to identify with the Liberal Party: women or men?

5.50 Social Networking Refer to the table in Exercise 5.45. A student is randomly chosen from this class.

a. Find the probability that this person spends less than five hours a week on Facebook given that they are male. In other words, what percentage of all males spend less than five hours a week on Facebook?

b. Find the probability that this person spends less than five hours a week on Facebook given that they are female. In other words, what percentage of all females spend less than five hours a week on Facebook?

c. If this person spends more than five hours a week on Facebook, find the probability that they are female. In other words, what percentage of all students in the class spending more than five hours a week on Facebook are female?

d. If this person spends more than five hours a week on Facebook, find the probability that they are male. In other words, what percentage of all students in the class spending more than five hours a week on Facebook are male?

5.51 Left-handedness The percentage of left-handed people in Canada is estimated to be 13%. Men are about twice as likely to be left-handed as women. Are gender and handedness independent or related events? Explain.

5.52 Smoking Statistics Canada's survey of tobacco usage by Canadians (The Canadian Tobacco Use Monitoring Survey) reported in 2012 that the percentage of Canadians aged 20–24 living outside of Newfoundland who smoke is estimated to be 22%. The percentage of Canadians aged 20 to 24 living in Newfoundland who smoke is estimated to be 33%. Are smoking and whether the 20 to 24-year-old Canadian lives outside of Newfoundland or in Newfoundland independent or related events?

5.53 Independent? Using your general knowledge, label the following pairs of variables as independent or related. Explain your reasoning.

a. Hair colour and age for adults 20 to 30 years old

b. Hair colour and eye colour for adults

5.54 Independent? A 2009 Gallup poll of over 14,000 people showed that 68% of weekly church attendees felt negatively about the economy. It also showed that 81% of those who seldom or never attended church felt negatively about the economy. According to the poll, are attendance at church and opinion about the economy independent? Explain.

5.55 Same-Sex Marriage An Angus Reid poll in 2012 found that 60% of Canadians believed same-sex marriage should be legally allowed. The same poll found that 42% of Americans believed same-sex marriage should be legally allowed. Suppose that these figures are accurate (or nearly accurate) probabilities, and state whether nationality and opinion about same-sex marriage are independent or related. Explain.

5.56 Shopping A survey by Statistics Canada in 2009 found that 42% of men shopped online compared to 38% of women who shop online. Assuming these figures are accurate, state whether or not gender and one's decision to shop online are independent or related. Explain.

TRY **5.57 Political Leanings: Independent? (Example 13)** Refer to the table in Exercise 5.47. If a person is selected at random, is the event that the person best identifies with the NDP independent of the event of the person being male or female? Explain.

5.58 Political Leanings A person is randomly selected from the sample summarized in the table in Exercise 5.47. The probability of identifying with the NDP given that the person is female is 21.6%, the probability that the person is a female given that the person identifies with the NDP is 59.7%, and the probability of being both a female AND identifying with the NDP is 11.5%. Why is the last probability the smallest?

TRY **5.59 Hand Folding (Example 14)** When people fold their hands together with interlocking fingers, most people are more comfortable with one of two ways. In one way, the right thumb ends up on top and in the other way, the left thumb is on top. The table shows the data from one group of people. M means man, and W means woman; Right means the right thumb is on top, and Left means the left thumb is on top. Judging on the basis of this data set, are the events "right thumb on top" and male independent or related? Data were collected in a class taught by one of the authors but were simplified for clarity. The conclusion remains the same as that derived from the original data. *See page 239 for guidance.*

	M	W
Right	18	42
Left	12	28

5.60 Dice When two dice are rolled, is the event "the first die shows a 1 on top" independent of the event "the second die shows a 1 on top"?

TRY **5.61 Gender and Marijuana Use (Example 15)** Of the 108 first-year students surveyed in Exercise 5.45, each was asked if they had used marijuana in the past six months. The table summarizes the data collected.

	Used Marijuana	Not Used Marijuana
Male	11	37
Female	9	51

a. Add the marginal totals and the grand total to the table. Show the complete table with marginal totals.

b. Determine whether "using marijuana" is independent of being "male."

5.62 Gender and Marijuana Use Using the table in Exercise 5.61, determine whether "using marijuana" is independent of being "female."

TRY **5.63 Coin (Example 16)** Imagine flipping three fair coins.

a. What is the probability that all three will come up heads?

b. What is the probability that the first toss is tails AND the next two are heads?

5.64 Die Imagine rolling a fair six-sided die three times.

a. What is the probability that all three rolls of the die show a 1 on top?

b. What is the probability that the first roll of the die shows a 6 AND the next two rolls show a 1 on top?

TRY **5.65 Die Sequences (Example 17)** Roll a fair six-sided die five times and record the number of spots on top.
Which sequence is more likely? Explain.

Sequence A: 66666

Sequence B: 16643

5.66 Babies Assume that babies born are equally likely to be boys (B) or girls (G). Assume that a woman has six children, none of whom are twins. Which sequence is more likely? Explain.

Sequence A: GGGGGG

Sequence B: GGGBBB

TRY **5.67 Student Debt (Example 18)** The 2009 Canadian College Student Survey revealed that 60% of university students will graduate from their program with student debt. Suppose that you looked at two recent university graduates, selected randomly and independently from the population, to see whether each graduated with student debt.

a. What is the probability that neither person graduated with student debt?

b. What is the probability that at least one person graduated with student debt? (*Hint: "At least one had student debt is the complement of "neither one had student debt."*)

5.68 Gender of Newborns When a baby is born in Canada, the probability that it will be a boy is close to 51%.

a. What is the probability that a newborn will be a girl?

For the rest of the questions, assume that a woman gives birth to two babies who are not identical twins, and therefore the genders are independent.

b. What is the probability that they are both girls?

c. What is the probability of there being at least one boy?

5.69 Cervical Cancer (Example 19) According to a study published in *Scientific American*, about 8 women in 100,000 have cervical cancer (C), so P(C) = 0.00008. Suppose the chance that a Pap smear will detect cervical cancer when it is present is 0.84. Therefore,

$$P(\text{test pos}\,|\,C) = 0.84$$

What is the probability that a randomly chosen woman who has this test will both have cervical cancer AND test positive for it?

5.70 Cervical Cancer About 8 women in 100,000 have cervical cancer (C), so P(C) = 0.00008 and P(no C) = 0.99992. The chance that a Pap smear will incorrectly indicate that a woman without cervical cancer has cervical cancer is 0.03. Therefore,

$$P(\text{test pos}\,|\,\text{no C}) = 0.03$$

What is the probability that a randomly chosen woman who has this test will both be free of cervical cancer and test positive for cervical cancer (a false positive)?

TRY **5.71 Cervical Cancer (Example 20)** Recall the information given in Exercises 5.69 and 5.70. A Pap smear test result was randomly chosen. The test result was positive.

a. What is the probability that the woman who had this Pap smear has cervical cancer?

b. What is the probability that the woman who had this Pap smear does not have cervical cancer?

5.72 Cervical Cancer Recall the information given in Exercises 5.69 and 5.70. A Pap smear test result was randomly chosen. The test result was negative.

a. What is the probability that the woman who had this Pap smear has cervical cancer?

b. What is the probability that the woman who had this Pap smear does not have cervical cancer?

5.73 Prostate Cancer Prostate Cancer Canada states on its site that one out of every seven Canadian males will be diagnosed with prostate cancer (PC) at some point in his life. The prostate specific antigen blood test, or PSA, is used as a diagnostic test for prostate cancer. The chance that a PSA will detect prostate cancer when it is present is 0.75. The chance that a PSA will detect prostate cancer when it is not present is 0.03.

a. Which of the following statements describes the 0.75 probability?
  i. P(test pos | PC)
  ii. P(PC | test pos)
  iii. P(PC AND test pos)

b. Which of the following statements describes the 0.03 probability?
  i. P(test pos | not PC)
  ii. P(not PC | test pos)
  iii. P(not PC AND test pos)

c. A PSA test is chosen at random. If this PSA test is positive, what is the probability that the man who had the PSA test done has prostate cancer?

d. A PSA test is chosen at random. If a PSA test is negative, what is the probability that the man who had the PSA test done has prostate cancer?

5.74 Unequal Die You have two dice in your pocket. One is a normal six-sided die and the other is not normal, with all six faces being a 1. You randomly select one of these dice from your pocket. Without looking at the selected die, you give it a toss and observe the uppermost face. The die shows a 1. What is the probability that the die you threw is the normal die?

5.75 Warehouse Shipping A very large retailer in Canada has two warehouses, one in Mississauga and the other in Calgary, from which product is trucked to retail outlets. Mississauga handles 70% of the national shipping load, and Calgary handles the remainder. Shipments from each warehouse aren't perfect; 5% of the shipments from Mississauga are not complete, while 10% of the shipments from Calgary are not complete. A retail outlet has received a shipment from one of these two warehouses.

a. If the shipment is not complete, what is the probability that it came from Mississauga?

b. If the shipment is complete, what is the probability that it came from Calgary?

SECTION 5.4

TRY **5.76 Simulating Coin Flips (Example 21)**

a. Simulate flipping a coin 20 times. Use the line of random numbers below to obtain and report the resulting list of heads and tails. Use odd numbers (1, 3, 5, 7, 9) for heads and even numbers for tails (0, 2, 4, 6, 8).

14709   93220   89547   95320

b. Judging on the basis of these 20 trials, what is the probability of getting heads?

* **5.77 Simulation**

a. Explain how you could use digits from a random number table to simulate rolling a fair eight-sided die with outcomes 1, 2, 3, 4, 5, 6, 7, and 8 equally likely. Assume that you want to know the probability of getting a 1.

b. Carry out your simulation, beginning with line 5 of the random number table in Appendix A. Perform 20 repetitions of your trial. Using your results, estimate the probability of getting a 1, and compare it with the true probability of getting a 1.

 5.78 Law of Large Numbers Refer to histograms a, b, and c, which show the relative frequencies from experiments in which a fair six-sided die was rolled. One histogram shows the results from 20 rolls, one the results for 100 rolls, and another the results for 10,000 rolls. Which histogram do you think was for 10,000 rolls and why?

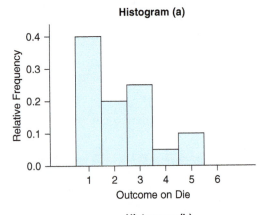

Histogram (a)

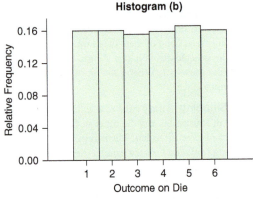

Histogram (b)

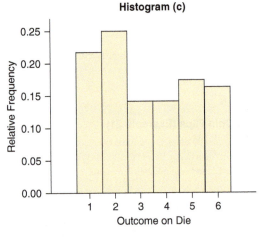

Histogram (c)

5.79 Law of Large Numbers The table shows the results of rolling a fair six-sided die.

Outcome on Die	20 Trials	100 Trials	1000 Trials
1	8	20	167
2	4	23	167
3	5	13	161
4	1	13	166
5	2	16	172
6	0	15	167

Using the table, estimate the probability of rolling a 1 for 20, 100, and 1000 trials. Report the true probability of rolling a 1 with a fair six-sided die. Compare the estimated probabilities to the theoretical probability, and explain what they show.

5.80 Coin Flips Imagine flipping a fair coin many times. Explain what should happen to the proportion of heads as the number of coin flips increases.

5.81 Coin Flips, Again Refer to the figure.

a. After a large number of flips, the overall proportion of heads "settles down" to nearly what value?

b. Approximately how many coin flips does it take before the proportion of heads settles down?

c. What do we call the law that causes this settling down of the proportion?

d. From the graph, determine whether the first flip was heads or tails.

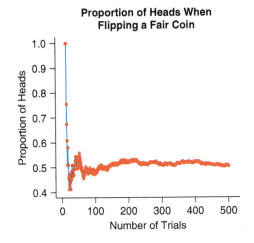

Proportion of Heads When Flipping a Fair Coin

* 5.82 Simulation: Four-Sided Die

a. Explain how you could use a random number table (or the random numbers generated by software or a calculator) to simulate rolling a fair *four-sided* die 20 times. Assume you are interested in the probability of rolling a 1. Then report a line or two of the random number table (or a computer or calculator) and the values that were obtained from it.

b. Report the approximate probability of rolling a 1 on the four-sided die from part a, and compare it with the true probability of rolling a 1.

* 5.83 Simulation: Six-Sided Die

a. Explain how you could use a random number table to simulate rolling a fair six-sided die 20 times. Assume you wish to find the probability of rolling a 1. Then report a line or two of the random number table (or a computer or calculator) and the values that were obtained from it.

b. Report the approximate probability of rolling a 1 from part a, and compare it with the true probability of rolling a 1.

CHAPTER REVIEW EXERCISES

5.84 Sabotage of Airplanes Between 1950 and 2009, there were 1300 fatal commercial airplane accidents worldwide for which a cause could be determined. Of those, 117 were due to sabotage (www.planecrashinfo.com). Using these data, estimate the probability that sabotage will be the cause of a fatal airplane accident.

5.85 Pilot Error Of the 1300 fatal commercial airplane accidents between 1950 and 2009 for which a cause could be determined, 377 were due to simple pilot error (without contributing weather problems or mechanical problems). Using these data, estimate the probability that simple pilot error will be the cause of a fatal airplane accident.

5.86 Independent Variables Use your general knowledge to label the following pairs of variables as independent or related. Explain.

a. For a sample of adults, gender and shoe size

b. For a sample of football teams, win/loss record for the coin toss at the beginning of the game and number of cheerleaders for the team

5.87 Independent Variables Use your general knowledge to label the following pairs of variables as independent or related. Explain.

a. The outcome on flips of two separate, fair coins

b. Breed of dog and weight of dog for dogs at a dog show

5.88 Ogopogo When two people meet, they are sometimes surprised they have similar beliefs. A survey of 801 British Columbians and 508 Albertans (aged 18 years of age or older) conducted by Insights West in 2015 found that 15% of Albertans and 16% of British Columbians believe that Ogopogo—a cryptic sea monster that has been reported to live in Okanagan Lake—is real. (http://www.insightswest.com/news/ufos-are-real-for-almost-half-of-western-canadians/)

a. If an Albertan and a British Columbian meet, what is the probability they both believe Ogopogo is real?

b. If an Albertan and a British Columbian meet, what is the probability that neither believe Ogopogo is real?

c. What is the probability that an Albertan and a British Columbian agree about Ogopogo's existence?

d. If an Albertan and a British Columbian meet, what is the probability they have opposing views on the belief that Ogopogo is real?

5.89 Impaired Driving Mother Against Drunk Driving (MADD) reported that in 2009, 38% of all traffic accidents involving a fatality were alcohol-related. Assume that this percentage is still accurate.

a. If four traffic accidents involving a death are randomly selected, what is the probability that all were alcohol-related?

b. If four traffic accidents involving a death are randomly selected, what is the probability that at least one was not alcohol-related?

5.90 Internet Access Statistics Canada's Internet Use Survey in 2010 found that close to 20% of Canadian households did not have access to the internet. Assume that this is still correct.

a. If two Canadian households are randomly chosen, what is the probability that they both have internet access?

b. If two Canadian households are randomly chosen, what is the probability that at least one will have internet access?

c. If two Canadians are randomly chosen from the same household, as opposed to two different Canadian households, explain why they would not be considered independent with regard to internet access.

5.91 Provincial Math Tests About 80% of Grade 12 students in Alberta pass the provincial Grade 12 Math Diploma Exam.

a. If two Alberta Grade 12 students are chosen randomly and independently, what is the probability that they will both pass the Grade 12 Math Diploma Exam?

b. If two Alberta Grade 12 students are selected from the same high school, do you think the probability of their passing the Grade 12 Math Diploma Exam is different from your answer in part a? Explain.

5.92 Birthdays Suppose all the days of the week are equally likely as birthdays. Alicia and David are two randomly selected, unrelated people.

a. What is the probability that they were both born on a Monday?

b. What is the probability that Alicia OR David was born on a Monday? *Hint:* The answer is not 2/7. Refer to Guided Exercise 5.25 if you need help.

5.93 Marijuana Use About 20% of first-year university students in Canada have used marijuana in the past six months. Suppose two first-year students are randomly selected and each is asked if they have used marijuana in the past six months.

a. What is the probability that both have used marijuana in the past six months?

b. What is the probability that one OR the other has used marijuana in the past six months?

c. What is the probability that one OR the other, but NOT BOTH, has used marijuana in the past six months?

5.94 Public Health Care A 2009 Harris/Decima poll of Canadians found that 82% of Canadians prefer the Canadian health care system to the U.S.-style health care system. If this percentage is still correct today and a poll of 2000 Canadians is taken, how many of the 2000 would you expect to prefer a Canadian health care system to a U.S.-style health care system?

5.95 Global Warming A 2010 poll of Canadians found that 80% believe that the earth is warming. The same poll of Americans found that 60% of Americans believe that the earth is warming. (Source: www.sustainableprosperity.ca/dl362)

a. If another poll of Canadians were to be taken and there were 1000 participants, how many would you expect to believe that the earth is warming?

b. If another poll of Americans were to be taken and there were 2000 participants, how many would you expect to believe that the earth is warming?

5.96 Insurance An insurance company classifies drivers as either "Normal" or "Accident Prone," with 80% of its clients being classified as "Normal," and 20% as "Accident Prone." 10% of its "Normal" clients have made an accident claim in the past year, while 40% of its "Accident Prone" clients have made an accident claim in the past year. The insurance company just received an accident claim. What is the probability that this claim is made by a "Normal" client?

5.97 Performance-Enhancing Drugs A 2009 confidential survey of retired National Football League (NFL) players revealed that 10% had used anabolic steroids during their playing days. A test used to detect anabolic steroid usage returns a positive reading 95% of the time on players who are using anabolic steroids (a positive reading here means the test detects anabolic steroids in the player's system). This test returns a positive reading 2% of the time on players who are not using anabolic steroids. Assume that the 10% number still holds today. From all test results, one is randomly selected. The result of this test was positive.

a. What is the probability of this outcome? That is, what is the probability of a positive test?

b. What is the probability that the player who had this positive test result is using anabolic steroids?

c. If the test result was not positive, what is the probability that the player taking the test is using anabolic steroids?

5.98 Income Gap and Internet Access Exercise 5.90 reported some of the findings from Statistics Canada's 2010 Canadian Internet Use Survey. The survey reported that 97% of households having a household income exceeding $87,000 (the top 25% of all households) have home internet access. For households with an income of less than $30,000 (the bottom 25%), 54% have home internet access. For households with incomes between $30,000 and $87,000, 85% have home internet access. A Canadian household is randomly chosen. This household does have home internet access.

a. What is the probability that the income of this household is less than $30,000?

b. What is the probability that the income of this household is more than $87,000?

5.99 Fighting in Professional Hockey A 2011 Forum Research survey of Canadians aged 18 years or older who watch or follow hockey asked each respondent the following question: "Should fighting be banned from professional hockey?" The response seemed to depend on the province in which the respondent lived: 67% of those living in Quebec agreed with a fighting ban, along with 61% in Ontario, 57% in Atlantic Canada, 55% in British Columbia, and 51% in the Prairies (including Territories). Of all Canadians, 24% of the population live in Quebec, 38% in Ontario, 7% in the Maritimes, 13% in British Columbia, and the remainder in the Prairies (and Territories). Assume that the regional breakdown of the percentage of Canadians aged 18 years or older who follow/watch professional hockey is similar to that of the general population.

a. What is the probability that a randomly selected Canadian (who is a follower/watcher of professional hockey) will support a fighting ban in professional hockey?

b. A Canadian who is at least 18 years old and watches or follows hockey is randomly chosen. This person does support a fighting ban in professional hockey. What is the probability that this person lives in the Prairies (including Territories)?

c. Suppose the person mentioned in part b does not support a fighting ban. What is the probability that this person lives in Quebec?

* **5.100 Independent** Imagine rolling a red die and a blue die. From this trial, name a pair of independent events.

* **5.101 Mutually Exclusive** Imagine rolling a red die and a blue die. From this trial, name a pair of mutually exclusive events.

* **5.102** Construct a two-way table with 60 women and 80 men in which both groups show equal percentages of right-handedness.

* **5.103** Construct a two-way table with 60 women and 80 men in which there is a higher percentage of right-handed women.

* **5.104 Simulating Guessing on a Multiple-Choice Test** Suppose a student takes a 10-question multiple-choice quiz, and for each question on the quiz there are five possible options. Only one option is correct. Now suppose the student, who did not study, guesses at random for each question. A passing grade is 3 (or more) correct. We wish to design a simulation to find the probability that a student who is guessing can pass the exam.

a. In this simulation, a single trial consists of a "student" guessing on 10 multiple-choice "questions." We will simulate this by selecting 10 single digits from the random number table. Using the random number table below, use 0 and 1 to represent correct answers, and use 2 through 9 to represent incorrect answers. Explain why this is a fair approach for the exam questions with five possible answers. (This completes the first two steps of the simulation given in online Section 5.4.)

b. Write the sequence of numbers from the first trial. Also write how this translates to correct and incorrect answers.

c. Step 3 in a simulation is to identify the response variable. The outcome here is the number of correct responses the student gets. What was the outcome for the first trial?

d. Step 4 is to describe the event of interest. In this simulation, this is whether or not the student got 3 or more questions correct. Did we achieve that in the first trial?

e. Perform a second simulation of the student taking this 10-question quiz by guessing randomly. Use the second line of the table given. What score did your student get? Did the event of interest occur this time?

f. Repeat the trial twice more, using lines 3 and 4 below. On the basis of these four trials, what is the approximate probability of passing the exam by guessing?

```
11373   96871
52022   59093
14709   93220
31867   85872
```

* **5.105 Simulating Guessing on a True/False Test** Perform a simulation of a student guessing on a true/false quiz with 10 questions. You will use the same four lines that are given for the preceding question. Write out each of the six steps outlined in online Section 5.4. What numbers will you use to represent correct answers and what numbers for incorrect answers? Explain why your choice is logical. Do four repetitions, each trial consisting of 10 questions. Estimate the probability of getting more than 5 correct out of 10.

* **5.106 Law of Large Numbers** A famous study by Amos Tversky and Nobel laureate Daniel Kahneman asked people to consider two hospitals. Hospital A is small and has 15 babies born per day. Hospital B has 45 babies born each day. Over one year, each hospital recorded the number of days that it had more than 60% girls born. Assuming that 50% of all babies are girls, which hospital had the most such days? Or do you think both will have about the same number of days with more than 60% girls born? Answer, and explain. (Source: Amos Tversky. 2004. *Preference, Belief, and Similarity: Selected Writings*, ed. Eldar Shafir. Cambridge, Mass.: MIT Press, p. 205)

* **5.107 Law of Large Numbers** A certain professional basketball player typically makes 80% of his basket attempts, which is considered

to be good. Suppose you go to several games at which this player plays. Sometimes the player attempts only a few baskets, say 10. Other times, he attempts about 60. On which of those nights is the player most likely to have a "bad" night, in which he makes much fewer than 80% of his baskets?

* 5.108 Red Light/Green Light A busy street has three traffic lights in a row. These lights are not synchronized, so they run independently of each other. At any given moment, the probability that the light is green is 60%. Assuming there is no traffic, follow the steps below to design a simulation to estimate the probability that you will get three green lights.

    a. Identify the actions that make up a single trial on the busy street.

    b. Using the random number table in Appendix A, describe how to simulate a single trial. Which digits will represent a green light and which a non-green light?

    c. The response variable is the number of "green lights" in one trial. Describe the event of interest—that is, the event for which we wish to estimate a probability.

    d. Carry out 20 repetitions of your trial, beginning with the first digit on line 11 of the random number table. For each trial, list the random digits, the outcomes they represent, and the value of the response variable.

    e. What is the approximate probability that you get three green lights?

* 5.109 Soft Drink A soda-bottling plant has a flaw in that 20% of the bottles it fills do not have enough soda in them. The sodas are sold in six-packs. Follow these steps to carry out a simulation to find the probability that three or more bottles in a six-pack have not enough soda.

    a. Identify the actions that make up a single trial for a six-pack.

    b. Using the random number table in Appendix A, describe how to simulate a single trial. Which digits will represent a "good" soda bottle and which will represent a "bad" (not full) soda bottle?

    c. What is the response variable?

    d. Describe the event of interest—that is, the event for which we wish to estimate a probability.

    e. Carry out 10 repetitions of your trial, beginning with the first digit on line 15 of the random number table. For each trial, list the random digits, the outcomes they represent, and the value of the response variable.

    f. What is the experimental probability that you get three or more "bad" bottles in a six-pack?

GUIDED EXERCISES

g 5.25 Political Leanings Referring to the table, one person is chosen randomly from the 1948 people in the table. Answer the questions below the table by following the numbered steps.

	LIB	CP	NDP	BLOC	GRN	OTH	Total
Male	213	368	151	119	54	6	911
Female	261	372	224	106	67	7	1037
Total	474	740	375	225	121	13	1948

QUESTION What is the probability that the person is a female OR identifies with the NDP?

Step 1 ▶ What is the probability that the person is a female?

Step 2 ▶ What is the probability that the person identifies with the NDP?

Step 3 ▶ If the events female and identifies with the NDP were mutually exclusive, you could just add the probabilities from step 1 and step 2 to find the probability that a person is female OR identifies with the NDP. Are they mutually exclusive? Why or why not?

Step 4 ▶ What is the probability that the person is female AND identifies with the NDP? Use numbers from the table; do not assume independence.

Step 5 ▶ Why should you subtract the probability that the person is female AND identifies with the NDP from the sum as shown in the given formula?

    P(female OR NDP) = P(female) + P(NDP) − P(female AND NDP)

Step 6 ▶ Do the calculation using the formula given in step 5 to find the probability that a person is female OR identifies with the NDP. It is more accurate to use the numbers from the table (fractions) than to use your percentages, which are rounded off.

Step 7 ▶ Finally, report the answer in a sentence.

g 5.59 Hand Folding When people fold their hands together with interlocking fingers, most people are more comfortable doing it in one of two ways. In one way, the right thumb ends up on top, and in the other way, the left thumb is on top. The table shows the data from one group of people.

	M	W
Right	18	42
Left	12	28

    M means man, W means woman, Right means the right thumb is on top, and Left means the left thumb is on top.

QUESTION Say a person is selected from this group at random. Are the events "right thumb on top" and "male" independent or associated?

    To answer, we need to determine whether the probability of having the right thumb on top given that you are a man is equal to the probability of having the right thumb on top (for the entire group). If so, the variables are independent.

Step 1 ▶ Figure out the marginal totals and put them into the table.

Step 2 ▶ Find the overall probability that the person's right thumb is on top.

Step 3 ▶ Find the probability that the right thumb is on top given that the person is a man. (What percentage of men have the right thumb on top?)

Step 4 ▶ Finally, are the variables independent? Why or why not?

TECH TIPS

For All Technology

EXAMPLE: GENERATING RANDOM INTEGERS ▶ Generate four random integers from 1 to 6, for simulating the results of rolling a six-sided die.

TI-83/84

Seed First Before the Random Integers

If you do not seed the calculator, everyone might get the same series of "random" numbers.

1. Enter the last four digits of your Social Insurance number or cell phone number and press **STO →** .

2. Then press **MATH**, choose **PRB**, and **ENTER ENTER** (to choose 1:rand).

You need to seed the calculator only once, unless you **Reset** the calculator. (If you want the same sequence later on, you can seed again with the same number.)

Random Integers

1. Press **MATH**, choose **PRB**, and press **5** (to choose 5:randInt).

2. See Figure 5A. Enter **1 ⟩ 6 ⟩ 4)** and press **ENTER**. (The comma button is above the 7 button.)

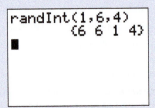

▲ **FIGURE 5A** TI-83/84.

The first two digits (1 and 6 in Figure 5A) determine the smallest and largest integers, and the third digit (4 in Figure 5A) determines the number of random integers generated. To get four more random integers, press **ENTER** again.

MINITAB

Random Integers

1. **Calc > Random Data > Integer**

2. See Figure 5B. Enter:

   Number of rows to generate, 4

   Store in column(s), c1

   Minimum value, 1

   Maximum value, 6

3. Click **OK**.

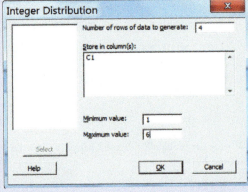

▲ **FIGURE 5B** Minitab.

EXCEL

Random Integers

1. Click **fx**, select a category **All,** and **RANDBETWEEN**.

2. See Figure 5C.

   Enter: **Bottom, 1; Top, 6.**

   Click **OK**.

   You will get one random integer in the active cell in the spreadsheet.

3. To get more random integers, put the cursor at the lower right corner of the cell containing the first integer until you see a black cross (+), and drag downward until you have as many as you need.

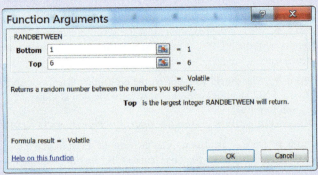

▲ **FIGURE 5C** Excel.

Random Integers

1. **Data** > **Simulate Data** > **Discrete Uniform**.
2. See Figure 5D.

   Enter **Rows**, **4**; **Columns**, **1**; **minimum**, **1**; **maximum**, **6** and leave **Split across columns** and **Use preset generator**.
3. Click **Simulate**.

   You will get four random integers (from 1 to 6) in the first empty column.

▲ **FIGURE 5D** StatCrunch.

SPSS

Random Integers

1. Starting with an empty spreadsheet, select the **Variable View** tab. In the first row, under the "Name" column give the output a name, like DieToss. Select the first row in the Decimals column and replace the number with 0.
2. Then select the **Data View** tab to take you back to the spreadsheet. Enter any number (1) in each of the first four rows. (To randomly generate numbers in SPSS you do need to tell SPSS that the variable DieToss has data.) Highlight all four entries.
3. Select **Transform** from the menu bar.
4. From the drop-down menu, select **Compute Variable**...
5. In the Target Variable box, type the variable name DieToss. Select the Arithmetic function in the Function group box. In the Functions and Special Variables box below, scroll to find then select the Rnd() function. Click on the up-arrow.
6. In the Numeric Expression box, you will see RND(?). In the Function group box, scroll to find, then select Random Numbers. Scroll to find and select Rv.Uniform. Click on the up-arrow. The ? should disappear. See Figure 5E.
7. Replace the RND(RV.UNIFORM(?,?)) with 1 and 6. Select **OK**. When asked to "Change existing variable?" select **OK**.

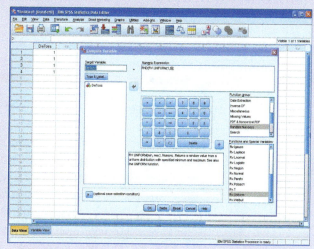

▲ **FIGURE 5E** SPSS.

6 Modelling Random Events: The Normal and Binomial Models

Elenathewise/Fotolia

LEARNING OBJECTIVES

After completing this chapter, you should be able to:

1. Explain the meaning of a random variable and make the distinction between discrete and continuous random variables.
2. Identify when the Normal probability model is appropriate and apply it to find probabilities.
3. Identify when the binomial probability model is appropriate and apply it to find probabilities.

Random events can seem chaotic and unpredictable. If you flip a coin 10 times, there's no way you can accurately predict how many heads will appear. In the same way, there is no way your local weatherperson can predict with probability 1 that it will snow tomorrow. But if we observe enough of these random events, we will discover that patterns emerge. From this we can understand which different outcomes are common and which ones are unusual.

Science fiction writer Isaac Asimov is often quoted as having said, "The most exciting phrase to hear in science, the one that heralds new discoveries, is not Eureka! (I found it!) but rather 'hmm . . . that's funny. . . .'" When such a "funny" outcome strikes us as being weird or unusual, it is because something unlikely has happened.

This is exciting because it means that a discovery has been made, and the world is not as we thought!

To understand if something unusual has occurred, we need to know how often it usually happens. That is, we need to know its probability. In the case study, you'll see an example where one of the authors was asked by a news organization to assess whether people who worked in places that sold lottery tickets in Manitoba were winning large prizes too often.

In this chapter, we will introduce the idea of a probability distribution. This is a tool we can use to show that random events have a pattern, or a behaviour. We'll look at two such probability distributions, the Normal and the binomial, and use these tools to ask, "Is this unusual?"

CASE STUDY

Keep an Eye on Your Winning Lottery Ticket

On October 26, 2006, *The Fifth Estate*—an investigative news program—aired an episode that investigated the frequency with which lottery retailers in Ontario—people who sell lottery tickets—were winning. It seemed as if they were winning too often. This came to light after an elderly gentleman living in southern Ontario won a prize of $250,000. When he took his ticket back to the lottery retailer, the clerk kept the ticket. She later maintained that the winning ticket was hers, and claimed the prize of $250,000. Was there widespread lottery fraud in Ontario? The Ontario Lottery and Gaming Corporation (OLG) denied any possibility of lottery fraud.

A thorough analysis was conducted by probabilist Dr. Jeffrey Rosenthal, after which the Ontario ombudsman investigated, and concluded that "insiders have won big over the years. . . . Millions of dollars have been paid out in what are dishonest claims." The scandal resulted in the firing of OLG's CEO, criminal charges being filed, and people being sent to jail. The OLG ended up changing its practices.

The Western Canada Lottery Corporation (WCLC) runs lotteries and gaming-related activities for the governments of Manitoba, Saskatchewan, and Alberta. Between June 1, 2007, and September 30, 2008, people who sell lottery tickets, or lottery retailers, in Manitoba won a total of 13 prizes of $10,000 or more. During the same time, 160 prizes of $10,000 or more were won in Manitoba by people who do not sell lottery tickets. What is so odd about these numbers? Well, the number of lottery retailers is approximately 10,075 compared to about 888,000 who are not lottery retailers, meaning that lottery retailers are winning $(13/10,075) \div (160/888,000) = 7.16$, or about seven *times more* than lottery players who do not sell lottery tickets.

Some people say that lottery retailers "play more," and that that's why there are more winners when compared to non-retailer lottery players. Okay, but still, is the difference between the number of wins of $10,000 or more by those who sell lottery tickets and those who don't due to randomness? After learning about the Normal and binomial probability distributions in this chapter, you will be able to determine whether or not this difference is due to random variation.

SECTION 6.1

Probability Distributions Are Models of Random Experiments

A **probability model** is a description of how a statistician thinks data are produced. We use the word *model* because the description does not explain how the data occurred; instead it is a representation of how the data behave. We can tell if a probability model is good or not by comparing the probabilities of the model with the real-life probabilities. Thus, if a model says that the probability of getting heads when we flip a coin is 0.60, but in fact we get heads 50% of the time, we suspect that the model is not a good match.

A **probability distribution** shows the pattern of "what can happen" by keeping track of the outcomes of a random experiment and showing the probabilities associated with such outcomes. For example, suppose the playlist on your mp3 player has 10 songs: 6 are Rock, 2 are Country, 1 is Hip-hop, and 1 is Opera. Put your player on shuffle. What is the probability that the first song chosen is Rock?

Outcome	Probability
Rock	6/10
Not Rock	4/10

▲ **TABLE 6.1** Probability distribution of songs.

The way the question is worded ("What is the probability . . . is Rock"?) means that we care about only two things: is the song classified as Rock or is the song the complement of Rock? We could write the probabilities as shown in Table 6.1.

Table 6.1 shows the distribution of probabilities (or probability distribution) to the two outcomes "Rock" and "Not Rock." It tells us all the possible outcomes *and* the probability of each outcome: 60% of the time your mp3 player will play a "Rock" song, and 40% of the time it will play a "Not Rock" song. Notice also how the probabilities of the outcomes add to 1. That is, $(6/10) + (4/10) = 1$, or 100%. This is because there are no other outcomes: you will either "Rock" or "Not Rock"!

KEY POINT A probability distribution tells us (1) all the possible outcomes of the random experiment, (2) the probability of each outcome, and (3) that the probabilities will add to 1.

 Looking Back

Distributions of a Sample

Probability distributions are similar to distributions of a sample, which were introduced in Chapter 2. A distribution of a sample tells us the values in the sample and their frequency. A probability distribution tells us the possible values of the random experiment and their probability.

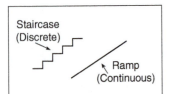

▲ **FIGURE 6.1** Visual representation of discrete and continuous changes in elevation. Note that for the staircase (discrete outcomes), you can count the stairs.

The idea of a probability distribution allows us to think of random experiments and their outcomes in terms of quantities. For example, how many heads do we observe in 10 flips of a coin? How long does it take you to commute from your home to school on a randomly chosen day? What is the annual income of a randomly selected person? In each situation, the outcome is measuring "how many" or "how much": How many heads? How many minutes (or hours) to commute to school? How much annual income (in $s or $10,000s)?

In the quantification of events, we can also see that there is variation in these numerical events. How many heads observed in 10 flips varies from 0 to 10; how much time it takes you to commute to school varies from day to day; how much income will vary from one randomly chosen person to another. In Chapter 1, we classified variables as either categorical or numerical. We can now treat random events that count or measure some quantity as numerical variables that fall into one of two categories. **Discrete random variables** (or discrete outcomes) are numerical events that you can list or count. The number of phone numbers stored on a person's phone is an example of a discrete random variable, since it can be counted. Furthermore, this count varies—the number of phone numbers on your phone is different from your friend's. **Continuous random variables** (or continuous outcomes) cannot be listed or counted because they occur over a range. The length of a phone call you make is a continuous variable because it can be a range of values, the length varying from one phone call to the next. Refer to Figure 6.1 for a visual comparison of these two terms.

This difference is important because if we can list the outcomes, as we can for a discrete random variable, then we have a nice way of displaying its probability distribution. But if we are working with a continuous random variable, we can't list all the outcomes and we then need to be more clever in describing its probability distribution. For this reason we treat discrete random variables (RVs) separately from continuous RVs.

EXAMPLE 1 Discrete or Continuous RV?

Consider these variables:

a. The weight of a submarine sandwich you're served at a sub shop.

b. The amount of time you spend waiting in line at your local grocery store.

c. The number of penalties your favourite hockey team takes in a period.

d. The blood alcohol level of a driver randomly stopped at a checkstop. (Blood alcohol level is measured as the percentage of the blood that is alcohol.)

e. The number of eggs laid by a randomly selected salmon as observed in a fish hatchery.

QUESTION Identify each of these numerical random variables as discrete or continuous.

SOLUTION The discrete random variables are found in c and e, because we are counting how many of some outcome have occurred.

Continuous random variables can take on any value in a range of values. For example, the sandwich may be 170 grams, or 171.5 grams. The amount of time you spent waiting at the check-out could be 3 minutes, or 4.5 minutes, or maybe 18.333 minutes. Blood-alcohol content, being a percentage, can be any value between 0 and 1 (or 0 to 100), including 0.075, 0.08, 0.11, or 0.15333, and so on.

TRY THIS! Exercise 6.1

Discrete Probability Distributions Can Be Tables or Graphs

A statistics class at the University of Calgary was approximately 40% male and 60% female. Let's arbitrarily code the males as 0 and the females as 1. If we select a person at random, what is the probability that the person is female?

Creating a probability distribution for this situation is as easy as listing both outcomes (0 and 1) and their probabilities (0.40 and 0.60). The easiest way to do this is in a table, as shown in Table 6.2. However, we could also do this as a graph (Figure 6.2).

Female	Probability
0	0.40
1	0.60

▲ **TABLE 6.2** Probability distribution of gender in a class.

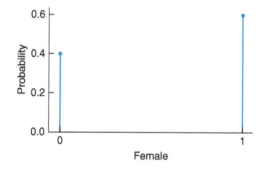

◄ **FIGURE 6.2** Probability distribution for selecting a person at random from a particular statistics class and recording whether the person is female (1) or not (0).

Amazon.ca invites customers to rate books on a scale of 1 to 5 stars. On a visit to the site on December 21, 2014, *To Kill a Mockingbird*, by Harper Lee, had received 1155 reviews. Suppose we were to randomly select a reviewer and base our decision to buy the book on how many stars this person gave it. Table 6.3 and Figure 6.3 show the different ways to represent the probability distribution for this random event. We note that rating is a discrete RV because it counts how many stars are given. We can see that the most likely outcome is that the reviewer gave the book 5 stars. The probability that the reviewer gave the book 5 stars is 0.756, or about 76%.

Number of Stars	Probability
1	0.033
2	0.020
3	0.035
4	0.156
5	0.756

▲ **TABLE 6.3** Distribution of number of stars.

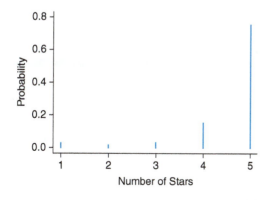

◄ **FIGURE 6.3** Probability distribution for the number of stars given, as a rating, to a particular book on amazon.ca by a randomly selected reviewer.

Notice how the probabilities in Table 6.3 add to 1, a needed property of a probability distribution. Also, notice how a higher rating (4 or 5 stars) is much more likely than a low rating (1 or 2 stars).

Discrete Distributions Can Also Be Equations

What if our discrete RV has too many values (outcomes) to list in a table? For example, suppose a married couple decides to keep having children until they have a girl. How many children will they have, assuming that boys and girls are equally likely and that the gender of one birth doesn't depend on any of the previous births? It could very well turn out that their first child is a girl and they therefore have only one child. Or that the first is a boy but the second is a girl. Or, just possibly, they might never have a girl. The value of this experiment could be any number 1, 2, 3, . . . up to infinity. (Okay, in reality, it's impossible to have that many children. But we can imagine!)

We can't list all these values and probabilities in a table, and we can only hint at what the graph might look like. But we *can* write them in a formula:

The probability of having x children until the first girl is $(1/2)^x$.

For example, the probability that they have 1 child is $(1/2)^1 = 1/2$.

The probability that they have 4 children is $(1/2)^4 = 1/16$.

The probability that they have 10 children is small: $(1/2)^{10} = 0.00098$.

In this book we will give the probabilities in either a table or a graph. It is good to try to understand the behaviour of the discrete random variable, and this can be done by visualizing its probability distribution. Figure 6.4 is part of the graph of the probability distribution for the number of children a couple can have until having a girl. We see that the probability that the first child is a girl is 0.50 (50%). The probability that the couple has two children is half this: 0.25. The probabilities continue to decrease, and each probability is half the one before it.

▶ **FIGURE 6.4** Probability distribution of the number of children born until the first girl.

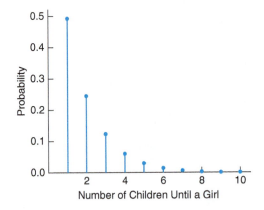

EXAMPLE 2 Playing Dice

Roll a fair six-sided die. A fair die is one in which each side is equally likely to end up on top. You will win $4 if you roll a 5 or a 6. You will lose $5 if you roll a 1. For any other outcome, you will win or lose nothing.

QUESTION Construct a table that shows the probability distribution for the amount of money you will win. Draw a graph of this probability distribution function.

SOLUTION There are three outcomes: you win $4, you win 0 dollars, you win −$5. (Winning negative five dollars is the same as losing five dollars.)

You win $4 if you roll a 5 or 6, so the probability is 2/6 = 1/3.

You win $0 if you roll a 2, 3, or 4, so the probability is 3/6 = 1/2.

You "win" −$5 if you roll a 1, so the probability is 1/6.

We can put the probability distribution in a table (Table 6.4), or we can represent it as a graph (Figure 6.5).

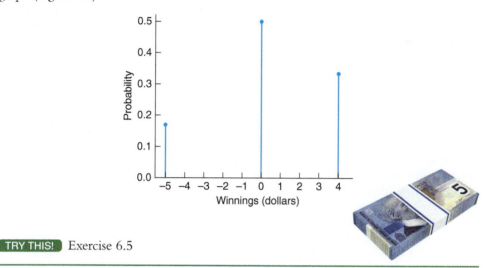

◀ **FIGURE 6.5** Probability distribution of the dice game.

Winnings	Probability
−5	1/6
0	1/2
4	1/3

▲ **TABLE 6.4** Probability distribution of the dice game (Example 2).

TRY THIS! Exercise 6.5

Continuous Probabilities Are Represented as Areas under Curves

Finding probabilities for continuous random variables is more complicated, because we cannot simply list all the possible values we might observe. What we can list is the *range of values* we might observe.

For example, suppose you want to know the probability that you will wait in line for between 3 and 4 minutes when you go to the coffee shop. You can't list all possible outcomes that could result from your visit: 1.0 minute, 1.00032 minute, 2.00000321 minute. It would take (literally) an eternity. But you can specify a range. Suppose this particular coffee shop has done extensive research and knows that everyone gets helped in under 5 minutes. So all customers get helped within the range of 0 to 5 minutes.

If we want to find probabilities concerning a continuous RV, we also need to give a range for the outcomes. For example, the manager wants to know the probability that a customer will wait less than 2 minutes; this gives a range of 0 to 2 minutes.

The probabilities for a continuous random variable are represented as areas under curves. This curve is represented by a **probability density function**, or pdf for short. In this instance, the 'pdf' is a curve, but this is not always the case. Regardless of the shape of the probability density function—a curve or a horizontally straight line—the total area beneath the pdf is 1, because it represents the probability that the outcome will be somewhere on the *x*-axis. To find the probability of waiting between 0 and 2 minutes, we find the area under the density curve between 0 and 2 (Figure 6.6).

◀ **FIGURE 6.6** Probability distribution of times waiting in line at a particular coffee shop.

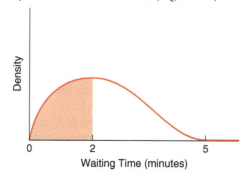

The *y*-axis of a continuous-RV pdf is labelled "Density." How the density is determined isn't important. What *is* important to know is that the units of density are scaled so that the area under the entire curve is 1.

You might wonder where this curve came from. How did we know the distribution was exactly this shape? In practice, it is very difficult to know which curve is correct for a real-life situation. Statisticians call these curves "probability models" because they are meant to mimic a real-life probability, but we don't know—and can never know for sure—that the curve is correct. On the other hand, we can compare our probability predictions to the actual frequencies that we see. If they are close, then our probability model is good. For example, if this probability model predicts that 45% of customers get coffee within 2 minutes, then we can compare this prediction to an actual sample of customers.

Finding Probabilities for Continuous Random Variables

Calculating the area under a curve is not easy. If you have a formula for the probability density, then you can sometimes apply techniques from calculus to find the area. However, for many commonly used probability densities, basic calculus is not helpful, and computer-based approximations are required.

In this book, you will always find areas for continuous random variables by using a table or by using technology. In Section 6.2 we introduce a table that can be used to find areas for one type of probability density that is very common in practice: the Normal curve.

EXAMPLE 3 Waiting for the Bus

The bus that runs near one of the authors' home arrives every 12 minutes. If the author arrives at the bus stop at a randomly chosen time, then the probability distribution for the number of minutes he must wait for the bus is shown in Figure 6.7.

▶ **FIGURE 6.7** Probability distribution function showing the number of minutes the author must wait for the bus if he arrives at a randomly determined time.

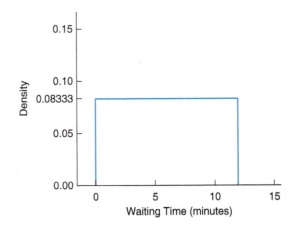

QUESTION Find the probability that the author will have to wait between 4 and 10 minutes for the bus. (*Hint:* Remember that the area of a rectangle is the width multiplied by its height.)

SOLUTION The distribution shown in Figure 6.7 is called a uniform distribution. Finding areas under this curve is easy because the curve is just a rectangular shape. The area we need to find is shown in Figure 6.8. The area of a rectangle is width times height. The width is (10 − 4) = 6, and the height is 0.08333.

The probability that the author must wait between 4 and 10 minutes is 6 × 0.08333 = 0.4998, or about 0.500. Visually, we see that about half of the area in Figure 6.8 is shaded.

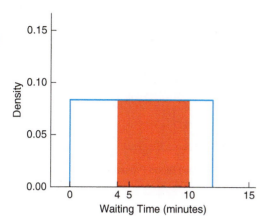

◄ **FIGURE 6.8** The shaded area represents the probability that the author will wait between 4 and 10 minutes if he arrives at the bus stop at a randomly determined time.

There is approximately a 50% chance that the author must wait between 4 and 10 minutes.

TRY THIS! Exercise 6.11

The Normal Model

The **Normal model** is the most widely used probability model for continuous random variables. One reason is that many continuous RVs in which researchers have been historically interested have probability distributions for which the Normal model provides a very good fit. Also, an important theorem (the Central Limit Theorem, to be introduced in Chapter 7) links the Normal model to several key statistical ideas, which provides good motivation for learning this model.

We begin by showing you what the Normal model looks like. Then we discuss how to find probabilities by finding areas underneath the Normal curve. We will illustrate these concepts with examples and also discuss why the Normal model is appropriate for these situations.

Visualizing the Normal Distribution

Figure 6.9 on the next page shows several histograms of measurements taken from a sample of about 1400 adult men. All of these graphs have similar shapes: they are unimodal and symmetric. We have superimposed smooth curves over the histograms that capture this shape. You could easily imagine that if we continued to collect more and more data, the histogram would eventually fill in the curve and match the shape almost exactly.

The curve drawn on these histograms is called the **Normal curve**, or the **Normal distribution**. It is also sometimes called the Gaussian distribution, after Karl Friedrich Gauss (1777–1855), the mathematician who first derived its formula. Statisticians and scientists recognized that this curve provided a model that pretty closely described a good number of continuous RV data distributions. Today, even though we have many other distributions to model real-life data, the Normal curve is still one of the most commonly used probability distributions in science.

Centre and Spread

In Chapters 2 and 3 we discussed the centre and spread of a distribution of *data*. These concepts are also useful for studying distributions of *probability*. The mean of a probability distribution sits at the balancing point of the probability distribution. The standard deviation

Looking Back

Unimodal and Symmetric Distributions
Symmetric distributions have histograms whose right and left sides are roughly mirror images of each other. Unimodal distributions have histograms with one mound.

Details

The Bell Curve
The Normal or Gaussian curve is also called the bell curve.

(a)

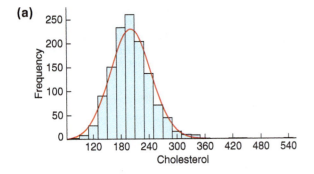

(b)

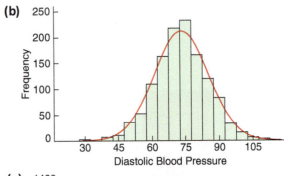

(c)

▲ **FIGURE 6.9** Measurements for a sample of men: **(a)** cholesterol levels, **(b)** diastolic blood pressure readings, and **(c)** height. For all three, a very similar shape appears: nearly symmetric and bell-shaped.

of a probability distribution measures the spread of the distribution by telling us how far away, typically, the values are from the mean. The conceptual understanding you developed for the mean and standard deviation of a sample still applies to probability distributions.

The notation we use is slightly different, so that we can distinguish means and standard deviations of probability distributions from means and standard deviations of data. The **mean of a probability distribution** is represented by the Greek character μ (mu, pronounced "mew"), and the **standard deviation of a probability distribution** is represented by the character σ (sigma). These Greek characters are used to avoid confusion of these concepts with their counterparts for samples of data, $\bar{x}$ and s.

The Mean and Standard Deviation of a Normal Distribution

The exact shape of the Normal distribution is determined by the values of the mean and the standard deviation. Because the Normal distribution is symmetric, the mean is in the exact centre of the distribution. The standard deviation determines whether the Normal curve is wide and low (large standard deviation) or narrow and tall (small standard deviation). Figure 6.10 shows two Normal curves that have the same mean but different standard deviations.

> **Looking Back**
>
> **Mean and Standard Deviation**
> In Chapter 3, you learned that the symbol for the mean of a *sample* of data is $\bar{x}$ and that the symbol for the standard deviation of a sample of data is s.

▶ **FIGURE 6.10** Two Normal curves with the same mean but different standard deviations.

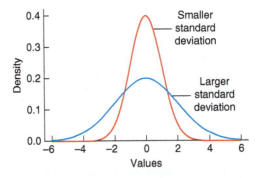

A Normal curve with a mean of 172.5 centimetres (cm) and a standard deviation of 7.5 cm provides a very good match for the distribution of heights of all adult men. Surprisingly, a Normal curve with the same standard deviation of 7.5 cm, but a smaller mean of about 160 cm, describes the distribution of adult women's heights. Figure 6.11 shows what these Normal curves look like.

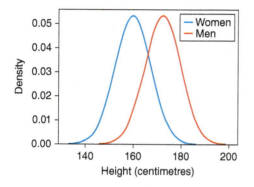

◀ **FIGURE 6.11** Two Normal models. The blue curve represents the distribution of women's heights and has a mean of 160 cm and a standard deviation of 7.5 cm. The red curve represents the distribution of men's heights and has the same standard deviation, but the mean is 172.5 cm.

The only way to distinguish among different Normal distributions is by their means and standard deviations. We can take advantage of this fact to write a short-hand notation to represent a particular Normal distribution. The notation $N(\mu, \sigma)$ represents a Normal distribution that is centred at the value of μ (the mean of the distribution) and whose spread is measured by the value of σ (the standard deviation of the distribution). For example, in Figure 6.11, the distribution of women's heights is $N(160, 7.5)$, and the distribution of men's heights is $N(172.5, 7.5)$.

 KEY POINT ▸ The Normal distribution is symmetric and unimodal ("bell-shaped"). The notation $N(\mu, \sigma)$ tells us the mean and standard deviation of the Normal distribution.

Finding Normal Probabilities

The Normal model $N(160, 7.5)$ gives a good approximation of the distribution of adult women's heights. Suppose we were to select a woman at random and record her height. What is the probability that she is taller than a specific height?

Because height is a continuous random variable, we can answer this question by finding the appropriate area under the Normal curve. For example, Figure 6.12 shows a Normal curve that models the distribution of heights of women in the population—the same curve as in Figure 6.11. The area of the shaded region gives us the probability of selecting a woman who is taller than 155 cm. The total area under this curve is 1.

In fact, Figure 6.12 represents the probability of selecting a woman taller than 155 cm as well as the probability of selecting a woman who is 155 *cm or taller* (or *at least* 155 cm tall). Because the areas for both regions (one that is strictly greater than 155, and the other that includes 155) are the same, the probabilities are also the same. This is a nice feature of continuous variables: we don't have to be too picky about our language when working with probabilities. As you will soon see, we do have to be picky in our language when we work with discrete random variables.

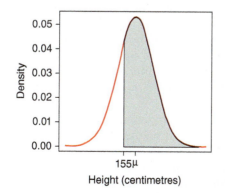

◀ **FIGURE 6.12** The area of the shaded region represents the probability of finding a woman taller than 155 cm from an $N(160, 7.5)$ distribution.

What if we instead wanted to know the probability that the chosen woman would be between 155 cm and 170 cm? The area would look like Figure 6.13.

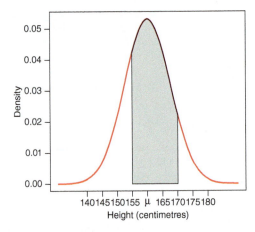

▶ **FIGURE 6.13** The shaded area represents the probability that a randomly selected woman is between 155 and 170 centimetres tall. The probability distribution shown is the Normal distribution with a mean of 160 cm and a standard deviation of 7.5 cm.

Figure 6.14 shows the area corresponding to the probability that this randomly selected woman is less than 150 centimetres tall.

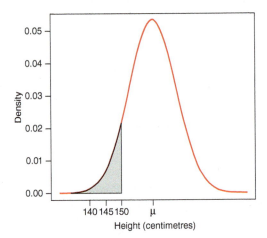

▶ **FIGURE 6.14** The shaded area represents the probability that the randomly selected woman is less than 150 centimetres tall.

> **KEY POINT** When you are finding probabilities with Normal models, the first and most helpful step is to draw the curve, label it appropriately, and shade in the region of interest.

A good habit is to always begin problems that concern Normal models with a drawing of the distribution. An advantage is that such a "visualization" may be all you need. For example, according to the McDonald's "Fact Sheet," each serving of ice cream in a cone is 90 grams. Now, we know that every ice cream cone sold at McDonald's is not going to weigh exactly 90 grams. Different employees who operate the ice cream machines may dispense a little more or a little less than 90 grams. Suppose the amount dispensed can be modelled by the Normal distribution with a mean of 90 grams and a standard deviation of 17 grams. What is the probability that a hungry customer will actually get less than 90 grams?

Figure 6.15a shows the scene. Without too much trouble, we can see that the area to the left of 90 is exactly half of the total area. The probability of getting less than 90 grams will then be 0.50. (Also, because the Normal distribution is symmetric, its mean is the "centre of gravity" and therefore is in the middle: the probability of getting a value less than the mean is 0.50.)

What if the true mean is actually greater than 90 grams? How will that affect the probability of getting a cone that weighs less than 90 grams? Imagine "sliding" the Normal curve to the right of 90 grams. Does the area to the left of 90 grams go up or down? Figure 6.15b shows that the area below 90 is now smaller than 50%. The larger the mean amount of ice cream dispensed, the less likely it is for a customer to complain about not getting enough.

(a)

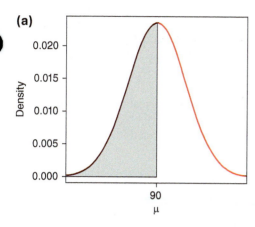

(b)

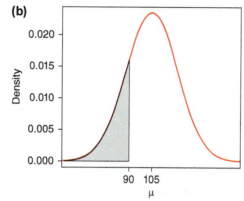

◀ FIGURE 6.15 (a) An *N* (90, 17) curve showing that the probability of getting a cone weighing less than 90 grams is 50%. (b) A Normal curve with the same standard deviation (17 grams), but a larger mean (105). The area below 90 is now much smaller.

Finding Probability with Technology

Finding the area of a Normal distribution is best done with technology. Most graphing calculators and many statistical software packages will show you how to do this. We illustrate one such package, available free on the internet, that you can use. We will also show you the "old-fashioned" way, which is useful when you do not have a computer handy. The old-fashioned way is also worth learning because it helps solidify your conceptual understanding of the Normal model.

Figure 6.16a is a screenshot from the SOCR (http://socr.stat.ucla.edu) calculator. It shows the probability that a randomly selected woman is between 155 and 170 centimetres tall if the $N(160, 7.5)$ model is a good description of the distribution of women's heights. To use the calculator, the user moves sliders to set the mean and standard deviation and then uses the mouse to shade in the appropriate area. The actual probability is given in a window below the graph (shown enlarged in Figure 6.16b).

TECH

(a)

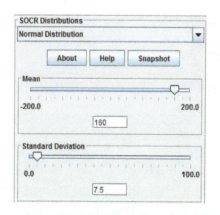

```
0.076





0   ( 138.324, 0.001 )
    130        155.0      170.0      190
```

Distribution Properties
Normal (160.0, 7.5) Distribution
Mean: 160.000000
Median: 160.000000
Variance: 56.250000
Standard Deviation: 7.500000
Max Density: .053192

Probabilities

Left: .252493
Between (Red-Shaded): .656296
Right: .091211

(b)

Distribution Properties
Normal (160.0, 7.5) Distribution
Mean: 160.000000
Median: 160.000000
Variance: 56.250000
Standard Deviation: 7.500000
Max Density: .053192

Probabilities

Left: .252493
Between (Red-Shaded): .656296
Right: .091211

▲ FIGURE 6.16 (a) Screenshot showing a calculation of the area under an $N(160, 7.5)$ curve between 155 and 170. (b) An enlarged view of the window below the $N(160, 7.5)$ curve. The shaded area is .656296. The area to the left is given as .252493. (We usually include a 0 before the decimal point when we report or work with these values.)

```
normalcdf(155,17
0,160,7.5)
         .6562962511
```

This particular calculation prints the probability next to the word "Between": .656296. Thus, the probability that the woman is between 155 and 170 centimetres tall is about 65.6%. Note that with no extra effort, we can find the probability that this person will be shorter than 155 centimetres (.252493, or about 25%) or taller than 170 centimetres (.091211, or about 9%).

To use the SOCR calculator to find probabilities for the Normal model, go to http://socr.stat.ucla.edu, click on Distributions, and select Normal.

Figure 6.17 shows output from a TI-83/84 for the same calculation.

EXAMPLE 4 Grizzly Bear Cubs

Some research has shown that the mean weight of a newborn grizzly bear cub is 650 grams ($\mu = 650$ grams)—about the size of a small chipmunk—and that the standard deviation is $\sigma = 20$ grams. Suppose that these weights follow the Normal model.

QUESTION Using the output in Figure 6.18, what is the probability that a randomly selected newborn grizzly bear cub is within one standard deviation of the mean weight of 650 grams?

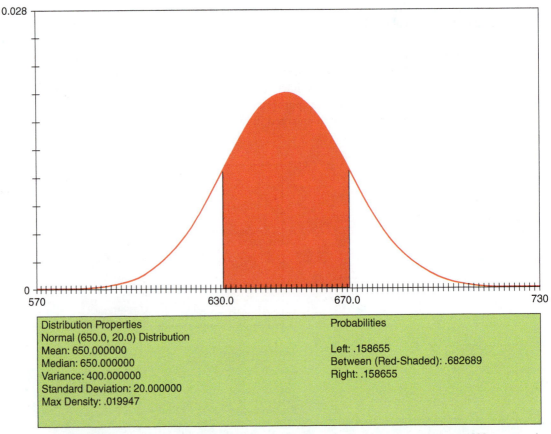

Distribution Properties
Normal (650.0, 20.0) Distribution
Mean: 650.000000
Median: 650.000000
Variance: 400.000000
Standard Deviation: 20.000000
Max Density: .019947

Probabilities

Left: .158655
Between (Red-Shaded): .682689
Right: .158655

▲ FIGURE 6.18 The shaded region represents the area under the Normal curve between 630 grams and 670 grams. That is, it represents the probability that the weight of a randomly selected grizzly bear cub is within one standard deviation of the mean.

SOLUTION The phrase "within one standard deviation of the mean weight" is one you will often see. (We used it in Chapter 3 when introducing the Empirical Rule.) It means that the cub's weight will be somewhere between

(mean − 1 standard deviation, mean + 1 standard deviation)

Because one standard deviation is 20 grams, the weight must be between

$$(650 - 20, 650 + 20)$$

or

$$(630 \text{ grams}, 670 \text{ grams})$$

From the results, we see that the probability that a randomly selected grizzly bear cub is within one standard deviation of the mean length is about 68% (from Figure 6.18, it is 68.2689%).

 TRY THIS! Exercise 6.17

Without Technology: The Standard Normal

Example 4 illustrates a principle that's very useful for finding probabilities from the Normal distribution without technology. This principle is the recognition that we don't need to refer to values in our distribution in the units in which they were measured. We can also refer to them in standard deviations. In other words, we can ask for the probability that a man's height is between 165 and 180 centimetres (measured units), but asking for the probability that his height is within one standard deviation of the mean, or has a z-score between -1 and $+1$, is asking the same thing.

You can still use the Normal model if you change the units to z-scores, but you must also convert the mean and standard deviation of the continuous random variable to z-scores. This is easy, because the mean is 0 standard deviations away from itself, and any point one standard deviation away from the mean has a z-score of 1. Thus, if the Normal model was a good model, then when you convert to z-scores, the $N(0, 1)$ model is appropriate.

This model—the Normal model with mean 0 and standard deviation 1—has a special name: the **standard Normal model**.

KEY POINT The standard Normal model is a Normal model with a mean of 0 ($\mu = 0$) and a standard deviation of 1 ($\sigma = 1$). It is represented by $N(0, 1)$.

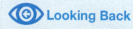 **Looking Back**

z-scores

z-scores (Chapter 3) tell us how many standard deviations from the mean an observation lies. z-scores are also called standard units.

The standard Normal model is an important concept, because it allows us to find probabilities for any Normal model. All we need to do is first convert to z-scores. We can then look up the areas in a published table that lists useful areas for the $N(0, 1)$ model. One such table is available in Appendix A.

Table 6.5 shows an excerpt from this table. The values within the table represent areas (probabilities). The numbers along the left margin, when joined to the numbers across the top, represent z-scores. For instance, the boldface value in this table represents

z	.00	.01	.02	.03	.04	.05	.06	.07	.08	.09
0.9	.8159	.8186	.8212	.8238	.8264	.8289	.8315	.8340	.8365	.8389
1.0	**.8413**	.8438	.8461	.8485	.8508	.8531	.8554	.8577	.8599	.8621
1.1	.8643	.8665	.8686	.8708	.8729	.8749	.8770	.8790	.8810	.8830
1.2	.8849	.8869	.8888	.8907	.8925	.8944	.8962	.8980	.8997	.9015

▲ **TABLE 6.5** Excerpt from the Normal table in Appendix A, which shows areas to the left of z in a standard Normal distribution. For example, the area to the left of z = 1.00 is 0.8413, and the area to the left of z = 1.01 is 0.8438.

the area under the curve *and to the left* of a *z*-score of 1.00. This represents the probability that a randomly selected person has a height *less than* 1 standard deviation above the mean. Figure 6.19 shows what this area looks like.

► **FIGURE 6.19** The area of the shaded region represents the probability that a randomly selected person (or thing) has a value less than 1.00 standard deviation above the mean, which is about 84%.

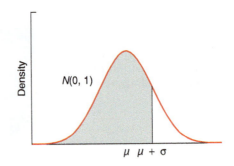

For example, imagine us finding the probability that a randomly selected woman is shorter than 150 centimetres (Figure 6.14). This person's height is then selected from a population (women) of values (heights) that follow $N(160, 7.5)$. To find this, we

1. Convert 150 centimetres to its *z*-score. We call this converted number *z*.

2. Look up the area below *z* in the table for the $N(0, 1)$ distribution.

> ### Details
>
> **z-Scores**
>
> In Chapter 3 we gave the formula for a *z*-score in terms of the mean and standard deviation of a sample:
>
> $$z = \frac{x - \bar{x}}{s}$$
>
> The same idea works for probability distributions, but we must change the notation to indicate that we are using the mean and standard deviation of a probability distribution:
>
> $$z = \frac{x - \mu}{\sigma}$$

EXAMPLE 5 Small Grizzly Bear Cubs

Small newborn cubs have a lower chance of survival. Suppose the weight of a grizzly bear cub follows a Normal distribution with a mean weight of 650 grams and a standard deviation of 20 grams.

QUESTION What is the probability that a newborn grizzly bear cub weighs less than 625 grams?

SOLUTION Begin by converting the weight of 625 grams to its *z*-score.

$$z = \frac{625 - 650}{20} = \frac{-25}{20} = -1.25$$

Next we sketch the area that represents the probability we wish to find (Figure 6.20). We want to find the area under the Normal curve that is to the left of 625 grams, or in *z*-scores, to the left of −1.25.

► **FIGURE 6.20** **(a)** A Normal distribution of the original continuous variable "weight," showing the area below 625 grams. **(b)** A standard Normal distribution, showing the z-score of −1.25 corresponding to a weight of 625 grams.

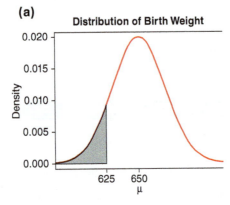

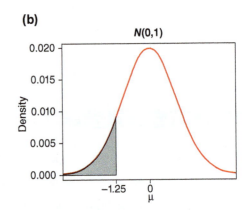

We can look this up in the standard Normal table in Appendix A. Table 6.6 on the next page shows the part we are interested in. We see that the area to the left/below of a *z*-score of −1.25 is 10.56%.

z	.00	.01	.02	.03	.04	.05	.06	.07	.08	.09
−1.3	.0968	.0951	.0934	.0918	.0901	.0885	.0869	.0853	.0838	.0823
−1.2	.1151	.1131	.1112	.1093	.1075	**.1056**	.1038	.1020	.1003	.0985

▲ **TABLE 6.6** Part of the standard Normal table. The value printed in boldface type is the area under the standard Normal density curve to the left of −1.25.

The probability that a newborn grizzly cub will weigh less than 625 grams is about 11% (rounding up from 10.56%).

TRY THIS! Exercise 6.25

EXAMPLE **6** A Range of Grizzly Cub Weights

Again, suppose that the $N(650, 20)$ model is a good description of how the weight of a grizzly bear cub is distributed.

QUESTION What is the probability that a newborn grizzly bear cub weighs between 608 and 675 grams?

SOLUTION This question is a bit tricky. The table gives us only the area below a given value. How do we find the area *between* two values?

We proceed in two steps. First we find the area below 675 grams. Then we find the area to the left of 608 grams, then take the difference between these two values of areas to the left. What remains is the region between 608 and 675, which turns out to be the probability. This is illustrated in Figure 6.21.

To find the area below 675 grams, we convert 675 to its z-score:

$$z = \frac{675 - 650}{20} = \frac{25}{20} = 1.25$$

(a)
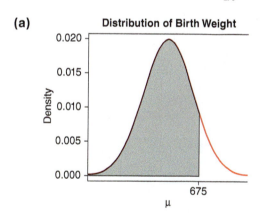

(b)
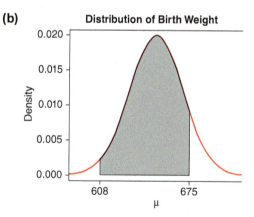

◄ **FIGURE 6.21** Steps for finding the area between 608 and 675 grams under an $N(650, 20)$ distribution. **(a)** The area below 675. **(b)** We cut off the area below 608, and the remaining (shaded) region is what we need.

Using the Standard Normal Table in Appendix A, we find that this probability is 0.8944. Next we find the area below 608 grams:

$$z = \frac{608 - 650}{20} = \frac{-42}{20} = -2.10$$

Using the same table, we find this area to be 0.0179. Now we subtract the smaller area from the larger area:

$$\begin{array}{r} 0.8944 \\ -0.0179 \\ \hline 0.8765 \end{array}$$

```
normalcdf(600,67
5,650,20)
        .8881404812
■
```

▲ **FIGURE 6.22** TI-83/84 output for finding the probability that a newborn grizzly cub will be between 608 and 675 grams.

CONCLUSION The probability that a newborn grizzly bear will weigh between 608 grams and 675 grams is about 88%. Figure 6.22 confirms that answer.

TRY THIS! Exercise 6.29

Finding Measurements from Percentiles for the Normal Distribution

So far, we have discussed how to find the probability that you will randomly select an object with a value that falls within a certain range. In Example 5, we found that if the weight of newborn grizzly cubs is modelled with an $N(650, 20)$ distribution, then the probability that a newborn grizzly cub will weigh less than 625 grams is (roughly) 11%.

Sometimes, we may be interested in what value of the continuous random variable is associated with a certain probability. For example, for 95% of the time, how long does it take you to commute to school? And during a police checkstop, 50% of all randomly inspected drivers will have a blood alcohol level of at most how much?

In Example 5, we found that 11% of newborn grizzly cubs will weigh at most 625 grams. This weight value can be called a **percentile**. In this case, 11% of a population consisting of newborn grizzly cubs will have a weight of 625 grams or less—11% of the values in the distribution of weights are below 625 grams.

Finding measurements from percentiles is simple with the right technology. The screenshot in Figure 6.23 shows how to use SOCR to find the height of a woman in the 25th percentile of an $N(160, 7.5)$. Simply move the cursor until the shaded region represents the lower 25th of the curve. (This area is given after the words "Between (Red-Shaded)" below the graph.) We see that the value that has 25.1% (as close as we could get to 0.2500) below it is 154.96. So we say that 154.96 (or 155) is the 25th percentile of this distribution.

> **Details**
>
> **Inverse Normal**
> Mathematicians sometimes call finding measurements from percentiles from Normal distributions finding "inverse Normal" values.

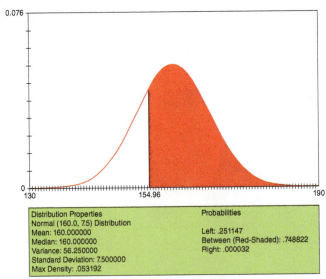

Distribution Properties	Probabilities
Normal (160.0, 7.5) Distribution	
Mean: 160.000000	Left: .251147
Median: 160.000000	Between (Red-Shaded): .748822
Variance: 56.250000	Right: .000032
Standard Deviation: 7.500000	
Max Density: .053192	

▲ **FIGURE 6.23** Technology shows that 154.96 is the 25th percentile, because it has 25% of the entire distribution below it. If a woman 155 centimetres tall, there is a 25% chance that another woman will be shorter than her.

Without technology, it takes a bit of effort. You first need to use the standard Normal curve $N(0, 1)$ to find the z-score corresponding to the percentile. Then you must work backward, converting the z-score to the units of the originating variable. So without technology, finding a percentile in terms of the Normal distribution involves two steps:

Step 1. Find the z-score from the percentile.

Step 2. Convert this z-score back to the original distribution.

Example 8 illustrates these steps.

EXAMPLE 7 Inverse Normal or Normal?

Suppose that the amount of money people keep in their online PayPal account follows a Normal model. Consider these two situations:

a. A PayPal customer wonders how much money he would have to put into his account to be in the 90th percentile.

b. A PayPal employee wonders what the probability is that a randomly selected customer will have less than $150 in his account.

QUESTION   For each situation, identify whether the question asks for a measurement or a Normal probability.

SOLUTIONS

a. This situation gives a percentile (the 90th) and asks for the measurement (in dollars) that has 90% of the other values below it. This is an inverse Normal question.

b. This situation gives a measurement ($150) and asks for a probability.

TRY THIS!   Exercise 6.41

EXAMPLE 8 Finding Percentiles by Hand

Assume that a woman's height is Normally distributed with a mean of 160 centimetres and a standard deviation of 7.5 centimetres: $N(160, 7.5)$. Earlier, we used technology to find that the 25th percentile was 155 centimetres (154.96).

QUESTION   Using the Normal table in Appendix A, confirm that the 25th percentile height is 155 centimetres.

SOLUTION   The question asks us to find a value, in centimetres, such that 25% of the values on the distribution are below it. Use the Normal table in Appendix A. This gives the probabilities and percentiles for a standard Normal distribution: $N(0, 1)$.

Step 1: Using tables somewhat limits us here. Generally, you will not find the exact value you are looking for, so simply take the value that is closest to it. This value, 0.2514, is underlined in Table 6.7, which is an excerpt from the Normal table in Appendix A.

z	.00	.01	.02	.03	.04	.05	.06	.07	.08	.09
−0.7	.2420	.2389	.2358	.2327	.2296	.2266	.2236	.2206	.2177	.2148
−0.6	.2743	.2709	.2676	.2643	.2611	.2578	.2546	.2514	.2483	.2451

▲ TABLE 6.7 Part of the standard Normal table.

You can see that the z-score corresponding to 0.2514 is −0.67. This relation between the z-score and the probability is shown in Figure 6.24.

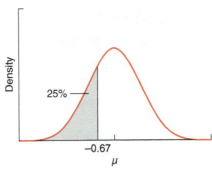

▲ **FIGURE 6.24** The percentile for 0.25 is −0.67 standard units, because 25% of the area under the standard Normal curve is below −0.67.

Step 2: Work backward to convert the z-score back to the original Normal distribution with a mean of 160 and a standard deviation of 7.5. In other words, find a woman's height that will convert to a z-score of −0.67.

A z-score of −0.67 informs us that we are 0.67 standard deviations *below* the mean. We convert this to a height in centimetres.

One standard deviation is 7.5 centimetres, so 0.67 standard deviations is

$$0.67 \times 7.5 = 5.025, \text{ or about 5 centimetres.}$$

So the 25th percentile of women's heights is 5 centimetres below the mean of the distribution. The mean is 160 centimetres, so the 25th percentile is

$$160 - 5 = 155 \text{ centimetres}$$

CONCLUSION   The woman's height at the 25th percentile is 155 centimetres, assuming that women's heights follow an $N(160, 7.5)$ distribution.

TRY THIS!   Exercise 6.47

Figure 6.25 shows some percentiles and the corresponding z-scores to help you visualize percentiles.

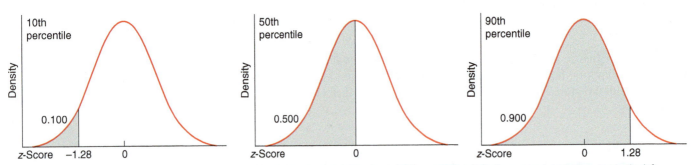

▲ **FIGURE 6.25** z-Scores and percentiles—the 10th, 50th, and 90th percentiles. A percentile corresponds to the percentage in the area to the left under the curve.

The Normal Model and the Empirical Rule

In Chapter 3 we mentioned the Empirical Rule, which was not so much a rule as a guideline for helping you understand how data are distributed. The Empirical Rule is meant to be applied to any symmetric, unimodal distribution. However, the Empirical Rule is based on the Normal model. For any arbitrary unimodal, symmetric distribution, the Empirical Rule is approximate. And sometimes very approximate. But if that distribution is the Normal model, the rule is exact.

In Example 4, we found that the area between −1 and +1 in a standard Normal distribution was 68%. This is exactly what the Empirical Rule predicts. We can also find the probability that a randomly selected observation will be between −2 and 2 standard deviations of the mean, if that observation comes from the Normal model. Figure 6.26 shows a sketch of the $N(0, 1)$ model, with the region between the z-scores of −2 and 2 shaded. From the table in the appendix, the area below +2 is 0.9772. Also from the table, the area below −2 is 0.0228. The difference is the shaded area and is $0.9772 - 0.0228 = 0.9544$, or about 95%, just as the Empirical Rule predicts.

These facts from the Empirical Rule help us interpret the standard deviation in the context of the Normal distribution. For example, because the heights of women are Normally distributed and have a standard deviation of 7.5 centimetres, we know that a majority of women (about 68%) have heights within 7.5 centimetres of the mean height of 160 centimetres: between 152.5 centimetres and 167.5 centimetres. Because nearly all women are within three standard deviations of the mean, we know not to expect too many women to be taller than $160 + (3 \times 7.5) = 182.5$ centimetres (about 6 feet 1 inch). Such women are very rare.

Looking Back

The Empirical Rule
The Empirical Rule says that if a distribution of a sample of data is unimodal and roughly symmetric, then about 68% of the observations are within one standard deviation of the mean, about 95% are within two standard deviations of the mean, and nearly all are within three standard deviations of the mean.

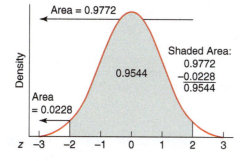

◀ **FIGURE 6.26** The area between z-scores of −2.00 and +2.00 on the standard Normal curve.

SNAPSHOT   THE NORMAL MODEL

WHAT IS IT? ▶	A model of a distribution for some numerical variables.
WHAT DOES IT DO? ▶	Provides us with a model of the distributions of probabilities for many real-life numerical variables.
HOW DOES IT DO IT? ▶	The probabilities are represented by the area underneath the bell-shaped curve.
HOW IS IT USED? ▶	If the Normal model is appropriate, it can be used for finding probabilities or for finding values associated with particular percentiles.
WHEN IS IT USED? ▶	If a histogram of your data appears to have a bell-curve shape.

Appropriateness of the Normal Model

The Normal model does not fit all distributions of numerical variables. For example, if we are randomly selecting people who submitted tax returns to the federal government, we cannot use the Normal model to find the probability that someone's return is higher than the mean value. The reason is that incomes are right-skewed, so the Normal model will not fit.

How do we know whether the Normal model is appropriate? Unfortunately, there is no checklist. However, the Normal model is a good first-choice model if you suspect that the distribution is symmetric and has one mode. Once you collected data, you can check to see whether the Normal model closely matches the data.

Statisticians have several ways to check whether the Normal model is an appropriate fit for the population, but the easiest way is for you to make a histogram of your data (as in Figure 6.27) and see if it looks unimodal and symmetric—do you see the "bell"? If so, the Normal model is likely to be an appropriate probability model of the data. In Chapter 13, you will learn about a more technical plot to determine whether your data follow a Normal model. QQ-plots will be covered in section 13.5.

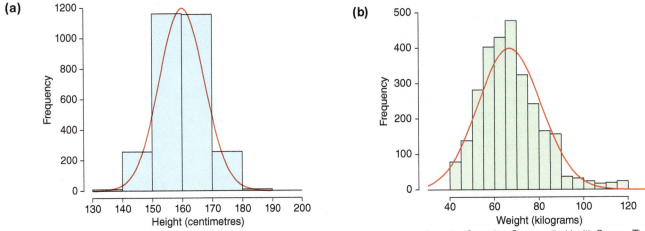

▲ **FIGURE 6.27** **(a)** A histogram of data from a large sample of adult women taken at random from the Canadian Community Health Survey. The curve is the Normal curve, which fits the shape of the histogram very well, indicating that the Normal model would be appropriate for these data. **(b)** A histogram of the weights for the same sample of women. Here, the Normal model is not a good fit for the data.

SECTION 6.3

The Binomial Model

The Normal model can be applied to many real-world, continuous random variables. The **binomial probability model** can be applied to instances when the random variable is discrete. As with the Normal model, we will explain what the binomial model looks like and how to find probabilities with it. We will also provide examples of situations where this model can be applied, and why.

A classic application of the binomial model is counting heads when flipping a coin. Let's say we flip a coin 10 times. What is the probability that we'll get 1 head? 2 heads? 10 heads? This is a situation where the binomial model fits quite well, and the probabilities of these outcomes are given by the binomial model. If we randomly select 10 people, what's the probability that exactly 4 voted for the current governing political party? What is the probability that Sidney Crosby will score on more than half of 30 shootout attempts? What is the probability that at least 20 of 100 randomly chosen women will develop breast cancer at some point in their lives? These are all situations where the binomial model can be applied.

How do we recognize a situation where the binomial model can be applied? The first sign is that the outcome from a random experiment is a count. Notice how we were looking for a count in each of the three examples mentioned in the previous paragraph. If this happens, then the following three conditions must be satisfied:

1. *A fixed number of trials.* We represent this with the letter n. For example, if we flip a coin 10 times, $n = 10$.

2. *Only two outcomes are possible for each trial.* We call these outcomes "success" and "failure." For example, we might consider the outcome of heads to be a success. Or we might be selecting people at random and counting females; in this case, of the two possible outcomes for each trial (a person), "female" would be considered a success.

3. *The trials are independent.* The outcome of one trial does not affect the outcome of any other trial. In Chapter 5, we discussed how independent events do not affect each other and that the probability of the event occurring does not change. Here, the probability of a success on each trial is the same. We represent this probability with the letter p. For example, the probability of getting heads after a coin flip is $p = 0.50$; because of independent trials, it does not change from one flip to another.

If these three conditions exist, the binomial model can be applied and you can easily find the probabilities by inspecting the binomial probability distribution.

KEY POINT The binomial model is used to find the probability that a random experiment will end in a certain count, this count being the number of successes that occur. Three conditions must exist:

1. Fixed number of trials: n.

2. Each trial is either a success or failure.

3. The trials are independent, meaning the probability of success p is the same for each trial.

EXAMPLE 9 Extrasensory Perception (Mind Reading)

Zener cards are special cards used to test whether people can read minds (telepathy). Each card in a Zener deck has one of five special designs: a star, a circle, a plus sign, a square, and three wavy lines (Figure 6.28). In an experiment, one person, the "sender," selects a card at random, looks at it, and thinks about the symbol on the card. Another person, the "receiver," cannot see the card (and in some studies cannot even see the sender), and guesses which of the symbols was chosen. A researcher records whether the guess was correct. The card is then placed back in the deck, the deck is shuffled, and another card is drawn. Suppose this happens 10 times (10 guesses are made). The receiver gets 3 guesses correct, and the researcher wants to know the probability of this happening if the receiver is simply guessing.

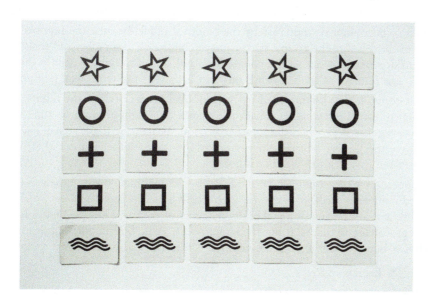

◀ **FIGURE 6.28** Zener cards (ESP cards) show one of five shapes. A deck has equal numbers of each shape.

QUESTION Explain why the binomial model can be applied here.

SOLUTION First, we note that we are counting something: the number of successful guesses. We need to check if this experiment meets the three conditions of a binomial model: (1) The experiment consists of a fixed number of trials: $n = 10$. (2) The outcome of each trial is either a success or failure: the receiver either gets the answer right or not. (3) The trials are independent: as long as the cards are put back in the deck and thoroughly reshuffled, each trial is independent. Therefore, the probability of success on any trial is $p = 1/5 = 0.20$.

All three conditions are satisfied, so the experiment can be modelled by the binomial distribution.

TRY THIS! Exercise 6.57

EXAMPLE 10 Why Are They Not Modelled By the Binomial?

The following four experiments can almost, but not quite, be modelled by the binomial model.

a. Count the number of eye colours in a group of 50 randomly selected people.

b. A married couple decides to have children until a girl is born, but to stop at five children if they do not have any girls. How many children will the couple have?

c. Suppose the probability that a flight will arrive on time (within 15 minutes of the scheduled arrival time) at Pearson International Airport in Toronto is 75%. How many flights arrive on time out of 300 flights scheduled to land on a day in January?

d. A student guesses on every question of a test that has 10 multiple-choice questions and 10 true/false questions. Count the number of questions the student gets right.

QUESTION In each instance, explain which of the three conditions are not satisfied.

SOLUTIONS

a. This count cannot be modelled by the binomial model because there are more than two eye colours, so each trial can produce more than two outcomes. If we reduced the eye colours to two categories, say to observing if a person's eye colour is brown or not, then we could model the count with the binomial distribution.

b. This count cannot be modelled by the binomial model because the number of trials is not fixed before the couple starts to have children. The number of "trials" (children) depends on whether the couple has a girl, and if so, which child is the first girl. The number of trials depends on what happens—the word *until* tells you that.

c. This count cannot be modelled by the binomial model because the flights are not independent. If the weather is bad, the chance of a flight arriving on time will be lower compared to when the weather is good. When one flight arrives late (during bad weather), there will be a higher probability that another flight will arrive late compared to when the weather is good.

d. It appears as if this count can be modelled by the binomial, because there is (1) a fixed number of trials ($n = 20$); (2) each trial is a success (right answer) or failure (not right); and (3) the guessing makes the outcome of each trial independent. However, the probability of success is not the same: $p = \frac{1}{4} = 0.25$ if the question is multiple-choice, but $p = \frac{1}{2} = 0.50$ if the question is true/false. This situation is tricky.

TRY THIS! Exercise 6.59

Visualizing the Binomial Distribution

All binomial models have the three conditions listed above, but the list gives us flexibility in the values of n and p. For example, if we had flipped 6 coins instead of 10, we could still use the binomial model. Also, if the coin was weighted in favour of heads, with $p = 0.60$, we could still use the binomial model. Differing values of n and p affect only the appearance of the binomial distribution.

Figure 6.29 shows that the binomial distribution for $n = 3$ and $p = 0.5$ is symmetric. We can read from the graph that the probability of getting exactly 2 successes (2 heads in 3 flips of a coin) is almost 0.40, and that the probability of getting 0 successes is the same as the probability of getting all successes.

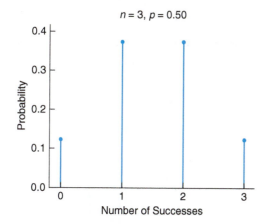

FIGURE 6.29 Binomial distribution with $n = 3$, $p = 0.50$.

If n is bigger but p remains fixed at 0.50, the distribution is still symmetric because the chance of a success is the same as the chance of a failure, as shown in Figure 6.30.

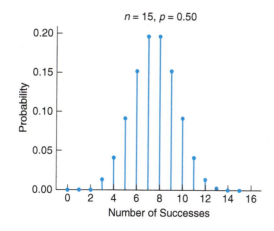

FIGURE 6.30 Binomial distribution with $n = 15$, $p = 0.50$.

If the probability of success is not 50%, the distribution might not be symmetric. Figure 6.31 on the next page shows the distribution for $p = 0.3$, which means we're less likely to get a large number of successes than a smaller number, so the probability "spikes" are taller for smaller numbers of successes. The plot is now right-skewed.

However, even if the distribution is not symmetric, if we increase the number of trials, it becomes symmetric. The shape of the distribution depends on both n and p.

▶ **FIGURE 6.31** Binomial distribution with $n = 15$, $p = 0.30$.

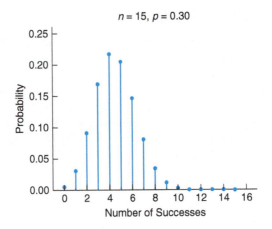

If we keep $p = 0.3$ but increase n to 100, we get a more symmetric shape, as shown in Figure 6.32.

▶ **FIGURE 6.32** Binomial distribution with $n = 100$, $p = 0.30$. Note that we show x only for values between 15 and 45. The shape is symmetric, even though p is not 0.50.

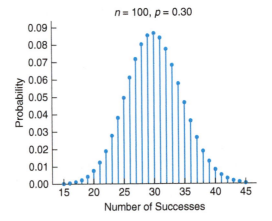

Binomial distributions have the interesting property that if the number of trials is large enough, the distributions are symmetric.

KEY POINT The shape of a binomial distribution depends on both n and p. Binomial distributions are symmetric when $p = 0.5$, but they are also symmetric when n is large, even if p is close to 0 or 1.

Finding Binomial Probabilities

Once you have identified that the count of a random experiment can be modelled by the binomial distribution, then you need to identify the values of n and p. As we have seen, the binomial distribution and its probabilities depend on n and p. We use the notation $b(n, p, x)$ to represent a binomial probability of getting x successes in n independent trials with probability of success p on each trial. For example, imagine tossing a coin 10 times. If each side is equally likely, what is the probability of getting 4 heads? We represent this with $b(10, 0.50, 4)$.

The easiest and most accurate way to find binomial probabilities is to use technology. Statistical calculators and software have the binomial distribution built in and can easily calculate probabilities for you.

EXAMPLE 11 Texting and Driving

According to a Leger Marketing survey in 2010, 8% of Canadians admit to the practice of texting while driving.

QUESTIONS For now, accept that the three conditions needed to use the binomial model are satisfied. Write the notation for the probability that exactly 11 drivers out of 200 are texting while driving.

SOLUTION The number of trials is 200, the probability of success is 0.08, and the number of successes is 11. Therefore, we can write the binomial probability as $b(200, 0.08, 11)$.

The command and output for finding this probability on a TI-83/84 are shown in Figure 6.33. The command binompdf stands for "binomial probability distribution function." The results show that the probability of exactly 11 drivers texting, out of 200 inspected, is about 4.77% (0.04769643).

TRY THIS! Exercise 6.63

TECH

▲ **FIGURE 6.33** TI-83/84 output for a binomial trial.

Although we applied the binomial model to the texting and driving example, we had to assume that the trials were independent. A "trial" in this context consists of a person in the act of driving, and a "success" occurs if a person is texting. The condition of independence assumes that all drivers have a cell phone, or at least have their cell phone handy while they are driving. If a person does not have a cell phone, then the chance that he or she will be texting while driving will be zero, different from the probability of a driver texting if he or she has her cell phone accessible while driving. Sometimes we have to impose such assumptions to complete a problem, but we need to be sure to check these conditions when we can, and then be prepared to change our answer if these conditions do not apply.

Another approach to finding binomial probabilities is to use a table. Published tables are available that list binomial probabilities for a variety of combinations of values for n and p. One such table is provided in Appendix A. This table lists binomial probabilities for values of n between 2 and 15 and for several different values of p.

EXAMPLE 12 Post-Secondary Education

According to Statistics Canada's National Household Survey, in 2011 about 60% of Canadians between the ages of 25 and 64 had a post-secondary education.

QUESTION Pretend that one person having a post-secondary education (or not) does not affect another person having a post-secondary education (or not). Using Table 6.8 on the next page, which shows binomial probabilities for $n = 15$ and for various values of p, find the probability that exactly 8 out of 15 randomly selected Canadians aged 25 to 64 will have a post-secondary education.

SOLUTION Substituting the numbers, you can see that we are looking for $b(15, 0.60, 8)$. Referring to Table 6.8, you can see—by looking in the table for $n = 15$, the row $x = 8$, and the column $p = 0.6$—that the probability that exactly 8 Canadians between the ages of 25 and 64 have a post-secondary education is 0.177, or about an 18% chance.

x	0.1	0.2	0.25	0.3	0.4	0.5	0.6	0.7	0.75	0.8	0.9
6	.002	.043	.092	.147	.207	.153	.061	.012	.003	.001	.000
7	.000	.014	.039	.081	.177	.196	.118	.035	.013	.003	.000
8	.000	.003	.013	.035	.118	.196	<u>.177</u>	.081	.039	.014	.000
9	.000	.001	.003	.012	.061	.153	.207	.147	.092	.043	.002
10	.000	.000	.001	.003	.024	.092	.186	.206	.165	.103	.010
11	.000	.000	.000	.001	.007	.042	.127	.219	.225	.188	.043
12	.000	.000	.000	.000	.002	.014	.063	.170	.225	.250	.129
13	.000	.000	.000	.000	.000	.003	.022	.092	.156	.231	.267
14	.000	.000	.000	.000	.000	.000	.005	.031	.067	.132	.343
15	.000	.000	.000	.000	.000	.000	.000	.005	.013	.035	.206

▲ **TABLE 6.8** Binomial probabilities with a sample of 15 and *x*-values of 6 or higher.

```
binompdf(15,.6,8
)
          .1770836617
```

▲ **FIGURE 6.34** TI-83/84 output for
b(15, 0.6, 8).

Using a TI-83/84 as shown in Figure 6.34, we can see another
way to get the same answer.

TRY THIS! Exercise 6.65

Finding (Slightly) More Complex Probabilities

EXAMPLE 13 ESP with 10 Trials

For a test of psychic abilities, researchers have asked the sender to draw 10 cards at random from a large deck of Zener cards (see Example 9). Assume that the cards are replaced
in the deck after each use and that the deck is shuffled. Recall that this deck contains
equal numbers of 5 unique shapes. The receiver guesses which card the sender has drawn.

QUESTIONS

a. What is the probability of getting *exactly 5* correct answers (out of 10 trials) if the
receiver is simply guessing (and has no psychic ability)?

b. What is the probability that the receiver will get *5 or more* of the cards correct out
of 10 trials?

c. What is the probability of getting *fewer than 5* correct in 10 trials with the ESP
cards?

SOLUTIONS

a. In Example 9, we identified that the binomial model can be applied. With that
done, we must now identify *n* and *p*. The number of trials is 10, so $n = 10$. If the
receiver is guessing, then the probability of a correct answer is $p = 1/5 = 0.20$.
Therefore, we wish to find $b(10, 0.2, 5)$.

Figure 6.35a on the next page gives the TI-83/84 output, where you can see
that the probability of getting 5 right out of 10 is only about 0.0264. Figure 6.35b
shows the Minitab output for the same question.

(a)

```
binompdf(10,.2,5
)
      .0264241152
▮
```

(b)

Probability Density Function
Binomial with n = 10 and p = 0.2
x   P
5   0.0264241

◀ **FIGURE 6.35** Technology output for *b*(10, 0.2, 5). **(a)** Output from a TI-83/84. **(b)** Output from Minitab.

Figure 6.36a shows a graph of the probability distribution of this particular count. The probability $b(10, 0.2, 5)$ is so small that it's hard to read off the graph. The graph shows that it's unusual to get exactly 5 correct when the receiver is guessing.

b. The phrase *5 or more* means we need the probability that the receiver gets 5 correct **or** 6 correct **or** 7 **or** 8 **or** 9 **or** 10. The outcomes 5 correct, 6 correct, and so on are mutually exclusive, because if you get exactly 5 correct, you cannot possibly also get exactly 6 correct. Therefore, we can find the probability of 5 or more correct by adding the individual probabilities together:

$$b(10, 0.2, 5) + b(10, 0.2, 6) + b(10, 0.2, 7) + b(10, 0.2, 8) + b(10, 0.2, 9) + b(10, 0.2, 10)$$
$$= 0.026 \quad + \quad 0.006 \quad + \quad 0.001 \quad + \quad 0.000 \quad + \quad 0.000 \quad + \quad 0.000$$
$$= 0.033$$

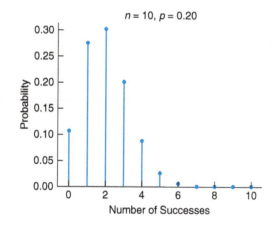

◀ **FIGURE 6.36(a)** The theoretical numbers of successes for 10 trials with the Zener deck, assuming guessing.

These probabilities are circled in Figure 6.36b.

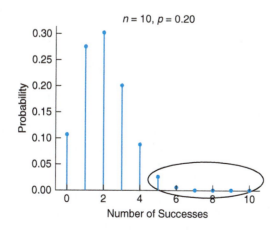

◀ **FIGURE 6.36(b)** Summing the probabilities represented by the circled bars gives us the probability of getting 5 or more correct.

c. The phrase *fewer than 5 correct* means 4, 3, 2, 1, or 0 correct. These probabilities are circled in Figure 6.36c.

▶ **FIGURE 6.36(c)** Summing the probabilities represented by the circled bars gives the probability of getting fewer than 5 correct.

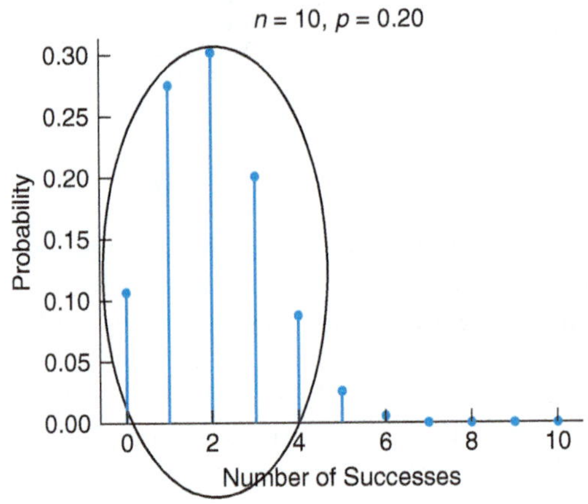

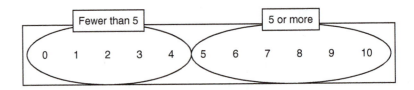

$n = 10, p = 0.20$

The event that we get fewer than 5 correct is the complement of the event that we get 5 or more correct, as you can see in Figure 6.37, which shows all possible numbers of successes with 10 trials. *Fewer than 5* is the same event as *4 or fewer* and is shown in the left oval in the figure.

▶ **FIGURE 6.37** The possible numbers of successes out of 10 trials with binomial data. Note that *fewer than 5* is the complement of *5 or more*.

Fewer than 5					5 or more				
0	1	2	3	4	5	6	7	8	9	10

Because we know the probability of 5 or more, we can find its complement by subtracting from 1:

$$1 - 0.033 = 0.967$$

CONCLUSIONS

a. The probability of exactly 5 correct is 0.026.

b. The probability of 5 or more correct is 0.033.

c. The probability of fewer than 5 (that is, of 4 or fewer) is 0.967.

TRY THIS! Exercise 6.73

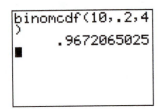

```
binomcdf(10,.2,4
)
         .9672065025
∎
```

▲ **FIGURE 6.38** TI-83/84 output for $n = 10$, $p = 0.2$, and 4 or fewer successes.

Most technology also offers you the option of finding binomial probabilities for x *or fewer*. In general, probabilities of x *or fewer* are called **cumulative probabilities**. Figure 6.38 shows the cumulative binomial probabilities provided by the TI-83/84; notice the c in binom**c**df.

The probability of getting 5 or more correct is different from the probability of getting more than 5 correct. This very small change in the wording gives very different results. Figure 6.39 shows that *5 or more* includes the outcomes 5, 6, 7, 8, 9, and 10, whereas *more than 5* does not include the outcome of 5.

When finding Normal probabilities, we did not have to worry about such subtleties of language, because for a continuous random variable, the probability of getting 5 or more is the same as the probability of getting more than 5.

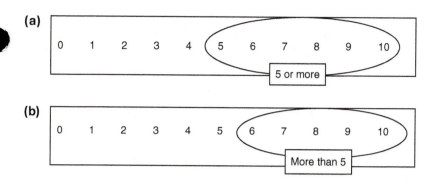

◄ **FIGURE 6.39** Interpretation of words for discrete counts with *n* of 10. **(a)** Results for *5 or more*; **(b)** results for *more than 5*. Note that they are different.

Finding Binomial Probabilities by Hand

When the number of trials is small, we can find probabilities by relying on the probability rules in Chapter 5 and listing all possible outcomes. In fact, there is a general pattern we can exploit to find a formula that will give us the probabilities for any value of *n* or *p*. Listing all the outcomes will help us see why this formula works.

Suppose we are testing someone using the Zener cards that have five different shapes. After each card is guessed, it is returned to the deck, and the deck is shuffled before the next card is drawn. We want to count how many correct guesses a potential psychic makes in four trials. We can have five different outcomes for this binomial experiment: 0 correct answers, 1 correct, 2 correct, 3 correct, and all 4 correct.

The first step is to list all possible outcomes after four attempts. At each trial, the guesser is either right or wrong. Using R for right and W for wrong, we list all possible sequences of right or wrong results in four trials.

4 Right	3 Right	2 Right	1 Right	0 Right
RRRR	RRRW	RRWW	RWWW	WWWW
	RRWR	RWRW	WRWW	
	RWRR	RWWR	WWRW	
	WRRR	WWRR	WWWR	
		WRWR		
		WRRW		

There are 16 equally likely possible outcomes for four guesses, giving five possible outcomes for the binomial experiment that are not all equally likely.

Now we find the probabilities of getting 4 right, 3 right, 2 right, 1 right, and 0 right. Because there are five shapes, and all five are equally likely to be chosen, if the receiver is simply guessing and has no psychic ability, then the probability of a right answer at each trial is $1/5 = 0.2$, and the probability of guessing wrong is 0.8.

Four right means "right AND right AND right AND right." Successive trials are independent (because we replace the card and reshuffle every time), so we can multiply the probabilities using the multiplication rule.

$$P(RRRR) = 0.2 \times 0.2 \times 0.2 \times 0.2 = 0.0016$$

This probability is just $b(4, 0.2, 4) = 1(0.0016) = 1(0.2)^4$. (We multiply by 1 because there is only one way that we can get all 4 right to happen, which is also why there is only one outcome listed in the "4 right" column.)

 Looking Back

AND

The multiplication rule was Probability Rule 5c in Chapter 5 and applies only to independent events: $P(A \text{ AND } B) = P(A) P(B)$.

The probability of getting 3 right and 1 wrong includes all four options in the second group. The probability for each of these options is obtained by calculating the probability of 3 right and 1 wrong, and all of these probabilities will be the same. To get the total probability, therefore, we multiply by 4.

$$P(RRRW) = 0.2 \times 0.2 \times 0.2 \times 0.8 = 0.0064$$

$$P(3 \text{ right and } 1 \text{ wrong, in any order}) = 4(0.0064) = 0.0256$$

$$b(4, 0.2, 3) = 4(0.2)^3(0.8)^1 = 0.0256$$

The probability of getting 2 right and 2 wrong includes all six options in the third column. The probability for each of these options is obtained by calculating the probability of 2 right and 2 wrong; then, to get the total, we multiply by 6.

$$P(RRWW) = 0.2 \times 0.2 \times 0.8 \times 0.8 = 0.0256$$

$$P(2 \text{ right and } 2 \text{ wrong, in any order}) = 6(0.0256) = 0.1536$$

$$b(4, 0.2, 2) = 6(0.2)^2(0.8)^2 = 0.1536$$

The probability of getting 1 right and 3 wrong includes all four options in the fourth column. We obtain the probability for each of the options by calculating the probability of 1 right and 3 wrong; then we multiply by 4 to get the total.

$$P(RWWW) = 0.2 \times 0.8 \times 0.8 \times 0.8 = 0.1024$$

$$P(1 \text{ right and } 3 \text{ wrong, in any order}) = 4(0.1024) = 0.4096$$

$$b(4, 0.2, 1) = 4(0.2)^1(0.8)^3 = 0.4096$$

Finally, the probability of getting all four wrong is

$$P(WWWW) = 0.8 \times 0.8 \times 0.8 \times 0.8 = 0.4096$$

Because there is only one way for this to happen, we multiply 0.4096 by 1. Thus

$$b(4, 0.2, 0) = 1(0.8)^4 = 0.4096$$

Table 6.9 summarizes the results.

If you add the probabilities, you will see that they add to 1, as they should, because this list includes all possible outcomes that can happen.

Figure 6.40 shows a graph of the probability distribution. Note that the graph is right-skewed because the probability of success is less than 0.50. Also note that the probability of getting 4 out of 4 right with the Zener cards is very small.

You might compare these probabilities with those in the binomial table. You will find that they agree, if you round off the numbers we found "by hand" to three decimal places.

Number Right	Probability
4 right	0.0016
3 right	0.0256
2 right	0.1536
1 right	0.4096
0 right	0.4096

▲ **TABLE 6.9** A summary of the probabilities of all possible numbers of successes in four trials with the Zener cards.

▶ **FIGURE 6.40** Probability distribution using the Zener cards with four trials.

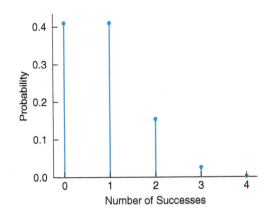

The Formula

This approach of listing all possible outcomes is tedious when $n = 4$, and the tedium increases for larger values of n. (For $n = 5$ we have to list 32 possibilities, and for $n = 6$

there are 64.) However, mathematicians have derived a formula that finds probabilities for the binomial distribution. The binomial table in this book and the results of your calculator are based on this formula:

$P(x$ successes in n trials of a binomial experiment) $=$
(number of different ways of getting x successes in n trials) $p^x(1 - p)^{(n-x)}$

For example, for our alleged psychic who gets four guesses with the Zener cards, the probability of 3 successes $(x = 3)$ in four trials $(n = 4)$ is

(number of ways of getting 3 successes in 4 trials) $(0.2)^3(0.8)^1$

$= 4 \, (0.2)^3(0.8)^1$

$= 0.0256$

The Shape of the Binomial Distribution: Centre and Spread

Unlike the Normal distribution, the mean and standard deviation of the binomial distribution can be easily calculated. Their interpretation is the same as with all distributions: the mean tells us where the distribution balances, and the standard deviation tells us how far values are, typically, from the mean.

For example, in Figure 6.41, the binomial distribution is symmetric, so the mean sits right in the centre at 7.5 successes.

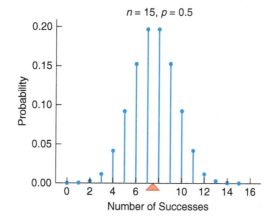

◀ **FIGURE 6.41** A binomial distribution with $n = 15$, $p = 0.50$. The mean is at 7.5 successes.

If the distribution is right-skewed, the mean will be just to the right of the peak, closer to the right tail, as shown in Figure 6.42. This is a binomial distribution with $n = 15$, $p = 0.3$, and the mean sits at the balancing point: 4.5 successes.

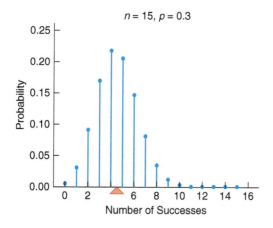

◀ **FIGURE 6.42** A binomial distribution with $n = 15$, $p = 0.3$. The mean is at the balancing point of 4.5 successes.

The mean, μ, of a binomial probability distribution can be found with a simple formula:

$$\mu = np$$

In words, the mean number of successes in a binomial experiment is the number of trials times the probability of a success.

This formula should make intuitive sense. If you toss a coin 100 times, you would expect about half of the tosses to be heads. Thus the "typical" outcome is $(1/2) \times 100 = 50$, or $np = 100 \times 0.5$.

The standard deviation, σ, of a binomial probability distribution, which measures the spread, is less intuitive:

$$\sigma = \sqrt{np(1 - p)}$$

For example, Figure 6.42 shows a binomial distribution with $n = 15$, $p = 0.30$. The mean is $15 \times 0.3 = 4.5$. The standard deviation is $\sqrt{15 \times 0.3 \times 0.7} = \sqrt{3.15} = 1.775$.

> **KEY POINT**
>
> For a binomial experiment, the mean is
>
> $$\mu = np$$
>
> For a binomial experiment, the standard deviation is
>
> $$\sigma = \sqrt{np(1 - p)}$$

Interpreting the Mean and Standard Deviation

The mean of any probability distribution, including the binomial, is sometimes called the **expected value**. This name gives some intuitive understanding. If you were to actually carry out a binomial experiment, you would *expect* about μ successes. If we flip a coin 100 times, we would *expect* about 50 heads. If, in an ESP study, 10 trials are made and the probability of success at each trial is 0.20, we *expect* about 2 successes due to chance ($10 \times 0.2 = 2$).

Will we get exactly 50 heads? Will the ESP receiver get exactly 2 cards correct? Sometimes, yes. Usually, no. Although we expect μ successes, we usually get μ give or take some amount. That give-or-take amount is what is measured by σ.

In 100 tosses of a fair coin, we expect $\mu = 50$ heads, give or take $\sigma = \sqrt{100 \times 0.5 \times 0.5} = 5$ heads. We expect 50, but we will not be surprised if we get between 45 and 55 heads. In the Zener card experiment with 10 trials, we expect the receiver to guess about 2 cards correctly, but in practice we expect him or her to get 2 give or take 1.3, because

$$\sqrt{10 \times 0.2 \times 0.8} = \sqrt{1.6} = 1.26$$

 SNAPSHOT **THE BINOMIAL DISTRIBUTION**

WHAT IS IT? ▶	A distribution for some discrete variables.
WHAT DOES IT DO? ▶	Gives probabilities for the number of successes observed in a fixed number of trials in a binomial experiment.
HOW DOES IT DO IT? ▶	If the conditions of the binomial model are met, once you identify n (number of trials), p (the probability of success), and x (the number of successes), it gives the probability.
HOW IS IT USED? ▶	The probabilities are generally provided in the form of a table or a formula, but if you need to calculate them, use a calculator or technology.
WHEN IS IT USED? ▶	When you are computing the probability of how many successes occur in n independent trials.

EXAMPLE **14** Shooting Percentage of the Great One

During the 1981–82 NHL season, Wayne Gretzky set a record for the most goals scored in a season, tallying 92 goals in 80 games. He scored on 92 of 369 shots taken, for a shooting percentage of 25% (24.93%). Assume that each shot he makes on goal is independent of another; that is, success or failure on one shot does not change the chance of success on another shot on goal.

QUESTION Suppose you were to pick any 200 shots-on-goal Gretzky took in 1981–82. How many would you expect him to score, give or take how many?

SOLUTION We can use the binomial model. (Why?) The number of trials is $n = 200$, and the probability of success on each trial is $p = 0.25$. You would expect Wayne Gretzky to score on 25% of his shots-on-goal, or 50 goals:

$$\mu = np = 200(0.25) = 50$$

The give-or-take amount is measured by the standard deviation:

$$\sigma = \sqrt{200 \times 0.25 \times 0.75} = 6.1237$$

You should expect him to score on about 50 of 200 shots-on-goal, give or take about 6.1.

$$50 - 6.1 = 43.9$$
$$50 + 6.1 = 56.1$$

CONCLUSION You expect Gretzky to score between 43 and 56 goals, out of 200 shots-on-goal.

TRY THIS! Exercise 6.77

Surveys: An Application of the Binomial Model

We are exposed to applications of the binomial model daily. The most common of these is in survey sampling. Imagine a large population of people; for example, the 27 million or so people who are eligible to vote in Canada. Some proportion of them, call it p, have a certain characteristic. If we choose 10 people at random (with replacement), we can ask what the probability is that all of them, none of them, three of them, or seven of them have the characteristic.

EXAMPLE **15** Survey on Canadian Youth Optimism

An Ipsos Reid survey found that 57% of Canadian youths aged 18 to 21 feel as if they can achieve anything they want. Suppose we were to randomly pick 100 from this population of Canadians aged 18 to 21.

QUESTIONS If, as is claimed, 57% of this population feel they can achieve anything they want, how many youths in our sample would we expect to say they can achieve anything they want? What is the give or take of this count? Would you be surprised if 72 people in this sample said they could achieve anything they want?

SOLUTION Assuming that the three properties of the binomial model are satisfied, then we would expect 57% of our sample of 100 to say they can achieve anything they want—that is, 57 people. The standard deviation is $\sqrt{100 \times 0.57 \times 0.43} = 4.95 \approx 5$. We should expect 57 people, give or take 5, to say they can achieve anything they want. We should not be surprised if we got as many as $57 + 5 = 62$ people. But 72 people is quite a bit more than one standard deviation above what we expect. In fact, 72 is three standard deviations above what we would expect, so it would be a very optimistic number of people.

TRY THIS!   Exercise 6.81

If we are counting the number of people who have a certain characteristic in a survey where the people are picked at random, then the three conditions of the binomial model are usually satisfied:

1. A fixed number of people are surveyed. In Example 15, $n = 100$.

2. The outcome for each person is observed as a success (believes they can achieve anything they want) or a failure (doesn't believe they can achieve anything they want).

3. The trials are independent. This means that if one person has the characteristic, this will not affect another person having the characteristic. As a result, the probability that each of $n = 100$ people will have the characteristic is the same, $p = 0.57$.

If the people are selected with replacement—meaning that once a person is selected and inspected they are placed back into the population to be possibly selected (and inspected) again—then the probability of success is the same for each trial.

With surveys, we usually don't report the number of people who have the characteristic; instead we report the proportion, or percentage, of people surveyed who have it. We would not report that 57 people in our sample of 100 felt they could achieve anything they want; we would report that 57% of our sample felt they could achieve anything they want. But the binomial model still applies, because we are simply converting our count to a percentage.

In reality, surveys don't select people with replacement. The most basic surveys sample people without replacement, which means that, strictly speaking, the probability of a success is different after each trial. Imagine if the first youth chosen feels they can achieve anything they want. If there are few of these people left in the population, the chance that the next youth chosen will have this same characteristic will be less than 57%. However, as you can imagine, this is not a problem if the population is very large. In fact, if the population size is very large relative to the sample size (at least 10 times bigger), then this difference is so slight that characteristic 3 is essentially met.

Taking a random sample, either with or without replacement, of a large and diverse population such as all voters is quite complicated. In practice, the surveys we read about in the papers or hear about on the news use a modified approach that is slightly different from what we've discussed here. Random selection is still at the heart of these modified methods, though, and the binomial model often provides a good approximation for probabilities, even under these more complex schemes.

CASE STUDY REVISITED

Between June 1, 2007, and September 30, 2008, lottery retailers in Manitoba won 13 prizes of $10,000 or more, about seven times more than the general population. Is this difference because lottery retailers "play more"? Or are lottery retailers winning more because of random chance?

Studies have indicated that lottery retailers do play lotteries more than you do (assuming you do not have a job that involves selling lottery tickets). Specifically, retailers play anywhere between 1.52 to 1.9 times more. (This is called "gaming intensity.")

Each time a person buys a lottery ticket, a win of $10,000 or more can be classified as a "success"; otherwise, the outcome of the lottery play is a "failure." The outcome of each lottery play—a win or a loss—is independent of other lottery plays. By counting the number of lottery wins of $10,000 or more, we can use the binomial model.

In total, there were 170 winners during this time period. Combining retailer and non-retailer lottery ticket players makes up about 898,000 Manitobans. (Note, not all people in Manitoba play lotteries.) The probability of any person winning a prize of $10,000 or more is about $p = \frac{170}{898,000} \approx 0.0002$. We then find the number of times lottery retailers played lotteries over this time period, and taking into account that they do play more often than people who do not sell lottery tickets, n can be found to be around 15318.

The expected number of lottery wins of $10,000 or more for lottery retailers in Manitoba is then $\mu = np = 15318(0.0002) = 3.0634 \approx 3.06$. The standard deviation of this count is $\sigma = \sqrt{np(1-p)} = \sqrt{15318(0.0002)(0.9998)} = 1.7501 \approx 1.75$. We should expect lottery retailers to win 3.06 prizes of $10,000 or more, give or take 1.75. That is, we should expect the number of wins to be somewhere between $(3.06 \pm 1.75) = (1.31, 4.81)$.

The observed number of lottery retailer wins of $10,000 or more was 13. This value is $\frac{13-3.06}{1.75} = 5.68$ standard deviations *above* the expected number of wins. The probability of observing such an extreme outcome is about 0.00001995, or about 0.002%. In other words, the fact that retailers of lottery tickets were winning more than non-retail lottery players by a factor of about 7 is not due to chance. Perhaps lottery fraud *was* occurring in Manitoba during this time period!

Two weeks after a local CBC newscast aired the story about irregularities in the number of $10,000 or more wins by lottery retailers, Manitoba's ombudsman re-opened an investigation into western Canada's lottery system. In August 2011, a gas bar clerk in Winnipeg was arrested on fraud charges for telling a 61-year-old man that his lottery ticket was good for several more draws. The gas bar clerk did not return the ticket, and attempted to cash it in and collect its $90,641.40. The clerk was charged with theft and fraud.

EXPLORING STATISTICS

CLASS ACTIVITY

ESP with Coin Flipping

GOALS	MATERIALS
Apply the binomial model to a real situation.	One coin for each pair of students.

ACTIVITY

Choose a partner. One of you will play the role of the "sender" and the other will be the "receiver." The sender will flip a coin so that the receiver can't see the outcome (heads or tails). The sender will then look at the coin and concentrate, trying to mentally send a thought about whether the coin landed heads or tails. The receiver writes down (quickly) the outcome he or she believes was sent. (Just write the first thing that comes to mind.) The sender should make a tally of the number of right answers the receiver achieved in 10 trials. Now switch roles and try it again. Each of you should be prepared to report how many you got correct in your 10 trials.

BEFORE THE ACTIVITY

1. With 10 trials, how many would you expect to guess correctly if there is no ESP? If there are 20 people trying this, do you expect all of them to have the same results?

2. Find the standard deviation—the "give-or-take value"—of the number of correct guesses in 10 trials. Assuming that the receiver does not have ESP, what's the smallest number of correct guesses you might expect? What's the largest? How does the standard deviation help you determine this?

AFTER THE ACTIVITY

1. Make a histogram of the class results. Where is the distribution centred? Is this what you expected?

2. Are all the results within the range of results predicted above?

3. Are any of the results unusually good? Does that show that the person with unusually good results has ESP? Why or why not? Explain.

CHAPTER REVIEW

Summary of Learning Objectives

1. **What is a random variable and how can I distinguish between its two types, continuous and discrete?** Often what is of interest is how much of something or how often an event occurs when a random experiment has finished. Because the "how much/many" can vary in numerical value from one random experiment to another, it is called a random variable. A random variable can be either continuous or discrete. Since a continuous random variable is one that measures how much of something occurs, this measurement often takes on one of infinite possible values. A discrete random variable counts how often something happens, and can be one of finite possible values.

2. **What is the Normal probability model and how is it used to find probabilities?** Probability models attempt to explain the behaviour of numerical events that result from a real-life random experiment. The Normal probability model—or the Normal distribution—is one that can be applied when a histogram of data collected appears to be unimodal and symmetric.

    Probabilities are found by finding the area under the appropriate region of the Normal curve. This is done by converting the value of a numerical outcome to a standardized score through the formula:

$$z = \frac{x - \mu}{\sigma}$$

x is the value of a numerical outcome of a Normal random variable

μ is the mean of the probability distribution

σ is the standard deviation of the probability distribution

3. **What is the binomial probability model and how is it used to find probabilities?** The binomial probability model can be applied to all discrete variables that count how many times an event occurs over the duration of a random experiment. Three conditions must be satisfied to apply this model:

    1. There must be a fixed number of trials, n.
    2. Each trial has two outcomes: a success or a failure.
    3. The trials are independent of each other. As a result of this, the probability of each trial being a success is the same and is represented by the letter p.

For binomial models:

$\mu = np$ is the mean

$\sigma = \sqrt{np(1 - p)}$ is the standard deviation

Important Terms

Probability model, *243*

Probability distribution, *243*

Discrete random variable, *244*

Continuous random variable, *244*

Probability density function, *247*

Normal model: Notation, $N(\mu, \sigma)$, *249*

Normal curve, *249*

Normal distribution, *249*

Mean of a probability distribution, μ, *250*

Standard deviation of a probability distribution, σ, *250*

Standard Normal model Notation, $N(0, 1)$, *255*

Percentile, *258*

Binomial probability model Notation, $b(n, p, x)$, *262*

n is the number of trials

p is the probability of success on one trial

x is the number of successes

Cumulative probabilities, *270*

Expected value, *274*

Sources

Broadband Report. Canadian Radio-television and Telecommunications Commission. www.crtc.gc.ca (accessed July 15, 2013).

Education Statistics at a Glance. *The Calgary Herald*, June 26, 2013 (accessed July 2, 2013).

Elections Canada. www.electionscanada.ca (accessed July 7, 2013).

McCarty, C., and House, M., et al. Effort in phone survey rates: The effects of vendor and client-controlled factors. *Field Methods* 18(2), May 2006.

Men's cholesterol levels and blood pressures throughout this chapter: NHANES. www.cdc.gov/nchs/nhanes

Men's heights throughout this chapter: CCHS. http://www23.statcan.gc.ca (accessed July 2, 2013).

Rosenthal, Jeffrey S. Statistics and the Ontario lottery retail scandal. http://probability.ca/jeff/ftpdir/lotteryartref.pdf (accessed December 17, 2014).

Survey: Dramatic Decline in Happiness, Optimism of Canadians During Late Teens. http://www.ipsos-na.com/news-polls/pressrelease.aspx?id=6677 (accessed December 23, 2014).

Survey: Three-quarters of Canadians drive while distracted. http://www.wirelessindustrynews.org/news-oct-2010/2142-100410-win-news.html (accessed July 2, 2013).

Women's heights and weights throughout this chapter: CCHS. http://www23.statcan.gc.ca (accessed July 2, 2013).

SECTION EXERCISES

SECTION 6.1

6.1–6.4 Directions Determine whether each of the following random variables would best be modelled as continuous or discrete.

TRY **6.1 (Example 1)**

a. The number of A's earned by students in statistics one semester at your school

b. The distance between two cars on the freeway

6.2 a. The number of newborn puppies in a litter

b. The weight of a randomly chosen puppy from this litter

6.3 a. The number of songs on a student's mp3 player

b. The length of a newborn baby

6.4 a. The height of a skyscraper in Toronto.

b. The number of people who have climbed to the top of the skyscraper

TRY **6.5 Loaded Die (Example 2)** A magician has shaved an edge off one side of a six-sided die, and as a result, the die is no longer "fair." The figure shows a graph of the probability distribution. Show this probability distribution in table format by listing all six possible outcomes and their probabilities.

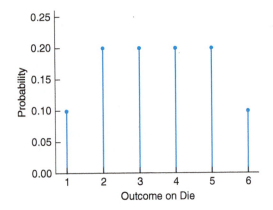

6.6 Fair Die Toss a fair six-sided die. The probability distribution is given in table form. Draw a graph of the probability distribution for the outcome of the topside of the die.

Number of Spots	1	2	3	4	5	6
Probability	1/6	1/6	1/6	1/6	1/6	1/6

★ **6.7 Fair Die, Again** Roll a fair six-sided die. You win $3 if you roll a 1, you lose $4 if you roll a 5 or a 6, and for any other outcome you win or lose nothing.

a. Complete the table that shows the probability distribution.

b. Complete the probability distribution graph.

Winnings	Probability
$3	1/6
$0	—
−$4	—

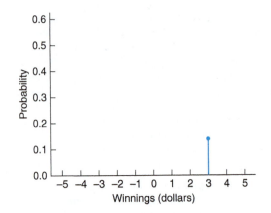

6.8 Fair Coin Flip a fair coin once. You win $10 if it comes up heads and lose $15 if it comes up tails.

a. Create a table that shows the probability distribution of *winning*. For the loss of $15 use −$15.

b. Create a graph that shows the probability density function.

c. If someone offered to play this game with you, would it be sensible to play? Explain.

6.9 Two roommates, Ken and Billy, play the following game: each throws a pair of fair dice, and the first one to throw a sum of 7 does not have to pay next month's rent (the other roommate has to pay the rent in full: $800). If Ken throws first, the probability that Ken eventually wins—and does not have to pay this month's rent—is 0.55.

a. Create a table that shows the probability distribution of Ken's winnings. For a loss, use a negative dollar amount.

b. Make a graph showing the probability distribution of Ken's winnings.

c. If you were Billy, would it be sensible to play this game (and go second), or would you rather be Ken (and go first)? Explain.

6.10 Snow Depth Juliana wants to go skiing tomorrow, but only if there is 10 centimetres or more of new snow. According to the weather report, any amount of new snow between 5 and 25 centimetres is equally likely. The probability density curve for tomorrow's new snow depth is shown. Find the probability that the new snow depth will be 10 centimetres or more tomorrow. Copy the graph and shade the appropriate area, and then calculate its numerical value to the find the probability. Remember, the total area is 1.

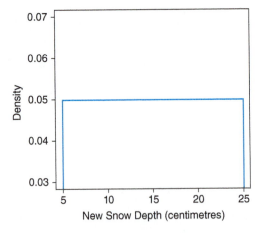

TRY **6.11 Snow Depth (Example 3)** Refer to Exercise 6.10. What is the probability that the amount of new snow will be between 7 and 15 centimetres? Copy the graph from Exercise 6.10, shade in the appropriate area, and find the probability.

6.12 Commuting Time The amount of time, in minutes, it takes Nayda to commute to her part-time job is a continuous random variable that varies from day to day in accordance with the probability distribution that is given in the graph below. The probability that it will take Nayda between 45 and 60 minutes to get to her job is found to be 0.0878, or about 9%. Copy the graph and shade in the area that corresponds to this probability.

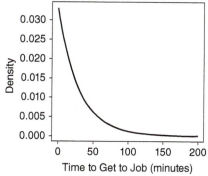

SECTION 6.2

6.13 Applying the Empirical Rule with *z*-Scores The Empirical Rule gives rough approximations to probabilities for any unimodal, symmetric distribution. But for the Normal distribution we can be more precise, as the figure shows. Use the figure and the fact that the Normal curve is symmetric to answer the questions. Do not use a Normal table or technology.

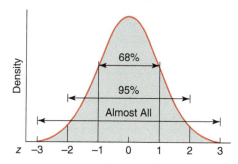

According to the Empirical Rule:

a. Roughly what percentage of *z*-scores are between −2 and 2?
   i. almost all   ii. 95%   iii. 68%   iv. 50%
b. Roughly what percentage of *z*-scores are between −3 and 3?
   i. almost all   ii. 95%   iii. 68%   iv. 50%
c. Roughly what percentage of *z*-scores are between −1 and 1?
   i. almost all   ii. 95%   iii. 68%   iv. 50%
d. Roughly what percentage of *z*-scores are more than 0?
   i. almost all   ii. 95%   iii. 68%   iv. 50%
e. Roughly what percentage of *z*-scores are between 1 and 2?
   i. almost all   ii. 13.5%   iii. 50%   iv. 2%

6.14 IQs Wechsler Intelligence Quotients, or IQs, are approximately Normally distributed with a mean of 100 and standard deviation of 15. Use the probabilities shown in the figure

in Exercise 6.13 to answer the following questions. Do *not* use the Normal table or technology. You may want to label the figure with Empirical Rule probabilities to help you think about this question.

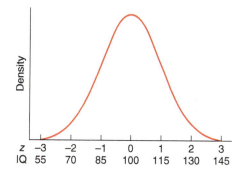

a. Roughly what percentage of people have IQs more than 100?
   i. almost all   ii. 95%   iii. 68%   iv. 50%
b. Roughly what percentage of people have IQs between 100 and 115?
   i. 34%   ii. 17%   iii. 2.5%   iv. 50%
c. Roughly what percentage of people have IQs below 55?
   i. almost all   ii. 50%   iii. 34%   iv. almost none
d. Roughly what percentage of people have IQs between 70 and 130?
   i. almost all   ii. 95%   iii. 68%   iv. 50%
e. Roughly what percentage of people have IQs above 130?
   i. 34%   ii. 17%   iii. 2.5%   iv. 50%
f. Roughly what percentage of people have IQs above 145?
   i. almost all   ii. 50%   iii. 34%   iv. almost none

6.15 PAT (Provincial Achievement Test) Scores Quantitative PAT scores in Alberta vary from student to student with a mean of 65% and a standard deviation of 10%. On the horizontal axis of the graph, indicate the PAT scores that correspond to the provided *z*-scores. (See the labelling in Exercise 6.14.) Answer the questions using only your knowledge of the Empirical Rule and symmetry.

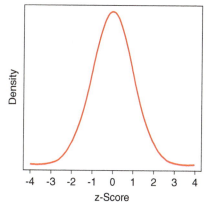

a. Roughly what percentage of students earn PAT scores more than 65%?
   i. almost all   ii. 75%   iii. 50%   iv. 25%   v. almost none
b. Roughly what percentage of students earn PAT scores between 55% and 75%?
   i. almost all   ii. 95%   iii. 68%   iv. 34%   v. almost none
c. Roughly what percentage of students earn PAT scores more than 95%?
   i. almost all   ii. 95%   iii. 68%   iv. 34%   v. almost none
d. Roughly what percentage of students earn PAT scores below 35%?
   i. almost all   ii. 95%   iii. 68%   iv. 34%   v. almost none

e. Roughly what percentage of students earn PAT scores between 45% and 85%?

    i. 95%   ii. 68%   iii. 34%   iv. 13.5%   v. 2.5%

f. Roughly what percentage of students earn PAT scores between 75% and 85%?

    i. 95%   ii. 68%   iii. 34%   iv. 13.5%   v. 2.5%

6.16 Women's Heights Assume that the height of women attending post-secondary school is a variable that can be modelled by the Normal distribution with a mean of 160 centimetres and a standard deviation of 7.5 centimetres. On the horizontal axis of the graph, indicate the heights that correspond to the z-scores provided. (See the labelling in Exercise 6.14.) Answer the questions using only your knowledge of the Empirical Rule and symmetry.

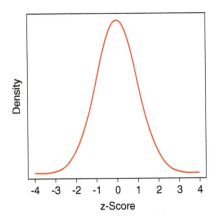

a. Roughly what percentage of women's heights are more than 182.5 centimetres?

    i. almost all   ii. 75%   iii. 50%   iv. 25%   v. about 0%

b. Roughly what percentage of women's heights are between 145 and 175 centimetres?

    i. almost all   ii. 95%   iii. 68%   iv. 34%   v. about 0%

c. Roughly what percentage of women's heights are between 160 and 167.5 centimetres?

    i. almost all   ii. 95%   iii. 68%   iv. 34%   v. about 0%

d. Roughly what percentage of women's heights are between 167.5 and 175 centimetres?

    i. 95%   ii. 68%   iii. 34%   iv. 13.5%   v. 2.5%

e. Roughly what percentage of women's heights are less than 137.5 centimetres?

    i. 95%   ii. 68%   iii. 34%   iv. 2.5%   v. about 0%

f. Roughly what percentage of women's heights are between 175 and 182.5 centimetres?

    i. 68%   ii. 34%   iii. 13.5%   iv. 2.5%   v. 2%

TRY 6.17 IQs (Example 4) Wechsler IQs have a population mean of 100 and a population standard deviation of 15 and are approximately Normally distributed. Use one of the StatCrunch outputs to find the probability that a randomly selected person will have an IQ of 95 or above. State which output is correct for this question, figure (a) or figure (b).

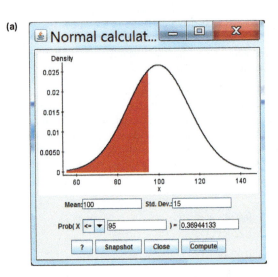

(a)

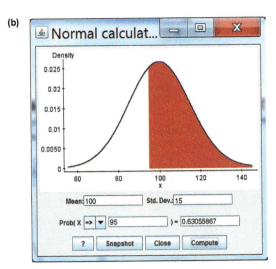

(b)

6.18 PAT Scores Each student writing a PAT will have a score, and this population of values can be approximately modelled by the Normal distribution with a mean of 67 (in percent) and a standard deviation of 10. Find the probability that a randomly chosen student who wrote the PAT will have a score of 70% or less by looking at the StatCrunch output.

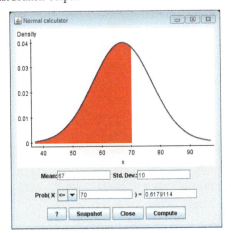

6.19 Standard Normal Use the table or technology to answer each question. Include an appropriately labelled sketch of the Normal curve for each part. Shade the appropriate region.

a. Find the area in a standard Normal curve to the left of 1.02 by using the Normal table. (See the excerpt provided.) Note the shaded curve.

b. Find the area in a standard Normal curve to the right of 1.02. Remember that the total area under the curve is 1.

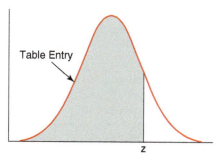

Table Entry

z

Format of the Normal Table: The area given is the area to the *left* of (less than) the given z-score.

z	.00	.01	.02	.03	.04
0.9	.8159	.8186	.8212	.8238	.8264
1.0	.8413	.8438	.8461	.8485	.8508
1.1	.8643	.8665	.8686	.8708	.8729

6.20 Standard Normal Use a table or technology to answer each question. Include an appropriately labelled sketch of the Normal curve for each part. Shade the appropriate region.

a. Find the area to the left of a z-score of −0.50.

b. Find the area to the right of a z-score of −0.50.

6.21 Standard Normal Use a table or technology to answer each question. Include an appropriately labelled sketch of the Normal curve for each part. Shade the appropriate region.

a. Find the probability that a z-score will be 1.76 or less.

b. Find the probability that a z-score will be 1.76 or more.

c. Find the probability that a z-score will be between −1.3 and −1.03.

6.22 Standard Normal Use a table or technology to answer each question. Include an appropriately labelled sketch of the Normal curve for each part. Shade the appropriate region.

a. Find the probability that a z-score will be −1.00 or less.

b. Find the probability that a z-score will be more than −1.00.

c. Find the probability that a z-score will be between 0.90 and 1.80.

6.23 Extreme Positive z-Scores For each question, find the area to the right of the given z-score in a standard Normal distribution. In this question, round your answers to the nearest 0.000. Include an appropriately labelled sketch of the N(0, 1) curve.

a. z = 4.00

b. z = 10.00 (*Hint:* Should this tail proportion be larger or smaller than the answer to part a? Draw a picture and think about it.)

c. z = 50.00

d. If you had the *exact* probability for these tail proportions, which would be the biggest and which would be the smallest?

e. Which is equal to the area in part b: the area below (to the left of) z = −10.00 or the area above (to the right of) z = −10.00?

6.24 Extreme Negative z-Scores For each question, find the area to the right of the given z-score in a standard Normal distribution. In *this* question, round your answers to the nearest 0.000. Include an appropriately labelled sketch of the N(0, 1) curve.

a. z = −4.00

b. z = −8.00

c. z = −30.00

d. If you had the *exact* probability for these right proportions, which would be the biggest and which would be the smallest?

e. Which is equal to the area in part b: the area below (to the left of) z = 8.00 or the area above (to the right of) z = 8.00?

TRY
g
6.25 Females' Math PAT Scores (Example 5) According to data provided by Alberta Education, the PAT math scores of all females writing in June 2012 had a mean of 63 (in percent). Assume that these scores can be modelled by the Normal distribution with a standard deviation of 10 (in percent). What percentage of females writing the math PAT had scores above 80%? Include a well-labelled Normal curve as part of your answer. *See page 289 for guidance.*

6.26 Males' Math PAT Scores According to Alberta Education, the PAT math scores of all males writing in June 2012 had a mean of 70 (in percent). Assume that these scores can be modelled by the Normal distribution with a standard deviation of 10 (in percent). If a male who wrote the math PAT is randomly chosen, what is the probability that he will score higher than 65%?

6.27 Stanford–Binet IQs Stanford–Binet IQ scores for children are approximately Normally distributed and have $\mu = 100$ and $\sigma = 15$. What is the probability that a randomly selected child will have an IQ below 115?

6.28 Stanford–Binet IQs Stanford–Binet IQ scores for children are approximately Normally distributed and have $\mu = 100$ and $\sigma = 15$. What is the probability that a randomly selected child will have an IQ of 115 or higher?

TRY **6.29 Gestation Periods (Example 6)** The human gestation period (length of pregnancy) is 270 days with a standard deviation of 9 days and is approximately Normally distributed (assuming spontaneous labour). What is the probability that a randomly selected woman's gestation period will be between 261 and 279 days?

6.30 Birth Weights According to Statistics Canada, the weight of full-term babies is a variable that can be modelled by the Normal distribution, with a mean weight of 3.4 kilograms and a standard deviation of 0.5 kilograms. Some physicians believe that a birth weight of 2.5 kilograms or less is dangerous.

a. For a randomly selected full-term pregnancy, what is the probability that the baby's birth weight is 2.5 kilograms or less?

b. For a randomly selected full-term pregnancy, what is the probability that a baby's birth weight is between 3 and 4 kilograms?

c. If there were 600 full-term babies born at a hospital, how many of them would you expect to weight 2.5 kilograms or less?

6.31 Total Cholesterol According to the U.S. Center for Disease Control (CDC), the mean total cholesterol for men between the ages of 20 and 29 is 180 micrograms per decilitre with a standard deviation of 36.2. A healthy total cholesterol level is less than 200, 200–240 is borderline, and above 240 is dangerous. Assume that the distribution is approximately Normal.

a. For a randomly selected man from this group, what is the probability that his total cholesterol level is 200 or more?

b. For a randomly selected man from this group, what is the probability that his total cholesterol level is 240 or more?

c. If two randomly selected men are chosen from this group, what is the probability that both will have a total cholesterol level of 200 or more? Assume independence.

d. If 750 randomly selected men are chosen from this group, how many (the count, not the percentage) would you expect to have a total cholesterol level of 200 or more?

6.32 ACT Scores In 2009, ACT reading scores had a mean of 21.4 (www.act.org). Suppose the population standard deviation is five and the distribution of ACT reading scores is approximately Normal.

a. What percentage of people scored between 18 and 22?

b. What percentage of people scored 25.8 or higher?

c. If scores for 880 randomly selected people were obtained, how many would you expect to be 25.8 or higher?

6.33 Fire Department Response Times in Toronto In 2010, the total response time—from the time a 911 call was made until the firefighters showed up on the scene—for calls to a fire department in Toronto was about 5.5 minutes, based on an article published by the City of Toronto. Suppose the distribution of the total response time can be modelled by the Normal distribution with a standard deviation of 1.5 minutes. What is the probability that the response time for a 911 call is less than 5 minutes? (Source: http://www.toronto.ca/budget2012/pdf/op12_bn_fireresponse.pdf)

6.34 Fire Department Response Times in Calgary The average response time—from the time a 911 call was made until firefighters show up on the scene—in Calgary is about 7 minutes. Assume that the distribution of the response times in Calgary can be modelled by the Normal distribution with a standard deviation of 1.5 minutes. What is the probability that the total response time to a 911 call in Calgary exceeds the Province of Alberta's standard, which is 10 minutes?

6.35 Heights of Three-Year-Old Boys According to the CDC, three-year-old boys have a mean height of 96.5 centimetres and a standard deviation of 5 centimetres. The distribution is approximately Normal.

a. What percentage of three-year-old boys have a height of 100 centimetres or more?

b. What percentage of three-year-old boys have a height of 90 centimetres or less?

6.36 Heights of 10-Year-Old Girls According to the CDC, 10-year-old girls have a mean height of 138 centimetres and a standard deviation of 6.4 centimetres. The distribution is approximately Normal.

a. What percentage of 10-year-old girls have a height of 130 centimetres or more?

b. What percentage of 10-year-old girls have a height of 150 centimetres or less?

6.37 Winnipeg Weather Winnipeg's mean daily maximum temperature in January 2013 was −11°C (accuweather.com). The standard deviation of this variable was 7.5°C. Suppose the daily maximum temperature can be modelled by the Normal distribution. What percentage of days is the daily maximum temperature in January below −30°C?

6.38 Kelowna Weather Kelowna's mean daily maximum temperature in July 2013 was 30°C (accuweather.com). The standard deviation of this variable was 3.6°C. Suppose the daily maximum temperature can be modelled by the Normal distribution. What percentage of days is the daily maximum in July above 37°C?

* **6.39 Women's Heights** Assume for this question that the heights of university women can be modelled by the Normal distribution with a mean of 164 centimetres and a standard deviation of 7 centimetres. Draw a well-labelled Normal curve for each part.

a. Find the percentage of women who should have heights of 162.5 centimetres or less.

b. In a sample of 123 women, according to the probability obtained in part a, how many should have heights of 162.5 centimetres or less?

c. The table shows the frequencies of heights for a sample of women, collected by the statistician Brian Joiner in his statistics class. Count the women who have heights of 162.5 centimetres or less by looking at the table. They are bracketed.

d. Are the answers in parts b and c close or far off? Explain.

Height (cm)	Frequency
150	2
152.5	5
155	7
157.5	10
160	16
162.5	23
165	19
167.5	15
170	9
172.5	6
175	6
177.5	3
180	1
182.5	1

6.40 Probability or Originating Value (Inverse)? The Normal model $N(270, 9)$ describes the length of pregnancies, in days, for women who go into spontaneous labour. Which of these statements is asking for an originating value (is an inverse Normal question) and which is asking for a probability?

a. If 60% of women have a pregnancy length below this number of days, what is the number of days?

b. If we select, at random, a woman who goes into spontaneous labour, what is the probability that her pregnancy will be 279 days or fewer?

TRY **6.41 Probability or Originating Value (Inverse)? (Example 7)** The Normal model $N(100, 15)$ describes Wechsler IQs. Which of these statements is asking for an originating value (is an inverse Normal question) and which is asking for a probability?

a. What percentage of people have IQs above 130?

b. To get into Mensa, a high-IQ group, you must have an IQ in the upper 2%. What IQ is this?

6.42 Inverse Normal, Standard In a standard Normal distribution, if the area to the left of a z-score is about 0.6666, what is the approximate z-score?

First locate the number closest to 0.6666 in the table. Then find the z-score by adding 0.4 and 0.03; refer to the table. Draw a sketch of the Normal curve showing the area and z-score.

z	.00	.01	.02	.03	.04	.05
0.4	.6554	.6591	.6628	**.6664**	.6700	.6736
0.5	.6915	.6950	.6985	.7019	.7054	.7088
0.6	.7257	.7291	.7324	.7357	.7389	.7422

6.43 Inverse Normal, Standard In a standard Normal distribution, if the area to the left of a z-score is about 0.1000, what is the approximate z-score?

6.44 Inverse Normal, Standard In a standard Normal distribution, if the area to the left of a z-score is 0.8000, what is the approximate z-score?

6.45 Inverse Normal, Standard Assume a standard Normal distribution. Draw a separate, well-labelled Normal curve for each part.

a. Find the z-score that gives a left area of 0.7123.

b. Find the z-score that gives a left area of 0.1587.

6.46 Inverse Normal, Standard Assume a standard Normal distribution. Draw a separate, well-labelled Normal curve for each part.

a. Find an approximate z-score that gives a left area of 0.7000.

b. Find an approximate z-score that gives a left area of 0.9500.

TRY **6.47 Females' Math PAT Scores (Example 8)** According to Alberta Education, the mean score for females who wrote the Math Provincial Achievement Test in June 2012 was 63%. Assume that these scores can be modelled by the Normal distribution with a standard deviation of 10%. A scholarship committee wants to give awards to females who score at the 96th percentile or above on their math PAT. What score does an applicant need? Include a well-labelled Normal curve as part of your answer. *See page 290 for guidance.*

6.48 Males' Math PAT Scores According to Alberta Education, the mean score for males who wrote the Math Provincial Achievement Test in June 2012 was 70%. Assume that these scores can be modelled by the Normal distribution with a standard deviation of 10%. A scholarship committee wants to give awards to males who score at the 98th percentile or above on their math PAT. What score does an applicant need? Include a well-labelled Normal curve as part of your answer.

6.49 Males' Body Temperatures A study showed that males' body temperatures are approximately Normally distributed with a mean of 36.7°C and a population standard deviation of 0.4°C. What body temperature does a male have if he is at the 90th percentile? Draw a well-labelled sketch to support your answer.

6.50 Females' Body Temperatures A study showed that females' body temperatures are approximately Normally distributed with a mean of 36.9°C and a population standard deviation of 0.4°C. Find the female body temperature at the 90th percentile. Draw a well-labelled sketch to support your answer.

6.51 Women's Heights The height of university women can be modelled by the Normal distribution with a mean of 160 centimetres and a standard deviation of 7.5 centimetres. What height is at the 25th percentile? Include an appropriately labelled Normal curve to support your answer.

6.52 Men's Heights The height of university men can be modelled by the Normal distribution with a mean of 172.5 centimetres and a standard deviation of 7.5 centimetres. What height is at the 10th percentile? Include an appropriately labelled Normal curve to support your answer.

6.53 Wechsler IQs Wechsler IQs have a mean of 100 and a standard deviation of 15 and are approximately Normally distributed.

a. The Wechsler IQ at the 25th percentile is 90. What is the Wechsler IQ at the 75th percentile?

b. The interquartile range is Q3 minus Q1. Find the interquartile range for Wechsler IQs.

c. Is the interquartile range larger or smaller than the standard deviation, 15 IQ points?

6.54 Gestation Period The gestation period for humans is approximately Normally distributed with a mean of 270 days and population standard deviation of nine days, assuming spontaneous labour. The gestation period at the 25th percentile is 264 days.

a. Find the gestation period at the 75th percentile.

b. Find the interquartile range of the gestation period.

c. Using the distribution of gestation periods, is the standard deviation larger or smaller than the interquartile range?

6.55 Child and Adult Height for Males According to the National Center for Health Statistics, three-year-old-boys have a mean height of 96.5 centimetres and a standard deviation of 5 centimetres. Assume that the distribution can be modelled by the Normal distribution.

a. Find the percentile value associated with a three-year-old boy who is 100 centimetres tall.

b. If this three-year-old boy grows up to be a man with a height at the same percentile, what will his height be? Use a population mean of 172.5 centimetres and a population standard deviation of 7.5 centimetres.

6.56 Child and Adult Height for Females According to the National Center for Health Statistics, 10-year-old-girls have a mean height of 138 centimetres and a standard deviation of 6.4 centimetres. Assume that the distribution can be modelled by the Normal distribution.

a. Find the percentile value associated with a 10-year-old girl who is 150 centimetres tall.

b. If this 10-year-old girl grows up to be a woman with a height at the same percentile, what will her height be? Use a population mean of 160 centimetres and a population standard deviation of 7.5 centimetres.

SECTION 6.3

TRY **6.57 Gender of Children (Example 9)** A married couple plans to have four children, and they are wondering how many boys they should expect to have. Assume that none of the children will be twins or other multiple births. Also assume the probability that a child will be a boy is 0.50. Explain why this is a binomial experiment. Check all three required conditions.

6.58 Coin Flip A coin will be flipped three times, and the number of heads recorded. Explain why this is a binomial experiment. Check all three required conditions.

TRY **6.59 Coin Flips (Example 10)** A teacher wants to find out whether coin flips of pennies have a 50% chance of coming up heads. In the last five minutes of class, he has all the students flip pennies until the end of class and then report their results to him. Which condition or conditions for use of the binomial model is or are not met?

6.60 Twins In Exercise 6.57 you are told to assume that none of the children will be twins or other multiple births. Why? Which of the conditions required for a binomial experiment would be violated if there were twins?

6.61 Divorce Suppose that the probability that a randomly selected person who has recently married for the first time will get a divorce within five years is 0.2. Suppose we follow 12 married couples (24 people) for five years and record the number of people divorced. Why is the binomial model inappropriate for finding the probability that at least 7 of these 24 people will be divorced within five years? List all binomial conditions that are not met.

6.62 Divorce Suppose that the probability that a randomly selected person who has recently married for the first time will be divorced within five years is 0.2, and that the probability that a randomly selected person who has recently married for the second time will be divorced within five years is 0.30. Take a random sample of 10 people married for the first time and 10 people married for the second time. The sample is chosen such that no one in the sample is married to anyone else in the sample. Why is the binomial model inappropriate for finding the probability that exactly 4 of the 20 people in the sample will be divorced within five years? List all of the binomial conditions that are not met.

TRY **6.63 Identifying n, p, and x (Example 11)** For each situation, identify the sample size n, the probability of success p, and the number of successes x. Give the answer in the form $b(n, p, x)$. Do *not* go on to find the probability. Assume that the three conditions for a binomial experiment are satisfied.

a. In the 2011 federal election, 38% of votes cast were for the Conservative Party. What is the probability that 44 out of 100 randomly chosen Canadian voters voted Conservative?

b. The manufacturer of LoJack Stolen Vehicle Recovery System claims that the probability that a stolen vehicle using LoJack will be recovered is 90%. What is the probability that exactly 9 out of 10 independently stolen vehicles with LoJack will be recovered?

c. A student is taking a 10-question multiple-choice test. Each question has four options: a, b, c, and d. One of these four options is correct and three of them are incorrect. What is the probability that the student correctly answers exactly 6 of the 10 questions on the test by guessing?

d. Thirty percent of all your received text messages are from your best friend. You randomly select 20 recent text messages that you have received today. What is the probability that 8 of them are from your best friend?

6.64 Identifying n, p, and x For each situation, identify the sample size n, the probability of success p, and the number of successes x. Give the answer in the form $b(n, p, x)$. Do *not* go on to find the probability. Assume that the three conditions for a binomial experiment are satisfied.

a. Research suggests that about 30% of people respond to telephone surveys. Fifty people are randomly chosen to participate in a telephone survey. What is the probability that 10 out of the 50 will respond?

b. Data from the National Comprehensive Auto Theft Research System (CARS) showed that 75% of motor vehicles stolen in Australia from 2005 to 2006 were recovered. What is the probability that in a sample of 10 stolen cars, 6 out of 10 will be recovered, assuming the same rate of recovery?

c. A student is taking a 10-question multiple-choice test. Each question has five options: a, b, c, d, and e. For each question, one of these five choices is correct and four of them are incorrect. What is the probability that the student correctly answers exactly 6 of the 10 questions on the test by guessing?

d. Twenty percent of all the fish in a river are brown trout. A person catches 10 fish. What is the probability that none of the 10 fish caught are brown trout?

TRY **6.65 Stolen Bicycles (Example 12)** According to the *Sidney Morning Herald*, 40% of bicycles stolen in Holland are recovered. (In contrast, only 5% of bikes stolen in Toronto are recovered.) Find the probability that, in a sample of six randomly selected cases of bicycles stolen in Holland, exactly two out of six bikes are recovered.

6.66 Youth Recidivism Rate The two-year recidivism rate of male youths (teens aged 12–17) in Canada is about 50%; that is, 50% of male youths end up back in the criminal justice system within two years (*Responding to Youth Crime in Canada*, Doob, A. and Cesaroni, C.). Assume that whether one male youth ends up back in the criminal justice system is independent of whether another does.

a. Find the probability that exactly 8 out of 20 male youths who have been in the criminal justice system will be back in the system within two years.

b. Find the probability that 8 or less of 20 male youths who have been in the criminal justice system will be back in the system within two years.

6.67 Retirement A 2013 poll (theglobeandmail.com) found that 8% of Canadians have taken money out of their RRSP (registered retirement savings plan) to pay for a vacation. Assume that whether one person withdraws money from their RRSP to pay for a vacation is independent of whether another one does.

a. Find the probability that at most 2 out of 10 Canadians will withdraw from their RRSP to pay for a vacation.

b. Find the probability that at least 3 out of 10 Canadians will withdraw from their RRSP to pay for a vacation.

c. Find that probability that anywhere between 1 and 3 out of 10 Canadians will withdraw from their RRSP to pay for a vacation. The 1 to 3 is inclusive, meaning that it includes 1, 2 and 3.

6.68 Guessing on Exams Suppose you are taking an exam with 10 questions and you are required to get 7 or more right answers to pass.

a. With a 10-question true/false test, what is the probability of getting at least 7 answers correct by guessing?

b. With a 10-question multiple-choice test where there are three possible choices for each question, what is the probability of getting at least 7 answers correct by guessing? Only one of the choices is correct for each question.

c. With a 10-question multiple-choice test where there are five possible choices for each question, only one of which is correct, what is the probability of getting at least 7 answers correct by guessing?

d. Which test (of those described in parts a, b, and c in this exercise) would be easiest to pass by guessing, which would be hardest, and why?

6.69 Newborn Gender Assume that half of all children born are male and half are female. In the following cases, we will assume that there are no twins (or triplets or more) and that the conditions of the binomial model are satisfied.

a. If a woman plans to have two children, what is the probability that both will be girls?

b. If a woman plans to have three children, what is the probability that all will be girls?

c. If a woman plans to have three children, what is the probability that she will have at least one boy? ("At least one boy" is the complement of "all girls.")

d. Does this mean that the more children a woman has, the more likely she will be to have at least one boy? Explain.

6.70 Employment Rates According to a study by the Canadian Labour Congress, almost 28% of Canadians between the ages of 18 and 25 are underemployed. That means they are either unemployed or have a job working few hours than they would like. (Homemakers and other people not seeking employment are not included in the data.)

a. For one randomly selected person between the age of 18 and 25, what is the probability that the person is fully employed (not underemployed)?
For parts b and c, assume that you randomly select five people and inquire about their employment, but you do not include those seeking employment.

b. What is the probability that all five people are fully employed?

c. What is the probability that at least one of the five is underemployed?

6.71 Late Flights For commercial flights in 2009, approximately 80% arrived on time (within 15 minutes of scheduled arrival time), according to the U.S. Bureau of Transportation Statistics.

a. Assuming that this success rate still holds, if you randomly select three flights and assume they are independent, what is the probability that all three will arrive on time?

b. What is the probability that at least one of the three flights will be late?

c. If all three flights are on the same day in December and all three are flights to Toronto, explain why the binomial model is not appropriate for finding the probability that at least one flight will be late.

6.72 Guns and Homicide Statistics Canada reported that in 2011, 27% of all homicides committed were a result of a shooting. Consider 10 independently chosen homicides in 2011.

a. What is the probability that all homicides were the result of a shooting?

b. What is the probability that none of these homicides were the result of a shooting?

c. What is the probability that at least one of these homicides was a result of a shooting?

d. On average, how many of these 10 homicides would you expect to be a result of a shooting?

TRY **6.73 Drinking and Driving (Example 13)** A survey of Canadians in 2010 revealed that about one-quarter, or 25%, admitted to driving after consuming alcohol in the past year (http://digitaljournal.com/article/301211). Assume that this percentage has not changed since 2010.

a. If 20 people are independently chosen, how many would you expect to have driven after consuming alcohol?

b. What is the probability that exactly 7 out of 20 independently selected people have driven after consuming alcohol in the past year?

c. What is the probability that 7 or fewer have driven after consuming alcohol in the past year?

6.74 Broadband Internet Access The Canadian Radio-television and Telecommunications Commission (CRTC) reported that in 2013, 90% of Canadian households had high-speed internet.

a. Suppose 100 Canadian households are randomly chosen. How many of these would you expect to have high-speed internet?

b. Suppose 10 households were randomly chosen. What is the probability that 8 have high-speed internet?

c. Of the 10 households in part b, what is the probability that 7 or fewer have high-speed internet?

d. Of the 10 households in part b, what is the probability that 8 or more have high-speed internet?

6.75 Cell Phone Only According to a cbc.ca article, 26% of Canadians have only cell phones. Assume that two people are randomly chosen and asked whether they have only a cell phone.

a. If a person has only a cell phone, we will record Y (for Yes). If not, we will record N. List all possible outcomes of Y and N for this experiment.

b. For each outcome, find by hand the probability that it will occur, assuming each person's response is independent.

c. What is the probability that neither of the two randomly chosen people has only a cell phone?

d. What is the probability that exactly one of the two people has only a cell phone?

e. What is the probability that both people have only a cell phone?

6.76 Texting While Driving According to a Pew poll in 2010, one in four teens of driving age have reported having sent or received a text message while driving. Assume that we randomly sample two teens of driving age.

a. If a teen has texted while driving, record Y; if not, record N. List all possible sequences of Y and N for this experiment.

b. For each sequence, find by hand the probability that it will occur, assuming each outcome is independent.

c. What is the probability that neither of the two randomly selected teens has texted?

d. What is the probability that exactly one out of the two teens has texted?

e. What is the probability that both have texted?

TRY **6.77 Coin Flip (Example 14)** A fair coin is flipped 50 times.

a. What is the expected number of heads?

b. Find the standard deviation for the number of heads.

c. How many heads should you expect, give or take how many? Give the range of the number of heads based on these numbers.

6.78 Alberta Drivers According to a 2003 cbc.ca article, 10% of Alberta drivers are uninsured. If 500 Alberta drivers are randomly checked, how many would you expect to be driving without insurance? Give or take how many? Pretend the 10% figure holds today.

6.79 Online Dating According to a 2012 Leger Marketing survey, 25% of Canadians had participated in online dating. If 200 Canadians are randomly selected, how many would you expect to have participated in online dating? Give or take how many?

6.80 Women without Children According to a Pew Research poll in 2010, 20% of women have ended their childbearing years without having children. (In the 1970s, this number was 10%.)

a. If we randomly select 300 women, how many would we expect to have had no children? Give or take how many?

b. Give the range of likely values from one standard deviation above the mean to one standard deviation below the mean.

c. If you found that 62 out of 300 randomly sampled women ended their childbearing years without having children, would you be surprised? Why or why not?

TRY **6.81 Breast Cancer (Example 15)** According to the Canadian Cancer Society, about one in nine women (11%), will develop breast cancer at some point in their lives. Suppose 100 randomly selected women are to be surveyed.

a. How many of these 100 women will develop breast cancer at some point in their lives?

b. Give the range of likely values from one standard deviation above the mean to one standard deviation below the mean.

c. If you found that 25 of these 100 women will have developed breast cancer at some point in their lives, would you be surprised by this? Explain.

CHAPTER REVIEW EXERCISES

6.82 Birth Length A study of births published on the website *Medscape from WebMD* reported that the average birth length of babies was 52 centimetres and that the standard deviation was about 2.3 centimetres. Assume the distribution is approximately Normal. Find the percentage of babies with birth lengths of 56 centimetres or less.

6.83 Birth Length A study of births published on the website *Medscape from WebMD* reported that the average birth length of babies was 52 centimetres and that the standard deviation was about 2.3 centimetres. Assume the distribution is approximately Normal. Find the percentage of babies with birth lengths of 48 centimetres or less.

6.84 Males' Body Temperature A study of human body temperatures using healthy men showed a mean of 36.7°C and a standard deviation of 0.4°C. Assume that the temperatures are approximately Normally distributed.

a. Find the percentage of healthy men with temperatures below 37.0°C (that temperature was considered typical for many decades).

b. What temperature does a healthy man have if his temperature is at the 76th percentile?

6.85 Females' Body Temperature A study of human body temperatures using healthy women showed a mean of 36.9°C and a standard deviation of about 0.4°C. Assume that the temperatures are approximately Normally distributed.

a. Find the percentage of healthy women with temperatures below 37.0°C (this temperature was considered typical for many decades).

b. What temperature does a healthy woman have if her temperature is at the 76th percentile?

6.86 Baby's Gender A woman with five sons and no daughters becomes pregnant. What is the likelihood that her next child will be a girl? Write a sentence or two explaining your answer.

6.87 Coin Flip You flip a coin and get heads four times in a row. What is the likelihood that the next flip will show heads? Write a sentence or two explaining your answer.

6.88 Good Neighbours According to a 2013 Gallup poll, 91% of Americans view Canada as a favourable country.

a. If there were 2000 independent Americans surveyed, how many would you expect to have a favourable view toward Canada, give or take how many?

b. Judging on the basis of your answer in part a, what range of Americans would you expect to have a favourable view toward Canada?

6.89 Caesarean Births According to the CDC, the rate of caesarean births in 2007 was 32%.

a. If 200 independent births were surveyed in 2007, how many of those would you expect to be caesarean, give or take how many?

b. Would it be unusual for a hospital with 200 births to have 110 caesareans? Explain.

6.90 Leukemia Survival Rate The five-year survival rate for chronic myelogenous leukemia (CML) for those on the drug Gleevec is about 90%. Before Gleevec was introduced, the five-year survival rate was about 40%.

a. Suppose four patients have just been diagnosed with CML and will be using Gleevec. Assume that one patient's survival is independent of the survival of the others.

    i. What is the probability that the patients will all be alive in five years?

    ii. What is the probability that at least one will die within five years?

  b. Suppose four patients had been diagnosed with CML 25 years ago, before Gleevec was available. Assume that one patient's survival was independent of the survival of the others.

    i. What is the probability that they all would have stayed alive for five years?

    ii. What is the probability that at least one would have been dead within five years?

  c. Why is the answer to Question ii in part a smaller than the answer to Question ii in part b?

6.91 Assisted Suicide According to a 2013 Environics poll, 63% of Canadians would support a law that allows doctor-assisted suicide in Canada. Assume that 63% is the percentage of all Canadians who support such a law.

  a. If 300 randomly selected people were asked if they support a law allowing doctor-assisted suicide, how many of them would you expect to answer yes? Give or take how many?

  b. Would you be surprised if 185 of the 300 indicated that they would support such a law? Explain.

GUIDED EXERCISES

6.25 Females' Math PAT Scores According to data provided by Alberta Education, the PAT math scores of all females writing in June 2012 had a mean of 63 (in percent). Assume that these scores can be modelled by the Normal distribution with a standard deviation of 10 (in percent). What percentage of females writing the math PAT had scores above 80%?

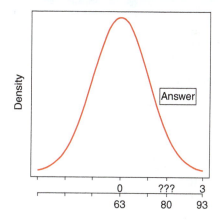

Question

What percentage of females writing the math PAT had scores above 80%? Answer this question by following the numbered steps.

Step 1 ▶ Find the z-score

To find the z-score for 80, subtract the mean of 63 and then divide this difference by the standard deviation of 10. Report the z-score.

Step 2 ▶ Explain the location of 63

Refer to the Normal curve. Explain why the PAT score of 63 is right below the z-score of 0. The tick marks on the axis mark the location of z-scores that are integers from −3 to 3.

Step 3 ▶ Label with PAT scores

Carefully sketch a copy of the curve. Pencil in the PAT scores of 33, 43, 53, 63, 73, 83, and 93 in the correct places.

Step 4 ▶ Add the line, z-score, and shading

Draw a vertical line through the curve at the location of 80. Just above the 80, put in the corresponding z-score. We want to find what percentage of females had scores *above* 80. Therefore, we shade the area to the *right* of this boundary, because numbers to the right are larger.

Step 5 ▶ Use the table for the left area

Use the following excerpt from the Normal table to find and report the area to the left of the z-score that was obtained from a PAT math score of 80. This is the area of the unshaded region.

Step 6 ▶ Answer

Because you want the area to the right of the z-score, you will have to subtract the area you obtained in step 5 from 1. This is the area of the shaded region. Put it where the box labelled "Answer" is. Check to see if that number makes sense. For example, if the shading is less than half the area, the answer should not be more than 0.5000.

Step 7 ▶ Sentence

Finally, write a sentence stating what you found.

z	.00	.01	.02	.03	.04	.05	.06	.07	.08	.09
1.6	.9452	.9463	.9474	.9484	.9495	.9505	.9515	.9525	.9535	.9545
1.7	**.9554**	.9564	.9573	.9582	.9591	.9599	.9608	.9616	.9625	.9633
1.8	.9641	.9649	.9656	.9664	.9671	.9678	.9686	.9693	.9699	.9706

6.47 Females' Math PAT Scores

According to Alberta Education, the mean score for females who wrote the Math Provincial Achievement Test in June 2012 was 63%. Assume that these scores can be modelled by the Normal distribution with a standard deviation of 10%. A scholarship committee wants to give awards to females who score at the 96th percentile or above on their math PAT. What score does an applicant need? Include a well-labelled Normal curve as part of your answer.

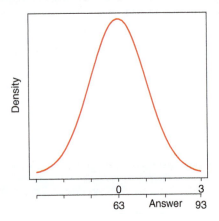

Question

What math PAT score represents the 96th percentile? Answer this question by following the numbered steps.

Step 1 ▶ Think about it

Will the math PAT score be above the mean of 63 or below it? Explain.

Step 2 ▶ Label z-scores

Label the curve with z-scores. The tick marks represent the position of integer z-scores from −3 to 3.

Step 3 ▶ Use the table

The 96th percentile has 96% of the area to the left because it is higher than 96% of all the scores. The table below gives the areas to the *left* of z-scores. Therefore, we look for 0.9600 in the interior part of the table.

Use the excerpt of the Normal table given above for Exercise 6.25 to locate the area *closest* to 0.9600.

Report the z-score for that area.

Step 4 ▶ Add the z-score, line, and shading to your graph

Add the just found z-score in step 3 to your graph, then draw a vertical line from the z-score to the top of the curve. Shade in the left side because this area to the left represents the 96th percentile.

Step 5 ▶ Find the math PAT score

Find the math PAT score that corresponds to the z-score found in step 3. The score should be z standard deviations above the mean, so the 96th percentile in terms of the math PAT score can be found by

$$x = \mu + z\sigma$$

Step 6 ▶ Add the math PAT score to the graph

Add the math PAT score resulting from your application of the equation in step 5 to the graph where it says "Answer."

Step 7 ▶ Write a sentence

Finish it up with a closing sentence stating what you have found.

For All Technology

All technologies will use the two examples that follow.

EXAMPLE A: NORMAL ▶ Wechsler IQs have a mean of 100 and standard deviation of 15 and are Normally distributed.

a. Find the probability that a randomly chosen person will have an IQ between 85 and 115.

b. Find the probability that a randomly chosen person will have an IQ that is 115 or less.

c. Find the Wechsler IQ at the 75th percentile.

Note: If you want to use technology to find areas from *z*-scores, use a mean of 0 and a standard deviation of 1.

EXAMPLE B: BINOMIAL ▶ Imagine that you are flipping a fair coin (one that comes up heads 50% of the time in the long run).

a. Find the probability of getting 28 or fewer heads in 50 flips of a fair coin.

b. Find the probability of getting exactly 28 heads in 50 flips of a fair coin.

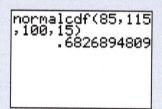

Normal

a. Between Two Values

1. Press **2ND DISTR** (located below the four arrows on the keypad).

2. Select **2:normalcdf** and press **ENTER**.

3. Enter: (left boundary, right boundary, μ, σ), in this example **85 , 115 , 100 , 15**), and press **ENTER**. (The comma button is above the 7 button.)

Your screen should look like Figure 6A, which shows that the probability that a randomly selected person will have a Wechsler IQ between 85 and 115 is equal to 0.6827.

▲ **FIGURE 6B** TI-83/84 normalcdf with indeterminate left boundary.

Caution: The negative button **(−)** is to the left of the **ENTER** button and is not the same as the minus button that is above the plus button.

If you have an indeterminate right boundary, then to find the probability that the person's IQ is 85 or more, for example, use a right boundary (such as 1000000) that is clearly above all the data.

c. Inverse Normal

If you want a value on the original Normal distribution (such as an IQ) associated with a percentile:

1. Press **2ND DISTR**.

2. Select **3:invNorm** and press **ENTER**.

3. Enter: (left proportion, μ, σ) and press **ENTER**. Be sure to include the commas between the numbers.

Figure 6C shows the Wechsler IQ at the 75th percentile, which is 110. Note that the 75th percentile is entered as **.75**.

```
normalcdf(85,115
,100,15)
          .6826894809
```

▲ **FIGURE 6A** TI-83/84 normal**c**df (c stands for "cumulative").

b. Some Value or Less

1. Press **2ND DISTR**.

2. Select **2:normalcdf** and press **ENTER**.

3. Enter: (left boundary, right boundary, μ, σ) and press **ENTER**.

The probability that a person's IQ is 115 *or less* has an *indeterminate* left boundary, for which you may use negative 1000000 or any extreme value that is clearly out of the range of data. Figure 6B shows the probability that a randomly selected person will have an IQ of 115 or less.

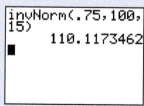

▲ **FIGURE 6C** TI-83/84 inverse normal.

Binomial

a. Cumulative (or Less)

1. Press **2ND DISTR**.
2. Select **B:binomcdf** (you will have to scroll down to see it) and press **ENTER**. (On a TI-83, it is **A:binomcdf**.)
3. See Figure 6D. Enter: (*n*, *p*, *x*) and press **ENTER**. Be sure to include the commas between the numbers.

   The answer will be the probability for *x or fewer*. Figure 6D shows the probability of 28 *or fewer* heads out of 50 flips of a fair coin. (You could find the probability of 29 *or more* heads by subtracting your answer from 1.)

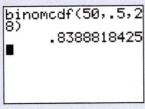

▲ **FIGURE 6D** TI-83/4 binom**c**df (cumulative).

b. Individual (Exact)

1. Press **2ND DISTR**.
2. Select **A:binompdf** and press **ENTER**. (On a TI-83, it is **0:binompdf**.)
3. Enter: (*n*, *p*, *x*) and press **ENTER**. Be sure to include the commas between the numbers.

   Figure 6E shows the probability of *exactly* 28 heads out of 50 flips of a fair coin.

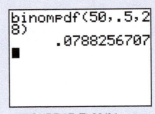

▲ **FIGURE 6E** TI-83/84 binom**p**df (individual).

MINITAB

Normal

a. Between Two Values

1. Enter the upper boundary, **115**, in the top cell of an empty column; here we use column C1, row 1. Enter the lower boundary, **85**, in the cell below; here column C1, row 2.
2. **Calc > Probability Distributions > Normal**.
3. See Figure 6F. Choose **Cumulative probability**. Enter: **Mean**, 100**; Standard deviation**, 15**; Input column**, C1**; Optional storage,** C2.
4. Click **OK**.
5. Subtract the lower probability from the larger shown in column C2.

   $0.8413 - 0.1587 = 0.6826$ is the probability that a Wechsler IQ is between 85 and 115.

b. Some Value or Less

1. The probability of an IQ of 115 *or less*, 0.8413, is shown in column C2, row 1. (In other words, do as in part a above, except do *not* enter the lower boundary, 85.)

c. Inverse Normal

If you want a value on the original Normal distribution (such as an IQ or height) associated with a percentile:

1. Enter the decimal form of the left proportion (**.75** for the 75th percentile) into a cell in an empty column in the spreadsheet; here we used column C1, row 1.
2. **Calc > Probability Distributions > Normal**.
3. See Figure 6G. Choose **Inverse cumulative probability**. Enter: **Mean**, 100**; Standard deviation**, 15**; Input column**, **c1**; and **Optional storage**, c2 (or an empty column).
4. Click **OK**.

You will get **110**, which is the Wechsler IQ at the 75th percentile.

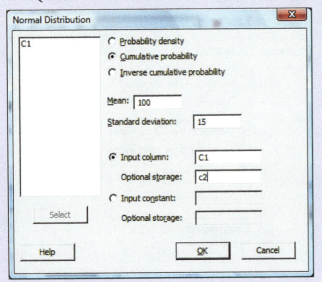

▲ **FIGURE 6F** Minitab normal.

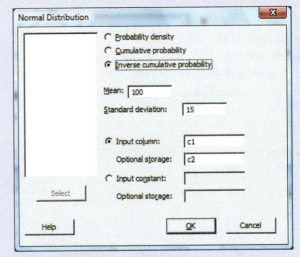

▲ **FIGURE 6G** Minitab inverse normal.

Binomial

a. Cumulative (or Less)

1. Enter the upper bound for the number of successes in an empty column; here we use column C1, row 1. Enter **28** to get the probability of 28 or fewer heads.

2. **Calc > Probability Distributions > Binomial**.

3. See Figure 6H. Choose **Cumulative probability**.

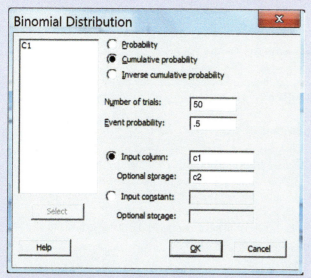

▲ **FIGURE 6H** Minitab binomial.

Enter: **Number of trials**, 50; **Event probability**, .5; **Input column**, c1; **Optional storage**, c2 (or an empty column).

4. Click **OK**.

Your answer will be 0.8389 for the probability of 28 or fewer heads.

b. Individual (Exact)

1. Enter the number of successes at the top of column 1, **28** for 28 heads.

2. **Calc > Probability Distributions > Binomial**.

3. Choose **Probability** (at the top of Figure 6H) instead of **Cumulative Probability** and enter: **Number of trials**, 50; **Event probability**, .5; **Input column**, c1; **Optional storage**, c2 (or an empty column).

4. Click **OK**.

Your answer will be 0.0788 for the probability of *exactly* 28 heads.

EXCEL

Normal

Unlike the TI-83/84, Excel makes it easier to find the probability that a random person has an IQ of 115 or less than to find the probability that a random person has an IQ between 85 and 115. This is why, for Excel, part b appears before part a.

b. Some Value or Less

1. Click *fx* (and **select a category All**).

2. Choose **NORMDIST**.

3. See Figure 6I. Enter: **X**, 115; **Mean, 100; Standard_dev, 15; Cumulative, true** (for 115 *or less*). The answer is shown as 0.8413. Click **OK** to make it show up in the active cell on the spreadsheet.

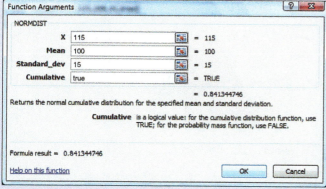

▲ **FIGURE 6I** Excel normal.

a. Between Two Values

If you want the probability of an IQ between 85 and 115:

1. First, follow the instructions above for part b. *Do not change the active cell in the spreadsheet.*

2. You will see **=NORMDIST(115,100,15,TRUE)** in the *fx* box. Click in this box, to the right of **TRUE**, and put in a minus sign.

3. Now repeat the steps for part b starting by clicking *fx*, except enter 85 instead of 115 for X. The answer, **0.682689**, will be shown in the active cell.

   Alternatively, just repeat steps 1−3 for part b using 85 instead of 115. Subtract the smaller probability value from the larger (0.8413 − 0.1587 = 0.6826).

c. Inverse Normal

If you want a value on the original Normal distribution (such as an IQ or height) associated with a percentile:

1. Click *fx*.

2. Choose **NORMINV** and click **OK**.

3. See Figure 6J on the next page. Enter: **Probability**, .75 (for the 75th percentile); **Mean, 100: Standard_dev, 15**. You may read the answer off the screen or click **OK** to see it in the active cell in the spreadsheet.

   The IQ at the 75th percentile is 110.

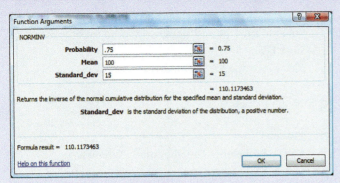

▲ FIGURE 6J Excel inverse normal.

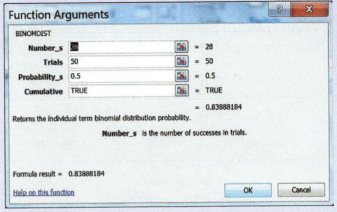

▲ FIGURE 6K Excel binomial.

Binomial

a. Cumulative (or Less)

1. Click f_x.
2. Choose **BINOMDIST** and click **OK**.
3. See Figure 6K. Enter: **Number_s, 28**; **Trials, 50**; **Probability_s, .5**; and **Cumulative, true** (for the probability of 28 *or fewer*).

   The answer (**0.8389**) shows up in the dialogue box and in the active cell when you click **OK**.

b. Individual (Exact)

1. Click f_x.
2. Choose **BINOMDIST** and click **OK**.
3. Use the numbers in Figure 6K, but enter **False** in the Cumulative box. This will give you the probability of getting *exactly* 28 heads in 50 tosses of a fair coin.

   The answer (**0.0788**) shows up in the dialogue box and in the active cell when you click **OK**.

STATCRUNCH

Normal

Unlike the TI-83/84, StatCrunch makes it easier to find the probability for 115 or less than to find the probability between 85 and 115. This is why part b is done before part a.

b. Some Value or Less

1. **Stat > Calculators > Normal**
2. See Figure 6L. To find the probability of having a Wechsler IQ of 115 or less, enter: **Mean, 100**; **Std Dev, 15**. Make sure that the arrow to the right of **Prob(X** points left (for less than). Enter the **115** in the box above **Snapshot**.
3. Click **Compute** to see the answer, **0.8413**.

a. Between Two Values

To find the probability of having a Wechsler IQ between 85 and 115, use steps 1, 2, and 3 again, but use **85** instead of **115** in the box above **Snapshot**. When you find that probability, subtract it from the probability found in Figure 6L.

$$0.8413 - 0.1587 = 0.6826$$

c. Inverse Normal

If you want a value on the original Normal distribution (such as an IQ or height) associated with a percentile:

1. **Stat > Calculators > Normal**
2. See Figure 6M. To find the Wechsler IQ at the 75th percentile, enter: **Mean, 100**; **Std. Dev., 15**. Make sure that the arrow to the right of **Prob(X** points to the left, and enter **0.75** in the box above **Compute**.

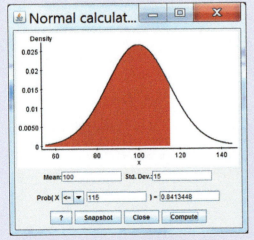

▲ FIGURE 6L StatCrunch normal.

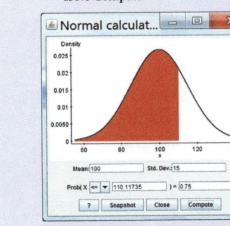

▲ FIGURE 6M StatCrunch inverse normal.

3. Click **Compute,** and the answer (**110**) is shown above **Snapshot**.

Binomial

a. Cumulative (or Less)

1. **Stat > Calculators > Binomial**

2. See Figure 6N. To find the probability of 28 or fewer heads in 50 tosses of a fair coin, enter: **n, 50;** and **p, 0.5.** The arrow after **Prob(X** should point left (for *less than*). Enter **28** in the box above **Snapshot**.

3. Click **Compute** to see the answer (**0.8389**).

b. Individual (Exact)

1. **Stat > Calculators > Binomial**

2. To find the probability of exactly 28 heads in 50 tosses of a fair coin, use a screen similar to Figure 6N, but to the right of **Prob(X** choose the equal sign. You will get **0.0788**.

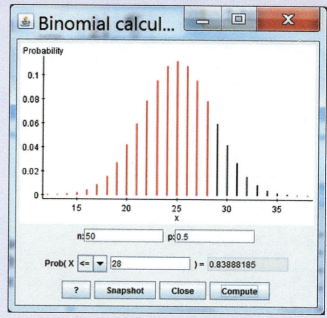

▲ **FIGURE 6N** StatCrunch binomial.

SPSS

Normal

a. Between Two Values

1. Enter the upper boundary, 115, in the top cell of an empty column; here we use var, row1. Enter the lower boundary, 85, in the cell below; here var, row2.

2. **Transform > Compute Variable. . . .**

3. In the box labelled Function group, choose **CDF & Noncentral CDF**. In the Functions and Special Variables box, choose **Cdf .Normal**; select the up-pointing arrow to the left of this box.

4. In the Numerical Expression box, you will see **CDF.NORMAL(?,?,?).** Replace the first ? with **VAR00001,** the second with **100** (the mean), and the third with **15** (the standard deviation). In the Target Variable box, enter any text. For now, enter Answer. See Figure 6O. Press **OK**.

5. In the spreadsheet, select the first cell of the Answer column. This shows .8413 (rounded to four decimals). See Figure 6P. Select the second row in the same column; it reads .1587. Subtract the smaller probability from the larger probability in your Answer column.

$0.8413 - 0.1597 = 0.6826$ is the probability that a Wechsler IQ is between 85 and 115.

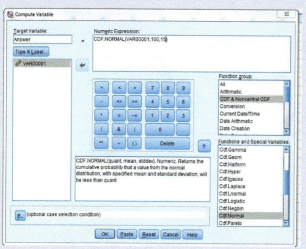

▲ **FIGURE 6O** SPSS normal.

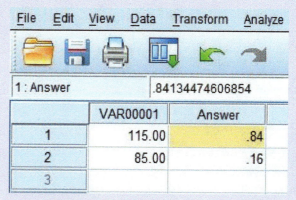

▲ **FIGURE 6P** SPSS spreadsheet.

b. Some Value or Less

1. The probability of an IQ of 115 or less, .8413 (rounded to four decimals), is shown in column Answer, row 1. (That is, repeat the steps in part a except *do not enter* the lower boundary, 85.)

c. Inverse Normal

If you want a value on the original Normal distribution (such as an IQ or a height) associated with a percentile:

1. Enter the decimal form of the percentile, or the left area (0.75 for the 75th percentile), into a cell in an empty column in the spreadsheet: here we use the first column, row 1.

2. **Transform > Compute Variable. . . .**

3. In the box labelled Function group, choose **Inverse DF**. In the Functions and Special Variables box, choose **Idf.Normal**; select the up-pointing arrow to the left of this box.

4. In the Numerical Expression box, replace the first ? with **VAR00001**, the second ? with **100** (the mean), and the third with **15** (the standard deviation). See Figure 6Q. Select **OK.**

5. Row 1 in the Answer column will be 110.12, which is the Wechsler IQ at the 75th percentile. See Figure 6R.

Binomial

a. Cumulative (or Less)

1. In the first cell of an empty column, enter: 28. (Here we use var, row 1.)

2. **Transform > Compute Variable. . . .**

3. In the box labelled Function group, choose **CDF & Noncentral CDF**. In the Functions and Special Variables box, choose **Cdf .Binom**; select the up-pointing arrow to the left of this box.

4. In the Numerical Expression box, you will see **CDF. BINOM(?,?,?).** Replace the first ? with **VAR00001**, the second with **50** (the value of n), and the third with **0.5** (the value of p).

5. In the Target Variable box, enter any text. For now, enter Answer. Press **OK.** See Figure 6S.

6. Row 1 of the Answer column gives the probability of x *or less*. Your answer of .83888 is the probability of 28 *or less* heads. See Figure 6T.

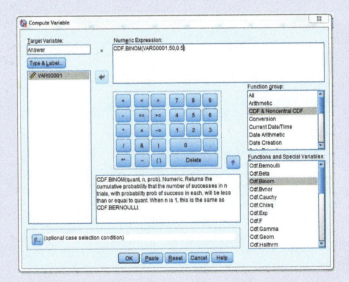

▲ **FIGURE 6S** SPSS binomial.

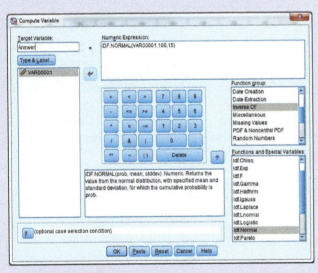

▲ **FIGURE 6Q** SPSS inverse normal.

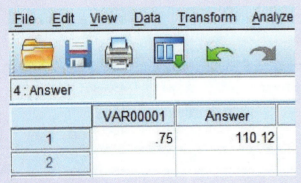

▲ **FIGURE 6R** SPSS spreadsheet.

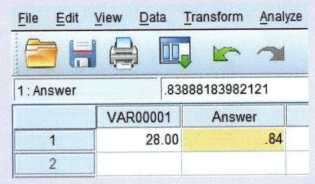

▲ **FIGURE 6T** SPSS spreadsheet.

b. Individual (Exact)

1. Enter the number of successes: **28** in row 1 of an empty column. (Here we use var, row 1.)

2. **Transform > Compute Variable. . . .**

3. In the box labelled Function group, choose **PDF & Noncentral PDF**. In the Functions and Special Variables box, choose **Pdf.Binom**; select the up-pointing arrow to the left of this box.

4. In the Numerical Expression box, you will see **PDF .BINOM(?,?,?)**. Replace the first ? with **VAR00001**, the second with **50** (the value of *n*), and the third with **0.5** (the value of *p*). In the Target Variable box, enter any text. For now, enter Answer. Press **OK**. See Figure 6U.

5. Row 1 of the Answer column is .0788, the probability of 28 *or less* heads. See Figure 6V.

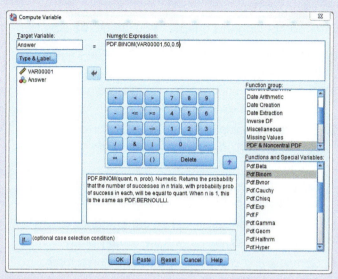

▲ **FIGURE 6U** SPSS binomial.

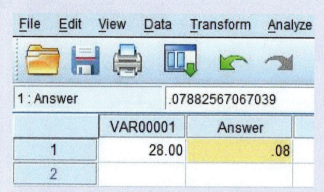

▲ **FIGURE 6V** SPSS spreadsheet.

7 Survey Sampling and Inference

zimmytws/Shutterstock

LEARNING OBJECTIVES

After completing this chapter, you should be able to:

1. Differentiate between a non-random sample and a random sample.
2. Describe why random sampling reduces potential biases in a survey.
3. Estimate the value of a population proportion with the sample proportion and determine how far off your estimate is.
4. Explain the Central Limit Theorem and how it applies to the sample proportion.
5. Employ the Central Limit Theorem to find approximate probabilities associated with the sample proportion.
6. Compute and interpret a confidence interval for the population proportion.
7. Calculate the required sample size for a given margin of error when doing a survey.

Somewhere in your town or city, possibly at this very moment, people are participating in a survey. Perhaps they are filling out a customer satisfaction card at a restaurant. Maybe their television is automatically transmitting information about which show is being watched so that marketers can estimate how many people are viewing their ads. They may even be text messaging in response to a television survey. Most of you will receive at least one phone call from a survey company that will ask whether you are satisfied with local government services or plan to vote for one candidate over another. The information gathered by these surveys is used to piece together, bit by bit, a picture of the larger world.

You've reached a pivotal point in the book. In this chapter, the data summary methods you learned in Chapters 2 and 3, the probability you learned in Chapter 5, combined with the Normal and binomial distributions studied in Chapter 6 will allow us to generalize our understanding of a small sample—a snapshot—to a larger group, or the big picture. Politicians rely on surveys of 1000 people not because they care how those 1000 people will vote. Such surveys are important to politicians because they help them learn how *all* people will vote. In this and later chapters, we learn how reliable such a projection from a sample to the larger population is.

When we make a judgement about a big group based on observations from a small part of this group, we are making an inference. Inferential reasoning lies at the foundation of science but is far from foolproof. As the following case study illustrates, when we make an inference we can never be absolutely certain of our conclusions. But applying the methods introduced in this chapter ensures that if we collect data carefully, we can measure how certain or uncertain we are in our inference.

CASE STUDY

Online Polls: Be Careful What You Ask For

ENMAX is a public utility—owned by the City of Calgary—that provides electricity, natural gas, and renewable energy to customers in southern Alberta. In 2011, its CEO resigned after a series of scandals, which included (1) a company-wide email to all ENMAX employees blasting news media coverage of his $2.7 million salary package in 2008, which was approved by the board of directors; (2) private house parties featuring performances by famous rock stars; and (3) a paid vacation to the French Riviera by SAP, a German software company that held a software-providing contract with ENMAX. The CEO resigned in January 2012 with a $4.6 million severance package.

Approximately two months later, a local councillor posted a survey on her publicly accessible webpage. The survey was intended to ask people in the area she represents—about 82,000 persons—to provide their opinion regarding the ENMAX board of directors. The question asked: Was the board doing a sufficient job, or not? The results of the survey suggested that about 66% of people who responded said the board was doing a sufficient job.

There were 800 responses to the survey, a relatively large number of respondents compared to other surveys this councillor regularly posts on her webpage. A random sample that size would allow us to state that the survey had a margin of error of ± 3 percentage points at the 95% level of confidence. In that case, we would be very confident that the true percentage of people the councillor represents who believed that the ENMAX board of directors was doing a sufficient job was somewhere between 63% and 69%, a very strong majority. However, this statement does not appear to match the general opinion of the people in Calgary, who were at the time very upset about how the board of directors of a public company supported the CEO's multimillion dollar severance package (among other things).

Online polls are the subject of many disagreements. Can the results of online polls be trusted? If so, what sort of understanding can we gain from online polls? In this chapter, you'll see why the method used to collect data is so important to inference, and how we use probability, under the right conditions, to calculate the margin of error to quantify how precise our inference is. At the end of the chapter, you'll see why the 66% figure is suspicious.

SECTION 7.1

Learning about the World through Surveys

Surveys are probably the most often encountered application of statistics. Various forms of media report on surveys or polls several times a week—and during a major election, several times a day. We can learn quite a bit through a survey if the survey is done correctly.

Survey Terminology

A **population** is a big group of people or objects we wish to study. Usually this group is very large—say the group of all Canadian citizens, or all Canadian citizens over the age of 65. However, it could be smaller, such as all first-year students in your school, or all the grizzly bears living in the Canadian Rockies. Whatever the group, we wish to know the value of a **parameter**, a numerical property that summarizes a characteristic of the population. For example, a pollster will want to know the percentage of voters who say they will vote for a certain political party in an upcoming election. Opponents of drunk driving will be interested in the percentage of Canadian teenagers who have driven after consuming alcohol. Designers of passenger airplanes will want to know the mean length of passengers' legs so that they can put the seats closer together without discomfort. Senior management of a national store chain will want to know the mean household income in an area they are considering for a new store location.

In this book we focus on two frequently used parameters: the mean of a population and the population proportion. This chapter deals with population proportions.

If the population is relatively small, we can find the exact value of the parameter by conducting a census. A **census** is a survey where every member of the population is measured. For example, if you wish to know the percentage of people in your classroom who are left-handed, you can perform a census. The students in your class, including yourself, are the population, and the parameter is the percentage of left-handers. We sometimes try to take a census with a large population (such as Statistics Canada's Census), but such undertakings are too expensive for nongovernmental organizations and are filled with complications caused by trying to track down and count people who may be hard to find. (For example, Statistics Canada's Census of 2011 failed to count people living on 31 Indian reserves and settlements.)

In reality, most populations we want to investigate are simply too big to take a census. For this reason, we instead observe a smaller portion of the population. This smaller group is called a **sample**, which is a small group of people or objects taken from the population of interest.

Once a sample is collected, we measure the characteristic we're interested in. A **statistic** is a numerical property of the sample. We use the *computed value* of the statistic as an estimate of the unknown value of the parameter. For instance, we may be interested in the proportion of Canadian voters that will vote for the governing political party in the next federal election. The proportion of all Canadian voters who will vote for the governing political party is our *parameter*, the value of which is unknown. We estimate this value by surveying a small sample of Canadian voters. The proportion of those sampled who say they will vote for the governing political party in the next federal election is a *statistic*.

Statistics are sometimes called **estimators**, and the value of a statistic an **estimate**, because it "estimates" the unknown value of the parameter. For example, suppose that the proportion of sampled Canadian voters who say they will vote for the governing political party in the next federal election is computed to be 0.39. This statistic, 0.39, is our *estimate* of the proportion of all Canadian voters who will vote for the governing political party in the next federal election.

Statistical inference is the science of drawing conclusions about a population on the basis of observing a sample from this population. Statistical inference always has uncertainty, so a vital component of "inference making" is measuring our uncertainty.

KEY POINT

1. A statistic is computed from data appearing in the sample. Its value is used to estimate the unknown value of its corresponding population parameter. Because of this a statistic is sometimes called an estimator.

2. Using the computed value of a statistic to estimate the unknown value of a parameter is a scientific process called statistical inference.

EXAMPLE 1 Poll: Millennials and Social Media

In June 2012, Angus Reid Public Opinion surveyed 223 Canadians between the ages of 18 and 32 (Generation Y "millennials"). Common wisdom suggests that this group is in tune with the internet and social media. The survey found that 48% of the respondents personally need to check social media (Facebook, Twitter, etc.) after waking up in the morning.

QUESTIONS Identify the population and the sample. What is the parameter of interest? What is the statistic?

CONCLUSION The *population* we wish to study is all Canadians between the ages of 18 and 32, or all "Gen-Yers." The *sample,* which is taken from the population, consists of 223 Gen-Yers. The *parameter* of interest is the percentage of all Gen-Yers who personally need to check social media when waking up in the morning. The value of the *statistic,* which is the computed percentage of the sample that has this characteristic, is 48%.

TRY THIS! Exercise 7.1

An important difference between statistics and parameters is that the values of statistics can be computed. Any time we collect data, we can calculate the value of a statistic. In Example 1, we know that 48% of 223 people surveyed between the ages of 18 and 32 personally need to check social media after they wake up in the morning. On the other hand, the value of a parameter is generally unknown. We are not certain about the percentage of all Canadians between the ages of 18 and 32 who personally need to check social media after they have woken in the morning. The only way to find out would be to take a *census,* and we have neither the time nor the money to do this. Table 7.1 compares the known and unknown in this situation.

Unknown	Known
Population All Canadians between the ages of 18 and 32, or Gen-Yers	*Sample* A small number of Canadians between the ages of 18 and 32
Parameter Percentage of Gen-Yers who personally need to check social media when they wake up Mean debt level of all Gen-Yers	*Statistic* Percentage of Gen-Yers who personally need to check social media when they wake up, computed from the sample Mean debt level of Gen-Yers, computed from the sample

◀ **TABLE 7.1** Some examples of unknown quantities we might wish to estimate, and their knowable counterparts.

Statisticians have developed notation for keeping track of parameters and statistics. In general, Greek characters are used to represent population parameters. For example, μ (mu, pronounced "mew," as in the beginning of *music*) represents the mean of a population. Also, σ (sigma) represents the standard deviation of a population. Statistics (estimates based on a sample) are represented by English letters: $\bar{x}$ (pronounced "x-bar") is the mean of a sample, and s is the standard deviation of a sample, for instance.

One frequently encountered exception is the use of the letter p to represent the proportion of a population and $\hat{p}$ (pronounced "p-hat") to indicate the proportion of a sample. Table 7.2 summarizes this notation. You've seen most of these symbols before, but this table organizes them in a new way that is important for statistical inference.

Details

The Sample Proportion: $\hat{p}$
The sample proportion $\hat{p}$, pronounced "p-hat," is the number of successes divided by the number of trials.

► **TABLE 7.2** Notation for some commonly used statistics and parameters.

Statistics (based on data)		Parameters (typically unknown)	
Sample mean	$\bar{x}$ (x-bar)	Population mean	μ (mu)
Sample standard deviation	s	Population standard deviation	σ (sigma)
Sample variance	s^2	Population variance	σ^2
Sample proportion	$\hat{p}$ (p-hat)	Population proportion	p

What Could Possibly Go Wrong? The Problem of Bias

Unfortunately, it is much easier to conduct a bad survey than a good one. One of the many ways in which we can reach a wrong conclusion about a population is to use a survey method that is biased.

A survey method is **biased** if it tends to produce "untrue data," which then produces inaccurate statistical inferences. This can occur two ways. The first is through **sampling bias**, which happens when the collected sample is not representative of the population. Another way is **measurement bias**, which comes from asking questions that do not produce a true answer. For example, if we ask people "What is your income?," there is a tendency for respondents to exaggerate the value: the exaggerated income will produce a positive (or "upward") bias, resulting in a "higher than should be" value of the statistic. Measurement bias can occur when measurements recorded in the survey tend to be larger or smaller than the true value.

A third way occurs because some statistics are naturally biased. For example, if you use the statistic 10 times the sample mean, or $10\bar{x}$, you will typically get an estimate for the μ that is 10 times too large. When steps have been taken to eliminate sampling bias and measurement bias, you must still take care to use a statistic that is not biased.

Measurement Bias

In October 2002, the *Calgary Herald* reported on a recent survey to determine Alberta residents' opinion of the Kyoto Protocol. In this agreement, countries would voluntarily commit to either limit or reduce their greenhouse gas emissions. Alberta is a province that is rich in natural resources, but the process to extract them is industrially intensive and results in a large amount of greenhouse gas emissions. The Government of Alberta hired Environics West to survey 1200 Albertans. Environics asked the question:

> "As you may know, the United States has withdrawn from the Kyoto protocol and developing countries such as China, India, and Mexico are currently exempt from meeting reduction targets under Kyoto. If Canada ratifies the Kyoto protocol, some people say that Canada will be at an economic disadvantage because industry and investment will leave Canada for the U.S. and other countries where they will not have to incur the extra costs of meeting Kyoto protocol targets. Other people say Canada will NOT be at an economic disadvantage because technology will emerge that will allow companies in Canada to remain competitive. Which view is your own?"

Seventy percent of respondents said Canada would be at a *disadvantage*.

In the previous May, another polling company, Ipsos-Reid, asked a random sample of Albertans the following question:

> "As you may know, the Kyoto Accord or Protocol is an agreement to reduce greenhouse gas emissions. Under this agreement, Canada has committed to reduce its greenhouse gas emissions to 6 percent below 1990 levels by the period from 2008 to 2012. The Government of Canada is currently considering ratifying the agreement, thereby making it binding on our country. Thinking of the Kyoto Protocol as it now stands, how do you think the Government of Canada should proceed? Should they withdraw from the Kyoto Protocol and develop a made-in-Canada plan for reducing greenhouse gas emissions, or ratify the Kyoto Protocol?"

Seventy-two percent of respondents to this survey *supported* the ratification of the Kyoto Protocol (Simpson 2012). One or both of these surveys have measurement bias.

 Caution

Bias

Statistical bias is different from the everyday use of the term *bias*. You might perhaps say a friend is biased if she has a strong opinion that affects her judgment. In statistics, bias is a way of measuring the performance of a method over many different applications.

A more famous example occurred in 1993, when, on the basis of the results of a Roper Organization poll, many U.S. newspapers published headlines similar to this one from the *New York Times*: "1 in 5 in New Survey Express Some Doubt About the Holocaust" (April 20, 1993). Almost a year later, the *New York Times* reported that this alarmingly high percentage of alleged Holocaust doubters could be due to measurement error. The actual question respondents were asked contained a double negative: "Does it seem possible, or does it seem impossible to you, that the Nazi extermination of the Jews never happened?" When Gallup repeated the poll but did not use a double negative, only 9% expressed doubts (*New York Times* 1994).

Sampling Bias

Writing good survey questions to reduce measurement bias is an art and a science. However, the focus of this book is on sampling bias, which happens when the estimation of the parameter uses a sample that does not represent the population. (By "not representing" the population we mean that the sample is fundamentally different from the population.)

Have you ever heard of Alfred Landon? Unless you're a political science student, you probably haven't. In 1936, Landon was the Republican candidate for U.S. president, running against Franklin Delano Roosevelt. The *Literary Digest*, a popular news magazine, conducted a survey with over 10 million respondents and predicted that Landon would easily win the election with 57% of the vote. The fact that you probably haven't heard of Landon suggests that he didn't win, and indeed, he lost big, setting a record at the time for the lowest number of electoral votes received by a major-party candidate. What went wrong? The *Literary Digest* had a biased sample. The journal relied largely on polling its own readers, and its readers were more well-to-do than the general public and more likely to vote for a Republican. The reputation of the *Literary Digest* was so damaged that two years later it disappeared and was absorbed into *Time* magazine.

The U.S. presidential elections of 2004 and 2008 both had candidates who claimed to have captured the youth vote, and both times, candidates claimed that the polls were biased. The reason given was that the surveys used to estimate candidate support relied on landline phones, and many young voters don't own landlines, relying instead on their cell phones. Reminiscent of the 1936 *Literary Digest* poll, these surveys were potentially biased because their sample systematically excluded an important part of the population: those who do not use landlines (Cornish 2007).

In fact, a Pew Foundation study in 2010 found that U.S. polls that excluded cell phones had a sampling bias that favoured Republican candidates.

These days, the most commonly encountered biased samples involve surveys done over the internet. These are often found on news organization websites (for example, "Do you think the monarchy in Canada should be abolished?," www.lethbridgeherald.com, May 21, 2001; "Do you think the Canadian national anthem needs a change?," www.cbc.ca/news, March 3, 2010). Internet polls such as these are rife with **voluntary-response bias**. This type of sampling bias tends to occur when people have strong feelings about the survey topic. The intensity of these feelings provokes them to participate in these surveys; otherwise, why bother? As a result, the group of participators is likely to be quite different in makeup from the population, and therefore not representative of the population. Even if the population does consist of only readers of the *Lethbridge Herald*, the online survey may not accurately reflect the views of all readers of the *Lethbridge Herald*! The voluntary nature of going online and responding to this survey means that people responding will be biased with their views. In this case, the City of Lethbridge has a significant senior-citizen population, many of whom have a fondness for the Queen and the monarchy. In addition, not every reader of the *Lethbridge Herald* had access to the internet in 2001. Moreover, what would prevent a person from responding multiple times to this survey?

To warn readers of these problems, most online polls will have a disclaimer: "This is not a scientific poll." This means that "we should not take the results of this survey seriously." The results of such online surveys simply summarize how the participants feel; inferences to the larger population should not be made.

Another form of bias happens when those being surveyed fail to answer a question or respond to a survey. Such **nonresponse bias** occurs when people selected to participate in the survey refuse to do so. Refusal can happen for mundane reasons (they're eating dinner when the pollster calls) or for reasons that might have a more serious effect on the results (because people are embarrassed or offended by the question). Those who choose not to respond might have different views about the survey's topics from those who do. For example, questions about income might be refused by those who are embarrassed by what they feel is too low, or too high, an income. If a large percentage declines to participate, then a biased survey could result.

> **KEY POINT** When reading about a survey, it is important to know
>
> 1. what percentage of people who were asked to participate actually did so.
> 2. whether the researchers randomly chose people to participate in the survey or people volunteered to participate.
>
> If a large percentage chosen to participate refused to answer questions, nonresponse bias could result. If people volunteered to participate, there will be voluntary-response bias. If a survey suffers from these problems, its conclusions are suspect.

Simple Random Sampling Saves the Day

How do we collect a sample that has as little bias as possible and is representative of the population? Only one way works: to take a random sample.

As we explained in Chapter 5, statisticians have a precise definition of *random*. If we stand on a street corner and stop whomever we like then ask if they would like to participate in our survey, we are taking a **convenience sample**—we are stopping people because they are convenient to reach and not on the basis of some randomization. A random sample must be taken in such a way that every person in the population has a chance of being in the sample.

A true random sample is difficult to achieve. Pollsters have devised many clever ways of pulling this off, often with good success. Of the many ways to take a random sample from a population (many of which are beyond the focus of this book), one that's easy to understand but difficult to employ is **simple random sampling (SRS)**.

In SRS, subjects are drawn from the population at random and without replacement in such a way that every person in the population has the same chance of being selected. Without replacement means that once a person is picked, that person cannot be picked again. This is like dealing cards from a deck: once a card is dealt for a hand, it cannot be dealt again. A result of SRS is that every conceivable sample of a fixed size is equally likely to be chosen. For example, every five-card hand has the same chance of being picked. The result of this is that we can come up with a statistic that is unbiased, and then use its computed value to estimate the population parameter of interest. Finally, we can measure how "close or far off" our estimate is.

It can't be emphasized enough that if our sample is not random, there's really nothing we can learn about the population. We can't measure a survey's precision, and we can't know how large or small the bias might be. An unscientific survey is a useless survey for the purposes of learning about a population.

In theory, we can take an SRS by assigning a number to each and every member of the population. We then use a random number table or other random number generator to select our sample, ignoring numbers that appear twice.

EXAMPLE 2 Taking a Simple Random Sample

Alberto, Justin, Michael, Audrey, Brandy, and Nicole are in a class.

QUESTION Select an SRS of three names from these six names.

SOLUTION First assign each person a number, as shown:

> **Details**
>
> Simple random sampling is not the only valid method for statistical inference. Statisticians collect representative samples using other methods as well (for example, sampling with replacement). What these methods all have in common is that they take samples randomly.

Alberto	1
Justin	2
Michael	3
Audrey	4
Brandy	5
Nicole	6

Next, select three of these numbers without replacement. Figure 7.1 shows how this is done in StatCrunch, and almost all statistical technologies let you do this quite easily.

TECH

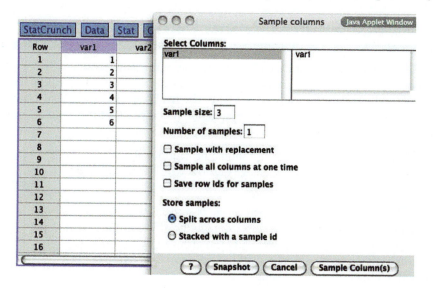

◄ FIGURE 7.1 StatCrunch will randomly select, without replacement, three numbers from the six shown in the var1 column.

Using technology, we got these three numbers: 1, 2, and 6. These correspond to Alberto, Justin, and Nicole.

If technology is not available, a random number table, such as the one provided in Appendix A, can be used. Here are two lines from such a table:

$$7\,7\,5\,9\,8 \quad 2\,9\,5\,1\,1 \quad 9\,8\,1\,4\,9 \quad 6\,3\,9\,9\,1$$
$$3\,1\,9\,4\,2 \quad 0\,4\,6\,8\,4 \quad 6\,9\,3\,6\,9 \quad 5\,0\,8\,1\,4$$

You can start at any row or column you please. Here, we choose to start at the upper left (shown in bold face). Next, read off digits from left to right, skipping digits that are not in our population. Because no one has the number 7, skip this number, twice. The first person selected is number 5: Brandy. Then skip 9 and 8 and select number 2: Justin. Skip 9 and 5 (because you already selected Brandy) and select number 1: Alberto.

CONCLUSION Using technology, our sample consisted of Alberto, Justin, and Nicole. Using the random number table, we got a different sample: Brandy, Justin, and Alberto.

TRY THIS! Exercise 7.11

Sampling in Practice

In practice, an SRS is difficult to collect and often inefficient. In most situations, we can't make a list of all people in Canada and assign each of them a number. To get around this, we use alternative techniques. We'll discuss examples of some other sampling methods in Chapter 12.

Also, random sampling is not the superhero that solves all issues that result from sampling. Nonresponse bias can still occur after an SRS is taken, and there is always the chance that methods of taking a random sample are flawed (as when telephone surveys use randomly selected landline numbers when many in the population of interest have only a cell phone).

Statistics Canada reported in 2013 that 21% of Canadian households no longer have landlines and use only their cell phones. For Canadian households in the 18 to 34 age bracket, this percentage is 60%. Among households made up of people over the age of 50, only 6% used only a cell phone. As a result, telephone surveys that involve automated dialing of landlines can produce bias, since older households are more likely to be sampled than younger households, which may not reflect the population of interest. Telephone surveys of cell phone users are also open to nonresponse bias, since cell phone users do not want to waste valuable air time on answering survey questions, which may take anywhere from a few to 15 minutes to complete. These people may also be in the "middle of something" that requires their attention, such as attending a meeting or driving a vehicle, compared to people using landlines at home.

EXAMPLE 3 Survey on Sexual Harassment

A newspaper at a large post-secondary institution wants to determine whether sexual harassment is a problem on campus. The paper takes a simple random sample of 1000 students and asks each person whether he or she has been a victim of sexual harassment on campus. About 35% of those surveyed refuse to answer. Of those who do answer, 2% say they have been victims of sexual harassment.

QUESTION Give a reason why we should be cautious about using the 2% value as an estimate for the population percentage of those who have been victims of sexual harassment.

CONCLUSION There is a large percentage of students who did not respond. Those who did not respond might be different from those who did, and if their answers had been included, the results could have been quite different. When those surveyed refuse to respond, it can create a biased sample.

TRY THIS! Exercise 7.17

There will always be some people who refuse to participate in a survey, but a good statistical investigator will anticipate this and do everything necessary to keep the problem of nonresponse to a minimum to reduce this bias, such as assuring participants that the data they provide will be confidential and ensuring that the data provided from the survey are anonymous.

SECTION 7.2

Measuring the Quality of a Survey

A common complaint about surveys is that the "sample size is too small." How can it be possible that a survey based on 1000 people tells us what all people in Canada are thinking? To an extent, the "how many surveyed" is important, but not as important as we might think. A survey based on a random sample of 1000 Canadians can tell us to a certain degree of accuracy what all Canadians are thinking. But other interesting questions can be raised: How can we judge whether the statistics from our survey are working? Are they good estimators of the parameter? What separates a good method to estimate the parameter from one that is bad?

It's difficult, if not impossible, to judge whether any particular survey is good or bad. Sometimes we can find obvious sources of bias, but often we don't know whether a survey has failed unless we later learn the true parameter value. (This sometimes occurs in elections, when we learn that a survey must have had bias because it severely missed predicting the actual outcome.) Instead, statisticians evaluate the *method* used to estimate a parameter, not the outcome of a particular survey.

Statisticians evaluate the method used for a survey, not the outcome of a single survey.

Before we talk about the judging of surveys, imagine this: we are going to take many surveys, each to be of 1000 randomly chosen people. We send out an army of pollsters, and each pollster is to randomly sample 1000 people, where all the pollsters are to use the same method of collecting the sample. Each pollster is to ask the same question to his or her 1000 people, after which a statistic is to be computed to estimate the proportion of people in the population who would answer "yes" to the question, or the "target." When all the pollsters are done, we will see many different values of the statistic—one from each pollster—each being an estimate of the population proportion. We expect some of these values to be closer to the target than others because of random variation. What we really want to know is how our army of pollsters did as a whole. For this reason, we talk about evaluating the *estimation method*, not the estimate/statistic it produces.

An estimation method is a lot like a golfer. To be a good golfer, we need to get the ball closest to the target—the cup—as much as possible. A good golfer is both *accurate* (tends to hit the ball near the cup) and *precise* (even when she misses, she doesn't miss by very much).

It is possible to be precise and yet be inaccurate, as shown in Figure 7.2b. Also, it is possible to aim in the right direction (be accurate) but be imprecise, as shown in Figure 7.2c. (Naturally, some of us are bad at both, as shown in Figure 7.2d.) But the best golfers can both aim in the right direction and manage to be very consistent, which Figure 7.2a shows us.

> **⚠ Caution**
>
> **Estimator and Estimates**
> We often use the word **estimator** to mean the same thing as "estimation method." An **estimate**, on the other hand, is the value of a statistic produced by our estimation method.

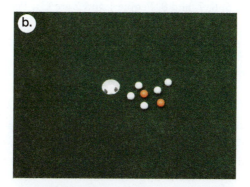

◀ **FIGURE 7.2 (a)** Shots from a golfer with good aim and precision; the balls are tightly clustered and centred around the cup. **(b)** Shots from a golfer with good precision but poor aim; the balls are close together but centred to the right of the cup. **(c)** Shots from a golfer with good aim—the balls are centred around the cup—but bad precision. **(d)** The worst-case scenario: bad precision *and* bad aim.

Think of the cup as the population parameter, and think of each golf ball as an estimate, a value of $\hat{p}$, is that results from a different survey. We want an estimation method that aims in the right direction. Such a method will, on average, get the correct value of the population parameter. We also need a precise method, so that if we repeated the survey, we would arrive at nearly the same estimate.

The aim of our method, which is the *accuracy*, is measured in terms of *bias*. The *precision* represents "how-far-away" $\hat{p}$ is from the true value of the population proportion, and is to be measured by the *standard deviation of* $\hat{p}$. Discussion of simulation studies in the next sections will help clarify how accuracy and precision are measured. These simulation studies show how bias and standard deviation are used to quantify the uncertainty in our inference.

Using Simulations to Understand the Behaviour of Estimators

The three simulations that follow will help measure how well the sample proportion works as an estimator of the population proportion.

In the first simulation, imagine doing a survey of four people in a very small population with only eight people. You'll see that the estimator of the population proportion is accurate (no bias) but, because of the small sample size, not terribly precise.

In the second simulation, the first simulation is repeated, using a larger population and sample. The estimator is still unbiased, and you will see a perhaps surprising change in precision. Finally, the third simulation will reveal that using a much larger sample size makes the result even more precise.

To learn how our estimation method behaves, we're going to create a very unusual, unrealistic situation: we're going to create a world in which we know the truth. In this world, there are two types of people: those who like dogs and those who like cats. No one likes both. Exactly 25% of the population are Cat People, and 75% are Dog People. We're going to take a random sample of people from this world and see what proportion of our sample are Cat People. Then we'll do it again. And again. From this repetition, we'll see some interesting patterns emerge.

Simulation 1: Statistics Vary from Sample to Sample

To get started, let's create a very small world. This world has eight people named 1, 2, 3, 4, 5, 6, 7, and 8. People 1 and 2 are Cat People. See Figure 7.3.

▶ **FIGURE 7.3** The entire population of our simulated world; 25% are Cat People.

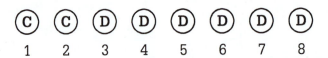

From this population, we use the random number table to generate four random numbers between 1 and 8. When a person's number is chosen, he or she steps out of the population and into our sample.

Before we tell who was selected, think for a moment about what you expect to happen. What proportion of our sample will be Cat People? Is it possible for 0% of the sample to be Cat People? For 100%?

Below is our random sample. Note that we sampled without replacement, as in a real survey. We don't want the same person to be in our sample twice.

6	8	4	5
D	D	D	D

None of those selected are Cat People, as Figure 7.4 indicates. The proportion of Cat People in our sample is 0%. We call this the *sample proportion* because it comes from the sample, not the population.

▶ **FIGURE 7.4** The first sample, which has 0% Cat People.

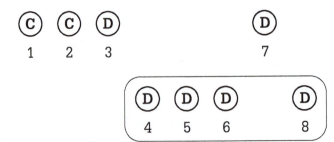

Let's take another random sample. It is possible that we will again get 0%, but it is also possible that we will get a different percentage.

7	2	6	3
D	C	D	D

This time, our sample proportion is 25%.
One more time:

2	8	6	5
C	D	D	D

Again, our sample proportion is 25%.

Table 7.3 shows what has happened so far. Even though we have done only three repetitions, we can make some interesting observations.

Repetition	Population Parameter	Sample Statistic
1	$p = 25\%$ Cat People	$\hat{p} = 0\%$ Cat People
2	$p = 25\%$ Cat People	$\hat{p} = 25\%$ Cat People
3	$p = 25\%$ Cat People	$\hat{p} = 25\%$ Cat People

◄ **TABLE 7.3** The results of three repetitions of our simulation.

First, notice that the population proportion, p, never changes. It can't, because in our made-up world, the population always has the same eight people and the same two are Cat People. However, the sample proportion, $\hat{p}$, can be a different value in each sample. In fact, $\hat{p}$ is treated as a random variable because its value (1) varies from one sample to the next and (2) is computed from the random sample.

KEY POINT No matter how many different samples we take, the value of p (the population proportion) is always the same. The value of the sample proportion, $\hat{p}$, is a random variable because it changes from one sample to another.

This simulation is a random experiment and $\hat{p}$ is our outcome. We learned in Chapter 6 that random variables (discrete or continuous) have a probability distribution. Because $\hat{p}$ is a random variable, it too has a probability distribution, which is called the **sampling distribution**. This term reminds us that $\hat{p}$ is a statistic whose value changes from one sample to the next and that its value is used to estimate the population proportion p.

Because our world has only eight people and we are taking samples of four, we can write down all the different samples that exist and the value of $\hat{p}$ for each sample, of which there are 70. By doing this, we can see exactly how often $\hat{p}$ will be 0%, how often 25%, and how often 50%. (Notice that it can never be more than 50%.) These probabilities are listed in Table 7.4, which presents the sampling distribution for $\hat{p}$. Figure 7.5 visually represents this sampling distribution.

Value of $\hat{p}$	Probability of Seeing That Value
0%	0.2143
25%	0.5714
50%	0.2143

▲ **TABLE 7.4** The sampling distribution for $\hat{p}$, based on our random sample.

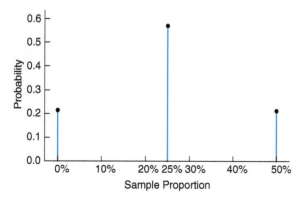

◄ **FIGURE 7.5** Graphical representation of Table 7.4, the sampling distribution for $\hat{p}$ when p is 0.25.

From Table 7.4 and Figure 7.5, we learn several things:

1. Our estimator, $\hat{p}$, is not always the same as our parameter, p. Sometimes $\hat{p}$ turns out to be 0%, sometimes it is 50%, and sometimes it hits the target value of 25%.

2. The mean of this distribution is 25%—the same value as p.

3. Even though $\hat{p}$ is not always the "true" value, p, we are never more than 25 percentage points away from the true value.

Why are these observations important? Let's consider each one separately.

The first observation reminds us that statistics based on random samples are random. We cannot be absolutely sure exactly what estimates our survey will produce.

The second observation tells us that our estimator has no bias. This means that, *on average*, it will be the same value as the parameter. **Bias** is measured as the distance between the average value of the estimator (the centre of the sampling distribution) and the population parameter. In this case, the centre of the sampling distribution and the population parameter are both 0.25, so the difference is 0. There is no bias.

The third observation is about precision. We know that our estimator is, on average, the same as the parameter, but the sampling distribution tells us how far away, typically, the estimator might stray from average. **Precision** is reflected in the spread of the sampling distribution. We have learned that this spread is measured by the standard deviation. Seeing that the sample proportion is a statistic that is a random variable, we can say that the sample proportion has a standard deviation. In this simulation the **standard deviation of the sample proportion** is 0.16366, or roughly 16%.

The standard deviation of the sample proportion measures how much this estimator will vary from one sample to the next. Thus, in the above example, if we survey four people, we usually get 25% Cat People, but this typically varies by plus or minus 16.4% (16.4 percentage points). Looking at the graph in Figure 7.5, we might think that the variability is typically plus or minus 25 percentage points, but we must remember that the standard deviation measures how spread out observations are from the average value. Many observations are identical to the average value, so the typical, or "standard," deviation from average is only 16.4 percentage points.

KEY POINT   Bias is measured using the centre of the sampling distribution: it is the distance between the centre and the population value.

Precision is measured using the standard deviation of the sample proportion, $\hat{p}$. The smaller the standard deviation the more precise $\hat{p}$ is as an estimator.

SNAPSHOT   SAMPLING DISTRIBUTION

WHAT IS IT? ▶	A special name for the probability distribution of a statistic.
WHAT DOES IT DO? ▶	It tells us that the statistic is a random variable.
WHAT IS IT USED FOR? ▶	It shows us how the statistic behaves: how often we can expect to see particular values of the statistic we are using as an estimator. It will reveal the central point and the standard deviation, from which we can determine its bias (or lack thereof) and its precision.
HOW IS IT USED? ▶	It is used for making inferences about a population.
WHEN IS IT USED? ▶	When computing probabilities associated with the statistic to determine its precision.

Simulation 2: The Size of the Population Does Not Affect Precision

In our first simulation, the bias of the estimator was 0. This is good because it means that we have an accurate estimator. That is, the statistic $\hat{p}$ is an accurate estimator of the population proportion p. However, the precision was poor because of the large standard deviation. How can we improve the precision? To understand, consider a more realistic simulation.

This time, we'll use the same world but make it bigger. Let's assume we have 1000 people (instead of 8) and 25% are Cat People ($p = 0.25$). We take a random sample of 10 people and find the proportion of the sample that are Cat People, or $\hat{p}$.

We've already seen how this is done, so we're going to skip some steps and just show the results. This time the different outcomes are too numerous to list (there are just under 263.5 *trillion different values* of $\hat{p}$), so we just do a simulation:

1. Take a random sample, without replacement, of 10 people.

2. Calculate $\hat{p}$: the proportion of Cat People in our sample.

3. Repeat steps 1 and 2 a total of 10,000 times. Each time, calculate $\hat{p}$ and record its value.

Here are our predictions:

1. We predict that $\hat{p}$ will not be the same value every time because it is based on a random sample, so the value of $\hat{p}$ will vary randomly.

2. We predict that the mean outcome, the typical value for $\hat{p}$, will be 25%—the same as the population parameter—because our estimator is unbiased.

3. Precision: this one is left to you. Do you think the result will be more precise or less precise than in the last simulation? In the last simulation, only four people were sampled and the standard deviation of the sample proportion was about 16%. This time more people (10) are being sampled, but the population is much larger (1000). Will the standard deviation be larger (less precise) or smaller (more precise) than 16%?

Figure 7.6 shows the sampling distribution of $\hat{p}$. Figure 7.6 is not the true sampling distribution because the histogram is based on one simulation of 10,000 random samples of 10 each. The frequencies in this figure, when divided by 10,000, are estimates of the probabilities, not the true probabilities. Still, it is a very good approximation of the true sampling distribution of $\hat{p}$.

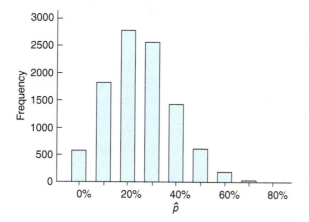

◄ **FIGURE 7.6** Simulation results for $\hat{p}$. This histogram is a simulation of the sampling distribution. The true value of p is 25%. Each sample is based on 10 people, and we repeated the simulation 10,000 times.

The centre of the estimated distribution is at 0.2501, which indicates that essentially no bias exists, because the population parameter is 0.25.

The outcomes ranged from $\hat{p} = 0$ to $\hat{p} = 0.8$. We can find the precision by finding the standard deviation of the estimate $\hat{p}$. This turns out to be about 13.56%.

The value of the standard deviation tells us that if we were to take another sample of 10 people, we would expect to get about 25% Cat People, give or take 13.6 percentage points.

From Figure 7.6 we learn important information:

1. The bias of $\hat{p}$ is still 0, even though we used a larger population and a larger sample.

2. The variation of $\hat{p}$ is less; this estimator is more precise, even though the population is larger. In general, as long as the population is large relative to the sample size, the precision has *nothing* to do with the size of the *population*, but only with the size of the *sample*.

Many people are surprised to learn that precision is not affected by population size. How can the level of precision for a survey in a town of 10,000 people be the same as for one in a country of 35 *million* people?

Figure 7.7 provides an analogy. The bowls of soup represent two populations: a big one (a country, perhaps) and a small one (a city). Our goal is to taste each soup (take a sample from the population) to judge whether we like it. If both bowls are well stirred, the size of the bowl doesn't matter—using the same-size spoon, we can get the same amount of taste from either bowl.

▶ **FIGURE 7.7** The bowls of soup represent two populations and the sample size is represented by the spoons. The precision of an estimate depends only on the size of the sample, not the size of the population.

 KEY POINT   The precision of an estimator does not depend on the size of the population; it depends only on the sample size. An estimator based on a sample size of 10 is just as precise in a population of 1000 people as in a population of a million.

Simulation 3: Large Samples Produce More Precise Estimators

Let's do one more simulation. This time the only change we'll make is to increase the sample size from 10 to 100 people from the population of 1000, with Cat People still representing 25% of the population. How will the larger sample change the precision of the simulated sampling distribution from Figure 7.6?

Figure 7.8 shows the result. Note that the centre of this simulated sampling distribution is still at 25%, so our estimation method remains unbiased. However, the shape looks pretty different. First, because many more outcomes are possible for $\hat{p}$, this histogram looks as though it belongs more to a continuous-valued random variable than to a discrete one. Second, it is much more symmetric than Figure 7.6. You will see in Section 7.3 that the shape of the sampling distribution of $\hat{p}$ depends on the size of the random sample.

An important point to note is that this estimator is much more precise because it uses a larger sample size. By sampling more people, we get more information, so we can end up with a more precise estimate. The standard deviation in the distribution of the sample proportion shown in Figure 7.8 is now 4.2 percentage points, compared to 16% in the first simulation.

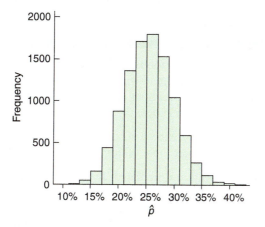

◀ **FIGURE 7.8** Simulated sampling distribution of a sample proportion of Cat People, based on a random sample of 100 people. The simulation was repeated 10,000 times.

Table 7.5 shows a summary of the three simulations.

Simulation	Population Size	Sample Size	Mean	Standard Deviation
1	8	4	25%	16.4%
2	1000	10	25%	13.5%
3	1000	100	25%	4.2%

Increasing Sample Size ↓   *Increasing Precision* ↓

◀ **TABLE 7.5** Increasing sample size results in increasing precision (measured as decreasing standard deviation).

Here is what we learned from Figure 7.8, which is based on sample sizes of 100 "people":

1. The estimator $\hat{p}$ is unbiased for all sample sizes (as long as we take random samples).

2. The precision improves as the sample size gets larger.

3. The shape of the sampling distribution is more symmetric for larger sample sizes.

KEY POINT ▸ Surveys based on larger sample sizes have a smaller standard deviation (SD) and are therefore more precise. Increasing the sample size improves the precision of the survey.

Finding the Bias and the Standard Deviation

We've shown how to estimate bias and precision by running a simulation. But we can also do this mathematically, without running a simulation. Bias and standard deviation are easy to find for a sample proportion under the following conditions:

Condition 1. The sample must be randomly selected from the population of interest, either with or without replacement. The population parameter to be estimated is the proportion of people (or objects) with some characteristic. This proportion is denoted as p.

Condition 2. If the sampling is without replacement, the population needs to be much larger than the sample size n; at least 10 times bigger is a good general rule.

When these two conditions are met, the bias of $\hat{p}$ is 0, and its standard deviation is

$$SD = \sqrt{\frac{p(1 - p)}{n}}$$

EXAMPLE **4** Pet World

Suppose that in Pet World, the population is 1000 people and 25% of the population are Cat People. Cat People love cats but hate dogs. We are planning a survey in which we take a random sample of 100 people, without replacement. We calculate the proportion of people in our sample who are Cat People.

QUESTION What value should we expect for our sample proportion? What's the standard deviation? How do we interpret these values?

SOLUTION The sample proportion is unbiased, so we expect it to be the same as the population proportion: 25%.

The standard deviation is $\sqrt{\dfrac{p(1-p)}{n}} = \sqrt{\dfrac{0.25 \times 0.75}{100}} = \sqrt{\dfrac{0.1875}{100}}$

$$= \sqrt{0.001875} = 0.04330, \text{ or about } 4.3\%.$$

This formula is appropriate because the population size is big with respect to the sample size. The population size is 1000, and the sample size is 100; $100 \times 10 = 1000$, so the population is 10 times larger than the sample size.

CONCLUSION We interpret the values to mean that if we were to take a survey of 100 people from Pet World, we would expect about 25% of them to be Cat People, give or take about 4.3%. The "give or take" means that if you were to draw a sample of 100 and I were to draw a sample of 100, our sample proportions would typically differ from the expected 25% by about 4.3 percentage points.

TRY THIS! Exercise 7.29

Real Life: We Get Only One Chance

Simulation studies, like the one we just did, allow us to repeat the survey many times to understand what will happen. In real life, we have only one shot: we take a random sample, find the value of $\hat{p}$, and then go from there.

It is important to realize that bias and precision are both measures of what happens if we could repeat our survey many times. Bias indicates the typical outcome of surveys repeated again and again. If the bias is 0, we will usually get the right value. If the bias is 0.10, then our estimate will characteristically be 10 percentage points too high. Precision measures how much our estimator will vary from the typical value if we do the survey again. To put it slightly differently, if someone else does the survey, precision helps determine how different her or his estimate could be from ours.

How small must the standard deviation be for a "good" survey? The answer varies, but the basic rule is that the precision should be small enough to be useful. A typical election poll having a sample of roughly 1000 registered voters has a standard deviation of about 1.5 percentage points. If the candidates are many percentage points apart, this is good precision. However, if they are neck and neck, this might not be good enough. In Section 7.4, we will discuss how to make decisions about whether the standard deviation is small enough.

In practice, we don't know the true value of the population proportion, p. This means that we can't compute the value of the standard deviation of $\hat{p}$. However, we can come very close by replacing the p term with $\hat{p}$. If p is unknown, then

$$SD_{est} = \sqrt{\dfrac{\hat{p}(1-\hat{p})}{n}}, \text{ the estimated standard deviation,}$$

is a useful approximation to the true standard deviation of the sample proportion.

The Central Limit Theorem for Sample Proportions

From Chapter 5, we learned that probability tells us the proportion of times an event happens if we repeat a random experiment a very large—theoretically an infinite—number of times. For example, the sampling distribution of $\hat{p}$ gives us a distribution of the values this statistic can have for a given sample size, as well as the probabilities of $\hat{p}$ being certain values. In summary, it tells us how often we would see particular values of $\hat{p}$ if we were able to take an infinite number of surveys. In our simulation we repeated our fake survey 10,000 times—which is a lot, but a long way from infinity.

In our three simulations in Section 7.2, we observed through Figures 7.5, 7.6, and 7.8 that the shape of the sampling distribution of $\hat{p}$ changed as the sample size increased. As the sample size increased, the sampling distribution became more and more symmetric. If we used an even larger sample than our last simulation—the survey of 100—would we find the same Normal pattern in the sampling distribution of $\hat{p}$? Well, it so happens that we don't need to conduct a fourth simulation. There is a wonderful theorem, called the **Central Limit Theorem (CLT)**, that gives us a very good approximation of the sampling distribution of $\hat{p}$ without performing any simulations!

The Central Limit Theorem is needed because we are estimating the value of a parameter with a statistic computed from a random sample. By knowing the sampling distribution of the statistic we are using, along with its bias and precision (standard deviation), we are allowed to measure "how good" our estimation method is. Because of this, we can use the sampling distribution to find the probability that the value of our estimate falls a specified distance from the population value. For example, we don't want to just know that 40% of our customers are satisfied with their service; we also want to know the probability that the true percentage is more than a particular value, such as 50%.

Meet the Central Limit Theorem for Sample Proportions

The Central Limit Theorem has several versions. The one we will see now applies to estimating the value of a population proportion based on the sampling distribution of $\hat{p}$. If some basic conditions are satisfied, the sampling distribution of $\hat{p}$ is close to the Normal distribution.

These conditions are the same as those used in finding bias and precision by using $\hat{p}$ to estimate the true value of p, but with one new condition:

Condition 1. *Random and Independent.* The sample is collected randomly from the population and observations are independent of each other. The sample can be collected either with or without replacement.

Condition 2. *Large Sample.* The sample size, n, is large enough that the sample expects at least 10 successes (yes's) and 10 failures (no's).

Condition 3. *Big Population.* If the sample is collected without replacement, then the population size must be much (at least 10 times) bigger than the sample size.

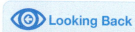 **Looking Back**

Normal Notation
Recall that the notation N(mean, standard deviation) designates a particular Normal distribution.

The sampling distribution for $\hat{p}$ is then approximately Normal, with mean p (the population proportion) and standard deviation:

$$SD = \sqrt{\frac{p(1-p)}{n}}$$

KEY POINT   The Central Limit Theorem (CLT) for sample proportions tells us that if we take a random sample from a population, and if the sample size is large and the population size much larger than the sample size, then the sampling distribution of $\hat{p}$ is approximately

$$N\left(p, \sqrt{\frac{p(1-p)}{n}}\right)$$

If you don't know the value of p, then you can substitute the value of $\hat{p}$ to estimate the standard deviation.

Figure 7.9 illustrates the CLT for proportions. Figure 7.9a is based on simulations in which the sample size was just 10 people, which is too small for the CLT to apply. In this case, the simulated sampling distribution does not look Normal; it is right-skewed and has large gaps between values. Figure 7.9b is based on simulations of samples of 100 observations. Because the true population proportion is $p = 0.25$, a sample size of 100 is large enough for the CLT to apply, and our simulated sampling distribution looks very close to the Normal model. Figure 7.9b is actually a repeat of Figure 7.8 with the Normal curve superimposed. Now that the graphs are shown on the same scale, we can see that the sample size of 100 gives better precision than the sample size of 10—the distribution is narrower.

▶ **FIGURE 7.9 (a)** Revision of Figure 7.6, a histogram of 10,000 sample proportions, each based on $n = 10$ with a population percentage p equal to 25%. **(b)** Revision of Figure 7.8, a histogram of 10,000 sample proportions, each based on $n = 100$ percentage and with the population percentage p equal to 25%.

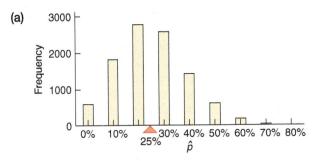

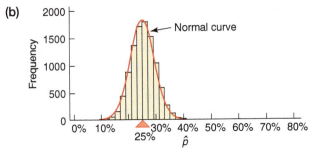

The Normal curve shown in Figure 7.9b has a mean of 0.25 because $p = 0.25$, and a standard deviation of 0.0433 because

$$\sqrt{\frac{0.25 \times 0.75}{100}} = 0.0433$$

Before illustrating how to use the CLT, we show how to check conditions to see whether the CLT applies.

Checking Conditions for the Central Limit Theorem

The first condition states that the sample must be collected randomly. There is no way to check this just by looking at the data; you have to trust the researcher's report on how the data were collected, or, if you are the researcher, to take care that you use sound random sampling methods.

The second condition dictates that the sample size must be large enough. This we *can* check by looking at the data. The CLT says that the sample size needs to be sufficiently large to get at least 10 successes and 10 failures in our sample. If the probability of a success is p, then we would expect about np successes and $n(1 - p)$ failures. One problem, though, is that we usually don't know the value of p. In this case, we instead check that

$$n\hat{p} \geq 10 \text{ and } n(1 - \hat{p}) \geq 10$$

For example, if our sample has 100 people and we are estimating the proportion of females in the population, and if our sample has 49% females, then we need to verify that both $100(0.49) \geq 10$ and $100(0.51) \geq 10$.

The third condition applies only to random samples done without replacement. In this case, the population must be at least 10 times bigger than the sample. In symbols, if N is the number of people in the population and n is the number in the sample, then

$$N \geq 10n$$

If this condition is not met, and the sample was collected without replacement, then the actual standard deviation will be a little smaller than what our formula says it should be.

In most real-life applications, the population size is much larger than the sample size. Over 35 million people live in Canada, so the typical survey of 1000 easily meets this condition.

You can see how these conditions are used in the examples that follow.

Using the Central Limit Theorem

The following examples use the CLT to find the probability that the sample proportion will be near (or far from) the population value.

EXAMPLE 5 Pet World Revisited

Let's return to Pet World. The population is 1000 people, and the proportion of Cat People is 25%. We'll take a random sample of 100 people.

QUESTION What is the approximate probability that the proportion in our sample will be bigger than 29%? Begin by checking conditions for the CLT.

SOLUTION First we check conditions to see whether the Central Limit Theorem can be applied. The sample size is large enough because $np = 100(0.25) = 25$ is greater than 10 and $n(1 - p) = 100(0.75) = 75$, which is also greater than 10. Also, the population size is 10 times larger than the sample size, because $1000 = 10(100)$. Thus $N = 10(n)$; the population is just large enough. We are told that the sample was collected randomly.

According to the CLT, the sampling distribution will be approximately Normal. The mean is the same as the population proportion: $p = 0.25$. The standard deviation is:

$$SD = \sqrt{\frac{p(1 - p)}{n}} = \sqrt{\frac{0.25 \times 0.75}{100}} = \sqrt{\frac{0.1875}{100}} = \sqrt{0.001875} = 0.0433$$

We can use technology to find the probability of getting a value larger than 0.29 in an $N(0.25, 0.0433)$ distribution. Or we can standardize.

The z-score corresponding to 0.29 is

$$z = \frac{0.29 - 0.25}{0.0433} = 0.924$$

In an $N(0,1)$ distribution, the probability of getting a number bigger than 0.924 is, from Table A in the appendix, about 0.18, or 18%. Figure 7.10 on the next page shows the results using technology.

▶ **FIGURE 7.10** Output from SOCR (http://socr.stat.ucla.edu): there is about an 18% chance that $\hat{p}$ will be more than 4 percentage points above 25%.

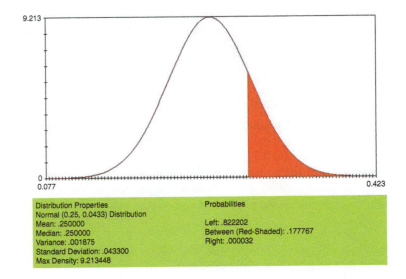

Distribution Properties
Normal (0.25, 0.0433) Distribution
Mean: .250000
Median: .250000
Variance: .001875
Standard Deviation: .043300
Max Density: 9.213448

Probabilities
Left: .822202
Between (Red-Shaded): .177767
Right: .000032

CONCLUSION With a sample size of 100, there is about an 18% chance that $\hat{p}$ will be more than 4 percentage points above 25%.

TRY THIS! Exercise 7.33

SNAPSHOT — THE SAMPLE PROPORTION: $\hat{p}$ (p-HAT)

WHAT IS IT? ▶ The proportion of people or objects in a sample that have a particular characteristic in which we are interested.

WHAT IT IS USED FOR? ▶ To estimate the proportion of people or objects in a population that have that characteristic.

WHY DO WE USE IT? ▶ If the sample is drawn at random from the population, then the sample proportion is unbiased and has standard deviation $\sqrt{\dfrac{p(1-p)}{n}}$.

HOW IS IT USED? ▶ As long as the sample size is at least 10% of the population size, the Central Limit Theorem holds, and the distribution of the sample proportion can be modelled by the Normal distribution.

WHEN IS IT USED? ▶ To find probabilities associated with the sample proportion.

EXAMPLE 6 Federal Election Survey

In an emotionally charged federal election, the current prime minister is seeking re-election. In the previous federal election the governing political party, of which the prime minister is the leader, received 40% of the country's vote. For now, let's assume that voter preference has not changed since the last federal election. Suppose a random sample of 1000 Canadians is to be taken and each will be asked who they are going to vote for.

QUESTIONS What percentage of the sample should be expected to say they would vote for the governing political party of which the current prime minister is leader? What is the standard deviation for this sample proportion? Does the Central Limit Theorem apply? If so, what is the approximate probability that the sample proportion will fall within two standard deviations of the population value of $p = 0.40$?

SOLUTION Because we have collected a random sample, the sample proportion has no bias (assuming there are no problems in collecting the sample). We then expect that 40% of our sample will vote for the governing party of which the leader is currently prime minister.

Because the sample size, $n = 1000$, is small relative to the population (which is over 25 million voters), we can calculate the standard deviation with

$$SD = \sqrt{\frac{(0.40)(0.60)}{1000}} = 0.0155$$

We can interpret this to mean that we expect the value of the sample percentage to be 40%, give or take 1.55 percentage points.

Because the sample size is fairly large (the expected number of successes and failures—$np = 1000 \times 0.40 = 400$, and $n(1 - p) = 1000 \times 0.60 = 600$—are both at least 10), the CLT says we can use the Normal distribution. That is, the distribution of $\hat{p}$ is close to being Normally distributed, or $N(0.40, 0.0155)$.

We are asked to find the probability that the sample proportion will fall within two standard deviations of 0.40. Or that it will fall somewhere between the two values

$$0.40 - 2SD$$
and
$$0.40 + 2SD$$

Because this is a Normal distribution, we know that this probability will be close to 95% (by the Empirical Rule). Let's find the probability without the use of the Empirical Rule.

$$0.40 - 2SD = 0.40 - 2(0.0155) = 0.40 - 0.031 = 0.369$$

$$0.40 + 2SD = 0.40 + 2(0.0155) = 0.40 + 0.031 = 0.431$$

We want to find the area between 0.369 and 0.431 in an $N(0.40, 0.0155)$ distribution. Figure 7.11 shows the result using technology, which tells us this probability is 0.9545.

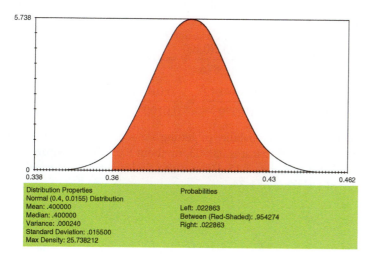

Distribution Properties
Normal (0.4, 0.0155) Distribution
Mean: .400000
Median: .400000
Variance: .000240
Standard Deviation: .015500
Max Density: 25.738212

Probabilities
Left: .022863
Between (Red-Shaded): .954274
Right: .022863

CONCLUSION If 40% of the population will vote for the political party that the current prime minister is leader of, then we'd expect our sample proportion to be about 0.40 (or 40%). There is about a 95% chance that the sample proportion falls within two standard deviations of 40%.

TRY THIS! Exercise 7.35

The conclusion from Example 6 is useful because it implies that, in general, we can predict where $\hat{p}$ will fall, relative to p. It indicates that $\hat{p}$ is very likely to fall within two standard deviations of the true value, as long as the sample size is large enough. If, in addition, we have a small standard deviation, we know that $\hat{p}$ is quite likely to fall close to p.

Looking Back

Empirical Rule
Recall that the Empirical Rule says that roughly 68% of observations should be within one standard deviation of the mean, about 95% within two standard deviations of the mean, and nearly all within three standard deviations of the mean. In this context, the standard deviation is for the sampling distribution of $\hat{p}$.

◄ **FIGURE 7.11** The probability that a sample proportion based on a random sample of 1000 people taken from a population in which $p = 0.40$ has about a 95% chance of falling within two standard deviations of 0.40.

KEY POINT If the conditions of a survey sample satisfy those required by the CLT, then the probability that a sample proportion will fall within two standard deviations of the population value is approximately 95%.

EXAMPLE 7 Morse and the Proportion of E's

Samuel Morse (1791–1872), the inventor of Morse code, claimed that the letter used most frequently in the English language was E and that the proportion of E's was 0.12. We took a simple random sample with replacement from a modern-day book. Our sample consisted of 876 letters, and we found 118 E's, so $\hat{p} = 0.1347$.

QUESTION Find the probability that, if we were to take another random sample of 876 letters, the sample proportion would be greater than or equal to 0.1347. Assume that the true proportion of E's in the population is, as Morse claimed, 0.12. As a first step, check that the Central Limit Theorem can be applied in this case.

SOLUTION To check whether we can apply the Central Limit Theorem, we need to make sure the sample size is large enough. Because $p = 0.12$, we check:

$$np = 876(0.12) = 105.12, \text{ which is at least 10,}$$

and

$$n(1 - p) = 876(0.88) = 770.88, \text{ which is also at least 10}$$

The book contains far more than 8760 letters, so the population size is much larger than the sample size.

We can therefore use the Normal model for the distribution of sample proportions. The mean of this distribution is

$$p = 0.12$$

The standard deviation is

$$SD = \sqrt{\frac{p(1-p)}{n}} = \sqrt{\frac{0.12(0.88)}{876}} = 0.010979$$

$$z = \frac{\hat{p} - p}{SD} = \frac{0.1347 - 0.12}{0.010979} = \frac{0.0147}{0.010979} = 1.34$$

normalcdf
lower:.1347
upper:1.00
μ:.12
σ:.010979
Paste
normalcdf(.1347▸
.0902984603

▲ **FIGURE 7.12** TI-83/84 output.

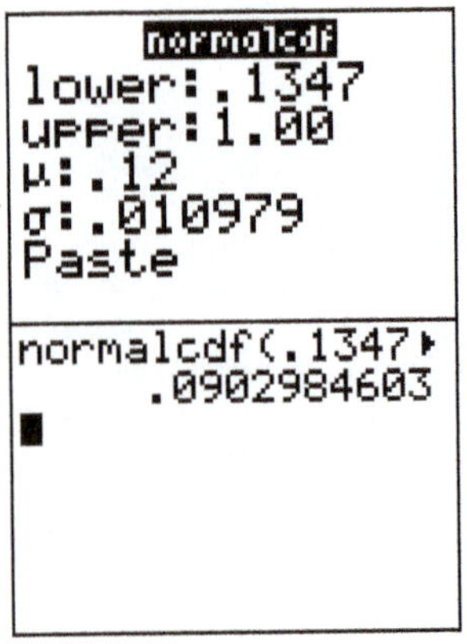

We therefore need to determine the probability of getting a z-score of 1.34 or larger. We use technology (Figure 7.12) to find that it is 0.0903, or about 9.0%. This probability is represented by the shaded area in Figure 7.13. We can also find it with the Normal table; it is the area to the right of a z-score of 1.34.

0.10
0.11
0.12
0.13
0.1347
p̂

▶ **FIGURE 7.13** The shaded area represents the probability of finding a sample proportion of 0.1347 from a population with a proportion of 0.12.

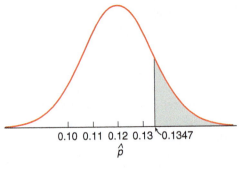

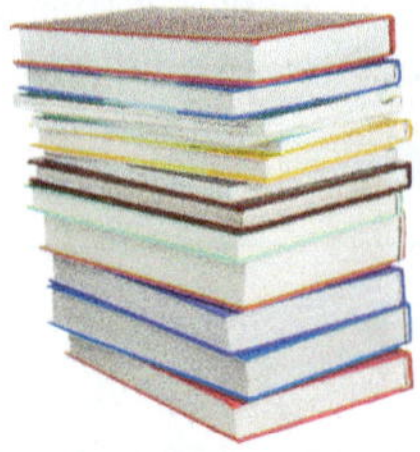

CONCLUSION If the sample is 876 letters, the probability of getting a sample proportion of 0.1347 or larger, when the true proportion of E's in the population is 0.12, is about 9%.

TRY THIS! Exercise 7.37

Estimating the Population Proportion with Confidence Intervals

Up until now, all of our examples have described scenarios where the population proportion, p, is a known value. In Example 7, p represented the proportion of E's found in the English language, and we assumed that $p = 0.12$. However, in the real-world the value of p is usually unknown. This is why we survey, because we don't know the value of p.

To illustrate this point, we look at a real survey. A survey of 2207 Canadian adults was taken in November 2012 by Leger Marketing. In this sample, 74% of the 2207 people said that universal health care as a symbol of Canada was a very important source of Canadian pride. However, this percentage simply informs us about the sample. What percentage of all Canadians view universal health care as a proud symbol of Canada? That is, what is the value of p? Is it larger or smaller than 74%, and if so, by how much? Can we say that more than three-quarters, or 75%, of all Canadians feel the same way?

We don't know the value of p, but we do know the value of $\hat{p} = 0.74$. We also know, from preceding sections, that:

1. Our statistic $\hat{p}$ is unbiased. Even though our estimate of 0.74 may not be exactly equal to the population parameter, we are probably off by a little.

2. The standard deviation of $\hat{p}$ can be estimated as

$$SD_{est} = \sqrt{\frac{\hat{p}(1 - \hat{p})}{n}} = \sqrt{\frac{(0.74)(1 - 0.74)}{2207}} = 0.0093, \text{ about } 0.9\%.$$

   This means that the population parameter must be close by, because the standard deviation of 0.9 percentage point means that this statistic is a very precise estimator.

3. Because the sample size is large, the CLT kicks in. This means that the probability distribution of $\hat{p}$ is very close to being Normally distributed and is centred at the true value of the population proportion. There is about a 68% chance that $\hat{p}$ is closer than one standard deviation away from the population proportion, and close to a 95% chance that it is closer than two standard deviations away (see Example 6). Finally, there is almost a 100% probability (99.7%, to be specific) that the sample proportion is closer than three standard deviations from the population proportion. We can be almost *certain* that the proportion of Canadians who feel pride in universal health care being a symbol of Canada is within three standard deviations of 0.74. Three standard deviations is 3(0.9%) = 2.7%.

In other words, we can place a high *level of confidence* in the population parameter being between these two numbers:

$$74\% - 2.7\% \quad \text{to} \quad 74\% + 2.7\%, \text{ or}$$
$$71.3\% \quad \text{to} \quad 76.7\%$$

We have just calculated what statisticians call a **confidence interval**. Confidence intervals are often reported with a "plus or minus" amount, which is often called the **margin of error**.

$$74\% \text{ plus or minus } 2.7\%, \text{ or } 74\% \pm 2.7\%$$

This margin of error of 2.7% tells us how far off from the population value our estimate is very likely to be.

A confidence interval gives us two vital pieces of information: (1) a range of possible values that the population parameter could be equal to (71.3% to 76.7%), and (2) a **confidence level**, which expresses how confident we are in this calculated interval. The high level of confidence of 99.7% figure assures us that we can be very confident that the percentage of all Canadians who feel pride in universal health care being a symbol of Canada is at least 71.3% to at most 76.7%, which does include three-quarters of Canadians!

To help further explain a confidence interval, imagine trying to capture the mystical creature Ogopogo that lurks in the waters of B.C.'s Okanagan Lake. Let's assume for now that it stays in one location in this rather large lake. One way is to bait Ogopogo by getting a very large fishing rod with a very strong line, at the end of which is something yummy that it will grab. We throw the line into a section of Okanagan Lake, and wait. We hope that the bait is close enough to Ogopogo that it will detect the yummyness; then we hope that it's hungry and will bite. This approach to catching Ogopogo is similar to using *only the value* of the estimate.

However, we can increase our chance of catching Ogopogo by throwing into the lake a very strong net, which is like our confidence interval. We are more likely to catch Ogopogo in a net than on a fishing line that has been baited. Also, the larger the net, the more confident we will be in nabbing Ogopogo. If our net has a standard size, we will be 68% confident in capturing Ogopogo; if we double the size of the net, we will be more confident in catching the beast—about 95% confident. If we increased the size of the net three times, we would be about 99% confident in catching it. (If our net was the size of lake, we would be 100% confident in catching Ogopogo.)

In this analogy, Ogopogo is the population proportion that is stationary—it has a location and we don't know where it is. The bait is the sample proportion, in that we can be very close or very far off. The net is our confidence interval, where we have a much better chance of capturing Ogopogo. The larger the net, the greater the confidence we have in nabbing Ogopogo *somewhere* in the net.

Setting the Confidence Level

If our confidence interval estimate is successful, then the value of the population proportion will fall somewhere inside it. The confidence level tells us the percentage of times our estimation method will be successful. Our method is to take a random sample and calculate a confidence interval estimate of the population proportion. If the method has a 10% confidence interval, it will contain—or capture, as mentioned in the Ogopogo analogy—the value of p 10% of the time. On the other hand, a 100% confidence interval means that the interval will capture the value of p 100% of the time.

The confidence level can be thought of as the capture percentage, telling us the percentage of times our confidence interval based on a random sample will capture the value of the population proportion. Like Ogopogo, the population proportion is a stationary value that never moves. However, our confidence interval will change from one sample to another, just as each time we cast out the net it will not fall in the same place. Thus, the confidence interval measures the percentage of times our method is successful, and not the success of any one particular interval.

KEY POINT The confidence level measures the capture rate for our method of finding confidence intervals.

Figure 7.14 demonstrates what we mean by a 95% confidence level. Let's suppose that in Canada, 51% of all voters favour stricter laws with respect to buying and selling guns. We simulate taking a random sample of 1000 people. We calculate the percentage of the sample who favour stricter laws, and then we find the confidence interval that gives us a 95% confidence level. We do this again and keep repeating. Figure 7.14 shows 100 simulations.

Each blue point and each orange point represent a sample percentage. Note that the points are centred around the population percentage of 51%. The horizontal lines

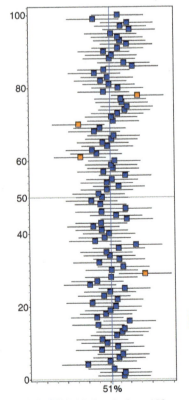

▲ **FIGURE 7.14** Results from 100 simulations in which we draw a random sample and then find and display a confidence interval with a 95% confidence level. The orange squares indicate "bad" intervals.

represent the confidence interval: the sample percentage plus or minus the margin of error. The margin of error was chosen so that the confidence level is 95%. Notice that most of the lines cross the vertical line at 51%. These are successful confidence intervals that capture the population value of 51% (in blue). However, a few sample percentages miss the mark; these are indicated by orange points. In 100 trials, our method failed 4 times and was successful 96 times. In other words, it worked in 96% of the trials. When we use a 95% confidence level, our method works in approximately 95% of all surveys we conduct.

We can change the confidence level by changing the margin of error. The greater the margin of error, the higher our confidence level. For example, we can be 100% confident that the true percentage of Canadians who favour stricter gun laws is between 0% and 100%. We're 100% confident in this interval because it can never be wrong. Of course, it will also never be useful. We really don't need to spend money on a survey to learn that the answer lies between 0% and 100%, do we?

It would be more helpful—more precise—to have a smaller margin of error than "plus or minus 50 percentage points." However, if the margin of error is too small, then we are more likely to be wrong. Think of the margin of error as a lacrosse stick. The bigger the mesh, the more confident you are of catching the ball. Choosing an interval that ranges from 0% to 100% is like using a lacrosse stick that fills the entire field—you will definitely catch the ball, but not because you are a good lacrosse player. If the netting of the stick is too small, you are less confident of catching the ball, so you don't want it too small. Somewhere between too big and too small is just right.

Selecting a Margin of Error

We select a margin of error that will produce the desired confidence level. For instance, how can we choose a margin of error with a confidence level of 95%? We already know that if we take a large enough random sample and find the sample proportion, then the CLT tells us that 95% of the time, the sample proportion is within two standard deviations of the population proportion. This is what we learned from Example 6. It stands to reason, then, that if we choose a margin of error that is two standard deviations, then we'll cover the population proportion in 95% of our samples.

This means that

$$\hat{p} \pm 2SD$$

is a confidence interval with a 95% confidence level. More succinctly, we call this a 95% confidence interval.

Using the same logic, we understand that the interval

$$\hat{p} \pm 1SD$$

is a 68% confidence interval and that

$$\hat{p} \pm 3SD$$

is a 99.7% confidence interval.

Figure 7.15 shows four different margins of error for a sample in which $\hat{p} = 0.50$.

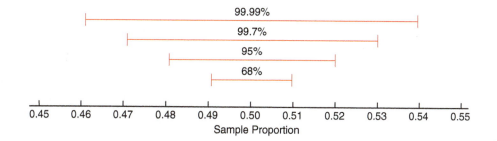

◄ **FIGURE 7.15** Four confidence intervals with confidence levels ranging from 99.99% (plus or minus four standard deviations— top) to 68% (plus or minus one standard deviation). Notice how the interval gets wider with increasing confidence level.

This figure illustrates one reason why a 95% confidence interval is so desirable. If we increase the margin of error from two standard deviations to three, we gain only a small amount of confidence; the level goes from 95% to 99.7%. However, if we decrease from two standard deviations to one, we lose a lot of confidence; the level falls from 95% to 68%. Thus, the choice of two standard deviations is very economical.

The margin of error has this structure:

$$\text{Margin of error} = z^* SD$$

where z^* is a number that tells how many standard deviations to include in the margin of error. If $z^* = 1$, the confidence level is 68%. If $z^* = 2$, the confidence level is about 95%. Table 7.6 summarizes the margin of error for four commonly used confidence levels.

▶ **TABLE 7.6** We can set the confidence level to the value we wish by choosing the appropriate margin of error.

Confidence Level	Margin of Error Is . . .
99%	2.58 standard deviations
95%	1.96 (about 2) standard deviations
90%	1.645 standard deviations
80%	1.28 standard deviations

Reality Check: Finding a Confidence Interval When *p* Is Not Known

As we have seen, a confidence interval for a population proportion has this structure:

$$\hat{p} \pm m$$

where m is the margin of error. Substituting for the margin of error, we can also write

$$\hat{p} \pm z^* SD$$

Finding the standard deviation requires us to know the value of p:

$$SD = \sqrt{\frac{p(1 - p)}{n}}$$

However, in real life, we don't know p. So instead, we substitute our sample proportion and use this estimated standard deviation:

$$SD_{est} = \sqrt{\frac{\hat{p}(1 - \hat{p})}{n}}$$

The result is a confidence interval with a confidence level close to, but not exactly equal to, the correct level. This tends to be close enough for most practical purposes.

In real life, then, Formula 7.1 is the method we use to find approximate confidence intervals for a population proportion.

Formula 7.1: $\hat{p} \pm m$ where $m = z^* SD_{est}$ and $SD_{est} = \sqrt{\frac{\hat{p}(1 - \hat{p})}{n}}$

where:

m is the margin of error
$\hat{p}$ is the sample proportion of successes, or the proportion of people in the sample with the characteristic we are interested in
n is the sample size
z^* is a multiplier that is chosen to achieve the desired confidence level (Table 7.6)
SD_{est} is the estimated standard deviation of the sample proportion

EXAMPLE 8 Ipsos Poll on Tattoos

What proportion of Canadians have a tattoo? A 2012 Ipsos poll involved a random sample of 1005 Canadian adults, and found that 22% of those sampled have at least one tattoo.

QUESTIONS Find the standard deviation of this statistic. Find an approximate 95% confidence interval for the percentage of Canadians who have at least one tattoo. Can we say that one-fifth of Canadians have at least one tattoo?

SOLUTION Before we can proceed, we first make sure that the conditions of the Central Limit Theorem apply. We are told that Ipsos took a random sample. It is not clear that the pollsters sampled with replacement or without replacement, but since the population of Canadian adults is very large—easily more than 10 times 1005—we can relax about this.

Next, we check that the sample is large enough to apply the CLT. We do not know the value of p, the proportion of all Canadians who have at least one tattoo. We only know $\hat{p}$ (equal to 0.22), which Ipsos calculated from their sample. This means that our sample has at least 10 successes (at least 10 people in the sample have at least one tattoo) because $1005(0.22) = 221$, which is larger than 10. Also, we know that there are at least 10 failures (people who do not have at least one tattoo) in the sample, as $1005(0.78)$ is also larger than 10.

Our next step is to estimate the standard deviation of the sample proportion.

$$SD_{est} = \sqrt{\frac{(0.22)(0.78)}{1005}} = 0.013067$$

The problem asks us for a 95% confidence interval, which can be achieved by using a margin of error of about two standard deviations.

$$\hat{p} \pm 2SD_{est} = 0.22 \pm 2(0.013067) = 0.22 \pm 0.0261,$$
$$\text{or } 22\% \pm 2.61\%$$

Expressing as an interval, we get

$$22\% - 2.61\% = 19.39\%$$
$$22\% + 2.61\% = 24.61\%$$

The 95% confidence interval is 19.39% to 24.61%.

CONCLUSION This confidence interval narrows down the possible values of the population proportion. We can infer that it is indeed plausible for one-fifth (20%) of Canadians to have at least one tattoo, since the lower bound of our confidence interval is *lower* than 20% and the upper bound is *more* than 20%. That is, the 95% confidence interval captures the value of 20%.

TRY THIS! Exercise 7.51

Interpreting Confidence Intervals

A confidence interval for a sample proportion gives a set of values that are plausible for the population proportion. If a value is not in the confidence interval, we conclude that it is implausible. It's not impossible that the population value is outside the interval, but it would be pretty surprising.

Suppose a candidate for political office conducts a poll and finds that a 95% confidence interval for the proportion of voters who will vote for him is 42% to 48%.

He would be wise to conclude that he does *not* have 50% of the population voting for him. The reason is that the value 50% is not in the confidence interval, so it is implausible to believe that the population value is 50%.

There are many common misinterpretations of confidence intervals you must avoid. The most common mistake that students (and, indeed, many others) make is trying to turn confidence intervals into some sort of probability statement. For example, if asked to interpret a 95% confidence interval of 19.41% to 24.59%, many people would mistakenly say, "This means there is a 95% chance that the population proportion is between 19.41% and 24.59%."

What's wrong with this statement? Remember that probabilities are long-run frequencies. This sentence claims that if we were to repeat this survey many times, then in 95% of the surveys the true population percentages would be a number between 19.41% and 24.59%. This claim is wrong, because the true population percentage doesn't change. It is either *always* between 19.41% and 24.59% or it is *never* between these two values. It can't be between these two numbers 95% of the time and somewhere else the rest of the time. In the Ogopogo analogy, a stationary Ogopogo resembles the population parameter in that it doesn't wander or move. Similarly, the value of the population proportion does not move—it is always the same value.

To help make this clear, let's look at another analogy. A factory that produces composite hockey sticks says that 95% of the composite hockey sticks are perfect, meaning they have no structural defects. But due to tiny imperfections in the manufacturing process, 5% of the sticks do have structural defects. When you buy a composite hockey stick that has been made at this factory, you don't say there is a 95% chance that it's a good stick. It is either "good" or "defective" (unknown to you, of course! If you could know in the store, then store workers wouldn't put out the defective sticks for sale). A confidence interval is similar to a composite hockey stick: it either contains the parameter of interest (the stick is good) or it does not (the stick is defective). The "95% confidence" refers to the "factory" that "manufactures" confidence intervals: 95% of its products are good, 5% are defective.

Our confidence is in the process, not the product.

KEY POINT   Our confidence is in the process that produces confidence intervals, not in any particular interval. It is incorrect to say that a particular confidence interval has a 95% (or any other percent) chance of including the true population parameter. Instead, we say that the *process* that produces intervals captures the true population parameter with a 95% probability.

EXAMPLE 9 Distracted Driving in British Columbia

A 2012 Ipsos poll of 1021 randomly chosen British Columbian drivers with cell phones found that, during the previous six months, 40% had used their cell phones (non-hands-free device) while driving. Ipsos reports that "the margin of error is plus or minus 3.1 percentage points, 19 times out of 20."

QUESTION   State the confidence interval. How would you interpret the confidence interval? What does the "19 times out of 20" mean?

CONCLUSION   We are told that the margin of error is 3.1 percentage points, or 0.031. In interval form, the confidence interval is

$$40\% - 3.1\% \quad \text{to} \quad 40\% + 3.1\%$$
$$36.9\% \quad \text{to} \quad 43.1\%$$

We interpret this to mean that we are "19 times out of 20," or $19/20 = 95\%$, confident that the true proportion of British Columbia drivers who own cell phones and have used them while driving in the past six months is between 36.9% and 43.1%. The 95% confidence level means that if we were to repeat this survey many times, about 95% of them would result in confidence intervals that include the population proportion.

TRY THIS! Exercise 7.55

Example 10 demonstrates the use of confidence intervals to make decisions about population proportions.

EXAMPLE **10** Credit Card Debt

To "carry a balance" means that the amount owing on a credit card is not completely paid off. Polls indicate that about half of all Americans who own credit cards carry a monthly balance. What about the percentage of Canadian credit card holders that carry a monthly balance? Is this the same, lower, or higher when compared to the United States? A poll conducted by Abacus Data in 2013 stated that 30% of Canadians carried a monthly balance on their credit cards. Suppose that out of 1000 randomly chosen Canadian credit card holders, 300 carry a monthly balance.

TECH

QUESTION Find a 95% confidence interval for p, the percentage of Canadian credit card holders who carry a monthly balance.

SOLUTION The best approach is to use technology. Figure 7.16 shows the Minitab output that gives the 95% confidence interval as

$$(0.2716, 0.3284) \quad \text{or} \quad (27.16\% \text{ to } 32.84\%)$$

CI for One Proportion

Sample	X	N	Sample p	95% CI
1	300	1000	0.300000	(0.271597, 0.328403)

▲ **FIGURE 7.16** Minitab output for a confidence interval for the proportion of Canadians who carry a monthly credit card balance.

If you do not have access to statistical technology, then the first step is to find the value of the sample proportion, $\hat{p} = 300/1000 = 0.30$.

The estimated standard deviation is

$$SD_{\text{est}} = \sqrt{\frac{\hat{p}(1 - \hat{p})}{n}} = \sqrt{\frac{(0.30)(0.70)}{1000}} = 0.0144914$$

Because we want a 95% confidence interval, our margin of error is plus or minus 1.96 standard deviations:

$$\text{Margin of error} = 1.96SD_{\text{est}} = 1.96(0.0144914) = 0.028403$$

The interval boundaries are

$$\hat{p} \pm 1.96SD_{est} = 0.30 \pm 0.028403$$

Lower end of interval: $0.30 - 0.028403 = 0.271597$
Upper end of interval: $0.30 + 0.028403 = 0.328403$

This confirms the result we got using technology: a 95% confidence interval is (0.2716 to 0.3284). Notice how this interval *does not* include the value of 0.50, or 50%.

CONCLUSION We are 95% confident that p, the proportion of Canadian credit card holders who carry a monthly balance, is between 0.2716 and 0.3284. It is not plausible for p to be 0.50, as this value is not captured by this confidence interval, meaning that the percentage of Canadians who carry a monthly balance is less than the percentage of Americans who carry a monthly balance.

TRY THIS! Exercise 7.63

SECTION 7.5

Margin of Error and Sample Size for Proportions

In practice, many surveys are taken after the researchers set the margin of error they wish the survey to have. Many surveys and polls we see in the news media use a 95% confidence interval ("accurate to 19 times out of 20" is how it is commonly reported) and a margin of error of around 3 percentage points.

To find the approximate sample size needed to get a margin of error of size m (written as a decimal, not as a percentage), we could use this formula:

$$n = \left(\frac{z^*}{m}\right)^2\left(\frac{1}{4}\right)$$

In this formula, z^* represents the multiplier we use in our confidence interval, chosen from Table 7.6. For instance, for a 95% confidence interval, $z^* = 1.96$, or about 2. For a 90% confidence interval, $z^* = 1.65$.

If we are using a 95% confidence level, this formula simplifies greatly. For a 95% confidence interval, $z^* = 1.96$. Rounding this up to 2.0, we get $(z^*)^2 = 2^2 = 4$, and 4 times $(1/4) = 1$, so the formula becomes

Formula 7.2: $n = \dfrac{1}{m^2}$

Usually this formula will compute a value of n that has a decimal. As a result, we always *round up* to the next integer. This formula gives the minimum sample size needed for a 95% level of confidence and a given margin of error m.

EXAMPLE **11** Finding the Sample Size

Many professional polls use a 95% confidence interval and report a margin of error of 0.03 (3 percentage points).

QUESTION Find the sample size needed in a survey of a large population if the margin of error for a 95% confidence interval must be 0.03 (3 percentage points).

SOLUTION Use Formula 7.2, with $m = 0.03$.

$$n = \frac{1}{0.03^2} = \frac{1}{0.0009} = 1111.11$$

Sample at least 1112 people.

CONCLUSION We must randomly sample 1112 people. Next time you see a poll published in a paper or on a website, check the sample size. You can bet it's around 1000 people.

For example, Ipsos published a survey in May 2012 showing that 36% of Canadians were vaccinated against the flu in the previous year. Ipsos used a sample size of $n = 1019$ to achieve a margin of error of $m = 0.03$.

TRY THIS! Exercise 7.65

CASE STUDY REVISITED

What was wrong with the online survey we discussed at the beginning of the chapter? It indicated that about 66% of people residing in the area the councillor represents believed the ENMAX board of directors was doing a sufficient job. This statistic seemed unreal, given the board's recent allowance of a $4.6 million severance package to its resigned CEO.

This was a volunteer-response survey, a non-scientific way to collect data. The intended population was all residents in the area of the city this councillor represents, about 82,000 people. However, anyone with a computer and internet access could fill out this survey. It was open to people who weren't part of the intended population! Another problem: the councillor discovered that about 500 of the 800 responses came from the Internet Protocol (IP) address that belongs to ENMAX, and that about 82% of these respondents said that the board was doing a sufficient job. Of the remaining 300 respondents who were not ENMAX employees, only about 39% indicated that the board was doing a sufficient job. Perhaps ENMAX employees were encouraged to participate in the survey?

From this survey, it is impossible to find a confidence interval for the true proportion of all area residents who believe that the ENMAX board of directors is doing a sufficient job. The sample proportion is biased because (1) the survey was open to a larger population of people than intended; (2) anyone could respond to this survey, and some people may have responded more than once; and (3) the resulting sample was not random. People who feel strongly about this issue—in this case, employees at the utility it seems—are more likely to participate in such haphazard surveys. The statistical results of surveys like this are meaningless, and any attempt to make statistical inferences from such surveys should not be trusted.

CLASS ACTIVITY

Simple Random Sampling Prevents Bias

GOALS	MATERIALS
In this activity, you'll see how the sampling method affects our estimation of the population proportion.	• A box of Smarties • A blank piece of 8.5″ by 11″ paper • A random number table or other method of obtaining random numbers

ACTIVITY

Smarties are a sugar-coated candy treat, with each Smartie varying in colour.

With your box of Smarties, you will attempt to estimate the percentage of Smarties that are in your box.

You will use two estimation procedures, compare them, and decide which one works better. One method is informal; the other is based on random sampling. Your instructor will give you detailed information about each method.

A box of Smarties has been emptied, with each piece of candy placed in a grid on the blank 8.5″ by 11″ piece of paper in such a way that there are six pieces in a row. Below are the first four rows of one opened box, or 24 candies (your placement will not look exactly like this).

BEFORE THE ACTIVITY

1. What proportion of the candies in the first two rows in Figure A are red?

2. Randomly select 12 of the 24 candies. Calculate the proportion of these candies that are red. How does this differ from the proportion found from the first two rows?

001	002	003	004	005	006
○	○	●	○	○	○
007	008	009	010	011	012
○	●	○	○	○	○
013	014	015	016	017	018
○	○	○	○	○	○
019	020	021	022	023	024
○	○	○	○	○	●

▲ **FIGURE A** The first 24 candies arranged in four rows of six.

AFTER THE ACTIVITY

Your instructor will give you data from the entire class. The data will consist of a list of estimates of the proportion of red candies in a box of Smarties based on the "informal method," and a list based on the simple random sampling method. Make a dotplot of the informal estimates and a second dotplot of the estimates obtained using simple random sampling.

1. Compare the distributions from the two methods. (Comment on the shape, centre, and the spread of the distributions.)

2. Judging on the basis of your comparison of the dotplots, why is simple random sampling preferred over the informal method for collecting data?

This exercise is based on an activity from an INSPIRE workshop, which was based on an activity from Workshop Statistics, © 2004, Dr. Allan Rossman and Dr. Beth Chance, California Polytechnic State University.

CHAPTER REVIEW

Summary of Learning Objectives

1. **What is the difference between a random and a non-random sample?** A random sample differs from a non-random sample in that it involves the random selection of people or objects from a population, with the condition that everyone/thing in what makes up the population has a chance of being chosen. After that, the variable of interest is then measured. Non-random samples such as convenience and volunteer-response samples will produce biased results.

2. **Why does random sampling reduce potential biases in a survey?** Random sampling is an important part of statistical inference methods because it eliminates potential statistical biases by ensuring that a measurement from one sampled person/object is independent of the measurement from a different sampled person/object. This means that the collected data are independent of each other and that the statistics computed from the sample are likely to have no bias.

3. **How is the value of the population proportion estimated from the sample?** The proportion of the random sample that has the particular characteristic, represented by $\hat{p}$, is computed and then used as an estimate of the unknown value of the population parameter p. Because the sample proportion will vary in its value from one sample to the next, is precision can be measured.

4. **What is the Central Limit Theorem and how does it apply to the sample proportion?** The Central Limit Theorem (CLT) applied to the sample proportion tells us that the sample proportion is a random variable whose behaviour is approximately

$$N\left(p, \sqrt{\frac{p(1-p)}{n}}\right)$$

This is used to infer the true value of the population proportion from the proportion of the sample having the particular characteristic.

5. **How is the CLT used to find probabilities associated with the sample proportion?** The CLT says that the sample proportion can be closely modelled by the Normal distribution. When computing probabilities of a random variable that is approximately Normal, the sample proportion is converted to a z-value by subtracting its mean, then dividing this difference by its standard deviation.

For the application of the CLT to be effective, the first step is to make sure that the sample size is large enough. This means that we need the sample size times the sample proportion to be at least 10 and that we need the sample size times (1 minus the sample proportion) to be at least 10.

6. **How is a confidence interval for the population proportion computed?** A confidence interval for the population proportion p is found with:

Formula 7.1: $\hat{p} \pm m$, where $m = z^* \times SD_{est}$

and $SD_{est} = \sqrt{\dfrac{\hat{p}(1-\hat{p})}{n}}$

where

m is the margin of error,
n is the sample size, and
z^* is the multiplier that is chosen to achieve the desired confidence level.

The computed confidence interval may or may not capture the true value of the population proportion. However, we are confident that it will because the method works for 95% of all samples.

5. **When surveying a population, how large should the random sample be?** When designing a survey, we typically choose the margin of error in advance and then find the sample size that will give us this margin of error. A conservative formula for the required sample size is

Formula 7.2: $n = \dfrac{1}{m^2}$ for 95% confidence

Important Terms

Population, *300*	Statistical inference, *300*	Simple random sample (SRS), *304*	Confidence interval, *321*
Parameter, *300*	Biased, *302*	Sampling distribution, *309*	Margin of error, *321*
Census, *300*	Sampling bias, *302*	Bias (accuracy), *310*	Confidence level, *322*
Sample, *300*	Measurement bias, *302*	Precision, *310*	
Statistic, *300*	Voluntary-response bias, *303*	Standard deviation of the sample	
Estimator, *300*	Nonresponse bias, *304*	proportion, *310*	
Estimate, *300*	Convenience sample, *304*	Central Limit Theorem (CLT), *315*	

Sources

Angus Reid. Coffee is an essential component of the morning for most Canadians. http://www.angus-reid.com/polls/45521/coffee-is-anessential-component-of-the-morning-for-most-canadians (accessed November 5, 2012).

Calgary Herald. October 2002.

Cornish, A. 2007. Do polls miss views of young and mobile? National Public Radio. October 1. http://www.npr.org (accessed March 29, 2010).

Canadian Press. 2012. Canadians most proud of universal health care says poll (accessed November 26, 2012).

CBC News. 2010, March 3. Do you think the Canadian national anthem needs change? http://www.cbc.ca/news/pointofview/2010/03/-introcopy-here-do.html (accessed November 6, 2012).

CBC News. Enmax hijacked online survey about company: Alderman. http://www.cbc.ca/news/canada/calgary/enmax-hijacked-onlinesurvey-about-company-alderman-1.987146 (accessed January 4, 2015).

CBC News. Marijuana still preferred drug in Canadian army, while cocaine gains ground. http://www.cbc.ca/news/canada/marijuana-still-preferreddrug-in-canadian-army-while-cocaine-gains-ground-1.2880624 (accessed January 6, 2015).

Diabetes in Canada: Facts and figures from a public health perspective. Public Health Agency of Canada. http://www.phac-aspc.gc.ca/cd-mc/publications/diabetes-diabete/facts-figures-faits-chiffres-2011/highlightssaillants-eng.php (accessed December 4, 2012).

Harris Decima Poll. 2012. Canadian consumer confidence rises. http://www.harrisdecima.ca/news/releases/201206/1425-canadian-consumerconfidence-rises (accessed December 1, 2012).

Huffington Post. Worst prime minister: Harper most popular choice in new poll of leaders since 1968. http://www.huffingtonpost.ca/2012/09/25/worst-prime-minister-harper-poll_n_1913250.html (accessed January 5, 2015).

Ipsos Poll. 2012. Canada's first flu report: The results are in: Canada fails the flu test! http://www.ipsos-na.com/news-polls/pressrelease.aspx?id=5624 (accessed November 30, 2012).

Ipsos Poll. 2012. Four in ten still using cell phone while driving. http://www.ipsos-na.com/news-polls/pressrelease.aspx?id=5733 (accessed November 26, 2012).

Ipsos Poll. 2013. Two in ten Canadians have a tattoo. http://www.ipsos-na.com/news-polls/pressrelease.aspx?id=5490 (accessed January 2, 2015).

Lethbridge Herald. 2001, May 21.

New York Times. 1993, April 20. 1 in 5 in new survey express some doubt about the Holocaust.

Simpson, S. 2012. Private communication.

Statistics Canada. 2014, April. Residential telephone service survey, 2013. http://www.statcan.gc.ca/daily-quotidien/140623/dq140623a-eng.htm (accessed September 13, 2015).

Statistics Canada. Labour Force Survey. http://www.statcan.gc.ca/pub/81-004-x/2010004/article/11360-eng.htm (accessed December 1, 2012).

Strategic Counsel. 2011. Assessment of Canada's banks. http://www.cba.ca/en/media-room/50-backgrounders-on-banking-issues/123-credit-cards (accessed November 26, 2012).

SECTION EXERCISES

SECTION 7.1

TRY 7.1 Parameter vs. Statistic (Example 1) Explain the difference between a parameter and a statistic.

7.2 Sample vs. Census Explain the difference between a sample and a census. Every five years, Statistics Canada takes a census. What does this mean?

7.3 $\bar{x}$ vs. μ Two symbols are used for the mean: μ and $\bar{x}$.
   a. Which represents a parameter and which a statistic?
   b. In determining the mean age of all students at your school, you survey 30 students and find the mean of their ages. Is this mean $\bar{x}$ or μ?

7.4 $\bar{x}$ vs. μ The mean GPA of all 5000 students at a small university is 2.78. A sample of 50 GPAs from this school has a mean of 2.93. Which number is μ and which is $\bar{x}$?

7.5 Ages of Prime Ministers Suppose you knew the age of each Canadian prime minister when he/she became prime minister for the first time. Could you use that data to make inferences about ages of past prime ministers? Why or why not?

7.6 Heights of Basketball Team Suppose you find *all* the heights of the members of the men's basketball team at your school. Could you use those data to make inferences about heights of all men at your school? Why or why not?

7.7 Sample vs. Census You are receiving a large shipment of batteries and want to test their lifetimes. Explain why you would want to test a sample of batteries rather than the entire population.

7.8 Sampling Meat Products You are receiving a big shipment of processed meat from a large meat processing plant, and you want to check if the meat in the shipment contains *E. coli* bacteria. You check a few packages of meat, ones that are easy to get at in the truck that has the shipment. Would your findings from this sampling method be representative? Explain.

7.9 Sampling with and Without Replacement Explain the difference between sampling with replacement and sampling without replacement. Suppose you have the names of 10 students, each written on a 3 by 5 notecard, and you want to select two names. Describe both procedures.

7.10 Simple Random Sampling Is simple random sampling usually done with or without replacement?

TRY 7.11 Finding a Random Sample (Example 2) You need to select a simple random sample of four from eight friends who will participate in a survey. Assume that the friends are numbered 1, 2, 3, 4, 5, 6, 7, and 8.

Select four friends, using the two lines of numbers in the next column from a random number table.

Read off each digit, skipping any digit not assigned to one of the friends. The sampling is without replacement, meaning that you cannot select the same person twice. Write down the numbers chosen. The first person is number 7.

0 7 0 3 3   7 5 2 5 0   3 4 5 4 6
7 5 2 9 8   3 3 8 9 3   6 4 4 8 7

Which four friends are chosen?

7.12 Finding a Random Sample You need to select a simple random sample of two from six friends who will participate in a survey. Assume that the friends are numbered 1, 2, 3, 4, 5, and 6.

Use technology to select your random sample. Indicate what numbers you obtained and how you interpreted them.

If technology is not available, use the line from a random number table that corresponds to the day of the month on which you were born. For example, if you were born on the fifth day of any month, you would use line 05. Show the digits in the line and explain how you interpreted them.

7.13 Criticize the Sampling Billy is interested in whether a proposal to raise tuition fees for students taking professional programs (Engineering, Law, Business) will be supported by students. He goes to the law library at the university and takes a poll of 100 students, of which 70 are against the proposed tuition-fee hike. Since 70% of these students are against the proposed increase, Billy believes that the proposal will not pass. Is Billy's inference correct? Explain.

7.14 Criticize the Sampling Molly supports a ban on smoking in all public places. She attends a local gym and asks everyone who is there working out if smoking in all public places should be banned. Because 85% of the people she asks supports a ban on smoking in all public places, she infers that around 85% of all Canadians would support such a ban. Is Molly's inference correct? Explain.

7.15 Bias In 2003, shortly after the U.S. invasion of Iraq, www.TimeEurope.com posed a question to European readers of *Time* magazine on the internet: "Who really poses the greatest danger to world peace: Iraq, North Korea, or the United States?" The site received 706,842 responses: 6.7% said North Korea, 6.3% Iraq, and 86.9% the United States. Identify the population, and explain why the results might not reflect true opinions in the population.

7.16 Polling When men and women live together, women are more likely to answer the telephone. When polling agencies call homes, they often ask to speak to the adult with the most recent birthday. Give at least one reason why polling agencies take this approach.

TRY 7.17 Questionnaire Response (Example 3) A teacher at a community college sent out questionnaires to evaluate how well the administrators were doing their jobs. All teachers received questionnaires, but only 10% returned them. Most of the returned questionnaires contained negative comments about the administrators. Explain how an administrator could dismiss the negative findings of the report.

7.18 Survey on Social Security A phone survey asked whether Old Age Pensions should be continued or abandoned immediately. Only landlines (not cell phones) were called. Do you think this would introduce bias? Explain.

7.19 Random Sampling? If you walked around your school campus and asked people you met how many books they were carrying, would you be obtaining a random sample? Explain.

7.20 Biased Sample? You want to find the mean weight of the students at your school. You calculate the mean weight of a sample of members of the football team. Is this method biased? If so, would the mean of the sample be larger or smaller than the true population mean for the whole school? Explain.

7.21 Views on Differential Tuition Fees Many colleges and universities charge more tuition for students who are in professional programs, such as Nursing, Engineering, Law, and Business. To measure support for differential tuition fees, a student asked a question two ways:

1. With persuasion: "Students in programs such as Engineering, Law, and Business typically get high-paying jobs after they graduate. Do you support or oppose students in these programs paying more tuition because they have higher earning potential?"

2. Without persuasion: "Do you support or oppose students in these programs paying more tuition?"

Here is a breakdown of the student's data.

Men

	With Persuasion	Without Persuasion
Support	21	8
Oppose	4	17

Women

	With Persuasion	Without Persuasion
Support	20	12
Oppose	4	12

a. What percentage of those persuaded oppose differential tuition fees?

b. What percentage of those not persuaded oppose differential tuition fees?

c. Compare the percentages in parts a and b. Is this what you expected? Explain.

7.22 Views on Differential Tuition Fees Use the data given in Exercise 7.21.

Make the two given tables into one table by combining men supporting differential fees into one group, men opposing them into another, women supporting them into a third group, and women opposing them into a fourth group. Show your two-way table.

The student who collected the data could have made the results misleading by trying persuasion more often on one gender than on the other, but she didn't do this. She used persuasion on 24 of 48 women (50%) and on 25 of 50 men (50%).

a. What percentage of women oppose differential tuition fees? What percentage of men oppose them?

b. On the basis of these results, if you were campaigning against differential tuition fees, would you seek out men or women to help your cause?

SECTION 7.2

7.23 Targets: Bias or Lack of Precision?

a. If a rifleman's gunsight is adjusted incorrectly, he might shoot bullets consistently close to 60 centimetres left of the bull's-eye target. Draw a sketch of the target with the bullet holes. Does this show lack of precision or bias?

b. Draw a second sketch of the target if the shots are both unbiased and precise (have little variation).

The rifleman's aim is not perfect, so your sketches should show more than one bullet hole.

7.24 Targets: Bias or Lack of Precision?, Again

a. If a rifleman's gunsight is adjusted correctly but he has shaky arms, the bullets might be scattered widely around the bull's-eye target. Draw a sketch of the target with the bullet holes. Does this show variation (lack of precision) or bias?

b. Draw a second sketch of the target if the shots are unbiased and have precision (little variation).

The rifleman's aim is not perfect, so your sketches should show more than one bullet hole.

7.25 Bias? Suppose that, when taking a random sample of 4 from 123 women, you get a mean height of only 152 centimetres. The procedure may have been biased. What else could have caused this small mean?

7.26 Bias? Four women selected from a photo of 123 were found to have a sample mean height of 180 centimetres. The population mean for all 123 women was 164 centimetres. Is this evidence that the sampling procedure was biased? Explain.

7.27 Proportion of Odd Digits A large collection of one-digit random numbers should have about 50% odd and 50% even digits because five of the ten digits are odd (1, 3, 5, 7, and 9) and five are even (0, 2, 4, 6, and 8).

a. Find the proportion of odd-numbered digits in the following lines from a random number table. Count carefully.

5 5 1 8 5   7 4 8 3 4   8 1 1 7 2
8 9 2 8 1   4 8 1 3 4   7 1 1 8 5

b. Does the proportion found in part a represent $\hat{p}$ (the sample proportion) or p (the population proportion)?

c. Find the error in this estimate, the difference between $\hat{p}$ and p (or $\hat{p} - p$).

7.28 Proportion of Odd Digits 1, 3, 5, 7, and 9 are odd and 0, 2, 4, 6, and 8 are even. Consider a 30-digit line from a random number table.

a. How many of the 30 digits would you expect to be odd, on average?

b. If you actually counted, would you get exactly the number you predicted in part a? Explain.

TRY 7.29 Smarties (Example 4) According to Nestlé, packages of Smarties contain 18% blue candies. Suppose we examine 100 randomly selected candies.

a. What percentage of the sample should we expect to be blue candies?

b. What is the standard deviation?

c. Use your answers to fill in the blanks:
We expect ____% of blue candies, give or take ____%.

7.30 Random Letters Samuel Morse suggested in the nineteenth century that the letter T made up 9% of the English language. Assume that this is still correct. A random sample of 1000 letters is taken from a large, randomly selected book and the T's are counted.

a. What value should we expect for our sample percentage of T's?

b. Calculate the standard deviation.

c. Use your answers to fill in the blanks:
We expect ____% T's, give or take ____%.

7.31 What Is the Proportion of Seniors? A population of university students is taking an advanced math class. In the class are three third-year students ("juniors") and two fourth-year students ("seniors"). Using numbers 1, 2, and 3 to represent juniors and 4 and 5 to represent seniors, sample without replacement. Draw a sample of two people four times (once in each of parts a, b, c, and d), and then fill in the following table.

a. Use the first line (reprinted here) from the random number table to select your sample of two. (The selections are underlined.)

0 **2** 7 7 9   7 2 6 **4** 5   3 2 6 9 9   8 6 0 0 9

Report the percentage of seniors in the sample. (Count the number of 4s and 5s and divide by the sample size.)

b. Use the next line to select your sample of two.

3 1 8 6 7   8 5 8 7 2   9 1 4 3 0   4 5 5 5 4

Report the percentage of seniors in the sample.

c. Use the next line to select your sample of two.

0 7 0 **3** 3   7 5 2 5 0   3 4 5 4 6   7 5 2 9 8

Report the percentage of seniors in the sample.

d. Use the last line to select your sample of two.

0 9 0 8 4   9 8 9 4 8   0 9 5 4 1   8 0 6 2 3

Report the percentage of seniors in the sample.

e. Fill in the rest of the table below, showing the results of the four samples:

Repetition	p (population proportion of seniors)	$\hat{p}$ (sample proportion of seniors)	Error: $\hat{p} - p$
1 (from part a)	$2/5 = 0.4$	$1/2 = 0.5$	$0.5 - 0.4 = 0.1$
2 (from part b)			
3			
4			

7.32 Simulation From a very large population (essentially infinite), of which half are men and half are women, you take a random sample, with replacement. Use the following random number table and assume that each single digit represents the selection of one person; the odd numbers (1, 3, 5, 7, 9) represent women and the even numbers (0, 2, 4, 6, 8) men.

a. Start on the left side of the top line (with 118) and count 10 people. What percentage of the sample will be men?

1 1 8 4 8   8 0 8 0 9   2 5 8 1 8   3 8 8 5 7
2 3 8 1 1   8 0 9 0 2   8 5 7 5 7   3 3 9 6 3
9 3 0 7 6   3 9 9 5 0   2 9 6 5 8   0 7 5 3 0

b. Start in the middle of the second line (with 857) and count 20 people. What percentage of the sample will be men?

c. If you were to repeat parts a and b many times, which sample would typically come closer to 50%—the sample of 10 or the sample of 20? Why?

SECTION 7.3

7.33 Smarties (Example 5) Return to Exercise 7.29 and find the approximate probability that a random sample of 100 candies will contain 24% or more blue candies.

7.34 Random Letters Return to Exercise 7.30 and find the approximate probability that a random sample of 1000 letters will contain 8.1% or fewer T's.

TRY 7.35 Jury Selection (Example 6) Juries should have a racial makeup similar to that of the community from which they're chosen.

According to Statistics Canada (2001), about 10% of the residents of Winnipeg are First Nations people. A Winnipeg court randomly selects 100 Winnipeggers to participate in a jury pool.

Use the Central Limit Theorem (and the Empirical Rule) to find the approximate probability that the proportion of available First Nation jurors is beyond two standard deviations from the population value of 0.10.

Keep in mind that the conditions for using the CLT are satisfied because (1) the sample is random, (2) the population is more than 10 times 100, and (3) n times p is 10, and n times $(1-p)$ is 90, both being at least 10.

7.36 Mercury in Freshwater Fish According to *The New York Times* (August 19, 2009), 25% of freshwater fish have mercury levels that are beyond safe levels for human consumption. Suppose a fish market has 250 fish that we can consider as a random sample from the population of edible freshwater fish.

Use the Central Limit Theorem (and the Empirical Rule) to find the approximate probability that the market will have a proportion of fish with beyond-human-consumption levels of mercury that are more than two standard deviations above 0.25.

You can use the CLT because (1) the fish were randomly sampled, (2) the population is more than 10 times 250, and (3) n times p is 62.5, and n times $(1 - p)$ is 187.5, both being at least 10.

TRY 7.37 Law School Graduation and Articling (Example 7)
g According to the Law Society of Upper Canada (Ontario), 15% of law school graduates in Ontario did not find an articling position (*Law Times*, May 7, 2012). A random sample of 70 recent law school graduates in Ontario was taken. Find the approximate probability that at least 12% of these graduates will not find an articling position. (In other words, find the probability that at least about 8 of the 50 will not find an articling position.) *See page 341 for guidance.*

7.38 Single Occupant Vehicles and Traffic The City of Calgary reported in May 2012 that the percentage of single-occupancy vehicles (SOVs) entering the downtown core during morning rush hour is 80%. Two hundred vehicles entering the downtown core early one morning are randomly surveyed. On any given weekday, the city's traffic department reports that about 20,000 vehicles enter the downtown core during peak morning hours.

Find the probability that of the 200 vehicles surveyed, the percentage of SOVs is more than 85%.

7.39 Renting Chairs for a Meeting You have sent out 4000 invitations to hear a speaker, and you must rent chairs for the people who come. In the past, usually about 8% of the people invited have come to hear the speaker.

a. On average, what proportion of those invited should we expect to attend?

b. Suppose you assume that 8.5% of those invited will attend, and so you rent 340 chairs (because 0.085 times 4000 is 340). What is the approximate probability that more than 8.5% of those invited will show up and you will not have enough chairs? Refer to the TI-83/84 output given. Recall that this gives the Normal cumulative probability in the following format:

Normalcdf (left boundary, right boundary, mean, standard deviation)

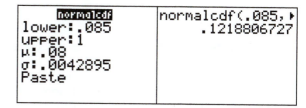

Draw a well-labelled sketch of the Normal curve, and shade the appropriate region to represent the probability.

c. What is the approximate probability that more than 9% of the 4000 invited will show up? How many chairs would you have to rent if exactly 9% of those invited attended?

d. Why is your answer to part c smaller than your answer to part b? Draw a Normal probability distribution with a centre at a proportion of 0.08 and vertical lines at about 0.085 and 0.090 so that you can visualize the size of the right-tail area.

7.40 High School Diplomas Statistics Canada reported in 2011 that 90% of Canadians aged 20–24 have a high school diploma.

a. Suppose you took a random sample of 2000 Canadians between the ages of 20 and 24. What proportion would you expect to have a high school diploma? How many young Canadians is this? What proportion would you expect not to have a high school diploma? How many young Canadians is this? Are both numbers at least equal to 10, as required by the Central Limit Theorem?

b. If you took a random sample of 2000 Canadians between the ages of 20 and 24, find the probability that 91% or more will have earned a high school diploma. Refer to Example A in the TechTips for one approach to this question.

7.41 Passing a Test by Guessing A true/false test has 40 questions. A passing grade is 60% or more correct answers.

a. What is the probability that a person will guess correctly on one true/false question?

b. What is the probability that a person will guess incorrectly on one question?

c. Find the approximate probability that a person who is just guessing will pass the test.

d. If a similar test were given with multiple-choice questions with four choices for each question, would the approximate probability of passing the test by guessing be higher or lower than the approximate probability of passing the true/false test? Why?

7.42 Gender: Randomly Chosen? A large community college district has 1000 teachers, of whom 50% are men and 50% are women. In this district, administrators are promoted from among the teachers. There are currently 50 administrators, and 70% of these administrators are men.

a. If administrators are selected randomly from the faculty, what is the approximate probability that the percentage of male administrators will be 70% or more?

b. If administrators are selected randomly from the faculty, what is the approximate probability that the percentage of female administrators will be 30% or less?

c. How are part a and part b related?

d. Do your answers suggest that it is reasonable to believe the claim that the administrators have been selected randomly from the teachers? Answer yes or no, and explain your answer.

SECTION 7.4

7.43 Canadian Military and Drugs According to a 2013 report on drug use by Canadian military members, of the 4198 participants who submitted to a drug test, 223 were detected as having used marijuana. Using the output given, find a 95% confidence interval for the proportion of all people in the Canadian military who use marijuana. Copy the statement that follows, filling in the blanks.

I am 95% confident that the proportion of all people in the Canadian military who use marijuana is somewhere between _____ and _____.

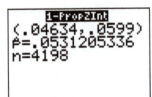

7.44 Drug to Prevent Heart Attacks In June of 2009, a Pew poll asked 1005 people: Which over-the-counter drug do doctors recommend to help prevent heart attacks? Is it aspirin, cortisone, or antacids? (Options were rotated.)

Of 1005, 914 correctly chose aspirin. Report a 95% confidence interval for the population proportion of those who know the correct answer. Use the output provided to find the interval. Copy the statement below, inserting the left and right endpoints of the interval.

I am 95% confident that the proportion of all people who know that aspirin is used to prevent heart attacks is between _____ and _____.

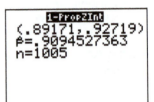

7.45 State of the Economy A 2012 Harris-Decima telephone poll of 2000 Canadians found that 920 of the respondents believe there will be good times financially for Canada in the next five years.

a. What percentage of the sample believe there will be good times financially for Canada in the next five years?

b. Report a 95% confidence interval for the population percentage who believe there will be good times financially for Canada in the next five years. Refer to the Minitab output, and round the boundaries sensibly.

Sample	X	N	Sample p	95% CI
1	920	2000	0.460000	(0.438157, 0.481843)

7.46 Best Prime Minister Since 1968 A 2012 Ipsos poll of 1510 adults asked, "Who do you think is the best prime minister since 1968? Harper, Martin, Chrétien, Campbell, Mulroney, Trudeau, or Clark?" The order was rotated to avoid biasing the response. Of 1510 surveyed, 574 chose Trudeau. Refer to the Minitab output.

Sample	X	N	Sample p	95% CI
1	574	1510	0.380132	(0.355649, 0.404616)

a. What percentage of the respondents chose Trudeau?

b. From the Minitab output, report a 95% confidence interval for the population percentage who said that Trudeau has been the best prime minister since 1968.

7.47 Voting A random sample of likely voters showed that 55% planned to vote for Candidate X, with a margin of error of 2 percentage points and with 95% confidence.

a. Use a carefully worded sentence to report the 95% confidence interval for the percentage of voters who plan to vote for Candidate X.

b. Is there evidence that Candidate X could lose?

c. Suppose the survey was taken on the streets of Toronto and the candidate was running for prime minister. Explain how that would affect your conclusion.

7.48 Voting A random sample of likely voters showed that 49% planned to support Measure X. The margin of error is 3 percentage points with a 95% confidence level.

a. Using a carefully worded sentence, report the 95% confidence interval for the percentage of voters who plan to support Measure X.

b. Is there evidence that Measure X will fail?

c. Suppose the survey was taken on the streets of Halifax and Measure X was province-wide. Explain how that would affect your conclusion.

7.49 Estimating the Proportion of Odd Digits (with Given Standard Deviation)

a. Find the proportion of odd-numbered digits in the following lines from a random number table. Count carefully; circle them!

55185   74834   81172

89281   48134   71185

b. The estimated standard deviation for the sample proportion of odd digits is 0.090. Find the margin of error for a 95% confidence interval for the proportion of odd digits in the entire random number table by multiplying the estimated standard deviation by 1.96.

c. Find a 95% confidence interval for the population proportion of odd-numbered digits in the entire random number table by adding the margin of error to the sample proportion to find the upper boundary and subtracting it to find the lower boundary.

d. The estimated standard deviation is 0.090. Find an 80% confidence interval for the population proportion of odd-numbered digits. For calculations by hand, multiply the estimated standard deviation by 1.28 to find the margin of error, since z^* for 80% confidence is 1.28.

e. Find a 99% confidence interval for the population proportion of odd-numbered digits. For calculations by hand, z^* for 99% is 2.58.

f. State which interval is widest and which is narrowest. Explain why.

7.50 Proportion of Odd Digits (with Given Standard Deviation)

a. Find the proportion of odd-numbered digits in the following lines from a random number table, and then find a 95% confidence interval for the population proportion of odd-numbered digits in the entire random number table. Count carefully!

87964   43751   80971

50613   51441   30505

b. The estimated standard deviation is 0.090. Find an 80% confidence interval for the population proportion of odd-numbered digits in the full random number table. For calculations by hand, z^* for 80% is 1.28.

c. Find a 99% confidence interval for the population proportion of odd-numbered digits. For calculations by hand, z^* for 99% is 2.58.

d. State which interval is wider and which is narrower. Explain why.

TRY 7.51 High School Diplomas (Example 8) In a simple random sample of 1500 Canadians aged 20–24, 1350 had earned a high school diploma.

a. What is the estimated standard deviation for the sample percentage of all Canadians aged 20–24 who earned a high school diploma?

b. Find the margin of error, using a 95% confidence level, for estimating the proportion of all Canadians aged 20–24 who earned a high school diploma.

c. Report the 95% confidence interval for the proportion of all Canadians aged 20–24 who earned a high school diploma.

d. Suppose that in the past, 85% of all Canadians aged 20–24 had earned a high school diploma. Does the confidence interval you found in part c support or refute the claim that the proportion of Canadians aged 20–24 who have earned a high school diploma has increased? Explain.

7.52 Diabetes In a simple random sample of 1200 people from the First Nations population in Canada, the proportion with diabetes was found to be 0.175 (or 17.5%, 210 out of 1200).

a. What is the estimated standard deviation for the sample percentage of First Nations people who have diabetes?

b. Find the margin of error, using a 95% confidence level, for estimating this proportion.

c. Report the 95% confidence interval for the proportion of all First Nation people in Canada who have diabetes.

d. Statistics Canada reported in 2009 that 6.8%, or 0.068, of non-First Nations Canadians have diabetes. Does the confidence interval you found in part c support or refute the claim that the proportion of First Nations people in Canada who have diabetes is higher than the proportion of non–First Nations people? Explain.

7.53 Dreaming in Colour In a 2003 study on dreaming, an investigator attempted to replicate an experiment done by Middleton in 1942 (Schwitzgebel, *Perceptual and Motor Skills* 2003). In the study from 2003, 92 of 113 people said they dream in colour.

a. What percentage of people in 2003 said they dreamed in colour?

b. Find a 95% confidence interval for the proportion who dreamed in colour in 2003. The margin of error is 0.0717.

c. In the study from 1942, 29.24% of people reported dreaming in colour. Does the interval for the data from 2003 capture 29.24%? Is 29.24% plausible as the 2003 population percentage? Explain.

7.54 Morning Coffee Fix In a May 2012 Angus poll of 1019 randomly chosen Canadian adults, 62%, or 0.62, said that they needed to have a cup of coffee after waking up. The margin of error is 3.1 percentage points.

a. Assuming that the level of confidence is 95%, find a 95% confidence interval for the proportion of all Canadian adults that need to have a cup of coffee after waking up.

b. Suppose you and your friends are sitting around a table having a cup of coffee, and one says to you, "I think two-thirds (67%) of Canadians need to have a cup of coffee after waking up." Does the confidence interval in part a support or refute your friend's statement? Explain.

TRY 7.55 Understanding the Meaning of Confidence Levels: 90% (Example 9) Each student in a class of 40 was randomly assigned one line of a random number table. Each student then counted the odd-numbered digits in a 30-digit line. (Remember that 0, 2, 4, 6, and 8 are even.)

a. *On average*, in the list of 30 digits, how many odd-numbered digits would each student find?

b. If each student found a 90% confidence interval for the percentage of odd-numbered digits in the entire random number table, how many intervals (out of 40) would you expect *not* to capture the population percentage of 50%?

7.56 Understanding the Meaning of Confidence Levels: 80% Each student in a class of 30 was assigned one random line of a random number table. Each student then counted the even-numbered digits in a 30-digit line.

a. *On average*, in the list of 30 digits, how many even-numbered digits would each student find?

b. If each student found an 80% confidence interval for the percentage of even-numbered digits, how many intervals (out of 30) would you expect *not* to capture 50%? Explain how you arrived at your answer.

7.57 Percentage of Female MPs In May 2011, of the 308 members of Parliament, 76 were female. Find a 95% confidence interval for the proportion of all MPs (in May 2011) who were female, or explain why you should not find a confidence interval for the proportion of MPs who were female in May 2011.

7.58 Closest Canadian Federal Election In the 1972 federal election, 3,717,804 Canadians voted for Pierre Trudeau (Liberal); 3,388,980 voted for Robert Stanfield (of Stanfield's underwear fame, PC); 1,725,719 voted for David Lewis (NDP); and 730,759 voted for Réal Caouette (Social Credit). (www.elections.ca)

a. What percentage of voters chose Trudeau?

b. Would it be appropriate to find a confidence interval for the proportion of all voters who chose Trudeau? Why or why not?

7.59 Relevance of Newspapers to Young Canadians The Canadian Media Research Consortium surveyed 561 randomly chosen Canadians between the ages of 18 and 34, finding that 84 prefer to access news and information by way of printed newspaper.

a. Find the proportion of Canadians between the ages of 18 and 34 sampled who prefer to access news and information by way of printed newspaper.

b. Find a 95% confidence interval for the proportion of all Canadians between the ages of 18 and 34 who prefer to access news and information by way of printed newspaper.

c. Find a 90% confidence interval for the proportion of all Canadians between the ages of 18 and 34 who prefer to access news and information by way of printed newspaper.

d. Which interval, the one in part b or part c, is wider, and why?

7.60 Human Cloning In a Gallup poll, 441 of 507 adults said it was "morally wrong" to clone humans.

a. What proportion of the respondents believed it is morally wrong to clone humans?

b. Find a 95% confidence interval for the population proportion who believed it is morally wrong to clone humans. Assume that Gallup used a simple random sample.

c. Find an 90% confidence interval (using a z^* of 1.65 if you are calculating by hand).

d. Which interval is wider, and why?

7.61 Desire to Lose Weight In a Gallup poll from November 2008, 525 of 1009 Canadian adults surveyed said they wanted to lose weight.

a. What percentage of the sample wanted to lose weight?

b. Find a 95% confidence interval for the proportion of people in the population who wanted to lose weight.

c. Would a 99% confidence interval be wider or narrower?

7.62 Support for Nuclear Energy Some people fear the use of nuclear energy because of potential accidents. However, an Innovative Research Group poll in 2012 indicated that 42% of men supported the use of nuclear energy to produce electricity. The sample size was 626.

a. In this poll, how many men supported the use of nuclear energy?

b. Report a 95% confidence interval for the proportion of all men in Canada who support the use of nuclear energy.

c. Would a 90% interval be wider or narrower?

TRY 7.63 Do People Think Astrology Is Scientific? (Example 10) In the 2008 General Social Survey, people were asked their opinions on astrology—whether it was very scientific, somewhat scientific, or not at all scientific. Of the 1438 who responded, 74 said astrology was very scientific.

a. Find the proportion of people in the survey who believe astrology is very scientific.

b. Find a 95% confidence interval for the population proportion with this belief.

c. Suppose a TV news anchor said that 5% of people in the general population think astrology is very scientific. Would you say that is plausible? Explain your answer.

7.64 Do People Think the Sun Goes around the Earth? In the 2008 General Social Survey, people were asked whether they thought the sun went around Earth or vice versa. Of 1381 people, 310 thought the sun went around Earth.

a. What proportion of people in the survey believed the sun went around Earth?

b. Find a 95% confidence interval for the proportion of all people with this belief.

c. Suppose a scientist said that 30% of people in the general population believe the sun goes around Earth. Using the confidence interval, would you say that was plausible? Explain your answer.

SECTION 7.5

TRY 7.65 Voters' Poll (Example 11) A polling agency wants to determine the size of a random sample needed to estimate the percentage of votes that Candidate X will receive in the next city council election in a mid-sized city. The estimate should have a margin of error of no more than 1.5 percentage points at a 95% level of confidence.

a. How large a sample should the agency take? Because a 95% interval is desired, use the shortcut formula: $n = \dfrac{1}{m^2}$. Recall that for this formula, the margin of error must be in decimal form.

b. Would a 1% margin of error require a larger or a smaller sample than that in part a?

c. If the degree of confidence were lowered to 90%, with the margin of error no more than 1.5%, would that require a larger or a smaller sample size than the result for part a?

7.66 Poll of Voters A polling agency is deciding how many voters to poll.

a. The agency wants to estimate the percentage of voters in favour of extending tax cuts, and it wants to provide a margin of error of no more than 1.8 percentage points. Using 95% confidence, how many respondents must the agency poll?

b. If the margin of error is to be no more than 1.7%, with 95% confidence, should the sample be larger or smaller than that determined in part a? Explain your reasoning.

c. If the degree of confidence were lowered to 90%, with the margin of error no more than 1.8%, would that require a larger or a smaller sample size than the result for part a?

7.67 Ratio of Sample Sizes Find the sample size required for a margin of error of 3 percentage points, and then find one for a margin of error of 1.5 percentage points; for both, use 95% confidence. Find the ratio of the larger sample size to the smaller sample size. To reduce the margin of error to half, what do you need to multiply the sample size by?

7.68 Ratio of Sample Sizes Find the sample size required for a margin of error of 4 percentage points, and then find one for a margin of error of 1 percentage point; for both, use 95% confidence. Find the ratio of the larger sample size to the smaller sample size. To reduce the margin of error to one-quarter of what it was, what do you need to multiply the sample size by?

CHAPTER REVIEW EXERCISES

7.69 Heart Attacks and Exposure to Traffic In 2004, *The New England Journal of Medicine* published a study of Germans who had suffered heart attacks and survived. Within the first 24 hours of the heart attack, the 691 subjects were interviewed about what they were doing before the heart attack. Of the 691 subjects, 515 reported exposure to traffic within an hour prior to the heart attack. Most of these people had been travelling in cars or trucks, although some had used public transportation and some had been riding motorcycles.

a. What percentage of people had been exposed to traffic?

b. Find a 95% confidence interval for the percentage of all heart attack victims exposed to traffic.

c. Can you conclude that traffic definitely causes heart attacks? Why or why not?

7.70 Bariatric Surgery and Diabetes A study published in *JAMA* in 2004 examined past results of other studies on bariatric surgery. Bariatric surgery is done to reduce the size of the stomach in various ways. It is typically used only on obese patients, and one form of surgery had a 1% mortality rate (death rate) caused by the surgery. However, in the studies reporting on the effect of this surgery on diabetes, 1417 of 1846 diabetic patients recovered completely from diabetes after surgery. These patients no longer needed diabetes medication such as insulin.

a. Find the percentage of patients who recovered from diabetes.

b. Find a 95% confidence interval for the percentage of recovery from diabetes.

c. If you had a morbidly obese relative with diabetes, what would you tell him or her about bariatric surgery? Explain.

7.71–7.72 Polls: Sample Size and Margin of Error In June 2012 the *National Post* ran an article about Canadians being able to buy private insurance for all forms of medically necessary treatment (such as cancer care and heart surgery), which could then be accessed outside the public health care system. The article cited a June 2012 Ipsos poll about Canadians' opinions of this practice, and included the following Ipsos statement about its survey methods:

Results based on a simple random sample of 1101 Canadians would have an estimated margin of error of 3.0 percentage points, 19 times out of 20 (or 95% confidence).

7.71 Verify the statement by calculation, and find the margin of error from the sample size. Round your margin of error to the nearest whole percentage.

7.72 Suppose that only 500 Canadians comprised the simple random sample reported in this poll. What would be the survey's margin of error? (Use 95% confidence.)

7.73 Canadians' Opinion on Supplemental Health Insurance An Ipsos poll of 1101 Canadian adults (Exercise 7.71) asked the following question.

To what extent do you support the following: Canadians being allowed to buy private health insurance for all forms of medically necessary treatment that can be obtained outside the current system.

Of the 1101 respondents, 838 supported the idea of being able to purchase private health insurance for all forms of medically necessary treatment that could be obtained outside the current system.

a. What percentage of Canadians sampled supported the ability to purchase private health insurance to access medically necessary treatment available outside the current public system?

b. Find and interpret a 95% confidence interval for the percentage of Canadians who support being able to purchase private health insurance for all forms of medically necessary treatment that could be obtained outside the current system.

c. Is it plausible that more than two-thirds of all Canadians share the same feelings about being able to buy private health insurance?

d. Suppose the sample size were 419, or half the size. Would the percentage of Canadians who supported the ability to purchase private health insurance be the same as or different from the percentage in part a? Would the interval be wider or narrower? If you don't know, try it!

* 7.74 Polls: Canadians, Holiday Shopping Habits In a November 2012 Strategic Counsel survey of 1000 randomly chosen adult Canadians, 352 said that they would "self-gift" (buy themselves a Christmas present).

a. What percentage of the sample said they would self-gift?

b. Find and interpret a 95% confidence interval for the percentage of Canadians who would buy themselves a gift in the 2012 holiday season.

c. Is it plausible that more than one-third of all Canadians would self-gift in 2012?

d. Suppose that the sample size were 2000, twice as large, and that the number who said they would self-gift was 704, also twice as large. Would the percentage of Canadians who said they would self-gift be the same as or different from the percentage reported in part a? Would the interval be wider or narrower? If you don't know, try it!

e. Referring to your answer in part d, does increasing the sample size from 1000 to 2000 increase the precision of the 95% confidence interval? Why or why not? Explain.

7.75 Buying Private Health Insurance: Ontario and British Columbia In the Ipsos poll (Exercise 7.73), 363 of the Canadians sampled were from Ontario. Of these, 307 responded that they supported being allowed to buy private health insurance. Let's consider a population of only Ontario residents.

a. What percentage of Ontario residents sampled said they support being allowed to buy private health insurance?

b. Find and interpret a 95% confidence interval for the percentage of Ontario residents who support being allowed to buy private health insurance.

c. The same poll indicated that the proportion of all British Columbia residents who support being allowed to buy private health insurance is 0.70. Does the interval in part b indicate that there is a difference in the percentage of British Columbians and the percentage of Ontarians? Why or why not?

7.76 Buying Private Health Insurance and Household Income The Ipsos poll (Exercise 7.73) randomly selected 189 individuals with an annual income exceeding $100,000. Of these people, 143 said they support being allowed to buy private health insurance to access medically necessary treatments.

a. What percentage of sampled Canadians with an annual income exceeding $100,000 support being able to buy private health insurance?

b. Find and interpret a 95% confidence interval for the percentage of all Canadians having an annual income exceeding $100,000 who support being able to buy private health insurance.

c. Now consider a separate population made up of Canadians with an annual income of between $40,000 and $60,000. Do you think this population's percentage of those who support buying private health care insurance will differ from that of Canadians with an income exceeding $100,000? Why or why not?

d. A 95% confidence interval for the percentage of the population in part (c) who supports being able to buy private health insurance to access medically necessary treatments available outside the current system has a lower boundary of 75.5% and an upper boundary of 85.6%. Using your answer in part b, is there a difference in the percentage of Canadians with an annual income between $40,000 and $60,000 and the percentage of Canadians with an income exceeding $100,000 who support buying private health insurance? Why or why not?

7.77 Terri Schiavo In 2005, Terri Schiavo was said to have been in a "persistent vegetative state" for many years. Her husband wanted her feeding tube removed, and her parents wanted it left in place. In a Gallup poll taken in 2005, 56% of adults polled answered yes to the following question: "Should Terri Schiavo's feeding tube have been removed?" The margin of error was given as 4 percentage points, assuming a 95% confidence level. Assuming the sampling was random, does this suggest that a majority of adults believe the feeding tube should have been removed? Show your work and explain your answer.

7.78 Wording Confidence Interval Statements From Exercise 7.77, a 95% confidence interval for the percentage who would answer yes to whether Terri Schiavo's feeding tube should have been removed was (52%, 60%).

Which of the following is the best interpretation? Explain why the other wordings are incorrect.

a. We are 95% confident that the boundaries for the interval are 52% and 60%.

b. There is a 95% probability that the population percentage is between 52% and 60%.

c. There is a 95% chance that the boundaries 52% and 60% capture the population percentage.

d. Ninety-five percent of all sample percentages based on samples of the same size will be between 52% and 60%.

e. We are 95% confident that the population percentage is between 52% and 60%.

GUIDED EXERCISES

7.37 Law School Graduation and Articling According to the Law Society of Upper Canada (Ontario), 15% of law school graduates in Ontario did not find an articling position (*Law Times*, May 7, 2012).

Question
A random sample of 70 recent law school graduates in Ontario was taken. Find the approximate probability that at least 12% of these graduates will not find an articling position.

Step 1 ▶ Population proportion
The sample proportion is 0.12. What is the population proportion?

Step 2 ▶ Check conditions
Because we are asked for an approximate probability, we might be able to use the Central Limit Theorem. In order to use the CLT for a sample proportion, we must check the conditions under which we are allowed.

a. Randomly sampled? Yes

b. Sample size? In a simple random sample of 70 independent recent law school graduates in Ontario, how many would we expect not to get an articling position? Calculate *n* times *p*. Also calculate how many would expect to get an articling position, *n* times $1 - p$. State whether these are both at least 10.

c. Assume the population size is at least 10 times the sample size, which would be at least 700.

Step 3 ▶ Calculate
Part of the standardization follows. Finish it, showing all the numbers.
First, find the standard deviation of the sample proportion:

$$SD = \sqrt{\frac{p(1-p)}{n}} = \sqrt{\frac{0.15(0.85)}{70}} = ?$$

Then find the corresponding *z*-score:

$$z = \frac{\hat{p} - p}{SD} = \frac{0.12 - 0.15}{?} = ?$$

Find the approximate probability that at least 0.12 do not get articling positions by finding the area to the right of the *z*-value of -0.70 in the Normal curve. Show a well-labelled curve, starting with what is given in Figure A.

Step 4 ▶ Explain
Explain why the tail area in Figure A represents the correct probability.

Step 5 ▶ Answer the question
Find the area of the shaded region in Figure A.

For another approach to this type of problem, see Example A in TechTips.

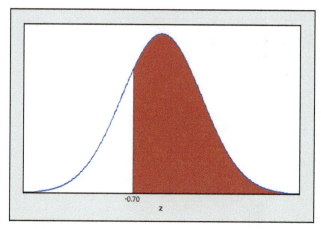

▲ FIGURE A

Example A: One-Proportion Probability Using Normal Technology

According to a 2012 Statistics Canada survey of Canadians aged 20 to 24, 90% had earned a high school diploma. If you took a random sample of 2000 Canadians aged 20 to 24, what is the approximate probability that 91% or more of the sample will have earned their high school diploma? To use the "Normal" steps from Chapter 6, we just need to evaluate the mean and standard deviation of the sample proportion. The mean of the distribution of the sample proportion is 0.90. The standard deviation is

$$SD = \sqrt{\frac{p(1-p)}{n}} = \sqrt{\frac{0.90(1-0.90)}{2000}} = \sqrt{\frac{0.09}{2000}} = 0.006708$$

Now you can use the "Normal" TechTips steps (for TI-83/84, Minitab, Excel, SPSS, or StatCrunch) from Chapter 6 starting on page 291. Figure 7A shows TI-83/84 ouput.

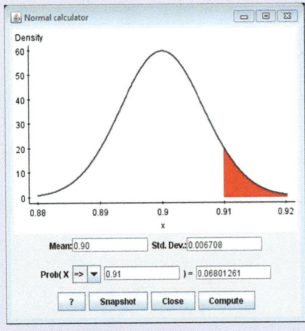

▲ **FIGURE 7A** TI-83/84 normal output.

Figure 7B shows StatCrunch output.

The probability is around 7%.

▲ **FIGURE 7B** StatCrunch normal output.

Example B: Finding a Confidence Interval for a Proportion

Find a 95% confidence interval for the population proportion of sixes appearing when a fair die is tossed 100 times and 23 sixes are observed.

Confidence Interval for One Proportion

1. Press **STAT**, choose **Tests, A: 1-PropZInt**.
2. Enter: **x, 23; n, 100; C-level, .95**.
3. Press **ENTER** when **Calculate** is highlighted.
4. Figure 7C shows the 95% confidence interval of (.14752, .31248).

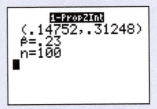

▲ **FIGURE 7C** TI-83/84 output for one-proportion z-interval.

Confidence Interval for One Proportion

1. **Stat > Basic Statistics > 1 Proportion**.
2. Choose **Summarized data**.
   Enter: **Number of events, 23; Number of trials, 100**.
3. Click **Options** and Check **Use test and interval based on normal distribution**.
4. In the **1 Proportion - Options** box, if you want a confidence level different from 95%, change it.
5. Click **OK**.

The relevant part of the output is

```
            95% CI
    (0.147518, 0.312482)
```

Confidence Interval for One Proportion

1. Click on **Add-Ins, XLSTAT, Parametric Text, Tests for one proportion**.
2. See Figure 7D. Enter: Frequency, 23; Sample size, 100; Test Proportion, 0.1667. Leave the **z-test** option checked, uncheck the **Continuity correction** option.
3. Select the Options tab. Beneath the **Confidence Interval:** section, select **Wald**. Beneath the **Variance (confidence interval):** option, select **Test Proportion**.

   (If you wanted an interval other than 95%, you would change the significance level in the Significance Level (%) field. For a 99% interval, you would use 1. For a 90% interval, use 10.)

The relevant part of the output is 95% confidence interval for the proportion (Wald):

(0.148, 0.312)

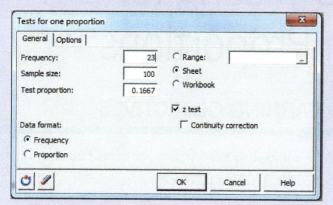

▲ **FIGURE 7D** XLSTAT input for one proportion.

Confidence Interval for One Proportion

1. **Stat > Proportion Stats > One sample > with Summary**
2. Enter: **number of successes, 23; number of observations, 100**.
3. Select the **Confidence Interval** option.

   Leave the default 0.95 for a 95% interval or change the **Level**. For **Method**, leave the default **Standard-Wald**.
4. Click **Compute!**

The relevant part of the output is shown. "L. Limit" is the lower boundary of the interval and "U. Limit" is the upper boundary of the interval.

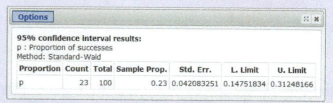

▲ **FIGURE 7E** STATCRUNCH output for one proportion confidence interval.

SPSS

SPSS can be used to compute a 95% confidence interval for the proportion of times this die will show a six. However, it requires the raw data. This means that for each six and non-six observed, the SPSS user would have to enter a value of 1 or 0 in a column. In this instance, that means entering 23 1s and 77 0s.

8 Hypothesis Testing for Population Proportions

LEARNING OBJECTIVES

After completing this chapter, you should be able to:

1. Formulate a statistical hypothesis concerning a population proportion and a hypothesis concerning the comparison of two population proportions.

2. State the conditions required for the collection of evidence to perform a statistical hypothesis test involving proportions.

3. Evaluate the evidence through a p-value calculation and interpretation.

4. Decide on the statistical hypothesis based on the level of significance.

Rick Eglinton/ZUMAPRESS/Newscom

In medicine, industry, science, and everyday life, we often have to make decisions on the basis of incomplete information. For example, a national coffee-and-doughnut chain might need to determine the percentage of its customers who would buy a bacon-flavoured doughnut before an investment is made to make the item available in all its locations. They can't test this doughnut on all its customers—they have to test it on a small sample of customers. An educational psychologist wonders whether kids who receive music training become more creative than other children. The test she uses to measure creativity does in fact show an increase, but might this increase be explained by chance alone? A sample of people who watched violent TV when they were children turn out to exhibit more violent behaviour than a comparison sample made up of people who did not watch violent TV when young.

Could this difference be due to chance, or is something else going on?

Hypothesis testing is another type of statistical inference. In Chapter 7, we used confidence intervals to estimate the value of a parameter and provided a margin of error for our estimate. In this chapter, we make decisions about the population based on the information provided by our sample. If we knew everything about the population, we would definitely know what decision to make. However, we do not have such a privilege. Making a decision about the population from a sample makes the decision tougher to make. As we did in Chapter 7, we can determine how correct our decision is when testing a hypothesis. In this chapter we continue to work with proportions. In the next chapter, we'll see how to find confidence intervals and perform hypothesis tests for population means.

CASE STUDY

Violence on TV

Does watching violence on TV as a child lead to violent behaviour as an adult? Psychologists wishing to shed some light on this question examined 329 children and divided them into two groups: those who watched a high level of violent content on television, and those who did not. Fifteen years later, when the children were in their early twenties, the researchers interviewed them again. This time they asked about acts of aggression or violence (Husemann et al. 2003).

The researchers examined many different types of violence, and one form of violence recorded was whether the now-adults had pushed, grabbed, or shoved their spouse or partner. They found that about 38% of those who reported watching violent television had pushed, grabbed, or shoved their spouse or partner, while only 22% of those who had not watched a lot of TV violence reported engaging in the same behaviours. The difference between these two groups is 16 percentage points. Is this difference due to some real behavioural differences between these two groups of people? Or is the difference due merely to chance? After all, the researchers examined only 329 adults, which is a far cry from the entire population of all adults who watched television as children. Is it possible that even if there were no real differences between these two groups of people, we might see a difference of 16 percentage points or even more? How likely is this? Should we attribute this difference to random variation, or should we conclude that something deeper is going on?

Researchers had to make a decision: either the difference in behaviours was real or it was due to chance. In this chapter, you will see how to make this decision using a formal hypothesis-testing approach. At the end of the chapter, we will come back to this case study and see what the researchers decided and how they made their decision.

SECTION 8.1

The Requirements of a Hypothesis Test

A well-known story goes something like this: four students missed the midterm for their statistics class. They went to the professor together and said, "Please let us make up the exam. We carpool together, and on our way to the exam, we got a flat tire. That's why we missed the exam." The professor didn't believe them, but instead of arguing he said, "Sure, you can make up the exam. Be in my office tomorrow at 8." The next morning, they met in his office. He sent each student to a separate room and gave them an exam. The exam consisted of only one question: "Which tire?"

We don't know the outcome of this story, but let's imagine that all four students answer, "left rear tire." The professor is surprised. He had assumed that the students were lying. "Maybe," he thinks, "they just got lucky. After all, if they just guessed, they could still all choose the same tire." But then he does a quick calculation and figures out that *if the students were lying*, then the probability that all four students would answer the same tire is only 0.0156. On the basis of this probability calculation, he concludes that the students were not lying and allows the students to make up their exam.

The statistics professor has just carried out a hypothesis test. **Hypothesis testing** is a statistical inference procedure that enables us to choose between two hypotheses when we do not know all the information about the population. We call hypothesis testing a "procedure" because it is a process that involves unique terminology and a specific set of steps. However, we will show you that this process lends itself to common sense.

This chapter is divided into five sections. In the first section, you will learn the requirements and basic terminology of a hypothesis test through the presentation of a simple example. Then we will develop the procedure through two more examples. In the third section we will further explore the ideas developed in the first two sections. We will expand our understanding of hypothesis testing and apply the concepts to more complex situations. The last section we will devote to a discussion of some of the subtleties of hypothesis testing.

But before reading further, get a loonie.

Football games and tennis matches begin with a coin toss to determine which team or player gets to start by playing offence. Coin tosses, where the coin is flipped high into the air, are used because flipping a coin is believed to be "fair." The coin is equally likely to land heads or tails, so each side has an equal chance of winning.

But what if we spin the loonie (on a hard, flat surface) rather than flipping it in the air? We claim that, because the heads side of a loonie bulges out, the lack of symmetry will cause the spinning coin to land on one side more often than on the other. In other words, we believe a spun loonie is not fair. Some people—and they may include you—will find this claim to be outrageous and will insist it is false. So how do we decide? Let's collect some data!

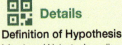

Details

Definition of Hypothesis
Merriam-Webster's online dictionary defines a hypothesis as "a tentative claim made in order to draw out and test its logical or empirical consequences."

1. Start with: A Pair of Hypotheses

We now have a claim: a spun loonie is not fair. This is our first step in the process toward determining whether the "loonie is not fair" statement is true or false. Our first step is not complete, though, since we need to be precise in explaining what we mean by "fair."

When a coin is flipped or spun, it has some probability of landing heads. Let's call that probability p. For a fair coin, $p = 0.5$. We are claiming for a loonie that is spun, p is not equal to 0.5.

We now have a pair of competing claims about this loonie: that p is not equal to 0.5, and that p is equal to 0.5.

Common sense would lead us to believe that this loonie is fair. There is no reason to believe it is not fair. The claim of a "fair loonie" is called the *null hypothesis*, which we write as

$$p = 0.5$$

The "not fair loonie" claim is called the *alternative hypothesis*. We write this as

$$p \neq 0.5$$

In a hypothesis test, hypotheses are *always statements about the value of a population parameter*. Here our population consists of an infinite number of spins of the loonie, and p represents the proportion of times the loonie shows heads, or the probability of heads.

KEY POINT   Hypotheses are *always* statements about the values of the population parameters; they are *never* statements about the values of sample statistics.

Hypotheses come in pairs:

The **null hypothesis**, which we write as H_0 (and pronounce "H-oh," "H-naught," or simply "the null hypothesis"), represents the status-quo, business-as-usual statement about the *value* of the population parameter. In the context of researching new ideas, the null hypothesis represents the "no change," "no effect," or "no difference" scenario. The null hypothesis is the "state of the world" that is *assumed to be true*.

The **alternative hypothesis**, H_A (pronounced "H-eh"), is the opposite of the null hypothesis. It is usually a statement associated with the value of the parameter that is to be tested. It is the complement of the null hypothesis, or "not the H_0," representing the "state of the world" that *is assumed to be false.*

The most important step of a hypothesis test is the selection of the hypotheses. In fact, there are really only two steps of a hypothesis test that a computer cannot do, and this is one of those steps. (The other step is checking to make sure that the conditions necessary for the probability calculations to be valid are satisfied.)

Hypothesis tests are like criminal trials. In a criminal trial, two conflicting views—or hypotheses—are placed before a jury. The defendant is not guilty, or he is guilty. These hypotheses are not given equal weight, however. The jury is told to assume that the defendant is not guilty until the evidence overwhelmingly suggests this is not so. That is, a decision of "guilty" is made if the evidence is "beyond all reasonable doubt."

Hypothesis tests follow the same principles. The statistician plays many roles: that of the Crown attorney, the defence lawyer, and the jury. The null hypothesis is chosen to represent the status quo, or the neutral statement. Just as in a jury trial, where we ask the jury to believe that the defendant is not guilty unless the evidence against this belief is overwhelming, we will believe that the null hypothesis is true in the beginning. After we thoroughly examine the evidence, we may find that it's overwhelmingly against the "not guilty" belief, and so we'll reject it in favour of the "guilty" belief.

> **KEY POINT** The null hypothesis always gets the benefit of the doubt and is *assumed* to be true throughout the hypothesis-testing procedure. If we decide at the last step that the observed outcome is extremely unusual under this assumption, then and only then do we reject the null hypothesis.

Our hypotheses about spinning a coin are competing predictions about what we will see when we collect data. If the null hypothesis is true, then when we spin the loonie a number of times, about half of the outcomes should be heads. If the null hypothesis is false, we will see either a larger or small proportion of heads. Now stop reading this book and spin a loonie 20 times. Record the number of heads and calculate the sample proportion of heads, $\hat{p}$. This will only take a minute. We'll wait.

Are your results consistent with the claim that $p = 0.5$?

Looking Back

Statistic vs. Parameter
In Chapter 7 you learned that $\hat{p}$, a statistic, represents the proportion of successes in a sample and that p, a parameter, represents the proportion of successes in the population.

EXAMPLE **1** Student Debt

Since the start of the new millennium, tuition fees in Canada have increased dramatically. In 2000, the average yearly tuition fee for a full-time undergraduate student was $3380, and 54% of undergraduates finishing their studies graduated with debt. According to Statistics Canada, the current average fee is around $6000. A student union president at a university believes that the increase in tuition fees over the past decade has caused more and more students to graduate with student debt. A survey of recent graduates from undergraduate programs was taken to determine whether the incidence of debt among recent graduates is indeed higher than it was in 2000. The percentage of recent graduates surveyed who have debt was 58%. To do a hypothesis test, the following hypotheses were written.

$$H_0: \hat{p} = 0.58$$

$$H_A: \hat{p} > 0.58$$

where $\hat{p}$ represents the proportion of the sample of recent graduates who graduated with debt.

QUESTION What is wrong with these hypotheses? Rewrite them so they are correct.

SOLUTION First, these hypotheses are written about the sample proportion $\hat{p}$. We know that 58% of the sample had debt upon graduation, so there is no need to make a hypothesis about it. What we do not know is what proportion of the population of all recent graduates have debt. The hypothesis is a statement about the value of the population parameter and has to be written in such terms. Here the hypothesis should be written in terms of p, the population proportion.

A second problem is with the alternative hypothesis. The question the president of the student union wants to answer is not if 58% of recent graduates have debt. She wants to know if the percentage of students currently graduating with debt has *increased* since the year 2000.

The correct hypotheses are

H_0: $p = 0.54$ (proportion of students graduating with debt has not increased from 2000)

H_A: $p > 0.54$ (proportion of students graduating with debt has increased from 2000)

where p represents the proportion of all recent graduates from undergraduate programs who graduate with debt.

TRY THIS! Exercise 8.5

Details

p Can Be Either a Proportion or a Probability

The parameter p can represent both. For example, if we were describing the percentage of voters in a city who would vote for a certain mayoral candidate, we might say that $p = 0.57$. Then p is a proportion. But if we selected a voter at random, we might say that the probability this voter will vote for this candidate is $p = 0.57$.

2. Consider: Potential Mistakes

Mistakes are an inevitable part of the hypothesis-testing process. The trick is not to make them too often.

One mistake we might make is to reject the null hypothesis when it is true. For example, even a fair loonie can turn up heads in 20 out of 20 flips. If that happened, we might conclude that the coin was unfair when it really was fair. We can't prevent this mistake from happening, but we can try to make it happen infrequently.

The **significance level** is the name of a *type* of probability: it is the probability of rejecting the null hypothesis when, in fact, the null hypothesis is true. It represents the probability of making a very particular type of error. In our experiment, the significance level is the probability that we conclude the spinning loonie is *not* fair when, in fact, it really *is* fair. In a criminal justice setting, the significance level is the probability that we conclude that the suspect is guilty, *when in fact he is actually not guilty*. The significance level has its own symbol, the Greek lowercase alpha: α.

Naturally, we want a procedure with a small significance level, because we want to have a low probability of making this type of error. How small? Most statisticians use a significance level of 0.05. In some situations it makes sense to allow the significance level to be bigger, while other situations require a smaller significance level. Should a suspect be on trial for a serious crime that has a minimum penalty of 25 years in prison, we would want the significance level to be very small. But $\alpha = 0.05$ is a good place to start.

KEY POINT The significance level, α (Greek lowercase alpha), represents the probability of rejecting the null hypothesis when the null hypothesis is true. In most applications, $\alpha = 0.05$ is an acceptable value, but 0.01 and 0.10 are also sometimes used.

EXAMPLE 2 Significance Level for Student Debt

In Example 1, the president of a student union gave a pair of hypotheses about p, the proportion of all recent graduates who have debt. Recall that in 2000 this proportion was equal to 0.54, and the student union president wishes to see whether this percentage has increased.

$$H_0: p = 0.54$$

$$H_A: p > 0.54$$

QUESTION Describe the significance level in context.

SOLUTION The significance level is the probability of rejecting H_0 when in fact it should not be rejected (it is true). In this context, α represents the probability that the student union president will conclude that a larger proportion of graduates from undergraduate programs will graduate with debt than in 2000 when, in fact, the proportion has not changed from 2000.

TRY THIS! Exercise 8.13

3. Gather Evidence: The Test Statistic

A **test statistic** compares the outcome we observed from the sample to the outcome the null hypothesis would produce. For example, in our loonie-spinning example, we observed 7/20, or 0.35, heads. The null hypothesis tells us that we should expect half of the spins to be heads: 0.5. The test statistic compares the observed value of the sample proportion to the expected value of the sample proportion should the null hypothesis be true.

A useful test statistic in this situation is the **one-proportion z-test** statistic.

Formula 8.1: The one-proportion z-test statistic

$$z = \frac{\hat{p} - p_0}{SD}$$

$$\text{where } SD = \sqrt{\frac{p_0(1 - p_0)}{n}}$$

The symbol p_0 represents the value of p claimed to be true by the null hypothesis. For example, for the loonie-spinning example, p_0 is 0.5. Most of the test statistics you will see in this book have the same structure as Formula 8.1:

$$\text{Test Statistic Observed} = \frac{\text{observed value} - \text{null value}}{SD}$$

Because we observe a sample proportion of $\hat{p}$, the observed value of the test statistic from our experiment is

$$z = \frac{0.35 - 0.50}{\sqrt{\dfrac{0.50(1 - 0.50)}{20}}} = -1.34$$

Note that the observed value of the test statistic is negative, because the observed value of the sample proportion $\hat{p}$ was less than the value we expected to observe if the null hypothesis was true.

 Looking Back

In Chapter 7 we learned about the Central Limit Theorem and how $\hat{p}$ has a sampling distribution that is approximately Normal with a mean p and a standard deviation of

$$SD = \sqrt{\frac{p(1 - p)}{n}}$$

This allowed us to find the percentage of times a sample proportion will be within a given interval of percentages by "standardizing" $\hat{p}$ to a z-score and finding the area with either technology or the Normal table. Formula 8.1 simply replaces p with the hypothesized value p_0.

Why Is the *z*-Statistic Useful?

The **z-test statistic** is useful because it takes into account the sampling distribution of the sample proportion and allows us to compare its observed value, $\hat{p}$, with the null hypothesis value, p_0. If the observed value of $\hat{p}$ is close to p_0, then the test statistic will be close to 0. The further the value of the test statistic is away from 0 (or, the larger its absolute value), the more suspicious we become of the null hypothesis. Also, knowing the sampling distribution of the sample proportion allows us to verify that we are getting the correct significance level.

> **KEY POINT**   If the null hypothesis is true, then the observed value of the z-test statistic will be close to 0. The further away from 0 the value of the z-test statistic is, the more evidence there is against the null hypothesis.

EXAMPLE 3 Test Statistic for Spinning Heads

The authors observed 7 heads when they spun their coin 20 times, and they calculated a test statistic of $z = -1.34$. A friend of the authors observed 12 heads out of 20 spins.

QUESTION   What value of the test statistic should the friend report?

SOLUTION   The observed sample proportion is $12/20 = 0.60$. Using Formula 8.1, the friend's observed test statistic is

$$z = \frac{0.60 - 0.50}{\sqrt{\dfrac{0.50\,(1 - 0.50)}{20}}} = 0.89$$

CONCLUSION   The observed value of the test statistic is 0.89. Note that the friend has a positive-valued test statistic, because he observed more than the expected number of heads.

TRY THIS!   Exercise 8.15

4. The Strength of the Evidence: A p-Value

In a court of law, the null hypothesis of 'not guilty' is rejected in favour of the 'guilty' alternative hypothesis only when the evidence presented is so strong, it leads the judge (or jury) to be suspicious of the 'not guilty' assumption. A decision is then made, a 'guilty' verdict is rendered and the 'non-guilty' assumption is rejected.

This reasoning also applies to a hypothesis test. The null hypothesis tells us what to expect from our data. If our data show something that is unexpected—the outcome is inconsistent with what we expect to happen—we should then have some doubts about the null hypothesis. Furthermore, if the data are wildly inconsistent with what we would expect to happen, or we get a surprising outcome, then we should reject the null hypothesis and lean toward believing the alternative hypothesis.

Figure 8.1 shows all possible outcomes of our loonie-spinning experiment. According to the null hypothesis, getting between about 6 and 15 heads is not that unusual; these outcomes are quite common when one is spinning a fair coin. But getting less than 6 heads (5, 4, 3, 2, 1, or 0) or more than 15 (16, 17, 18, 19, or 20) is unusual. If this happened to us, we would be surprised and might be inclined to reject the null hypothesis.

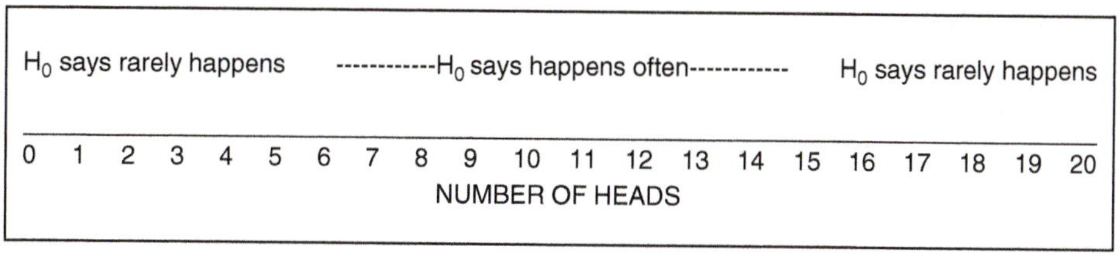

H_0 says rarely happens	------------H_0 says happens often------------	H_0 says rarely happens

```
0  1  2  3  4  5  6  7  8  9  10  11  12  13  14  15  16  17  18  19  20
                        NUMBER OF HEADS
```

◀ **FIGURE 8.1** Possible outcomes from spinning a loonie 20 times and counting the number of heads. If the probability of heads is 0.50, then when spinning or tossing a coin 20 times, we would get between 6 and 14 heads quite often. The numbers 5 or fewer are rare, as are 15 or more.

Because we are statisticians, we have a way of quantifying the outcome and determining if we are observing a surprise or not. The **p-value** measures how surprised we are by reporting the following: if the null hypothesis is true, compute the probability of taking another sample, observing the test statistic of this sample, and finding this value to be as extreme or more extreme than the value we initially observed. Small p-values (closer to 0) mean that we have observed a surprise: our observed outcome is not consistent with the null hypothesis. Large p-values (closer to 1) mean that the outcome is not a surprise: the outcome is consistent with the null hypothesis. For instance, we can calculate the probability of getting four or fewer heads when spinning a fair loonie to be 0.0059. This tells us that getting four or fewer heads is not likely to occur *if the null hypothesis $p = 0.5$ is true.* We therefore would be very surprised by observing four heads or less!

KEY POINT The p-value is a probability. Assuming that the null hypothesis is true, the p-value is the probability that another random sample of the same size would produce a test statistic value that is as surprising or more surprising than the one you have observed. A small p-value suggests that a surprising outcome has occurred, and therefore your result is statistical evidence that discredits the null hypothesis.

For example, in our test to see whether a spun loonie is fair, we spun it 20 times and saw 7 heads. The p-value associated with this outcome can be found to be about 0.18. This tells us that if spinning a loonie is really fair (and $p = 0.5$), then the outcome we observed was not that surprising. The probability of observing an outcome that is just as surprising or more surprising is close to 1 in 5. We would probably think that this does not discredit the null hypothesis of $p = 0.5$, or that the coin is fair.

EXAMPLE **4** Increased Debt for Recent Graduates

The president of the student union in Examples 1 and 2 wants to find out if the proportion of recent graduates from undergraduate programs who graduate with debt has increased since 2000. Data are collected from a random sample of recent graduates, and it is found that from this sample 58%, or $\hat{p} = 0.58$, have graduated with debt. The student union president performs a hypothesis test and finds a p-value of 0.006. The null and alternative hypotheses are

$$H_0: p = 0.54$$

$$H_A: p > 0.54$$

QUESTION Explain the meaning of this p-value, 0.006, in context.

SOLUTION The p-value of 0.006 means that if the proportion of recent graduates from undergraduate programs who have debt has not increased since the year 2000, and is still equal to 54%, then the probability of another random sample of recent graduates producing a sample proportion that is as high or higher than 58% is 0.006. This is a surprising outcome—one that occurs only 6 out of 1000 times—which is an unlikely outcome *if* the null hypothesis is true.

TRY THIS! Exercise 8.17

SECTION 8.2

Finding p-Values

Understanding how to interpret the p-value is vital to understanding hypothesis testing. Technology might provide us with the p-value, but we need to be able to understand how the technology did this calculation. Technology may do the calculation for us, but it will not tell us what the p-value means.

The p-Value Is All about Extremes

The meaning of the phrase "as extreme or more extreme" depends on the alternative hypothesis. There are three basic pairs of hypotheses, shown in Table 8.1.

► **TABLE 8.1** These three pairs of hypotheses can be used in a hypothesis test.

Two-tailed	One-tailed (Left)	One-tailed (Right)
$H_0: \ p = p_0$	$H_0: \ p = p_0$	$H_0: \ p = p_0$
$H_A: \ p \neq p_0$	$H_A: \ p < p_0$	$H_A: \ p > p_0$

If the alternative hypothesis is

$H_A: p \neq p_0$ (the true value of p is either bigger
or smaller than what the null hypothesis claims)

then "as extreme as or more extreme than" means "even farther away from 0 than the value you observed." This corresponds to finding the probability in both tails of the $N(0, 1)$ distribution. This is called a **two-tailed hypothesis**.

If the alternative hypothesis is

$H_A: p < p_0$ (the true value is less than the value claimed by the null hypothesis)

then we have a **one-tailed hypothesis**. The "as extreme or more extreme" means "less than or equal to the observed value of the z-test statistic." This type of one-tailed test can also be called a **left-tailed hypothesis**, because the sign in the alternative hypothesis "points to the left." This is important, because it provides us with a guide to finding the p-value. The p-value is the probability in the left tail of the $N(0, 1)$ distribution.

Finally, if the alternative hypothesis is

$H_A: p > p_0$ (the true value is greater than the value claimed by the null hypothesis)

then "as extreme as or more extreme than" means "greater than or equal to the observed value." This is another one-tailed test, called a **right-tailed hypothesis**, because the sign in the alternative hypothesis points "to the right." To find the p-value of this type of test, we find the probability of being to the right of the observed value of our test statistic in the $N(0, 1)$ distribution.

Notice how the null hypothesis in each of the three hypotheses tests in Table 8.1 has an "=" sign. This is not by accident, but rather by design. The null hypothesis is a bold statement about the value of the population parameter, and since we assume the null hypothesis to be true until we have enough statistical evidence—a small p-value—to suggest otherwise, we set the value of p *equal to* some value.

To illustrate, suppose the observed value of the test statistic is $z = 1.56$. Figure 8.2 shows the p-value (represented by the shaded region) for each of these three possible alternative hypotheses.

KEY POINT ▶ A null hypothesis about the population proportion will always be associated with the $p = p_0$ portion of the hypotheses, because a hypothesis test is a statement about the value of the population proportion. Under the null hypothesis, we assume it to be equal to a specific value, which is p_0.

(a)

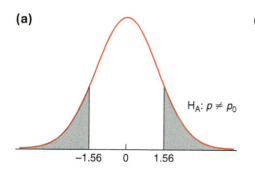

(b)

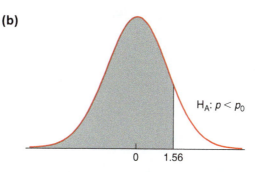

(c)

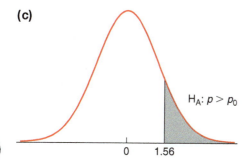

◀ **FIGURE 8.2** The shaded areas represent p-values for three different alternative hypotheses when the observed value of the test statistic is $z = 1.56$. **(a)** The p-value for a two-tailed alternative hypothesis (0.119). **(b)** The p-value for a left-tailed hypothesis (0.941). **(c)** The p-value for a right-tailed hypothesis (0.059).

Our loonie-spinning experiment is an example of a two-tailed hypothesis. Figure 8.3 shows the area corresponding to the p-value for getting an outcome as extreme as or more extreme than a sample proportion of 0.35 for this two-tailed alternative hypothesis. (The output in Figure 8.3 does not show the "proportion of heads" but, rather, it shows the observed value of the z-statistic.)

As an example of a one-tailed p-value, consider Figure 8.4, which illustrates the p-value for a scenario in Example 4. In that example, the president of a student union was checking if the proportion of recent graduates from undergraduate programs has increased since 2000, or $p > 0.54$. As extreme or more extreme that the observed outcome means "as big or bigger than" what the null hypothesis tells the president to expect. (In Figure 8.4, the p-value shown is about 0.030. You can see that about 3% of the area under the curve is shaded.)

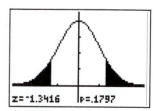

▲ **FIGURE 8.3** The shaded area represents the p-value: the probability of getting a proportion as extreme as or more extreme than 0.35 in 20 spins of a coin. Note that both the left and right tails are shaded.

◀ **FIGURE 8.4** The shaded area represents the p-value for a z-statistic of 1.84. Because the alternative hypothesis is one-tailed ("the proportion of recent undergraduates who graduate with debt is larger than 0.54"), the p-value is the area in the right tail.

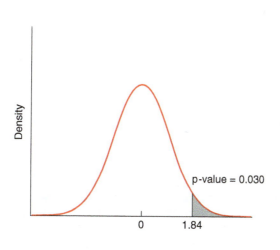

EXAMPLE 5 Identify the p-Values

Figure 8.5 shows sketches of three probability distributions. The shaded areas represent probabilities.

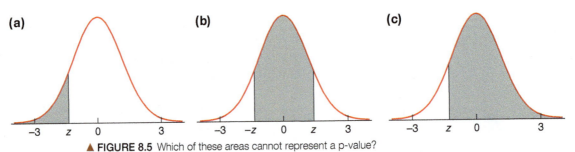

(a)   (b)   (c)

▲ **FIGURE 8.5** Which of these areas cannot represent a p-value?

QUESTION   Which of these three sketches cannot represent a p-value? Explain your reasoning.

SOLUTION   Figure 8.5b cannot represent a p-value because it is not a tail probability. Figure 8.5b represents the probability of getting an outcome between two values. Figure 8.5a represents the probability of getting an outcome as small or smaller than the observed outcome, and Figure 8.5c represents the probability of getting an outcome as big or bigger than the observed outcome. Both Figure 8.5a and Figure 8.5c, therefore, could represent p-values.

TRY THIS!   Exercise 8.19

Conditions Required for Calculating an Approximate p-Value

Note that in Figures 8.4 and 8.5 we used a Normal distribution to illustrate finding the p-value. This is no coincidence; under certain conditions, the standard Normal distribution, $N(0, 1)$, provides a good model for the sampling distribution of the z-test statistic.

These conditions are listed here and will be referred to throughout the remainder of the chapter.

1. *Random sample*: The sample is collected randomly from the population.

2. *Large enough sample size*: The sample size, n, is large enough that the sample has at least 10 expected successes and 10 expected failures; in other words, $np_0 \geq 10$ and $n(1 - p_0) \geq 10$.

3. *Without replacement*: If the sample is collected without replacement, then the population size is at least 10 times bigger than the sample size.

4. *Independence*: Each observation or measurement must have no influence on any others.

5. *Null hypothesis*: The null hypothesis is true.

If these conditions are satisfied, then the conditions for using the Central Limit Theorem for sample proportions (Chapter 7) have been met, and the z-test statistic for the one-proportion z-test can be closely modelled by the standard Normal distribution.

KEY POINT   Under the right conditions, the sampling distribution of the z-test statistic can be approximated by the standard Normal distribution, $N(0, 1)$.

Calculating the p-Value

Because the sampling distribution of the z-test statistic can be modelled by the standard Normal distribution, use the same techniques described in Section 6.2 to find p-values. We recommend that you use technology to find the area under the standard Normal curve that represents the p-value. If you don't have technology, you can use Table 2 in Appendix A.

Figure 8.6 illustrates how the p-value depends on the observed outcome of our loonie-spinning study. Each graph represents the p-value for a different outcome, with the loonie spun 20 times in each case. The null hypothesis in all cases is $p = 0.5$, and the alternative is the two-tailed hypothesis that the probability of heads is *not* 0.5. Note that the closer the number of heads is to 10, the closer the z-value is to 0 and the larger the p-value is. Also note that the p-value for an outcome of 11 heads is the same as for 9 heads, and the p-value for an outcome of 12 heads is the same as for 8 heads. This happens because the alternative hypothesis is two-tailed and the Normal distribution is symmetric.

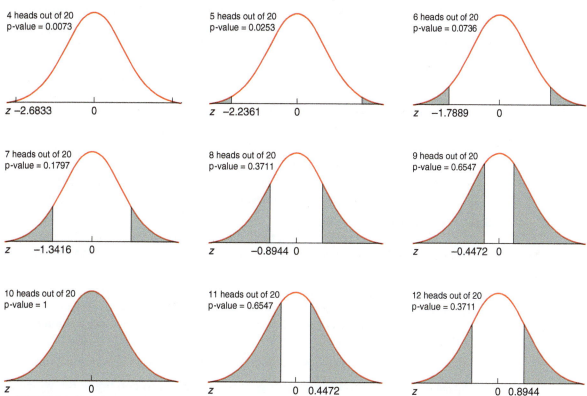

▲ **FIGURE 8.6** Each graph shows the p-value (shaded) for a different number of heads out of 20 spins of a loonie, with the assumption that the loonie is fair and using a two-tailed alternative hypothesis. Note that the closer the number of heads is to 10 (out of 20), the closer the z-value is to 0 and the larger the p-value. Also, as the number of heads gets farther from 10, the z-value gets farther from 0 and the p-value gets smaller.

EXAMPLE 6 p-Values for Loonie Spinning

Two different students each did the loonie-spinning experiment with a two-tailed alternative. Their test statistics follow.

$$\text{Study 1: } z = 1.98$$

$$\text{Study 2: } z = -2.02$$

 QUESTION Which of these test statistics has the smaller p-value and why?

> ⚠ **Caution**
>
> **So Many p's**
> p is the population proportion. p_0 is the value of the population proportion according to the null hypothesis.
> $\hat{p}$ is the sample proportion. The p-value is the probability that if the null hypothesis is true, our test statistic will be as extreme as or more extreme than the value we actually observed.

SOLUTION If the null hypothesis is correct, then the test statistic should be close to 0. Values farther from 0 are more surprising and so have smaller p-values. Because −2.02 is farther from 0 than 1.98, the area under the Normal curve in the tails is smaller for −2.02 than it is for 1.98. Thus −2.02 has the smaller p-value.

TRY THIS! Exercise 8.21

SECTION 8.3

Hypothesis Testing in Four Steps

Now that you've seen the requirements of hypothesis testing, it's time to learn the process.

We present hypothesis testing as a four-step procedure. In this chapter we focus on tests about population proportions. In Chapter 9 you will see tests about population means, and in later chapters we will introduce other tests.

Step 1: Hypothesize.
State your hypotheses about the value of the population proportion. Your null hypothesis will always contain the term "$p = p_0$." The sign in the alternative hypothesis will either be "<" (left-tailed test), ">" (right-tailed test), or "≠" (two-tailed test).

Step 2: Prepare.
Get ready to test: state and choose a significance level. Choose a test statistic appropriate for the hypotheses. State and check conditions required for future computations, and state any assumptions that must be made.

Step 3: Compute to compare.
Compute the observed value of the test statistic, and compare it to what the null hypothesis said you would get. Find the p-value to measure your level of surprise.

Step 4: Interpret and conclude.
Interpret the meaning of the p-value and compare it to the level of significance, α. Do you reject or not reject the null hypothesis? What does the decision made mean in the context of the data?

Now we will examine in detail how these steps are applied to two different situations.

Situation 1: In an NHL game that goes to a shootout to determine the winner, does the team that shoots first have an advantage? Data from a random sample of games decided by a shootout were collected from nhl.com.

Situation 2: Do we dream in colour? Historically, before the age of television, colour movies, and video games, 29% of the American population reported dreaming in colour. A psychologist suspects that the present-day proportion might be higher, now that we are surrounded with colour imagery. The data consist of a random sample of 113 people, taken in the year 2001 (Schwitzgebel 2003).

Step 1: Hypothesize

Recall that the hypotheses consist of a null and an alternative hypothesis. The null hypothesis represents the status-quo condition, the alternative being "not the null" hypothesis. The null hypothesis is assumed to be true until the last step in our procedure.

Let's see how to create a pair of hypotheses for these two situations.

Situation 1: Does the team that goes first in an NHL shootout have an advantage?

Most people would think that when given the choice of going first in a game where all players take a turn, the player with the first turn has the advantage. Remember the last time you played a board game with your friends or family, and before the game started a process took place to see who would go first? If the player having the first turn does not have an advantage, then why do we fret to determine who will go first? The player with the first turn might even have a disadvantage. If the team going first in an NHL shootout has either an advantage or a disadvantage, then the team shooting first will win either more than 50% of the shootout games (an advantage exists) or less than 50% of the games (a disadvantage). This is the alternative hypothesis: should there be an advantage or a disadvantage to the team going first in a shootout, then the percentage of games won by the team going first is not 50%. The neutral, or status-quo, hypothesis is that there is no advantage or no disadvantage to going first in a shootout.

The null and alternative hypotheses can now be stated in both words and symbols.

H_0: There is no advantage to shooting first. The percentage of games won by the team shooting first is the same as the percentage of games lost by the team shooting first.

H_A: There is either an advantage or a disadvantage to shooting first. The percentage of games won by the team shooting first is either greater or less than 50%:

$$H_0: p = 0.50$$
$$H_A: p \neq 0.50$$

Situation 2: Dreaming

The researcher hopes to establish that a greater proportion of people today report that they dream in colour than the proportion who reported dreaming in colour historically. In the past, before colour TV and movies, this proportion was 0.29. The researcher has interviewed a random sample of 113 people.

We state the null and alternative hypotheses in words and symbols.

H_0: The proportion of those who report dreaming in colour in the population is the same as it has historically been: 0.29.

H_A: The proportion of those who report dreaming in colour has increased.

$$H_0: p = 0.29$$
$$H_A: p > 0.29$$

This alternative hypothesis is a one-tailed hypothesis, because the hypothesis considers only the possibility that the true population proportion might be greater than—to the right of—the hypothesized value of 0.29.

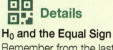

Details

H_0 and the Equal Sign
Remember from the last Key Point that the null hypothesis will always contain an "=" sign.

EXAMPLE 7 Age Discrimination

According to Statistics Canada's 2006 census, about 34% of Alberta's population is between the ages of 40 and 65. A fired employee (an Albertan) of an oil and gas corporation who is in his fifties feels that he was a victim of age discrimination, given that only 20% of the company's 3000 employees are between the ages of 40 and 65. Here is what he wants to investigate: if this company hires at random, is this information enough evidence that it has a preference for younger employees?

QUESTION State the null and alternative hypotheses in words, then in symbols. Use the symbol p to represent the proportion of all employees at this company who are between 40 and 65.

SOLUTION

H_0: The proportion of employees at this company who are between 40 and 65 is 0.34, the same as that for the general population.

H_A: The proportion of employees at this company who are between 40 and 65 is less than that for the general population.

$$H_0: p = 0.34$$
$$H_A: p < 0.34$$

TRY THIS! Exercise 8.25

Step 2: Prepare

Before we can choose a test statistic, compute a p-value, then make a decision about the null hypothesis being true, we need to set the significance level.

Set the Significance Level

The significance level of a hypothesis test is the probability that we will reject the null hypothesis when in fact we should not—because the null hypothesis is actually true! Most scientific journals require this probability to be low: 0.05. In symbols,

$$\alpha = 0.05$$

Select a Test Statistic

Choosing the correct test statistic is not a big deal at this point, because you have seen only one test statistic to choose from—the one-proportion z-test. This test statistic works well, because when the null hypothesis is true we tend to get small values (close to 0), and when the null hypothesis is not true we tend to get values far from 0. The test statistic is also useful because we know a good approximation to its sampling distribution and so can compute the significance level and the p-value.

In Section 8.4 you will study a new test statistic used when comparing two population proportions. Later in the book, you will see test statistics for comparing means, and then for comparing slopes and intercepts for regression lines. It's important, therefore, to understand which test statistic is appropriate for the context you are working with.

Check the Sampling Distribution Conditions

We know the distribution of our test statistic. In order to use it, you should check to see if the conditions under which the test statistic can be used, listed in Section 8.2, hold. These conditions are (1) random sample, (2) large enough sample size, (3) sampling without replacement, and (4) independence. Condition (5), that the null hypothesis is true, is a condition we will assume to be met for the time being. If these conditions are not met, then other approaches are needed. (Some examples will be given in Chapter 13.)

KEY POINT If the null hypothesis is true, and if the four conditions for applying the Central Limit Theorem hold, then the test statistic z follows an $N(0, 1)$ distribution. Extreme values rarely occur in an $N(0, 1)$ distribution, so if we see an extreme value, this will produce a small p-value and evidence that the null hypothesis is not true.

EXAMPLE 8 Preparing for Situation 1: Advantage to Shooting First

Is there an advantage or disadvantage to going first in a shootout to settle the outcome of an NHL hockey game? The hypotheses for this test are

$$H_0: p = 0.50$$

$$H_A: p \neq 0.50$$

where p is the proportion of all shootout games in which the team going first wins. The data are from a random sample of 87 recent NHL contests that were decided by a shootout.

QUESTION Check that the conditions hold so that the sampling distribution of the z-test statistic will approximately follow the standard Normal distribution.

SOLUTION We are told that the data come from a random sample, and this satisfies the first condition of randomization. Next we check that the sample size is large enough to produce at least 10 successes and 10 failures.

   If the null hypothesis is true, then the probability of success is $p_0 = 0.50$. Because $n = 87$,

$$np_0 = 87 \times 0.50 = 43.5 > 10$$

$$n(1 - p_0) = 87 \times (1 - 0.50) = 43.5 > 10$$

The third condition is true if the population—all NHL overtime games that are decided by a shootout—is more than 10 times bigger than the sample size, or

$$\text{Population size is bigger than } 10 \times 87 = 870$$

We confess we do not know how many games were decided by a shootout. Data from nhl.com show that from the introduction of the shootout in the 2005/2006 season to the time this was written, there were 948 games decided by a shootout.

CONCLUSION If the null hypothesis is true (as we assume when beginning these tests), then the conditions hold and the one-proportion z-test can be applied.

TRY THIS! Exercise 8.31

Step 3: Compute to Compare

At last, we are at the step where we consider actual data. Our test statistic, usually calculated with technology, will compare the value of the statistic provided by the data ($\hat{p}$) with the value that the null hypothesis says we should see (p_0). We then find the p-value to determine whether this value is unusual, given our assumption that the null hypothesis is true.

Find the Observed Value of the Test Statistic

Let's see how this works for the first team to shoot in an NHL game decided by a shootout. In the sample of 87 games, it was found that the team shooting first won 43 times. In Example 8 we found that the one-proportion z-test is appropriate. Let's now find the observed value of the z-test statistic. The hypotheses of this test are

$$H_0: p = 0.50$$

$$H_A: p \neq 0.50$$

The data: in the sample of 87 games that ended with a shootout, 43 were won by the team shooting first. The sample proportion is then $\hat{p} = (43/87) = 0.4943$. We now compare this value to 0.50, the value we would expect if the null hypothesis is true. We do so by finding the value of the z-test statistic (Formula 8.1), which requires us to find the standard deviation of the sample proportion from Chapter 7.

$$SD = \sqrt{\frac{p_0(1 - p_0)}{n}} = \sqrt{\frac{0.50(1 - 0.50)}{87}} = 0.053606$$

Now we substitute the standard deviation into our z-test statistic:

$$z = \frac{\hat{p} - p_0}{SD} = \frac{0.4943 - 0.50}{0.053606} = -0.1063, \text{ or } -0.11$$

Find the p-Value

If the null hypothesis is true, how surprised are we by this outcome? Recall from Section 8.1 that the p-value measures our surprise. If the null hypothesis is true, it is the probability of getting a z-test statistic value that is as extreme, or more extreme, than the one we observed. Here, it has to be as extreme or more extreme than -0.11.

TECH

EXAMPLE 8 *(continued)* Is the Outcome Surprising Enough?

In our example involving the team going first in an NHL shootout, our observed value of the z-test statistic was -0.11, and the alternative hypothesis was

$$H_A: p \neq 0.50$$

We have verified the conditions required for the distribution of the z-test statistic to be approximated by the $N(0, 1)$ distribution.

QUESTION Find the p-value.

SOLUTION The p-value is the probability of getting a test statistic that is as extreme or more extreme than -0.11. Because our alternative hypothesis is two-tailed, the p-value translates to "the probability of getting a test statistic even farther way from 0 than -0.11 is." Visually, it looks like Figure 8.7, with the shaded area representing the p-value.

The p-value can be found using methods discussed in Chapter 6 to find probabilities from the standard Normal distribution, or we can take advantage of the fact that many software packages provide the p-value automatically when asked to perform a hypothesis test. Figure 8.8 shows the p-value as calculated by the T1-83/84 one-proportion z-test.

CONCLUSION If the null hypothesis is true, and there is no advantage or disadvantage to an NHL team shooting first, then the probability of getting a z-test statistic that is as extreme or more extreme than the observed value of -0.11 is 0.9146. This is a rather large probability, suggesting that if the null hypothesis is true, the outcome of $\hat{p} = (43/87) = 0.4943$ is not that surprising.

Here's another way to look at the p-value: if another 87 games were randomly chosen, the probability of this second sample producing a result that is as extreme or more extreme than the current result is very likely, 0.9146, which would mean that the current result is strong evidence in support of the null hypothesis.

TRY THIS! Exercise 8.33

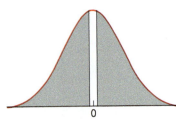

▲ **FIGURE 8.7** The p-value as a shaded area. This value is from a two-tailed test for which z comes out to be -0.11. The area has been enlarged a bit so that it can be seen readily.

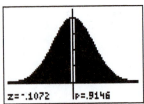

▲ **FIGURE 8.8** TI-83/84 output for the team that shoots first. The p-value is given as 0.9146.

EXAMPLE **9** Dreaming in Colour

In situation 2, the researchers are wondering whether a greater proportion of people now dream in colour than did so before colour television and movies became as prominent as they are today. The hypotheses they are checking are

$$H_0: p = 0.29$$

$$H_A: p > 0.29$$

The researchers took a random sample of 113 people. Of these 113 people, 92 reported dreaming in colour.

QUESTION Find the value of the sample proportion, $\hat{p}$. Find the observed value of the test statistic, and then find the p-value associated with this observed value. In the conclusion, interpret the p-value in context. Assume that the conditions that must be met in order for us to use the $N(0, 1)$ distribution as the sampling distribution are satisfied.

SOLUTION

The sample proportion is $\hat{p} = \dfrac{92}{113} = 0.814159$.

We can then compute the observed value of the test statistic:

$$z = \frac{0.814159 - 0.29}{\sqrt{\dfrac{0.29(1 - 0.29)}{113}}} = \frac{0.524159}{0.042686} = 12.28$$

The p-value is the area under the $N(0, 1)$ curve to the right of (above) 12.28. We know, without looking, that this area must be quite small, because it is extremely rare for a value from an $N(0, 1)$ distribution to be greater than 3, so 12.28 is a very large number. Therefore, the p-value is quite small, and we report that it is less than 0.001.

CONCLUSION If the proportion of people who now dream in colour is the same as it was before colour television, then the probability of getting a z-test statistic as extreme or more extreme than 12.28 is less than 0.001. Or, if another sample were taken, the probability that this second sample would give an outcome that as is surprising or more surprising than the observed outcome is very small (less than 0.001).

The small p-value, being less than 0.001, means that we're not likely to get more extreme—or stronger—statistical evidence against the null hypothesis than the evidence we have.

TRY THIS! Exercise 8.35

You should always draw a sketch before you compute the p-value, even if you use technology (as we strongly recommend) to find the probability.

EXAMPLE **10** Improving Attendance in Calculus

A very large calculus class at a university has been troubled by a high attrition rate: over the last five years, 15% of the students who started the class did not finish. An instructor thinks that one reason for this is that some students need help with algebra. She randomly selects 100 students and assigns them to meet weekly with teaching assistants to study algebra. At the end of the semester, she will see what proportion of these 100 students have dropped the course. If p represents the proportion of all students who drop the course and had algebra tutoring, her hypotheses can be written as

$$H_0: p = 0.15$$
$$H_A: p < 0.15$$

After the study is finished, she finds that her test statistic is $z = -1.68$. Assume that all the required conditions hold for the one-proportion z-test.

QUESTION Three possible p-values are shown. One of them corresponds to the p-value for the alternative hypothesis $p > 0.15$, one to the alternative hypothesis $p < 0.15$, and one to the two-tailed alternative hypothesis $p \neq 0.15$. Without using any technology or referring to Normal tables, indicate which of the following numbers is the correct p-value. Explain.

   a. p-value $= 0.0930$
   b. p-value $= 0.0465$
   c. p-value $= 0.9535$

SOLUTION Draw a sketch, as in Figure 8.9. This sketch shows that the p-value must be less than 50%, which eliminates answer c. Answer a is twice as big as answer b, so answer a must correspond to the two-tailed alternative. The correct answer is therefore answer b: p-value $= 0.0465$.

TRY THIS! Exercise 8.37

p-value = 0.0465

z -1.68 0

▲ **FIGURE 8.9** A representation of the p-value when the alternative hypothesis is left-tailed and the z-statistic is -1.68.

Step 4: Interpret and Conclude

The p-value measures our surprise (or lack of surprise) at the outcome of our test, but what should we do about this number? When is the outcome so unusual that we should reject the null hypothesis?

We apply a simple rule: reject the null hypothesis if the p-value is smaller than (or equal to) the value chosen for the significance level, α. If the p-value is larger than the significance level, do not reject the null hypothesis. For most applications, this means you reject the null hypothesis if the p-value is less than or equal to 0.05.

Following this rule ensures that our significance level is achieved. In other words, by following this rule and rejecting the null hypothesis when the p-value is less than or equal to 0.05, we know that there is only a 5% chance that we are mistakenly rejecting the null hypothesis (rejecting H_0 even though H_0 is true).

In Example 8, we found the p-value to be 0.9124. This is quite a bit larger than the significance level of 0.05. As a result, the null hypothesis is not rejected. We can conclude from the data that the team to shoot first in an NHL game whose outcome is to be decided by a shootout has neither an advantage nor a disadvantage. The data confirm $H_0: p = 0.50$.

The dreaming in colour p-value was less than 0.001, and therefore less than the significance level of 0.05. The null hypothesis is then rejected. We can conclude from these data that the proportion of people who dream in colour is higher when compared to a time when colour television and movies were not as prominent. The data support rejecting $H_0: p = 0.29$ in favour of $H_A: p > 0.29$.

KEY POINT Reject the null hypothesis if the p-value is less than (or equal to) α. If the p-value is greater than α, do not reject the null hypothesis.

You should always state your decision: reject the null hypothesis or do not reject the null hypothesis, and describe this decision in the context of the problem.

Now that we have illustrated all four steps, it's time to tackle an entire hypothesis test.

EXAMPLE **11** Creative Kids and Music

Some arts educators reasoned that exposure to music instruction would help students think more creatively in a variety of educational situations than students who did not receive music instruction. To test this, elementary school children were randomly assigned, with their parents' consent, to participate either in a standard music instruction course (the treatment group) or in a recreation course (the control group). All students were given the Torrance Test of Creative Thinking, which measures several components of creativity, both before the music course began (in October) and after the course ended (in May). This test is fairly complex, and a student's score could change slightly just by chance. Of the 30 students in the treatment group, 19 increased their creativity scores by the end of the course. (The others' scores either were unchanged or decreased.) Is this evidence that the music program is effective? If the program had no effect, we would expect, due to chance, that about half of the children would exhibit an increase in creativity and half would exhibit a decrease.

QUESTION Test the hypothesis that the probability that a child's creativity score will increase after participating in this music program is better than 50%. Assume that the children are a random sample from a larger population of elementary school children. Use a 5% significance level.

SOLUTION

Step 1: Hypothesize
Let p represent the probability that a child's creativity score will improve.

$$H_0: p = 0.50$$

$$H_A: p > 0.50$$

Step 2: Prepare
Use the one-proportion z-test. The children are assumed to be a random sample, and the measurements of their creativity scores can be assumed to be independent of each other. Thirty children is enough of a sample because $np_0 = 30(0.5) = 15$; and $n(1 - p_0) = 30(0.5) = 15$, and both are bigger than 10.

Step 3: Compute to compare

$$\hat{p} = \frac{19}{30} = 0.633333$$

We now compare the observed proportion to the hypothetical value of 0.50.

$$z = \frac{0.633333 - 0.50}{\sqrt{\dfrac{(0.50)(1 - 0.50)}{30}}} = \frac{0.133333}{0.091287} = 1.46$$

The p-value is the area under an $N(0, 1)$ curve and to the right of 1.46. This area, which is shown in Figure 8.10 and also in Figure 8.11, gives us

$$\text{p-value} = 0.072$$

Step 4: Interpret and conclude
If the null hypothesis is true, there is a 7.2% probability that another sample of 30 will provide an outcome that is just as extreme or more extreme than the current outcome.

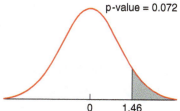

▲ **FIGURE 8.10** The shaded area represents the p-value, the probability of getting a test statistic as large as or larger than 1.46 when the true proportion is 0.50.

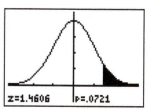

▲ **FIGURE 8.11** TI-83/84 output for 19 out of 30, one-tailed, for which H_A is $p > 0.50$. (Choose Draw to get the curve.)

Caution

Do Not Accept

For reasons we'll explain in Section 8.5, it is incorrect to imply that we accept the null hypothesis. We do *not* say, "The music program was ineffective." Instead, we say, "We do not have enough evidence to show that the program is effective."

Because the p-value is greater than 0.05, we cannot reject H_0. In other words, we do not have enough evidence to conclude that creativity scores increased. This is not the same as saying that the music program was ineffective; we are simply concluding that if it *is* effective, we do not have enough evidence to detect that effectiveness.

Most statistical software packages show you both z and the p-value at once. Some packages (see Figure 8.11) even show the Normal curve with the p-value shaded.

TRY THIS! Exercise 8.43

SNAPSHOT   ONE-PROPORTION z-TEST

WHAT IS IT? ▶ A procedure for choosing between two hypotheses about the true value of a single population proportion. The test statistic is

$$z = \frac{\hat{p} - p_0}{SD} \text{ where } SD = \sqrt{\frac{p_0(1 - p_0)}{n}}$$

WHAT DOES IT DO? ▶ Because estimates of population parameters are uncertain, a hypothesis test gives us a way of making a decision while knowing the probability that we will incorrectly reject the null hypothesis.

HOW DOES IT DO IT? ▶ The z-test statistic compares the sample proportion to the hypothesized population proportion. Very large or very small values of the test statistic tend to discredit the null hypothesis.

HOW IS IT USED? ▶ When the conditions are right: the data must be from an independent, random sample that must be larger than 10% of the population. Then the z-test statistic has an approximate $N(0, 1)$ distribution.

WHEN IS IT USED? ▶ When making hypotheses about one population proportion.

SECTION 8.4

Comparing Proportions from Two Populations

You have now seen how to carry out a hypothesis test for a single population proportion. With very few changes, this procedure can be altered to accommodate a more interesting situation: comparing proportions from two populations.

Consider as an example euthanasia, or medically assisted suicide. Many people believe that if they are diagnosed with an incurable disease that will bring about a slow and painful death, they should have the right to intervene in the treatment of their disease through a doctor-assisted suicide. Clearly this is controversial. Suicide, doctor-assisted or not, goes against the religious beliefs of many people. In addition, advocates suggest that the allowing of euthanasia would leave the vulnerably sick without legal protection. Angus Reid has kept track of Canadians' attitudes about euthanasia through surveys of the Canadian population. Such surveys raise the question of whether Canadians' support for the legalization of euthanasia has changed since 2010, when 63% of Canadians generally supported laws allowing for doctor-assisted suicide. Angus Reid sampled the Canadian population again in 2014, and 79% supported laws for doctor-assisted suicide. Can we conclude that support for the legalization of euthanasia in Canada has changed from 2010 to 2014? Are the differences between these two sample proportions due to chance variation in the sampling procedure?

This problem involves two populations. One population consists of Canadians in 2010, and the second population consists of Canadians in 2014. Each population has a true proportion who support the laws allowing for doctor-assisted suicide, but in each case we do not know the true value. We have a random sample taken from each of the two populations, and we must estimate the two population proportions from these two samples.

We outline the changes to a hypothesis test that will allow us to compare the proportions from two populations.

Changes to the Requirements: The Hypotheses

Since we now have two populations to contend with, we need some new notation. We'll let p_1 be the proportion of Canadians who supported laws allowing for doctor-assisted suicide in 2010 and p_2 be the proportion of Canadians who supported such laws in 2014.

We are not interested in the actual values of p_1 and p_2, as we were when dealing with just one population proportion. Rather, we are interested in whether they are the same value or not. If they are the same value, then the proportion of Canadians who support laws allowing for doctor-assisted suicide has not changed from 2010 to 2014. The "no change" can be formalized as our status-quo hypothesis. We write this as

$$H_0: p_1 = p_2$$

The opposite of this statement is that there has been "a change" from 2010 to 2014. If this happened, then the values of p_1 and p_2 would be different. This would be our alternative hypothesis:

$$H_A: p_1 \neq p_2$$

Notice the similarity to a hypothesis test of a single population proportion? The null hypothesis contains "=" and we have a two-tailed hypothesis. One-tailed hypotheses are also possible. If we wanted to see whether the proportion of Canadians who support laws allowing for doctor-assisted suicide had decreased in 2014, we would have the left-tailed alternative

$$H_A: p_1 < p_2$$

We could also test to see whether the proportion had increased from 2010 to 2014, and write the alternative of the right-tailed test as

$$H_A: p_1 > p_2$$

These options lead to three pairs of hypotheses, as shown in Table 8.2. You choose the pair that corresponds to the research question your study hopes to answer. Note that the null hypothesis is always $p_1 = p_2$ because the neutral position is always that the two proportions are the same.

Hypothesis	Symbols	The Alternative in Words
Two-tailed	$H_0: p_1 = p_2$ $H_A: p_1 \neq p_2$	The proportions are different in the two populations.
One-tailed (left)	$H_0: p_1 = p_2$ $H_A: p_1 < p_2$	The proportion in population 1 is less than the proportion in population 2.
One-tailed (right)	$H_0: p_1 = p_2$ $H_A: p_1 > p_2$	The proportion in population 1 is greater than the proportion in population 2.

◀ **TABLE 8.2** Possible hypotheses for a two-proportion hypothesis test.

Changes to the Requirements: The Test Statistic

We are interested in how p_1 and p_2 differ, so our test statistic is based on the difference between our sample proportions from the two populations. The test statistic we will use has the same structure as the one-sample z-statistic:

$$z = \frac{\text{estimator} - \text{null value}}{SD}$$

However, the estimator for the **two-proportion z-test** is $\hat{p}_1 - \hat{p}_2$ because we are estimating the difference $p_1 - p_2$. Here $\hat{p}_1$ and $\hat{p}_2$ are just the sample proportions for the different samples. In our case, $\hat{p}_1$ is the sample proportion for the people surveyed in 2010 (reported as 0.63), and $\hat{p}_2$ is the sample proportion for the people surveyed in 2014 (reported as 0.79).

The null value is 0, because the null hypothesis claims that these proportions are the same, so $p_1 - p_2 = 0$.

The standard deviation, SD, is more complicated than in the one-sample case, because the null hypothesis no longer tells us the value of the population proportion. All it tells us is that both populations have the same value. For this reason, when we estimate this single value, we pool the two samples together. Formula 8.2 shows you how to do this.

Formula 8.2: The two-proportion z-test statistic

$$z = \frac{\hat{p}_1 - \hat{p}_2 - 0}{SD}$$

where

$$SD = \sqrt{\hat{p}(1 - \hat{p})\left(\frac{1}{n_1} + \frac{1}{n_2}\right)}$$

n_1 = sample size in sample 1

n_2 = sample size in sample 2

$$\hat{p} = \frac{\text{number of successes in sample 1} + \text{number of successes in sample 2}}{n_1 + n_2}$$

$$\hat{p}_1 = \text{proportion of successes in sample 1} = \frac{\text{number of successes in sample 1}}{n_1}$$

$$\hat{p}_2 = \text{proportion of successes in sample 2} = \frac{\text{number of successes in sample 2}}{n_2}$$

Formula 8.2 is perhaps the most elaborate formula we have shown you so far. As usual, it is much more important to be able to use technology to perform this test than to apply the formula. Still, studying the formula does help us understand why the test statistic is useful.

EXAMPLE 12 Angus Reid Survey on Euthanasia

The pollsters from Angus Reid surveyed two random samples, one in 2010 and one in 2014, with the 2010 sample having 1005 Canadians and the 2014 sample having 1504. (Of note, the sample taken in 2014 was prior to the Supreme Court ruling on February 6, 2015, that allows for doctor-assisted suicide in Canada.) The data are summarized in Table 8.3.

	2010	2014	Total
Support Legalization of Euthanasia	633	1188	1821
Do Not Support Legalization of Euthanasia	372	316	688
Total	1005	1504	2509

◀ TABLE 8.3 Data for the Angus Reid survey.

QUESTION Find the observed value of the z-test statistic to test the hypotheses

$$H_0: p_1 = p_2$$
$$H_A: p_1 \neq p_2$$

where p_1 is the proportion of Canadians who supported the legalization of euthanasia in 2010 and p_2 is the proportion of Canadians who supported it in 2014.

SOLUTION We must find all the individual calculations needed in the z-test statistic:

$$\hat{p}_1 = \frac{633}{1005} = 0.63 \text{ (a value we knew already from the 2010 survey)}$$

$$\hat{p}_2 = \frac{1188}{1504} = 0.79 \text{ (again, we knew this value from the 2014 survey)}$$

$$\hat{p} = \frac{633 + 1188}{1005 + 1504} = 0.7258 \text{ (a pooled estimate of the sample proportion)}$$

$$SD = \sqrt{0.7258(1 - 0.7258)\left(\frac{1}{1005} + \frac{1}{1504}\right)} = 0.01818$$

Inserting the values of the various components, the observed value of the z-test statistic is

$$z = \frac{0.63 - 0.79 - 0}{0.01818} = -8.80$$

TRY THIS! Exercise 8.51

Looking Back

Two-Way Tables
Two-way tables, such as the one used to summarize the data in Example 12, were first presented in Chapter 1.

Details

The Sign of z
In a two-proportion test, whether z is positive or negative depends on which population you call "1" and which you call "2." It's important to pay attention to which proportion is subtracted from which!

Changes to the Requirements: Checking Conditions

The conditions we need to check for a two-sample test of proportions are similar to those for a one-sample test, but with some additional things to consider.

1. *Large Samples*: Both sample sizes must be large enough. Because we don't know the value of p_1 or p_2, we must use an estimate. The null hypothesis says that these two proportions are the same, so we use $\hat{p}$, the pooled sample proportion, to check this condition. Do not use $\hat{p}_1$ or $\hat{p}_2$. This means that we need

   a. $n_1\hat{p} \geq 10$ and $n_1(1 - \hat{p}) \geq 10$
   b. $n_2\hat{p} \geq 10$ and $n_2(1 - \hat{p}) \geq 10$

2. *Random Samples*: The samples are drawn randomly from the appropriate population. In practice, this condition is often impossible to check unless we were present when the data were collected. In such cases, we have to assume that it is true.

3. *Independent Samples*: The samples are independent of each other. This condition is violated if, for example, the same individuals are in both samples we are comparing.

4. *Independent Within Samples*: The observations within each sample must be independent of one another.

5. *Null Hypothesis*: The null hypothesis is true.

If the first four conditions hold, then, assuming the null hypothesis to be true, z approximately follows an $N(0, 1)$ distribution.

EXAMPLE **13** Caffeine for Babies

Apnea of prematurity occurs when premature babies have shallow breathing or stop breathing for more than 20 seconds. One therapy for this condition is to give caffeine to the premature infants. Medical researchers conducted an international study in which one sample of premature infants was randomly assigned to receive caffeine therapy, and another sample received a placebo therapy. Researchers compared the rate of severely negative outcomes (death and severe disabilities) in the two groups to determine whether the caffeine therapy would lower the rate of such bad events.

The caffeine therapy group included 937 infants. Of these 937 infants, 377 suffered from death or disability. The placebo group had 932 infants, and of these, 431 suffered from death or disability (Schmidt et al. 2007). These data are summarized in Figure 8.12.

QUESTION Perform a four-step hypothesis test to test whether the caffeine therapy was effective (that is, whether it succeeded in lowering the death or disability proportion).

SOLUTION As always, hypotheses are about populations, not samples. In this example, we have two samples, consisting of 937 and 932 infants, but our hypothesis is about *all* premature infants who might receive caffeine or placebo therapy.

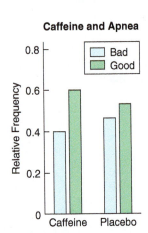

▲ **FIGURE 8.12** Bar graph for caffeine treatment for apnea of prematurity.

Let p_1 represent the proportion of death or disability in all infants who could receive caffeine therapy, and let p_2 represent the proportion of death or disability in all infants who could receive the placebo therapy.

Step 1: Hypothesize
The null hypothesis is neutral; it states that the therapy changes nothing. If so, then the proportions of both populations are the same.

$$H_0: p_1 = p_2$$

The alternative hypothesis is that the therapy will help, so the proportion of bad events in the caffeine therapy group should be lower than that in the placebo group.

$$H_A: p_1 < p_2$$

Step 2: Prepare
We use a significance level of $\alpha = 0.05$.

We are comparing proportions from two populations, so we need to make sure that we can use the two-proportion z-test. Here are the conditions we check:

1. Are both samples large enough?
   We find that

   $$\hat{p} = \frac{377 + 431}{937 + 932} = \frac{808}{1869} = 0.432317$$

   First sample: $n_1 \times 0.432317 = 937 \times 0.432317 = 405.08$, which is greater than 10, and $937 \times (1 - 0.432317) = 531.92$, which is also greater than 10.

   Second sample: $n_2 \times 0.432317 = 932 \times 0.432317 = 402.92$, which is greater than 10, and $932 \times (1 - 0.432317) = 529.08$, which is also greater than 10.

2. Are the samples drawn randomly from the appropriate population?
   We are not told whether the samples are random, but for the purpose of this exercise we will assume that they are.

3. Are the samples independent of each other?
   The samples are independent of each other because the caffeine treatment is given to a different group of babies from those who received the placebo.

4. We are not told if the observations within each sample are independent or not. However, we will assume that data observed within the placebo group are independent of each other, as well as the data observed within the caffeine, or treatment, group.

With these four conditions checked, we can proceed to step 3.

Step 3: Compute to compare
We must find the individual pieces of Formula 8.2. We defined p_1 to be the proportion of babies who could receive caffeine therapy in the population and who suffer from bad events. So let $\hat{p}_1$ be the proportion of babies in the caffeine therapy sample who suffered these bad events. The sample size in this group was $n_1 = 937$, and 377 suffered bad events. Then

$$\hat{p}_1 = \frac{377}{937} = 0.4023$$

The sample proportion for the placebo group is

$$\hat{p}_2 = \frac{431}{932} = 0.4624$$

To find the standard deviation, we need to use $\hat{p}$, the proportion of bad events that happen in the sample if we ignore the fact that the babies belong to two different groups. Above we found that $\hat{p} = 0.4323$.
The standard deviation is then

$$SD = \sqrt{0.432317(1 - 0.432317)\left(\frac{1}{937} + \frac{1}{932}\right)} = 0.022918$$

Putting it all together yields

$$z = \frac{0.402348 - 0.462446}{0.022918} = \frac{-0.060098}{0.022918} = -2.62$$

Now that we know the observed value, we must measure our surprise. The null hypothesis assumes that the two population proportions are the same and that our sample proportions differed only by chance. The p-value will measure the probability of getting an outcome as extreme as or more extreme than -2.62, assuming that the population proportions are the same.

The p-value is calculated exactly the same way as with a one-proportion z-test. Our alternative hypothesis is a left-tailed hypothesis, so we need to find the probability of getting a value less than the observed value (Figure 8.13).

Figure 8.14 shows the z-value and the p-value from technology.

$$\text{p-value} = 0.004$$

Step 4: Interpret and conclude
If the null hypothesis is true, the probability that another experiment would give an outcome that is as surprising or more surprising than our current outcome of -2.62 is 0.004. This p-value is less than our significance level of 0.05, so we reject the null hypothesis. From the data, we conclude that caffeine therapy does help: a lower proportion of babies will die or suffer disability with this therapy.

Note that because this is a controlled, randomized experiment (the researchers randomly assigned babies to treatment groups), we can make a cause-and-effect conclusion about the effectiveness of the treatment.

 Exercise 8.53

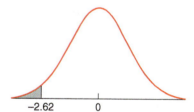

▲ **FIGURE 8.13** The shaded area represents the area to the left of a z-value of -2.62.

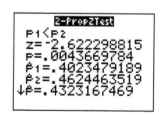

▲ **FIGURE 8.14** TI-83/84 output for the p-value of the test of caffeine on babies.

TWO-PROPORTION z-TEST

WHAT IS IT? ▶	A hypothesis test.
WHAT DOES IT DO? ▶	The null hypothesis is always that the proportions are the same, and this procedure gives us a way to reject or fail to reject that hypothesis.
HOW DOES IT DO IT? ▶	The test statistic z compares the differences between the sample proportions and the value 0 (which is what the null hypothesis says this difference should be):

$$z = \frac{\hat{p}_1 - \hat{p}_2 - 0}{SD} \text{ where } SD = \sqrt{\hat{p}(1 - \hat{p})\left(\frac{1}{n_1} + \frac{1}{n_2}\right)}$$

Values of z far from 0 tend to discredit the null hypothesis.

HOW IS IT USED? ▶	When the conditions are right for each sample. The data must come from two independent, random samples, and each sample must be larger than 10% of the population. Then the p-value can be computed for the z-test statistic, which can be approximately modelled by the $N(0, 1)$ distribution.
WHEN IS ITUSED? ▶	When making a hypothesis that compares two population proportions, p_1 to p_2.

SECTION 8.5

Understanding Hypothesis Testing

Now that you've seen how to do a hypothesis test, you need to know about a few subtleties before you can become an expert.

If Conditions Fail

If the conditions fail to be met for the hypothesis test, the z-test statistic will not follow a Normal distribution when the null hypothesis is true. This means that we cannot find the p-value using the Normal curve (using Table 2 in Appendix A or technology). However, other approaches often exist.

Sample Sizes Too Small

The Normal distribution is only an approximation to the true distribution of the z-test statistic. If the sample sizes are large enough, then the approximation is very good. If the sample sizes are too small, then the approximation may not be good, but other tests can be used. Fisher's Exact Test is one such test that, under certain conditions, can find the exact p-value (not the approximate p-value found with the Normal curve) for two proportions. We will discuss Fisher's Exact Test in Chapter 10.

Samples Not Independent

Suppose we survey a sample of consumers and determine the proportion that will buy a new car in the next year. This same sample then watches a car commercial, and by asking again whether they plan to buy a new car in the next year, we determine a second proportion. We do this because we want to know whether the commercial changed minds. In other words, has the proportion that will buy a new car increased after the sample watched the commercial? Two populations are being studied: those who have not seen the commercial and those who have. However, the two samples we collect consist of the same people, because we interview each person both before and after the commercial. Thus the samples are *not* independent. If you find yourself in this situation, all is not lost, but you should consult a statistician to consider your options.

Samples Not Randomly Selected

In Chapter 7, we learned how non-random samples such as convenience samples and voluntary-response samples do not allow us to proceed with the process of statistical inferences. This is because the requirement of independent data, which is necessary for the statistical techniques outlined in this text, probably does not hold. Sometimes, random samples are rare in certain situations. For example, medical researchers cannot take a random sample of people with a medical condition they wish to study: they rely on recruiting patients who come into their clinics/hospitals. Psychologists at universities often study students, particularly students who are willing to submit to a study for a small amount of money or to earn a credit on a part of their course. It is difficult for them to take a random sample from the population and cover their expenses to get them to the university to participate in their experiment.

Sometimes we get around such potential problems by assuming that the samples taken are random, or that the samples are representative of the population under study. However, we have no guarantee that the conclusions we make with such assumptions are valid or useful.

In many situations, though, researchers are not that interested in generalizing to the larger population. For example, in the study of apnea in premature infants, the researchers were interested in knowing whether caffeine therapy worked for this group of infants or if, instead, the differences between the caffeine therapy infants and the placebo infants could be explained by chance. They concluded that the differences were too large to be due to chance, so they felt confident concluding that at least for this group, the treatment was effective. Research with other groups is still needed to see whether the results obtained are **replicable**, but the study is at least an encouraging start because researchers know the therapy works with some infants. In Chapter 13 we study some tests that more thoroughly address this situation, in which samples are not necessarily drawn at random.

Controlling Mistakes: The Role of Sample Size

In Section 8.1 we mentioned one type of bad decision we might make when carrying out a hypothesis test. This mistake occurs when we reject the null hypothesis even though it is true. The probability of making this mistake was called the significance level.

Another type of bad decision we might make is to *fail* to reject the null hypothesis when the null hypothesis *should be* rejected. We might make one of these two types of bad decisions—but not both—when doing a hypothesis test.

If you are a jury member and you convict a defendant as guilty when, in fact, he is innocent, you have made the first type of error. You are making the second type of error when you decide that the defendant is not guilty when in fact he did commit the crime.

But why be so negative? Rather than focusing on what can go wrong if we mistakenly fail to reject the null hypothesis, we instead focus on its complement: correctly rejecting the null hypothesis, or, in the context of a criminal trial, correctly convicting a guilty person. The probability of rejecting the null hypothesis when the null hypothesis is wrong—the probability of doing the right thing—is called the **power** of the statistical test.

We can ensure that the significance level is set at 5% just by rejecting H_0 whenever the p-value is less than or equal to 0.05, but the power is a little more difficult to control. This is because the null hypothesis can be wrong in many different ways, so it is harder to measure the probability of correctly rejecting the null.

The power depends on three factors:

1. Just how wrong the null hypothesis truly is. If the null hypothesis value, p_0, is very close to the true value of p, then the probability of correctly identifying that they are different is small, because the two values are very similar. So

 Details

Replicable Results
The results of a study are said to have been replicated when researchers using new subjects come to the same conclusion.

 Caution

Cause and Effect
Remember that we can conclude that there is a cause-and-effect relationship between a treatment variable and a response variable only when we have a controlled experiment that uses random assignment, includes a placebo (or comparison) treatment, and is double-blind.

Details

Mistakes (Errors)
We are not referring here to calculation mistakes. The mistakes we refer to occur because sometimes, just by chance, we get sample data that are very unusual and come to a mistaken conclusion about the population from which the data came.

the power will be low and we are unlikely to make the right decision. On the other hand, if the true value of p is very different from p_0, then it is easy to tell them apart, and the probability of making the correct decision is high. The basic idea here is that it is easier to confuse a beaver with an otter than to confuse it with a mouse.

2. The sample size. The larger the sample size, the bigger the power. More is always better (although more expensive) when it comes to sample size. With a larger sample, it's easier to tell the beavers from the otters.

3. The significance level. The smaller the significance level, the smaller the power. (Remember: small power, bad; small significance level, good.) If you want a small probability of mistakenly rejecting the null hypothesis when it is in fact true, then you must live with a smaller probability that you will correctly reject it when it is false. We discuss this tradeoff after the next paragraph.

Calculating the power is tricky and somewhat complex, in part because it requires that we know the true value of the population proportion. We leave this calculation to a future statistics course. For now, be aware that if you do a hypothesis test and do not reject the null, then there is always the chance that you have made an error because your power is too low. You simply don't have enough evidence to tell the difference between the null hypothesis and the truth.

The Tradeoff Between Significance Level and Power

We are free to choose any value we wish for the significance level. Typically, we set this probability at 0.05, but sometimes we go as low as 0.01. But why don't we make it arbitrarily small? Say 0.0000001? That way, we'd almost never make the mistake of rejecting a true null hypothesis.

We can't make the significance level as small as we would like because we have a price to pay. The price is that if we make the significance level smaller, then the power gets smaller too!

To see this, think about our criminal justice example. The null hypothesis is that the defendant is innocent. The alternative is that he is guilty. An error occurs when we convict an innocent man (mistakenly reject the null hypothesis). Another type of error occurs when we free a guilty man (fail to reject the null hypothesis even though it is false). We can make the significance level, the probability of convicting an innocent man, 0 by following a simple rule: free every defendant. If everyone goes free, then it is impossible to convict an innocent person because you are convicting no one. But now the power—the probability of correctly convicting a guilty person—is 0%.

 KEY POINT We cannot make the significance level arbitrarily small because doing so lowers the power—the probability that we will correctly reject the null hypothesis.

Of course, we could increase the power by changing course and convicting every defendant. Now the power is 100% because every guilty person will be convicted. But the significance level has gone to 100% as well, because every innocent person also gets convicted.

There is only one way out if you want to lower the significance level and keep the power high: increase the sample size. This relationship between power and significance level is summarized in Table 8.4.

▶ **TABLE 8.4** Relationship between power and significance level.

	Reject H_0	Fail to Reject H_0
H_0 True	Bad (The probability of doing this is called the significance level.)	Good
H_0 False	Good (The probability of doing this is called the power.)	Bad

So What? Statistical Significance vs. Practical Significance

Researchers call a result "statistically significant" when they reject the null hypothesis. This means that the difference between their data-estimated value for a parameter and the null hypothesis value is so large that it cannot be explained by chance. However, just because a difference is statistically significant does not mean it is useful or meaningful. A *practically significant* result is both statistically significant and meaningful.

For example, suppose that the proportion of people who get a certain type of cancer is one in 10 million. However, a statistical analysis finds that those who talk on their cell phones every day have a statistically significant greater risk of getting that cancer, and that the risk is doubled. It may be true that using your cell phone is therefore more dangerous than not using it, but would you really stop talking on the phone if your risk would change from two in 10 million to one in 10 million? That's a pretty big change of habit for a pretty small change in risk. Most people would conclude that the difference in risk is statistically significant, but not practically significant.

> **KEY POINT** : Statistically significant findings do not necessarily mean that the results are useful.

Don't Change Hypotheses!

A researcher sets up a study to see whether caffeine affects our ability to concentrate. He has a large number of subjects, and he gives them a task to complete when they have not had any caffeine. The task takes some concentration to complete, and he records how long it takes them. Later, he asks them to complete the same task, only this time the subjects have had a dose of caffeine. Again he records the time, and he's interested in the proportion who take longer to complete the task with caffeine than without.

He isn't sure just what the effect of caffeine will be. It might help people concentrate, in which case only a small proportion of people will take longer. On the other hand, it might make people jittery so that a large proportion will take longer to complete the task. If caffeine has no effect, probably half will take the same amount of time or more, and half will take the same amount of time or less.

The researcher chooses a significance level of $\alpha = 0.05$ to test this pair of hypotheses:

$$H_0: p = 0.5$$

$$H_A: p \neq 0.5$$

The parameter p represents the proportion of all people who would take longer to complete the task with caffeine than without. His alternative hypothesis is two-tailed because he does not know what the effect will be—that is, whether it will increase or decrease concentration.

He collects his data and gets a z-test statistic of -1.81. This leads to a p-value of 0.07—and to a moral dilemma! (Figure 8.15 illustrates this p-value.) The researcher needs a p-value less than or equal to 0.05 if he is to publish this paper, because no one wants to hear about an insignificant result. Also, he needs to publish more papers if he is going to get that promotion he really wants.

However, it occurs to this researcher that if he had a different alternative hypothesis, his p-value would be different. Specifically, if he had used

$$H_A: p < 0.50$$

then the p-value would have been the area in just the lower tail. In that case, his p-value would be 0.035 and he would reject the null hypothesis.

What the researcher has just done is the sort of thing that small children do in a contest: they change the rules midway through so that they can win. As they say in the

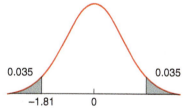

▲ **FIGURE 8.15** The shaded areas represent the p-value of 0.070 for a test statistic of $z = -1.81$ in a two-tailed hypothesis test.

western movies, "You gotta dance with the gal/guy that brung ya." You can't choose your hypotheses to fit the data. By doing so, you are increasing the true significance level of your test.

Hypothesis-Testing Logic

Statisticians and scientists are rather touchy when it comes to talk about "proving" things. They often use softer words, such as "Our data demonstrate that . . ." or "Our data are consistent with the theory that. . . ." One reason is that in mathematical and scientific circles, the word *prove* has a very precise and very definite meaning. If something is proven, then it is absolutely, positively, and without any doubt true. However, in real life, and particularly in statistics and science (which we consider to be part of real life), you can never be completely certain. For this reason we avoid saying, for example, that we have proven that more people now believe they dream in colour than thought so in the past.

On a similar note, it is improper (maybe even impolite!) to say that you have "accepted" the null hypothesis when your p-value is bigger than 0.05. Instead, we say "We have failed to reject H_0" or "We cannot reject H_0." The reason for this is that several factors might make it difficult to determine whether the null hypothesis is false. It could be that our statistical power was low, and we couldn't detect that the null hypothesis was false because we didn't have enough evidence.

In Example 11, we examined a study that asked whether music instruction improved children's creativity scores. We concluded that we could not reject the null hypothesis and that there was not enough evidence to show that the scores increased. Could we make a stronger statement? Specifically, could we conclude that the music instruction was *not* effective?

No. We might have had low power; that is, the probability of detecting a difference between the students' increase in scores for an effective music instruction program was too low. With a larger sample size, we might see that, in fact, the program is effective.

 KEY POINT   Don't say you "proved" something with statistics. Say you "demonstrated" it or "showed" it. Similarly, don't say you "accept the null hypothesis"; say, rather, that you "cannot reject the null hypothesis" or that you "failed to reject the null hypothesis" or that "there is insufficient evidence to reject the null hypothesis."

CASE STUDY REVISITED

Does watching violence on TV as a child lead to violent behaviour as an adult? To find out, researchers examined two independent groups of subjects. One group had watched a lot of violent television as children; the other group had not. The researchers recorded whether the subjects enacted a form of violence with their partners or spouses, including whether they had pushed or shoved a partner or spouse, which was defined as physical abuse. About 38% of those who had watched violent television as children said yes, compared to 22% of the watchers of nonviolent TV. Can we conclude, then, that these groups are truly different? Or might the observed difference be due simply to chance?

To find out, the researchers performed a hypothesis test. We can do a similar test with what we've learned in this chapter. The data are summarized in Table 8.5 and in Figure 8.16.

▶ **TABLE 8.5** Two-way table for the relationship between TV violence and physical abuse.

	High TV Violence	Low TV Violence	Total
Yes, Physical Abuse	25	57	82
No, Physical Abuse	41	206	247
Total	66	263	329

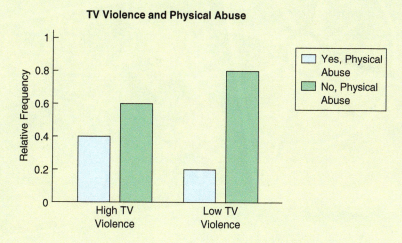

TV Violence and Physical Abuse

◀ FIGURE 8.16 Bar chart for the relationship between TV violence and physical abuse.

As it turns out, the differences between the two groups in the proportions of those who committed an act of violence is too large to be attributed to chance alone. Because this is an observational study, we cannot conclude that watching violent TV as a child causes adults to behave violently toward their spouses. Complicating factors could exist. For example, perhaps children raised by parents who behave violently toward each other are more likely to watch violent television *and* more likely to reenact their parents' behaviour when they become adults. Still, we can rule out the possibility that these sample proportions differ only because of chance.

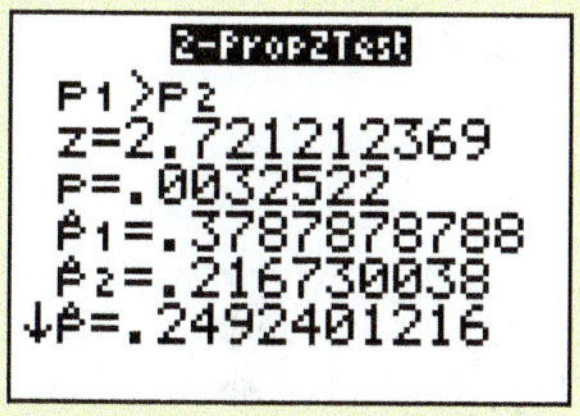

To come to this conclusion, we performed a two-proportion z-test with a significance level of $\alpha = 0.05$. The two populations consist of all the 20-something adults who watched a lot of violent TV as children (population 1) and all the 20-something adults who did not watch violent TV as children (population 2). The proportion of this first population who commit acts of violence directed at their partners we call p_1. The proportion of this second population who commit acts of violence against their partners we call p_2.

$H_0: p_1 = p_2$ Both groups have the same proportion of violent acts.

$H_A: p_1 > p_2$ The TV violence group has a greater proportion of violent acts.

A quick check shows that the sample sizes are large enough, and the other conditions can be assumed to hold as well. (One questionable condition is the one requiring random samples. However, we can assume the samples are random to see what the conclusion would be in this case. The fact that they are not really random means our results might not generalize to a larger group.)

The observed value of the z-statistic, calculated with technology, is $z = 2.72$ (see Figure 8.17). The p-value for this one-tailed hypothesis is 0.003. This small value tells us that the outcome was rather unusual if, in fact, the proportion of violent acts is the same in both populations. The fact that such an outcome is so rare leads us to reject the null hypothesis and conclude that those who watch violent TV as children do tend to commit more acts of violence toward their spouses as adults than do people who did not watch violent TV.

```
2-PropZTest
P1>P2
z=2.721212369
P=.0032522
p̂1=.3787878788
p̂2=.216730038
↓p̂=.2492401216
```

▲ FIGURE 8.17 TI-83/84 output for a two-proportion z-test using a one-tailed alternative hypothesis, where the sample proportions are 25/66 and 57/263. Here p_1 is the proportion of those who watched violent TV who subsequently abused a partner, and p_2 is the proportion of those who did not watch violent TV who later abused a partner.

EXPLORING STATISTICS

CLASS ACTIVITY

Identifying Flavours of Gum Through Smell

GOALS

To use a hypothesis test to determine how well a person can distinguish between flavours based on smell alone.

MATERIALS

- Gum (or candy) in two different flavours. We will call these flavour A and flavour B. Each student will need one piece of each flavour.
- A paper towel for each student.

ACTIVITY

Pair up. One student will take the role of the sniffer, and the other will act as the researcher. Both students must know the two flavours that are being tested.

Researcher: ask the sniffer to turn his or her back, then select a piece of gum at random and record the flavour of the gum on a sheet of paper. Place the gum on a sheet of paper towel.

Hold the gum about five centimetres below the sniffer's nose and ask him or her to identify which of the two flavours is in the hand. Sniffers may take as long as they like. Record whether the sniffer's response was correct next to the flavour that you wrote down for this trial.

Do 20 trials, then work together to determine the proportion of correct responses. If time permits, change roles.

BEFORE THE ACTIVITY

1. Let p represent the probability that the sniffer makes a correct identification. If the sniffer is simply guessing and cannot tell the difference, what value would p have?

2. If the sniffer is not guessing and really can tell the difference, would p be bigger than, less than, or the same as the value you found in Question 1?

3. Suppose the sniffer cannot tell the difference between the two flavours. In 20 trials, about how many would you expect the sniffer to get right? What proportion is this? What is the greatest number of trials you'd expect the sniffer to get right if she or he were just guessing? What proportion is this?

4. How many trials would the sniffer have to get right before you would believe that he or she can tell the difference? All 20? 19? Explain.

5. Write a pair of hypotheses to test whether the sniffer is just guessing or can really tell the difference. Write the hypotheses in both words and symbols, using the parameter p to represent the probability that the sniffer correctly identifies the scent.

AFTER THE ACTIVITY

1. Report the proportion of trials the sniffer got right.

2. Does this show that the sniffer could tell the difference in the scents? Explain.

3. If the sniffer is just guessing, what is the probability that he or she would have gotten as many right as, or more right than, the actual number recorded?

    a. Pretty likely: between 50% and 100%   b. Maybe: between 10% and 50%

    c. Fairly unlikely: between 5% and 10%   d. Very unlikely: between 0% and 5%

CHAPTER REVIEW

Summary of Learning Objectives

1. **What is a statistical hypothesis about the population proportion, or one that compares proportions of two populations?** A statistical hypothesis has two parts, the null hypothesis H_0 and the alternative hypothesis H_A. H_0 represents the status quo and is assumed to be the true state of affairs. For this reason, it always contains an "=" sign. For tests about the population proportion, $H_0 : p = p_0$. For tests that compare two population proportions, $H_0 : p_1 = p_2$. H_A is "not the null hypothesis," and can be "less than" ($<$), "greater than" ($>$), or "not equal to" ($\neq$). This is Step 1 of the Requirements of a Hypothesis Test.

2. **How is the evidence of a test about the population proportion, or a test comparing two population proportions, gathered?** The evidence of the statistical test comes together in the form of a single number that is calculated from the sample(s). This computed value is called a test statistic. The z-test statistic is calculated for a test of the population proportion (one-proportion z-test) or two population proportions (two-proportion z-test). The conditions required for using the standard Normal distribution to model the behaviour of this z-test statistic are (1) independence of the data by random sampling, (2) expectation of observing at least 10 successes and 10 failures in each sample, and when comparing two population proportions, (3) the samples are independent of each other. Making sure these conditions hold is to prepare to compute the value of the z-test statistic. This is Step 2 of the Requirements of a Hypothesis Test.

3. **How is the evidence computed and evaluated by a p-value?** The data gathered from the sample (one-proportion z-test) or both samples (two-proportion z-test) are summarized by observing, through computation, the value of the z-test statistic.

    For a one-proportion z-test:

    Formula 8.1: $z = \dfrac{\hat{p} - p_0}{SD}$

    where

    $$SD = \sqrt{\dfrac{p_0(1 - p_0)}{n}}$$

p_0 is the hypothesized value of the population proportion in H_0, $\hat{p}$ (p-hat) is the proportion of people/objects sampled that have the particular characteristic n is the sample size.

For a two-proportion z-test:

Formula 8.2: $z = \dfrac{\hat{p}_1 - \hat{p}_2 - 0}{SD}$

where

$$SD = \sqrt{\hat{p}(1 - \hat{p})\left(\dfrac{1}{n_1} + \dfrac{1}{n_2}\right)}$$

where

$$\hat{p} = \dfrac{\text{number of successes in both samples}}{n_1 + n_2}$$

$\hat{p}_1$ is the proportion of successes observed in the random sample of n_1 from the first population, and $\hat{p}_2$ is the proportion of successes observed in the random sample of n_2 from the second population.

   The p-value is then computed from the observed value of the z-test statistic, and depends on the alternative hypothesis. Figure 8.18 shows, from left to right, the p-values for a two-tailed test, a right-tailed test, and a left-tailed test. This is Step 3 of the Requirements of a Hypothesis Test.

4. **How is a decision made about the null hypothesis?** If the null hypothesis is true, then the computed p-value is the chance that another random sample (one-proportion z-test) or random samples (two-proportion z-test) will give stronger evidence against the null hypothesis than the current sample/samples. The smaller the p-value, the more unexpected the observed value of the test statistic becomes. This is then compared to the significance level, which is the probability of rejecting the null hypothesis when it should not be rejected. If the p-value is less than the significance level α, then the null hypothesis is rejected. The conclusion is then that the data appearing in the sample(s) do not support the null hypothesis. This is Step 4 of the Requirements of a Hypothesis Test.

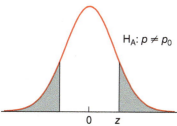
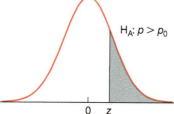
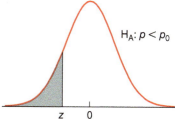

▲ **FIGURE 8.18** Representations of possible p-values for three different alternative hypotheses. The area of the shaded regions represents the p-value.

Important Terms

Hypothesis testing, *345*
Null hypothesis, H_0, *346*
Alternative hypothesis, H_A, *347*
Significance level, α (alpha), *348*

Test statistic, *349*
One-proportion z-test, *349*
z-test statistic, *350*
p-value, *351*

Two-tailed hypothesis, *352*
One-tailed hypothesis, *352*
Left-tailed hypothesis, *352*
Right-tailed hypothesis, *352*

Two-proportion z-test, *366*
Replicable results, *371*
Power, *371*

Sources

Angus Reid Institute. 2014, December 16. Most Canadians support assisted suicide, but under which circumstances reveal much deeper divides (accessed January 11, 2015).

Angus Reid Public Opinion. 2012, June 13. Three in five Canadians OK with banning plastic shopping bags (accessed March 1, 2013).

Angus Reid Public Opinion. Canadians and Britons are more open to same-sex relations than Americans (accessed March 8, 2013).

Angus Reid Public Opinion. Global warming skepticism higher in the U.S. and Britain than in Canada. http://www.angus-reid.com/polls/45431/global-warming-skepticism-higher-in-u-s-and-britain-than-canada (accessed March 1, 2013).

cnews.canoe.ca. 2011. Most Canadians say death penalty is OK. cnews.canoe.ca/CNEWS/Politics/2011/01/25/17031436.html (accessed March 3, 2013).

The Daily, Statistics Canada. 2000, August 28. www.statcan.gc.ca/daily-quotidien/000828/dq000828b-eng.htm (accessed March 1, 2013).

Digital Journal. 2010, December 8. Survey: 27 percent of Canadian drivers admit to driving impaired. http://digitaljournal.com/article/301211 (accessed March 1, 2013).

Gallup. 2001, December 10. The right to bear arms: U.S. and Canada. http://www.gallup.com/poll/7381/right-bear-arms-us-canada.aspx (accessed March 9, 2013).

Globe and Mail. 2011, October 31. With Harper cruising in poll, Rae surpasses Turmell on leadership (accessed March 9, 2013).

Health Canada. A federal report on comparable health indicators. www.hc-sc.gc.ca/hcs-sss/pubs/system-regime/2010-fed-comp-indicat/index-eng.php#t19 (accessed March 8, 2013).

Husemann, L. R., J. Moise-Titus, C. Podolski, and L. D. Eron. 2003. Longitudinal relations between children's exposure to TV violence and their aggressive and violent behavior in young adulthood: 1977–1992. *Development Psychology 39*(2), 201–221.

National Post. 2012, September 11. Get ready for $10K tuition: Canadian university fees rising faster than inflation, report says (accessed March 1, 2013).

Pundits Guide. 2011, September 18. Pollsters divided on final shifts in Ontario during last May's federal election. www.punditsguide.ca/tag/exit-polls (accessed March 9, 2013).

Schmidt, B. et al. for the Caffeine for Apnea of Prematurity Trial Group, 2007. Long-term effects of caffeine therapy for apnea of prematurity. *New England Journal of Medicine 357*, 1893–1902.

Schwitzgebel, E. 2003: Do people still report dreaming in black and white? An attempt to replicate a questionnaire from 1942. *Perceptual & Motor Skills 96*, 25–29.

Vancouver Sun. 2013, March 8. Unemployment rates in selected Canadian cities.

SECTION EXERCISES

SECTION 8.1

8.1 Choose one of the answers given. The null hypothesis is always a statement about a _____ (sample statistic or population parameter).

8.2 Choose one of the answers in each case. In statistical inference, measurements are made on a _____ (sample or population), and generalizations are made to a _____ (sample or population).

8.3 With a two-tailed test, if the z-test statistic is far from 0, will the p-value be large (closer to 1) or small (closer to 0)?

8.4 With a two-tailed test, if the z-test statistic is 0 or close to 0, will the p-value be large (closer to 1) or small (closer to 0)?

TRY 8.5 Coin Flips (Example 1) A coin is flipped 30 times and lands on heads 18 times. You want to test the hypothesis that the coin does not come up 50% heads in the long run.

Pick the correct null hypothesis for this test.

    i. $H_0: \hat{p} = 0.60$

    ii. $H_0: p = 0.50$

    iii. $H_0: p = 0.60$

    iv. $H_0: \hat{p} = 0.50$

8.6 Die Rolls You roll a six-sided die 30 times and land on the "one" outcome 6 times. You want to test the hypothesis that the die does not come up as a one for one-sixth of the time; in other words, the die is not fair.

  a. Pick the notation that represents what you want to test.

    i. $p = 1/6$ ii. $p \neq 1/6$ iii. $\hat{p} = 1/6$ iv. $\hat{p} \neq 1/6$

  b. The notation you chose in part a would represent the _____ (null or alternative) hypothesis.

8.7 Biased Coin You flip a loonie 20 times and observe 15 heads. You want to test the hypothesis that the loonie is biased toward a heads outcome. That is, the loonie is more likely to come up heads than tails.

  a. Pick the notation that represents what you want to test.

    i. $p \neq 1/2$ ii. $\hat{p} \neq 1/2$ iii. $\hat{p} > 1/2$ iv. $p > 1/2$

  b. The notation you chose in part a would represent the _____ (null or alternative) hypothesis.

8.8 Guessing a Card A friend claims he can predict the suit of a card drawn from a standard deck of 52 cards. There are four suits and equal numbers of cards in each suit. The parameter, p, is the probability of success, and the null hypothesis is that the friend is just guessing.

  a. Which is the correct null hypothesis?

    i. $p = 1/4$ ii. $p = 1/13$ iii. $p > 1/4$ iv. $p > 1/13$

  b. Which hypothesis best fits the friend's claim? (This is the alternative hypothesis.)

    i. $p = 1/4$ ii. $p = 1/13$ iii. $p > 1/4$ iv. $p > 1/13$

8.9 Predicting a Die Roll A friend claims he can predict how a six-sided die will land. The parameter, p, is the long-run likelihood of success, and the null hypothesis is that the friend is guessing.

  a. Pick the correct null hypothesis.

    i. $p = 1/6$ ii. $p > 1/6$ iii. $p < 1/6$ iv. $p > 1/2$

  b. Which hypothesis best fits the friend's claim? (This is the alternative hypothesis.)

    i. $p = 1/6$ ii. $p > 1/6$ iii. $p < 1/6$ iv. $p > 1/2$

8.10 Breast Cancer Forty percent of breast cancer patients who are treated with a certain chemotherapy are in remission six months after the start of their treatment. A new chemotherapy to be used in the treatment of breast cancer is to be tested to see if it is more effective than the current chemotherapy. p is the proportion of all breast cancer patients treated with the new chemotherapy who are in remission six months after the start of treatment.

  a. Pick the correct null hypothesis.

    i. $p = 0.40$ ii. $p > 0.40$ iii. $p < 0.40$ iv. $p \neq 0.40$

  b. Which hypothesis represents the research hypothesis? (This is the alternative hypothesis.)

    i. $p = 0.40$ ii. $p > 0.40$ iii. $p < 0.40$ iv. $p \neq 0.40$

8.11 Heart Attack Prevention A new drug is being tested to see whether it can reduce the chance of heart attack in people who have previously had a heart attack. The rate of heart attack in the population of concern is 0.20. The null hypothesis is that p (the population proportion using the new drug who have a heart attack) is 0.2.

Pick the correct alternative hypothesis.

    i. $p \neq 0.2$ ii. $p > 0.2$ iii. $p < 0.2$

8.12 Stroke Survival Rate The proportion of people who live after suffering a stroke is 0.85. Suppose there is a new treatment that is used to increase the survival rate. Use the parameter p to represent the population proportion of people who survive after a stroke. For a hypothesis test of the treatment's effectiveness, researchers use a null hypothesis of $p = 0.85$. Pick the correct alternative hypothesis.

    i. $p \neq 0.85$ ii. $p > 0.85$ iii. $p < 0.85$

TRY 8.13 ESP (Example 2) We are testing someone who claims to have ESP by having that person predict whether a coin will come up heads or tails. The null hypothesis is that the person is guessing and does not have ESP, and the population proportion of success is 0.50. We test the claim with a hypothesis test, using a significance level of 0.05. Select an answer and fill in the blank.

The probability of concluding that the person has ESP when in fact she or he (does/does not) _____ have ESP is _____.

8.14 Multiple-Choice Test A teacher is giving an exam with 20 multiple-choice questions, each with four possible answers. The teacher's null hypothesis is that the student is just guessing, and the population proportion of success is 0.25. Suppose we do a test with a significance level of 0.01. Write a sentence describing the significance level in the context of the hypothesis test.

TRY 8.15 Votes for the Parti Québécois (Example 3) On the basis of experience, a political consultant suggested that 40% of all Quebecers will vote for the Parti Québécois in the next provincial election. Suppose you have surveyed 100 randomly chosen people who are eligible to vote in the election, and 36 say they will vote for the PQ. The null hypothesis is that the proportion of all votes cast for the PQ in the next provincial election is 40%. Give the value of the test statistic that would be used to test the null hypothesis.

8.16 Votes for the Parti Québecois Refer to Exercise 8.15. Suppose 44 out of the 100 voters surveyed say that they'll cast a vote for the PQ. The null hypothesis is that the proportion of all votes cast for the PQ in the next provincial election is 35%. Give the value of the test statistic that would be used to test the null hypothesis.

TRY * **8.17 Texting While Driving (Example 4)** The mother of a teenager has heard a claim that 25% of teenagers who drive and use a cell phone reported texting while driving. She thinks that this rate is too high and wants to test the hypothesis that fewer than 25% of these drivers have texted while driving. Her alternative hypothesis is that the percentage of teenagers who have texted when driving is less than 25%.

$$H_0: p = 0.25$$

$$H_A: p < 0.25$$

She polls 50 randomly selected teenagers, and 6 of them report having texted while driving, a proportion of 0.12.

a. Give the value of the test statistic used to test the hypotheses.

b. The p-value is 0.017. Explain the p-value in the context of this question.

* **8.18 True/False Test** A teacher giving a true/false test wants to make sure her students do better than they would if they were simply guessing, so she forms a hypothesis to test this. Her null hypothesis is that a student will get 50% of the questions on the exam correct. The alternative hypothesis is that the student is not guessing and should get more than 50% in the long run.

$$H_0: p = 0.50$$

$$H_A: p > 0.50$$

A student gets 30 out of 50 questions correct, or 60%.

a. Give the value of the test statistic used to test the hypotheses.

b. The p-value is 0.079. Explain the p-value in the context of this question.

SECTION 8.2

TRY **8.19 p-Values (Example 5)** For each graph, indicate whether the shaded area could represent a p-value. Explain why or why not. If yes, state whether the area could represent the p-value for a one-tailed or a two-tailed alternative hypothesis.

(a)

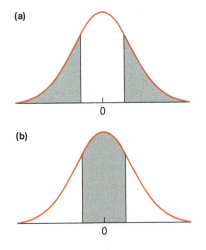

0

(b)

0

8.20 p-Values For each graph, state whether the shaded area could represent a p-value. Explain why or why not. If yes, state whether the area could represent the p-value for a one-tailed or a two-tailed alternative hypothesis.

(a)

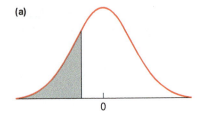

0

(b)

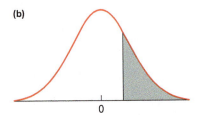

0

TRY **8.21 p-Values (Example 6)** A researcher carried out a hypothesis test using a two-tailed alternative hypothesis. Which of the following z-scores is associated with the smallest p-value? Explain.

   i. $z = 0.50$ ii. $z = 1.00$ iii. $z = 2.00$ iv. $z = 3.00$

8.22 Coin Flips A test is conducted in which a coin is flipped 30 times to test whether the coin is unbiased. The null hypothesis is that the coin is fair. The alternative is that the coin is not fair. One of the accompanying figures represents the p-value after getting 16 heads out of 30 flips, and the other represents the p-value after getting 18 heads out of 30 flips. Which is which, and how do you know?

(a)

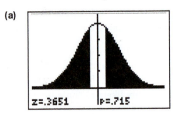

z=.3651   p=.715

(b)

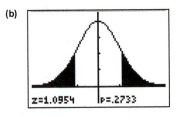

z=1.0954   p=.2733

8.23 ESP Suppose a friend says he can predict whether a coin flip will result in heads or tails. You test him, and he gets 10 right out of 20. Do you think he can predict the coin flip (or has a way of cheating)? Or could this just be something that occurs by chance? Explain without doing any calculations.

8.24 ESP Again Suppose a friend says he can predict whether a coin flip will result in heads or tails. You test him, and he gets 20 right out of 20. Do you think he can predict the coin flip (or has a way of cheating)? Or could this just be something that is likely to occur by chance? Explain without performing any calculations.

SECTION 8.3

8.25 Does Hand Washing Save Lives? (Example 7) In the mid-1800s, Dr. Ignaz Semmelweiss decided to make the doctors wash their hands with a strong disinfectant between patients at a clinic with a death rate of 9.9%. Semmelweiss wanted to test the hypothesis that the death rate would go down after the new hand-washing procedure was used. What null and alternative hypotheses should he have used? Explain, using both words and symbols. Explain the meaning of any symbols you use.

8.26 Retirement Suppose you wanted to test the claim that the majority of Canadians between the ages of 18 and 50 plan to keep working past the age of 65. Give the null and alternative hypotheses, and explain each in both words and symbols.

8.27 Drinking and Driving The Canadian Automobile Association (CAA) reported in 2010 that 27% of Canadians surveyed had admitted to driving impaired at least once in the past year. Suppose you are to survey randomly chosen Canadians to determine whether the proportion who have driven impaired at least once in the past year has *changed* from 2010.

    a. Give the null and alternative hypotheses to test whether the proportion of Canadians who have driven while impaired at least once in the past year has changed from 2010.

    b. The statistical hypothesis in part a is a _____ (right-tailed, left-tailed, or two-tailed) test.

8.28 Drinking and Driving, Again Refer to Exercise 8.27. Suppose you are to survey randomly chosen Canadians to determine whether the proportion who have driven while impaired at least once in the past year has decreased from 2010.

    a. Give the null and alternative hypotheses to test whether the proportion of Canadians who have driven while impaired at least once in the past year has decreased from 2010.

    b. The statistical hypothesis in part a is a _____(right-tailed, left-tailed, or two-tailed) test.

g 8.29 Gun Registry Support Conventional wisdom suggests that half of Canadians (50%) have supported the existence of the long-gun registry. The same wisdom suggests that the support for the long-gun registry is much lower in the provinces of Alberta, Saskatchewan, and Manitoba. An EKOS poll conducted in 2009 of 247 Canadians living in these three provinces showed that 44 support the long-gun registry. Assume that this survey was a random sample. Test the claim that the proportion of Canadians living in these provinces who are in favour of the long-gun registry is less than 50%. Perform a hypothesis test using a significance level of 0.05. Choose one of the following conclusions.

    i. The proportion is not significantly different from 50%. (A significant difference is one for which the p-value is less than or equal to 0.05.)

    ii. The proportion is significantly less than 50%.

8.30 Death Penalty An Abacus poll of 1105 Canadians in January 2011 showed that 729 believe the death penalty is appropriate for those convicted of murder. A Gallup poll done in 1978 indicated that 68% of Canadians supported the death penalty for those convicted of murder.

    a. Using the data from 2011, test the hypothesis that the support for the death penalty for those convicted of murder has changed since 1978. Use a value of 0.05 for the level of significance α.

    b. Explain the meaning of the p-value.

    c. Choose the appropriate decision.

        i. The level of support for the death penalty has not changed since 1978.

        ii. The level of support for the death penalty has changed since 1978.

TRY 8.31 Dreaming (Example 8) A 2003 study of dreaming found that out of a random sample of 113 people, 92 reported dreaming in colour. However, the rate of reported dreaming in colour that was established in the 1940s was 0.29 (Schwitzgebel 2003). Check to see whether the conditions for using a one-proportion z-test are met, assuming that the researcher wanted to test to see if the proportion dreaming in colour had changed since the 1940s.

8.32 Age Discrimination About 30% of the population in Silicon Valley, a region in California, are between the ages of 40 and 65, according to the U.S. Census. However, only 2% of the 2100 employees at a laid-off man's former Silicon Valley company are between the ages of 40 and 65. Lawyers might argue that if the company hired people regardless of their age, the distribution of ages would be the same as if it had hired people at random from the surrounding population. Check whether the conditions for using the one-proportion z-test are met.

TRY 8.33 Coin Spinning (Example 8 continued) Suppose you are testing the claim that a coin comes up tails more than 50% of the time when the coin is spun on a hard surface. Steps 1 and 2 of the hypothesis test are given. Suppose that you did this experiment and got 22 tails in 30 spins. Find the value of the test statistic z and explain the meaning of the p-value.

    p is the proportion of tails.

    Step 1: $H_0: p = 0.50$

              $H_A: p > 0.50$

    Step 2: Assume that the outcomes are random and the sample size is large enough because both np_0 and $n(1 - p_0)$ are 15.

8.34 Coin Spinning Repeat Exercise 8.33 assuming that you got 18 tails out of 30 spins.

TRY 8.35 Guessing on a True/False Test (Example 9) A true/false test has 50 questions. Suppose a passing grade is 35 or more correct answers. Test the claim that a student knows more than half of the answers and is not just guessing. Assume the student gets 35 answers correct out of 50. Use a significance level of 0.05. Steps 1 and 2 of a hypothesis test procedure are given. Show steps 3 and 4, and be sure to write a clear conclusion.

    Step 1: $H_0: p = 0.50$

              $H_A: p > 0.50$

    Step 2: Choose the one-proportion z-test. The sample size is large enough, because np_0 is $50(0.5) = 25$ and $n(1 - p_0) = 50(.5) = 25$, and both are more than 10. Assume the sample is random.

8.36 Guessing on a Multiple-Choice Test A multiple-choice test has 50 questions with four possible options for each question. For each question, only one of the four options is correct. A passing grade is 35 or more correct answers.

    a. What is the probability that a person will guess correctly on one multiple-choice question?

    b. Test the hypothesis that a person who got 35 right out of 50 is not just guessing, using an alpha of 0.05. Steps 1 and 2 of the hypothesis testing procedure are given. Finish the question by doing steps 3 and 4.

    Step 1: $H_0: p = 0.25$

              $H_A: p > 0.25$

Step 2: Choose the one-proportion z-test. n times p_0 is 50 times 0.25, which is 12.5. This is more than 10, and 50 times 0.75 is also more than 10. Assume a random sample.

TRY 8.37 Taste Test (Example 10) A taste test was done in which a blindfolded subject was asked to identify the spread on English muffins. Twenty bites were taken, and they were randomly arranged such that exactly half of the bites contained butter and half contained margarine.

$$H_0: p = 0.50$$

$$H_A: p > 0.50$$

The subject got 13 out of 20 correct. The graphs show p-values (as shaded areas) corresponding to the alternative hypotheses $p \neq 0.50$, $p > 0.50$, and $p < 0.50$, *though not necessarily in that order.*

Indicate which graph matches the given alternative hypothesis, $p > 0.50$.

(a)
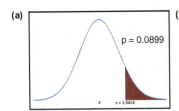

(b)
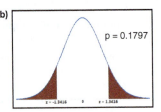

(c)
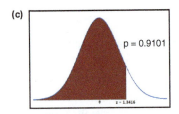

8.38 Penny Spinning Suppose we spin a coin 20 times to test whether it is biased. Let p represent the probability of heads.

$$H_0: p = 0.50$$

$$H_A: p \neq 0.50$$

Suppose that 8 heads were obtained out of 20 spins. The graphs show p-values (as shaded areas) corresponding to the alternative hypotheses $p \neq 0.50$, $p > 0.50$, and $p < 0.50$. Indicate which graph matches the given alternative hypothesis, $p \neq 0.50$.

(a)
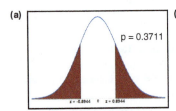

(b)
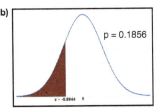

(c)
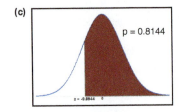

8.39 Banning Sugary Foods in Schools In a Rasmussen poll of 1000 adults in July 2010, 520 of those polled said that schools should ban sugary snacks and soft drinks.

a. Do a majority of adults (more than 50%) support a ban on sugary snacks and soft drinks? Perform a hypothesis test using a significance level of 0.05.

b. Explain the meaning of the p-value in part a.

c. Choose the best interpretation of the results you obtained in part a:

i. The percentage of all adults who favour banning is significantly more than 50%.

ii. The percentage of all adults who favour banning is not significantly more than 50%.

8.40 Year-Round School In July 2010, a Rasmussen poll of 1000 adults showed that 630 opposed students attending school year-round without the traditional summer break.

a. Test the claim that more than half of adults oppose year-round school. Use a significance level of 0.05.

b. Explain the meaning of the p-value in part a.

c. Choose the correct interpretation:

i. The percentage opposing year-round school is significantly more than 50%.

ii. The percentage opposing year-round school is not significantly more than 50%.

8.41 Global Warming An Angus Reid poll in June 2012 found that about 45% of Americans believed that the earth's temperature is rising (or that global warming is fact). In the same month, a survey of 1004 randomly chosen Canadian adults was taken, of whom 532 believed that global warming is fact.

a. What percentage of the Canadian sample believed global warming was fact in June 2012? Is it more or less than the proportion of Americans, or 45%?

b. Test the hypothesis that the proportion of Canadians who believe global warming is fact is different from the proportion of Americans who believe global warming is fact.

c. Explain the meaning of the p-value.

d. Choose the correct interpretation:

i. In 2012, the proportion of Canadians who believe global warming is fact is not different from the 45% of Americans who believe global warming is fact.

ii. In 2012, the proportion of Canadians who believe global warming is fact is different from the 45% of Americans who believe global warming is fact.

8.42 Plane Crashes According to one source, 50% of plane crashes are due at least in part to pilot error (http://www.planecrashinfo .com). Suppose that in a random sample of 100 separate airplane accidents, 62 of them were due to pilot error (at least in part).

a. Test the hypothesis that the proportion of airplane accidents due to pilot error is not 0.50. Use a significance level of 0.05.

b. Explain the meaning of the p-value in part a.

c. Choose the correct interpretation:

i. The percentage of plane crashes due to pilot error is not significantly different from 50%.

ii. The percentage of plane crashes due to pilot error is significantly different from 50%.

TRY 8.43 Mercury in Freshwater Fish (Example 11) Some experts believe that 25% of all freshwater fish have such high levels of mercury that they are dangerous to eat. Suppose a fish market has

250 fish tested, and 75 of them have dangerous levels of mercury. Test the hypothesis that this sample is *not* from a population with 25% dangerous fish. Use a significance level of 0.05.

Comment on your conclusion: Are you saying that the percentage of dangerous fish is definitely 25%? Explain.

8.44 Marijuana Use A statistics professor believes that the percentage of all first-year post-secondary education students who have used marijuana in the past six months is 20%. In a recent survey of 108 randomly sampled first-year students, 25 said that they had used marijuana in the past six months.

  a. Find the proportion of the sample who used marijuana in the past six months.

  b. Test the hypothesis that the proportion of students who say they've used marijuana in the past six months is higher than 20%.

  c. Explain the meaning of the p-value.

  d. Comment on your conclusion.

8.45 Morse's Proportion of T's Samuel Morse determined that the percentage of T's in the English language in the 1800 was 9%. A random sample of 600 letters from a current newspaper contained 48 T's. Test the hypothesis that the proportion of T's has changed in modern times, using the 0.05 level of significance. Treat the newspaper as a random sample of all letters used.

8.46 Morse's Proportion of A's Samuel Morse determined that the percentage of A's in the English language in the 1800s was 8%. A random sample of 600 letters from a current newspaper contained 60 A's. Test the hypothesis that the proportion of A's has changed in modern times, using the 0.05 level of significance. Treat the newspaper as a random sample of all letters used.

SECTION 8.4

g 8.47 Vioxx In the fall of 2004, drug manufacturer Merck Pharmaceutical withdrew Vioxx, a drug that had been used for arthritis pain, from the market after a study revealed that its use was associated with an increase in the risk of heart attack. The experiment was placebo-controlled, randomized, and double-blind. Out of 1287 people taking Vioxx there were 45 heart attacks, and out of 1299 people taking the placebo, there were 25 heart attacks (*Los Angeles Times*, October 23, 2004). Perform a hypothesis test to test whether those who took Vioxx had a greater rate of heart attack than those who took a placebo. Use a level of significance of 0.05. *See page 388 for guidance.* Choose i or ii:

  i. Those taking Vioxx did *not* have a significantly higher rate of heart attack than those taking the placebo.

  ii. Those who took Vioxx had a significantly higher heart attack rate than those who took the placebo.

Can we conclude that Vioxx *causes* an increased risk of heart attack?

8.48 Treating Traumatic Shock Dopamine and norepinephrine are two drugs that are effective for treating traumatic shock, which results in dangerously low blood pressure and can cause death. A study compared the outcomes for patients who were given these drugs. After 28 days it was noted whether the patient was alive or dead. Of the 858 patients randomly assigned dopamine, 450 were alive. Of the 821 patients randomly assigned norepinephrine, 398 were alive. (Source: De Backer et al., Comparison of dopamine and norepinephrine in the treatment of shock, *New England Journal of Medicine*, vol. 362: 779–789, March 4, 2010)

  a. Find and compare the sample percentages of patients alive for these groups.

  b. Test the hypothesis that the rate of success (being alive) is different in the two groups, using a significance level of 0.05.

8.49 Vaccine for Diarrhea A vaccine to prevent severe rotavirus gastroenteritis (diarrhea) was given to African children within the first year of life as part of a drug study. The study reported that of the 3298 children randomly assigned the vaccine, 63 got the virus. Of the 1641 children randomly assigned the placebo, 80 got the virus. (Source: Madhi et al., Effect of human rotavirus vaccine on severe diarrhea in African infants, *New England Journal of Medicine*, vol. 362: 289–298, January 28, 2010)

  a. Find the sample percentage of children who caught the virus in each group. Is the sample percentage lower for the vaccine group, as investigators hoped?

  b. Determine whether the vaccine is effective in reducing the chance of catching the virus, using a significance level of 0.05. Steps 1 and 2 of the hypothesis-testing procedure are given. Complete the question by doing steps 3 and 4.

Step 1: H_0: $p_v = p_p$ (p_v is the proportion who got the virus among those who took the vaccine, and p_p is the proportion who got the virus among those who took the placebo)
H_A: $p_v < p_p$

Step 2: Although we don't have a random sample, we do have random assignment to groups.

$$\hat{p} = \frac{63 + 80}{3298 + 1641} = \frac{143}{4939} = 0.028953$$

$n_p \times \hat{p} = 3298 \times 0.028953 = 95.49$, which is more than 10

$n_p \times \hat{p} = 1641 \times 0.028953 = 47.51$, which is more than 10 (and the other two products are larger)

* 8.50 Radiation for Breast Cancer Women with localized breast cancer are often given radiation treatment. A study tried to find out whether simplifying the treatment would lower the success rate. Each woman needing treatment was randomly assigned to receive whole-breast irradiation either at a standard dose of 50.0 Gy, a unit of absorbed radiation, in 25 treatments over a period of 35 days (the control group) or at a dose of 42.5 Gy in 16 treatments over a period of 22 days (the new treatment group). The new treatment had smaller doses and also fewer treatments, so it was feared that the new treatment would be less effective than the standard treatment.

Among the 612 women randomly assigned to the standard (old) treatment, 41 had a recurrence within 10 years. Among the 622 women randomly assigned to the new treatment, 39 had a recurrence within 10 years. (Source: Whelan et al., Long-term results of hypo-fractionated radiation therapy for breast cancer, *New England Journal of Medicine*, vol. 362: 513–520, February 11, 2010)

  a. Find the failure rate (rate of recurrence) for each treatment, and comment on the difference. Was this what was expected?

  b. Determine whether the new treatment increases the rate of recurrence, using a significance level of 0.05. The first two steps of the hypothesis-testing procedure are given. You may refer to the TI-83/84 output to do steps 3 and 4 to complete the answer.

Step 1: H_0: $p_{Old} = p_{New}$, where p_{New} is the probability of recurrence with the new treatment and p_{Old} is the probability of recurrence with the old treatment.

$$H_A: p_{Old} < p_{New}$$

Step 2: Although we don't have a random sample, we do have random assignment.

$$\hat{p} = \frac{41 + 39}{612 + 622} = \frac{80}{1234} = 0.064830$$

$n_{old}\hat{p} = 612 \times 0.064830 = 39.68$, which is more than 10.

$n_{new}\hat{p} = 622 \times 0.064830 = 40.32$, which is more than 10. The other two products are larger.

```
        2-PropZTest
P1<P2
z=.3061898787
P=.6202698963
p̂1=.0669934641
p̂2=.0627009646
↓p̂=.0648298217
```

TRY **8.51 Nicotine Gum (Example 12)** A study used nicotine gum to help people quit smoking. The study was placebo-controlled, randomized, and double-blind. Each participant was interviewed after 28 days, and success was defined as being abstinent from cigarettes for 28 days. The results showed that 174 out of 1649 people using the nicotine gum succeeded, and 66 out of 1648 using the placebo succeeded. Although the sample was not random, the assignment to groups was randomized. (Source Shiffman et al, Quitting by gradual smoking reduction using nicotine gum: A randomized controlled trial, *American Journal of Preventive Medicine*, vol. 36, issue 2, February, 2009)

  a. Find the proportion of people using nicotine gum who stopped smoking and the proportion of people using the placebo who stopped smoking, and compare them. Is this what the researchers had expected?

  b. Find the observed value of the test statistic, assuming that the conditions for a two-proportion z-test hold.

  c. Find and explain the meaning of the p-value.

  d. Does the data indicate that nicotine gum helps people quit smoking? Explain why or why not.

8.52 Treating Prostate Cancer A 2010 article reported the results of an experiment on reducing the likelihood that men develop prostate cancer. The investigators randomly assigned 3305 men to receive the drug dutasteride (the generic name for the drug sold under the brand name Avodart) and assigned 3424 men to receive a placebo. Of those receiving the drug, 659 developed prostate cancer, and of those receiving the placebo, 858 developed prostate cancer. (Source: Andriole et al., Effect of dutasteride on the risk of prostate cancer, *New England Journal of Medicine*, vol. 362: 1192–1202, April 1, 2010)

  a. Find the percentage of men who developed prostate cancer in each group. Was the sample percentage for those taking the drug lower than the sample percentage for those who took the placebo?

  b. Find the observed value of the test statistic, assuming that the conditions for a two-proportion z-test hold.

  c. Find and explain the meaning of the p-value.

  d. Does the data indicate that taking the drug lowers the chance of getting prostate cancer? Explain why or why not.

TRY **8.53 Smiling and Gender (Example 13)** In a 1997 study, people were observed for about 10 seconds in public places, such as malls and restaurants, to determine whether they smiled during the randomly chosen 10-second interval. The table shows the results for comparing males and females. (Source: M. S. Chappell, Frequency of public smiling over the life span, *Perceptual and Motor Skills*, vol. 45: 474, 1997)

	Male	Female
Smile	3269	4471
No Smile	3806	4278

  a. Find and compare the sample percentages of women who were smiling and men who were smiling.

  b. Treat this as though it were a random sample, and test whether there are differences in the proportion of men and the proportion of women who smile. Use a significance level of 0.05.

  c. Explain why there is such a small p-value even though there is such a small difference in sample percentages.

8.54 Smiling and Age Refer to the study discussed in Exercise 8.53. The accompanying table shows the results of the study for different age groups.

	\multicolumn{5}{Age Range}

	0–10	11–20	21–40	41–60	61+
Smile	1131	1748	1608	937	522
No Smile	1187	2020	3038	2124	1509

  a. For each age group, find the percentage who were smiling.

  b. Treat this as a random sample of people, and merge the groups 0–10 and 10–20 into one group (0–20) and the groups 21–40, 41–60, and 61+ into another age group (21–61+). Then determine whether these two age groups have different proportions of people who smile in the general population, using a significance level of 0.05. Comment on the results.

SECTION 8.5

8.55 If we reject the null hypothesis, can we claim to have *proved* that the null hypothesis is false? Why or why not?

8.56 If we do not reject the null hypothesis, is it valid to say that we *accept* the null hypothesis? Why or why not?

8.57 When a person stands trial for murder, the jury is instructed to assume that the defendant is innocent. Is this claim of innocence an example of a null hypothesis, or is it an example of an alternative hypothesis?

8.58 When, in a criminal court, a defendant is found "not guilty," is the court saying with certainty that he or she is innocent? Explain.

8.59 Arthritis A magazine advertisement claims that wearing a magnetized bracelet will reduce arthritis pain in those who suffer from arthritis. A medical researcher tests this claim with 233 arthritis sufferers randomly assigned to wear either a magnetized bracelet or a placebo bracelet. The researcher records the proportion of each group who report relief from arthritis pain after six weeks. After analyzing the data, he fails to reject the null hypothesis. Which of the following are valid interpretations of his findings? There may be more than one correct answer.

  a. The magnetized bracelets are not effective in reducing arthritis pain.

  b. There's insufficient evidence that the magnetized bracelets are effective in reducing arthritis pain.

  c. The magnetized bracelets had exactly the same effect as the placebo in reducing arthritis pain.

  d. There were no statistically significant differences between the magnetized bracelets and the placebos in reducing arthritis pain.

* 8.60 No-Carb Diet A weight-loss diet claims that it causes weight loss by eliminating carbohydrates (breads and starches) from the diet. To test this claim, researchers randomly assign overweight subjects to two groups. Both groups eat the same amount of calories, but one group eats almost no carbs, and the other group includes carbs in their meals. After two months, the researchers test the claim that the no-carb diet is better than the usual diet. They record the proportion of each group who lost more than 5% of their initial weight. They then announce that they failed to reject the null hypothesis. Which of the following are valid interpretations of the researchers' findings?

a. There were no significant differences in effectiveness between the no-carb diet and the carb diet.

b. The no-carb diet and the carb diet were equally effective.

c. The researchers did not see enough evidence to conclude that the no-carb diet was more effective.

d. The no-carb diet was less effective than the carb diet.

8.61 When comparing two sample proportions with a two-tailed alternative hypothesis, all other factors being equal, will you get a smaller p-value if the sample proportions are close together or if they are far apart? Explain.

8.62 When comparing two sample proportions with a two-tailed alternative hypothesis, all other factors being equal, will you get a smaller p-value with a larger sample size or a smaller sample size? Explain.

* 8.63 Banning Plastic Shopping Bags The Angus Reid Public Opinion organization surveyed Canadians in June 2012 by asking the question:

"Some cities and towns have prohibited retail stores from providing customers with single use plastic carryout (shopping) bags, urging customers to bring their own bags or boxes instead. Would you support or oppose banning plastic shopping bags in your own city or town?"

In response, 43% of Ontarians indicated that they would support such a ban, and 35% of Albertans said that they would support such a ban.

a. Assume that the poll surveyed 400 Ontarians and 400 Albertans. Determine the number of people in the sample from Ontario who supported the ban and the number of people in the sample from Alberta who supported the ban.

b. Do a test to see whether the proportion who support a ban on plastic bags is different in Ontario than it is in Alberta, using a significance level of 0.05.

c. Repeat the problem, assuming that the sample sizes were different, with 400 people from Ontario and 200 from Alberta.

d. Comment on the effect of the different sample sizes in part c on the p-value and the conclusion.

8.64 Weight Loss in Men Many polls have asked people whether they are trying to lose weight. A Gallup poll in November 2008 showed that 22% of men said they were seriously trying to lose weight. In 2006, 24% of men (with the same average weight of 194 pounds as the men polled in 2008) said they were seriously trying to lose weight. Assume that both samples contained 500 men.

a. Determine how many men in the sample from 2008 and how many in the sample from 2006 said they were seriously trying to lose weight.

b. Determine whether the difference in proportions is significant at the 0.05 level.

c. Repeat the problem with the same proportions but a sample size of 5000 instead of 500.

d. Comment on the different p-values and conclusions with different sample sizes.

* 8.65 Effectiveness of Financial Incentives A psychologist is interested in testing whether offering students a financial incentive improves their video-game-playing skills. She collects data and performs a hypothesis test to test whether the probability of getting to the highest level of a video game is greater with a financial incentive than without. Her null hypothesis is that the probability of getting to this level is the same with or without a financial incentive. The alternative is that this probability is greater. She gets a p-value from her hypothesis test of 0.003. Which of the following is the best interpretation of the p-value?

i. The p-value is the probability that financial incentives are *not* effective in this context.

ii. The p-value is the probability of getting exactly the result obtained, assuming that financial incentives are *not* effective in this context.

iii. The p-value is the probability of getting a result as extreme as or more extreme than the one obtained, assuming that financial incentives are *not* effective in this context.

iv. The p-value is the probability of getting exactly the result obtained, assuming that financial incentives *are* effective in this context.

v. The p-value is the probability of getting a result as extreme as or more extreme than the one obtained, assuming that financial incentives *are* effective in this context.

8.66 Is it acceptable practice to look at your research results, note the direction of the difference, and then make the alternative hypothesis one-tailed in order to achieve a significant difference? Explain.

8.67 Choosing a Test and Naming the Population For each of the following, state whether a one-proportion z-test or a two-proportion z-test would be appropriate, and name the populations.

a. A polling agency takes a random sample to determine the proportion of people in a certain riding who support Proposition X.

b. A student asks men and women at her institution whether they support capital punishment for some convicted murderers. She wants to determine whether the proportion of women who support capital punishment is less than the proportion of men who support it.

8.68 Choosing a Test and Naming the Population For each of the following, state whether a one-proportion z-test or a two-proportion z-test would be appropriate, and name the populations.

a. A student watches a random sample of men and women leaving a Hamilton supermarket with carts to see whether they put the carts back in the designated area. She wants to compare the proportions of men and women who put the carts in the designated area.

b. The pass rate for the Ontario bar exam is 65%. A random sample of graduates from Osgoode Hall Law School is examined to see whether their pass rate is significantly higher than 65%.

8.69 Choosing a Test and Giving the Hypotheses Give the null and alternative hypotheses for each test, and state whether a one-proportion z-test or a two-proportion z-test would be appropriate.

a. You test a person to see whether he can tell tap water from bottled water. You give him 20 sips selected randomly (half from tap water and half from bottled water) and record the proportion he gets correct to test the hypothesis.

b. You test students at your institution who stand on one foot with their eyes closed and determine who can stand for at least 10 seconds, comparing athletes and nonathletes.

8.70 Choosing a Test and Naming the Population(s) In each case, choose whether the appropriate test is a one-proportion z-test or a two-proportion z-test. Name the population(s).

a. A researcher takes a random sample of four-year-olds to find out whether girls or boys are more likely to know the alphabet.

b. A pollster takes a random sample of all Canadian voters to see whether more than 50% approve of the performance of the current prime minister.

c. A researcher wants to know whether a new heart medicine reduces the rate of heart attacks compared to an old medicine.

d. A pollster takes a poll in Saskatchewan about home schooling to find out whether the approval rate for men is equal to the approval rate for women.

e. A person is studied to see whether he or she can predict the results of coin flips better than chance alone.

CHAPTER REVIEW EXERCISES

8.71 Cola Taste Test A student who claims he can tell cola A from cola B is blindly tested with 20 trials. At each trial, cola A or cola B is randomly chosen and presented to the student, who must correctly identify the cola. The experiment is designed so that the student will have exactly 10 sips from each cola. He gets 6 identifications right out of 20. Can he tell cola A from cola B at the 0.05 level of significance? Explain.

8.72 Butter Taste Test A man is tested to determine whether he can tell butter from margarine. He is blindfolded and given small bites of English muffin to identify. At each trial, an English muffin with either butter or margarine is randomly chosen. The experiment is designed so that he will have exactly 15 bites with butter and 15 with margarine. He gets 14 right out of 30. Can he tell butter from margarine at the 0.05 level? Explain.

* 8.73 Death of a Leader Jack Layton—leader of the federal NDP—passed away in August 2011, three months after leading the NDP to their best federal election results, in which they received 30.6% of the national vote. Did Mr. Layton's passing have a negative effect on the NDP's popularity? A Nanos poll of 1202 randomly selected Canadians surveyed in October 2011 showed that 361 would vote for the NDP should there be a federal election in the near future. Test the hypothesis that the proportion of voters who would vote for the NDP declined after Mr. Layton's death. Use a significance level of 0.05.

8.74 Access to Health Care In 2007, the proportion of Canadians who reported not having a family doctor was 17%. A Decima Research poll in 2009 found that 13% of randomly surveyed Canadians did have a family doctor. If this poll surveyed 1000 Canadians, test the hypothesis that the proportion of Canadians who had a family doctor in 2009 decreased from 2007. Use a level of significance of 0.05.

8.75 Same-Sex Marriage Does the majority of the Canadian population wish for same-sex marriage to remain legal in Canada? In 2010, an Angus Reid poll of 1003 Canadian adults was taken, of whom 612 indicated that same-sex couples should continue to be allowed to legally marry in Canada. Test the hypothesis that the majority of Canadians in 2010 wished for same-sex marriage to remain legal in Canada. Use a level of significance of 0.05.

* 8.76 Biased Coin? A study is done to see whether a coin is biased. The alternative hypothesis used is two-tailed, and the obtained z-value is 2. Assuming that the sample size is sufficiently large and that the other conditions are also satisfied, use the Empirical Rule to approximate the p-value.

* 8.77 Biased Coin? A study is done to see whether a coin is biased. The alternative hypothesis used is two-tailed, and the obtained z-value is 1. Assuming that the sample size is sufficiently large and that the other conditions are also satisfied, use the Empirical Rule to approximate the p-value.

8.78 ESP A researcher studying ESP tests 200 students. Each student is asked to predict the outcome of a large number of coin flips. For each student, a hypothesis test using a 5% significance level is performed. If the p-value for the student is less than or equal to 0.05, the researcher concludes that the student has ESP. Out of 200 people who do *not* have ESP, about how many would you expect the researcher to declare *do* have ESP?

8.79 Coin Flips Suppose you tested 50 coins by flipping each of them many times. For each coin, you perform a significance test with a significance level of 0.05 to determine whether the coin is biased. Assuming that none of the coins is biased, about how many of the 50 coins would you expect to appear biased when this procedure is applied?

8.80 Voter Turnout In the 2011 federal election, the Conservative Party received 39.6% of the votes, followed by the NDP, which received 30.6% of the votes. Of those who had a religious identity, 42% voted Conservative. Of those who did not identify with a religion, 27% voted Conservative. Would it be appropriate to do a two-proportion z-test to determine whether the proportions of Conservative voters who did and did not identify with a religion were significantly different (assuming we know the number of voters who did and did not identify with a religion)? Explain.

8.81 Unemployment Rate In February 2013, Statistics Canada reported that the unemployment rate was 5.0% in Calgary and 6.1% in Ottawa. Would it be appropriate to do a two-proportion z-test to determine whether the unemployment rate was lower in Calgary than in Ottawa (assuming we know the total number of employable people in Calgary and Ottawa)? Explain.

8.82 Do Financial Incentives Help Smokers Quit? A controlled, randomized study compared smoking cessation for a group in which participants received $350 if they quit and a group who did not receive money. The study participants had to submit to a biochemical test to prove they had quit. Of the 442 people randomly assigned not to receive money, 52 had quit smoking after six months. Of the 436 people randomly assigned to receive money, 91 had quit smoking after six months. (Source: Volpp et al., A randomized, controlled trial of financial incentives for smoking cessation, *New England Journal of Medicine*, vol. 361: 4, 331–333, 2009) Determine whether the proportion of success was significantly greater for those who received money than for those who did not. Use a significance level of 0.05.

8.83 Two Countries and Guns

A 2013 Forum Research poll surveyed 1626 randomly chosen Canadians. When asked "Should gun control regulations in this country be more strict, less strict, or are they about right as they are?," 829 said "more strict." A Gallup poll that same year surveyed 1028 randomly chosen Americans, of whom 504 responded "more strict" when asked the same question.

Do these polls suggest that the proportion of Canadians who favour stricter gun control regulations in Canada is higher than the proportion of Americans who do so? Test this hypothesis with a significance level of 0.05.

8.84 Aspirin for Heart Disease in Women

The *New England Journal of Medicine* in March 2005 reported on a randomized, placebo-controlled study that was done to determine whether the use of aspirin could lower the risk of heart disease in women. It was already known that aspirin reduced heart disease in men. Researchers randomly assigned 39,876 healthy women 45 years of age or older to receive either placebo or 100 milligrams of aspirin on alternate days and then monitored them for 10 years for a first major cardiovascular event (such as a nonfatal myocardial infarction, a nonfatal stroke, or death from cardiovascular causes). The table shows the results. (Source: Ridke et al., A randomized trial of low-dose aspirin in the primary prevention of cardiovascular disease in women, *New England Journal of Medicine*, vol. 352: 1293–1304, March 31, 2005)

	Aspirin	Placebo
Heart Event	477	522
No Heart Event	19,457	19,420
Totals	19,934	19,942

a. Find the percentage of those taking aspirin who had a "heart event," and compare it with the percentage of those taking a placebo who had a "heart event."

b. Use the two-proportion z-test to determine whether aspirin lowered the rate of women who suffered from cardiovascular events, using a significance level of 0.05.

8.85 Support for Nuclear Energy

Some people fear the use of nuclear energy because of potential accidents. A Gallup poll in 2009 showed that 74% of men and 47% of women surveyed supported the use of nuclear energy to produce electricity. The overall sample size was 1012.

a. Assume that exactly half the sample were men and half were women, and determine the numbers of men and women who said they supported the use of nuclear energy and the numbers of men and women who opposed it. Round your frequencies to whole numbers and report them in a table. Put the labels "Men" and "Women" across the top.

b. Now using the numbers from part a, determine whether women are less supportive of nuclear energy than men at the 0.05 level of significance.

★ 8.86 Red Eyes from the Swimming Pool

A recent study reported on the red-eye effect one often experiences after swimming in a pool. Chlorine has been the culprit, but researchers at the Centers for Disease Control recently published a report to warn swimmers that the red-eye effect is the result of human urine depleting the chlorine, which in turn produces a chemical that irritates the eyes. So, what proportion of Canadians have admitted to peeing in a pool, and how does this compare to the proportion of Americans to have peed in a pool? The table below resulted from a travelzoo.com poll of 1005 randomly chosen Canadians and 1401 randomly chosen Americans.

	Canadian	American
Had urinated in a pool	586	897
Had not urinated in a pool	419	504
Totals	1005	1401

a. Compare the proportions of peeing-in-the-pool in these samples. Which proportion is higher, the proportion of Canadians who have peed in the pool or the proportion of Americans?

b. Treat this travelzoo.com survey as if it were a random sample of 1005 Canadians and 1401 Americans to determine if the proportion of Canadians who have peed in the pool is lower than the proportion of Americans who have peed in the pool. Use a 0.05 significance level.

8.87 Sleep Medicine for Shift Workers

Shift workers, who work during the night and must sleep during the day, often become sleepy when working and have trouble sleeping during the day. In a study done at Harvard Medical School, 209 shift workers were randomly divided into two groups: one group received a new sleep medicine (modafinil or Provigil), and the other group received a placebo. During the study, 54% of the workers taking the placebo and 29% of those taking the medicine reported accidents or near accidents commuting to and from work. Assume that 104 of the people were assigned the medicine and 105 were assigned the placebo. (Source: Czeisler et al., Modafinil for excessive sleepiness associated with shift-work sleep disorder, *New England Journal of Medicine*, vol. 353: 476–486, August 4, 2005)

a. State the null and alternative hypotheses. Is the alternative hypothesis one-tailed or two-tailed? Explain your choice.

b. Perform a statistical test to determine whether the proportion in the treatment group is significantly lower than the proportion in the placebo group at the 0.05 level.

GUIDED EXERCISES

8.29 Gun Registry Support Conventional wisdom suggests that half of Canadians—50%—have supported the existence of the long-gun registry. The same wisdom suggests that the support for the long-gun registry is much lower in the provinces of Alberta, Saskatchewan, and Manitoba. An EKOS poll conducted in 2009 of 247 Canadians living in these three provinces showed that 44 support the long-gun registry. Assume that this survey was a random sample.

Questions
Test the claim that the proportion of Canadians living in these provinces who are in favour of long-gun registry is less than 50%. Perform a hypothesis test, using a significance level of 0.05, by following the steps.

  i. The proportion is not significantly different from 50%. (A significant difference is one for which the p-value is less than or equal to 0.05.)

  ii. The proportion is significantly less than 50%.

Step 1 ▶ Hypothesize

H_0: The population proportion who supports the existence of the long-gun registry is 0.50, $p = $ _____.

H_A: p $(<, >, \neq)$ _____.

Step 2 ▶ Prepare

Choose the one-proportion z-test.

Random sample? Yes

Sample size: $np_0 = 247(0.50) = 123.5$, which is ____ (more, less, equal to) 10, and $n(1 - p_0) = 247(0.50) = $ ____.

Step 3 ▶ Compute to compare

$$\hat{p} = \_\_$$

$$SD = \sqrt{\frac{p_0(1 - p_0)}{n}} = \sqrt{\frac{0.50(1 - \_\_)}{247}} = \_\_$$

$$z = \frac{\hat{p} - p_0}{SD} = \frac{0.178138 - \_\_}{SD} = \_\_$$

p-value = __

Report your p-value with three decimal digits.

Check your answers with the accompanying output, generated with Minitab technology.

```
95% Upper
Sample   X    N   Sample p      Bound   Z-Value  P-Value
1       44   247  0.178138   0.218183   -10.12     0.000
```

Minitab output for one-proportion z-test.

Step 4 ▶ Interpret and conclude
Interpret the meaning of the p-value.

The p-value represents the following: Assuming that H_0 is _____ (true, false), the probability that another random sample of _____ residents from Alberta, Saskatchewan, and Manitoba will give an outcome that is just as _____ as the current outcome is _____. Reject H_0 (if the p-value is 0.05 or less) or do not reject H_0 and choose one of the following conclusions:

  i. The proportion is not significantly less than 50%. (The proportion is significantly less when the p-value is less than or equal to 0.05.)

  ii. The proportion is significantly less than 50%.

8.47 Vioxx In the fall of 2004, drug manufacturer Merck Pharmaceutical withdrew Vioxx, a drug that had been used for arthritis pain, from the market after a study revealed that its use was associated with an increase in the risk of heart attack. The experiment was placebo-controlled, randomized, and double-blind. Out of 1287 people taking Vioxx there were 45 heart attacks, and out of 1299 people taking the placebo there were 25 heart attacks. (Source: *Los Angeles Times*, October 23, 2004)

Questions
Perform a hypothesis test to test whether those who take Vioxx have a greater rate of heart attack than those who take a placebo. Use a level of significance of 0.05. Follow the steps below to answer the question. In order to be able to use the typical four steps without changing the numbering, we have called the first step, step 0. Can we conclude that Vioxx *causes* an increased risk of heart attack?

Step 0 ▶ Find the proportion of people in the sample taking Vioxx who had a heart attack and the proportion of people in the sample taking a placebo who had a heart attack. Compare these proportions.

Step 1 ▶ Hypotheses
Let p_V be the population proportion of those taking Vioxx who had a heart attack, and let p_p be the population proportion of those taking the placebo who had a heart attack.

$$H_0: p_V = p_p$$
$$H_A: \_\_$$

Step 2 ▶ Prepare
Choose the two-proportion z-test. Although we don't have a random sample, we have random assignment to groups. The pooled proportion of heart attacks is

$$\hat{p} = \frac{45 + 25}{1287 + 1299} = \frac{70}{2586} = 0.027069$$

$n_1 \times \hat{p} = 1287(0.027069) = 34.84$, which is more than 10

$n_1 \times (1 - \hat{p}) = \_\_$

$n_2 \times (1 - \hat{p}) = \_\_$

$n_2 \times \hat{p} = \_\_$

Step 3 ► **Compute to compare**

Refer to the accompanying figure.

$$z = \underline{\quad}$$

$$\text{p-value} = \underline{\quad}$$

```
Sample   X     N   Sample p
1       45  1287   0.034965
2       25  1299   0.019246
Difference = p (1) - p (2)
Estimate for difference:  0.0157195
95% lower bound for difference:  0.00521961
Test for difference = 0 (vs > 0):  Z = 2.46  P-Value = 0.007
```

Minitab output for two-proportion z-test.

Step 4 ► **Interpret and conclude**

Interpret the meaning of the p-value.

The p-value represents the following: assuming that H_0 is _____ (true, false), the probability that another experiment will give a(n) _____ that is just as _____ as the current outcome is _____.

Reject H_0 or do not reject H_0 and choose i or ii:

i. Those taking Vioxx did not have a significantly higher rate of heart attack than those taking the placebo.

ii. Those taking Vioxx had a significantly higher heart attack rate than those who took the placebo.

Causality

Does the experiment satisfy the conditions required to conclude that a cause-and-effect relationship exists between taking Vioxx and increased risk for heart attacks?

TECH TIPS

General Instructions for All Technology

All technologies will use the examples that follow.

Example A

Do a one-proportion z-test to determine whether you can reject the hypothesis that a coin is a fair coin if 10 heads are obtained from 30 flips of the coin. Find z and the p-value.

Example B

Do a two-proportion z-test: Find the observed value of the test statistic and the p-value that tests whether the proportion of people who support stem cell research changed from 2002 to 2007. In both years, the researchers sampled 1500 people. In 2002, 645 people expressed support. In 2007, 765 people expressed support.

TI-83/84

One-Proportion z-Test

1. Press **STAT**, choose **Tests**, and choose **5: 1-PropZTest**.
2. See Figure 8A.

Enter: p_0, **.5**; **x**, **10**; **n**, **30**.
Leave the default $\neq p_0$.
Scroll down to **Calculate** and press **ENTER**.

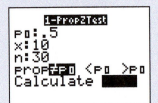

▲ **FIGURE 8A** TI-83/84 input for one-proportion z-test.

You should get a screen like Figure 8B. If you choose **Draw** instead of **Calculate**, you can see the shading of the Normal curve.

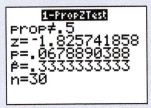

▲ **FIGURE 8B** TI-83/84 output for one-proportion z-test.

Two-Proportion z-Test

1. Press **STAT**, choose **Tests**, and choose **6: 2-PropZTest**.
2. See Figure 8C.

Enter: **x1**, **645**; **n1**, **1500**; **x2**, **765**; **n2**, **1500**.
Scroll down to **Calculate** (or **Draw**) and press **ENTER**.

▲ **FIGURE 8C** TI-83/84 input for two-proportion z-test.

You should get a screen like Figure 8D. The down arrow next to $\hat{p}$ means that there's more information below what is given. To see that information, scroll down, using the down arrow on your keypad.

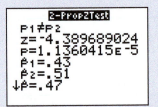

▲ **FIGURE 8D** TI-83/84 output for two-proportion z-test.

Caution! Beware of p-values that appear at first glance to be larger than 1. In Figure 8D, the p-value is 1.1 times 10 to the negative fifth power (−5), or 0.000011.

MINITAB

One-Proportion z-Test

1. **Stat** > **Basic Statistics** > **1-Proportion**.
2. Refer to Figure 8E. Click **Summarized data.** Enter: **number of events, 10**; **Number of trials, 30**; check **Perform hypothesis test, hypothesized proportion, .5**

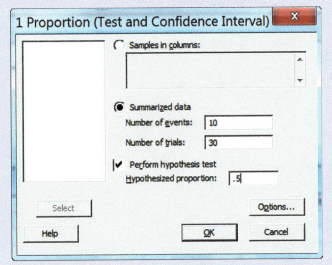

▲ **FIGURE 8E** Minitab input for one-proportion z-test.

3. Click **Options** and check the box that says **Use test and interval based on normal distribution**. (If you wanted to change the alternative hypothesis to one-tailed, you would do that also through **Options**.) Click **OK**.

You should get output that looks like Figure 8F. Note that you also get a 95% confidence interval (95% CI) for the proportion.

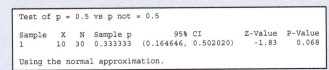

▲ **FIGURE 8F** Minitab output for one-proportion z-test.

Two-Proportion z-Test

1. **Stat > Basic Statistics > 2 Proportions**
2. See Figure 8G.

Click **Summarized data**.

Enter	Events	Trials
First	645	1500
Second	765	1500

3. Click **OK**.

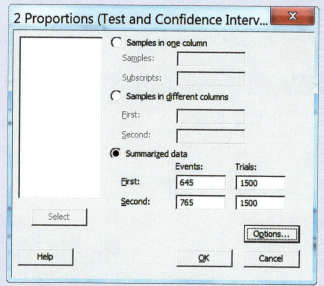

▲ **FIGURE 8G** Minitab input for two-proportion z-test.

Your output should look like Figure 8H. Note that it includes a 95% confidence interval for the difference between the proportions, as well as z and the p-value.

```
Test and CI for Two Proportions
Sample   X     N    Sample p
1       645  1500   0.430000
2       765  1500   0.510000


Difference = p (1) - p (2)
Estimate for difference:  -0.08
95% CI for difference:  (-0.115605, -0.0443955)
Test for difference = 0 (vs not = 0):  Z = -4.40   P-Value = 0.000
```

▲ **FIGURE 8H** Minitab output for two-proportion z-test and interval.

EXCEL

One-Proportion z-Test

1. Click **Add-ins**, **XLSTAT**, **Parametric Tests**, **Tests for one proportion**.
2. See Figure 8I.

Enter: **Frequency, 10**; **Sample size, 30**; **Test proportion, .5**.
(If you wanted a one-tailed hypothesis, you would click **Options**.)
Click **OK**.

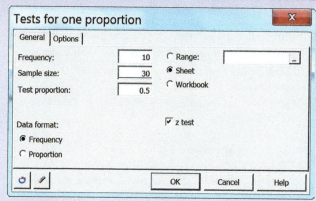

▲ **FIGURE 8I** Input for one-proportion z-test.

When the output appears, you may need to change the column width to see the answers. Click **Home**, and in the **Cells** group click **Format** and **AutoFit Column Width**. The relevant part of the output is shown here.

Difference	−0.167
z (Observed value)	−1.826
p-value (Two-tailed)	0.068

Two-Proportion z-Test

1. Click **Add-ins**, **XLSTAT**, **Parametric Tests**, **Tests for two proportions**.
2. See Figure 8J.

Enter: **Frequency 1**, 645; **Sample size 1**, 1500; **Frequency 2, 765**; **Sample size 2, 1500**.
(If you wanted a one-tailed alternative, you would click **Options**.)
Click **OK**.

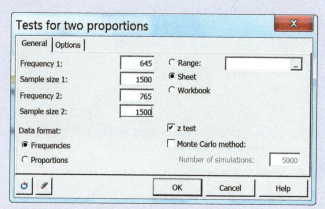

▲ **FIGURE 8J** XLSTAT input for two-proportion z-test.

The relevant parts of the output are shown.

Difference	−0.080
z (Observed value)	−4.404
p-value (Two-tailed)	<0.0001

STATCRUNCH

One-Proportion *z*-Test and Confidence Interval

1. **Stat** > **Proportions** > **One sample** > **with summary**
2. Enter: **number of successes, 10; number of observations, 30.**

   Click **Next** and select the **Hypothesis Test** or **Confidence interval** option.

   a. Leave Hypothesis test checked. Enter: **Null prop:=, 0.5.** Leave the **Alternative 2-tailed**, which is the default.

   b. For a Confidence interval, leave the **Level, 0.95** (the default). For **Method**, leave ***Standard-Wald***, the default.
3. Click **Calculate**.

   Figure 8K shows the output for the hypothesis test.

Proportion	Count	Total	Sample Prop.	Std. Err.	Z-Stat	P-value
p	10	30	0.33333334	0.09128709	-1.8257419	0.0679

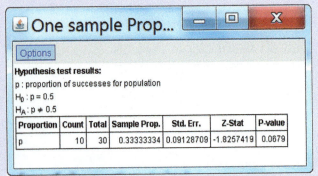

▲ **FIGURE 8K** StatCrunch output for one-proportion *z*-test.

Two-Proportion *z*-Test

1. **Stat** > **Proportions** > **Two samples** > **with summary**
2. Refer to Figure 8L.

Enter: **Sample 1: Number of successes, 645;**
Number of observations, 1500:
Sample 2: Number of successes, 765;
Number of observations, 1500.

3. If you want to change the alternative hypothesis from the two-tailed default (or want a confidence interval), click **Next**. Otherwise, click **Calculate**.

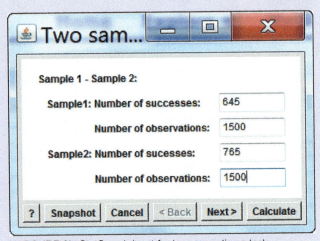

▲ **FIGURE 8L** StatCrunch input for two-proportion *z*-test.

Figure 8M shows the StatCrunch output.

Difference	Count1	Total1	Count2	Total2	Sample Diff.	Std. Err.	Z-Stat	P-value
$p_1 - p_2$	645	1500	765	1500	-0.08	0.018224526	-4.389689	<0.0001

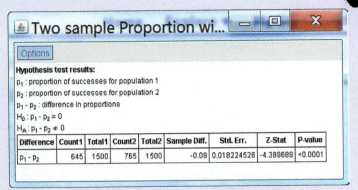

▲ **FIGURE 8M** StatCrunch output for two-proportion *z*-test.

SPSS

One-Proportion *z*-Test

1. Enter the categorical variable as one variable then the observed counts as the second variable. See Figure 8N.

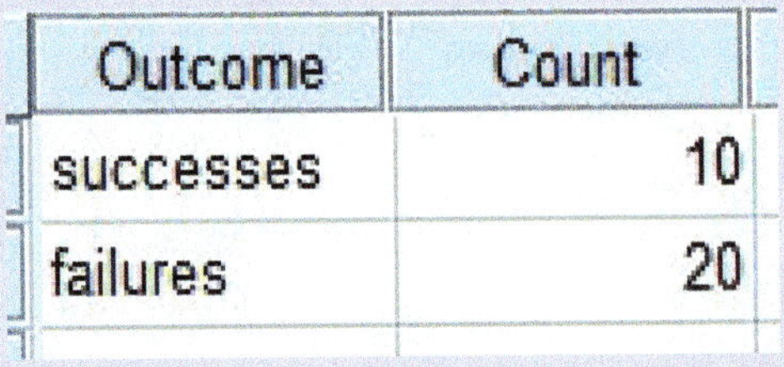

Outcome	Count
successes	10
failures	20

▲ **FIGURE 8N** Data in SPSS.

2. **Data > Weight.** Enter Count as the variable to Weight cases by. Click **OK**. See Figure 8O.

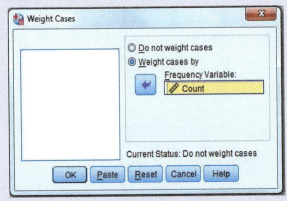

▲ **FIGURE 8O** SPSS input to weight counts.

3. **Analyze > Nonparametric Tests > Legacy Dialogs > Chi-square.** Enter Count as the Test Variable List. Click **OK**. See Figure 8P.

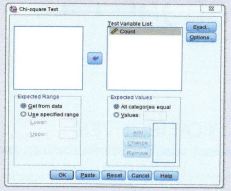

▲ **FIGURE 8P** SPSS input for one-proportion z-test.

4. From the SPSS output, the z-test statistic is the square root of the **Chi-Square Count**, $z = \sqrt{3.333} = 1.82565 \approx 1.83$
   z always has the same sign as $\hat{p} - p_0$
   $= \frac{10}{30} = -0.16667$, so $z = -1.83$

   See Figure 8Q.

Count

	Observed N	Expected N	Residual
10	10	15.0	-5.0
20	20	15.0	5.0
Total	30		

Test Statistics

	Count
Chi-Square	3.333[a]
df	1
Asymp. Sig.	.068

▲ **FIGURE 8Q** SPSS output for one-proportion z-test.

Two-Proportion z-Test

1. Enter the two populations (Year 2002 and Year 2007) as one variable, the two categories (support, do not support) as a second variable, and the observed counts from the sample as a third variable. See Figure 8R.

Year	Opinion	Count
Year 2002	support	645
Year 2002	do not support	855
Year 2007	support	765
Year 2007	do not support	735

▲ **FIGURE 8R** Data in SPSS.

2. **Data > Weight**

   This weights the Opinion variable by its observed counts. Enter Count as the variable to Weight cases by. Click **OK**. See Figure 8S.

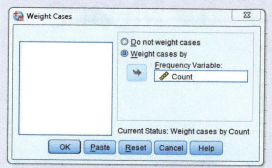

▲ **FIGURE 8S** SPSS input to weight counts.

3. **Analyze > Descriptive Statistics > Crosstabs**

   Select Year as the row variable and Opinion as the column variable. Then click **Statistics** and select **Chi-square**. Click **Continue**. Then select **OK**. See Figure 8T.

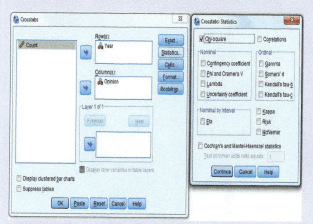

▲ **FIGURE 8T** SPSS input for two-proportion z-test.

4. From the SPSS output, the z-test statistic is the square root of the **Pearson Chi-Square Value**, $z = \sqrt{19.269} = 4.3896 \approx 4.39$
   z always has the same sign as $\hat{p}_1 - \hat{p}_2$
   $= \frac{645}{1500} = \frac{765}{1500} = -0.88$. $z = -4.39$

   See Figure 8U.

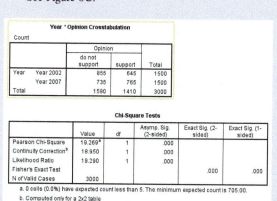

▲ **FIGURE 8U** SPSS output for two-proportion z-test.

9 Inferring Population Means

LEARNING OBJECTIVES

After completing this chapter, you should be able to:

1. Apply the Central Limit Theorem to conceptualize the distribution of the sample mean and see why the sample mean is a good estimate of the population mean.

2. Compute a confidence interval for a population mean and interpret its meaning.

3. Develop and conduct a statistical hypothesis about the value of a population mean, and make the distinction between a hypothesis test about a population mean and a confidence interval.

4. Distinguish between two independent samples and a paired (dependent) sample.

5. Compare two populations by computing a confidence interval of the difference between their means.

6. Formulate a statistical hypothesis from either two independent random samples or a dependent sample, and conduct the necessary statistical test.

7. Use the p-value and the significance level to decide if the data based on a random sample from a population, or two independent random samples, or a dependent sample support the null hypothesis or not.

Todd Klassy/Shutterstock

Brewing beer is a tricky business. Beer has only four main ingredients: malted barley, hops, yeast, and water. However, these four ingredients must be mixed in precise quantities at precise temperatures. Having some experience in trying to get this mix just right, in the late 1800s the Guinness brewery in Dublin, Ireland, began to hire the best and brightest science graduates to help them perfect the brewing process. One of these, hired in 1899 at the age of 23, was William Sealy Gosset (1876–1937), who had majored in chemistry and mathematics. One of Gosset's jobs was to measure the amount of yeast in a small sample of beer. On the basis of this sample, he was to estimate the mean amount of yeast in the beers produced. If this yeast amount was too high

or too low, then something was wrong and the process would have to be fixed.

Naturally, uncertainty played a role. Suppose the average yeast count in his sample was too high or too low. Did this indicate that the mean yeast count in the entire factory was off? Or was his sample different just because of chance? The statistical science of the day knew how to answer this question if the number of samples was large, but Gosset worked in a context in which large samples were just too expensive and time-consuming to collect. A decision had to be based on a small sample. Gosset solved the problem, and published his findings under the name "Student." His approach (called the *t*-test) is one of the most widely used techniques in statistics.

Estimating one or more population means is still an important part of science and public policy. How do we compare the effects of different drugs on epilepsy? Are home prices the same in Vancouver and Toronto? Are increases in tuition fees in Ontario the same as in Quebec? To answer these questions, we need good estimates of the population means, and these estimates must be based on reliable data from small samples.

In Chapters 7 and 8 you learned two important techniques for statistical inference: the confidence interval and the hypothesis test. In those chapters, we applied statistical inference for population proportions. In this chapter, we use the same two techniques for making inferences about means of populations. We begin with inference for one population and conclude with inferring the difference between the means of two populations. In later chapters we develop these techniques further to see how they apply, for example, to comparing categorical variables, regression, and other situations.

CASE STUDY

Epilepsy Drugs and Children

Epilepsy is a neurological disorder that causes seizures, which can range from mild to severe. It has been estimated (World Health Organization 2015) that over 50 million people around the world suffer from epilepsy. It is usually treated with drugs, and four drugs that are commonly used for this purpose are carbamazepine, lamotrigine, phenytoin, and valproate. In 2009 the *New England Journal of Medicine* reported that pregnant mothers who take valproate might risk impairing the cognitive development of their children, compared to mothers who take one of the other drugs. As evidence, on the basis of a sample of pregnant women with epilepsy, they estimated the mean IQ of three-year-old children whose mothers took one of these four drugs during their pregnancies. They gave 95% confidence intervals (CI) for the mean IQ, as shown in Table 9.1 (Meador et al. 2009).

Drug	95% CI
carbamazepine	(95, 101)
lamotrigine	(98, 104)
phenytoin	(94, 104)
valproate	(88, 97)

▲ **TABLE 9.1** 95% confidence intervals for the average IQ of children whose mothers took various epilepsy drugs during their pregnancies.

Why did these four intervals lead the researchers to recommend that pregnant women not use valproate as a "first choice" drug for epilepsy? The researchers wrote that "Although the confidence intervals for carbamazepine and phenytoin overlap with the confidence interval for valproate, the confidence intervals for the differences between carbamazepine and valproate and between phenytoin and valproate do not include zero." What does this tell us?

In this chapter we discuss how confidence intervals can be used to estimate characteristics of a population—in this case, the population of all children of women with epilepsy who took one of these drugs during pregnancy. Confidence intervals can also be used to judge between hypotheses about the means and about differences between means. The population of pregnant women with epilepsy is large, and yet if conditions are right, we can make decisions and reach an understanding about the entire population on the basis of a small sample. At the end of this chapter, we will return to this study and see if we can better understand its conclusions.

SECTION 9.1

Sample Means of Random Samples

As you learned in Chapter 7, we estimate the value of a population parameter by collecting a random sample from the population. From the data collected we compute a statistic, which is used to estimate the value of the parameter. It does not matter if we are using the statistic $\hat{p}$ to estimate the value of the parameter p or $\bar{x}$ to estimate μ, we want to know how close our estimate is to its true value. Is the statistic usually close to the parameter?

As we did in Chapter 7 with $\hat{p}$, we now examine the characteristics of the sample mean $\bar{x}$: its accuracy, its precision, and how it behaves (its probability distribution). From these we'll be able to measure how close or how far off $\bar{x}$ is from the unknown value of the population mean μ.

Table 9.2 is a reminder showing the relation between some commonly used statistics and the parameters they estimate. (This table originally appeared as Table 7.2.)

▶ **TABLE 9.2** Notation for some commonly used statistics and parameters.

Statistics (based on data)		Parameters (typically unknown)	
Sample mean	$\bar{x}$	Population mean	μ (mu)
Sample standard deviation	s	Population standard deviation	σ (sigma)
Sample variance	s^2	Population variance	σ^2
Sample proportion	$\hat{p}$ (p-hat)	Population proportion	p

This chapter uses much of the same vocabulary introduced in Chapters 7 and 8, and we'll remind you of important terms as we proceed. To help you see how the mean of a random sample behaves, we'll use simulation, which we used before to demonstrate the behaviour of $\hat{p}$ in Chapter 7. Our simulation is somewhat 'make belief,' because to carry out a proper simulation we need the entire population. After using simulation to see how the sample mean behaves in this 'make-belief,' electronic laboratory setting, we will discuss what to do when we face a real-world problem without knowing much about the population being studied.

Accuracy and Precision of a Sample Mean

The reason why the sample mean is a useful estimator for the population mean is that the sample mean is accurate and, with a sufficiently large sample size, very precise. The accuracy of an estimator, you'll recall, is measured by the **bias**, and the precision is measured by the standard deviation. You will see in our simulations that

1. The sample mean is **accurate** when it is used to estimate the population mean, meaning it has no bias. On average, the value of $\bar{x}$ will be the same as μ.

2. The **precision** of $\bar{x}$ depends on the variation in the population. However, the more data we have—the larger the sample size—the more precise $\bar{x}$ is.

The behaviour of the sample mean will be demonstrated through two simulations. For the first simulation, we'll use a population of adults (Shoemaker and College 1996). Data collected on people's heart rate, as measured by the number of times their heart beats in a minute, revealed that heart rate varies from person to person. The behaviour of the heart rates can be approximately modelled by a Normal distribution with a mean heart rate of 74 beats per minute and a standard deviation of 7 beats per minute, or $N(74, 7)$. Thinking of each person in the population as providing a heart rate number, our "population of values" is shown in Figure 9.1.

The population parameters are given in symbols,

$$\mu = 74$$

$$\sigma = 7$$

In our first simulation, we will randomly pick 30 people and record the heart rate of each. We'll repeat this many, many times (at this point in our discussion, the

Details

Mu-sings

The mean of a population, represented by the Greek character μ, is pronounced "mu" as in *music*.

Looking Back

Bias and Precision

Bias is the average distance between the sample statistic and the parameter whose value it is estimating. Precision is measured by the standard deviation of the statistic. This tells us how far off the statistic tends to deviate from its centre.

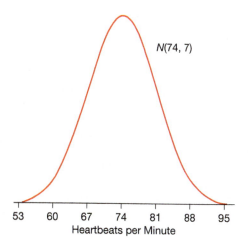

exact number of repetitions is not important). We are interested in three questions: (1) What is the typical value of the mean heart rate for a sample of 30 people? Is it the value of the population mean, 74? If so, then the statistic $\bar{x}$ has no bias. (2) How far away is $\bar{x}$ from 74? That is, how much spread is in the distribution of the statistic $\bar{x}$? (3) What is the behaviour of $\bar{x}$ based on a sample size of 30? Does it approximately follow a Normal distribution as well? Or is the distribution of the sample mean *not* Normal?

In our first simulated sample, the mean number of heartbeats per minute was 75.63, or $\bar{x} = 75.63$. This sample mean, as well as all the other sample means from each of the different random samples of 30 people, was plotted with a dotplot in Figure 9.2. The plot is on the same scale as Figure 9.1, the population of values, so you can see how much tighter the distribution of the sample mean of 30 observations is.

From the plot in Figure 9.2, we see that the value of the sample mean is typically the same as the population mean of 74, indicating that the sample mean is accurate. And we see that the sample mean is consistently close to 74, indicating that it is a precise statistic. All the sample means are within about plus or minus four heartbeats of the true value of the population mean of 74.

What is not clear from Figure 9.2 is the behaviour of $\bar{x}$. It appears to be approximately Normally distributed. This would mean that when we sample from a population of values, the mean of such a sample will be approximately Normally distributed as well.

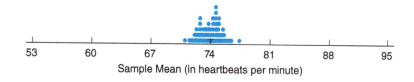

Sample Mean (in heartbeats per minute)

Figure 9.2 is a good approximation of the **sampling distribution** of the sample mean for samples of size 30. Recall that the sampling distribution is the distribution of a sample statistic, the statistic here being the sample mean. You can imagine the sampling distribution as the distribution of all possible sample means that would result from drawing repeated random samples of a certain size from the population.

When the sampling distribution of a statistic has a mean that is the same value as the population mean, we say the statistic is an **unbiased estimator.** This appears to be the case here, because the mean of the distribution of the sample means in Figure 9.2 is about 74, which is the same as the population mean of 74 beats per minute.

◄ **FIGURE 9.2** Each dot represents a sample mean based on 30 people randomly chosen from the population whose distribution is shown in Figure 9.1. Observe how the spread in the distribution of the sample mean is much smaller when compared to the population, but the centre looks to be at the same place: 74 heartbeats per minute.

Looking Back

Sampling Distribution
In Chapter 7 we introduced the sampling distribution of sample proportions. The sampling distribution of sample means is the same concept: it is a distribution that gives us probabilities for sample means drawn from a population. The sampling distribution is the distribution of all possible sample means.

The spread in the sampling distribution of the sample mean is quantified by its standard deviation. This measures the precision of the sample mean by telling us how much it varies from one sample of size n to another sample of the same size. By comparing the axes in Figures 9.1 and 9.2, we can see that the standard deviation of the sample mean is much less than the standard deviation of the population. Soon you'll see how to calculate the standard deviation of the sample mean.

What happens to the centre (accuracy) and the spread (precision) of the sample mean should we decide to take a larger sample? Let's restart our simulation, but this time we will increase the sample size to 100 people, calculate the mean of the sample, and repeat many times. Figure 9.3 shows the results for this simulation and for two new simulations where each sample mean is based on (a) 100 people, (b) 500 people and (c) 1000 people. The scale of the x-axis is the same as in Figure 9.1. Note how the distribution of the sample mean becomes tighter and tighter as the sample size increases—so much so that it is difficult to see a distribution shape.

(a)
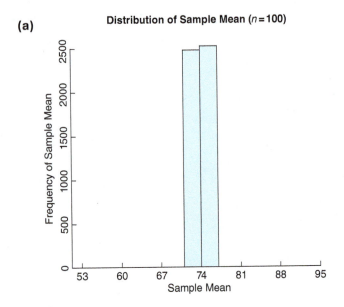

(b)
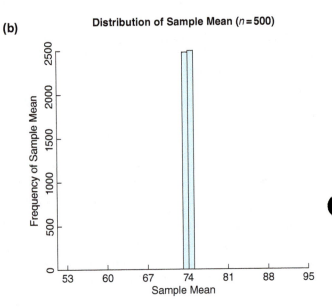

(c)
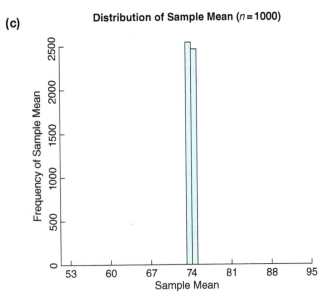

▶ **FIGURE 9.3** Histogram of a large number of sample means. **(a)** Sample means based on a sample of 100 people. **(b)** Sample means based on samples of 500 people. **(c)** Sample means based on samples of 1000 people. Each time, the sampling distribution becomes narrower, reflecting a smaller standard deviation.

What Have We Demonstrated with These Simulations?

Because the sampling distributions are always centred at the population mean, we have demonstrated that the sample mean is an unbiased estimator of the population mean. We saw this for only one type of population distribution: the Normal distribution. But in fact, this is the case for any population distribution.

We have also demonstrated that the standard deviation of the sample mean gets smaller as the sample gets larger. This happens *regardless* of how the population of values is distributed.

We can generalize our observations. If μ represents the mean of a population of values, and σ is the standard deviation of this population of values, then

1. The sampling distribution of the sample mean has a mean that is equal to μ. (This tells us that the statistic $\bar{x}$ is unbiased when we are estimating the population mean.)

2. The standard deviation of the sample mean is $\dfrac{\sigma}{\sqrt{n}}$ (which tells us that the standard deviation of the sample mean depends on the standard deviation of the population from where we take the sample and is smaller for larger samples).

> **KEY POINT**
>
> For all populations, the sample mean is unbiased when estimating the population mean. The standard deviation of the sample mean is $\dfrac{\sigma}{\sqrt{n}}$, so the sample mean is more precise for larger sample sizes.

Looking Back

Sample Proportions from Random Samples
Compare the properties of the sample mean to those of the sample proportion, $\hat{p}$, given in Chapter 7. The sample proportion is also an unbiased estimator (for estimating the population proportion, p). It has standard deviation

$$\sqrt{\dfrac{p(1-p)}{n}}$$

EXAMPLE 1 iTunes Library Statistics

A student's iTunes library of mp3s has a very large number of songs. The mean length of the songs is 243 seconds, and the standard deviation is 93 seconds. The distribution of song lengths is right-skewed. Using his mp3 player, this student will create a playlist that consists of 25 randomly selected songs.

QUESTIONS

a. Is the mean value of 243 seconds an example of a parameter or a statistic? Explain.

b. What should the student expect the average song length to be for his playlist?

c. What is the standard deviation for the mean song length of 25 randomly selected songs?

SOLUTIONS

a. The mean of 243 is an example of a parameter, because it is the mean of the population that consists of all the songs in the student's iTunes library.

b. The sample mean length can vary, but is typically the same as the population mean: 243 seconds.

c. The standard deviation is $\dfrac{\sigma}{\sqrt{n}} = \dfrac{93}{\sqrt{25}} = \dfrac{93}{5} = 18.6$ seconds.

TRY THIS! Exercise 9.11

The Central Limit Theorem for Sample Means

Looking Back

CLT for Proportions
In Chapter 7, you saw that the Central Limit Theorem applies to sample proportions. Here you'll see that it also applies to sample means.

Although it was difficult to see in the last simulation, the sampling distribution of the sample mean was approximately Normal. This seems reasonable, because we were sampling from a population of values that is Normally distributed.

What might surprise you is that the sample mean behaves in a way that is, at least, approximately Normal for sample sizes that are considered to be large. (We will see how large shortly.) This phenomenon is also true for populations of values that are not Normally distributed. This is the conclusion of the Central Limit Theorem, an important theorem that tells us that as long as the sample size is large, we can use the Normal distribution to assist us in making statistical inference—no matter how the population of data from which we sample is distributed.

The **Central Limit Theorem (CLT)** assures us that we do not need to know the distribution of the underlying population of values. If a sample is chosen such that the following conditions are satisfied, then the distribution of the sample mean will approximately follow a Normal distribution. The mean of this sampling distribution is the same as the population mean. The standard deviation of this distribution is the population standard deviation divided by the square root of the sample size. As a general rule, a sample size of at least 25 is considered to be a large sample.

Condition 1: *Random Sample.* Each observation is a result of a random sample of observations from a population of observations. The random selection means that each observation is independent of other observations in the sample.

Condition 2: *Normality.* Either the population of observations follows a Normal model or the sample size is large ($n \geq 25$).

Condition 3: *Big Population.* If the sample is collected without replacement, then the population must be at least 10 times larger than the sample size.

KEY POINT The sampling distribution of $\bar{x}$ is approximately $N\left(\mu, \dfrac{\sigma}{\sqrt{n}}\right)$, where μ is the mean of the population and σ is the standard deviation of the population. The larger the sample size, n, the better the approximation. If the population is Normal to begin with, then the sampling distribution is exactly a Normal distribution.

Visualizing Distributions of Sample Means

The histogram in Figure 9.4 shows the distribution of the salaries of NHL players for the 2013–2014 season in US$ millions (capgeek.com). The distribution is skewed to the right, indicating that most NHL players were making at most $1 million, with a very small proportion having salaries above $8 million.

The population consists of all players who had a contract with an NHL team in 2013–2014. Each player in this population provides a data value—a salary. We can then imagine a population of salaries. This histogram shows the distribution of the population, including all the players and their salaries. The mean of this population—the typical salary of an NHL player in the 2013–2014 season—is 2.442 (in US $1,000,000s).

Using this distribution, we now show the results of a simulation. First, we take a random sample of 30 NHL players. The distribution of the salaries is given in Figure 9.5. We find the mean salary of the 30 players in the sample and record this statistic; the mean $\bar{x}$ of this sample is about 2.2 (in $ millions).

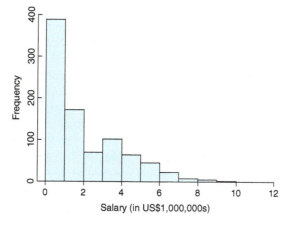

◀ **FIGURE 9.4** Distribution of salaries for NHL players for the 2013–2014 season.

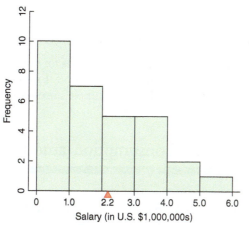

◀ **FIGURE 9.5** Distribution of a sample of 30 NHL players taken from the population of all NHL players in the 2013–2014 season. The mean of this sample, $2.2 million, is indicated.

We repeat this activity (that is, we sample another 30 NHL players from the population, finding the salary of each and then computing the mean of the sample) 500 times. When we are done, we will have 500 sample means—each being the mean salary of 30 NHL players. Figure 9.6a shows this distribution. Figure 9.6b shows the distribution of the sample mean when we sample 60 NHL players instead of 30, repeating 500 times. What differences do you see between the distribution of the population of NHL salaries (Figure 9.4), the distribution of a sample of 30 NHL salaries (Figure 9.5), and the distribution of the sample mean based on a sample size of 30 (Figure 9.6a) and 60 (Figure 9.6b)?

(a)

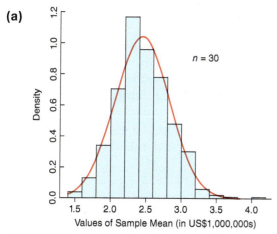

(b)

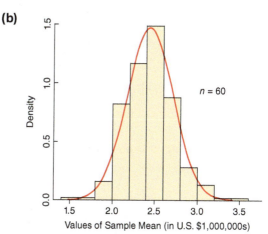

▲ **FIGURE 9.6** **(a)** Distribution of the sample means, where each sample mean is based on a sample size of $n = 30$ NHL players and is taken from the population shown in Figure 9.4. This is (approximately) the distribution of the sample mean $\bar{x}$ when $n = 30$. A Normal curve is superimposed. **(b)** The distribution of the sample mean $\bar{x}$ when $n = 60$.

Both of the sampling distributions in Figures 9.6a and 9.6b show us how the distribution of the sample mean $\bar{x}$ is approximately Normal, even though they are based on different sample sizes of 30 and 60. Furthermore, the behaviour of the mean of a sample from this population is *different* from the population (Figure 9.4). The Normal fit is not as good for $n = 30$ as it is for $n = 60$, but it is very close to Normal.

This is exactly what the CLT predicts. When the sample size is large enough, we can use the Normal distribution to find approximate probabilities for the values you may see for $\bar{x}$ when we take a random sample from the population.

The more observations you sample from the population, the more Normal the distribution of the sample mean becomes. Generally, the CLT provides a useful approximation of the true probabilities when the sample size is 25 or more. But this is just a general guideline. Be aware that in some scenarios you might need a larger sample size than 25. Unlike in Chapter 7, where we worked with the sample proportion, we can't provide a hard-and-fast rule for sample size. For nearly all the examples in this book, though not always in real life, 25 is big enough.

Applying the Central Limit Theorem

The Central Limit Theorem helps us find probabilities for sample means when those means are based on a random sample from a population. Example 2 demonstrates how we can answer probability questions about the sample mean even if we can't answer probability questions about individual outcomes.

EXAMPLE 2 Cigarette Consumption among Teenagers

According to a large study (Youth Smoking Survey 2009), the mean number of cigarettes consumed in a day by smoking Canadian teenagers is about six, and the standard deviation of this population is five cigarettes per day. The distribution of the number of cigarettes teenagers consume in a day is right-skewed.

QUESTIONS

a. Suppose we take a random sample of 36 Canadian teenagers who smoke and observe how many cigarettes each consumes in a day. What is the approximate probability that the mean number of cigarettes consumed in this sample will be below five or above seven? (In other words, what is the probability that it will be more than one cigarette per day away from the population mean of six?)

b. Can you find the probability that a single teenager, in a single day, will smoke more than two cigarettes away from the mean value of six?

SOLUTION

a. It doesn't matter that the distribution of the population variable is not Normal. This is because the sample size from the population is considered large at 36 (it is greater than 25), and the Central Limit Theorem tells us that the distribution of the mean of this sample will be approximately (but not exactly) Normal.

   The mean of this Normal distribution will be the same as the population mean: $\mu = 6$ cigarettes per day. The standard deviation of this distribution is

$$SD = \frac{\sigma}{\sqrt{n}} = \frac{5}{\sqrt{36}} = \frac{5}{6} = 0.833$$

To use the Normal table to find probabilities requires that the values of five cigarettes and seven cigarettes be converted to z-scores:

$$z = \frac{\bar{x} - \mu}{SD} = \frac{5 - 6}{0.833} = \frac{-1}{0.833} = -1.20$$

By symmetry (or direct calculation), the z-score corresponding to seven cigarettes is 1.20. Figure 9.7 shows the area that corresponds to the probability that the sample mean number of cigarettes consumed in a day will be more than 1.20 standard deviations away from the population mean number of cigarettes consumed in a day. This probability is calculated to be about 23%.

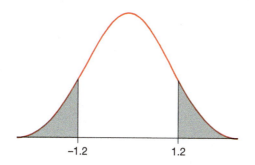

-1.2   1.2

◀ **FIGURE 9.7** Area of the Normal curve outside of z-scores of -1.20 and 1.20.

CONCLUSIONS

a. The approximate probability that the average number of cigarettes consumed by the sample of 36 teenage smokers in a day is less than five cigarettes or more than seven cigarettes is about 23%.

b. We cannot find probabilities concerning a single smoking teen because we do not know the probability distribution. We only know that it is skewed to the right, which is not enough information to find the actual probability.

TRY THIS! Exercise 9.13

> ❗ **Caution**
>
> **CLT Not Universal**
> The CLT does not apply to all statistics you run across. It does not apply to the sample median, for example. No matter how large the sample size, you cannot use the Normal distribution to find a probability for the median value. It also does not apply to the sample standard deviation.

Many Distributions

It's natural at this point to feel that you have seen a confusingly large number of types of distributions, but it's important that you keep them straight. The *population distribution* is the distribution of all the values in the population. Figure 9.4 (NHL salary in US $ millions) is an example of a population distribution because it shows the salary of each NHL player on NHL team rosters during the 2013–2014 season. Figure 9.1 (heart rates) is another example of a population distribution. For some populations, we don't know exactly how the variable of interest (salary in Figure 9.4, heartbeats per minute in Figure 9.1) is distributed. Sometimes we assume it is Normal, sometimes we know it is right-skewed or left-skewed, and sometimes we simply do not know.

When we know nothing about the population distribution, we sample n observations from this population. We can then make a histogram to understand how the data in this sample behave. As long as the sample is large enough and the sample was random, the distribution of the data in the sample should closely resemble the population distribution. Figure 9.5 is an example of the distribution of a sample of size $n = 30$ taken from a population of NHL players in the 2012–2013 season. Notice how closely the behaviour of the data in the sample mirrors the population distribution in Figure 9.4.

The *sampling distribution* is more abstract. If we take a random sample of data and find the sample mean (the centre of the distribution of the sample), and repeat this many, many times, we can then make a histogram of all the sample means to get the sampling distribution. In real life, we don't see the sampling distribution of the sample mean, because this would require us to take many, many samples of the same size. Figures 9.6a and 9.6b are examples of approximate sampling distributions for the sample mean based on samples of size 30 and 60, respectively, from a population made up of NHL player salaries. Note that these sampling distributions are not the same shape as the population distribution nor the sample seen in Figure 9.5; they are both approximately Normal.

EXAMPLE 3 Identify the Distribution

Figure 9.8 shows three distributions. One distribution is a population. The other two distributions are (approximate) sampling distributions. One sampling distribution is based on sample means of size 10, and the other is based on sample means of size 25.

(a)
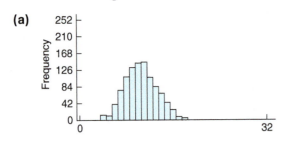

(b)
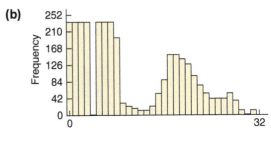

(c)
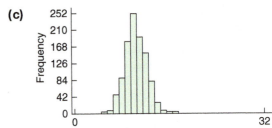

▶ **FIGURE 9.8** Three distributions, all on the same scale. One is a population distribution, and the other two are sampling distributions for means sampled from the population. (Source: Rice Virtual Lab in Statistics, http://onlinestatbook .com)

QUESTION Which graph (a, b, or c) is the population distribution? Which shows the sampling distribution for the mean with $n = 10$? Which with $n = 25$?

SOLUTION The Central Limit Theorem tells us that sampling distributions for means are approximately Normal. This implies that Figure 9.8b is not a sampling distribution, so it must be the population distribution from which the samples were taken. We know that the sample mean is more precise for larger samples, and because Figure 9.8a has the larger standard deviation (is wider), it must be the graph associated with $n = 10$. This means that Figure 9.8c is the sampling distribution of means with $n = 25$.

TRY THIS! Exercise 9.15

📷 SNAPSHOT THE SAMPLE MEAN ($\bar{x}$)

WHAT IS IT? ▶ The arithmetic average of the data in the sample.

WHAT DOES IT DO? ▶ The population mean μ represents the typical value for the population. The sample mean estimates the value of μ.

HOW DOES IT DO IT? ▶ If the sample was a random sample, then the sample mean is unbiased and we can make the precision of the estimator as good as we want by taking a large enough sample.

HOW IS IT USED? ▶ When the sample size is large enough ($n \geq 25$), the Central Limit Theorem says that the distribution of the sample mean is approximately Normal. If the population distribution is Normal, then the distribution of the sample mean is exactly Normal.

WHEN IS IT USED? ▶ The distribution of the sample mean is used to find the approximate probability that the sample mean will be any value within a certain range. This lets us know how close or far off our estimate for μ could be.

The *t*-Distribution

The confidence intervals and hypothesis tests that we will use for estimating and testing the mean are based on a statistic called the **t-statistic**:

$$t = \frac{\bar{x} - \mu}{\left(\dfrac{s}{\sqrt{n}}\right)}$$

The *t*-statistic is very similar to a *z*-statistic for the sample mean. In the numerator, we subtract the population mean from the sample mean. However, we divide differently: we divide by an *estimate* of the standard deviation of the sample mean.

It would be nice if we could divide by the true standard deviation. But in real life, we almost never know the value of σ, the population standard deviation. So instead, we replace it with an estimate: the sample standard deviation, *s*. This gives us an estimate for the standard deviation of the sample mean:

$$SD_{est} = \frac{s}{\sqrt{n}}$$

Compare the *t*-statistic to the *z*-statistic

$$z = \frac{\bar{x} - \mu}{\left(\dfrac{\sigma}{\sqrt{n}}\right)}$$

and you will see that we simply replaced σ in the *z*-statistic with *s*.

The *t*-statistic does *not* follow the Normal distribution. One reason for this is that the denominator changes with every sample. For this reason, the *t*-statistic is more variable than the *z*-statistic (whose denominator is always the same). Instead, the *t*-statistic follows a distribution called—surprise!—the **t-distribution**. This was Gosset's great discovery at the Guinness brewery. When small sample sizes were used to make inferences about the mean, even if the population was Normal, the Normal distribution just didn't fit the results that well. Gosset discovered a new distribution, which he called the *t*-distribution, that turned out to be a better model than the Normal for the sampling distribution of $\bar{x}$ when σ is not known.

The *t*-distribution shares many characteristics with the $N(0, 1)$ distribution. Both are symmetric, are unimodal, and might be described as "bell-shaped." However, the *t*-distribution has thicker tails. This means that in a *t*-distribution, it is more likely that we will see extreme values (values far from 0) than it is in a standard Normal distribution.

The *t*-distribution's shape depends on only one parameter, called the **degrees of freedom (df)**. The number of degrees of freedom is (usually) an integer: 1, 2, 3, and so on. If df is small, then the *t*-distribution has very thick tails. As the degrees of freedom get larger, the tails get thinner. Ultimately, when df is infinitely large, the *t*-distribution is exactly the same as the $N(0, 1)$ distribution.

Figure 9.9 shows *t*-distributions with 1, 10, and 40 degrees of freedom. In each case, the *t*-distribution is shown with an $N(0, 1)$ curve so that you can compare them. The *t*-distribution is the one whose tails are "higher" at the extremes. Note that by the time the degrees of freedom reach 40 (Figure 9.9c), the *t*-distribution and the $N(0, 1)$ distribution are too close to tell apart (on this scale).

Looking Back

Sample Standard Deviation
In Chapter 3 we gave the formula for the sample standard deviation:

$$s = \sqrt{\frac{\Sigma(x - \bar{x})^2}{n - 1}}$$

Details

Degrees of Freedom
Degrees of freedom are related to the sample size: generally, the larger the sample size, the larger the degrees of freedom. When estimating a single mean, as we are doing here, the number of degrees of freedom is equal to the sample size minus one.

$$df = n - 1$$

▶ **FIGURE 9.9** **(a)** A *t*-distribution with 1 degree of freedom, along with an *N*(0, 1) distribution. The *t*-distribution has much thicker tails. **(b)** The degrees of freedom are now equal to 10, and the tails are only slightly thicker in the *t*-distribution. **(c)** The degrees of freedom are now 40, and the two distributions are visually indistinguishable.

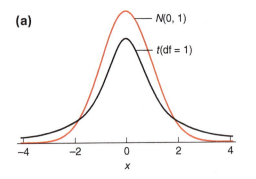

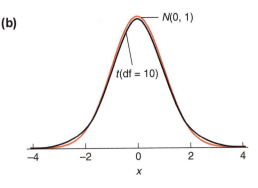

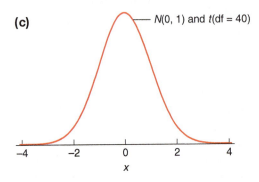

SECTION 9.3

Answering Questions about the Mean of a Population

Do you commute to school or work? If so, how long does it take? Is this amount typical among your friends? How about family members or friends living in different parts of the country? Does it take them about the same amount of time to commute as it does for you? What cities typically have the longest commute? Shortest commute? This information is important, and not just for those of us who fight traffic, navigate through winter driving conditions, and deal with bad drivers every day. It's also important to business leaders and government policy makers who make decisions about the cost of business and the quality of living. Statistics Canada periodically conducts surveys on the quality of life of Canadians, one aspect of which is commuting times. The 2010 General Social Survey (the latest GSS) found that, not surprisingly, Toronto, Montreal, and Vancouver had the longest commutes, with mean commuting times of 33 minutes, 31 minutes, and 30 minutes, respectively. In metropolitan areas with populations between 250,000 and 1 million residents, the mean commuting time was 25 minutes.

These figure are statistics—sample means computed from random samples of commuters taken from each city or metropolitan area—that are used to estimate the mean commuting time for all commuters. To find the true value of the mean commuting time in any city, we would have to inspect *each commuter*; that is, every individual in the population. Such a task is much too time consuming. We learned in Chapter 7 that taking such a census is not practical, due to the effectiveness of random sampling.

In this section we present two methods for answering questions about the value of the population mean. As we saw in Chapter 7, confidence intervals are used for estimating values of a parameter. In Chapter 8, we saw how hypothesis tests are used to decide whether a parameter is equal to a particular value, or not. We have seen these methods applied to proportions, but here you'll see how they are modified to work with means.

Estimation with Confidence Intervals

A **confidence interval** is a method for communicating the estimate of the population mean with a measure of uncertainty in that estimate. A confidence interval works to give us a range of values that are plausible for the population mean based on the data collected. For instance, the range of values for the mean commuting time of those living in cities of 250,000 to 1 million people is between 23.7 and 26.3 minutes.

Not all confidence intervals do an equally good job; the "job performance" of a confidence interval is therefore measured with something called the **confidence level**. The higher this level, the better the confidence interval performs. The confidence interval given above for the mean commuting time of someone living in a city of 250,000 to 1 million people has confidence level of 95%, which means we can be extremely confident that this interval contains the true mean.

Sometimes, you will be in a situation in which you will know only the sample mean and sample standard deviation. In these situations, you can use a calculator to find the confidence interval. However, if you have access to the actual data, you are much better off using statistical software to do all the calculations for you. We will show you how to respond to both situations.

No matter which situation you are in, you will need to judge whether a confidence interval is appropriate for the situation, and you will need to interpret the confidence interval. Therefore, we will discuss these essential skills before demonstrating the calculations.

When Are Confidence Intervals Useful?

A confidence interval is a useful answer to the following questions: "What's the typical value for a variable in this large group of objects or people? And how far away from the truth might this estimate of the typical value be?" You should provide a confidence interval whenever you are estimating the value of a population parameter on the basis of a random sample from that population. For example, judging on the basis of a random sample of 30 adults, what's the typical body temperature of all healthy adults? On the basis of a survey, how long does it take a student to commute to his or her college or university? A confidence interval is useful for answering questions such as these because it communicates the uncertainty in our estimate and provides a range of plausible values.

A confidence interval is not appropriate if there is no uncertainty in your estimate. This would be the case if your "sample" were actually the entire population. For example, it is not necessary to find a confidence interval for the mean score on your class's statistics exam. The population is your class, and all the scores are known. Thus the population mean is known, and there is no need to estimate it.

Checking Conditions

In order to measure the correct confidence level, the following conditions must hold:

Condition 1: *Random Sample.* Each observation is a result of a random sample of observations from a population of observations. The random selection means that each observation is independent of other data observed in the sample.

Condition 2: *Normality.* Either the population of observations follows a Normal model or the sample size is large ($n \geq 25$).

If these conditions do not hold, then we cannot measure the job performance of the interval; the confidence level may be incorrect. This means that we may advertise a 95% confidence level when, in fact, the true performance is much worse than this.

To check the first condition, you must know how the data were collected. This is not always possible, so rather than checking this condition you have to be somewhat trusting and assume that it holds. When we see the results of a poll, not often are we told that the persons surveyed were randomly chosen, rather we are told the 'margin of error' and that the results are accurate '19 times out of 20.'

The second condition is due to the Central Limit Theorem. If the population distribution is Normal, we have no concerns. However, if the population distribution is not Normal, then the CLT acts as a safety net: as long as the sample taken from the population distribution is large enough—at least 25—the distribution of the sample mean will be approximately Normal.

EXAMPLE 4 Is the Cost of Post-Secondary Education Going Up?

With increased pressure on provincial governments to implement cost-cutting in their yearly budgets, publicly funded post-secondary institutions face increasing pressures to provide access to post-secondary education with less financial resources. This usually leads to increases in tuition fees. Statistics Canada reported that the mean tuition fee across Canada (for Canadian citizens or residents) in 2010–2011 was $5146. A random sample of 34 colleges and universities found that the mean tuition for the 2012–2013 year was $5218, with a standard deviation of $893. Figure 9.10 shows the distribution of this sample. On the basis of this, a 95% confidence interval for the mean tuition fee at colleges and universities in Canada in 2012–2013 is $4906 to $5530.

▶ **FIGURE 9.10** Distribution of tuition fees for a random sample of 34 colleges and universities during the academic year 2012–2013.

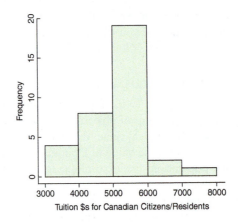

Tuition $s for Canadian Citizens/Residents

QUESTIONS

a. Describe the population. Is the number $5218 a parameter or a statistic?

b. Verify that the conditions for a valid confidence interval are met.

SOLUTIONS

a. The population consists of all publicly funded colleges and universities in Canada. (There are 92 of these institutions at the time of this writing.) The number $5218 is the mean tuition for Canadian citizens or residents of a sample of 34 colleges and universities. Since this number is computed from a sample, it is a statistic. Therefore $\bar{x} = 5218$.

b. The first condition is that the data represent a random sample of independent observations. We are told the sample was collected randomly, so we assume this is true. Independence here means that knowledge about one school's tuition tells us nothing about any other sampled school's tuition. The second condition requires that the population distribution be roughly Normally distributed or the sample size be at least 25. We do not know the distribution of the population, but because the sample size of 34 is at least 25, this condition is satisfied.

TRY THIS!   Exercise 9.17

Interpreting Confidence Intervals

To understand confidence intervals, you must know how to interpret a confidence interval and how to interpret a confidence level.

A confidence *interval* can be interpreted as a range of plausible values for the population parameter. In other words, we can be confident that if we were to learn the value of the population mean, it would be somewhere in the range of values given by our confidence interval. For example, Statistics Canada estimates that the mean commuting time of a person living in a city whose population is between 250,000 and 1 million is some-where between 23.7 and 26.3 minutes, with 95% confidence. We interpret this in the following way: we are 95% confident that the mean commuting time of *all* people living in a city of between 250,000 and 1 million people will be somewhere between 23.7 and 26.3 minutes. Yes, we could be wrong; the mean could be less than 23.7 minutes, or more than 26.3 minutes. Such a discovery would be very surprising though, as we are highly confident (95%) from the data collected that the mean will be within this interval.

KEY POINT A confidence interval can be interpreted as a range of plausible values of the population parameter.

EXAMPLE 5 Evidence for Increasing Post-Secondary Education Costs

Based on a random sample of 34 publicly funded colleges and universities, a 95% confidence interval for the mean tuition at all publicly funded colleges and universities for the 2012–2013 academic year is $4906 to $5530. In the academic year 2010–2011, the mean tuition at such schools was $5146.

QUESTION Does the confidence interval provide evidence that the mean tuition has increased?

SOLUTION No, it does not. Although we cannot know the mean tuition for all 92 publicly funded colleges and universities in the 2012–2013 academic year, we are 95% confident that this mean is somewhere between $4906 and $5530. This range includes the mean tuition for 2010–2011, $5146. Therefore, there is not enough evidence to conclude that the mean tuition has changed.

TRY THIS! Exercise 9.19

Measuring Performance with the Confidence Level

The confidence level, which in the case of the interval for the mean commuting time of a person living in a city of 250,000 to 1 million people was 95%, tells us about the method used to find the interval. A confidence level value of 95% says that Statistics Canada used a method that will capture the mean commuting time of all such people about 95% of the time. If we took many same-sized samples of people living in these cities and computed a 95% confidence interval for each sample, then about 95% of the intervals would contain the mean commuting time of all these city dwellers—μ.

The level of confidence does *not* tell us whether the interval (23.7 to 26.3) contains the population mean. Rather, the 95% tells us that we have a lot of trust in the method that produces the interval, and a lot of trust means the method is pretty good.

Suppose you decided to purchase a tablet online. You have your choice of several manufacturers, and they are rated in terms of their performance level. One manufacturer has a 90% performance level, which means that 90% of the tablets it produces are good ones, and 10% are defective. Some other manufacturers have lower levels: 80%, 60%, and worse. From whom do you buy? You choose to buy from the manufacturer with the 90% level, because you can be very confident that the tablet it sends you will be good. Of course, once the tablet arrives at your home, the confidence level isn't too useful. Your tablet either works or does not work; there's no 90% about it.

Confidence levels work the same way. We prefer confidence intervals with levels of confidence that are at least 90%, because then we know that the process that produced these levels is a good one, and therefore, we are confident in any decisions or conclusions we reach. But the level doesn't tell us whether this one particular interval sitting in front of us is good or bad. In fact, we shall never know that, unless we someday gain access to the entire population.

> **KEY POINT** The confidence level is a measure of how well the method used to produce the confidence interval performs. We can interpret the confidence level to mean that if we were to take many random samples of the same size from the same population, and for each random sample calculate a confidence interval, then the confidence level is the proportion of intervals that "work"—the proportion that contain the population parameter.

> ⚠️ **Caution**
> **Confidence Levels Are Not Probabilities**
> A confidence level, such as 95%, is not a probability. Saying we are 95% confident that the mean is between 23.7 and 26.3 minutes does *not* mean that there is a 95% chance that the mean is between these two values. It either is or isn't. There's no probability about it.

Figure 9.11 shows the meaning of a confidence interval. From a population of 89 movies showing in theatres in North America during the week of January 26, 2015 (www.the-numbers.com), a random sample of 25 movies was taken (with replacement) and the mean revenue per theatre was computed. This process was repeated for a total of 10 samples of 25 movies. Because the movies were chosen randomly, each sample of 25 movies gave a different value of the sample mean. For each of these 10 samples a 95% confidence interval was calculated, and the results are given in Figure 9.11a. Then 90 more random samples of 25 movies were taken, and from each of these a 95% confidence interval was found. These 90 intervals were added to the previous 10 for a total of 100 different confidence intervals for the population mean, as shown in Figure 9.11b.

(a)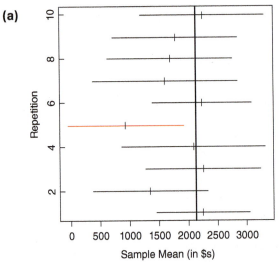

(b)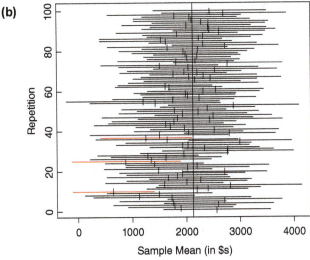

▲ **FIGURE 9.11 (a)** Ten different 95% confidence intervals, each based on a different random sample of 25 movies. The population mean of $2124 is shown by the black vertical bar. Nine of the 10 intervals capture the value of $2124, with the off interval shown in red. **(b)** One hundred confidence intervals, each based on a random sample of 25 movies. Because we are using a 95% confidence level, we expect about 95%, or 95, of these intervals to capture the value of $2124. Here, 97 netted the target of $2124. The red intervals are "bad" intervals because they do not capture $2124.

EXAMPLE 6 iPad Batteries

A consumer group wishes to test Apple's claim that the iPad has a 10-hour battery life. With a random sample of five iPads, and running them under identical conditions, the group finds a 95% confidence interval for the mean battery life of an iPad to be 9.5 hours to 12.5 hours. One of the following statements is a correct meaning of the confidence level. The other is a correct interpretation of the confidence interval.

(i) We are very confident that the mean battery life of all iPads is between 9.5 and 12.5 hours.

(ii) In about 95% of all samples of five iPads, the resulting confidence interval will contain the mean battery life of all iPads.

QUESTION Which of these statements is a valid interpretation of a confidence interval? Which of these statements is a valid meaning of a confidence level?

SOLUTION Statement (i) interprets a confidence *interval* (9.5, 12.5). Statement (ii) tells us the meaning of the 95% confidence *level*.

TRY THIS! Exercise 9.23

Calculating the Confidence Interval

Confidence intervals for means have the same basic structure as they did for proportions:

$$\text{Estimator} \pm \text{margin of error}$$

As in Chapter 7, the margin of error has the structure

$$\text{Margin of error} = (\text{multiplier}) \times SD$$

The standard deviation is $SD = \dfrac{\sigma}{\sqrt{n}}$. Because we usually do not know the standard deviation of the population and hence the SD, we replace the SD with its estimate. This leads to a formula similar in structure, but slightly different in details, from the one you learned for proportions.

Formula 9.1: One-Sample *t*-Interval

$$\bar{x} \pm m$$

where

$$m = t^* SD_{est} \text{ and } SD_{est} = \dfrac{s}{\sqrt{n}}$$

The multiplier t^* is a constant that is used to fine-tune the margin of error m so that it has the level of confidence we want. This multiplier is found using a t-distribution with $n - 1$ degrees of freedom. SD_{est} is the estimated standard deviation of the sample mean.

To compute a confidence interval for the mean, you first need to choose the level of confidence. After that, you need either the original data or these four pieces of information:

1. The sample average, $\bar{x}$, which you calculate from the data.

2. The sample standard deviation, s, which you calculate from the data.

3. The sample size, n, which you know from looking at the data.

4. The multiplier, t^*, which you look up in a table (or use technology) and which is determined by your confidence level and the sample size n. The value of t^* tells us how wide the margin of error is in terms of standard deviations. For example, if t^* is 2, then our margin of error is two standard deviations wide.

The first three steps are pretty straightforward, so let's spend a minute on finding t^*, the multiplier for the margin of error.

The multiplier is based on a t-distribution with $n - 1$ degrees of freedom. The correct values can be found in Table 4 in Appendix A, or you can use technology. Table 4 is organized so that each row represents possible values of t^* for each number of degrees of freedom. The columns contain the values of t^* for a given confidence level. For example, for a 95% confidence level and a sample size of $n = 30$, we use $t^* = 2.045$. We find this in the table by looking in the row with $df = n - 1 = 30 - 1 = 29$ and using the column for a 95% confidence level. Refer to Table 9.3, which is in part from the table in Appendix A.

EXAMPLE 7 Finding the Multiplier t^*

Suppose we collect a sample of 30 iPads and wish to calculate a 90% confidence interval for the mean battery life.

QUESTION Using Table 9.3, find t^* for a 90% confidence interval when $n = 30$.

▶ **TABLE 9.3** Critical values of t.

DF	Confidence Level			
	90%	**95%**	**98%**	**99%**
28	1.701	2.048	2.467	2.763
29	<u>1.699</u>	2.045	2.462	2.756
30	1.697	2.042	2.457	2.750
33	1.692	2.035	2.445	2.733

SOLUTION We find the number of degrees of freedom from the sample size,

$$\text{df} = n - 1 = 30 - 1 = 29$$

And so we find, from Table 9.3, that $t^* = 1.699$ (shown underlined).

TRY THIS! Exercise 9.25

**Looking Back**

Why Not 100%?
In Chapter 7, you learned that one reason why a 95% confidence level is popular is that increasing the confidence level by only a small amount beyond 95% requires a much larger margin of error.

It is best to use technology to find the multiplier, because most tables stop at 35 or 40 degrees of freedom. For a 95% confidence level, if you do not have access to technology and the sample size is bigger than 40, it is usually safe to use $t^* = 1.96$—the same multiplier that we used for confidence intervals for sample proportions (for 95% confidence). The precise value, if we used a computer, is 2.02, but this is only 0.06 unit away from 1.96, so the result is probably not going to be affected in a big way.

The wider the confidence interval, the more confident we will be that the interval captures the value of the population parameter. We can always increase our level of confidence by making the margin of error bigger. We do this by choosing larger values for t^*.

 ## EXAMPLE 8 Post-Secondary Education Tuition

A random sample of 34 publicly funded colleges and universities in 2012–2013 has a mean tuition of $5218, with a standard deviation of $893.

QUESTION Find a 90% confidence interval and a 95% confidence interval for the mean tuition for all publicly funded colleges and universities in 2012–2013. Interpret the intervals. Assume that the required conditions hold.

SOLUTION We are given the desired confidence level, the standard deviation of the sample, and the mean of the sample, so the next step is to compute the estimated standard deviation of the sample mean.

$$\bar{x} = \$5218$$

$$SD_{\text{est}} = \frac{s}{\sqrt{n}} = \frac{893}{\sqrt{34}} = 153.1482$$

$$\bar{x} \pm m = \bar{x} \pm t^* SD_{\text{est}}$$

We find the appropriate values of t^* (from Table 9.3):

$$t^* \text{ (for 90\%)} = 1.692$$
$$t^* \text{ (for 95\%)} = 2.035$$

For the 90% confidence interval,

$$\bar{x} \pm m = \bar{x} \pm t^* SD_{est} \text{ becomes } 5218 \pm (1.692 \times 153.1482) = 5218 \pm 259.1268$$

Lower limit: $5218 - 259.1268 = 4958.87$
Upper limit: $5218 + 259.1268 = 5477.13$

A 90% confidence interval for the mean tuition for all publicly funded colleges and universities in the 2012–2013 academic year is ($4959, $5477). That is, we are 90% confident that the mean tuition (or typical tuition) of these institutions is somewhere between $4959 and $5477.

For the 95% confidence interval,

$$\bar{x} \pm m = \bar{x} \pm t^* SD_{est} \text{ becomes } 5218 \pm (2.035 \times 153.1482) = 5218 \pm 311.6566$$

Lower Limit: $5218 - 311.6566 = 4906.34$
Upper Limit: $5218 + 311.6566 = 5529.66$

CONCLUSION The 90% confidence interval is ($4959, $5477). The 95% confidence interval is ($4906, $5530), which is wider. We are 90% confident that the mean tuition for all publicly funded colleges and universities is somewhere between $4959 and $5477. We are 95% confident that the mean tuition could be as low as $4906 and as high as $5530.

TRY THIS! Exercise 9.27

If you have access to the original data (and not just the statistics as we were given in Example 8), then it is always good practice to use a computer to find the confidence interval for you. In Figure 9.12, the StatCrunch output shows us what we would see if we used the full data for Example 8 and asked the software to find a 95% confidence interval for the mean tuition for all publicly funded colleges and universities. The output shows us the estimated mean ($5217.7354) and standard deviation (StatCrunch calls it the Std. Err.) ($153.12825), the degrees of freedom (33), the lower limit of the confidence interval ($4906.1934), and the upper limit ($5529.277). Note that these are not exactly the values given in Example 8. StatCrunch values are more accurate because there is no rounding when it computes this confidence interval.

TECH

95% confidence interval results:
μ : mean of Variable

Variable	Sample Mean	Std. Err.	DF	L. Limit	U. Limit
2012-2013 Tuition	5217.7354	153.12825	33	4906.1934	5529.277

◄ FIGURE 9.12 StatCrunch output showing the 95% confidence interval for the mean tuition for publicly funded colleges and universities in the academic year 2012–2013.

Reporting and Reading Confidence Intervals

There are two ways of reporting confidence intervals. Professional statisticians tend to report (lower boundary, upper boundary). This is what we've done so far in this chapter.

We reported the 95% confidence interval for the mean tuition of publicly funded colleges and universities in 2012–2013 as ($4906, $5530).

In the press, however, and in some scholarly publications, you'll also see confidence intervals reported as

$$\text{Estimate} \pm \text{margin of error}$$

For the mean tuition in 2012–2013, we calculated the margin of error to be 311.6566 for 95% confidence. Alternatively, we could report the confidence interval as

$$\$5218 \pm \$312$$

This form is useful because it shows our estimate of the population mean ($5218) as well as our uncertainty (the population mean could be $312 lower or $312 higher).

You're welcome to choose whichever you think best, although you should be familiar with both forms.

Testing a Mean

In Chapter 8 we established the foundations of hypothesis testing. Here, you'll see that the same four steps can be used to test hypotheses about means of populations. These four steps are

Step 1: Hypothesize.
State your hypotheses about the value of the population parameter.

Step 2: Prepare.
Get ready to test: choose and state a significance level. Choose a test statistic appropriate for the hypotheses. State and check conditions required for the computations, and state any assumptions that must be made.

Step 3: Compute to compare.
Compute the observed value of the test statistic in order to compare the null hypothesis value to our observed value. Find the p-value to measure your level of surprise.

Step 4: Interpret and conclude.
Interpret the meaning of the p-value and compare it to the significance level. Do you reject or fail to reject the null hypothesis? What does your decision mean in the context of the data?

As an example of testing a mean, consider a "study" done by one of the authors. In 2012, Tim Hortons added an extra-large coffee to its menu. This new size was supposed to hold a mean of 710 millilitres (ml) of coffee. To compare, a regular can of beer holds about 355 ml, and the maximum capacity of the human bladder is between 500 and 530 ml. A human server pours coffee into the extra-large cup, so we would expect some variation in the amount of coffee poured. What would happen if we measured the amount of coffee poured into all of Tim Hortons extra-large coffee cups? Would the mean amount be 710 ml? Or not?

One of the authors collected a sample by ordering five extra-large Tim Hortons coffees at five different locations. The amount of coffee poured into each cup was measured using a graduated cylinder (no cream, no sugar). The amount of coffee was then measured (in millilitres) as

$$710, 673, 713, 679, \text{ and } 710$$

We summarize the data as

$$\bar{x} = 697 \text{ ml}, \ s = 19.326 \text{ ml}$$

Do these data support the Tim Hortons claim that the mean amount of coffee poured into its extra-large coffee cups is 710 millilitres? Or is the mean amount poured a different value? We'll apply the four steps of a hypothesis test to come to a decision.

Step 1: Hypothesize

Hypotheses come in pairs and are always statements about the population. Here, the population consists of all extra-large cups of Tim Hortons coffee that have been poured, and will be poured. The parameter of this population is the mean amount of coffee poured into an extra-large cup.

The null hypothesis is the status-quo position, which is the Tim Hortons claim. Each extra-large cup of coffee will have varying amounts poured, but on average, the amount should be 710 ml.

We state the null hypothesis as

$$H_0: \mu = 710$$

Recall that the null hypothesis always contains an "=" sign.

The alternative hypothesis is "not the null hypothesis." Here, it's that the mean amount of coffee poured is anything but 710 millilitres. That is, the mean is not 710 ml.

$$H_A: \mu \neq 710$$

We have a two-tailed hypothesis. We will reject the null hypothesis if the average of our sample of extra-large sized coffee cups is either very small (they are under-filling) or very large (they are over-filling). It is possible to have a one-tailed hypotheses, as you will see later in this chapter.

> **KEY POINT** Hypotheses are always statements about population parameters. For the test you are about to learn, this parameter is always μ, the mean of the population.

Step 2: Prepare

The first step is to set the significance level α (alpha), as we discussed in Chapter 8. The significance level is a performance measure of the test. It helps us to evaluate the quality of the test procedure we are using. It is the probability of making the mistake of rejecting the null hypothesis when, in fact, the null hypothesis is true. Here, this is the probability of concluding that the mean amount poured into the extra-large Tim Hortons cup is not 710 millilitres when, in fact, it is.

The test statistic for this test, called the one-sample t-test, is very similar to the one-proportion z-test statistic. Unsurprisingly, given its name, this test is based on the t-statistic introduced in Section 9.2. The idea is simple: compare the observed value of the sample mean, $\bar{x}$, to the value claimed by the null hypothesis, μ_0.

Details

What Value for α?
For most situations, using a significance level of 0.05 is a good choice and is recommended by many scientific journals. Values of 0.01 and 0.10 are also commonly used.

Formula 9.2: Test Statistic for the One-Sample t-Test

$$t = \frac{\bar{x} - \mu_0}{SD_{est}}, \qquad \text{where} \qquad SD_{est} = \frac{s}{\sqrt{n}}$$

If conditions hold, the test statistic follows a t-distribution with df $= n - 1$.

This test statistic compares the value of the population mean that says the null hypothesis is true, or μ_0, to the estimate of its value that we have observed in our data. If this estimate is close to μ_0, then the t-statistic is close to 0. But if the estimate is far from μ_0, then the t-statistic is far from 0. The further the t-statistic is from zero, the stronger the evidence against the null hypothesis.

Anyone can make a decision, but we need to measure the probability that the decision is right or wrong. To do this, we need to know the sampling distribution of our test statistic.

The sampling distribution will follow the t-distribution under these conditions:

Condition 1: *Random Sample.* Each observation is a result of a random sample of observations from a population of observations. The random selection

Looking Back

The z-Test
Compare this to the z-test statistic for one proportion in Chapter 8, which has a very similar structure:

$$z = \frac{\hat{p} - p_0}{SD}$$

means that each observation is independent of other data observed in the sample.

Condition 2: *Normality.* Either the population of observations follows a Normal model or the sample size is large ($n \geq 25$).

Now let's apply this to our coffee problem. Because the amounts poured in our sample were from different Tim Hortons locations, we can safely say that the amount of coffee put into each of the extra-large cups is independent of each other amount poured. If all five cups were filled by the same person, independence could be questioned here—then we would be in some statistical trouble. If independence did not hold, our conclusions could be *very* wrong!

Second, the population for testing the mean amount of coffee poured into a extra-large Tim Hortons cup is a bit abstract, due to the constant stream of extra-large "Timmies" being poured. However, it does seem plausible that in some instances the amount of coffee poured is less than 710 ml, and in others the amount poured is slightly more (not too much more, though, as the cup would overfill). Given this, then the amounts poured should closely follow a Normal distribution. By making the population distribution Normal, the small sample size of $n = 5$ is not a problem for us.

Step 3: Compute to compare

By checking the conditions of the *t*-statistic, our data tell us that our test statistic should follow a *t*-distribution with $n - 1$ degrees of freedom. So, we move on to doing the calculations we need to compare our observed sample mean $\bar{x}$ to the hypothesized value of the population mean μ_0, then measure our surprise.

To find the observed value of the *t*-statistic, we need to find the sample mean and the standard deviation of our sample. These values are given above, but you can easily calculate them from the data, preferably with the help of software.

$$SD_{est} = \frac{s}{\sqrt{n}} = \frac{19.326}{\sqrt{5}} = 8.6428$$

$$t = \frac{\bar{x} - \mu_0}{SD_{est}} = \frac{697 - 710}{8.6428} = -1.504$$

The observed *t*-statistic was -1.504, between one and two standard deviations below the value the null hypothesis expects us to observe.

> **KEY POINT** The *t*-statistic measures how far away (how many standard deviations) our observed mean, $\bar{x}$, lies from the hypothesized value, μ_0. Values far from 0 tend to discredit the null hypothesis.

According to the null hypothesis, how unusual is the observed value of the *t*-statistic? The p-value tells us exactly that—the probability that we would get a result as surprising or more surprising than our *t*-statistic if we were to sample again and retest whether in fact the population mean is 710 millilitres.

Our alternative hypothesis says we should look out for *t*-statistic values that are much smaller or bigger than 0. Therefore, we must find the probability in both tails of our *t*-distribution. The p-value is shown by the shaded areas in Figure 9.13. Because our sample size is $n = 5$, our degree of freedom is $n - 1 = 5 - 1 = 4$.

The p-value is 0.2070.

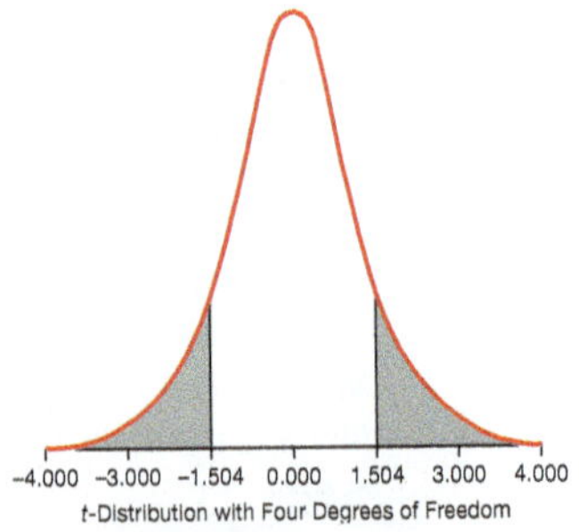

-4.000 -3.000 -1.504 0.000 1.504 3.000 4.000
t-Distribution with Four Degrees of Freedom

▲ FIGURE 9.13 The tail areas below −1.504 and above 1.504 are shown as the shaded areas in both tails of the *t*-distribution with four degrees of freedom. The p-value is 0.2070, the probability that if $\mu = 710$, another random sample of five observations will give a *t*-statistic that is smaller than −1.504 or larger than 1.504.

Step 4: Interpret and conclude

The last step involves the interpretation of the p-value, followed by its comparison to the level of significance. We then complete the problem by making a conclusion.

If the author were to collect data again in the same way that the five coffee amounts were collected, there is a 0.2070 probability that such a sample would produce a *t*-statistic value that is just as surprising as the one we observed, given that the null hypothesis is true (or $\mu = 710$).

Our p-value of 0.2070 is not less than the significance level we chose (0.05), so we should not reject the null hypothesis. From these data, we can conclude that the mean amount of coffee poured into an extra-large Tim Hortons coffee cup is as advertised, 710 millilitres.

Even though the sample from which the test is conducted is small, the method is statistically sound. Perhaps a Tim Hortons executive is breathing a sigh of relief. Surely it would be embarrassing if the data and the application of the one-sample t-test revealed that $\mu < 710$!

One- and Two-Tailed Alternative Hypotheses

The alternative hypothesis in the coffee-pouring test was two-tailed. As you learned in Chapter 8, alternative hypotheses can also be one-tailed. The exact form of the alternative hypothesis depends on the research question. In turn, the form of the alternative hypothesis tells us how to find the p-value.

You will always use one of the following three pairs of hypotheses for the one-sample t-test:

Two-Tailed	One-Tailed (Left)	One-Tailed (Right)
$H_0: \mu = \mu_0$	$H_0: \mu = \mu_0$	$H_0: \mu = \mu_0$
$H_A: \mu \neq \mu_0$	$H_A: \mu < \mu_0$	$H_A: \mu > \mu_0$

You choose the pair of hypotheses on the basis of your research question. For the coffee-pouring example, we asked if the mean amount poured is different from 710 millilitres, and proceeded with a two-tailed test. What if we wanted to see if Tim Hortons was short-pouring its customers? Then we would test whether the mean amount of coffee poured is less than 710 millilitres, and our one sample t-test would be *left*-tailed. Or, what if we wanted to see if Tim Hortons was pouring too much coffee in the extra-large cup? Here we would test that the population mean is greater than 710 millilitres, and our t-test would be *right*-tailed.

Your choice of alternative hypothesis determines how you calculate the p-value. Figure 9.14 shows how to find the p-value for each alternative hypothesis, all using the same t-statistic value of $t = 2.1$ and a sample size of $n = 30$.

(a)

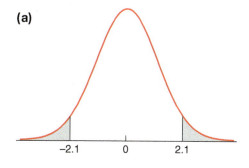

(b)

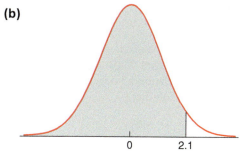

(c)

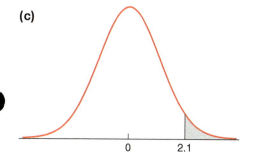

◀ **FIGURE 9.14** The distributions are t-distributions with $n - 1 = 29$ degrees of freedom. The shaded region in each graph represents a p-value when $t = 2.1$ for **(a)** a two-tailed alternative hypothesis, **(b)** a one-tailed (left) hypothesis, and **(c)** a one-tailed (right) hypothesis.

Looking Back

p-Values
In Chapter 8 you learned that the p-value is the probability that when the null hypothesis is true, we will get a test statistic as extreme as or more extreme than what we actually saw. (What is meant by "extreme" depends on the alternative hypothesis.) The p-value measures our surprise at the outcome.

Looking Back

What Does "as extreme as or more extreme than" Mean?
See Chapter 8 for a detailed discussion of how the p-value depends on the alternative hypothesis.

Note that the p-value is always an "extreme" probability; it's always the probability of the tails (even if the tail is pretty big, as it is in Figure 9.14b).

EXAMPLE 9 Dieting

People who want to lose weight have many different diets among which to choose. In one study (Dansinger et al. 2005), researchers compared results from four different diets. In this example, though, we look at only a small part of these data to examine whether one of the more popular diets, the Weight Watchers diet, is effective. The researchers examined 40 subjects who were randomly assigned to this diet. Researchers recorded the change in weight after 12 months. The distribution of amount of weight lost in this sample is shown in Figure 9.15. Only 26 of the 40 subjects stayed with the diet for that long, so we have data on only these 26 people.

QUESTION Test the hypothesis that people on the Weight Watchers diet tend to lose weight. Summary statistics are given below. (A negative weight change means the person lost weight.)

$$\bar{x} = -4.6 \text{ kg}, \quad s = 5.4 \text{ kg}$$

SOLUTION From Figure 9.15, we see that although a small number of people actually gained weight, the typical experience was a loss in weight. After a year, the average change in weight of the 26 people who stayed on the diet was -4.6 kilograms, with a standard deviation of 5.4 kilograms.

▶ **FIGURE 9.15** Change in weight for subjects after one year on a points-based plan (the Weight Watchers diet). Note that most values are negative, representing people who lost weight.

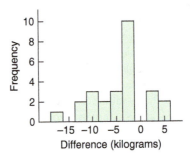

Our population of interest is the group of all overweight people who might go on the Weight Watchers diet and stick to the diet for one year. Could the mean weight change of this population be negative? If so, then, on average, we could say that people do lose weight on this diet.

Step 1: Hypothesize
Let μ represent the mean weight change of the population.

$$H_0: \mu = 0$$

$$H_A: \mu < 0$$

The null hypothesis says that the mean is 0, because the neutral position here is that no change occurs, on average. This is the same as saying that the diet is ineffective, or not different from no diet at all.

The alternative is that the mean change is negative. This differs from the coffee-pouring example, where we only wanted to know whether or not the mean amount poured was 710 millilitres. Here we care about the direction of the weight change: Did it go down?

Step 2: Prepare

We will test using a 5% significance level.

We need to check the conditions required in order for the *t*-statistic to follow the *t*-distribution (approximately).

Condition 1: *Random Sample.* The subjects in the study were not randomly chosen from the population of all dieters. But they were selected randomly from a larger group of dieters, because one-fourth of the subjects in this study were randomly assigned to Weight Watchers and the rest to other diets. We will assume that the researchers took care so that observations were independent.

Condition 2: *Normality.* The distribution of the sample does not look Normal, which leads us to suspect that the population distribution is not Normal. But because the sample size is larger than 25, the condition is satisfied.

Step 3: Compute to compare

$$SD_{est} = \frac{s}{\sqrt{n}} = \frac{5.4}{\sqrt{26}} = 1.0590$$

$$t = \frac{\bar{x} - \mu}{SD_{est}} = \frac{-4.6}{1.0590} = -4.34$$

This tells us that our test statistic is 4.34 standard deviations below what the null hypothesis expected.

Our p-value here is the area below the observed value, because the alternative cares only whether we get values that are smaller than expected. (Remember, this is a one-tailed hypothesis.) We find the p-value, using technology, to be 0.0001 (Figure 9.16). We use a *t*-distribution with $n - 1 = 25$ degrees of freedom.

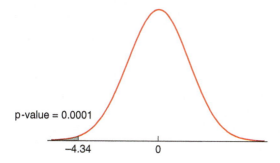

p-value = 0.0001

−4.34   0

◀ **FIGURE 9.16** The p-value (shaded) for the diet data. The area has been enlarged so that it can be seen.

Step 4: Interpret and conclude

The p-value of 0.0001 means that if the null hypothesis is true and the mean weight change is zero, then the chance that another random sample of 26 people who stay on the Weight Watchers diet for a year would produce a *t*-statistic that is just as surprising or more so than the one we observed is 0.0001, or about 1 in 10,000. In other words, we are not very likely to get stronger evidence against the null hypothesis than the evidence we have. Since the p-value of 0.0001 is less than 0.05, we reject the null hypothesis. From this sample, we can conclude that the mean weight change is negative, meaning that *on average* people do tend to lose weight after one year on the diet.

TRY THIS! Exercise 9.31

TECH

If you have access to the original data, then you should use statistical software to perform the *t*-test. Figure 9.17 shows the results from using StatCrunch to carry out the hypothesis test. We had to tell the computer only the null and alternative hypotheses, and it did the rest. Note that, because of rounding, the values are not precisely the same as those we calculated by hand in the example.

▶ **FIGURE 9.17** Output from StatCrunch, showing the test that the mean weight loss under Weight Watchers was a negative value (Example 8). The small p-value leads us to conclude that, on average, the dieters lost weight.

One sample T statistics with data

Options

Hypothesis test results:
Where: DIET="Weight Watchers" and weightloss <>0
μ : mean of Variable
$H_0 : \mu = 0$
$H_A : \mu < 0$

Variable	Sample Mean	Std. Err.	DF	T-Stat	P-value
weightloss	−4.5923076	1.0575868	25	−4.3422513	0.0001

SNAPSHOT — ONE-SAMPLE *t*-TEST

WHAT IS IT? ▶ A procedure based on the *t*-statistic $t = \dfrac{\bar{x} - \mu_0}{SD_{est}}$, where $SD_{est} = \dfrac{s}{\sqrt{n}}$

WHAT DOES IT DO? ▶ It tests hypotheses about the value of the population mean μ.

HOW DOES IT DO IT? ▶ Because σ is unknown, the standard deviation of $\bar{x}$ needs to be estimated from the data with $SD_{est} = \dfrac{s}{\sqrt{n}}$. Since this ratio will vary from sample to sample, there is an extra random component in the process. The *t*-distribution accounts for this.

HOW IS IT USED? ▶ The value of the *t*-statistic is used to compute the p-value. If the value of the *t*-statistic is close to zero, an outcome in line with the null hypothesis is observed and the p-value will not be small. If the *t*-statistic is far from zero, the outcome is not in line with the null hypothesis and the p-value will be small. This leads to a rejection of the null hypothesis.

WHEN IS IT USED? ▶ When conducting a hypothesis test about the value of the population mean and the standard deviation in the population of values is unknown. Either the population distribution is Normal or $n \geq 25$.

SECTION 9.4

Comparing Two Population Means

Do gas prices in Vancouver differ from those in Toronto? Do Ontario post-secondary students pay the same tuition fees as those in Alberta? Is the price of wine the same at two competing wine stores? Does your ability to smell depend on whether you are sitting up or lying down?

If we wanted to see if gas prices were different in Vancouver and Toronto, we could proceed in the following way: we first take a random sample of gas stations in Vancouver, and another random sample of gas stations in Toronto. We then record the price of a litre of gasoline at each of the Vancouver and Toronto gas stations chosen. When we are finished, we have two sets of numbers. In a statistics context, we treat each set of numbers as a sample of values from a population of values. Here we have two populations, Vancouver gas prices and Toronto gas prices, each having a population mean.

How can we investigate whether the two means of these populations are the same? We can find a confidence interval for each population mean—one for the mean price of a litre of gasoline in Vancouver (μ_1) and another for the mean price of a litre of gasoline in Toronto (μ_2)—using the method outlined in Section 9.3. But we can be more precise in this comparison by looking at the difference between the two population means, or $\mu_1 - \mu_2$.

When comparing two populations of values, it is important to pay attention to whether the data sampled from the populations are two **independent samples** or **paired (dependent) samples**. Independent samples are taken when the values observed in the sample from one population are not related to values observed in the sample from the second population. In our hypothetical samples of gas stations in Vancouver and Toronto, the price per litre at a gas station in Vancouver has nothing to do with the price per litre at a gas station in Toronto, and vice versa.

Paired (dependent) samples occur when you randomly pick an individual, or thing, from a population of individuals (things). Then we observe a variable on that individual (or thing) under two different settings. Each setting can be thought of as a distinct population. If we wanted to compare the price of wine at two different—and competing—wine stores, we could look at a few different brands of wine sold at both stores and observe the price of each brand at both stores. We then have pairs of wine prices for each wine: the price of Wine A at store 1 and the price of Wine A at store 2. This is an example of paired, or dependent, samples. The two settings are the two competing wine stores. These types of data are called dependent because the pairs of data—pairs of wine prices—depend on the items the data are coming from, in this instance the brand of wine.

Sometimes the dependence results when the objects being measured are related somehow, as in the case of comparing twins, siblings, or spouses. Other times, dependence occurs when the experimenters have deliberately matched subjects in the two populations so that each pair of subjects has similar characteristics.

> **⚠ Caution**
>
> **Paired (Dependent) vs. Independent Samples**
> One indication that you have paired samples is that each observation in one group is coupled with *one particular observation* in the other group. In this case, the two groups will have the same sample size (assuming no observations are missing).

EXAMPLE 10 Independent or Dependent Samples?

Here are four descriptions of research studies.

a. Subjects were tested for their sense of smell twice: once when lying down, once while sitting up. Researchers want to know whether the mean ability to detect smells differs depending on whether one is sitting up or lying down.

b. Men and women each had their sense of smell measured. Researchers want to know whether, typically, men and women differ in their ability to sense smells.

c. Researchers randomly assigned overweight people to one of two diets: Weight Watchers and Atkins. Researchers want to know whether the mean weight loss on Weight Watchers was different from that on Atkins.

d. The number of years of education for husbands and wives are compared to see whether the means are different.

QUESTION For each study, state the two populations and whether it involves two independent samples or paired (that is, dependent) samples.

SOLUTIONS

a. This study has two populations as the data being observed are from two different settings: a lying-down setting and a sitting-up setting. We can think of the first population as all people lying down, the variable being their ability to detect smells. The second population is the same people, but in the sitting-up setting. The variable is the same as in the first population: a person's ability to detect smells. Because data are being collected on the same people in two different settings—lying down or sitting up—these samples are *paired* (or *dependent*).

b. The two populations are the population of men and the population of women. For each population, the data to be collected are the same: the ability to sense smells. A measurement from a man could not tell us anything about the measurement from a woman. These are *independent* samples.

c. The two populations are the people on the Weight Watchers diet (Population 1) and the people on the Atkins diet (Population 2). We are told that the two samples consist of different people; people are randomly assigned to one diet or the other, but not both. These are *independent* samples.

d. The two populations, or settings, are the husband and the wife. The number of years of education is observed under each setting: the husband and the wife. Because the number of years of education of one may be related to the number of years of education of the other, the samples are *dependent*. Or, for each husband and wife pair, years of education is observed, hence the sample is *paired*.

TRY THIS! Exercise 9.47

Soon you will see that we analyze paired samples differently from two independent samples. The data collected from paired samples are turned into "difference" data: we subtract one value in each pair from the other to create a single variable, a "difference variable," then analyze these differences using the one-sample methods seen in Section 9.3. The weight loss data in Example 9 was an example of this. Participants were measured before the diet, in one setting. Then they were measured after the diet, in a different setting. These pairs of values were subtracted to produce a difference between the before and after diet weights, a weight loss measure.

Estimating the Mean Difference with Confidence Intervals (Independent Samples)

The Weight Watchers diet uses a personalized points system to restrict calories. The Atkins diet, on the other hand, limits the amount of carbohydrates. Which diet is more effective? Researchers compared these two diets (as well as two others) by randomly assigning overweight subjects to the two diet groups. The boxplots in Figure 9.18 show summary statistics for the samples' weight losses after one year. The mean weight loss of the Weight Watchers dieters was 4.6 kilograms and the mean loss of the Atkins dieters was 3.9 kilograms (Dansinger et al. 2005). Was the Weight Watchers diet more effective

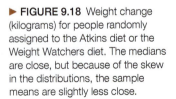

► **FIGURE 9.18** Weight change (kilograms) for people randomly assigned to the Atkins diet or the Weight Watchers diet. The medians are close, but because of the skew in the distributions, the sample means are slightly less close.

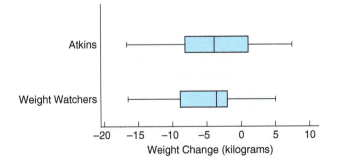

than the Atkins diet, or could the observed difference in mean weight loss be due to chance? How can we estimate the difference between the two means with confidence?

To guarantee a particular confidence level—for example, 95%—requires that certain conditions hold:

Condition 1: *Random Samples*. Both samples are randomly taken from their populations. This means that observations in each sample are independent of each other.

Condition 2: *Normality*. The population distributions are approximately Normal, or the sample size in each is at least 25. (In some cases, you might need even larger sample sizes.)

If these conditions hold, we can use the following procedure to find an interval for the difference between the two population means, $\mu_1 - \mu_2$, with a given confidence level.

A confidence interval for the difference between the two population means allows us to compare their values. The formula for this confidence interval, when the data are from independent samples, has the same structure as before:

$$(\text{Estimate}) \pm \text{margin of error}$$

which is

$$(\text{Estimate of difference}) \pm t^*(SD_{\text{estimate of difference}})$$

We estimate the difference with

$$(\text{Mean of first sample}) - (\text{mean of second sample})$$

The standard deviation of this estimator depends on the sample sizes of both samples and also on the standard deviations of both samples:

$$SD_{\text{est}} = \sqrt{\frac{s_1^2}{n_1} + \frac{s_2^2}{n_2}}$$

We can put these together to form a confidence interval for the difference between the two population means, $\mu_1 - \mu_2$:

Formula 9.3: Two-Sample t-Interval

$$(\bar{x}_1 - \bar{x}_2) + t^*\sqrt{\frac{s_1^2}{n_1} + \frac{s_2^2}{n_2}}$$

The multiplier t^* is based on an approximate t-distribution. If a computer is not available, you can conservatively calculate the degrees of freedom for the t^* multiplier as the smaller of $n_1 - 1$ and $n_2 - 1$, but a computer provides a more accurate value.

Choosing the value of t^* (the critical value of t) by hand to get your desired level of confidence is tricky. For reasons requiring advanced mathematics to show, the sampling distribution is close to, or approximately, a t-distribution. And, for the approximation to be good requires that the degrees of freedom be computed using a long and complex formula—which we will not get into. If you must do these calculations by hand, we recommend using the "quick and easy" (but also safe and conservative) approach. For t^*, use a t-distribution with degrees of freedom equal to the smaller of $n_1 - 1$ and $n_2 - 1$. That is, use the smaller of the two samples, and subtract 1. For a 95% confidence level, if both samples contain 40 or more observations, you can use 1.96 for the multiplier.

If we apply this procedure to the dieting data, we find that a 95% confidence interval for the difference in weight loss after one year for the Weight Watchers and the Atkins diets is 0.7 ± 2.5 kilograms, or about $(-1.8, 3.2)$. This interval captures 0, so we cannot rule out the possibility that the difference is 0. In other words, we are 95% confident that the weight loss means for both diets are the same.

🌐 EXAMPLE **11** Comparing Men's and Women's Senses of Smell

Researchers studying people's sense of smell devised a measure of smelling ability (Lundström et al. 2006). If you score high on this scale, you can detect smells better than others. We can use the data collected by these researchers to determine whether women and men differ in their ability to detect smells. The fact that the researchers felt it was important to record the gender of the study participants suggests that there may be some reason to think this sense might vary by gender.

For this example, we compare two populations—men and women—whose sense of smell was measured while they were lying down. (The subjects' sense of smell was also measured when they were sitting up.) Treating the men as Population 1 and the women as Population 2, the summary statistics of these two independent samples are

$$\text{Men:} \quad \bar{x}_1 = 10.0694, \quad s_1 = 3.3583, \quad n_1 = 18$$

$$\text{Women:} \quad \bar{x}_2 = 11.1250, \quad s_2 = 2.7295, \quad n_2 = 18$$

Boxplots are shown in Figure 9.19.

▶ **FIGURE 9.19** Distribution of smelling ability for men and women. There is slight skew, and there is one potential outlier (indicated by the dot).

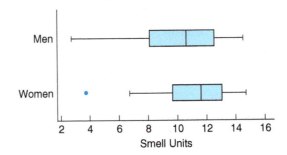

QUESTION It looks like the women tend to have a better sense of smell, as indicated by their higher smell scores when compared to the men. But can this perceived difference be due to chance? Or do women really have a better sense of smell than men? If so, then the mean smell score for men will be lower than the mean smell score for women. Find a 95% confidence interval for the difference in mean smelling ability between men and women, or $\mu_1 - \mu_2$. Interpret the meaning of this interval. Assume that the participants are random samples from a population of all adult men and another population of all adult women.

SOLUTION These data consist of two independent samples: 18 men and 18 women. You might expect that the ability to smell would be Normally distributed across the population, with some people a little better than average and some people a little worse. The boxplots show some skew (and one potential outlier), but with a sample of size 18, it can be hard to tell whether a distribution is Normal on the basis of the boxplot (or histogram). Thus, even though we are not certain that the Normal condition is fulfilled, we will proceed by assuming that it is. Our assumption is based on some theoretical beliefs about how some biological traits such as sense of smell are distributed.

Because the sample sizes of both groups are the same (18), our number of degrees of freedom for t^* is conservatively estimated as the smaller of $18 - 1$ and $18 - 1$, which equals 17. For an approximate 95% confidence interval, we use Table 4 in Appendix A to find $t^* = 2.110$.

Let's call the group of men group 1. (It doesn't matter which we choose for group 1 and which for group 2.)

$$\text{Estimate of difference: } 10.0694 - 11.1250 = -1.0556$$

$$m = t^*\sqrt{\frac{s_1^2}{n_1} + \frac{s_2^2}{n_2}} = t^*\sqrt{\frac{3.3583^2}{18} + \frac{2.7295^2}{18}} = t^*1.0200$$

$$m = 2.110 \times 1.0200 = 2.1522$$

Therefore, a 95% confidence interval for $\mu_1 - \mu_2$ is

$$-1.0556 \pm 2.1522, \text{ or about } (-3.2, 1.1)$$

We are 95% confident that the true value of the difference between the mean smelling ability for men and women, $\mu_1 - \mu_2$, is somewhere between −3.2 and 1.1. Since this interval captures the value of 0, we cannot rule out the scenario where $\mu_1 - \mu_2 = 0$. Therefore, this finding suggests that on average, men and women may not differ in their ability to smell.

TRY THIS! Exercise 9.53

With access to the full data set, and not just to the summary statistics that were provided in Example 11, we can use statistical software to get more accurate calculations. Figure 9.20 shows StatCrunch output for the 95% confidence interval for the difference in the mean smelling ability of men and women. The confidence interval is (−3.1, 1.0), which is slightly different (and narrower) than what we found by hand. The computer-produced interval is more accurate.

TECH

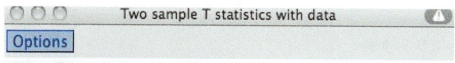

◄ **FIGURE 9.20** StatCrunch output for smelling ability confidence interval.

95% confidence interval results:

μ_1 : mean of Lying Down where Sex="man"
μ_2 : mean of Lying Down where Sex="woman"
$\mu_1 - \mu_2$: mean difference
(with pooled variances)

Difference	Sample Mean	Std. Err.	DF	L. Limit	U. Limit
$\mu_1 - \mu_2$	−1.0555556	1.0200313	34	−3.1285086	1.0173975

Testing Hypotheses about Mean Differences

Hypothesis tests to compare two means from independent samples follow the same structure we discussed in Chapter 8, except that we now have more parameters to compare. We show this structure by revisiting the study to investigate whether men and women differ in their ability to detect smells. In Example 11 you found a confidence interval for the difference in the mean smelling ability of men and women. Here we approach the same data with a hypothesis test.

In Example 11 we used boxplots to investigate the shape of the distribution of smelling ability. Here, we examine histograms (Figure 9.21), which show a more detailed picture of the distributions. Both distributions have roughly the same amount of spread, and the histograms show only a little left skew.

We label men as "Population 1" and women as "Population 2." The mean smelling ability for all men (while lying down) is then μ_1, and the mean smelling ability (while lying down) for all women is μ_2.

If, on average, there is no difference between men and women in their ability to smell while lying down, then $\mu_1 = \mu_2$. If a difference, on average, exists between men and women, then $\mu_1 \neq \mu_2$. We can now state the hypotheses that test whether men and women do differ.

▶ **FIGURE 9.21** Distributions of smelling ability for a sample of 18 men and 18 women.

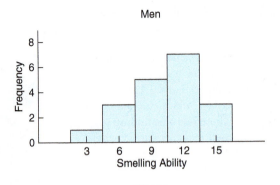

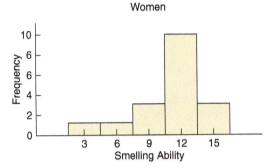

Step 1: Hypothesize

$H_0: \mu_1 = \mu_2$ (men and women have the same mean sense of smell)

$H_A: \mu_1 \neq \mu_2$ (men and women differ in their mean sense of smell)

Step 2: Prepare

The conditions for testing two means are not very different from those for testing one mean, and are identical to those for finding confidence intervals of the difference between two means.

Condition 1: *Random Samples.* Observations are taken at random from each of two populations, producing two different samples. Observations within each sample are independent of each other. That means knowing one person's smell ability—male or female—does not influence another person's smell ability. Also the two random samples are independent of each other. Knowing a man's smell ability does not influence a woman's smell ability.

Condition 2: *Normality.* The population distributions are approximately Normal, or the sample size in each is at least 25. (In some cases, you might need even larger sample sizes.)

We might expect the population distributions to be Normally distributed, because measures of some biological traits, such as sense of smell, often follow the Normal model. The sample distributions show a little bit of left skew, but even Normal populations sometimes produce skewed samples when the sample sizes are small, as they are here. The skew is not so great that we would doubt that the populations are Normally distributed, so we assume that condition 2 holds. We must assume that condition 1 (random samples and independence) holds, because we don't know whether the people were randomly sampled. (In fact, they probably were not, because this is rather difficult to do for such studies.) We will assume it is true, understanding that if these people are not representative of the population, we might have substantial bias in our results. It is also safe to assume that these are independent samples, because they are two distinct groups of people.

(If researchers had sampled married couples, for example, then this assumption would have been violated.)

Another step in our preparation is to choose a significance level. It is common to use $\alpha = 0.05$, and we will do so for this example.

Step 3: Compute to compare

The test statistic used to test this hypothesis is based on the difference between the sample means. Basically, the test statistic measures how far away the observed difference in sample means is from the hypothesized difference in population means. Yes, you guessed it: the distance is measured in terms of the standard deviation of the difference between the two sample means.

$$t = \frac{(\text{difference in sample means} - \text{what null hypothesis says the difference is})}{SD_{est}}$$

Using the test statistic is made easier by the fact that the null hypothesis almost always says that the difference is 0.

Formula 9.4: Two-Sample t-Test

$$t = \frac{\bar{x}_1 - \bar{x}_2 - 0}{SD_{est}}, \quad \text{where} \quad SD_{est} = \sqrt{\frac{s_1^2}{n_1} + \frac{s_2^2}{n_2}}$$

If conditions hold, the test statistic follows an approximate t-distribution, where the degrees of freedom are conservatively estimated to be the smaller of $n_1 - 1$ and $n_2 - 1$.

To compare the mean sense of smell between men and women:

$$\text{Difference in sample means} = \bar{x}_1 - \bar{x}_2 = 10.0694 - 11.125 = -1.0556$$

$$SD_{est} = \sqrt{\frac{s_1^2}{n_1} + \frac{s_2^2}{n_2}} = \sqrt{\frac{3.3583^2}{18} + \frac{2.7295^2}{18}} = 1.0200$$

$$t = \frac{-1.0556}{1.0200} = -1.0349$$

This statistic tells us that the observed difference, -1.0556, is about one standard deviation below what the null hypothesis told us to expect.

We now measure how surprising this is if the null hypothesis is true. To do this, we need to know the sampling distribution of the test statistic t, because we measure surprise by finding the probability that if the null hypothesis is true, we would see a value as extreme as or more extreme than the value we observed. In other words, we need to find the p-value.

If the conditions listed in the Prepare step hold, then t follows, approximately, a t-distribution with minimum $(n_1 - 1, n_2 - 1)$ degrees of freedom. This approximation can be made even better by adjusting the degrees of freedom, but this adjustment is, for most cases, too complex for a "by hand" calculation. For this reason, we recommend using technology for two-sample hypothesis tests, because you will get more accurate p-values.

Both sample sizes are 18, so $n_1 = 18$ and $n_2 = 18$. Thus we use $18 - 1 = 17$ for the degrees of freedom.

Our alternative hypothesis is two-tailed and says that the true difference might be much bigger than 0 or much smaller than 0. We therefore find the area under both tails of the t-distribution. Figure 9.22 shows this probability as the shaded area under the appropriate t-distribution.

The p-value (found using technology) is 0.3152.

> **Details**
>
> **Null Hypotheses for Two Means**
> Mathematically, we can easily adjust our test statistic if the null hypothesis claims that the difference in means is some value other than 0. But in almost all scientific, business, and legal settings, the null hypothesis value will be 0.

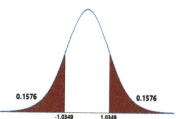

0.1576   0.1576

-1.0349   1.0349
t-Distribution with 17 Degrees of Freedom, p-value = 0.3152

▲ **FIGURE 9.22** The shaded area represents the p-value for this test: the probability of getting a t-statistic more than 1.03 standard deviations away from 0 when the null hypothesis is true.

Step 4: Interpret and conclude

The p-value of 0.3152 tells us that if we were to measure the smelling ability of 18 randomly selected men and 18 women again, there is about a 0.3152 probability that this would give an outcome that is as surprising or more surprising than our current outcome of $t = -1.0349$, *if the null hypothesis is true*. If the p-value is less than or equal to the significance level α, we reject the null hypothesis. Here, the p-value of 0.3152 is not less than 0.05. The value of our test statistic was not a surprise, if the null hypothesis is true. As a result, we do not reject the null hypothesis. These data suggest that the mean ability for men to smell is the same as the mean ability for women to smell, or $\mu_1 = \mu_2$. Note how the conclusion of our hypothesis test finding is the same as the inference we made in Example 11.

The previous analysis was done using only the summary statistics provided. If you have the raw data, then you should use computer software to do the analysis. You will get more accurate values and save yourself lots of time. Figure 9.23 shows StatCrunch output for testing whether the mean sense of smell differs between men and women. Notice how the p-value of 0.3084 provided by StatCrunch is slightly different. This is because StatCrunch uses the long, complicated formula for finding the degrees of freedom.

▶ **FIGURE 9.23** StatCrunch output in a test of whether, on average, men's ability to smell is different from women's.

TECH

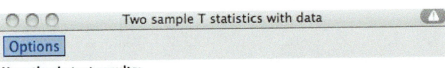

Two sample T statistics with data

Options

Hypothesis test results:

μ_1 : mean of Lying Down where Sex="man"
μ_2 : mean of Lying Down where Sex="woman"
$\mu_1 - \mu_2$: mean difference
$H_0 : \mu_1 - \mu_2 = 0$
$H_A : \mu_1 - \mu_2 \neq 0$
(without pooled variances)

Difference	Sample Mean	Std. Err.	DF	T-Stat	P-value
$\mu_1 - \mu_2$	-1.0555556	1.0200313	32.636784	-1.0348266	0.3084

Caution

Don't Accept!

Remember from Chapter 8 that we do not "accept" the null hypothesis. It is possible that the sample size is too small (the test has low power) to detect the real difference that exists. Instead, we say that there is not enough evidence for us to reject the null.

Into the Pool

Some software packages, and some textbooks too, provide for another version of this *t*-test, called the "pooled two-sample *t*-test." We have presented the unpooled version (you can see this in the StatCrunch output above the table, where it says "without pooled variances"). The unpooled version is preferred over the other version because the pooled version works only in special circumstances (when the population standard deviations are equal). The unpooled version works reasonably well in all situations, as long as the listed conditions hold.

Caution

Don't Pool

When using software to do a two-sample *t*-test, make sure that it does the unpooled version. You might have to tell the software explicitly. The unpooled version is more accurate in more situations than the pooled version.

Test of Two Means: Dependent Samples

With paired samples, we turn two samples into one. We do this by finding the difference in each pair.

Recall the study to evaluate smelling ability. Earlier, you saw there were no differences in mean smelling ability between men and women. Are there differences, however, that depend on position? Researchers carried out this study to determine whether people differ in their ability to smell depending on whether they are sitting up or lying down.

SNAPSHOT   TWO-SAMPLE *t*-TEST (FROM INDEPENDENT SAMPLES)

WHAT IS IT? ▶ A procedure for determining whether two population means, μ_1 and μ_2, are different.

WHAT DOES IT DO? ▶ It tests the null hypothesis that the two population means are equal compared to any one of three alternative hypotheses: (i) $\mu_1 > \mu_2$, (ii) $\mu_1 < \mu_2$, and (iii) $\mu_1 \neq \mu_2$.

HOW DOES IT DO IT? ▶ The observations appearing in the random samples from each of the two populations are processed to compute a *t*-test statistic:

$$t = \frac{\bar{x}_1 - \bar{x}_2 - 0}{SD_{est}}, \text{ where } SD_{est} = \sqrt{\frac{s_1^2}{n_1} + \frac{s_2^2}{n_2}}$$

HOW IS IT USED? ▶ Exactly as the one-sample *t*-test. The value of the *t*-statistic is used to compute the p-value. A value close to 0 means that the outcome is in line with the null hypothesis, the p-value will not be small, and the null hypothesis is supported. If the *t*-statistic is far from zero, the outcome is not in line with the null hypothesis, the p-value will be small, and the null hypothesis is rejected.

WHEN IS IT USED? ▶ When conducting a hypothesis test that compares two population means and the standard deviation in each population of values is unknown. Either the population distributions are Normal or both sample sizes are at least 25.

To test this idea, they measured each subject's sense of smell under two settings: once while sitting and once while lying down. This is a test of two means, as we have two populations:

> Population 1: All people lying down; μ_1 represents the mean ability to smell while lying down.
> Population 2: All people sitting up; μ_2 represents the mean ability to smell while sitting up.

However, even though we have two populations, we do not have two *independent* samples. Rather, we have one sample of people who were measured twice. Thus we can change the problem slightly so that, instead of measuring the ability to smell in each position, we measure the *difference* in ability when a person goes from sitting up to lying down.

The first few lines of the data are shown in Table 9.4a.

Subject Number	Sex	Sitting	Lying
1	woman	13.5	13.25
2	woman	13.5	13
3	woman	12.75	11.5
4	man	12.5	12.5

◀ **TABLE 9.4a** Smelling ability for the first four people sitting and lying.

We create a new variable, call it *difference*, and define it to be the difference between a subject's smelling ability sitting up and smelling ability lying down. We show this new variable in Table 9.4b.

Subject Number	Sex	Sitting	Lying	Difference
1	woman	13.5	13.25	0.25
2	woman	13.5	13	0.50
3	woman	12.75	11.5	1.25
4	man	12.5	12.5	0

We take the differences computed from the pairs of data and treat these differences as a random sample from a *population of differences*. Imagine every person in this population has their ability to smell while sitting, then their smelling ability is measured while they are lying down. The difference in the sitting and lying down smelling abilities for all in the population would create a population of differences. The mean of this population of differences is $\mu_{\text{difference}}$.

If there is no difference between a person's smelling ability when sitting or lying down, then the mean of this population of differences will be zero. We can state our hypotheses in terms of this mean difference:

$$H_0: \mu_{\text{difference}} = 0 \quad (\text{or } \mu_{\text{sitting}} = \mu_{\text{lying}})$$

$$H_A: \mu_{\text{difference}} \neq 0 \quad (\text{or } \mu_{\text{sitting}} \neq \mu_{\text{lying}})$$

We find $\bar{x}$ by averaging all the differences computed between the paired-data:
$\bar{x}_{\text{difference}} = 0.8681$.

We find $s_{\text{difference}}$ by finding the standard deviation of the computed differences:
$s_{\text{difference}} = 2.3946$.

There were 36 participants, and therefore 36 computed differences. So,

$$SD_{\text{est}} = \frac{2.3946}{\sqrt{36}} = 0.3991$$

and then

$$t = \frac{0.8681}{0.3991} = 2.18$$

To find the p-value, we use a *t*-distribution (assuming the conditions for a one-sample *t*-test hold) with $n - 1$ degrees of freedom, where n is the number of data pairs. Figure 9.24 shows a *t*-distribution with 35 degrees of freedom. The shaded areas represent the (two-sided) p-value of 0.0365.

The p-value means that if the null hypothesis is true, there is a 0.0365 probability that another sample of 36 people whose smelling ability is measured while sitting and while lying down will produce an outcome that is just as or more surprising than our outcome of $t = 2.18$. We reject the null hypothesis, since 0.0365 is less than 0.05. The data are evidence to show that the mean of the population of differences is not zero, and therefore our sense of smell is affected by the position of the body.

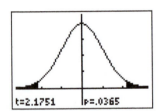

▲ **FIGURE 9.24** A *t*-distribution with $n - 1 = 35$ degrees of freedom. The shaded area represents the p-value for the smell study (sitting vs. lying) and illustrates that if there is no difference in our ability to smell, then our outcome was very unusual and surprising.

t=2.1751   p=.0365

Paired *t*-Test vs. Two-Sample *t*-Test

If you have paired data and (incorrectly) do the two-sample *t*-test, you will generally get a p-value that is too big. Figures 9.25 and 9.26 compare the results of doing a two-sample *t*-test on paired data (Figure 9.25) and doing a paired *t*-test on the same data (Figure 9.26). Note that the test statistic is much larger when you (correctly) use the paired *t*-test to test the paired data; as a result, the p-value is much smaller.

(a)  **(b)**

◄ **FIGURE 9.25** TI-83/84 **(a)** input and **(b)** output for two-sample *t*-test.

The tests produce different values because when we convert the paired data to differences, the resulting differences have a smaller standard deviation than does either sample by itself. This smaller standard deviation leads to a smaller standard deviation in the *t*-statistic. So even though the numerators of both *t*-statistics (the paired and the two-sample) are the same, the paired *t*-statistic is larger because its denominator is smaller. In Chapter 12 you'll learn more about why studies designed with paired data can be powerful.

▲ **FIGURE 9.26** TI-83/84 output for paired *t*-test.

📷 SNAPSHOT   PAIRED *t*-TEST (PAIRED/DEPENDENT SAMPLES)

WHAT IS IT? ▶ A procedure for determining whether two paired, or dependent, samples come from populations that have different means.

WHAT DOES IT DO? ▶ It computes the difference of each pair of data observed in the sample and treats these differences as a random sample from a population of differences. The null hypothesis that the population of differences has a mean $\mu_{\text{difference}} = 0$ is compared to any of the three alternative hypotheses: (i) $\mu_{\text{difference}} > 0$, (ii) $\mu_{\text{difference}} < 0$, and (iii) $\mu_{\text{difference}} \neq 0$.

HOW DOES IT DO IT? ▶ The mean and the standard deviation of the computed differences are found to compute the *t*-statistic:

$$t = \frac{\bar{x}_{\text{difference}} - 0}{SD_{\text{est}}}, \quad \text{where} \quad SD_{\text{est}} = \frac{s_{\text{difference}}}{\sqrt{n}}$$

The *t*-statistic has $n - 1$ degrees of freedom.

HOW IS IT USED? ▶ The value of the *t*-statistic is used to compute the p-value. If $\mu_{\text{difference}} = 0$, the *t*-statistic will be close to zero and the p-value will not be small. If the *t*-statistic is far from zero, what is observed is not in line with the null hypothesis and the p-value will be small. This suggests that the mean of the population of differences is not zero.

WHEN IS IT USED? ▶ Typically used in comparing treatments when people/objects of the population are measured in two different settings. It may be used to compare a control to a treatment, a treatment to a placebo, or two different treatments.

SECTION 9.5

Overview of Analyzing Means

We hope you've been noticing a lot of repetition. The hypothesis test for two means is very similar to the test for one mean, and the hypothesis test for paired data is really a special case of the one-sample *t*-test. Also, the hypothesis tests use almost the same calculations as the confidence intervals, and they impose the same conditions, arranged slightly differently.

All the test statistics (for one proportion, for one mean, for two means, and for two proportions) have this structure:

$$\text{Test statistic} = \frac{(\text{estimated value}) - (\text{null hypothesis value})}{SD_{est}}$$

All the confidence intervals have this form:

$$\text{Estimated value} \pm (\text{multiplier}) \, SD_{est}$$

Not all confidence intervals used in statistics have this structure, but most that you will encounter do.

The method for computing a p-value is the same for all tests, although different distributions are used for different situations. The important point is to pay attention to the alternative hypothesis, which tells you whether you are finding a two-tailed or a one-tailed (and *which* tail) p-value.

Confidence Intervals and Hypothesis Tests

In the preceding examples, we reached exactly the same conclusion about men and women and their sense of smell, whether we used a confidence interval or a hypothesis test. This is no coincidence. In fact, it has to be that way. If you have a *two-tailed* alternative hypothesis, then you actually have two choices for how to do the test. Both choices always reach the same conclusion.

Choice 1: Perform the hypothesis test as described above with significance level α.

Choice 2: Find a $(1 - \alpha) \times 100\%$ confidence interval (using methods given above). Reject the null hypothesis if the value does *not* appear in the interval.

Confidence Level	Equivalent α (Two-Tailed)
99%	0.01
95%	0.05
90%	0.10

▲ **TABLE 9.5** Equivalences between confidence intervals and tests with two-tailed alternative hypotheses.

KEY POINT A 95% confidence interval is equivalent to a test with a two-tailed alternative with a significance level of 0.05. Table 9.5 shows some other equivalences. All are true only for *two-tailed* alternative hypotheses.

EXAMPLE **12** Calcium Levels in the Elderly

The boxplots in Figure 9.27 show the results of a study to determine whether calcium levels differ substantially between senior men and senior women (all older than 65 years). Calcium is associated with strong bones, and people with low calcium levels are believed to be more susceptible to bone fractures. The researchers carried out a hypothesis test to see whether the mean calcium levels for men and women were the same. Figure 9.28 shows the results. Calcium levels (the variable *cammol*) are measured in millimoles per litre (mmol/L).

▶ **FIGURE 9.27** Boxplots of calcium levels (mmol/L) for males and females.

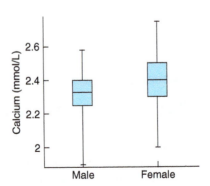

○ ○ ○   Two sample T statistics with data

Options

Hypothesis test results:
μ_1 : mean of cammol where female=1
μ_2 : mean of cammol where female=0
$\mu_1 - \mu_2$: mean difference
$H_0 : \mu_1 - \mu_2 = 0$
$H_A : \mu_1 - \mu_2 \neq 0$
(without pooled variances)

Difference	Sample Mean	Std. Err.	DF	T-Stat	P-value
$\mu_1 - \mu_2$	0.07570534	0.019790715	168.45009	3.825296	0.0002

◄ **FIGURE 9.28** StatCrunch output for testing whether mean calcium levels in men and women differ. The difference estimated is mean of females minus mean of males.

QUESTIONS

a. Assuming that all conditions necessary for carrying out *t*-tests and finding confidence intervals hold, what conclusion should the researchers make on the basis of this output? Use a significance level of 0.05.

b. Suppose the researchers calculate a confidence interval for the difference between the two means. Will this interval include the value 0? If not, will it include all negative values or all positive values? Explain.

SOLUTIONS

a. The p-value, 0.0002, is less than 0.05, so the researchers should reject the null hypothesis and conclude that men and women have different calcium levels.

b. Because we rejected the null hypothesis, we know that the confidence interval cannot include the value 0. If it did, then 0 would be a plausible difference between the means, and our hypothesis test says 0 is not plausible. The estimated difference between the two means is, from the output, 0.0757. Because this value is positive, and because the interval cannot include 0, all values in the interval must be positive.

TRY THIS! Exercise 9.67

Hypothesis Test or Confidence Interval?

If you can use either a confidence interval or a hypothesis test, how do you choose? First of all, remember that these two methods produce the same results only when you have a two-tailed alternative hypothesis, so you need only make the choice when you have a two-tailed alternative.

These two approaches answer slightly different questions. The confidence interval answers the questions "What's the estimated value? And how much uncertainty do you have in this estimate?" Hypothesis tests are designed to answer the question "Is the parameter's value one thing, or another?"

For many situations, the confidence interval provides much more information than the hypothesis test. It not only tells us whether or not we should reject the null hypothesis but also gives us a plausible range for the population value. The hypothesis test, on the other hand, simply tells us whether to reject or not (although it does give us the p-value, which helps us see just how unusual our result is if the null hypothesis is true).

For example, in our test of whether people have a different sense of smell depending on whether they are sitting up or lying down, we rejected the null hypothesis and concluded that the sense of smell was affected by body position. But that is all we can say with a two-tailed test: the means are different. If we want to ask, "How much does the sense of smell change when we sit up?," then a confidence interval for the difference in these two means helps. The 95% confidence interval (smelling ability while sitting up minus smelling ability while lying down) is (0.06, 1.68). This interval tells us that the ability to smell doesn't change very much with body position.

CASE STUDY REVISITED

The researchers reported 95% confidence intervals for the mean IQ of three-year-old children whose mothers took one of four drugs for epilepsy, as shown in Table 9.6.

▶ **TABLE 9.6** Confidence intervals for IQs.

Drug	95% CI
carbamazepine	(95, 101)
lamotrigine	(98, 104)
phenytoin	(94, 104)
valproate	(88, 97)

The researchers could not observe all women on these drugs, so they based their observations on a random sample. If we think of these women as being sampled randomly, then the confidence intervals represent a range of plausible values for the mean IQ for the population of all three-year-olds whose mothers took these drugs.

It is helpful to display these confidence intervals graphically (as the researchers do in their paper), as shown in Figure 9.29.

▶ **FIGURE 9.29** Four confidence intervals for mean IQs of children whose mothers took different drugs for epilepsy.

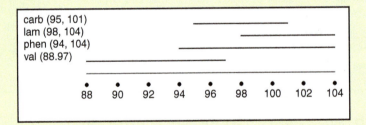

From the figure, we see that the confidence interval for valproate does not overlap with that for lamotrigine. This suggests to us visually that it is *not* plausible that the mean IQ for children whose mothers took these drugs could be the same. The confidence interval for valproate has little overlap with the others, which makes us wonder how much different the mean IQs for the children of valproate users are from those for the children of the other mothers.

For this reason, we need to focus our attention on the differences between the means, not on the individual values for the means. If we do this, as the researchers did, we will find the confidence intervals shown in Table 9.7.

Difference	95% CI
carbamazepine − valproate	(0.6, 12.0)
lamotrigine − valproate	(3.1, 14.6)
phenytoin − valproate	(0.2, 14.0)

◀ **TABLE 9.7** Confidence intervals for differences in mean IQs.

The first interval tells us that the difference between the mean IQ of those under carbamazepine and that of those under valproate could be as small as 0.6 IQ point or as large as 12.0 points. None of these intervals contains 0. This tells us that if we do a hypothesis test to see whether the means are the same, we will have to reject the null hypothesis and conclude that the means are different.

EXPLORING STATISTICS

CLASS ACTIVITY

Pulse Rates

GOALS	MATERIALS
Learn to use a confidence interval (and/or a hypothesis test) to compare the means of two populations.	• A clock on the wall with a second hand or a watch with a second hand (for the instructor) • A computer or calculator

ACTIVITY

You will take your pulse rate before and after an activity to measure the effect of the activity on your pulse rate and/or to compare pulse rates between groups.

Try to find your pulse; it is usually easiest to find in the neck on one side or the other.

After everyone has found his or her pulse, your instructor will say, "Start counting," and you will count beats until the instructor says, "Stop counting." If your instructor uses a 30-second interval, double the count to get beats per minute.

Option A: Breathe in and out 10 times, taking slow and deep breaths. Now measure your pulse rate again.

Option B: Stand up and sit down five times and then measure your pulse rate again.

Your instructor will collect this data and display the values (before and after each activity) for the class.

BEFORE THE ACTIVITY

1. Try finding your pulse (in your neck) to see how to do it.

2. Do you think that either activity (breathing slowly or standing up and sitting down) will change your heart rate? If so, by how much, and will it raise or lower it?

3. How would you measure the typical pulse rate of the class before and after the activity? How would you measure the change in pulse rate after each activity?

4. Do you think men and women have different mean heart rates before the activities?

5. Do you think the change in pulses will be different for men and women? (*Note:* If the class includes only one gender, your instructor may ask you to compare athletes to nonathletes or the taller half to the shorter half.)

AFTER THE ACTIVITY

1. State a pair of hypotheses (in words) for testing whether the breathing activity changes the mean pulse rate of the class. Do the same for the standing and sitting activity.

2. State a pair of hypotheses (in words) for whether men and women have the same mean resting pulse rate.

3. Calculate a 95% confidence interval for the change in pulse rates after the activity. What does this confidence interval tell us about the effect of the activity on the mean heart rate? Suppose you did a two-sided hypothesis test. On the basis of the confidence intervals, can you tell what the conclusions of the hypothesis test will be?

436

CHAPTER REVIEW

Summary of Learning Objectives

1. **How does the Central Limit Theorem apply to the sample mean?** The Central Limit Theorem (CLT) tells us how the average of a random sample behaves. When a random sample is taken from a population of values that is Normal, the distribution of the sample mean is Normal. Otherwise, if the sample size is at least 25 then the distribution of the sample mean $\bar{x}$ is approximately Normal. The sample mean is an estimator for the population mean because, on average, it is equal to the population mean. The precision of $\bar{x}$ is measured by its standard deviation. The mean and the estimated standard deviation of the sampling distribution of the sample mean are

$$\mu \text{ and } SD_{\text{est}} = \frac{s}{\sqrt{n}}$$

The CLT is used to infer how close or far off the observed value of $\bar{x}$ is to the true value of μ.

2. **How is a confidence interval for the population mean computed and what does it mean?** The unknown value of μ can be captured by the computation of a confidence interval for the population mean. As discussed in Chapter 7, the form of the confidence interval is

Estimate $\pm$ margin of error

The confidence interval computed for a population mean uses the t-distribution to take into account that the standard deviation of the distribution of $\bar{x}$ is being estimated by SD_{est}. The computed confidence interval indicates that the true value of the population mean will fall somewhere between the lower and upper bound aries with a $100(1 - \alpha)\%$ level of confidence.

A confidence interval for the population mean is computed with the formula

Formula 9.1: One-Sample Confidence Interval for the Mean

$$\bar{x} \pm m$$

where $m = t^* SD_{\text{est}}$ and $SD_{\text{est}} = \frac{s}{\sqrt{n}}$

The multiplier t^* is obtained from the t-distribution with $n - 1$ degrees of freedom.

3. **How does one formulate and conduct a statistical hypothesis about the population mean, and how does a hypothesis test differ from a confidence interval?** The hypothesis test for the value of the population mean follows the same structure described in Chapter 8. As with confidence intervals, if the necessary conditions hold, then a one-sample t-test can be applied to the data collected using the statistic

Formula 9.2: The One-Sample t-Test for the Mean

$$t = \frac{\bar{x} - \mu_0}{SD_{\text{est}}}, \quad \text{where} \quad SD_{\text{est}} = \frac{s}{\sqrt{n}}$$

and t follows a t-distribution with $n - 1$ degrees of freedom.

The application of the one-sample t-test for the mean differs from a confidence interval in that the one-sample t-test is used to test if the population mean is equal to a particular value. In the case of a random sample from a population, the null hypothesis always assigns the population mean to the particular value μ_0. The alternative hypothesis will be that μ is either (i) less than ($<$), (ii) greater than ($>$), or (iii) not equal to ($\neq$) μ_0. This is different from how a confidence interval works, as the "CI" gives a range of possible values for μ.

4. **What is the difference between two independent random samples and a paired, or dependent, sample?** When data are collected from two independent random samples, it is done to compare the means of two different populations, μ_1 to μ_2. The two samples are said to be independent because the data appearing in one sample are not influenced by the data collected in the other sample. Paired, or dependent, sampling happens when data are collected from the same person/object (or strikingly similar persons/objects) under two different scenarios. This produces a pair of observations for each person or object. The difference between each data pair is then computed.

5. **What is a confidence interval for the difference between two population means?** When two independent samples are taken from two different populations, a confidence interval for the differences between the two population means $\mu_1 - \mu_2$ can be computed using the formula

Formula 9.3: Two-Sample Confidence Interval

$$(\bar{x}_1 - \bar{x}_2) \pm t^* \sqrt{\frac{s_1^2}{n_1} + \frac{s_2^2}{n_2}}$$

If the conditions hold, t^* is from the t-distribution. If no computer is available, the degrees of freedom are conservatively estimated as the smaller of $n_1 - 1$ or $n_2 - 1$.

If this confidence interval captures the value of 0, then it can be said that the two different populations have the same mean, or $\mu_1 = \mu_2$.

6. **Can statistical hypothesis testing about the mean be extended to testing if two different populations have equal means?** When two independent samples are taken, the null hypothesis states that the two populations have the same mean: $H_0: \mu_1 = \mu_2$. The alternative hypothesis can be one of the three: (i) $H_A: \mu_1 < \mu_2$, (ii) $H_A: \mu_1 > \mu_2$, or (iii) $H_A: \mu_1 \neq \mu_2$. If the required conditions hold, then a two-sample t-test can be applied to the data with the formula

Formula 9.4: Two-Sample t-Test (Unpooled)

$$t = \frac{\bar{x}_1 - \bar{x}_2}{SD_{\text{est}}}, \quad \text{where} \quad SD_{\text{est}} = \sqrt{\frac{s_1^2}{n_1} + \frac{s_2^2}{n_2}}$$

and t approximately follows a t-distribution where the degrees of freedom, df, are conservatively estimated to be the smaller of $n_1 - 1$ and $n_2 - 1$. (There exists a pooled version which requires a special condition that is not covered in this text. So please don't use it.)

When the data have been collected with dependent, or paired, samples, the null hypothesis is almost always that the observed differences between the paired data values come from a population of differences that has a mean of 0, or $H_0: \mu = 0$. The alternative hypothesis will be either (i) $H_A: \mu < 0$, (ii) $H_A: \mu > 0$, or (iii) $H_A: \mu \neq 0$. If the conditions required hold, the test statistic is a t-statistic that looks like the paired version of Formula 9.2:

Paired: $t = \dfrac{\bar{x}_{\text{difference}} - 0}{SD_{\text{est}}}$,   where $SD_{\text{est}} = \dfrac{s_{\text{difference}}}{\sqrt{n}}$

$\bar{x}_{\text{difference}}$ is the average of the differences and $s_{\text{difference}}$ is the standard deviation of the differences.

This t-statistic has $n - 1$ degrees of freedom, where n is the number of data pairs.

7. After the statistical test is applied, how is the p-value found and a decision about the plausibility of the null hypothesis made? The p-value is found using the t-distribution. When the data collected come from a single sample, then the p-value is determined from the t-distribution with df $= n - 1$. If the data collected consist of n-pairs of observations, the p-value is also determined with the same t-distribution with df $= n - 1$. Should the data be in the form of two independent samples from two different populations of values, then the p-value is computed form an approximate t-distribution where df is the smaller of $n_1 - 1$ and $n_2 - 1$. Whatever test is applied, if the p-value is less than the significance level then the null hypothesis is rejected. Otherwise the null hypothesis is not rejected.

Important Terms

You may want to review the following terms, which were introduced in Chapters 7 and 8.

Chapter 7: statistic, estimator, bias, precision, sampling distribution, confidence interval, confidence level, margin of error
Chapter 8: null hypothesis, alternative hypothesis, significance level, test statistic, p-value, one-tailed hypothesis, two-tailed hypothesis

Accuracy, *396*
Bias, *396*
Precision, *396*
Sampling distribution, *397*

Unbiased estimator, *397*
Central Limit Theorem
 (CLT), *400*
t-statistic, *405*

t-distribution, *405*
Degrees of freedom (df), *405*
Confidence interval, *406*
Confidence level, *407*

Independent samples, *421*
Paired (dependent) samples, *421*

Sources

Canadian Association of University Teachers Almanac: Post-Secondary Education in Canada. 76.

Canadians spend the most time online, says Study. 2015, March 27. http://www.torontosun.com/2015/03/27/canadians-spend-the-most-time-online-study (accessed September 18, 2015).

The Chronicle of Higher Education, Facts & Figures. 2008. http://chronicle.com/premium/stats/tuition/2008 (accessed July 2009).

The Daily. Statistics Canada. 2011, August 24. http://www.statcan.gc.ca/daily-quotidien/110824/dq110824b-eng.htm (accessed April 7, 2013).

Dansinger, M., J. Gleason, J. Griffith, H. Selker, and E. Schaefer. 2005. Comparison of the Atkins, Ornish, Weight Watchers, and Zone diets for weight loss and heart disease risk reduction: A randomized trial. *Journal of the American Medical Association* 293(1), 43–53.

Encyclopedia Americana, International Edition. Danbury, CT: Grolier, 2001.

The great pricing battle that doesn't exist. 2013, April 4. *National Post.*

Lundström, J., J. Boyle, and M. Jones-Gotman. 2006. Sit up and smell the roses better: Olfactory sensitivity to phenyl ethyl alcohol is dependent on body position. *Chemical Senses* 31(3), 249–252. doi:10.1093/chemse/bjj025

Manske, S., S. Brown, M. Thompson, et al. The Youth Smoking Survey, 2008–2009.

MBA programs by the numbers. 2013, March. *Financial Post* magazine.

Meador, K. J., et al. 2009. Cognitive function at 3 years of age after fetal exposure to antileptic drugs, *New England Journal of Medicine* 360(16), 1597–1605.

National Health and Nutrition Examination Survey (NHANES). Centers for Disease Control and Prevention (CDC). National Center for Health Statistics (NCHS). National Health and Nutrition Examination Survey Data. Hyattsville, MD: U.S. Department of Health and Human Services, Centers for Disease Control and Prevention, 2003–2004.

Shoemaker, A. L., and C. College. 1996. What's normal? Temperature, gender, and heart rate. *Journal of Statistics Education* 4(2).

Survey of Household Spending 2011. 2013, January 30. *The Daily*, Statistics Canada (accessed April 18, 2013).

Tim Hortons supersizes its coffee cups. 2012, January 16. *Toronto Star* (accessed April 11, 2013).

Tuition fees by university. http://www.aucc.ca/canadian-universities/facts-and-stats/tuition-fees-by-university

Undergraduate tuition fees for full time Canadian students, by discipline, by province. Statistics Canada. 2012, October 3. http://www.statcan.gc.ca/tables-tableaux/sum-som/l01/cst01/educ50a-eng.htm (accessed April 9, 2013).

World Health Organization. 2015. Epilepsy; Fact Sheet No. 999. http://www.who.int/mediacentre/factsheets/fs999/en (accessed July 20, 2015).

SECTION EXERCISES

SECTION 9.1

9.1 Library Books An exhaustive cataloguing of all hardbound books at a university library revealed that the mean age was 54.4 years, with a standard deviation of 15.5 years. Recently, the librarian commissioned a study to determine the condition of the books. A random sample of 500 books was assembled, and the mean age of this collection was found to be 50.2 years, with a standard deviation of 18.0 years.

a. Which of these numerical values are parameters?

b. Which of these numerical values are statistics?

9.2 Canadian Internet Usage The 2015 Canada Digital Future in Focus found that in 2014 the amount of time Canadians spent on the internet per month averaged 36.3 hours. Is this 36.3 number a statistic or a parameter? Explain.

9.3 Exam Scores The distribution of the scores on a certain exam is $N(70, 10)$, which means that the exam scores are Normally distributed with a mean of 70 and a standard deviation of 10.

a. Sketch the curve and label, on the x-axis, the position of the mean, the mean plus or minus one standard deviation, the mean plus or minus two standard deviations, and the mean plus or minus three standard deviations.

b. Find the probability that a randomly selected score will be bigger than 80. Shade the region under the Normal curve whose area corresponds to this probability.

9.4 Exam Scores The distribution of the scores on a certain exam is $N(70, 10)$, which means that the exam scores are Normally distributed with a mean of 70 and a standard deviation of 10.

a. Sketch the curve and label, on the x-axis, the position of the mean, the mean plus or minus one standard deviation, the mean plus or minus two standard deviations, and the mean plus or minus three standard deviations.

b. Find the probability that a randomly selected score will be between 50 and 90. Shade the region under the Normal curve whose area corresponds to this probability.

9.5 Bats A biologist is interested in studying the effect that applying insecticide to a fruit farm has on the local bat population. She collects 23 bats from a grove of fruit trees with the insecticide and finds the mean weight of this sample to be 503.4 grams. Assuming that the selected bats are a random sample, she concludes that because the sample mean is an unbiased estimator of the population mean, the mean weight of bats in the population is also 503.4 grams. Explain why this is an incorrect interpretation of what it means to have an unbiased estimator.

9.6 Cellphone Calls Answers.com claims that the mean length of all cell phone conversations is 3.25 minutes (3 minutes and 15 seconds). Assume that this is correct, and also assume that the standard deviation is 4.2 minutes. (Source: wiki.answers.com, accessed January 16, 2011)

a. Describe the shape of the distribution of the length of cell phone conversations in this population. Do you expect it to be approximately Normally distributed, right-skewed, or left-skewed? Explain your reasoning.

b. Suppose that, using a phone company's records, we randomly sample 100 phone calls. We calculate the mean length from this sample and record the value. We repeat this thousands of times. What will be the (approximate) mean value of the distribution of these thousands of sample means?

c. Refer to part b. What will be the standard deviation of this distribution of thousands of sample means?

9.7 Household Spending Every few years, Statistics Canada surveys a large sample of Canadian households to get an idea of their economic health. The most recent survey, which inspected about 18,000 households, estimated that couples with children will spend a mean of \$55,151 on goods and services in a year. Suppose we were to make a histogram of all the household expenditures in this sample. Would the histogram be a display of the population distribution, the distribution of the sample, or the sampling distribution of the sample mean? Explain.

9.8 Time Employed A human resources manager for a large company takes a random sample of 50 employees from the company database. She calculates the mean time they have been employed. She records this value and then repeats the process: she takes another random sample of 50 names and calculates the mean employment time. After she has done this 1000 times, she makes a histogram of the mean employment times. Is this histogram a display of the population distribution, the distribution of a sample, or the sampling distribution of the sample mean?

9.9 Waiting Times The manager of a hospital emergency room (ER) takes a random sample of 40 patients who are waiting to receive medical attention. He observes the time each of the 40 patients waits until they are attended to, to the nearest minute. He finds the mean waiting time, then repeats the process by taking another random sample of 40 patients and finding the mean waiting time of this sample.

a. If the manager had done this for a total of 1000 times and made a histogram of the mean waiting times, would this display the population distribution, the distribution of the sample, or the sampling distribution of the mean?

a. If the manager made a histogram of the waiting times for one of the samples, would this display the population distribution, the distribution of the sample, or the sampling distribution?

9.10 Waiting Times To get an idea of the behaviour of the waiting times at the ER mentioned in Exercise 9.9, would you consult a histogram of (i) the distribution of the sample, or (ii) the sampling distribution of the sample mean? Explain.

TRY **9.11 Women's Weights (Example 1)** The weight of all 20-year-old women is a variable that has a distribution that is right-skewed. The mean weight of this population, μ, is 58 kilograms. The population standard deviation, σ, is 9 kilograms (http://www .kidsgrowth.com). Suppose we take a random sample of 100 20-year-old women and record the weight of each.

a. What value should we expect for the mean weight of this sample? Why?

b. Of course, the actual sample mean will not be exactly equal to the value you gave in part a. The amount it typically differs from this value is given by the standard deviation of the sample mean. What is the standard deviation for a sample mean taken from this population?

9.12 Men's Weights The weight of all 20-year-old men is a variable that has a distribution that is skewed to the right, and the mean weight of this population, μ, is 70 kilograms. The population standard deviation, σ, is 10 kilograms (http://www.kidsgrowth.com). Suppose we take a random sample of 75 20-year-old men and record the weight of each.

a. What value should we expect for the mean weight of this sample? Why?

a. Of course, the actual sample mean will not be exactly equal to the value you gave in part a. The amount it typically differs from this value is given by the standard deviation of the sample mean. What is the standard deviation for a sample mean taken from this population?

SECTION 9.2

TRY **9.13 Women's Weights (Example 2)** The weight of all 20-year-old women has a population mean of 58 kilograms and a population standard deviation of 9 kilograms. The distribution of these weights is right-skewed. Suppose we take a random sample of 100 20-year-old women and record the weight of each. You will find the probability that the sample mean will be more than 1 kilogram from the population mean. The Normal curve in figure (a) is the distribution of the sample mean and therefore not skewed.

(a)

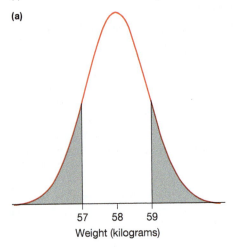

Weight (kilograms)

a. The sample mean is random. Why is the sample size large enough for us to use the Central Limit Theorem?

b. What are the mean and standard deviation of the sampling distribution? (*Hint*: Refer to Exercise 9.11)

c. Find the probability that the sample mean will be more than 59 kilograms or less than 57 kilograms, as shown in Figure (a). Figure (b)

shows the Minitab output for finding the probability that the mean will be less than 57, but you want to find the probability that the mean will be less than 57 or more than 59.

(b)

Cumulative Distribution Function

```
Normal with mean = 58 and standard deviation = 0.9

x    P( X <= x )
57     0.133260
```

9.14 Men's Weights The weight of all 20-year-old men has a population mean of 70 kilograms and a population standard deviation of 10 kilograms. The distribution of these weights is right-skewed. Suppose we take a random sample of 75 20-year-old men and record the weight of each.

a. Explain why the Central Limit Theorem is applicable.

b. Sketch the distribution of the sample mean. Label the mean, the mean plus or minus one standard deviation, the mean plus or minus two standard deviations, and the mean plus or minus three standard deviations.

c. Using your sketch of the distribution of the sample mean, shade the area that corresponds to the probability of sample mean being between 68.85 kilograms and 71.15 kilograms.

d. What is this probability?

TRY **9.15 Length of Cell Phone Calls (Example 3)** One histogram below shows the distribution of the length of cell phone calls for one of the authors in one month, and the other shows many sample means, in which each is the mean length for 10 randomly selected calls from the author's phone records for that month. Which is which? Explain.

(a)

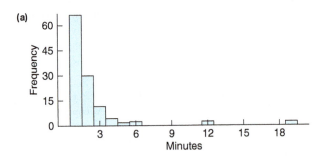

(b)

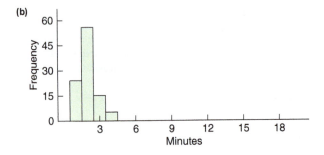

9.16 AC/DC Song Length One histogram below shows a histogram of the length of each of 151 songs taken off all AC/DC studio albums/CDs (at the time of this writing). The other three graphs show the distributions of means of random samples taken from the same population of AC/DC studio albums/CDs. One histogram shows the means based on a sample of 2 songs, another shows a distribution of means based on a sample of 5 songs, another shows means based on a sample of 10 songs. Each distribution of sample means is based on many repetitions. Which distribution is which, and why?

(a)

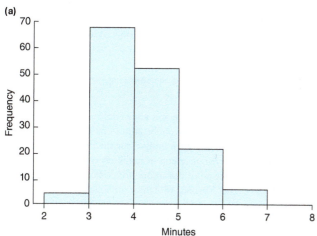

(b)

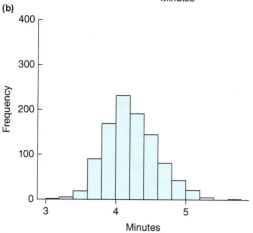

(c)

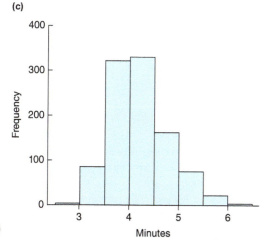

(d)

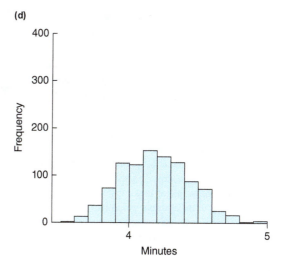

TRY **9.17 AC/DC Song Length (Example 4)** The mean length of all 151 songs taken off AC/DC's studio albums/CDs was 4.21 minutes (about 4 minutes and 13 seconds) with a standard deviation of 0.82 minutes (about 49 seconds). The distribution of song length is right-skewed. The program manager of a radio station wishes to play a three-hour (180-minute) uninterrupted block of AC/DC songs using a random sample of 40 songs from these 151. He finds the mean length of the 40 songs to be 4.10 minutes and the standard deviation of the 40 songs to be 0.89 minutes.

 a. Which of these four numerical values are parameters and which are statistics?

 b. $\mu = ?\ \sigma = ?\ s = ?\ \bar{x} = ?$

 c. Are the conditions for using the CLT satisfied? What would be the shape and the approximate distribution of the sample mean based on a sample of 40 songs?

9.18 Student Ages The mean age of all 2550 students at a small university is 22.8 years with a standard deviation of 3.2 years, and the distribution is right-skewed. A random sample of four students' ages is obtained, and the mean is 23.2 with a standard deviation of 2.4 years.

 a. $\mu = ?\ \sigma = ?\ \bar{x} = ?\ s = ?$

 b. Is μ a parameter or a statistic?

 c. Are the conditions for using the CLT fulfilled? What would be the shape of the approximate sampling distribution of many means, each from a sample of four students? Would the shape be right-skewed, Normal, or left-skewed?

SECTION 9.3

TRY **9.19 Grades of Statistics Students (Example 5)** A random sample of 30 students taking statistics at a community college was asked their cumulative average. The sample mean was 81.25, and the margin of error for a 95% confidence interval was 4.5.

 a. Decide whether each of the following three statements is a correctly worded or an incorrectly worded interpretation of the confidence interval, and fill in the blanks for the correct one(s).

  i. We are 95% confident that the *population* mean cumulative average of *statistics* students at the school is between ____ and ____.

ii. We are 95% confident that the recorded *sample* mean cumulative average of *statistics* students at the school is between _____ and _____.

iii. We are 95% confident that the population mean cumulative average for *all* the students in the school is between _____ and _____.

b. What does the interval tell us about the population mean cumulative average for *statistics* students at the school? Can you reject 72 as the mean cumulative average for statistics students? Explain.

9.20 Gas Prices Some students who live in Edmonton but go to school in Calgary wanted to see whether the mean price of a litre of gas in and around Calgary was the same as the mean price of gas in Edmonton, which was $1.049 for a litre of regular grade unleaded gasoline. They took a random sample of 16 gas stations in Calgary. The distribution of the gas prices in their sample was roughly symmetric, so we will assume that gas prices in Calgary were approximately Normal. The sample mean was $1.088, and the margin of error was $0.011.

a. Describe the population.

b. Decide whether each of the following three statements is a correctly worded or an incorrectly worded interpretation of the confidence interval, and fill in the blanks for any option(s) with correct wording.

i. There is a 95% probability that all the next random samples of 16 stations will have sample mean between _____ and _____.

ii. We are 95% confident that the population mean is between _____ and _____.

iii. We are 95% confident that the boundaries for the interval are _____ and _____.

c. On the basis of this confidence interval, what should the students conclude? Are gas prices in and around Calgary different from those in Edmonton?

9.21 Smarties A statistics instructor randomly selected five boxes of Smarties, and counted the number of Smarties that were in each box. Answers.com indicates that there are a mean of 56 Smarties in a box (accessed April 19, 2013). The number of Smarties in the five boxes was 56, 61, 54, 52, and 52. Assume that the number of Smarties in a box is Normal. Find a 95% confidence interval for the mean number of Smarties in a box of Smarties. Use technology for your calculations.

a. Decide whether each of the three statements is a correctly worded interpretation of the confidence interval, and fill in the blanks for the correct option(s).

i. I am 95% confident that the population mean is between _____ and _____.

ii. There is a 95% chance that all intervals will be between _____ and _____.

iii. I am 95% confident that the sample mean is between _____ and _____.

b. Does the interval capture 56 Smarties? Is there enough evidence to reject the claim that on average there are 56 Smarties in a box of Smarties? Explain.

9.22 Carrots The weights of four randomly chosen bags of horse carrots, each bag labelled 9 kilograms, were 9.3, 9.0, 9.4, and 9.0 kilograms. Assume that the distribution of weights is Normal. Find a 95% confidence interval for the mean weight of all bags of horse carrots. Use technology for your calculations.

a. Decide whether each of the three statements is a correctly worded interpretation of the confidence interval, and fill in the blanks for the correct option(s).

i. 95% of all sample means based on samples of the same size will be between _____ and _____.

ii. We are 95% confident that the population mean is between _____ and _____.

iii. We are 95% confident that the boundaries are _____ and _____.

b. Can you reject a population mean of 9 kilograms? Explain.

TRY 9.23 Human Body Temperature (Example 6) A random sample of 10 people's body temperatures was taken in degrees Celsius, and the 95% confidence interval for the mean was (36.4, 37.1). Distributions of body temperatures are approximately Normal. Which of the following statements is the correct interpretation of the confidence *level*, and which is the correct interpretation of the confidence *interval*?

a. In about 95% of all samples of 10 body temperatures, the resulting confidence interval will contain the population mean body temperature.

b. We are very confident that the mean body temperature is between 36.4 and 37.1.

9.24 Extra-Large Coffee The amount of coffee poured into a random sample of five extra-large coffee cups from Tim Hortons was measured, and the 95% confidence interval for the mean amount poured into an extra-large coffee cup in millilitres was (673.0, 721.0). Assume that the distribution of the amount of coffee poured into an extra-large coffee cup is Normal. Which of the following statements is the correct interpretation of the confidence *level*, and which is the correct interpretation of the confidence *interval*?

a. We are very confident that the mean amount of coffee poured into an extra-large Tim Hortons coffee cup is between 673 and 721 millilitres.

b. In about 95% of all samples of 5 extra-large Tim Hortons coffee cups, the resulting confidence intervals will contain the mean amount of coffee poured in all extra-large cups of Tim Hortons coffee.

TRY 9.25 t* (Example 7)

a. A researcher collects a sample of 30 measurements from a population and wishes to find a 90% confidence interval for the population mean. What value should he use for t^*? (Recall that df $= n - 1$ for a one-sample *t*-test or interval.)

b. If he instead decides to use a 95% confidence interval, will the interval be wider, be narrower, or stay the same? Why?

df	Confidence Level		
	90%	95%	99%
28	1.701	2.048	2.763
29	1.699	2.045	2.756
30	1.697	2.042	2.750
33	1.692	2.035	2.733

9.26 t*

a. A researcher collects a sample of 34 measurements from a population and wishes to find a 99% confidence interval for the population mean. What value should he use for t^*?

b. If he instead decides to use a 95% confidence interval, will the interval be wider, or be narrower, or stay the same? Why?

TRY 9.27 Dancers' Heights (Example 8) A random sample of 20 female university-aged dancers showed a sample mean height of 160.8 centimetres and a sample standard deviation of 5.51 centimetres. Assume that this distribution of heights is Normal.

	Confidence Level		
df	90%	95%	99%
14	1.761	2.145	2.977
15	1.753	2.131	2.947
16	1.746	2.120	2.921
17	1.740	2.110	2.898
18	1.734	2.101	2.878
19	1.729	2.093	2.861

a. Find a 95% confidence interval for the population mean height of dancers. Interpret the interval. Refer to the table.

b. Find a 99% confidence interval for the population mean height. Interpret the interval.

c. Which interval is wider and why?

9.28 Women's Pulses A random sample of 15 women's resting pulse rates from the National Health and Nutrition Examination Survey (NHANES) showed a mean of 73.5 beats per minute and standard deviation of 17.1 beats per minute. Assume that pulse rates are Normally distributed.

a. Are the mean and standard deviation that are provided statistics or parameters? Why?

b. Find a 95% confidence interval for the population mean pulse rate of women, and report it in a sentence. For t^* refer to the table for Exercise 9.27.

c. Find a 90% confidence interval.

d. Which interval is wider and why?

9.29 Confidence Interval Changes State whether each of the following changes would make a confidence interval wider or narrower. (Assume that nothing else changes.)

a. Changing from a 90% confidence level to a 99% confidence level.

b. Changing from a sample size of 30 to a sample size of 200.

c. Changing from a standard deviation of 9 kilograms to a standard deviation of 11 kilograms.

9.30 Confidence Interval Changes State whether each of the following changes would make a confidence interval wider or narrower. (Assume that nothing else changes.)

a. Changing from a 95% level of confidence to a 90% level of confidence.

b. Changing from a sample size of 30 to a sample size of 20.

c. Changing from a standard deviation of 5 centimetres to a standard deviation of 3 centimetres.

TRY **9.31 Human Body Temperature (Example 9)** A random sample of 10 healthy people showed the following body temperatures (in degrees Celsius):

g

36.9, 36.8, 37.2, 35.7, 36.8, 37.1, 36.2, 37.3, 37.1, 36.2

Assume that body temperatures for healthy people are Normal. Test the hypothesis that the population mean is not 37. *See page 451 for guidance.*

9.32 Reaction Distance Data on the website show reaction distances in centimetres for the dominant hand for a random sample

of 40 independently chosen students. Smaller distances indicate quicker reactions.

a. Make a graph of the distribution of the sample, and describe its shape.

b. Find, report, and interpret a 95% confidence interval for the population mean.

c. Suppose a professor said that the population mean should be 10 centimetres. Test the hypothesis that the population mean is not 10 cm, using the four-step procedure, with a significance level of 0.05.

9.33 MBA Tuition A random sample of 20 MBA programs was taken from all MBA programs in the country. For each MBA program, the in-province annual tuition was recorded. The mean tuition was found to be $36,625 and the standard deviation was $24,645. Assume that the annual in-province tuition fees are Normally distributed.

a. Determine whether the mean in-province tuition for all MBA programs in Canada is more than $30,000. Use a level of significance of 0.05.

b. Suppose a sample of 30 MBA programs, instead of 20, gave the same sample statistics. Repeat the test in part a.

c. Explain why the t-values and p-values for parts a and b are different.

9.34 Vegetarian Weights The mean weight of all 20-year-old women is 58 kilograms (http://www.kidsgrowth.com). A random sample of 40 vegetarian women who are 20 years old showed a sample mean of 55.45 kilograms and a standard deviation of 6.82 kilograms.

a. Determine whether the mean weight for all 20-year-old vegetarian women is less than 58 kilograms, the mean weight for all 20-year-old women, using a significance level of 0.05.

b. Now suppose the sample consists of 100 vegetarian women who are 20 years old. Repeat the test in part a.

c. Explain what causes the difference between the p-values for parts a and b.

9.35 Provincial Achievement Scores Of all students who wrote the Provincial Achievement Test (PAT) for Grade 12 Alberta math in June 2012, 30 were randomly chosen. The percentage score of each student was observed. Assume that scores on the June 2012 PAT in math are Normally distributed.

a. Find the sample mean.

b. Find the sample standard deviation.

c. The Minister of Education claims that the mean score on the June 2012 PAT in math was not less than 70%. Compare the value of the sample mean found in part a to 70. Does this mean that the population mean is less than 70? Explain.

d. Use the four-step procedure to test the claim in part c. Use a significance level of 0.05.

9.36 AC/DC Song Length A random sample of 40 songs was taken from the population of songs on all AC/DC studio albums/CDs. Assume that the length of all the studio-recorded AC/DC songs is Normally distributed.

a. Find the sample mean.

b. Find the sample standard deviation.

c. It has been claimed that the mean length of an AC/DC song is more than four minutes long. Compare the value in part a to four. Does this mean that the population mean is more than four? Explain.

d. Use the four-step procedure to test the claim in part c. Use a significance level of 0.05.

9.37 Pulse and Meditation Eleven students took their pulses while in class. Then they were asked to meditate by sitting with their eyes closed and counting their breaths for 5 minutes. After this, they took their pulse rates again. (The pulse was counted for 15 seconds and multiplied by 4 to get the number of beats per minute.) The data recorded provide differences: pulse before meditation minus pulse after meditation. A negative value, then, means that the pulse rates increased after meditation. Treat these students as a random sample of students and perform a hypothesis test to determine whether the mean pulse rate decreased after meditation. In other words, determine whether the mean difference is positive. Clearly state all four steps. Assume that the conditions for using a *t*-test are met.

$$12, 4, 4, 0, -8, -8, 0, 12, 8, 0, 8$$

 9.38 Amazon Textbook Prices Amelia Suragairin, a statistics student, was interested in the prices of textbooks and went online to the Amazon.com U.S. and Amazon.com U.K. websites to compare prices. The prices in the U.K. were in pounds and were converted to dollars using the exchange rate at that time. The data provide the differences (U.S. minus U.K.) in price between the two countries (rounded to the nearest dollar). Negative signs indicate that the U.K. price was higher. Treat these samples as random samples from their populations and perform a hypothesis test to determine whether the mean difference is significantly different from 0, using a significance level of 0.05. Clearly state all four steps. Assume that the conditions for using a *t*-test are met.

$$-4, 0, 0, -22, -21, -14, -12, 14, 3, -7, 13, -6, -12,$$
$$-11, -7, 12, -2, 2, 1, -13$$

9.39 Carrots, Three Tests The weights of four randomly chosen bags of horse carrots, each bag labelled 9 kilograms, were 9.3, 9.0, 9.4, and 9.0 kilograms. Assume that the distribution of weights in the population is Normal. In each case, report the alternative hypothesis, the *t*-value, and the p-value, and interpret the meaning of the p-value and the conclusion for each of the three parts.

a. Test the hypothesis that the population mean weight is not 9 kilograms.

b. Test the hypothesis that the population mean weight is less than 9 kilograms.

c. Test the hypothesis that the population mean weight is more than 9 kilograms.

9.40 Soft Drink Serving Size A consumer advocate wants to find out whether the soft drinks sold at a fast-food restaurant contain less than the advertised 470 millilitres (16 fluid ounces). A random sample of 10 independently chosen drinks produced a mean of 488 millilitres with a standard deviation of 12 millilitres. Assume that the distribution of serving sizes in the population is Normal.

a. State the null hypothesis in both words and symbols, using μ as the population mean amount of soft drink of all the drinks labelled 470 millilitres at this fast-food restaurant.

b. State the alternative hypothesis in both words and symbols.

c. Carry out the appropriate test using a 5% significance level. Interpret the meaning of the p-value and explain what conclusions the consumer advocate should reach.

d. Explain why no calculations are needed to show that the population mean is not significantly less than 470 millilitres.

9.41 Student Spending on Textbooks A 95% confidence interval for the mean amount that first-year business students at the University of Calgary spent on textbooks in the fall 2010 term, based on a random sample taken by one of the authors, was ($483.20, $560.80). Assuming that nothing else changed, what would have been the effect on the confidence interval if the author used a smaller

sample size? Assuming that the necessary conditions for finding a confidence interval hold, choose the best answer.

a. The confidence interval would have been wider.

b. The confidence interval would have been narrower.

c. The confidence level would have been higher.

d. The confidence level would have been lower.

e. Answers a and c are both correct.

f. Answers b and d are both correct.

9.42 Student Spending on Textbooks A 95% confidence interval for the mean amount that first-year business students at the University of Calgary spent on textbooks in the fall 2010 term, based on a random sample taken by one of the authors, was ($483.20, $560.80). To obtain this confidence interval, he multiplied the estimate of the standard deviation of the sample mean by 1.983, which was the value used for t^*. What would have happened if he had multiplied the estimate of the standard deviation of the sample mean by 1.660 instead? Choose the best answer.

a. The confidence interval would have been wider.

b. The confidence interval would have been narrower.

c. The confidence level would have been higher.

d. The confidence level would have been lower.

e. Answers a and c are both correct.

f. Answers b and d are both correct.

9.43 Student Ages Suppose that 200 statistics students each took a random sample (with replacement) of 50 students at their school and recorded the ages of the students in their sample. Then each student used his or her data to calculate a 95% confidence interval for the mean age of all students at the school. How many of the 200 intervals would you expect to capture the true population mean age, and how many would you expect not to capture the true population mean? Explain by showing your calculation.

9.44 Ages of Married Couples Suppose that 300 statistics students each collected a random sample of 40 married couples from their province and recorded the ages. From the ages of these couples, they calculated the difference in ages: husband's age minus wife's age. Then each found a 90% confidence interval for the population mean age difference. How many of the 300 intervals would you expect to capture the true population mean difference, and how many would you expect to miss the true population mean difference? Explain by showing your calculation.

9.45 Prime Ministers' Ages A 95% confidence interval for the ages of the first five prime ministers when they first took office was (50.36, 77.78). Either interpret the interval or explain why it should not be interpreted.

9.46 Bank of Canada Governors' Ages A 95% confidence interval for the ages of the first five governors of the Bank of Canada when they were appointed is (39.20, 56.00). Either interpret the interval or explain why it should not be interpreted.

SECTION 9.4

TRY **9.47 Independent or Paired? (Example 10)** State whether each situation has independent or paired (dependent) samples.

a. A researcher wants to know whether men and women at University X have different mean cumulative averages. She gathers two random samples: one of cumulative averages from 50 men and the other from 50 women.

b. A researcher wants to know whether husbands and wives have different mean overall cumulative averages. He collects a sample of husbands and wives who have both earned a bachelor's degree and has each person report his or her overall cumulative average in university.

9.48 Independent or Paired? State whether each situation has independent or paired (dependent) samples.

a. A researcher wants to know whether hypnosis tends to reduce pain. Research subjects place their hands in ice water to see how long they can tolerate it before the pain becomes unbearable. Then the subjects are hypnotized and again put their hands in ice water to see whether they tend to leave them in the water longer after hypnosis.

b. A researcher wants to know whether male or female professors at his university tend to have longer recorded greetings on their voice mails. He calls 40 random male and 40 random female professors over the weekend and times their messages.

g 9.49 Televisions The table shows the Minitab output for a two-sample *t*-test for the number of televisions owned in households of random samples of students at two different community colleges. Each individual was randomly chosen independently of the others; the students were not chosen as pairs or in groups. One of the schools is in a wealthy community (MC), and the other (OC) is in a less wealthy community. Test the hypothesis that the population means are not the same, using a significance level of 0.05. *See page 452 for guidance.*

```
Two-sample T for OCTV vs MCTV

        N     Mean    StDev   SE Mean
OCTV   30     3.70    1.49    0.27
MCTV   30     3.33    1.49    0.27

Difference = mu OCTV - mu MCTV
Estimate for difference: 0.367
95% CI for difference: (-0.404, 1.138)
T-Test of difference = 0 (vs not =): T-Value = 0.95  P-Value = 0.345
```

9.50 Pulse Rates Using data from NHANES, we looked at the pulse rates of nearly 800 people to see whether men or women tended to have higher pulse rates. Refer to the Minitab output provided.

a. Report the sample means and state which group had the higher sample mean pulse rate.

b. Use the Minitab output to test the hypothesis that pulse rates for men and women are not equal, using a significance level of 0.05. The samples are large enough so that Normality is not an issue.

```
Two-sample T for Pulse

Sex       N    Mean   StDev   SE Mean
Female   384   76.3   12.8    0.65
Male     372   72.1   13.0    0.67

Difference = mu (Female) - mu (Male)
Estimate for difference: 4.248
95% CI for difference: (2.406, 6.090)
T-Test of difference = 0 (vs not =): T-Value = 4.53  P-Value = 0.000
```

9.51 Triglycerides Triglycerides are a form of fat found in the body. Using data from NHANES, we looked at whether men have higher triglyceride levels than women.

a. Report the sample means and state which group had the higher sample mean triglyceride level. Refer to the Minitab output in figure (a).

b. Carry out a hypothesis test to determine whether men have a higher mean triglyceride level than women. Refer to the Minitab output provided in figure (a). Output for three different alternative hypotheses is

provided—see figures (b), (c), and (d)—and you must choose and state the most appropriate output.

(a)

```
Two-Sample T-Test and CI: Triglycerides, Gender

Two-sample T for Triglycerides

Gender    N    Mean    StDev   SE Mean
Female   44    84.4    40.2    6.1
Male     48   139.5    85.3    12

Difference = mu (Female) - mu (Male)
Estimate for difference: -55.1
95% CI for difference: (-82.5, -27.7)
```

(b)

```
B: T-Test of difference = 0 (vs <): T-Value = -4.02  P-Value = 0.000
```

(c)

```
C: T-Test of difference = 0 (vs >): T-Value = -4.02  P-Value = 1.000
```

(d)

```
D: T-Test of difference = 0 (vs not =): T-Value = -4.02  P-Value = 0.000
```

9.52 Systolic Blood Pressures When you have your blood pressure taken, the larger number is the systolic blood pressure. Using data from NHANES, we looked at whether men and women have different systolic blood pressure levels.

a. Report the two sample means and state which group had the higher sample mean systolic blood pressure. Refer to the Minitab output in figure (a).

b. Refer to the Minitab output given in figure (a) to test the hypothesis that the mean systolic blood pressures for men and women are not equal, using a significance level of 0.05. Although the distributions of blood pressures in the population are right-skewed, the sample size is large enough for us to use *t*-tests. Choose from figures (b), (c), and (d) for your p-value, and explain.

(a)

```
Two-sample T for BPSys

gender    N    Mean    StDev   SE Mean
Female   404   116.8   22.7    1.1
Male     410   118.7   18.0    0.89

Difference = mu (Female) - mu (Male)
Estimate for difference: -1.93
95% CI for difference: (-4.75, 0.89)
```

(b)

```
B: T-Test of difference = 0 (vs not =): T-Value = -1.34  P-Value = 0.180
```

(c)

```
C: T-Test of difference = 0 (vs >): T-Value = -1.34   P-Value = 0.910
```

(d)

```
D: T-Test of difference = 0 (vs <): T-Value = -1.34   P-Value = 0.090
```

TRY **9.53 Triglycerides, Again (Example 11)** Report and interpret the 95% confidence interval for the difference in mean triglycerides between men and women (refer to the Minitab output in Exercise 9.51). Does this support the hypothesis that men and women differ in mean triglyceride level? Explain.

9.54 Blood Pressures, Again Report and interpret the 95% confidence interval for the difference in mean systolic blood pressure for men and women (refer to the Minitab output in Exercise 9.52). Does this support the hypothesis that men and women differ in mean systolic blood pressure? Explain.

9.55 Clothes Spending A random sample of 14 university women and a random sample of 19 university men were separately asked to estimate how much they spent on clothing in the last month. The table shows the data.

Test the hypothesis that the population mean amounts spent on clothes are different for men and women. Use a significance level of 0.05. Assume that the distributions are Normal enough for us to use the *t*-test.

Sex	$ Clothes	Sex	$ Clothes
m	175	f	80
f	200	m	200
m	150	m	80
f	200	m	100
f	100	m	120
f	100	m	80
f	200	m	25
m	100	f	80
m	100	m	50
f	200	m	100
m	200	m	30
m	200	f	20
m	200	f	50
f	250	m	60
f	150	f	100
m	100	f	350
m	0		

9.56 NHL Salaries A random sample of 25 NHL players was taken in 2007. Twenty-five players were randomly selected in 2013. The salary of each player, in $ millions, was recorded. The table shows the unstacked data (in $ millions). Assume that the

distributions of both data sets are not Normal, and that the sample sizes of 25 are large enough for the Central Limit Theorem to apply.

2007 Salary ($ millions)	2013 Salary ($ millions)	2007 Salary ($ millions)	2013 Salary ($ millions)
3.500	2.500	0.450	4.500
0.450	0.925	0.500	1.500
0.600	3.250	0.775	0.800
0.525	0.600	0.606	0.750
3.040	1.750	0.575	4.500
2.400	2.500	1.600	4.250
1.200	1.600	2.000	3.500
2.500	1.850	0.450	6.500
3.268	1.400	1.900	6.875
4.250	3.000	1.900	0.700
0.800	1.200	5.000	1.300
2.000	0.850	0.575	11.000
5.269	0.525		

Determine whether the mean salary of an NHL player in 2007 is less than the mean salary of an NHL player in 2013, using a level of significance of 0.05.

* **9.57 Clothes Spending** In Exercise 9.55 you could not reject the null hypothesis that the mean amount spent by men and the mean amount spent by women for clothing are the same, using a two-tailed test with a significance level of 0.05.
  a. If you found a 95% confidence interval for the difference between means, would it capture 0? Explain.
  b. If you found a 99% confidence interval, would it capture 0? Explain.
  c. Now go back to Exercise 9.55. Find a 95% confidence interval for the difference between means, and explain what it shows.

* **9.58 NHL Salaries** In Exercise 9.56, you could not reject the null hypothesis that the mean salaries of NHL players in 2007 and 2013 were equal using a left-tailed test with a significance level of 0.05.
  a. If you found a 95% confidence interval for the differences between means, would it capture 0? Explain.
  b. If you found a 90% interval, would it capture 0? Explain.
  c. Now go back to Exercise 9.56. Find a 95% confidence interval for the difference between means, and explain what it shows.

9.59 Criminology In April 2005, the *Journal of Experimental Criminology* published the results of a 1998 study in which 121 rental properties that had already been the target of drug law enforcement were randomly divided into two groups. In the experimental group, the tenants received a letter from the police describing the enforcement tactics in place. For the control group, there was no letter. The table gives summary statistics for the number of crimes reported over a 30-month interval.

	Experimental	Control
Mean	3.2	5.1
SD	4.1	6.3
n	79	42

Determine whether the letter from the police was effective in *reducing* the number of crimes at the 0.05 level. Although the distribution of number of crimes is not Normal, assume that the sample size is large enough for the Central Limit Theorem to apply. (Source: David P. Farrington and Brandon C. Welsh, Randomized experiments in criminology: What have we learned in the last two decades?" *Journal of Experimental Criminology* (2005), 1: 9–38)

9.60 Criminology In April 2005, the *Journal of Experimental Criminology* reported on a study done in Washington in which 171 children were randomly divided into two groups. The experimental group went to a special cognitive preschool, and the control group went to a traditional preschool. The summary statistics for the number of self-reported criminal offences by the age of 15 are given in the table. Although the number of criminal offences is not Normally distributed, sample sizes are large enough that the Central Limit Theorem applies. Test the hypothesis that the mean number of self-reported offences is not the same for each group, using a 0.05 level of significance. (Source: David P. Farrington and Brandon C. Welsh, Randomized experiments in criminology: What have we learned in the last two decades?" *Journal of Experimental Criminology* (2005), 1: 9–38)

	Experimental	Control
Mean	12.62	11.05
SD	14.27	13.66
n	90	81

9.61 Females: Pulse Rates Before and After a Fright In a statistics class taught by one of the authors, students took their pulses before and after being frightened. The frightening event was having the teacher scream and run from one side of the room to the other. The pulse rates (beats per minute) of the women before and after the scream were obtained separately and are shown in the table. Treat this as though it were a random sample of female community college students. Test the hypothesis that the mean of college women's pulse rates is higher after a fright, using a significance level of 0.05. *See page 452 for guidance.*

| Women | | Women | |
Pulse Before	Pulse After	Pulse Before	Pulse After
64	68	84	88
100	112	80	80
80	84	68	92
60	68	60	76
92	104	68	72
80	92	68	80
68	72		

9.62 Males: Pulse Rates Before and After a Fright Follow the instructions for Exercise 9.61, but use the data for the men in the class. Test the hypothesis that the mean of community college men's pulse rates is higher after a fright, using a significance level of 0.05.

| Men | |
Pulse Before	Pulse After
50	64
84	72
96	88
80	72
80	88
64	68
88	100
84	80
76	80

9.63 Used Textbook Prices, U of C vs. Amazon.ca A random sample of textbooks at the University of Calgary Bookstore was obtained in 2013. The used-textbook price of each textbook was observed, then compared to the used-textbook price of the same textbook on Amazon.ca. Assume that the distribution of the differences in the used-textbook prices is Normal enough to proceed.

a. Find both sample means and compare them.

b. Test the hypothesis that the mean price of a used textbook at the U of C Bookstore is the same as the mean price of a used textbook on Amazon.ca. Use a level of significance of 0.05.

9.64 New Textbook Prices, U of C vs. Amazon.ca A random sample of textbooks at the University of Calgary Bookstore was obtained in 2013. The price of a new textbook was observed, then compared to the new price of the same textbook on Amazon.ca. Assume that the distribution of the differences in the new prices is Normal enough to proceed.

a. Find both sample means and compare them.

b. Test the hypothesis that the mean price of a new textbook at the U of C Bookstore is the same as the mean price of a new textbook on Amazon.ca. Use a level of significance of 0.05.

9.65 Ages of Brides and Grooms Data for the ages of grooms and their brides for a random sample of 31 couples were obtained.

a. Compare the sample means.

b. Test the hypothesis that there is a significant difference in mean ages of brides and grooms, using a significance level of 0.05.

c. If the test had been done to determine whether the mean for the grooms was significantly larger than the mean for the brides, how would that change the alternative hypothesis and the p-value?

9.66 Big-Box Store Price Comparison On April 4, 2013, The *Financial Post* ran a price comparison between Walmart and a recently opened Target. The prices of a basket of "stuff" were recorded at both Walmart and Target. Assume that the items in the basket were randomly chosen, and that the distribution of the differences is approximately Normal.

a. Report and compare the sample means.

b. Test the hypothesis that there is no difference in the mean price of goods at Walmart and Target. Use a level of significance of 0.05.

TRY **9.67 Self-Reported Heights of Men (Example 12)** A random sample of students reported what they believed to be their height in inches, which were then converted to centimetres. Then the students measured each other's heights in centimetres, without shoes. The data shown are for the men. Assume that the conditions for *t*-tests hold.

a. Find a 95% confidence interval for the mean difference in the reported height and the actual height. Does it capture 0? What does that show?

b. Perform a *t*-test to test the hypothesis that the means are not the same. Use a significance level of 0.05, and show all four steps.

Height (cm) (reported in inches and converted to cm)	Height (cm) Measured
167.64	166
172.72	172
185.42	184
170.18	166
193.04	191
172.72	173
175.26	174
193.04	191
177.8	178
175.26	177
180.34	181
175.26	175
170.18	171
170.18	170
182.88	184

9.68 Female Self-Reported Heights Follow the instructions for Exercise 9.67, but use the data for women. Assume that the heights are Normally distributed in the population and that the sample is random.

Height (cm) (reported in inches and converted to cm)	Height (cm) Measured	Height (cm) (reported in inches and converted to cm)	Height (cm) Measured
160.02	160	160.02	158
160.02	160	157.48	159
160.02	158	177.80	180
154.94	155	154.94	156
170.18	172	152.40	155
167.64	167	160.02	159
154.94	153	180.43	179
162.56	161	177.80	175
157.48	156	162.56	163
157.48	157	154.94	159
160.06	161	162.56	162
157.48	155	154.94	154
177.80	175	157.48	159

9.69 Anchoring To demonstrate how supplying a starting point for a numerical answer can be a source of bias in surveys, students in a statistics class were randomly assigned a quantity, either 10% or 65%. The students were first asked whether they thought the percentage of member states of the United Nations that are in Africa was higher or lower than that quantity, and then they were asked to estimate the correct percentage. (The actual percentage is 28%.) The data can be found in the text's website.

a. Report and compare the sample means.

b. Carry out a hypothesis test to determine whether the mean estimate of students who were supplied a starting point of 10% is lower than the mean estimate of those who were supplied a starting point of 65%. Assume that the conditions for a two-sample *t*-test hold. Use a level of significance of 5%.

9.70 Eating Out Jacqueline Loya, a statistics student, asked students with jobs how many times they went out to eat in the last week. There were 25 students who had part-time jobs and 25 students who had full-time jobs. Carry out a hypothesis test to determine whether the mean number of meals out per week for students with full-time jobs is greater than that for those with part-time jobs. Use a significance level of 0.05. Assume that the conditions for a two-sample *t*-test hold. The data can be found in Exercise 3.12 on page 113.

CHAPTER REVIEW EXERCISES

9.71 Which *t*-Test? State whether you would use a one-sample, two-sample, or paired *t*-test for each part, assuming the conditions required for *t*-tests hold.

a. The weights of a random sample of 25 people are measured before and after going on a diet. You want to test the hypothesis that weights tend to be lower at the end of the diet.

b. The number of felony convictions for each prisoner in a random sample of 10 prisoners at Prison A and a random sample of 10 prisoners at Prison B are obtained. You want to test the claim that the prisoners in Prison A tend to have more felony convictions than the prisoners in Prison B.

c. A random sample of 20 rock songs and 20 country songs is taken. You want to test the claim that the mean length of rock songs is less than the mean length of country songs.

9.72 Which *t*-Test? State whether you would use a one-sample, two-sample, or paired *t*-test for each part, assuming the conditions required for *t*-tests hold.

a. The weights of a random sample of 10 male weight-lifters at Gold's Gym are measured. You want to test the hypothesis that the weight-lifters tend to weigh more than men in the general population, for which the population mean is 82 kilograms.

b. The ages of the people in a randomly selected group of community college students are obtained. You want to find out whether the male and female students have significantly different mean ages.

c. A random sample of 40 properties is taken from a suburb of a large city. The market value of each property five years ago is recorded, along with the property's current market value. You want to test whether the market value has increased, on average.

9.73 Marathon Times The results from the 2014 Victoria Marathon contain times for a random sample of both men and women. Below is the Minitab output for a two-sample *t*-test.

a. Test the hypothesis that men (m) are quicker, on average, than women (f) at the 0.05 level of significance. The completion times are in seconds (14,715 seconds is about 4 hours and 5 minutes).

b. Interpret the 95% CI (confidence interval).

```
Two-Sample T-Test and CI: time in secs, gender

Two-sample T for time in secs

gender N  Mean StDevSE Mean
f    772 16338 2926  105
m    798 14715 2737   97


Difference = μ (f) - μ (m)
Estimate for difference:1624
95% CI for difference:(1343, 1904)
T-Test of difference = 0 (vs ≠): T-Value =11.35 P-Value = 0.000DF = 1552
```

9.74 Risks In a study aimed at understanding how people perceive risk, researchers asked subjects to consider various activities and rate them in terms of how risky they thought the activities were (0 for no risk to 100, the greatest possible risk). The results for the perceived risk of using a household appliance are given below for both men and women.

a. Use the Minitab output to determine whether the mean risk of using appliances for women is significantly different from the mean for men. The women are indicated with a 0 and the men with a 1.

b. Interpret the 95% CI (confidence interval).

```
Two-Sample T-Test and CI: appl, gender

gender   N   Mean  StDev  SE Mean
0      353  20.6   20.8     1.1
1      214  18.3   20.0     1.4


Difference = mu (0) - mu (1)
Estimate for difference: 2.30
95% CI for difference: (-1.16, 5.76)
T-Test of difference = 0 (vs not =): T-Value = 1.30  P-Value = 0.193
```

9.75 Heart Rate Before and After Coffee Elena Lucin, a statistics student, collected the data in the table showing heart rate (beats per minute) for a random sample of coffee drinkers before and 15 minutes after they drank coffee. Carry out a complete analysis, using the techniques you learned in this chapter. Use a 5% significance level to test whether coffee increases heart rates. The same amount of caffeinated coffee was served to each person, and you may assume that conditions for a *t*-test hold.

Before	After		Before	After
90	92		74	78
84	88		72	82
102	102		72	76
84	96		92	96
74	96		86	88
88	100		90	92
80	84		80	74
68	68			

* 9.76 Exam Grades The final exam grades for a sample of daytime statistics students and evening statistics students at one community college are reported. The classes had the same instructor, covered the same material, and had similar exams. Using graphical and numerical summaries, write a brief description of how grades differ for these two groups. Then carry out a hypothesis test to determine whether the mean grades are significantly different for evening and daytime students. Assume that conditions for a *t*-test hold. Select your significance level.

Daytime grades: 100, 100, 93, 76, 86, 72.5, 82, 63, 59.5, 53, 79.5, 67, 48, 42.5, 39

Evening grades: 100, 98, 95, 91.5, 104.5, 94, 86, 84.5, 73, 92.5, 86.5, 73.5, 87, 72.5, 82, 68.5, 64.5, 90.75, 66.5

9.77 Hours of Television Viewing The number of hours per week of television viewing for random samples of Grade 5 boys and Grade 5 girls were obtained. Each student logged his or her hours for one Monday-through-Friday period. Assume that the students were independent; for example, that there were no pairs of siblings who watched the same shows.

Using graphical and numerical summaries, write a brief description of how the hours differed for the boys and girls. Then carry out a hypothesis test to determine whether the mean hours of television viewing are different for boys and girls. Evaluate whether the conditions for a *t*-test are met, and state any assumptions you must make in order to carry out a *t*-test.

9.78 Reaction Distances Reaction distances in centimetres for a random sample of 40 students were obtained. Shorter distances indicate quicker reactions. The students tried the experiment by catching a metre stick first with their dominant hand and then with their nondominant hand.

Examine the summary statistics, and explain what we can learn from them. Then do an appropriate test to see whether the mean reaction distance is shorter for the dominant hand. Use a significance level of 0.05.

9.79 Work Hours: Men and Women Random samples of 50 men and 50 women reported how many hours they worked in the last week as part of the 2008 General Social Survey. (People who did not work were not included.)

a. Two different analyses were performed to test the claim that the population means are not the same. Choose the correct output, and carry out the hypothesis test. Both analyses were done using two-tailed alternative hypotheses.

b. Use the correct output to report and interpret an appropriate 95% confidence interval for the difference in means.

```
Two-sample T for 50 men vs 50 women

               N    Mean   StDev   SE Mean
50 men        50    49.8   16.8      2.4
50 women      50    37.8   12.2      1.7

Difference = mu (50 men) - mu (50 women)
Estimate for difference: 12.02
95% CI for difference: (6.18, 17.86)
T-Test of difference = 0 (vs not =): T-Value = 4.09  P-Value = 0.000
```

Output a

```
Paired T for 50 men - 50 women

                N    Mean   StDev   SE Mean
50 men         50    49.80  16.81     2.38
50 women       50    37.78  12.24     1.73
Difference     50    12.02  19.91     2.82

95% CI for mean difference: (6.36, 17.68)
T-Test of mean difference = 0 (vs = 0): T-Value = 4.27  P-Value = 0.000
```

Output b

9.80 Number of Children Random samples of 100 men and 100 women were collected from the 2008 General Social Survey, with each person reporting the number of children he or she had.

a. What do the sample means tell us about the differences between men and women in terms of the number of children they report having?

b. Two analyses were carried out to test the claim that the mean number of children for men is not the same as the mean number of children for women. Only one analysis is appropriate for these data. Carry out an appropriate hypothesis test, including all four steps. The sample sizes are large enough so that the shapes of the population distributions are not a concern.

c. Report and interpret the 95% confidence interval for the difference in means.

```
Two-sample T for 100 men vs 100 women

                N    Mean   StDev   SE Mean
100 men        100   1.49   1.76     0.18
100 women      100   1.85   1.57     0.16

Difference = mu (100 men) - mu (100 women)
Estimate for difference: -0.360
95% CI for difference: (-0.825, 0.105)
T-Test of difference = 0 (vs not =): T-Value = -1.53  P-Value = 0.128
```

Output a

```
Paired T for 100 men - 100 women

                N    Mean   StDev   SE Mean
100 men        100   1.490  1.755    0.176
100 women      100   1.850  1.572    0.157
Difference     100  -0.360  2.259    0.226

95% CI for mean difference: (-0.808, 0.088)
T-Test of mean difference = 0 (vs = 0): T-Value = -1.59  P-Value = 0.114
```

Output b

9.81 Sleep and Age Data were obtained on the number of minutes slept the night before the interview, by age, for a random sample of respondents to the 2010 General Social Survey. The

summary statistics are given in the table for two age groups: 15 to 24, and 25 to 34.

Test the hypothesis that the 15 to 24 age group slept more, on average, than the 25 to 34 group. Use a level of significance of 0.05 and assume that conditions for *t*-tests hold. Begin by choosing the appropriate output, the TI-83/84 output shown in figure (a) or that shown in figure (b), and explain your choice. In the output, 1 indicates the 15 to 24 age group, and 2 indicates the 25 to 34 age group.

	15 to 24	25 to 34
Mean	487	507
SD	112	176
n	30	30

(a)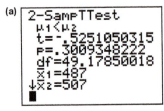

(b)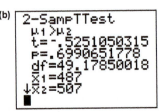

TI-83/84 Output   TI-83/84 Output

9.82 Sleep and Age Data were obtained on the number of minutes slept the night before the interview, by age, for a random sample of respondents to the 2010 General Social Survey. The summary statistics are given in the table for two age groups: 35 to 44, and 45 to 54.

Test the hypothesis that the 35 to 44 age group slept more, on average, than the 45 to 54 group. Use a level of significance of 0.05 and assume that conditions for *t*-tests hold. Begin by choosing the appropriate output, the TI-83/84 output shown in figure (a) or that shown in figure (b), and explain your choice. In the output, 1 indicates the 35 to 44 age group, and 2 indicates the 45 to 54 age group.

	35 to 44	45 to 54
Mean	463	431.5
SD	164	85
n	30	30

(a)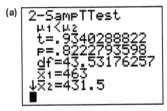

(b)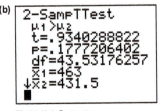

TI-83/84 Output   TI-83/84 Output

* 9.83 Why Is *n* − 1 in the Sample Standard Deviation? Why do we calculate *s* by dividing by *n* − 1 rather than just *n*?

$$s^2 = \frac{\sum (x - \bar{x})^2}{n - 1}$$

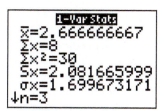

TI-83/84 Output

The reason is that if we divide by $n - 1$, then s^2 is an unbiased estimator of σ^2, the population variance.

We want to show that s^2 is an unbiased estimator of σ^2, sigma squared. The mathematical proof that this is true is beyond the scope of an introductory statistics course, but we can use an example to demonstrate that it is.

First we will use a very small population that consists of only these three numbers: 1, 2, and 5.

You can determine that the population standard deviation, σ, for this population is 1.699673 (or about 1.70), as shown in the TI-83/84 output. So the population variance, sigma squared, σ^2, is therefore 2.888889 (or about 2.89).

Now take all possible samples, with replacement, of size 2 from the population, and find the sample variance, s^2, for each sample.

Sample	s	s^2
1, 1	0	0
1, 2	0.7071	0.5
1, 5	2.8284	8.0
2, 1		
2, 2		
2, 5		
5, 1		
5, 2		
5, 5		

This process is started for you in the table. Average these sample variances (s^2), and you should get approximately 2.88889. If you do, then you have demonstrated that s^2 is an unbiased estimator of σ^2, sigma squared.

Show your work by filling in the accompanying table and show the average of s^2.

9.84 Is s an Unbiased Estimator of σ? Use the data given in Exercise 9.83 to find out whether s is a biased or an unbiased estimator of σ, sigma. To do this, add the standard deviations (s) for the nine samples, and divide by 9 to get the average. Report this average. Is it larger than, smaller than, or the same size as 1.69967? Is it a biased estimator of sigma or an unbiased estimator?

* **9.85** Construct two sets of body temperatures (in degrees Celsius, such as 36.9°C), one for men and one for women, such that the sample means are different but the hypothesis test shows the population means are not different. Each set should have three numbers in it.

* **9.86** Construct heights for three or more sets of twins (six or more people). Make the twins similar, but not exactly the same, in height. Put all the shorter twins in set A and all the taller twins in set B. Create the numbers such that a two-sample t-test will *not* show a significant difference in the mean heights of the shortest of each pair and the mean heights of the tallest of each pair but the paired t-test *will* show a significant difference. (*Hint:* Make one of the pairs really tall, one of the pairs really short, and one of the pairs in between.) Report all the numbers and the t- and p-values for the tests. Explain why the paired t-test shows a difference and the two-sample t-test does not show a difference.

GUIDED EXERCISES

9.31 Human Body Temperature A random sample of 10 healthy people showed the following body temperatures (in degrees Celsius):

36.9, 36.8, 37.2, 35.7, 36.8, 37.1, 36.2, 37.3, 37.1, 36.2

The Minitab output of the results of a one-sample t-test is shown.

```
One-Sample T: BodyTemp

Test of mu = 37 vs not = 37


Variable   N    Mean   StDev  SE Mean      95% CI          T      P
BodyTemp  10   36.730  0.525   0.166   (36.354, 37.106)  -1.63  0.138
```

Questions

Test the hypothesis that the population mean is not 37°C, using a level of significance of 0.05. Write out the steps given, filling in the blanks.

Step 1 ▶ Hypothesize

$H_0: \mu = 37$

$H_A:$ _____

Step 2 ▶ Prepare

A stemplot is shown that is somewhat skewed, suggesting that the distribution of the population may or may not be approximately Normal. Assume that the population is Normal. Comment on the data collection, and state the test to be used. State the significance level.

35	7
36	22
36	889
37	1123

Step 3 ▶ Compute to compare

$$t = \underline{\hspace{3cm}}$$

$$\text{p-value} = \underline{\hspace{3cm}}$$

Step 4 ▶ Interpret and conclude

If the _____ is true, the probability that another random sample of 10 body temperatures will give an outcome that is just as surprising or more surprising than our outcome is _____%.

Reject or do not reject H_0 and choose the decision i, ii, or iii:

i. The population mean is definitely 37°C on the basis of these data at the 0.05 level.

ii. We can reject the null hypothesis on the basis of these data, at the 0.05 level. The population mean is not 37°C.

9.49 Televisions Minitab output is shown for a two-sample t-test for the number of televisions owned in households of random samples of students at two different community colleges. Each individual was randomly chosen independently of the others; the students were not chosen as pairs or in groups. One of the schools is in a wealthy community (MC), and the other (OC) is in a less wealthy community.

```
Two-Sample T-Test and CI: OCTV, MCTV

        N     Mean    StDev   SE Mean
OCTV    30    3.70    1.49    0.27
MCTV    30    3.33    1.49    0.27


Difference = mu OCTV - mu MCTV
Estimate for difference: 0.367
95% CI for difference: (-0.404, 1.138)
T-Test of difference = 0 (vs not =): T-Value = 0.95  P-Value = 0.345
```

Question

Complete the steps to test the hypothesis that the mean number of televisions per household is different in the two communities, using a significance level of 0.05.

Step 1 ▶ Hypothesize

Let μ_{oc} be the population mean number of televisions owned by families of students in the less wealthy community (OC), and let μ_{mc} be the population mean number of televisions owned by families of students in the wealthier community (MC).

H_0: $\mu_{oc} = \mu_{mc}$

H_A: _____ __

Step 2 ▶ Prepare

Choose an appropriate t-test. Because the sample sizes are 30, the Normality condition of the t-test is satisfied. State the other conditions, indicate whether they hold, and state the significance level that will be used.

Step 3 ▶ Compute to compare

$$t = \underline{\hspace{3cm}}$$

$$\text{p-value} = \underline{\hspace{3cm}}$$

Step 4 ▶ Interpret and conclude

If the _____ is true, the probability that another random sample of 30 students from the less wealthy community (OC) and 30 students from the wealthy community (MC) will give an outcome that is just as surprising or more surprising than our outcome is _____%.

Reject or do not reject the null hypothesis. Then choose the correct conclusion:

i. At the 5% significance level, we cannot reject the null hypothesis that the mean number of televisions of all students in the wealthier community is the same as the mean number of televisions of all students in the less wealthy community.

ii. At the 5% significance level, we conclude that the mean number of televisions of all students in the wealthier community is different from the mean number of televisions of all students in the less wealthy community.

Confidence Interval

Report the confidence interval for the difference in means given by Minitab, and state whether it captures 0 and what that shows.

9.61 Females: Pulse Rates Before and After a Fright In a statistics class taught by one of the authors, students took their pulses before and after being frightened. The frightening event was having the teacher scream and run from one side of the room to the other. The pulse rates (beats per minute) of the women before and after the scream were obtained separately and are shown in the table. Treat this as though it were a random sample of female community college students.

Question

Test the hypothesis that the mean of college women's pulse rates is higher after a fright, using a significance level of 0.05, by following the steps below.

Women		Women	
Pulse Before	Pulse After	Pulse Before	Pulse After
64	68	84	88
100	112	80	80
80	84	68	92
60	68	60	76
92	104	68	72
80	92	68	80
68	72		

Step 1 ▶ Hypothesize

μ is the mean number of beats per minute.

H_0: $\mu_{\text{before}} = \mu_{\text{after}}$

H_A: μ_{before} _____ μ_{after}

Step 2 ▶ Prepare

Choose a test: Should it be a paired t-test or a two-sample t-test? Why? Assume that the sample was random and that the distribution of differences is sufficiently Normal. Mention the level of significance.

Step 3 ▶ Compute to compare

$$t = \underline{\hspace{3cm}}$$

$$\text{p-value} = \underline{\hspace{3cm}}$$

Step 4 ▶ Interpret and conclude

Interpret the meaning of the p-value, then reject or do not reject H_0. Then write a sentence that includes "significant" or "significantly" in it. Report the sample mean pulse rate, before the scream and after the scream.

TECH♀TIPS

General Instructions for All Technology

Because of the limitations of the algorithms, precision, and rounding involved in the various technologies, there can be slight differences in the outputs. These differences can be noticeable, especially for the calculated p-values involving *t*-distributions. It is suggested that the technology that was used be reported along with the p-value, especially for two-sample *t*-tests.

Example A (One-Sample *t*-Test and Confidence Interval)

A box of Smarties is supposed to have, on average, 56 Smarties. A random sample of five boxes was taken and the number of Smarties in each box was counted: 56, 61, 54, 52, 52. Test the hypothesis that the mean number of Smarties in a box of Smarties is 56. Report the *t*-statistic and p-value. Also find the 95% confidence interval for the population mean.

Example B (Two-Sample *t*-Test and Confidence Interval)

Below are the GPAs for random samples of men and women.

Men: 3.0, 2.8, 3.5

Women: 2.2, 3.9, 3.0

Perform a two sample *t*-test to determine whether you can reject the hypothesis that the population means are equal. Find the *t*- and p-values. Also find a 95% confidence interval for the difference in means.

Example C (Paired *t*-Test)

Here are the pulse rates (in beats per minute) before and after exercise for three randomly selected people.

Person	Before	After
A	60	75
B	72	80
C	80	92

Determine whether you can reject the hypothesis that the population mean change is 0 (in other words, that the two population means are equal). Find the *t*- and p-values.

TI-83/84

One-Sample *t*-Test

1. Press **STAT** and choose **EDIT**, and type the data into **L1** (list one).
2. Press **STAT**, choose **TESTS**, and choose **2: T-Test**.
3. Note this but don't do it: if you did not have the data in the list and wanted to enter summary statistics such as $\bar{x}$, s, and n, you would put the cursor over **Stats**, press **ENTER**, and put in the required numbers.
4. See Figure 9A. Because you have raw data, put the cursor over **Data** and press **ENTER**.

Enter: μ_0, 56; List, L1; Freq: 1; put the cursor over ≠ and press **ENTER**; scroll down to **Calculate** and press **ENTER**.

▲ FIGURE 9A TI-83/84 input for one-sample *t*-test.

Your output should look like Figure 9B.

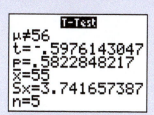

▲ FIGURE 9B TI-83/84 output for one-sample *t*-test.

One-Sample *t*-Interval

1. Press **STAT**, choose **TESTS**, and choose **8:TInterval**.
2. Choose **Data** because you have raw data. (If you had summary statistics, you would choose **Stats**.) Choose the correct **List** (to select **L1**, press **2nd** and **1**) and **C-Level**, here 0.95. Leave **Freq:1**, which is the default. Scroll down to **Calculate** and press **ENTER**.

The 95% confidence interval reported for the mean number of Smarties is (50.354, 59.646).

Two-Sample *t*-Test

1. Press **STAT**, choose **EDIT**, and put your data (GPAs) in two separate lists (unstacked). We put the men's GPAs into **L1** and the women's GPAs into **L2**.
2. Press **STAT**, choose **TESTS**, and choose **4:2-Samp-TTest**.

453

3. For **Inpt**, choose **Data** because we put the data into the lists. (If you had summary statistics, you would choose **Stats** and put in the required numbers.)

4. In choosing your options, make sure that the lists chosen are the ones containing the data; leave the **Freq** as 1, choose $\neq$ as the alternative, and choose **Pooled No** (which is the default). Scroll down to **Calculate** and press **ENTER**.

You should get the output shown in Figure 9C. The arrow down on the left-hand side means that you can scroll down to see more of the output.

▲ **FIGURE 9C** TI-83/84 output for two-sample *t*-test.

Two-Sample *t*-Interval

1. After entering your data into two lists, press **STAT**, choose **TESTS**, and choose **0:2-SampTInt**.

2. Choose **Data** because you have raw data. (If you had summary statistics, you would choose **Stats**.) Make sure that the lists chosen are the ones with your data. Leave the default for **Freq1:1**, **Freq2:1**, and **Pooled No**. Make sure the **C-Level** is .95. Scroll down to **Calculate** and press **ENTER**.

The interval for the GPA example will be (−1.744, 1.8774) if the men's data corresponded to **L1** and the women's to **L2**.

Paired *t*-Test

1. Enter the data given in Example 3 into **L1** and **L2**, as shown in Figure 9D.

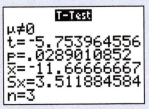

▲ **FIGURE 9D** Obtaining the list of differences for the TI-83/84.

2. See Figure 9D. Use your arrows to move the cursor to the top of **L3** so that you are in the label region. Then press **2ND L1 - 2ND L2**. For the minus sign, be sure to use the button above the plus button. Then press **ENTER**, and you should see all the differences in **L3**.

3. Press **STAT**, choose **TESTS**, and choose **2: T-Test**.

4. See Figure 9E. For **Inpt** choose **Data**. Make sure that μ_0 is 0 because we are testing to see whether the mean difference is 0. Also make sure to choose **L3**, if that is where the differences are. Scroll down to **Calculate** and press **ENTER**.

▲ **FIGURE 9E** TI-83/84 input for paired *t*-test.

Your output should look like Figure 9F.

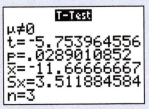

▲ **FIGURE 9F** TI-83/84 output for paired *t*-test.

MINITAB

One-Sample *t*-Test and Confidence Interval

1. Type the number of Smarties in each box sampled in **C1** (column 1).

2. **Stat > Basic Statistics > 1-Sample t**

3. See Figure 9G. Click in the empty white box below **Samples in columns:** a list of columns containing data will appear to the left. Double click on C1 to choose it. Check **Perform hypothesis test**, and put in 56 as the **Hypothesized mean**. (If you wanted a one-tailed test or a confidence level other than 95%, you would use **Options**.)

4. Click **OK**.

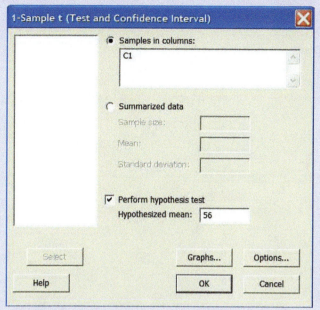

▲ **FIGURE 9G** Minitab input screen for one-sample *t*-test.

The output is shown in Figure 9H.

```
One-Sample T: C1

Test of mu = 56 vs not = 56

Variable   N    Mean   StDev   SD Mean      95% CI            T      P

C1         5   55.00    3.74      1.67   (50.35, 59.65)   -0.60   0.582
```

▲ **FIGURE 9H** Minitab output for one-sample *t*-test and confidence interval.

Note that the Minitab output (Figure 9H) includes the 95% confidence interval for the mean weight (3.22, 4.14) as well as the *t*-test.

Two-Sample *t*-Test and Confidence Interval

Use stacked data with all the GPAs in one column. The second column will contain the categorical variable that designates groups: male or female.

1. Upload the data from the disk or use the following procedure: Enter the GPAs in the first column. In the second column put the corresponding **m** or **f**. (Complete words or coding are also allowed for the second column, but you must decide on a system for one data set and stick to it. For example, using F one time and f the other times within one data set will create problems.) Use headers for the columns: **GPA** and **Gender**.

2. **Stat > Basic Statistics > 2-Sample t**

3. Refer to Figure 9I. Choose **Samples in one column,** because we have stacked data. Click in the small box to the right of **Samples** at the top to activate the box. Double click **GPA** and then double click **Gender** to get it into the **Subscripts** box. If you wanted to do a one-tailed test or to use a confidence level other than 95%, you would click **Options.**

   (If you had unstacked data, you would choose **Samples in different columns**, and choose both columns of data.)

4. Click **OK.**

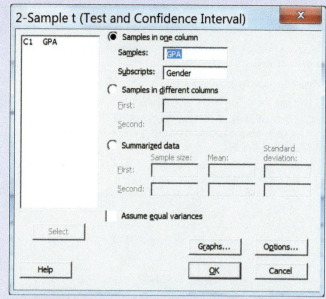

▲ **FIGURE 9I** Minitab input screen for two-sample *t*-test and confidence interval.

The output is shown in Figure 9J. Note that the confidence interval is included.

```
Two-Sample T-Test and CI: GPA, Gender
Two-sample T for GPA
Gender   N    Mean   StDev   SE Mean
f        3   3.033   0.850      0.49
m        3   3.100   0.361      0.21

Difference = mu (f) - mu (m)
Estimate for difference:  -0.067
95% CI for difference:  (-2.361, 2.228)
T-Test of difference = 0 (vs not =): T-Value = -0.13 P-Value = 0.912 DF = 2
```

▲ **FIGURE 9J** Minitab output for two-sample *t*-test and confidence interval.

Paired *t*-Test and Confidence Interval

1. Type the numbers (pulse rates) in two columns. Label the first column "**Before**" and the second column "**After**."

2. **Stat > Basic Statistics > Paired t**

3. Double click **Before** and then double click **After**. (If you wanted a one-tailed test or a confidence level other than 95%, you would click **Options**.)

4. Click **OK**.

Figure 9K shows the output.

```
Paired T-Test and CI: Before, After
Paired T for Before - After

            N    Mean   StDev   SE Mean
Before      3   70.67   10.07      5.81
After       3   82.33    8.74      5.04
Difference  3  -11.67    3.51      2.03

95% CI for mean difference: (-20.39, -2.94)
T-Test of mean difference = 0 (vs not = 0): T-Value = -5.75 P-Value = 0.029
```

▲ **FIGURE 9K** Minitab output for paired *t*-test and confidence interval.

EXCEL

We are saving the one-sample *t*-test for last, because we have to treat it strangely.

Two-Sample *t*-Test

1. Type the GPAs in two columns side by side.

2. Click on **Data** and **Data Analysis**, and then scroll down to **t-Test: Two-Sample Assuming Unequal Variances** and double click it.

3. See Figure 9L. For the **Variable 1 Range** select one column of numbers (don't include any labels). Then click inside the box for **Variable 2 Range**, and select the other column of numbers.

   You may leave the hypothesized mean difference empty, because the default value is 0, and that is what you want.

4. Click **OK**.

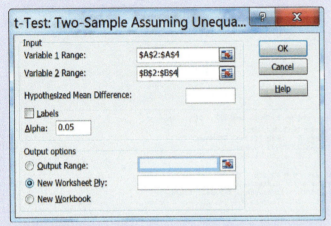

▲ **FIGURE 9L** Excel input for two-sample *t*-test.

To see all of the output you may have to click **Home**, **Format** (in the **Cells** group), and **AutoFit Column Width**.

Figure 9M shows the relevant part of the output.

t Stat	0.125
P(T<=t) one-tail	0.454214709
P(T<=t) two-tail	0.908429419

▲ **FIGURE 9M** Part of the excel output for two-sample *t*-test.

For a one-tailed alternative hypothesis, the Excel always reports one-half the p-value for the two-tailed hypothesis. This is the correct p-value only when the observed value of the test statistic is consistent with the direction of the alternative hypothesis. (In other words, if the alternative hypothesis is ">", then the observed test statistic is positive; if "<", then the observed value is negative.) If this is not the case, to find the correct p-value, calculate 1 minus the reported one-tailed p-value.

Paired *t*-Test

1. Type the data into two columns.

2. Click on **Data**, **Data Analysis**, and **t test: Paired Two Sample for Means**, and follow the same procedure as for the two-sample *t*-test.

One-Sample *t*-Test

1. You need to use a trick to force Excel to do this test. Enter the weights of the cones in column A, and put zeros in column B so that the columns are equal in length, as shown in Figure 9N.

▲ **FIGURE 9N** Excel data entry for one-sample *t*-test.

2. Click **Data**, **Data Analysis**, and **t-Test: Paired Two Sample for Means**.

3. See Figure 9O. After selecting the two groups of data, you need to put the hypothesized mean in the box labelled **Hypothesized Mean Difference**. For the way we set up this example, it is **56**. (If you had entered 56's in column B, you would put in 0 for the Hypothesized Mean Difference.)

4. Click **OK**.

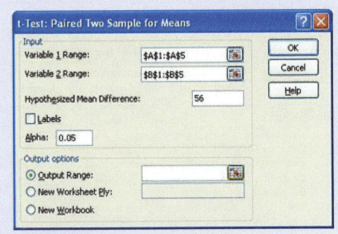

▲ **FIGURE 9O** Excel input for one-sample *t*-test.

Figure 9P shows the relevant part of the Excel output.

Hypothesized Mean Difference	56
df	4
t Stat	-0.597614305
P(T<=t) one-tail	0.291142411
t Critical one-tail	2.131846782
P(T<=t) two-tail	0.582284822
t Critical two-tail	2.776445105

▲ **FIGURE 9P** Relevant part of the excel output for one-sample *t*-test.

STATCRUNCH

One-Sample *t*-Test

1. Type the numbers of Smarties into the first column.
2. **Stat > T statistics > one sample > with data**

   (If you had summary statistics, then after **one sample**, you would choose **with summary**.)
3. Click on the column containing the data, **var1**, and click **Next**.
4. See Figure 9Q. Put in the **Null mean**, which is **56** for the Smarties. Leave the default not equal for the **Alternative**, and click **Calculate**.

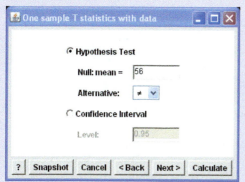

▲ **FIGURE 9Q** Part of StatCrunch input for one-sample *t*-test.

You will get the output shown in Figure 9R.

Hypothesis test results:
μ : mean of Variable
$H_0 : \mu = 56$
$H_A : \mu \neq 56$

Variable	Sample Mean	Std.Dev.	DF	T-Stat	P-value
var1	55	1.67332	4	−0.5976143	0.5823

▲ **FIGURE 9R** StatCrunch output for one-sample *t*-test.

One-Sample Confidence Interval
Go back and perform the same steps as for the one-sample *t*-test, but when you get to step 4, check **Confidence Interval**. You may change the confidence level from the default 0.95 if you want. See Figure 9Q.

Two-Sample *t*-Test
Use stacked data with all the GPAs in one column. The second column will contain the categorical variable that designates groups: male or female.

1. Upload the data from the disk or follow these steps: Enter the GPAs in column 1 (**var1**). Put **m** or **f** in column 2 (**var2**) as appropriate. (Complete words or coding for column 2 are also allowed, but whatever system you use must be maintained

within the data set.) Put labels at the top of the columns, changing **var1** to **GPA** and **var2** to **Gender**.

2. **Stat > T statistics > Two sample > with data**
3. See Figure 9S. For **Sample 1** choose **GPA**. For the first **Where** put **Gender=m**. For **Sample 2** choose **GPA** and for the second **Where** put **Gender=f**. Click off **Pool Variances**. (If you had unstacked data you would choose the two lists for the two samples and not use the **Where** boxes.)

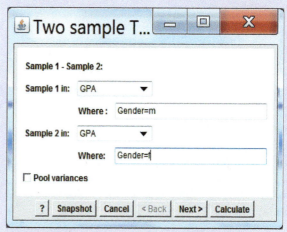

▲ **FIGURE 9S** StatCrunch input for two-sample *t*-test (stacked data).

4. Click **Next** if you want to change the alternative (the default is not equal) or want a confidence interval.
5. Click **Calculate**.

Figure 9T shows the output.

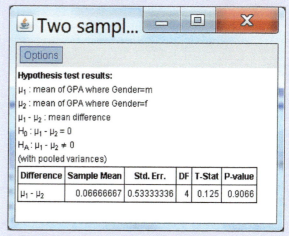

▲ **FIGURE 9T** StatCrunch output for two-sample *t*-test.

Two-Sample Confidence Interval
1. Go back and do the preceding first three numbered steps.
2. When you get to step 4, click **Next**, and check **Confidence Interval**.
3. Click **Calculate**.

Paired *t*-Test

1. Type the pulse rates Before in column 1 and the pulse rates After in column 2. The headings for the columns are not necessary.
2. **Stat > T statistics > Paired**
3. Select the two columns. Ignore the **Where** and **Group by** boxes. If you want to change your alternative hypothesis from the default two-tailed, click **Next**.
4. Click **Calculate**.

Figure 9U shows the output.

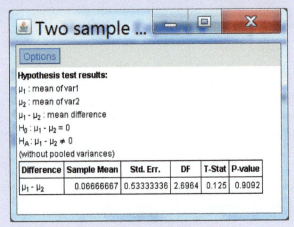

▲ **FIGURE 9U** StatCrunch output for paired *t*-test.

One-Sample *t*-Test and Confidence Interval

1. Type the number of Smarties in **var** (column 1).
2. **Analyze > Compare Means > One Sample T-Test…**
3. See Figure 9V. Select the arrow, moving VAR00001 into the **Test Variable(s)** box. Enter 56 in the **Test Value** box.
4. Press **OK**.

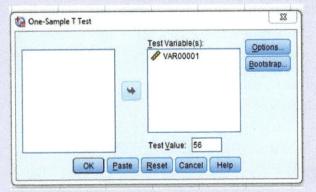

▲ **FIGURE 9V** SPSS input screen for one-sample *t*-test.

One-Sample Test

	Test Value = 56					
	t	df	Sig. (2-tailed)	Mean Difference	95% Confidence Interval of the Difference	
					Lower	Upper
VAR00001	−.598	4	.582	−1.00000	−5.6459	3.6459

▲ **FIGURE 9W** SPSS output for one-sample *t*-test and confidence interval.

Two-Sample *t*-Test and Confidence Interval

Use stacked data with all GPAs in one column. The second column will contain a categorical variable that designates groups: male or female.

1. Upload the data from the disk or use the following procedure: Enter the GPAs for the men and the women in the first column (VAR00001). In the second column put the corresponding **m** or **f** (VAR00002).

2. **Analyze > Compare Means > Independent-Samples T-Test…**
3. Using the arrow, move VAR00001 into the **Test Variable(s)** box, then move VAR00002 into the **Grouping Variable** box.
4. See Figure 9X. Select **Define Groups…** For **Group 1** enter **m**, and for **Group 2** enter **w**. Click **Continue**.
5. Click **OK**.

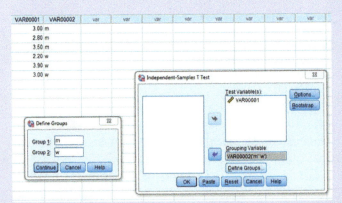

▲ **FIGURE 9X** SPSS input screen for two-sample *t*-test and confidence interval.

The output is shown in Figure 9Y. Pay attention to the "Equal variances not assumed" row.

Group Statistics

	VAR00002	N	Mean	Std. Deviation	Std. Error Mean
VAR00001	m	3	3.1000	.36056	.20817
	w	3	3.0333	.85049	.49103

Independent Sample Test

		Levene's Test for Equality of Variances		t-test for Equality of Means						
		F	Sig	t	df	Sig. (2-tailed)	Mean Difference	Std. Error Difference	95% confidence Interval of the Difference	
									Lower	Upper
VAR00001	Equal variances assumed	1.181	.338	.125	4	.907	.06667	.53333	−1.41410	1.54744
	Equal variances not assumed			.125	2.696	.909	.06667	.53333	−1.74404	1.87738

▲ **FIGURE 9Y** SPSS output screen for two-sample *t*-test and confidence interval.

Paired *t*-Test and Confidence Interval

Use stacked data with all GPAs in one column. The second column will contain a categorical variable that designates groups: male or female.

1. Upload the data from the disk or use the following procedure: Enter the before pulse rates in the first column (VAR00001). In the second column enter the matching after pulse rates (VAR00002).

2. **Analyze > Compare Means > Paired-Samples T-Test...**

3. Using the arrow, move VAR00001 into the **Variable 1** box for Pair 1, then move VAR00002 into the **Variable 2** box. See Figure 9Z.

4. Click **OK**.

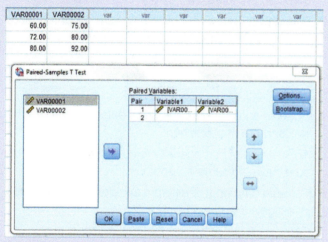

▲ **FIGURE 9Z** SPSS input screen for paired *t*-test.

The output is shown in Figure 9AA.

Paired Samples Statistics

		Mean	N	Std. Deviation	Std. Error Mean
Pair 1	VAR00001	70.6667	3	10.06645	5.81187
	VAR00002	82.3333	3	8.73689	5.04425

Paired Samples Test

		Paired Differences							
					95% confidence Interval of the Difference				
		Mean	Std. Deviation	Std. Error Mean	Lower	Upper	t	df	Sig. (2-tailed)
Pair 1	VAR00001 - VAR00002	−11.66667	3.51188	2.02759	−20.39067	−2.94266	−5.754	2	.029

▲ **FIGURE 9AA** SPSS output screen for paired *t*-test.

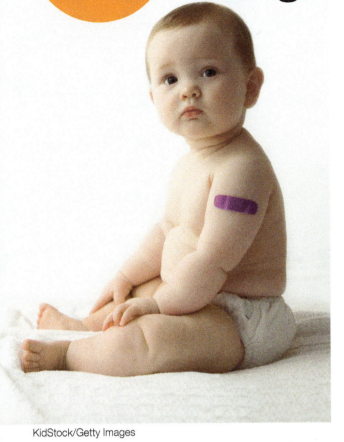

10 Relationships between Categorical Variables

LEARNING OBJECTIVES

After completing this chapter, you should be able to:

1. Determine the correct method for analyzing data collected on one or two categorical variables.

2. Differentiate between "how many were observed" and "how many were expected" in a sample of data.

3. Perform a goodness-of-fit test to determine if data collected on a categorical variable follow a certain distribution.

4. Observe and analyze categorical data collected from two or more populations.

5. Apply a test of homogeneity to determine if two populations have the same proportions.

6. Observe data on two different categorical variables to investigate if they are related.

7. Carry out a statistical test that determines if two categorical variables are independent.

As we have shown in the last few chapters, statistical tests are comparisons between two different views. One view is that if two samples have different means, it might be because the two populations are different. The other view is that randomness happens, and that this difference is due to chance. A sample of people who had watched violent TV as children may behave more aggressively toward their partners when adults. But this might just be due to chance. Changing the placement of an advertisement on an internet search results page might lead to a greater number of "follow-through" visits to the company that placed the ad. Or the difference could be due to chance—that is, if we were to repeat the study, we might see a very different outcome.

In this chapter we ask the same question as before: Are the results we see due to chance, or might something else be going on? In Chapter 8, we asked this question about one-sample and two-sample proportions. We now ask the same question with respect to categorical variables with multiple categories. For example, we might compare two categorical variables: Has a child had his or her mumps, measles, and rubella vaccination ("yes" or "no") and did the child develop autism before or after being vaccinated ("yes" or "no")? Or we might compare a single categorical variable to a proposed model: Are the proportions of Canadians who believe in global climate change living in different regions of the country the same as the proportions of the Canadian population living in these regions? If not, what is the reason behind the differing views?

A nice surprise in this chapter is that only one test statistic is needed to analyze the data collected under the situations described above. This same test statistic is used to perform different kinds of hypotheses: comparing the distributions of categorical variables, comparing proportions for two populations, and testing whether two categorical variables are independent of each other. You'll also be introduced in this chapter to a hypothesis test that requires no assumptions about the distribution of the population or the sample.

CASE STUDY

Do Vaccinations Cause Autism in Children?

In the past decade, there has been increasing scrutiny of vaccinations. A landmark 1998 study published in the prestigious British medical journal *The Lancet* suggested that seemingly healthy children who received the mumps, measles, and rubella (MMR) vaccine developed autism spectrum disorder (ASD) some time (days in some cases, weeks and months in others) after getting the MMR vaccine. ASD results in developmental regression—children lose their already acquired language skills and motor functions. This study's results spawned various celebrity public awareness campaigns warning about the dangers of vaccinations, prompting parents to opt their children out of receiving vaccinations. This had a dramatic effect. Prior to 1998, about 95% of Canadian children were getting the MMR vaccine. In 2013, this percentage had dropped to 84%. No parent wants their child to develop ASD after receiving the MMR vaccine.

So, does the MMR vaccine cause ASD in children?

The data in the accompanying table are from a study (Hornig et al. 2008) that investigated when the ASD symptoms began in a child and if their onset is related to when the child received the MMR vaccine. Children in the study had experienced a gastrointestinal (GI) event, which is a common side effect of the MMR vaccine.

Timing of Vaccination	Developed ASD	Did Not Develop ASD
Received MMR Vaccine Before GI	12	3
Received MMR Vaccine After GI	13	10

From the table, it looks like the onset of ASD symptoms is higher among children after they received the MMR vaccine (12 out of 15) compared to those children prior to receiving the MMR vaccine (13 out of 23).

What is the reason behind these different percentages? Are these outcomes due to chance? Or is there a connection between receiving the MMR vaccine and the onset of ASD symptoms? These variables—when the MMR vaccination was received (with two values: before or after) and the development of ASD symptoms (yes or no)—are both categorical. (At the time of this writing, a measles outbreak was occurring in various portions of Canada and the U.S. Children contracting measles was unheard of 15 years ago, because almost all parents were having their children vaccinated against MMR.)

In this chapter we will see the statistical methods used to test the claim that the timing of receiving the MMR vaccine is related to a child developing ASD.

SECTION 10.1

The Requirements for Testing with Categorical Variables

Hypothesis tests that involve categorical variables follow the same four steps you studied in Chapters 8 and 9. However, some of the details in these steps are slightly different. Here we introduce you to these different requirements: (1) data (sample) observed on categorical variables, (2) expected frequencies, (3) the chi-square statistic (our test statistic), and (4) the chi-square distribution.

To see the slight differences in how we approach a categorical variable, we will test whether a six-sided die is "fair." If it is, each side of the die will have the same chance of being the top side showing after the die is rolled. There is no reason to believe that the die is "not fair" because of its symmetrical shape. There could be variations in the manufacture of the die that could affect its fairness, but we would hope that these are very small and would not result in a biased die. Casinos, for example, would be very concerned if manufacturer variations in the different dice they use result in unfair dice.

We took a die from our favourite board game and decided to test whether it was fair. There is no reason to believe this die is not fair, so our null hypothesis is that the die is fair and therefore each side has the same chance of showing as the top side after it is rolled. The alternative hypothesis—"not the null hypothesis"—would be that the die is not fair. This means that all sides do not have the same chance of being the top side, or that *at least one* side is more likely to be the top side. We rolled this die 60 times, observing the number of dots showing on the top side of the die after each roll.

Before getting to the data, let's imagine what would happen in these 60 rolls if the null hypothesis of the die being fair is true. If we rolled a perfectly fair die an infinite number of times, the result of this experiment should look like Figure 10.1—each side will show as the top side of the die with an equal probability of 1/6—meaning the number of dots appearing on the top side is uniformly distributed.

▶ **FIGURE 10.1** Probability distribution for an ideal, fair die. Each outcome is equally likely (with probability 1/6).

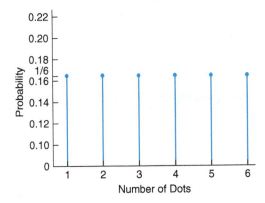

▶ **TABLE 10.1** Summary of outcomes with a six-sided die.

How did our real die compare to the perfect, ideal die? Table 10.1 provides a summary of the data.

Outcome:	•	••	•••	••••	•••••	••••••
Frequency	12	8	10	11	9	10
Relative Frequency	20%	13.33%	16.67%	18.33%	15%	16.67%

Figure 10.2 shows the graph of the results with this real die, tossed 60 times.

▶ **FIGURE 10.2** Observed frequency distribution for the real die, tossed 60 times. Comparing this to Figure 10.1, we see that it is less uniform. Is this irregularity due to chance, or is the die unfair?

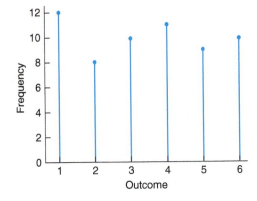

You can see more clearly from the graph than from the table that we did not get a perfectly uniform distribution. The question now is whether these deviations from the "perfect" model in Figure 10.1 occur because the die is not fair, or are due merely to chance.

1. Categorical Variables and Their Data

Recall that categorical variables are those whose values are categories as opposed to numbers. The outcome of the roll of a die can be thought of as a category, particularly if we don't care about the numerical values on the die.

When data are collected on two categorical variables, they are summarized and displayed in a **two-way table**. This table shows the frequency of all combinations of the categorical variables. Such tables can give the impression that the data are numerical, because you are seeing numbers in the table. But it's important to keep in mind that the numbers are *summaries* of variables whose values are *categories*.

For instance, the General Social Survey (GSS) asked respondents, "There are always some people whose ideas are considered bad or dangerous by other people. For instance, somebody who is against churches and religion. If such a person wanted to make a speech in your (city/town/community) against churches and religion, should he be allowed to speak, or not?" These respondents were also asked about their income and, depending on their response, were assigned to one of four annual income levels: $0–$20K, $20–$40K, $40–$70K, and $70K and more. The first four lines of the actual data would look something like Table 10.2. A value on the boundary would be assigned to the group with the larger incomes, so an income of $40K would be in the $40–$70K group.

Observation ID	Response	Income Level
1	allowed	20–40
2	allowed	20–40
3	not allowed	70 and over
4	allowed	0–20
. . .	. . .	. . .

◄ TABLE 10.2 The first four lines of the raw data (based on an actual data set) showing responses to two questions on the General Social Survey.

We have chosen to display another variable, *Observation ID*, which is useful simply for keeping track of the order in which the observations are stored.

A two-way table summarizes the responses observed on the two variables *Response* and *Income Level*, as shown as in Table 10.3.

Response	Income Level			
	0–20	20–40	40–70	70+
Allowed	2404	978	1015	971
Not Allowed	898	347	226	129

◄ TABLE 10.3 Two-way table summarizing the responses to the question about whether speeches opposed to church and religion should be allowed, and income level. (Source: GSS 1972–2008, http://www.teachingwithdata.org)

2. Expected Frequencies

The **expected frequencies** are the numbers we would see in a summary table if the null hypothesis were true. In the next few pages, we will look at a few different hypothesis tests and then see how these expected frequencies are calculated.

For example, Table 10.1 shows the frequencies observed when we rolled the six-sided die 60 times. If this die were truly fair—our null hypothesis—each of the six different sides of the die would have the same probability of showing as the top side, and we would expect each category of the "number showing" variable to occur with equal frequencies.

When the die is rolled 60 times, the expected frequencies are therefore 10 in each outcome category. Because the probability for each category is 1/6, we expect 1/6 of

Details

Expectations
Expected frequencies are actually long-run averages. When we say that we "expect" 10 observations in a cell of a table, we mean that if the null hypothesis were true and we were to repeat this data collection many, many times, then, on average, we would see 10 observations in that cell.

the total outcomes to fall in each category: $(1/6) \times 60 = 10$. Table 10.4 compares these expected frequencies with our observed frequencies.

▶ **TABLE 10.4** The expected (top) and observed (bottom) frequencies for rolling a fair die 60 times.

Outcome	•	••	•••	••••	•••••	••••••
Expected Frequency	10	10	10	10	10	10
Observed Frequency	12	8	10	11	9	10

For a slightly more complex (but still quite typical) example, consider a study of the link between TV viewing and violent behaviour. (We introduced these data in Chapter 8.) Researchers compared TV viewing habits for children, and then interviewed them about violent behaviour many years later (Husemann et al. 2003). Table 10.5 summarizes the results.

▶ **TABLE 10.5** A two-way summary of TV violence and later abusive behaviour.

	High TV Violence	Low TV Violence	Total
Yes, Physical Abuse	25	57	82
No Physical Abuse	41	206	247
Total	66	263	329

There are two categorical variables: *TV Violence* ("High" or "Low") and *Physical Abuse* ("Yes" or "No"). (Recall that the subjects were asked whether they had pushed, grabbed, or shoved their partner.) We want to know if these variables are related. Prior to the collection of the data, there is no reason to believe these two variables are related. Because of this, we can assume they are not related and make this our null hypothesis, and any patterns observed are due to chance.

What frequencies should we expect if these variables are truly not related to each other? That is, if the null hypothesis is true, what would we expect the table to look like? There are two ways of answering this question, and they both lead to the same answer. Let's look at them both.

Method One—Start with One Variable

Of the 329 people sampled, 82 said they had physically abused their partners, a sample proportion of 0.249240, or 24.92%. If the null hypothesis is true and abuse is independent of TV watching, then we should expect the same percentages of violent abuse in those who watched high TV violence and in those who watched low TV violence.

That is, we should expect 24.92% of the 66 people who watched high TV violence to have been physically abusive to their partners, or $0.24924 \times 66 = 16.45$ people. We would expect the same percentage of the 263 who watched low TV violence to have physically abused their partners, or $0.24924 \times 263 = 65.55$ people.

We use the same reasoning to find the other expected frequencies: 247 of 329 people sampled, or 0.75076, did not abuse their partner. If the null hypothesis of independence is true, we would expect this percentage of high TV violence watchers and low TV violence watchers to not abuse their partner. Working this out, we find the following:

In the "no physical abuse and high TV violence" group,

$$0.750760 \times 66 = 49.5502$$

In the "no physical abuse and low TV violence" group,

$$0.750760 \times 263 = 197.4499$$

(We are using many decimal places in these steps so that our answers for the expected frequencies are as accurate as possible.)

We then summarize these calculations in Table 10.6, which shows the expected frequencies in parentheses. We include the actual frequencies in the same table to make it easy to compare. Note the rounding to two decimal digits for ease of presentation.

Here we started with the Abuse categorical variable, or the "row" variable. If we started with the TV Violence variable—the "column" variable—we would have found the same expected frequencies.

	High TV Violence	Low TV Violence	Total
Yes, Physical Abuse	25 (16.45)	57 (65.55)	82
No Physical Abuse	41 (49.55)	206 (197.45)	247
Total	66	263	329

◀ **TABLE 10.6** TV violence: A two-way summary including expected frequencies (in parentheses).

If we call the values 82 and 247 row totals (for obvious reasons, we hope!), 66 and 263 column totals, and 329 the grand total, we can generate a formula for automatically finding expected frequencies for each cell. This formula is rarely needed. First, you can and should always think through the calculations as we did here. Second, most software will automatically do this for you.

Formula 10.1:   Expected frequency for a cell $= \dfrac{(\text{row total}) \times (\text{column total})}{\text{grand total}}$

Method Two—Formula 10.1 Works Like This

Where does Formula 10.1 come from? Let's begin by considering the *TV Violence* variable. We see that $66/329 = 0.200608$, or 20.06%, watched high TV violence. The rest, $263/329 = 0.799329$, or 79.94%, watched low TV violence. Furthermore, 82 of 329 people, 0.249240 or 24.92%, committed physical abuse, and $247/329 = 0.750760$, or 75.08%, did not.

In Chapter 5, you learned that if two events are independent, the probability of occurrence of both events is equal to the probabilities of each event multiplied together—called the multiplication rule.

Let's apply this rule: if the variables *TV Violence* and *Physical Abuse* are independent, the percentage of this sample that watched high TV violence *and* committed physical abuse would be $0.200608 \times 0.249240 = 0.049999$, or 4.9999%. Taking 4.9999% of 329 people leaves us with $0.04999 \times 329 = 16.45$ (rounded to two decimals). Similarly, we would expect $0.200608 \times 0.750760 = 0.150608$, or 15.0608%, to have watched high TV violence and not have committed physical abuse. We take 15.0608% of 329, or $0.150608 \times 329 = 49.55$.

The percentage of the 329 people sampled who we expect to "watch low TV violence and commit physical abuse" is

$$0.799329 \times 0.249240 = 0.199225$$

and for "watch low TV violence and not commit physical abuse," it is

$$0.799329 \times 0.750760 = 0.600104$$

Multiplying each of these percentages by 329 gives us the respective expected frequencies:

$$0.199225 \times 329 = 65.55 \text{ and } 0.600104 \times 329 = 197.45$$

You get the same result no matter what method you use!

Details

Fractions of People
Does it bother you that we have fractions of people in each category? It *is* a little strange, until you think about this in terms of an ideal model. These expected frequencies are like averages. We say the average family has 2.4 children, and we know very well that there is no single family with a 0.4 child. This number 2.4 is a description of the collection of all families. Our claim that we expect 16.45 people (in this group) who have seen high TV violence to be abusive is a similar idealization.

Looking Back

In Chapter 5, we learned that if events A and B are independent, then P(A AND B) = P(A) P(B).

EXAMPLE 1 Gender and Opinion about Same-Sex Marriage

Is there a difference between how men and women feel about the issue of same-sex marriage? An Ipsos Reid poll of 501 randomly chosen Canadians was taken in June 2013, recording the gender of each person and their opinion about same-sex couples being allowed to marry. The results are summarized in Table 10.7.

▶ **TABLE 10.7** Summary of gender and opinion about same-sex couples having the right to marry.

Opinion	Male	Female	Total
Allowed to Legally Marry	136	181	317
Be Allowed Legal Recognition, but Not to Marry	40	24	64
Not Be Allowed Any Kind of Legal Recognition	46	25	71
Not Sure	25	24	49
Total	247	254	501

QUESTION Assuming that the two variables *Opinion* and *Gender* are *not* related, find the expected number of males and females who believe that same-sex couples should be "allowed to legally marry."

SOLUTION We consider the column variable *Gender* first (although we could have just as easily chosen the row variable *Opinion* first). The percentage of men sampled is $(247/501 \times 100\%) = 49.30\%$. The percentage of women sampled is therefore $100\% - 49.30\% = 50.70\%$. If *Gender* is not related to *Opinion*, then if we look at the 317 people who believe same-sex couples should be allowed to legally marry, 49.30% of them should be male and 50.7% should be female.

CONCLUSION Expected frequency of males who believe in legal marriage for same-sex couples is $317 \times 0.4930 = 156.281$, or about 156.28. The expected frequency of females who believe in legal marriage for same-sex couples is $317 \times 0.5070 = 160.719$, or about 160.72.

TRY THIS! Exercise 10.9

3. The Chi-Square Statistic

Let's examine again our table of the relation of expected die tosses to our actual die tosses (Table 10.8).

▶ **TABLE 10.8** Sixty rolls of a six-sided die.

Outcome	⚀	⚁	⚂	⚃	⚄	⚅
Expected Frequency	10	10	10	10	10	10
Observed Frequency	12	8	10	11	9	10

We note that in the first category, we saw two more "ones" than expected. On the other hand, we saw two fewer "twos" and exactly the expected number of "threes" and "sixes." Are these differences big or small? If they are small, then we can believe that the deviations between observed and expected frequencies are just due to chance. But if they are big, then maybe the die is not fair.

The **chi-square statistic** is a statistic that measures the amount by which our expected frequencies differ from our observed frequencies. This statistic is shown in Formula 10.2.

$$\textbf{Formula 10.2: } \chi^2_{Obs} = \sum_{\text{all cells}} \frac{(\text{Observed} - \text{Expected})^2}{\text{Expected}}$$

where

Observed is the observed frequency in each cell
Expected is the frequency that we expect to happen in each cell
Σ means add the results from each cell

Why does this statistic work? The term (Observed − Expected) is the difference between what we observe to happen and what we expect to happen under the null hypothesis. To measure the total amount of deviation between Observed and Expected, it is tempting to just add together the individual differences. But this won't work, because the expected frequencies and the observed frequencies always add to the same value; if we sum up the differences, they will always add to 0.

You can see that the differences between Observed and Expected add to 0 in Table 10.9, where we've added the row of differences (Observed Frequencies minus Expected Frequencies). You'll notice that $2 - 2 + 0 + 1 - 1 + 0 = 0$.

Outcome						
Expected Frequency	10	10	10	10	10	10
Observed Frequency	12	8	10	11	9	10
Observed − Expected	2	−2	0	1	−1	0

▲ **TABLE 10.9** Sixty rolls of a six-sided die, emphasizing the observed minus expected values.

One reason why the chi-square statistic uses squared differences is that by squaring the differences, we always get a positive value, because even negative numbers multiplied by themselves result in positive numbers:

$$2^2 + (-2)^2 + 0^2 + 1^2 + (-1)^2 + 0^2 = 4 + 4 + 0 + 1 + 1 + 0 = 10$$

Why divide by the expected frequencies? The reason is that a difference between the expected and observed frequency of, say, 2 is a small difference if we were expecting a frequency of 1000. But if we were expecting only a frequency of 5, then this difference of 2 is substantial. By dividing by the expected frequencies, we're controlling for the size of the expected frequency. Basically, for each cell, we are finding what proportion of the expected frequency the squared difference is.

If we apply this formula to our test of whether the die is unbalanced, we get $\chi^2_{Obs} = 1.0$. We must still decide whether this value discredits the null hypothesis that the die is fair. Keep reading.

EXAMPLE **2** Viewing Violent TV as a Child and Abusiveness as an Adult

Table 10.10 on the next page shows summary statistics from a study that asked whether there was a relationship between watching violent TV as a child and aggressive behaviour toward one's spouse later in life. The table shows both observed frequencies and expected frequencies (in parentheses).

▶ **TABLE 10.10** A two-way summary of the effect of viewing TV violence on later abusiveness (expected values are shown in parentheses).

	High TV Violence	Low TV Violence	Total
Yes, Physical Abuse	25 (16.45)	57 (65.55)	82
No Physical Abuse	41 (49.55)	206 (197.45)	247
Total	66	263	329

QUESTION Find the chi-square statistic to measure the difference between the observed frequencies and expected frequencies for the study of the effect of violent TV on future behaviour.

SOLUTION We use Formula 10.2 with the values for Observed and Expected taken from Table 10.10.

$$\chi^2_{Obs} = \sum \frac{(\text{Observed} - \text{Expected})^2}{\text{Expected}}$$

$$= \frac{(25 - 16.45)^2}{16.45} + \frac{(57 - 65.55)^2}{65.55} + \frac{(41 - 49.55)^2}{49.55} + \frac{(206 - 197.45)^2}{197.45} = 7.4047$$

CONCLUSION

$$\chi^2_{Obs} = 7.40$$

Later we will see whether this is an unusually large value for two independent variables.

TRY THIS! Exercise 10.15

As you might expect, for tables with many cells, these calculations can quickly become tiresome. Fortunately, technology comes to our rescue. Most statistical software will calculate the chi-square statistic for you, given data summarized in a two-way table or presented as raw data as in Table 10.2, and some software will even display the expected frequencies alongside the observed frequencies. Figure 10.3 shows the output from StatCrunch for these data.

What happens to the chi-square statistic when the expected frequencies are exactly the same as the observed frequencies for every cell of a table? In our test to see whether a die was fair, we rolled the die 60 times. We expected 10 outcomes in each category. If we had gotten exactly 10 (for each cell), then our observations would have matched our expectations perfectly. In that case, the chi-square statistic would equal 0, because

$$(\text{Observed} - \text{Expected})^2 = (10 - 10)^2 = 0 \text{ in each cell}$$

Thus, when expectations and reality are exactly the same, the chi-square statistic is 0.

Even when the null hypothesis is true, our real-life observations will differ slightly from the expected frequencies just by chance. When this happens, the chi-square statistic will be a small value.

If reality is very different from what our null hypothesis claims, then our observed frequencies should differ substantially from the expected frequencies. When that happens, the chi-square statistic is a big value.

The trick, then, is to decide what values of the chi-square statistic are "big." Big values discredit the null hypothesis. To determine whether an observed value is big, we need to know the probability distribution of the statistic when the null hypothesis is true.

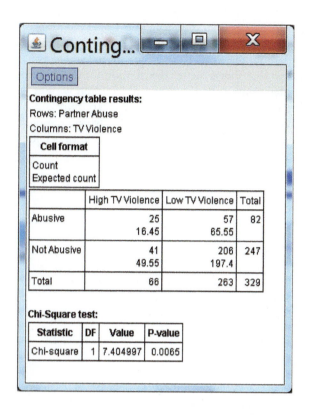

◄ **FIGURE 10.3** StatCrunch output for TV violence and abusiveness. The expected values are below the observed values.

TECH

> **KEY POINT** If the data support the null hypothesis, then the value of the chi-square statistic will be small. For this reason, large values of the chi-square statistic make us suspicious of the null hypothesis.

4. The Distribution of the Chi-Square Statistic

We are curious about whether our die is fair or biased. If fair, then the deviations between what we observe and what we expect should be small, meaning the chi-square statistic will compute to a small value. We found that $\chi^2_{Obs} = 1.0$ for the die. Is this small?

We are also wondering whether television-viewing habits as a child are related to violent behaviour as an adult. If there is *no* relationship, then the observed frequencies in Table 10.10 should be close to the ones we expect, and our chi-square statistic should be small. Here we found $\chi^2_{Obs} = 7.40$. Is this small?

To help us determine if the value of the chi-square statistic is small or not, we need to understand how this statistic behaves. That is, what is the probability distribution of this statistic? Once we understand how the statistic is distributed, we can visually locate the observed value on the distribution to determine if it is small or not.

Let's consider the value of $\chi^2_{Obs} = 1.0$. If we know how this statistic is distributed, we can use its probability distribution to find the chance of observing a value that is bigger than 1.0. If the probability of this is large, then 1.0 is not an unusually large number; should this probability be small, then 1.0 is an unusually large number.

For a large enough sample size, the probability distribution that closely models the behaviour of the chi-square statistic, or approximates its probability distribution, is called—not surprisingly—the **chi-square distribution**. It is represented by the Greek letter chi (pronounced ki, represented by χ) and raised to the second power, hence the symbol χ^2. (This is the reason why we express the *observed* value of the chi-square statistic as χ^2_{Obs}.)

Unlike the perfectly symmetric, centred-at-0 Normal and *t*-distributions, the χ^2 distribution is not symmetric. It is a right-skewed distribution that starts at zero. This means that the chi-square statistic will take on only positive values—it can *never be negative*.

There is one similarity between the shape of the *t*-distribution and the shape of the χ^2 distribution: they both depend on a parameter called the **degrees of freedom**, or **df**. For the χ^2 distribution, the smaller the df, the more right-skewed the shape of the χ^2 distribution. Figure 10.4 shows the χ^2 distribution for several different df values. For example, the blue distribution is the chi-square distribution with df = 2. The other distributions have df = 4 (red), df = 8 (green), and df = 16 (purple).

The df parameter is different, depending on what we are testing. However, the value of the df generally depends on the number of categories in the table that summarized the categorical variable(s).

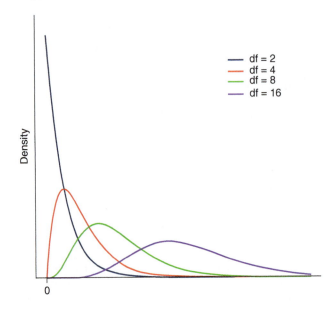

▶ **FIGURE 10.4** Four chi-square distributions with df = 2 (blue), df = 4 (red), df = 8 (green), and df = 16 (purple). Note how the right-skewness in the distribution tends to soften as the df increases. Also note that negative values are not possible, since the smallest possible value is 0.

The χ^2 distribution is only an approximation for the distribution of the chi-square statistic χ^2_{Obs}. The approximation is generally very good if all expected frequencies are 5 or bigger.

> **KEY POINT** The chi-square distribution provides a good approximation of the distribution of the chi-square statistic only if the sample size is large. For many applications, the sample size is large enough if each expected frequency is 5 or bigger.

At the start of this section, we asked whether the value we saw for the chi-square statistic when comparing an ideal die to our real die was big or small. Recall that the value was $\chi^2_{Obs} = 1.0$. As you will see in Section 10.2, df = 5 for this problem. Figure 10.5 shows that 1.0 is not a very big value. Specifically, about 96% of the total area of the chi-square distribution is above 1.0.

We also asked whether the value $\chi^2_{Obs} = 7.40$ was small for the problem of determining whether viewing TV violence was related with abusiveness later in life. We'll answer this question in Section 10.3.

▶ **FIGURE 10.5** A chi-square distribution with 5 degrees of freedom. The shaded area is the area above the value 1.0. This suggests that 1.0 is not a very large value for this distribution; most values are bigger than 1.0.

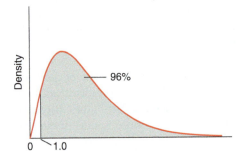

Finding p-Values without Technology

Not all calculators will produce the analyses we're about to show you. Also, not all calculators will let you find probabilities with the chi-square distribution. If you find yourself without technology, you will have to rely on a published table of probabilities, such as Table 5 in Appendix A.

Tables of chi-square probabilities cannot be complete, because there are too many different chi-square distributions (one for each df). The best we can do, then, is to approximate the p-value.

For example, Table 10.11 is from Table 5 in Appendix A and shows only a few "right-tailed" chi-square probabilities for a few different degrees-of-freedom parameters (df = 4, df = 5, and df = 6).

df	0.10	0.05	0.025	0.01	0.005
4	7.78	9.49	11.14	13.28	14.86
5	9.24	**11.07**	12.83	15.09	16.75
6	10.64	12.59	14.45	16.81	18.55

◀ **TABLE 10.11** Selected values of chi-square probabilities.

For example, the table tells us that for a chi-square distribution with 5 degrees of freedom, the probability that we will get a value bigger than 11.07 is 0.05, or 5%. The area under this distribution is illustrated in Figure 10.6.

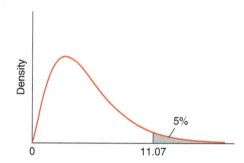

◀ **FIGURE 10.6** The table of chi-square probabilities in Appendix A shows you which values have right-tailed probabilities of 0.10, 0.05, 0.025, 0.01, and 0.005. This figure illustrates that the value 11.07 has a right-tailed probability of 0.05. This means that the probability that the chi-square statistic will be bigger than 11.07 is 0.05.

How can we use Table 5 in Appendix A to find the p-value for our chi-square statistic of 1.0 with 5 degrees of freedom? (This was the chi-square statistic we saw after tossing a die 60 times and comparing the outcomes to the expected frequencies from a fair die.) We can't get the exact p-value, but we can see that the p-value is going to be fairly large. If $\chi^2_{Obs} = 1.0$, we can see from Table 10.11 that this value is smaller than 9.24, the smallest value for the df = 5 row. Because the probabilities get larger as you move to the left, this means that whatever the p-value is, it must be bigger than 0.10. Thus, we can report simply that the p-value is bigger than 0.10, but using this table, we cannot be more precise.

Table 10.11 also tells us that if we plan to reject the null hypothesis whenever the p-value is less than 0.05, then if we have 5 degrees of freedom, we would reject the null hypothesis whenever the chi-square statistic is bigger than (or equal to) 11.07.

SECTION 10.2

The Chi-Square Test for Goodness of Fit

We will now show how the requirements of (1) data observed on a categorical variables, (2) expected frequencies, (3) the chi-square statistic, and (4) the χ^2 distribution can be incorporated into a hypothesis test that determines if the observed frequencies of a categorical variable follow a proposed distribution. This type of test is called a

goodness-of-fit test. Our experiment with the potentially unfair die was a goodness-of-fit test. We had a proposed distribution (each outcome is equally likely and happens with probability $1/6$) and an observed distribution that we got from rolling a real die.

The goodness-of-fit test is a hypothesis test, and it follows the same four-step procedure as the tests we presented in Chapters 8 and 9. It uses the chi-square statistic and is applied when you compare the observed frequency distribution of a categorical variable with the frequency distribution you would expect from its proposed distribution.

Step 1: Hypothesize

The hypotheses for a goodness-of-fit test are always the same:

> H_0: The population distribution of the variable is the same as the proposed distribution.
>
> H_A: H_0 is false. In other words, the population distribution of the variable is different from what is proposed.

For our die-testing example, we state the hypotheses as

> H_0: The die is fair (each side is equally likely to be the top side).
>
> H_A: H_0 is false—the die is not fair (or each side is not equally likely to be the top side).

Step 2: Prepare

We are testing whether the observed frequency distribution in Table 10.1 follows a proposed distribution (that the die is fair, meaning each side of the die will appear as the top side with equal probability). We use the chi-square statistic as the test statistic to compare the observed frequencies with those we would expect if the null hypothesis is true.

Recall that an important feature of a hypothesis test is being able to measure how often our conclusions will be wrong. To do this, we need to know the probability distribution of our test statistic so that we can find the p-value and significance level for our test. Under the following conditions, the chi-square distribution with $k - 1$ degrees of freedom gives good approximations for the p-value and significance level. Here, k is used to represent the number of categories for our variable. In the die example, $k = 6$, so we had $6 - 1 = 5$ degrees of freedom.

Conditions:

1. *Random Sample*. The sample was collected randomly. This condition means that the categorical variable measured on a person/object in the sample is independent of measurements observed on other persons/objects sampled.

2. *Large Sample*. The expected frequency is at least 5 in each cell.

The first condition should not be a surprise, as we have encountered this condition in previous chapters. In order for us to learn about the population, the sample must be representative of the population. The random sampling attempts to satisfy this. In addition, the random sample preserves the condition of independence of observations. This condition would be violated if you randomly sampled married couples and recorded their marriage status. In this case, one spouse's marital status will depend on his or her partner's marital status. Here the population consists of individuals, and not married couples.

The first condition is sometimes difficult to check, particularly when you are reading the summary of survey results in some form of media. In such an instance, you were not present at the time the data were collected. Or you might not have access to the data collection notes that detail how the data were collected. Nevertheless, we often know enough about the data collection to allow us to *assume* that this condition holds.

The second condition can be checked by looking at the data. This condition is another way of saying that a large sample is required. It must be large enough for us to *expect* at least 5 observations in each cell (each category). Note that we don't need to actually get 5 or more observations in each cell. We just need to *expect* 5 or more.

Goodness of Fit

We use the chi-square statistic (Formula 10.2) as a test statistic:

$$\chi^2_{Obs} = \sum_{\text{all cells}} \frac{(\text{Observed} - \text{Expected})^2}{\text{Expected}}$$

If the expected frequencies are large enough, the chi-square distribution with degrees of freedom = (number of categories − 1) is a good approximation for the distribution of χ^2_{Obs}.

To complete the "Prepare" step, you need to calculate the expected frequencies and verify that all are greater than or equal to 5. This can be time-consuming, and we recommend that you use technology.

Another important part of the "Prepare" step is to choose a significance level. This is nearly always chosen to be 0.05, but you are allowed to choose any small probability, as long as you state it clearly.

Step 3: Compute to compare

The chi-square statistic compares what we observed to what we should expect to happen. Calculating the value of this statistic is best done with technology, although for tables with only a few cells, it is not too tedious to do it by hand. Once we have the observed value of the chi-square statistic, we compute the p-value, which measures whether we should be surprised by how large the chi-square statistic is (if the null hypothesis is true).

The p-value is the probability that, if the null hypothesis is true, another sample will produce a statistic that is just as surprising as the value of the statistic produced by our sample. In the context of a goodness-of-fit test, it is the probability of observing the value of the chi-square test statistic that is just as big, or bigger, than the one we observed (χ^2_{Obs}). In other words, the p-value is the area to the right of χ^2_{Obs} under the appropriate χ^2 distribution. Figure 10.5 is an example of this. The shaded area represents the p-value for our die-rolling experiment. If the die really is fair (so that each outcome is equally likely), then the probability of getting a chi-square statistic as big as or bigger than 1.0 is about 96%.

Step 4: Interpret and conclude

The p-value of 96% means that if the die is fair (or the null hypothesis is true), there is a 0.96 probability that another experiment consisting of 60 rolls will produce an outcome that is just as big or bigger than $\chi^2_{Obs} = 1.0$. If this p-value is less than or equal to the significance level, α (alpha), then we reject the null hypothesis. If the p-value is larger than α, then we do not reject the null hypothesis. We can conclude from these data that the die is fair.

EXAMPLE 3 Global Climate Change

Table 10.12 shows the distribution of people (by region) of 1496 Canadians who responded "Yes" to the July 2013 Forum Research poll question "As far as you know, is Earth's climate changing?" (www.forumresearch.ca). The distribution is shown in Figure 10.7 on the next page.

TECH

Region	Observed Frequency	Expected Frequency
Maritimes/Atlantic Canada	141	104.89
Quebec	362	354.40
Ontario	549	575.70
Manitoba/Saskatchewan	107	101.24
Alberta/Territories	142	163.01
British Columbia	195	196.76

◄ TABLE 10.12 The observed number of Canadians who believe in climate change in each region, along with the frequency we would expect if this distribution is the same as that of the general population in these regions.

> **⚠ Caution**
>
> **Frequencies, Not Proportions**
> Sometimes, two-way tables present proportions (or percentages), not frequencies. Before carrying out these tests, you will need to convert the proportions to frequencies (if possible).

▶ **FIGURE 10.7** Distribution of believers in global climate change by region.

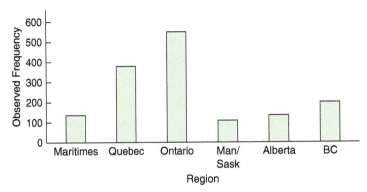

▶ **FIGURE 10.7** Distribution of believers in global climate change by region.

Do people in some regions believe more in global climate change than people in other regions? The Expected Frequency column shows the number of people we would expect from each region to believe in global climate change from the national sample of 1496 people. (For example, since 38.48% of the Canadian population lives in Ontario, we would expect 38.48% of the 1496 believers to live in Ontario, so the expected frequency for Ontario is $0.3848 \times 1496 = 575.7$, as seen in the table.) If these two distributions are the same, then the distribution of people in all regions of Canada who believe in global climate change is the same as the distribution of the general population among the different regions.

QUESTION Test whether the observed distribution of climate change believers fits the distribution of the Canadian population (shown in Table 10.12), using a significance level of 0.05.

SOLUTION The *Region* variable has six categories. Overall, there were 1496 people believing in climate change.

Step 1: Hypothesize

H_0: The distribution of people believing in climate change follows that of the Canadian population.

H_A: H_0 is false—the distribution of people believing in climate change does not follow that of the Canadian population.

Step 2: Prepare
We have one random sample of independent observations (or we assume so) and are measuring one categorical variable (*Region*) to see if it follows a proposed distribution, so we use the chi-square goodness-of-fit test to compare the distribution of believers in climate change to the distribution of the Canadian population, or the proposed distribution. The smallest expected frequency is 101.24, which is more than the required "at least 5," so we can use the chi-square distribution to approximate the p-value.

Step 3: Compute to compare
Figure 10.8 shows both the data as entered in StatCrunch and the output from the goodness-of-fit test. StatCrunch, like many other software packages, requires that you give it a column of observed frequencies and a different column of expected frequencies.

We see that the observed value of the chi-square test statistic is $\chi^2_{Obs} = 16.90$. This is a large value, larger than we would expect to observe if the null hypothesis is true. The small p-value of 0.0047 demonstrates this fact.

Step 4: Interpret and conclude
The p-value of 0.0047 means that if the null hypothesis is true, and the distribution of climate change believers among the regions of Canada is the same as the distribution of the general population among regions, the probability that another random sample of 1496 climate change believers will provide an outcome that is as surprising as the outcome we observed is 0.0047, or about 5 times in 1000. This is not likely to happen if the null hypothesis is true.

Looking Back

p-Value
Recall that the p-value is the probability of getting a test statistic as extreme as or more extreme than what was observed, assuming that the null hypothesis is true. For the chi-square statistic, "as extreme as or more extreme than" means "as big as or bigger than."

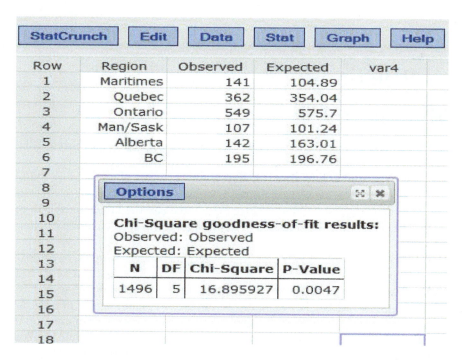

◀ **FIGURE 10.8** Data and the StatCrunch output from the goodness-of-fit test.

In closing, since the p-value of 0.0047 is less than 0.05, the null hypothesis is rejected. We can infer from these data that the distribution of climate change believers among the regions of Canada is *not the same* as the distribution of the general population among regions.

CONCLUSION The data from the sample suggest that Canadians who believe in climate change are distributed among the regions differently from the general population.

TRY THIS! Exercise 10.21

SNAPSHOT   **CHI-SQUARE TEST OF GOODNESS-OF-FIT**

WHAT IS IT? ▶ A test applied to data observed on one categorical variable.

WHAT DOES IT DO? ▶ It compares the observed frequencies with the frequencies that would be expected if the proposed distribution is the true distribution.

HOW DOES IT DO IT? ▶ If the sample size is large enough so that the conditions hold, then the chi-square statistic follows a chi-square distribution with df = (number of categories − 1). If there is not much difference between the observed and the expected frequencies, then the chi-square statistic will be small and the p-value will be large, supporting the null hypothesis. If the difference between what is observed and expected is remarkable, the chi-square statistic will be large and the p-value will be small, leading to a rejection of the null hypothesis.

HOW IS IT USED? ▶ The value of the chi-square statistic is computed using Formula 10.2. From this, the region above the chi-square statistic in the chi-square distribution is found. Its area represents the p-value.

WHEN IS IT USED? ▶ To see whether a sample of data collected on a single categorical variable follow a proposed distribution.

SECTION 10.3

Chi-Square Tests for Relationships Between Two Categorical Variables

There are two tests to investigate whether two categorical variables are related. Which test you will use depends on how the data were collected.

Example 2 showed us how data collected on two categorical variables are summarized in a two-way table. The reason for this is to help us identify if there is a relationship between these variables. Often we take for granted *how* the summarized data were collected. Data that can be summarized in a two-way table can be collected in one of two ways.

The first way is to collect two or more distinct independent samples, one from each population. Each object inspected is assigned a categorical value that keeps track of which sample, or group, it is from. Then, each object is measured with respect to a different categorical variable. For example, we can take a random sample of men and another random sample of women. We then ask them to provide their opinion on the extent to which they agree with the statement that same-sex couples should be allowed to marry legally: Yes, No with exceptions, No with no exceptions, or Unsure (see Example 1). The first categorical variable simply distinguishes which sample a person is from, the "male" or "female" sample, a variable we will call *Gender*. The second categorical variable is the response given by a person sampled with his/her opinion on the same-sex marriage matter, a variable we will call *Opinion*. Hence we have two samples and two categorical variables: *Gender* and *Opinion*. The *Gender* variable *distinguishes* which group a sampled person is from, and the *Opinion* variable *measures* the response.

The second way is to collect just one sample. For each object sampled, we measure two different categorical variables. For example, we may collect a large sample of people and measure their marital status (single, common-law, married, divorced, or widowed) and their highest level of education completed (high school, college/technical school, university, graduate school). From this one sample, we get responses on two categorical variables: *Marital Status* and *Highest Education Level*.

From either of these data collection methods, we are to investigate if there is a relationship between the two categorical variables. But because the data collection methods differ—at least two samples compared to one sample—the methods we use to complete our relationship investigation will also differ. Not to worry, though, since the *methodology is the same*: we compute the same chi-square test statistic, then use the same chi-square distribution and df to find the p-value, then make a decision that addresses the relational aspect of the two variables.

To distinguish these two methods, we call them different names. If we test a relationship based on two (or more) independent samples—a relationship between the categorical grouping variable and the categorical response variable—the method is called a test of **homogeneity**. A test of homogeneity amounts to testing whether the proportion of individuals in each category is the same for each of the groups sampled. If we test the existence of a relationship based on one sample, the method is called a test of **independence**. Two different data collection methods with two different names—but the same test!

> 📋 **Details**
>
> **Homogeneity**
> The word *homogeneity* is based on the word *homogeneous*, which means "of the same, or similar, kind or nature."

> **KEY POINT**
> There are two tests to determine whether two categorical variables are related. For two or more samples and one categorical response variable, we use a test of homogeneity. For one sample and two categorical response variables, we use a test of independence.

EXAMPLE **4** Independence or Homogeneity?

In 2014, comScore, a communications research firm, conducted a market research study to determine which type of smartphone dominates the Canadian smartphone market. Among Canadians who have a smartphone, Android was found to be the most popular, with 45% of the market share. comScore wants to repeat its market research study this year to determine whether Android still has the highest market share among smartphone users. Specifically, the firm wants to know whether there has been a change in Canadians' smartphone preferences from 2014 to the present and it plans to carry out a formal hypothesis test to see whether a relationship exists between the variables *Year* and *Own an Android*.

QUESTION Will this be a test of independence or a test of homogeneity?

SOLUTION comScore took two distinct samples: Canadians who have a smartphone in 2014 and those who currently have a smartphone. The variable *Year* tells us which group a respondent belongs to. There is one response taken from each Canadian: *Own an Android*. This is a categorical variable (Yes, No). This investigation has two samples and one response variable, and is therefore a test of homogeneity.

TRY THIS! Exercise 10.29

EXAMPLE **5** Independence or Homogeneity?

The Canadian Firearms Registry was introduced in 1993. Managed by the RCMP, it required people to register all their guns. Anecdotally, public support for this registry seemed to be very regional—strong support for it in Central Canada and very little support for it in Western Canada. Suppose we wanted to take a random sample of 1000 Canadians to determine if someone's support-level of the gun registry was related to the region of the country he/she resided. Each Canadian would be asked (a) Which region of the country do you live in? (Maritimes, Quebec, Ontario, Man/Sask, Alberta, BC, Territories), and (b) Do you support the Canadian Firearms Registry? (1—support, 2—neither support nor oppose, 3—do not support).

QUESTION Will this be a test of independence or a test of homogeneity?

SOLUTION Here one sample is to be taken, consisting of 1000 people. Each person is asked two questions, so there are outcomes on two different categorical variables: *Region* and *Level of Support*. This is a test of independence.

TRY THIS! Exercise 10.31

Tests of Independence and Homogeneity

Again, the tests follow the four-step procedure of all hypothesis tests. We'll give you an overview and then fill in the details with an example.

Step 1: Hypothesize
The hypotheses of both tests are the same:

   H_0: There is no relationship between the two categorical variables.

   H_A: There is a relationship between the two categorical variables.

Although the hypotheses are always the same, you should phrase these hypotheses in the context of the problem.

Step 2: Prepare

Whether you are testing independence or homogeneity, the test statistic you should use to compare frequencies is the chi-square statistic, shown in Formula 10.2 and repeated here.

$$\chi^2_{Obs} = \sum_{\text{all cells}} \frac{(\text{Observed} - \text{Expected})^2}{\text{Expected}}$$

If the conditions are right, then this statistic follows, approximately, a chi-square distribution with

$$df = (\text{number of rows} - 1)(\text{number of columns} - 1)$$

Conditions:

1. *Random Sample.* The sample was collected randomly. This condition means that the categorical variable measured on a person/object in the sample is independent of all other measurements in the sample.

2. *Large Sample.* The expected frequency is at least 5 in each cell.

Note that in a test of independence, there is always only one sample. But a test of homogeneity might have several independent samples.

Step 3: Compute to compare

This step is best done with technology. The p-value is the probability, assuming the null hypothesis is true, of getting a value as large as or larger than the observed chi-square statistic. In other words, the p-value is the probability, if the variables really are not related, that we would see an outcome as large or larger than the one observed. A small p-value therefore means a large test statistic, which casts doubt on the hypothesis that the variables are not related.

Step 4: Interpret and conclude

If the p-value is less than or equal to the stated significance level, we reject the null hypothesis and conclude that the variables are related.

EXAMPLE **6** Education and Marital Status

Is a person's level of education related to their marital status? From the Statistics Canada General Social Survey (GSS) conducted in 2011, we took a random sample of 924 adults (aged 18 and older), measuring the marital status of each (married, common-law, divorced, widowed, single) and their highest level of completed education (high school, college/technical school, university, graduate school). Figure 10.9 shows the output from StatCrunch.

QUESTION Is this a test of homogeneity or independence? Use the output provided to test whether marital status and highest education level completed are related.

SOLUTION Because there is one sample with two different response variables, this is a test of independence.

Step 1: Hypothesize

H₀: Among all Canadian adults, marital status and highest education level completed are not related (or are independent).

Hₐ: Among all Canadian adults, marital status and highest education level completed are related.

Step 2: Prepare

From the output we can see that all the expected frequencies are 5 or more (the smallest being 7). This means that we can use the chi-square distribution to approximate the p-value. The observed frequencies, along with the expected frequencies from a random sample of 924 adults, are displayed in Figure 10.9.

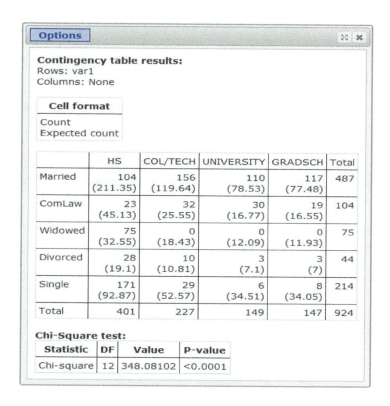

Contingency table results:
Rows: var1
Columns: None

Cell format

Count
Expected count

	HS	COL/TECH	UNIVERSITY	GRADSCH	Total
Married	104 (211.35)	156 (119.64)	110 (78.53)	117 (77.48)	487
ComLaw	23 (45.13)	32 (25.55)	30 (16.77)	19 (16.55)	104
Widowed	75 (32.55)	0 (18.43)	0 (12.09)	0 (11.93)	75
Divorced	28 (19.1)	10 (10.81)	3 (7.1)	3 (7)	44
Single	171 (92.87)	29 (52.57)	6 (34.51)	8 (34.05)	214
Total	401	227	149	147	924

Chi-Square test:

Statistic	DF	Value	P-value
Chi-square	12	348.08102	<0.0001

TECH

◄ **FIGURE 10.9** Two-way table with expected frequencies below each observed frequency, value of the chi-square statistic, and p-value to test whether marital status and highest education level completed are related.

Step 3: Compute to compare

The value of the chi-square statistic is $\chi^2_{Obs} = 348.08$ (rounded to two decimal digits). The chi-square distribution has 12 degrees of freedom:

$$\text{df} = (\text{number of rows} - 1)(\text{number of columns} - 1) = (5 - 1)(4 - 1) = 12$$

and the p-value is reported to be smaller than 0.0001 (< 0.0001).

Step 4: Interpret and conclude

A p-value that is less than 0.0001 says that if one's marital status and highest level of completed education were not related (the null hypothesis is true), then there is a less than 0.0001 probability that another random sample of 924 Canadians would give a chi-square statistic value that is at least as large as 348.08. That is, it is very unlikely that another sample will provide stronger statistical evidence against the null hypothesis than our sample.

Because the p-value is less than 0.05, we reject the null hypothesis. We can infer from these data that there is a relationship between a person's marital status and his or her highest level of education completed. These two variables are not independent.

TRY THIS! Exercise 10.35

EXAMPLE 7 Hungry Monkeys

Research in the past has suggested that mice and rats that are fed less food live longer and healthier lives. More recently, a study of rhesus monkeys was done that involved caloric restriction (less food). It is believed that monkeys have many similarities to humans, which is what makes this study so interesting.

Seventy-six rhesus monkeys, all young adults, were randomly divided into two groups. Half of the monkeys (38) were assigned to caloric restriction. Their food was decreased about 10% per month for three months, and as a result they were fed about 30% less food than the other 38 monkeys for the duration of the experiment.

For those on the normal diet, 14 out of 38 had died of age-related causes by the time the article was written. For those on caloric restriction, only 5 out of 38 had died of age-related causes (Colman et al. 2009).

Details

Random Assignment
Experiments that randomly assign subjects to treatment groups result in distinct, independent samples, so if other conditions are satisfied, they can be analyzed with tests of homogeneity.

QUESTION Because this is a randomized study, the hypothesis that diet is related to aging can be stated as a cause-and-effect hypothesis. Therefore, test the hypothesis that diet causes differences in aging. Will this be a test of homogeneity or of independence? The Minitab output is shown in Figure 10.10.

▶ **FIGURE 10.10** Minitab output showing *Diet* (normal or caloric) and *Aging* (died from age-related causes or not) for 76 monkeys.

Chi-Square Test: normal diet, caloric Restriction

Expected counts are printed below observed counts
Chi-Square contributions are printed below expected counts

	Normal Diet	Caloric Restriction	Total
Died	14	5	19
	9.50	9.50	
	2.132	2.132	
Not	24	33	57
	28.50	28.50	
	0.711	0.711	
Total	38	38	76

Chi-Sq = 5.684, DF = 1, P-Value = 0.017

SOLUTION There are two samples (monkeys with caloric restriction and monkeys without) and one outcome variable: whether the monkey died of age-related causes. Therefore, this is a test of homogeneity.

Step 1: Hypothesize

H_0: For these monkeys, the amount of calories in the diet is not related to aging.

H_A: For these monkeys, the amount of calories in the diet causes differences in aging. Because we do not have a random sample, our results do not generalize beyond this group of monkeys. But because we have randomized assignment to treatment groups, we are able to conclude that any differences we see in the aging process are caused by the diet.

Looking Back

Comparing Two Proportions
In Chapter 8, you learned to test two population proportions based on data from independent samples using the *z*-test. The test of diet in monkeys could have been done using this test. The chi-square test provides an alternative, but equivalent, approach.

Step 2: Prepare
Because we wish to use the chi-square test, we must confirm that the expected counts are all 5 or more. This is the case here, as Figure 10.10 confirms.

Step 3: Compute to compare
From the Minitab output in Figure 10.10, you can see that the chi-square value is 5.68 and the p-value is 0.017.

Step 4: Interpret and conclude

A p-value of 0.017 says that if a monkey's caloric intake and death due to age-related causes were not related (the null hypothesis is true), then there is a less than 1.7% chance that another randomized experiment of 76 rhesus monkeys would give a chi-square statistic value that is at least as large as 5.684. That is, it is not likely that another sample will provide stronger statistical evidence against the null hypothesis than our sample.

CONCLUSION Because the p-value is less than 0.05, we reject the null hypothesis. The proportion of monkeys who have died is not the same in both groups. We can infer from these data that the monkeys' deaths from age-related causes were caused by differences in the number of calories in the diet.

TRY THIS! Exercise 10.41

The article contains other information that suggests that monkeys on a restricted diet are generally healthier than monkeys on a normal diet. Figure 10.11 shows a photo of two monkeys. The one on the right had the restricted diet and shows fewer characteristics of old age.

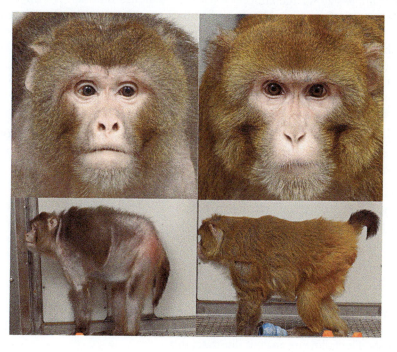

◄ FIGURE 10.11 The healthier monkey (on the right) was one of those on caloric restriction.

Random Samples and Randomized Assignment

You have now seen randomization used in two different ways. Random sampling is the practice of randomly selecting objects from the population, a practice commonly used in many surveys. From such a sample, we can make generalizations about the population. Random selection of the sample must occur to ensure that the sample is representative of the population. The General Social Survey (GSS) mentioned in Example 6 is an example of a study based on random sampling. We inferred from this sample that for all Canadians, a person's marital status and their highest level of completed education are related. Our concluding statement in Example 6 addresses the *entire* population of Canadians, extending the statistical analysis of 924 *randomly chosen* adult Canadians and projecting its findings onto a population of approximately 28 million adult Canadians.

In Example 7, on the other hand, there was no random sample. However, the monkeys were randomly assigned to a treatment group (low-calorie diet) or the control group (normal diet). Because the monkeys were not selected randomly, we have no means of generalizing about the population as a whole, statistically speaking. (There might be a biological argument, or an assumption, that a diet that works on

 **Looking Back**

Data Collection
Controlled experiments are those in which experimenters determine how subjects are assigned to treatment groups. In contrast, observational studies are those in which subjects place themselves into treatment groups, by behaviour or innate characteristics such as gender. Causal conclusions cannot be based on a single observational study.

one group of monkeys would work on any other group, but as statisticians, we have no data to support this assumption.) However, the researchers performed this study because they were interested in a cause-and-effect relationship: Does changing the calories in a monkey's diet change the monkey's health and longevity?

Because researchers controlled which monkeys got which diet, this is a controlled experiment. And because they used randomized assignment, and because we rejected the null hypothesis that diet and health were independent, we can conclude that in fact the caloric restriction *did* affect the monkeys' health.

SNAPSHOT   CHI-SQUARE TEST OF INDEPENDENCE OR HOMOGENEITY

WHAT IS IT? ▶ A test applied to data observed on two different categorical variables.

WHAT DOES IT DO? ▶ It compares the observed frequencies in each outcome category with the frequencies that would be expected if the two variables *are not related*.

HOW DOES IT DO IT? ▶ If the sample size is large enough so that the conditions hold, then the chi-square statistic follows a chi-square distribution with df = (number of rows − 1) × (number of columns − 1). In each outcome category, if there is not much difference between the observed and the expected frequencies, then the chi-square statistic will be small and the p-value will be large, supporting the null hypothesis. If the difference between what is observed and expected is remarkable, the chi-square statistic will be large and the p-value will be small, leading to a rejection of the null hypothesis.

HOW IS IT USED? ▶ The value of the chi-square statistic is computed using Formula 10.2. From this, the region above the chi-square statistic in the chi-square distribution is found. This area represents the p-value.

WHEN IS IT USED? ▶ To either compare proportions in two or more sampled populations (homogeneity) or to test whether two categorical variables are independent (independence).

Relation to Tests of Proportions

In the special case in which both categorical variables have only two categories, the test of homogeneity is identical to a *z*-test of two proportions, using a two-tailed alternative hypothesis. The following analysis illustrates this.

In a landmark study of a potential AIDS vaccine published in 2009, researchers from the U.S. Army and the Thai Ministry of Health randomly assigned about 8200 volunteers to receive a vaccine against AIDS and another 8200 to receive a placebo. (We rounded the numbers slightly to make this discussion easier.) Both groups received counselling on AIDS prevention measures and were promised lifetime treatment should they contract AIDS. Of those who received the vaccine, 51 had AIDS at the end of the study (three years later). Of those who received the placebo, 74 had AIDS (http://www.hivresearch.org, accessed September 29, 2009). We will show two ways of testing whether a relationship existed between receiving the vaccine and getting AIDS. The data are summarized in Table 10.13.

▶ **TABLE 10.13** Effect of the vaccine on AIDS.

	Vaccine	No Vaccine	Total
AIDS	51	74	125
No AIDS	8149	8126	16,275
Total	8200	8200	16,400

If we use the approach of this chapter, we would recognize that this is a test of homogeneity, because there are two samples (*Vaccine* and *Placebo*) and one response variable (*AIDS*). Although we cannot generalize to a larger population (because the volunteers were not randomly selected), we can make a cause-and-effect conclusion about whether differences in AIDS rates are due to the vaccine, because this is a controlled, randomized study.

As a first step, we calculate the expected frequencies, under the assumption that the two variables are not related.

Because the proportion of those who got AIDS was $125/16{,}400 = 0.007622$, if the risk of getting AIDS had nothing to do with the vaccine, then we should see about the same proportion of those getting AIDS in both groups. If the proportion of people who got AIDS in the *Vaccine* group was 0.007622, then we would expect $8200 \times 0.007622 = 62.5$ people to get AIDS in the *Vaccine* group.

Both groups are the same size, so we would expect the same number of AIDS victims in the *Placebo* group. This means that in both groups, we would expect $8200 - 62.5 = 8137.5$ not to get AIDS.

The results, with expected frequencies in parentheses to the right of the observed frequencies, are shown in Table 10.14.

	Vaccine	No Vaccine	Total
AIDS	51 (62.5)	74 (62.5)	125
No AIDS	8149 (8137.5)	8126 (8137.5)	16,275
Total	8200	8200	16,400

◀ **TABLE 10.14** Expected frequencies, assuming no relationship between variables, are shown in parentheses.

Note that all expected frequencies are much greater than 5.

The chi-square statistic is not difficult to calculate:

$$\chi^2_{Obs} = \sum_{\text{all cells}} \frac{(\text{Observed} - \text{Expected})^2}{\text{Expected}}$$

$$= \frac{(51 - 62.5)^2}{62.5} + \frac{(74 - 62.5)^2}{62.5} + \frac{(8149 - 8137.5)^2}{8137.5} + \frac{(8126 - 8137.5)^2}{8137.5}$$

$$= 4.26$$

The degrees of freedom of the corresponding chi-square distribution are calculated as

$$(\text{Number of rows} - 1)(\text{number of columns} - 1) = (2 - 1)(2 - 1) = 1 \times 1 = 1$$

The p-value is illustrated in Figure 10.12. It is the area under a chi-square distribution with 1 degree of freedom and to the right of 4.26. The p-value turns out to be 0.039. We therefore reject the null hypothesis and conclude that there is a relationship between getting the vaccination and contracting AIDS. The difference in the numbers of AIDS victims was caused by the vaccine.

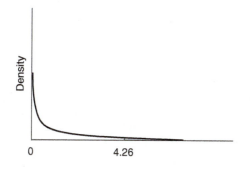

◀ **FIGURE 10.12** The area to the right of 4.26 represents the p-value to test whether there is a relationship between receiving the AIDS vaccine and contracting AIDS. The distribution is a chi-square distribution with 1 degree of freedom. The p-value is 0.039.

One thing that's disappointing about this conclusion is that the alternative hypothesis states only that the variables are related. That's nice, but what we really want to know is *how* they are related. Did the vaccine decrease the number of people who got AIDS? That's what the researchers wanted to know. They didn't want to know merely whether there was a relationship. They had a very specific direction in mind for this relation.

One drawback with chi-square tests is that they reveal only whether two variables are related, not how they are related. Fortunately, when both categorical variables have only two categories, we can instead do a two-proportion z-test.

Define p_1 to be the probability that someone given the vaccine will get AIDS, and define p_2 to be the probability that someone given the placebo will get AIDS. Then

Step 1: Hypothesize

H_0: $p_1 = p_2$
H_A: $p_1 < p_2$

In words, the null hypothesis says that the probability of getting AIDS is the same whether or not the individual gets the vaccine. The alternative hypothesis is one-tailed: if the individual gets the vaccine, the probability of contracting AIDS is less than if she or he got the placebo.

Step 2: Prepare

We plan to use the z-test for two independent proportions. Under the null hypothesis, the probability of getting AIDS is the same for both groups, and we estimate this probability with

$$\hat{p} = \frac{(51 + 74)}{16400} = 0.007622$$

(This is the same proportion we calculated above.)

We must check that both samples are large enough—both expected values must be bigger than 10. This is straightforward, because both samples are the same size:

$$8200 \times 0.007622 = 62.5$$

This means that we can use the standard Normal distribution (with mean 0 and standard deviation 1) to approximate the p-value.

Step 3: Calculate to compare

The observed value of the z-statistic is (Formula 8.2)

$$z = \frac{\hat{p}_1 - \hat{p}_2}{\sqrt{\hat{p}\left(1 - \hat{p}\right)\left(\frac{1}{n_1} + \frac{1}{n_2}\right)}}$$

Note that $\hat{p}_1 = 51/8200$, $\hat{p}_2 = 74/8200$, and both n_1 and n_2 are equal to 8200. Substituting, we get

$$z = -2.065068, \text{ or about } -2.07$$

It is no coincidence that if you square this value, you get the same value as our chi-square statistic. Recall that $\chi^2_{Obs} = 4.26$ and

$$z^2 = (-2.065068)^2 = 4.26$$

For the p-value, we find the area under the $N(0, 1)$ curve below -2.06. This probability is 0.0194582, or about 0.019.

Step 4: Interpret and conclude

The p-value of 0.019 means the following: if another experiment were performed where 16,400 people were equally divided into a vaccine and no-vaccine group, the probability that the statistical evidence from this experiment would be stronger against the null hypothesis than the current evidence is 0.019. Our current sample gives statistical evidence of $\chi^2_{Obs} = 4.26$; any value at least as big as 4.26 will give a small p-value, and therefore more evidence against the null hypothesis than we have. Because this was a randomized, controlled study, we can conclude that the vaccine caused a decrease in the probability of people getting AIDS.

Note that if we had doubled the p-value—that is, if we had instead used a two-tailed alternative hypothesis—we would have gotten $2 \times 0.019458 = 0.039$, almost exactly what we got for the chi-square test.

Although medical researchers were very excited about this study—not too many years before, it was thought to be impossible to develop an AIDS vaccine—they caution that this vaccine lowers risk by only about 30%. Many medical professionals consider a vaccine to be useful only if it lowers risk by at least 60%. There was also some controversy over this study: some argued that a few of the subjects who were dropped from the initial analysis (because of pre-existing medical conditions) should have been included. If these subjects had been included, then the vaccine would no longer have been judged effective, statistically speaking.

> **KEY POINT** For a 2-by-2 two-way table of frequencies, a two-proportion z-test with a two-tailed alternative is equivalent to a test of homogeneity.

When should you use the two proportion z-test, and when should you use the test for homogeneity? If you need to use a one-tailed alternative hypothesis, then you should use the z-test. However, if you plan to use a two-tailed alternative hypothesis, then it doesn't matter which test you use.

SECTION 10.4

Hypothesis Tests When Sample Sizes Are Small

We demonstrate two approaches for dealing with data in which the expected values are less than 5. One approach is to combine categories so that each of the new, larger categories has an expected frequency of 5 or more. The other approach is to use Fisher's Exact Test. Unlike the chi-square approach, which gives us approximate p-values, Fisher's Exact Test gives the actual p-value.

Combining Categories

The next example illustrates how to combine categories with small expected counts so that you can do a chi-square test.

 EXAMPLE 8 Gender and Method of Transportation

We encountered an example in Chapter 5 where 107 students taking an introductory statistics course—similar to the one you are taking—were randomly sampled. The students were asked their gender and the most common method of transportation they use to get to class. Table 10.15 shows the two-way table that summarized the data collected on *Gender* and *Most Common Method of Transportation*.

Gender	Most Common Method of Transportation					
	Drive Alone	Carpool	Transit	Walk	Bicycle	Total
Male	19	0	25	3	0	47
Female	22	6	25	5	2	60
Total	41	6	50	8	2	107

◀ **TABLE 10.15** Summary of the common methods of transportation, by gender, for a sample of 107 students from an introductory statistics course.

QUESTION Test the hypothesis that the type of transportation method most commonly used by students to get to class is related to their gender, using a significance level of 0.05. Use the Minitab output provided in Figure 10.13.

SOLUTION This is a test of independence. There is one sample, and two response categorical variables (*Gender* and *Most Common Method of Transportation*) are measured.

Step 1: Hypothesize

H_0: Among all students taking introductory statistics, the type of transportation method most commonly used is not related to (is independent of) their gender.

H_A: Among all students taking introductory statistics, the type of transportation method most commonly used is related to (not independent of) their gender.

Step 2: Prepare

We use the chi-square test of independence, since we assume the null hypothesis of independence between these two variables to be true. The problem we encounter here is that many of the expected frequencies are less than 5. Minitab even alerts us to this problem. We have highlighted these warnings in red for emphasis.

► FIGURE 10.13 Minitab output of the chi-square test of independence between *Gender* and *Most Common Method of Transportation*.

```
Chi-Square Test: DriveAlone, Carpool, Transit, Walk, Bicycle

Expected counts are printed below observed counts
Chi-Square contributions are printed below expected counts

          DriveAlone  Carpool  Transit   Walk  Bicycle  Total
   M            19        0       25       3        0      47
              18.01     2.64    21.96    3.51     0.88
              0.054    2.636    0.420   0.075    0.879

   F            22        6       25       5        2      60
              22.99     3.36    28.04    4.49     1.12
              0.043    2.064    0.329   0.059    0.688

Total          41        6       50       8        2     107

Chi-Sq = 7.247, DF = 4
WARNING: 1 cells with expected counts less than 1. Chi-Square approximation
```

Our solution, which can be a somewhat unsatisfying, is to combine categories so that each expected frequency is 5 or more. For example, you can see that when we combine the Carpool, Walk, and Bicycle categories, we get a new category that we call "Other." The expected frequency of this category is 2.64 + 3.51 + 0.88 = 7.03 males. We can also see that the expected number of females who fall into this Other category is 3.36 + 4.49 + 1.12 = 8.97.

We re-apply the chi-square test of independence using the observed frequencies of the three categories of *Most Common Method of Transportation*. The result is shown in Figure 10.14. We see from the Minitab output that all the expected frequencies are at least 5 and that the chi-square distribution can be used to approximate the p-value.

► FIGURE 10.14 Minitab output with groups combined so that all expected frequencies are 5 or bigger. "M" means the person was male, and "F" means the person was female.

```
Chi-Square Test: DriveAlone, Transit, Other

Expected counts are printed below observed counts
Chi-Square contributions are printed below expected counts

          DriveAlone  Transit  Other  Total
   M            19        25      3      47
              18.01     21.96   7.03
              0.054     0.420  2.309

   F            22        25     13      60
              22.99     28.04   8.97
              0.043     0.329  1.808

Total          41        50     16     107

Chi-Sq = 4.963, DF = 2, P-Value = 0.084
```

Step 3: Compute to compare
$\chi^2_{Obs} = 4.963$ (displayed in the output as Chi-sq = 4.963), df = $(2 - 1) \times (3 - 1) = 2$, and p-value = 0.084

Step 4: Interpret and conclude
The p-value of 0.084 indicates that if we were to randomly select 107 students from an introductory statistics class and observe the *Gender* and *Most Common Method of Transportation* of each, there is an 0.084 probability of this sample providing greater evidence against the null hypothesis in the form of a chi-square test statistic that is bigger than 4.963.

With this p-value not being smaller than 0.05, we do not reject the null hypothesis.

CONCLUSION We conclude from these data that a student's *Most Common Method of Transportation* is not related, or is independent of, their *Gender*.

TRY THIS! Exercise 10.51

Advantages and Disadvantages of Combining Categories

The advantage of combining categories is that it allows you to use the chi-square distribution to find a p-value, from which you can determine if a relationship exists between two categorical variables. If categories are not combined, the application of the chi-square distribution to find the p-value would give an inaccurate p-value, which may lead to an incorrect decision. In Example 8, if we did not combine classes, the output in Figure 10.13 would have given a p-value of 0.1234. We would have drawn the same conclusion, but this larger p-value would have indicated stronger evidence to support the hypothesis of independence between *Gender* and *Most Common Method of Transportation*.

The disadvantage is that we have less knowledge about the relationship. Collapsing the carpooling, walking, and biking categories together is not good practice, as carpooling is of course distinct from walking and bicycling.

Fisher's Exact Test

Another approach that works in some cases is Fisher's Exact Test. This test is called exact because in many situations we can find the exact p-value, not the approximate p-value found by the chi-square test.

Fisher's Exact Test depends on the idea that if the null hypothesis of no relationship between the two variables is true, then a two-way table of the data will be one where the column and row totals are fixed, but the observed frequencies within the table were determined by chance. These observed frequencies can then be any numbers, as long as they add up to the row and column totals. By mixing up these values at random, you can simulate the distribution for the null hypothesis.

To illustrate this approach, consider an example based on an actual study of the effectiveness of an experimental antivenom for scorpion stings in children (Boyer et al. 2009). The researchers randomly assigned 8 children suffering from scorpion stings to receive the antivenom, and 7 to receive a placebo. After several hours, they recorded which children showed substantial improvement. (The sting is not fatal, and the antivenom was not known to be a successful treatment.) The data are given in Table 10.16.

	Antivenom	Placebo	Total
No Improvement	1	6	7
Improvement	7	1	8
Total	8	7	15

◀ TABLE 10.16 Summary of data on children with scorpion bites.

The expected frequencies are too small for us to use the chi-square test. Besides that, the chi-square test can tell us only whether there is a relationship between the two variables. Here we want to know more—we want to know whether the antivenom group did better than the placebo group.

On the face of it, it looks like the antivenom group did in fact do better: 7 out of 8 children improved, as opposed to only 1 out of 7 who received the placebo. But could this difference be due to chance?

Note that it would have been possible to make an even stronger case for the antivenom if all the children who received it had improved. To see what this would look like, in the cell where "Improvement and Antivenom" intersect, we replace the 7 with an 8. This means changing all the other cells in order to keep the row and column totals the same. Table 10.17 shows this change.

► **TABLE 10.17** A hypothetical outcome even more extreme than the actual outcome and with the same marginal totals as in Table 10.16.

	Antivenom	Placebo	Total
No Improvement	0	7	7
Improvement	8	0	8
Total	8	7	15

If, instead, we had seen only 6 improvements in the antivenom group, this would have meant weaker support for the antivenom, because a lower proportion of children receiving the treatment would have recovered.

Now imagine that these cases are assigned to the table at random. The only restriction is that you always need 8 cases in the Antivenom column, 7 cases in the Placebo column, 7 cases in the No Improvement row, and 8 cases in the Improvement row. Maybe you throw darts or (more practically) use a computer to randomly assign cases to categories. After doing this many times, you'll see what the distribution of frequencies looks like when the null hypothesis is true and there is no relationship between variables.

To calculate an approximate p-value (the probability of getting a result as extreme as or more extreme than what we observed when the variables are not related), we use this generated distribution to calculate the approximate probability of getting the observed number of "Improved and Antivenom," or greater. In fact, we don't even need to use a computer simulation. A mathematical approach can provide an exact answer. (This is why it's called Fishers *Exact* Test!) These probabilities are found using a distribution called the hypergeometric function. Many software packages and on-line statistical calculators will find these probabilities for you. For example, to find the p-value using the SOCR website, we input the observed table, as in Figure 10.15.

► **FIGURE 10.15** Data input for SOCR's Fisher's Exact Test. Go to socr.stat.ucla.edu and click on Analyses.

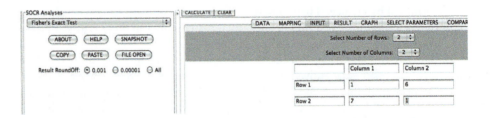

The result is shown in Figure 10.16. The p-value is 0.009, which is smaller than 0.05, so we reject the null hypothesis and conclude from these data that the antivenom is beneficial. (We can conclude that the antivenom *caused* this improvement because the researchers randomly assigned subjects to receive the treatment or a placebo.)

Fisher's Exact Test can be used for tables with more than two rows or columns, although then some technical considerations arise that are beyond an introductory course. You may have noticed that the two-tailed p-value is not simply twice the one-tailed p-value. This is one way in which Fisher's Exact Test differs from the *t*-test or *z*-test in earlier chapters.

The condition that the rows and columns remain fixed might strike you as somewhat odd. If the condition is not in fact met, the calculated p-value will be larger than the true p-value. This means that the test is conservative, which, for most purposes, is a good thing. (It also means that the test may not be very powerful—it might fail to detect real relationships.) However, when the condition does hold, the p-value is exactly right. We do not need to rely on approximations, as we do with the chi-square test.

Results of Fisher's Exact Test

Number of Rows = 2
Number of Columns = 2

	Column 1	Column 2	Row Total
Row 1	1.0	6.0	7
Row 2	7.0	1.0	8
Col Total	8	7	15

P-Value Cutoff = .009

1-Tail P-Value = .009

2-Tail P-Value = .010

◀ FIGURE 10.16 Output from SOCR website for Fisher's Exact Test. We used the one-tailed p-value.

CASE STUDY REVISITED

To better comprehend whether a relationship exists between a child's development (or not) of autism spectrum disorder (ASD) and when he or she received the MMR vaccine, we look at the data from a carefully conducted experiment in which the children are similar in age and the number of boys and girls is about the same. Each child had to have experienced a gastrointestinal (GI) event, as this is a common side effect of the MMR vaccination.

There are two categorical variables being observed in this study: whether the child experienced his or her first GI problem before or after having the MMR vaccine, and whether the child experienced symptoms consistent with ASD before or after receiving the MMR vaccine.

To test the contentious idea that the MMR vaccine is related to the onset of ASD symptoms, we assume that there is no relationship between when the child received the MMR vaccine and when ASD symptoms are first observed. The hypotheses follow.

H_0: The onset of ASD symptoms is independent of when the child receives the MMR vaccine.

H_A: The onset of ASD symptoms is related to when the child receives the MMR vaccine.

The results (and the table of observed frequencies) of the test of independence are shown by the Minitab output in Figure 10.17. The output shows that the expected frequencies are all greater than 5, so our sample size is large enough for the chi-square distribution (with 1 degree of freedom) to be a good approximation of the p-value.

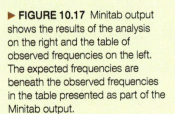

▶ **FIGURE 10.17** Minitab output shows the results of the analysis on the right and the table of observed frequencies on the left. The expected frequencies are beneath the observed frequencies in the table presented as part of the Minitab output.

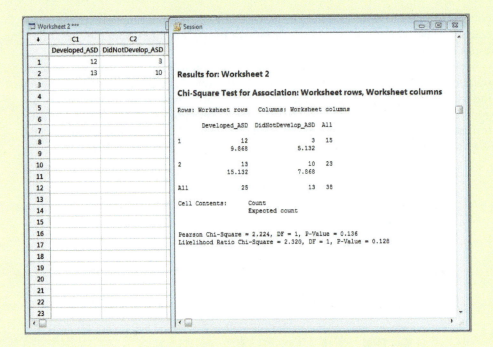

From the output, we can see that the chi-square test statistic has a value of χ^2_{Obs} = 2.224, and a p-value of 0.136. If we were to compare this to a significance level of 0.05, we would not reject the null hypothesis, since 0.136 is not less than 0.05. From these data, we can conclude that there is no relationship between the two categorical variables: the timing of the MMR vaccine and the onset of ASD symptoms are not related. In summary, there is no relationship between when a child experiences ASD symptoms and whether he or she had the MMR vaccine before or after onset.

It is worth noting that the landmark 1998 article published in *The Lancet* was later pulled from the journal because the study was biased. The lead author was found to have manipulated the data—the medical conditions of the 12 children in the study reported on were different from the hospital records of the same children. Today, the evidence showing that there is no relationship between a child receiving the MMR vaccine and the development of ASD continues to mount. Study after study continues to support the findings from the data collected in the Hornig et al. study.

An anecdote about the study: the 1998 problematic study was partially being funded by lawyers who were at the time representing clients who were in the process of suing vaccination manufacturers.

EXPLORING STATISTICS

CLASS ACTIVITY

Skittles

GOALS	MATERIALS
Apply a chi-square test to check whether two bags of Skittles candies contain the same proportions of colours.	• One small bag of Skittles for each student • Computer or TI-83/84

ACTIVITY

Open a bag of Skittles and count how many of each colour are in your bag. Fill in the numbers in the table below. Then find a partner and fill in the colours from his or her bag. (If someone does not have a partner, form a group of three and use three rows.)

	Purple	Red	Orange	Yellow	Green	Total
Yours						
Partner's						

BEFORE THE ACTIVITY

1. Do you think you and your partner(s) will get exactly the same number in each category?

2. Do you think you and your partner(s) will have significantly different distributions of colours? Why or why not?

AFTER THE ACTIVITY

1. Perform a hypothesis test to determine whether the two bags have a significantly different distribution of colours, using a significance level of 0.05.

2. Throw away, save, or eat the Skittles.

CHAPTER REVIEW

Summary of Learning Objectives

1. **How can I analyze data collected on a single categorical variable or two categorical variables?** Categorical data can be analyzed in one of three ways depending on how the data were collected. When data are collected on a single categorical variable, the data are presented in a table of frequencies and a goodness-of-fit test can be applied to determine if the data follow a proposed distribution. If the data are collected on two categorical variables, the data are presented in a two-way table and analyzed with either a test of homogeneity or a test of independence.

2. **What is the difference between the observed frequencies and the expected frequencies?** The observed frequencies count how many persons/objects sampled respond in a particular way to the categorical variable. The expected frequency represents how many persons/objects in the sample are expected to respond the same way according to the null hypothesis. In the case of two categorical variables, the observed frequency is how many are in each cell, and the expected frequency is computed with the formula

Formula 10.1:

$$\text{Expected frequency for a cell} = \frac{(\text{row total}) \times (\text{column total})}{\text{overall total}}$$

3. **How does the goodness-of-fit test work?** To consider whether the data follow a certain, or a proposed, distribution, the goodness-of-fit test is used to test these hypotheses:

H_0: The observed distribution is the same as the proposed distribution.
H_A: The observed distribution is different from the proposed distribution.

The *conditions* of the test are

1. *Random Sample.* The sample is collected randomly to ensure that (i) the population is represented in the sample and (ii) observations on each person/object in the sample are independent of all other observations.

2. *Large Sample.* The expected frequency is at least 5 in each category.

The chi-square statistic is computed with

Formula 10.2:

$$\chi^2_{Obs} = \sum_{\text{all cells}} \frac{(\text{Observed} - \text{Expected})^2}{\text{Expected}}$$

4. **How can I compare two or more populations using categorical data?** When two or more distinct independent samples are taken, and one categorical variable identifies the group from which a person/object was sampled, while a second variable represents a categorical response, then a test of homogeneity can be carried out. From the two-way table of data we can test whether the proportion of individuals in each response category is the same for each of the groups sampled.

5. **How does the test of homogeneity work?** If the proportion of individuals in each response category is the same for each of the groups sampled, then there is no relationship between the membership in the population (variable one) and the characteristic (variable two). The hypotheses to be tested are

H_0: The two categorical variables are not related.
H_A: The two categorical variables are related.

The conditions of this test are the same as the conditions of the goodness-of-fit test presented above. The chi-square statistic χ^2_{Obs} is computed using Formula 10.2. The p-value is then computed from an approximate chi-square distribution with degrees of freedom df = (number of rows − 1) × (number of columns − 1). A large p-value will support the null hypothesis. A p-value that is less than the significance level will result in the null hypothesis being rejected.

6. **How can I use data observed on two categorical variables to investigate whether the two variables are related?** When a single sample is collected and two categorical variables are measured on every person/object sampled, then a test of independence can be carried out. From the two-way table of data you can test whether the two variables are independent or not.

7. **How does the test of independence work?** The test of independence works the same way as the test of homogeneity. The hypotheses to be tested are

H_0: The two categorical variables are independent.
H_A: The two categorical variables are related.

This test needs the same conditions as outlined for the goodness-of-fit test. If the null hypothesis is true, the observed frequencies in the two-way table will be close to the frequencies expected, the chi-square statistic χ^2_{Obs} will be small in value, and the p-value will be large. If the value of χ^2_{Obs} is very large, then the p-value will be very small and the null hypothesis will be rejected in favour of the alternative hypothesis. When the large sample condition does not hold, Fisher's Exact Test can be applied to test these hypotheses.

Important Terms

Sources

Android has 43% of smartphone market share in Canada: comScore. www .mobilesyrup.com (accessed September 23, 2013).

Boyer, L. V., et al. 2009. Antivenom for critically ill children with neuro-toxicity from scorpion stings. *New England Journal of Medicine* 360, 2090–2098.

Colman, R. J., et al. 2009. Caloric restriction delays disease onset and mortality in Rhesus monkeys. *Science* 325, 201.

General Social Survey. 2013, April. Statistics Canada. www.statcan.gc.ca (accessed September 17, 2013).

Gun ownership database lives on despite long-gun registry repeal. www .huffingtonpost.ca (accessed September 15, 2013).

Hornig, et al. 2008. Lack of association between measles virus vaccine and autism with enteropathy: A case-control study. *PLoS One* 3(1).

Husemann, L. R., J. Moise-Titus, C. Podolski, and L. D. Eron. 2003. Longitudinal relations between children's exposure to TV violence and their aggressive and violent behavior in young adulthood: 1977–1992. *Developmental Psychology* 39(2), 201–221.

Kukuyeva, I. A., J. Wang, and Y. Yaglovskaya. 2008. Popcorn popping yield: An investigation. JSM Proceedings.

The Nanos number: Canadians less certain over country's direction. 2013, January 3. http://www.cbc.ca/news/politics/the-nanos-numbercanadians-less-certain-over-country-s-direction-1.1359566

Population and dwelling counts, for Canada, provinces and territories, 2006 and 2011 censuses. Statistics Canada. www.statcan.gc.ca (accessed September 14, 2013).

SECTION EXERCISES

SECTION 10.1

10.1 Tests

a. In Chapter 8, you learned some tests of proportions. Are tests of proportions used for categorical or numerical data?

b. In this chapter, you are learning to use chi-square tests. Do these tests apply to categorical or numerical data?

10.2 In Chapter 9, you learned some tests of means. Are tests of means used for numerical or categorical data?

10.3 Traditional Foods Consumption A study was conducted among Cree schoolchildren of the Mushkegowuk Territory First Nations in Northern Ontario. The purpose of the study was to investigate factors that influence consumption of wild game and other traditional foods. One of the factors under investigation was whether or not the child is concerned over potential environmental contaminants. The raw data on gender and concern over potential contaminants for the sample of children living in Fort Albany (one of the five communities in the study) are found in the table accompanying Exercise 1.45 on page 29 (c stands for concerned, n for not concerned, b for boy, and g for girl).

Create a two-way table to summarize the data. Are the two variables numerical or categorical? If you are doing this by hand, create a table with two rows and two columns. Label the columns Boy and Girl across the top. Label the rows Concerned and Not Concerned. Begin with a big table, making a tally mark in one of the four cells for each observation, then summarize these as observed frequencies.

10.4 Red Cars and Stop Signs The table shows the raw data for the results of a student survey of 22 cars and whether they stopped completely at a stop sign or not. In the colour column, "Red" means the car was red and "No" means the car was not red. In the Stop column, "Stop" means the car stopped and "No" means the car did not stop fully.

Create a two-by-two table to summarize these data. Use Red and No for the columns (across the top) and Stop and No for the rows. (We

gave you an orientation of the table so that your answers would be easy to compare.) Are the two variables categorical or numerical?

Colour	Stop	Colour	Stop
Red	Stop	No	No
Red	Stop	Red	Stop
Red	No	Red	No
Red	No	Red	No
Red	No	No	Stop
No	Stop	No	Stop
No	Stop	No	Stop
No	Stop	No	Stop
No	No	Red	Stop
Red	Stop	Red	No
Red	No	Red	No

10.5 The table summarizes the outcomes of a study that students carried out to determine whether humanities students had a higher mean GPA than science students. Identify both of the variables, and state whether they are numerical or categorical. If numerical, state whether they are continuous or discrete.

	Mean GPA
Science	3.4
Humanities	3.5

10.6 Finger Length There is a theory that relative finger length depends on testosterone level. The table shows a summary of the outcomes of an observational study that one of the authors carried out to determine whether men or women were more likely to have a ring finger that appeared longer than their index finger. Identify both of the variables, and state whether they are numerical or categorical. If numerical, state whether they are continuous or discrete.

	Men	Women
Ring Finger Longer	23	13
Ring Finger Not Longer	4	14

10.7 Internet Access According to a 2012 Statistics Canada survey, 83% of households had internet access. Let's say that you randomly selected 100 households and asked a person from each household if they had internet access or not. Suppose 84 say yes and 16 say no.

a. What is the observed proportion of people who say yes?

b. What is the observed frequency of people who say yes?

c. How many of the households sampled would you expect to say yes if the Statistics Canada survey is correct?

10.8 Fair Dice Suppose you roll two fair-dice 200 times. Each time you observe how many times the top sides sum to 7 dots. You observe that the top sides show a sum-to-7 outcome 30 times (the other 170 sum to something other than 7).

a. What is the observed proportion of times the dice sum to 7?

b. What is the observed frequency of a sum of 7?

c. If the two dice are fair, how many of the 200 rolls would you expect to show a sum of 7?

TRY **10.9 Effects of Television Violence on Men (Example 1)**
A study done by Husemann et al. and published in *Developmental Psychology* in 2003 compared men who had viewed high levels of television violence as children with those who had not in order to study the differences with regard to physical abuse of their partners as adults. The men categorized as physically abusive had hit, grabbed, or shoved their partners.

	High TV Violence	Low TV Violence
Yes, Physical Abuse	13	27
No Physical Abuse	18	95

a. Find the row, column, and grand totals, and prepare a table showing these values as well as the frequencies given.

b. Find the percentage of men overall who were abusive.

c. Find the expected number of men exposed to high levels of television violence who should say yes, if the variables are independent. Multiply the proportion overall who were abusive times the number of men exposed to high levels of television violence. Do not round off to a whole number. Round to two decimal digits.

d. Find the other expected values by knowing that the expected values must add to the row and column totals. Report them in a table with the same orientation as the one given for the data.

10.10 Effects of Television Violence on Women Refer to Exercise 10.9. This data table compares women who viewed high levels of television violence as children with those who did not in order to study the differences with regard to physical abuse of their partners as adults. The women categorized as physically abusive had hit, grabbed, or shoved their partners.

	High TV Violence	Low TV Violence
Yes, Physical Abuse	12	30
No Physical Abuse	23	111

a. Find the row, column, and grand totals and prepare a table showing these values.

b. Find the percentage of all women who were abusive (who answered yes).

c. Find the expected number of women exposed to high levels of television violence who should say yes, if the variables are independent. Do not round off to a whole number. Round to two decimal digits.

d. Find the other expected values. Report them in a table with the same orientation as the one for the data.

10.11 Mummies with Cardiovascular Disease According to the www.heartandstroke.com website, cardiovascular disease accounted for 29% of deaths in Canada (based on 2011 data). Many people believe this is due to modern-day factors such as high-calorie fast food and lack of exercise. However, a study published in the *Journal of the American Medical Association* in November 2009 (www.medicalnewstoday.com) reported on 16 mummies from the Egyptian National Museum of Antiquities in Cairo. The mummies were examined, and nine of them had hardening of the arteries, which seems to suggest that hardening of the arteries is not a new problem.

a. Calculate the expected number of mummies with artery disease (assuming the rate is the same as in the modern day). Then calculate the expected number of mummies without artery disease (the rest).

b. Calculate the observed value of the chi-square statistic for these mummies.

10.12 Internet Access We saw in Exercise 10.7 that 83% of Canadian households had internet access in 2012. Suppose you take a random sample of 100 households, of which 84 had internet access and 16 did not. Calculate the observed value of the chi-square statistic for testing the hypothesis that 83% of all households have internet access.

10.13 Violins Stradivarius violins, made in the 1700s by a man of the same name, are worth millions of dollars. They are prized by music lovers for their uniquely rich, full sound. In September 2009, an audience of experts took part in a blind test of violins, one of which was a Stradivarius. There were four other violins (modern-day instruments) made of specially treated wood. When asked to pick the Stradivarius after listening to all five violins, 39 got it right and 113 got it wrong (*Time magazine*, November 23, 2009).

a. If this group were just guessing, how many people (out of the 152) would be expected to guess correctly? And how many would be expected to guess incorrectly?

b. Calculate the observed value of the chi-square statistic by hand, showing your work.

10.14 Fair Dice In Exercise 10.8, two fair dice were rolled 200 times, and each time the sum of the dots on the top side was observed. You observed that a sum of 7 happened 30 times, and that something other than a sum of 7 happened 170 times. Calculate the observed value of the chi-square statistic, showing your work.

TRY 10.15 Effects of Television Violence on Men (Example 2) Refer to Exercise 10.9. The data table compares men who viewed high levels of television violence as children with those who did not in order to study the differences with regard to physical abuse of their partners as adults. Report the observed value of the chi-square statistic.

	High TV Violence	Low TV Violence
Yes, Physical Abuse	13	27
No Physical Abuse	18	95

10.16 Effects of Television Violence on Women Refer to Exercise 10.10. The data table compares women who viewed high levels of television violence as children with those who did not in order to study the differences with regard to physical abuse of their partners as adults. Calculate the observed value of the chi-square statistic.

	High TV Violence	Low TV Violence
Yes, Physical Abuse	12	30
No Physical Abuse	23	111

10.17 Colours in a Box of Smarties A study done by Zoon and GC Analytics in 2009 reported on the percentage of different colours that make up a box of Smarties. They reported the following: 13.2% of Smarties in a box are red, 16.2% are purple, 12.1% green, 11.6% blue, 14.5% orange, 11.7% yellow, 10.7% brown, and 10% pink. One of the authors, along with his children, sampled a few boxes of Smarties and observed the number of each colour. The distribution of the colours in this sample is summarized in the following table.

Colour	Red	Purple	Green	Blue	Orange	Yellow	Brown	Pink
Observed Frequency	4	10	7	17	14	17	14	4

From the percentage of times a colour appears in a box of Smarties reported in the study, calculate the observed value of the chi-square statistic, showing all your work.

10.18 Sidney Crosby and Wayne Gretzky Displayed in the table below (data from espn.go.com) is the observed frequency distribution of Sidney Crosby's points-per-game during all regular-season games played from the 2007–2008 season (his third) up to and including the 2012–2013 season.

Points in a Game	0	1	2	3	4	5 or More
Observed Frequency	77	97	79	39	11	3

In comparison, the following table shows Wayne Gretzky's points-per-game distribution starting in his third season (1981–1982) up to and including the 1985–1986 season.

Points in a Game	0	1	2	3	4	5 or More
Proportion of games	5.8%	21.1%	24.4%	22.3%	12.2%	14.2%

If Sidney Crosby's points-per-game performance were the same as Wayne Gretzky's, calculate the observed value of the chi-square statistic, showing your work.

SECTION 10.2

10.19 Fill in the blank by choosing one of the options given: Chi-square goodness-of-fit tests are applicable if the data consist of _____ (one categorical variable, two categorical variables, one numerical variable, or two numerical variables).

10.20 Fill in the blank by choosing one of the options given: Chi-square goodness-of-fit data are often summarized with _____ (one row or one column of observed frequencies, but not both; at least two rows and at least two columns of observed frequencies).

TRY g 10.21 Is Randomly Picking a Number Really Random? (Example 3) One of the authors collected data from a class to see whether humans made selections randomly, as a random number generator would. Each of 38 students had to pick an integer from one to five. The data are summarized in the table.

Integer	One	Two	Three	Four	Five
Frequency	3	5	14	11	5

A true random number generator would create roughly equal numbers of all five integers. Do a goodness-of-fit analysis to test the hypothesis that humans are not like random number generators. Use a significance level of 0.05, and assume that these data were from a random sample of students. *See page 505 for guidance.*

10.22 Is the Random Number Table Really Random? We counted ones, twos, threes, fours, and fives from a few lines of a random number table, and we should expect to get equal numbers of each. (We ignored the sixes, sevens, eights, nines, and zeros.) There were 14 ones, 12 twos, 16 threes, 11 fours, and 8 fives, which is 61 numbers in the categories selected. First, find the expected values, which should all be the same.

Then test the hypothesis that the random number table does not generate equal proportions of ones, twos, threes, fours, and fives, using a significance level of 0.05. Refer to the goodness-of-fit (GOF) output shown.

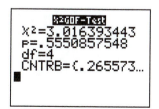

TI-84 GOF output.

10.23 Coin Spins A penny was spun on a hard, flat surface 50 times, landing on 15 heads and 35 tails. Using a chi-square test for goodness of fit, test the hypothesis that the coin is biased, using a 0.05 level of significance. Refer to the goodness-of-fit (GOF) output shown.

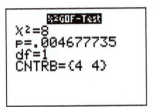

TI-84 GOF output.

10.24 Teens Texting According to a Harris Interactive (www .harrisinteractive.com) poll in June 2013, 57% of teenagers with driver's licences admit to texting while driving. Suppose we sample 100 teenagers, and 65 say they have texted while driving, while 35 say they have not. Test the hypothesis that the percentage who have texted while driving is not equal to the 57% claimed by this poll, using the goodness-of-fit test and a 0.05 level of significance.

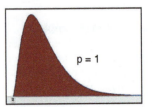

TI-84 GOF output.

10.25 Is the Six-Sided Die Fair? The table shows the results of rolling a six-sided die 120 times.

Outcome on Die	Frequency
1	27
2	20
3	22
4	23
5	19
6	9

Test the hypothesis that the die is not fair. A fair die should produce equal numbers of each outcome.

Use the four-step procedure with a significance level of 0.05, and state your conclusion clearly. Refer to the output shown.

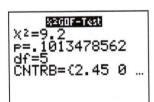

TI-84 GOF output.

10.26 Is the Six-Sided Die Fair? Repeat the chi-square test (all four steps) from Exercise 10.25, but this time assume that each of six possible outcomes occurred 20 times. Now refer to the figure below and explain it.

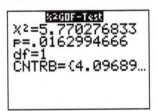

TI-84 GOF output for "draw."

10.27 Violins Professional musicians listened to five violins being played, without seeing the instruments. One violin was a Stradivarius, and the other four were modern-day violins. When asked to pick the Stradivarius (after listening to all five), 39 got it right and 113 got it wrong.

a. Use the chi-square goodness-of-fit test to test the hypothesis that the experts are not simply guessing. Use a significance level of 0.05. Refer to the output shown.

b. Perform a one-proportion z-test with the same data, using a one-tailed alternative that the experts should get more than 20% correct. Use a significance level of 0.05.

c. Compare your p-values and conclusions.

TI-84 GOF output.

10.28 Mummies with Cardiovascular Disease Exercise 10.11 on cardiovascular disease in mummies showed that 9 out of 16 mummies had hardening of the arteries.

Test the hypothesis that the proportion of mummies with hardening of the arteries is not the same as in modern Canada (whose proportion is 29%). Refer to the output below and use a significance level of 0.05.

TI-84 output.

SECTION 10.3

TRY **10.29 Political Party and Right Direction? (Example 4)** A Nanos poll in November 2012 asked the question "Would you say the country is moving in the right direction or wrong direction?" A random sample of 1000 Canadians was taken, and each was asked to respond "right" or "wrong." Suppose each Canadian was also asked "What federal political party do you currently support?" and the choices were Green, Liberal, New Democratic Party Conservative, and Other. If you were interested in determining whether there was a relationship between how a person responds to the direction question and which political party he or she currently supports, would you use a test of homogeneity or a test of independence? Explain.

10.30 Antibiotic or Placebo A large number of surgery patients get infections after surgery, which can sometimes be quite serious. Researchers randomly assigned some surgery patients to receive a simple antibiotic ointment after surgery, others to receive a placebo, and still others to receive just cleansing with soap. If we wanted to test the relationship between treatment and whether or not patients get an infection after surgery, would this be a test of homogeneity or of independence? Explain. (Source: Hospitals could stop infections by tackling bacteria patients bring in, studies find. *New York Times*, January 6, 2010)

TRY 10.31 Jet Lag Drug (Example 5) A study was conducted to determine whether the drug Nuvigil was effective at helping east-bound jet passengers adjust to jet lag. Subjects were randomly assigned either to one of three different doses of Nuvigil (low, medium, high) or to a placebo, flown to France in a plane in which they could not drink alcohol or coffee or take sleeping pills, and then examined in a lab where their state of wakefulness was measured and classified into categories (low, normal, alert). If we test whether treatments for jet lag are associated with wakefulness, are we doing a test of independence or of homogeneity? Explain. (Source: A drug's second act: Battling jet lag. *New York Times*, January 6, 2010)

10.32 Airlines and Flight Delays A poll of a 1000 randomly picked people who have flown in the past year is to be taken. Each person is to be asked two questions: "Was the last flight you were on delayed in departing?" and "What is the name of the airline you last flew with?" If you wanted to test whether there was a relationship between an airline and a delayed flight, would you use a test of homogeneity or a test of independence? Explain.

10.33 Population Getting Older? The table shows the distribution of the percentage of the Canadian population by age group taken from the 1996 census and the 2006 census (www .statcan.gc.ca). Can you use a chi-square test from these data? Explain.

	Less Than 15	15 to 64	65 or Older
1996	20.5	67.3	12.2
2006	17.8	68.7	13.7

10.34 Unemployment and Gender Canadian unemployment rates for all residents aged 18 and older are given in the table. The table does not include people who are actively seeking employment. Can you use a chi-square test from these data? Explain.

	Female	Male
1982	10.7	11.2
1992	10.2	12.0
2002	7.1	8.1
2012	6.8	7.7

http://www.indexmundi.com/g/g.aspx?c=ca&v=74

TRY g 10.35 Obesity and Marital Status (Example 6) A study reported in the medical journal *Obesity* in 2009 analyzed data from the National Longitudinal Study of Adolescent Health. Obesity was defined as having a body mass index (BMI) of 30 or more. The research subjects were followed from adolescence to adulthood, and all the people in the sample were categorized in terms of whether they were obese and whether they were dating, cohabiting, or married. Test the hypothesis that relationship status and obesity are related, using a significance level of 0.05. Can we conclude from these data that living with someone is making some people obese and that marrying is making people even more obese? Can we conclude that obesity affects relationship status? Explain. *See page 505 for guidance.*

	Dating	Cohabiting	Married
Obese	81	103	147
Not Obese	359	326	277

(Source: N. S. The and P. Gordon-Larsen. 2009. Entry into romantic partnership is associated with obesity. *Obesity* 17(7), 1441–1447)

10.36 Education Level and Income In Chapter 5 we looked at the results of a 2008 Statistics Canada Survey of Labour and Income Dynamics of 997 Canadians. Respondents were asked to indicate their highest completed level of education as well as their annual income. The sample was summarized in the two-way table below.

	Below $25,000	$25,000 to $50,000	$50,000 to $75,000	$75,000 to $100,000	Over $100,000
Less Than HS	159	58	13	4	5
High School	129	97	36	13	7
Two-Year Diploma/Degree	107	117	63	21	13
Four-Year Diploma/Degree	36	38	37	19	25

```
        below 25K  25K<50K  50K<75K  75K<100K  Over 100K  Total
NoHS       159        58       13        4         5       239
         103.32     74.31    35.72    13.66     11.99
          30.008     3.581   14.450    6.835     4.072

HS         129        97       36       13         7       282
         121.91     87.68    42.14    16.12     14.14
           0.413     0.990    0.896    0.605     3.607

2YR        107       117       63       21        13       321
         138.77     99.81    47.97    18.35     16.10
           7.272     2.961    4.707    0.382     0.596

4YR         36        38       37       19        25       155
          67.01     48.19    23.16     8.86      7.77
          14.348     2.156    8.264   11.599    38.177

Total      431       310      149       57        50       997

Chi-Sq = 155.917, DF = 12, P-Value = 0.000
```

Test the hypothesis that there is no relationship between a person's highest level of completed education and his or her income. Refer to the Minitab output, which shows the expected frequencies below the observed frequencies.

10.37 Effects of Television Violence on Men The data table compares men who viewed television violence with those who did not, in order to study the differences in physical abuse of the spouse. For the men in the table, test whether television violence and abusiveness are associated, using a significance level of 0.05. Refer to the Minitab output.

	High TV Violence	Low TV Violence
Yes, Physical Abuse	13	27
No Physical Abuse	18	95

(Source: L. R. Husemann et al. 2003. Longitudinal relations between children's exposure to TV violence and their aggressive and violent behavior in young adulthood: 1977–1992. *Developmental Psychology* 39(2), 201–221)

```
Chi-Square Test: High TV Violence, Low TV Violence
Expected counts are printed below observed counts
Chi-Square contributions are printed below expected counts

           High TV    Low TV
           Violence   Violence  Total
Yes, Ab      13         27        40
             8.10       31.90
             2.957      0.751

No           18         95       113
             22.90      90.10
             1.047      0.266

Total        31        122       153

Chi-Sq = 5.021, DF = 1, P-Value = 0.025
```

10.38 Effects of Television Violence on Women The data table compares women who viewed television violence with those who did not, in order to study the differences in physical abuse of the spouse (Husemann et al. 2003). Test whether television violence and abusiveness are associated, using a significance level of 0.05. Refer to the Minitab output.

	High TV Violence	Low TV Violence
Yes, Physical Abuse	12	30
No Physical Abuse	23	111

```
Chi-Square Test: High TV Violence, Low TV Violence
Expected counts are printed below observed counts
Chi-Square contributions are printed below expected counts

           High TV    Low TV
           Violence   Violence  Total
Yes, ab      12         30        42
             8.35       33.65
             1.593      0.395

No           23        111       134
             26.65     107.35
             0.499      0.124

Total        35        141       176

Chi-Sq = 2.612, DF = 1, P-Value = 0.106
```

10.39 Education Level and Travel A 2011 Statistics Canada survey was taken to understand the travelling habits of Canadians. The survey asked randomly chosen people many questions, two of which were "What is your highest level of completed education?" and "If you took a vacation this year, did you travel?" The two-way table shows both observed and (expected) frequencies.

	Travel for Vacation		
	No	Yes	Total
Less Than High School	158 (135.98)	26 (49.37)	184
High School Graduate	145 (137.45)	41 (49.91)	186
Some Post Secondary/ Post Secondary	309 (317.03)	120 (117.79)	429
University	127 (148.54)	74 (53.93)	201
Total	739	261	1000

a. If we carry out a test to determine whether these variables are related, would this be a test of independence, homogeneity, or goodness of fit?

b. Do a chi-square test with a significance level of 0.05 to determine whether highest level of completed education and travel during vacation are related.

(Source: Travel Survey of Residents of Canada, 2011. www.statcan.gc.ca)

10.40 Is Smiling Independent of Age? Randomly chosen people were observed for about 10 seconds in several public places, such as malls and restaurants, to see whether they smiled during that time. The table shows the results for different age groups.

	Age Group				
	0–10	11–20	21–40	41–60	61+
Smile	1131	1748	1608	937	522
No Smile	1187	2020	3038	2124	1509

(Source: M. S. Chapell. 1997. Frequency of public smiling over the life span. *Perceptual and Motor Skills* 85, 1326)

a. Find the percentage of each age group who were observed smiling, and compare these percentages.

b. Treat this as a single random sample of people, and test whether smiling and age group are related, using a significance level of 0.05. Comment on the results.

TRY 10.41 Preschool Attendance and High School Graduation Rates (Example 7) The Perry preschool project was created in the early 1960s by David Weikart in Ypsilanti, Michigan. One hundred and twenty three African American children were randomly assigned to one of two groups: one group enrolled in the Perry preschool, and one did not enroll. Follow-up studies were done for decades to answer the research question of whether attendance at preschool had an effect on high school graduation. The table shows whether the students graduated from regular high school or not. Students who received GEDs were counted as not graduating from high school. This table includes 121 of the original 123. This is a test of homogeneity, because the students were randomized into two distinct samples.

	Preschool	No Preschool
HS Grad	37	29
Not HS Grad	20	35

a. For those who attended preschool, the high school graduation rate was 37/57, or 64.9%. Find the high school graduation rate for those not attending preschool, and compare the two. Comment on what the rates show for *these* subjects.

b. Are attendance at preschool and high school graduation related? Use a 0.05 level of significance.

(Source: L. J. Schweinhart et al. 2005. Lifetime effects: The High/Scope Perry Preschool Study through age 40. *Monographs of the High/Scope Educational Research Foundation* 14. Ypsilanti, Michigan: High/Scope Press)

10.42 Preschool Attendance and High School Graduation Rates for Females The Perry preschool project data presented in Exercise 10.41 (Schweinhart et al. 2005) can be divided to see whether the preschool attendance effect is different for males and females. The table shows a summary of the data for females, and the figure shows Minitab output that you may use.

```
Chi-Square Test: Preschool, No Preschool: Girls
Expected counts are printed below observed counts

                    No
          Preschool  Preschool  Total

  Grad        21          8       29
            14.50      14.50

  No Grad      4         17       21
            10.50      10.50

Total         25         25       50

Chi-Sq = 13.875, DF = 1, P-Value = 0.000
```

Minitab output for the girls only

	Preschool	No Preschool
HS Grad	21	8
Not HS Grad	4	17

a. Find the graduation rate for those females who went to preschool, and compare it with the graduation rate for those who did not go to preschool.

b. Test the hypothesis that preschool and graduation rate are related, using a significance level of 0.05.

10.43 Preschool Attendance and High School Graduation Rates for Males The Perry preschool project data presented in Exercise 10.41 can be divided to see whether there are different

effects for males and females. The table shows a summary of the data for males (Schweinhart et al. 2005).

	Preschool	No Preschool
HS Grad	16	21
Not HS Grad	16	18

a. Find the graduation rate for males who went to preschool, and compare it with the graduation rate for those who did not go to preschool.

b. Test the hypothesis that preschool and graduation are related, using a significance level of 0.05.

c. Exercise 10.42 showed a relationship between preschool and graduation for just the females in this study. Write a sentence or two giving your advice to parents with preschool-eligible children about whether attending preschool is good for their children's future academic success, based on this dataset.

10.44 Drug for Atrial Fibrillation Atrial fibrillation is a heart problem in which the atrium (part of the heart) beats very rapidly. Researchers compared the drug valsartan with a placebo. People in the study had had at least one bout of atrial fibrillation in the previous six months. They were randomly assigned to receive valsartan or the placebo, and the frequencies are shown below. A "bad" outcome is when atrial fibrillation recurred again within one year, and a "good" outcome is when it did not recur during the one-year period.

	Valsartan	Placebo
Bad	371	375
Good	351	345

a. What percentage of those assigned valsartan had a bad outcome? What percentage of those assigned the placebo had a bad outcome? Compare these values.

b. Perform a hypothesis test to determine whether treatment is related with the outcome. Use a significance level of 0.05.

c. Would you recommend valsartan for a friend with atrial fibrillation?

(Source: The GISSI-AF Investigators. 2009. Valsartan for prevention of recurrent atrial fibrillation. *New England Journal of Medicine* 360, 1606–1617)

10.45 Gastric Surgery and Diabetes A study published in the *Journal of the American Medical Association* in 2008 reported on the effect of lap band surgery on diabetes. In this study, 55 obese patients with type 2 diabetes were randomly assigned to have lap band surgery or not. After two years, researchers recorded whether or not the subjects still had diabetes.

	Lap Band Surgery	No Surgery
Free from Diabetes	22	4
Not Free from Diabetes	7	22

a. What percentage of those who had the surgery were diabetes-free? What percentage of those who did not have the surgery were diabetes-free? Compare the two sample percentages.

b. Note the observed value of 4. Does this prevent us from using a chi-square test? Explain.

c. Test the hypothesis that lap bands and diabetes are related, using a significance level of 0.05.

(Source: J. B. Dixon et al. 2008. Adjustable gastric banding and conventional therapy for type 2 diabetes. *Journal of the American Diabetes Association* 299(3), 316–323)

10.46 Progressive Rewards A study was done on the effect of rewards on smokers' ability to refrain from smoking. All 60 smokers were adults who were *not* trying to quit smoking. Whether they were smoking or not was determined by a carbon monoxide meter. The smokers were studied for five days and tested three times each day. Each smoker was randomly assigned to one of three groups. The first group had "progressive rewards," in which the amount of money received per test gradually increased as they continued to refrain from smoking. The second group had "fixed rewards," in which they earned a fixed amount of money each time the test showed that they had refrained from smoking. The total dollar amounts for the first two groups were the same, assuming no smoking during the experiment. The control group did not receive any monetary reward.

The table shows whether the person smoked at all during the five days of the experiment.

	Progressive	Fixed	Control
No Smoking	10	6	1
Some Smoking	10	14	19

a. Compare the percentage of success (no smoking) for each group.

b. Note the observed value of 1, which is less than 5. Does this mean we cannot use chi-square on this data set? Explain.

c. Determine whether the treatment (group) was related with the outcome. Use the 0.05 level of significance.

d. Can we conclude that the type of encouragement changed smoking behaviours?

(Source: L. Shaffer and M. R. Merrens. 2001. *Research Stories for Introductory Psychology*. Boston: Allyn and Bacon. Original Source: J. M. Roll et al. 1996. An experimental comparison of three different schedules of reinforcement of drug abstinence using cigarette smoking as an exemplar. *Journal of Applied Behavioral Analysis* 29, 495–505)

10.47 Confederates and Compliance A study was done to see whether participants would ignore a sign that said "Elevator may stick between floors. Use the stairs." The people who used the stairs were said to be compliant, and those who used the elevator were noncompliant. The study was done in a university dormitory on the ground floor of a three-storey building. There were three different situations, two of which involved confederates. A confederate (Conf) is a person who is secretly working with the experimenter. In the first situation, there was no other person using the stairs or elevator—that is, no confederate. In the second, there was a compliant confederate (one who used the stairs). In the third, there was a noncompliant confederate (one who used the elevator). A summary of the data is given in the table and TI-83/84 output is given.

	No Conf	Compliant Conf	Noncompliant Conf
Participant Used Stairs	6	16	5
Participant Used Elevator	12	2	13

a. Find the percentage of participants who used the stairs in all three situations. What do these sample percentages say about the relationship between compliance and the existence of confederates?

b. From the figure, is the p-value 2.69? Explain. Report the actual p-value.

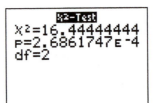

c. Determine whether there is a relationship between the three situations and whether the participant used the stairs (was compliant) or not. Use a significance level of 0.05.

(Source: L. Shaffer and M. R. Merrens. 2001. *Research Stories for Introductory Psychology*. Boston: Allyn and Bacon. Original Source: M. S. Wogalter et al. 1987. Effectiveness of warnings. *Human Factors* 29, 599–612)

10.48 Effects of Intensive Glucose Control in the ICU Adults admitted to a hospital intensive care unit (ICU) who were expected to be there three or more days were randomly assigned to undergo either intensive glucose (blood sugar) control or conventional glucose control. Intensive glucose control means an attempt was made to make sure the patients' glucose levels were within a narrow range of values (81–108 milligrams per decilitre). Conventional control means an attempt was made to keep the glucose level below 180 mg per dl. The subjects were observed for 90 days to see whether they died from any cause.

	Intensive Glucose Control	Conventional Glucose Control
Died	829	751
Did Not Die	2181	2261

a. What percentage of those who had intensive glucose control died? And what percentage of those who had conventional glucose control died? Compare these percentages, and comment on what the comparison shows.

b. Do a hypothesis test to see whether the treatment is related with whether the patient died. Use a significance level of 0.05.

c. Judging on the basis of these data, do you think that the glucose control method affects survival?

(Source: The NICE-SUGAR Study Investigators. 2009. Intensive versus conventional glucose control in critically ill patients. *New England Journal of Medicine* 360(13), 1283–1297)

10.49 Light at Night and Tumours A study was done on female mice to see whether the amount of light affects the risk of developing tumours. Fifty mice were randomly assigned to a regimen of 12 hours of light and 12 hours of dark (LD). Fifty similar mice were assigned to 24 hours of light (LL). The study began when the mice were two months old. The mice were observed for about two years. Four of the LD mice developed tumours, and 15 of the LL mice developed tumours.

a. What percentage of the LD mice in the sample developed tumours? And what percentage of the LL mice developed tumours? Compare these percentages and comment.

b. Create a two-way table showing the observed values. Label the columns (across the top) with LD and LL.

c. Test the hypothesis that the amount of light is related with tumours (at the 0.05 level of significance).

d. Some researchers are now starting to investigate whether this phenomenon occurs in humans. They are concerned about shift workers—workers (such as nurses) who may have night shifts. Why would this be a concern?

(Source: D. Baturin et al. 2001. The effect of light regimen and melatonin on the development of spontaneous mammary tumors. *Neuroendocrinology Letters* 22, 441–447)

10.50 Antidepressants for Bipolar Disorder Bipolar disorder is one in which patients cycle between mania and depression. In this study, done by G. S. Sachs et al. in 2007, the participants were randomly assigned to receive a mood stabilizer plus antidepressant or a mood stabilizer plus placebo for 26 weeks. A durable recovery means that the patients had a reasonably happy mood without being manic.

	Antidepressant	Placebo
Durable Recovery	42	51
Not Durable Recovery	137	136

a. What percentage of the patients on the antidepressant had a durable recovery? What percentage of the patients on the placebo had a durable recovery? Compare these percentages, and comment.

b. Test the hypothesis that the treatment is associated with the outcome, using a significance level of 0.05.

c. If you had a friend with bipolar disorder, would you suggest that she or he ask about taking an antidepressant in addition to the mood stabilizer already prescribed? Explain why or why not.

(Source: G. S. Sachs et al. 2007. Effectiveness of adjunctive antidepressant treatment for bipolar depression. *New England Journal of Medicine* 356(17), 1711–1722)

SECTION 10.4

TRY **10.51 Gender and Method of Transportation (Example 8)**
The data on students' gender and their most common method of transportation used to get to their classes are summarized in the table.

	Most Common Method of Transportation					
	Drive Alone	Carpool	Transit	Walk	Bicycle	Total
Male	19	0	25	3	0	47
Female	22	6	25	5	2	60
Total	41	6	50	8	2	107

Because some of the expected frequencies are less than 5, we should combine some groups. For this question, combine all the students who drive alone with those who carpool, and combine the students who walk and bicycle into another category called "Other." Show your new two-way table, then use it to test the hypothesis that there is a relationship between students' gender and their most common method of transportation used to get to class. Use a significance level of 0.05. Recall that these data were the result of a random sample of 107 first-year university students.

10.52 Gender and Political Views The table shows the observed (in black) and the expected (in red) frequencies that result from the random sample of 107 first-year students at a university in western Canada. In addition to their gender, they were asked which political party most reflects their political views: Liberal, Conservative, New Democratic Party (NDP), Green, or Other.

```
          Liberal     C    NDP   Green   Other   Total
 Male         7       26     3     3       9       48

             8.52   23.33  5.83  2.24    8.07


 Female      12       26    10     2       9       59

            10.48   28.67  7.17  2.76    9.93
```

a. We would like to perform a chi-square test with the data in the table. Check whether the conditions hold. If you cannot use the table for a chi-square test, explain why.

b. Combine the "Green" and "NDP" categories into one category. Create a new two-way table.

c. What percentage of females sampled have political views most closely represented by the Liberal Party? What percentage of males sampled have political views most closely represented by the Liberal Party? Compare them.

d. Do a chi-square test with a significance level of 0.05 to see whether the variables *Gender* and *Political View* are related.

10.53 Climate Change and Religion A 2013 Forum Research survey of randomly chosen Canadians asked the following questions: "As far as you know, is the Earth's climate changing?," to which the responses were Yes, No, or Don't Know. Respondents were also asked to provide their religious affiliation. The data are summarized in the table.

	Protestant Christian	Evangelical Christian	Catholic	Other Christian	Other	None	Total
Yes	377	62	492	126	105	325	1487
No	51	12	65	18	11	26	183
Don't Know	32	2	36	18	6	18	112
Total	460	76	593	162	122	369	1782

a. Find the expected frequencies and report the smallest. Could we use the table as is, without combining categories?

b. Create a new table, using the data from the table shown, with fewer categories. Merge the Evangelical Christian category with the Protestant Christian.

c. What percentage of people without religion believe that Earth's climate is changing? What percentage of people with religion believe Earth's climate is changing?

d. Do a chi-square test with a significance level of 0.05 to see whether the variables *Climate Change* and *Religion* are related.

(Source: www.forumresearch.ca)

10.54 Children and Happiness The data in the table come from the 2008 General Social Survey. The top row is the number of children reported for the respondents. The respondents also reported their level of happiness; Very H means Very Happy, and so on. The frequencies are shown in the table. Is happiness related with having at least one child?

	Number of Children								
	0	1	2	3	4	5	6	7	8 or More
Very H	129	99	151	112	51	24	6	7	8
Fairly H	188	110	189	98	53	21	9	5	5
Not Very H	22	13	20	12	7	6	0	2	0
Not at All H	6	3	3	1	2	2	0	1	0

a. Merge all the Number of Children categories into two groups: those who have 0 children and those who have at least one child. For the rows, merge the very happy and fairly happy into one group called Happy. Merge the not very happy and the not at all happy into one group called Unhappy. Report the new table, which should have two rows and two columns.

b. We wish to test whether happiness is related with having children. Why was it necessary to merge categories?

c. With the merged data, determine whether there is a relationship between happiness and whether a person has at least one child. Use a significance level of 0.05.

* **10.55 Scorpion Antivenom** A study was done on children, aged 6 months to 18 years, who had nonlethal scorpion stings. Each child was randomly assigned to receive an experimental antivenom or a placebo. "Good" results were no symptoms after four hours and no detectable plasma venom.

	Antivenom	Placebo	Total
No Improvement	1	6	7
Improvement	7	1	8
Total	8	7	15

The alternative hypothesis is that the antivenom leads to improvement. The p-value for a one-tailed Fisher's Exact Test with these data is 0.009.

a. Suppose the study had turned out differently, as in the following table.

	Antivenom	Placebo
Bad	0	7
Good	8	0

Would Fisher's Exact Test have led to a p-value larger or smaller than 0.009? Explain.

b. Suppose the study had turned out differently, as in the following table.

	Antivenom	Placebo
Bad	2	5
Good	6	2

Would Fisher's Exact Test have led to a p-value larger or smaller than 0.009? Explain.

c. Try the two tests, and report the p-values. Were you right? Search for a Fisher's Exact Test calculator on the internet, and use it.

(Source: L. V. Boyer et al. 2009. Antivenom for critically ill children with neurotoxicity from scorpion stings. *New England Journal of Medicine* 360(20), 2090–2098)

* **10.56 Traditional Foods Consumption** In Exercise 10.3, you read about a study conducted among Cree schoolchildren of the Mushkegowuk Territory First Nations in Northern Ontario. The purpose of the study was to investigate variables that influence consumption of wild game and other traditional foods. One of the variables under investigation was whether or not the child is concerned over potential environmental contaminants. The raw data on gender and concern over potential contaminants for the sample of children living in Fort Albany (one of the five communities in the study) are found in Exercise 1.45 on page 29.

a. Consult the two-way table of these data created in Exercise 10.3. Compare the percentages of girls and boys who are concerned about environmental contaminants.

b. Use a chi-square test with a significance level of 0.05 to test the hypothesis that gender and level of concern for contaminants are related.

c. Perform a Fisher's Exact Test using the same significance level. Report the two-tailed p-value and your conclusion. (Search for a Fisher's Exact Test calculator on the internet.)

d. Compare the p-values in parts b and c. Which one is more accurate?

e. Suppose the study had turned out differently. Create a new two-way table (with the same row and column totals) that yields a more extreme outcome in the direction you found. Report the p-value for this test, and compare it to the p-value in part d.

CHAPTER REVIEW EXERCISES

10.57 Perry Preschool Arrests The Perry preschool project discussed in Exercises 10.41–10.43 found that 8 of the 58 students who attended preschool had at least one felony arrest by age 40 and that 31 of the 65 students who did not attend preschool had at least one felony arrest (Schweinhart et al. 2005).

a. Compare the percentages descriptively. What does this comparison suggest?

b. Create a two-way table from the data and do a chi-square test on it, using a significance level of 0.05. Test the hypothesis that preschool attendance is related to being arrested.

c. Do a two-proportion z-test. Your alternative hypothesis should be that preschool attendance lowers the chances of arrest.

d. What advantage does the two-proportion z-test have over the chi-square test?

10.58 Parental Training and Criminal Behaviour of Children An experiment was done in Montreal with parents of children who were thought to have a high risk of committing crimes when they became teenagers. Some of the families were randomly assigned to receive parental training, and the others were not. Out of 43 children whose parents were randomly assigned to the parental training group, 6 had been arrested by the age of 15. Out of 123 children whose parents were not in the parental training group, 37 had been arrested by age 15.

a. Find and compare the percentages of children arrested by age 15. Is this what researchers might have hoped?

b. Create a two-way table from the data, and test whether the treatment program is related to arrests. Use a significance level of 0.05.

c. Do a two-proportion z-test, testing whether the parental training lowers the rate of bad results. Use a significance level of 0.05.

d. Explain the difference in the results of the chi-square test and the two-proportion z-test.

e. Can you conclude that the treatment causes the better result? Why or why not?

(Source: R. E. Tremblay et al. 1996. From childhood physical aggression to adolescent maladjustment: The Montreal prevention experiment. In R.D. Peters and R. J. McMahon, *Preventing childhood disorders, substance use and delinquency*. Thousand Oaks, California: Sage, pp. 268–298)

10.59 Market Share of Smartphones comScore, a communications research firm, reported that in the year 2013 the Android system made up 43% of the smartphone market in Canada, followed by Apple at 35%, BlackBerry at 19%, and Microsoft Windows at 2%, with the remaining 1% classified as "Other." Suppose a random sample of 1000 people was taken from a population of all Canadians with smartphones, and each was asked to indicate the type of smartphone he or she has. The observed frequencies are shown in the table.

Android	Apple	BlackBerry	Windows	Other
404	369	201	17	9

a. Find the percentage of people having each type of smartphone.

b. According to comScore's report, how many people in this sample would you expect to have each type of smartphone?

c. Perform a chi-square test of homogeneity to test the hypothesis that smartphone market share has changed from 2013, using a significance level of 0.05.

(Source: www.mobilesyrup.com)

10.60 Diet Drug A randomized, placebo-controlled study of the diet drug Meridia (sibutramine) was done on overweight or obese subjects and reported in the *New England Journal of Medicine*. The patients were all 55 years old or older with a high risk of cardiovascular events. Those who had a heart event experienced a heart attack, stroke, or death from heart-related factors. The table gives the counts.

	Drug	Placebo
Heart Event	559	490
No Heart Event	4347	4408

a. Compare the rates of heart event for the drug group and the placebo group.

b. Test for a relationship between the drug and a heart event, using a significance level of 0.05.

c. Can you conclude that the drug causes the difference in the rate of heart events? Why or why not?

(Source: W. P. James et al. 2010. Effect of sibutramine on cardiovascular outcomes in overweight and obese subjects. *New England Journal of Medicine* 363, 905–917)

10.61 Statin for Prevention of Blood Clots? A group of 17,802 healthy people with normal cholesterol readings were randomly assigned to take the cholesterol-lowering drug Crestor (a statin) or a placebo. They were then observed for about two years to see whether they developed pulmonary embolism, or blood clots. Assume that exactly half were assigned the drug, and half were assigned the placebo.

When the results were reported in 2009, 34 of those taking Crestor and 60 of those in the placebo group had developed pulmonary embolism, or blood clots.

a. Create a two-way table showing the numbers of those who developed blood clots. Use Crestor and Placebo as labels for the columns.

b. Compare the percentages of those who had blood clots for these two treatments.

c. Do a test to find out whether treatment and outcome are related, using a significance level of 0.05.

d. Can you conclude that using Crestor caused the difference? Why or why not?

(Source: R. J. Glynn et al. 2009. A randomized trial of rosuvastatin in the prevention of venous thromboembolism. *New England Journal of Medicine* 360(18), 1851–1861)

10.62 Scared Straight In the 1980s, the program Scared Straight was created. In this program young delinquents would go to a prison and meet prisoners who told them how difficult prison life is. The aim of the program was to scare the kids so that they would not commit crimes. A study was done in which half of the kids were randomly assigned to a Scared Straight program and half had no treatment. Then all the kids were observed for 12 months to see whether they were arrested.

Forty-three out of 53 of the Scared Straight kids were arrested, and 36 out of 53 of the group that did not see the prison were arrested.

(a)
```
        2-Prop2Test
      P1<P2
      z=1.560470435
      P=.9406756147
      p̂1=.8113207547
      p̂2=.679245283
    ↓p̂=.7452830189
```

(b)
```
        2-Prop2Test
      P1>P2
      z=1.560470435
      P=.0593243853
      p̂1=.8113207547
      p̂2=.679245283
    ↓p̂=.7452830189
```

a. Find the percentage of each group that was arrested, and comment on it.

b. Perform a chi-square test of homogeneity to determine whether the treatment and outcome (Arrest or No Arrest) are related. Use a significance level of 0.05.

c. Do a one-tailed two-proportion z-test to see whether Scared Straight decreases arrest rates. Which output shown is the correct one, output a or output b? Number 1 refers to the Scared Straight group, and number 2 refers to the control group with no treatment.

d. Compare the results of parts b and c. Include a comparison of p-values. Is there a relationship between the observed values of the z-statistic and the chi-square statistic? If so, what is it?

(Source: R. V. Lewis. 1983. Scared Straight—California style: Evaluation of the San Quentin Squires program. *Criminal Justice and Behavior* 10, 209–226)

10.63 Education Level and Opinion Example 1 reported on the results of a 2013 Ipsos poll of 501 randomly chosen people. They were asked their gender, their education level (low, medium, or high), and their opinion on same-sex marriage. The latter two results are given in the two-way table below.

Opinion	Low	Medium	High
Allowed to Legally Marry	117	145	55
Be Allowed Legal Recognition, but Not to Marry	23	27	14
Not Be Allowed Any Kind of Legal Recognition	28	29	13
Not Sure	18	22	10
Total	186	223	92

Using available technology, perform a chi-square test to see whether the variables *Education Level* and *Opinion* are related, using a significance level of 0.05.
(Source: ipsos-reid.ca)

10.64 Climate Change and Religion Exercise 10.53 reported on a 2013 Forum Research survey of randomly chosen Canadians who were asked the following question: "As far as you know, is the Earth's climate changing?," to which responses were Yes, No, or Don't Know. The level of education of each respondent was also measured as low (high school or less), medium (some college/university), or high (completed university/college). The data are summarized in the table.

Opinion	Low	Medium	High
Yes	321	415	756
No	44	60	81
Don't Know	42	25	38
Total	407	500	875

Using available technology, perform a chi-square test to see whether the variables *Education Level* and *Opinion* are related, using a significance level of 0.05. (Source: http://forumresearch.ca)

★ 10.65 Robot Cockroaches Cockroaches tend to rest in groups and prefer dark areas. In a study published in *Science* magazine in November 2007, cockroaches were introduced to a brightly lit, enclosed area with two different available shelters, one darker than the other. Each time a group of cockroaches was put into the brightly lit area will be called a trial. When groups of 16 real cockroaches were put in a brightly lit area, in 22 out of 30 trials, all the cockroaches went under the same shelter. In the other 8 trials, some of the cockroaches went under one shelter and some under the other one.

Another group consisted of a mixture of real cockroaches and robot cockroaches (4 robots and 12 real cockroaches). The robots did not look like cockroaches but had the odour of male cockroaches, and they were programmed to prefer groups (and brighter shelters). There were 30 trials. In 28 of the trials, all the cockroaches and robots rested under the same shelter, and in 2 of the trials they split up.

	Cockroaches Only	Robots Also
One Shelter Used	22	28
Both Shelters Used	8	2

Is the inclusion of robots associated with whether they all went under the same shelter? To answer these questions, assume the cockroaches are a random sample of all cockroaches.

a. Use a chi-square test for homogeneity with a significance level of 0.05 to see whether the presence of robots is related to whether roaches went into one shelter or two.

b. Repeat the question using Fisher's Exact Test. (If your software will not perform the test for you, search for Fisher's Exact Test on the internet to do the calculations.) Conduct a two-tailed hypothesis test so that the test is consistent with the test in part a.

c. Compare the p-values and conclusions from part a and part b. Which statistical test do you think is the better procedure in this case? Why?

(Source: J. Halloy et al. 2007. Social integration of robots into groups of cockroaches to control self-organized choices. *Science* 318(5853), 1155–1158)

★**10.66 Robot Cockroaches** Refer to the description in Exercise 10.65. There were 22 trials with only cockroaches (no robots) that went under one shelter. In 16 of these 22 trials, the group chose the darker shelter, and in 6 of the 22 the group chose the lighter shelter. There were 28 trials with a mixture of real cockroaches and robots that all went under one shelter. In 11 of these trials, the group chose the darker shelter, and in 17 the group chose the lighter shelter. The robot cockroaches were programmed to choose the lighter shelter (as well as preferring groups).

	All Under One Shelter	
	Cockroaches Only	Robots Also
Darker	16	11
Lighter	6	17

Is the introduction of robot cockroaches related to the type of shelter when the group went under one shelter? Assume that cockroaches were randomly sampled from some meaningful population of cockroaches.

a. Use the chi-square test to see whether the presence or absence of robots is related to whether they went under the darker or the brighter shelter. Use a significance level of 0.05.

b. Do Fisher's Exact Test with the data. If your software does not do Fisher's Exact Test, search the internet for a Fisher's Exact Test calculator and use it.

c. Compare the p-values for parts a and b. Which do you think is the more accurate procedure? The p-values that result from the two methods in this question are closer than the p-values in the previous question. Why do you think that is?

GUIDED EXERCISES

10.21 Is Randomly Picking a Number Really Random?

One of the authors collected data from a class to see whether humans made selections randomly, as a random number generator would. Each of 38 students had to pick an integer from one to five. The data are summarized in the table.

Integer:	One	Two	Three	Four	Five
Times Chosen:	3	5	14	11	5

A true random number generator would create roughly equal numbers of all five integers.

Question

Test the hypothesis that humans are not like random number generators by following the steps below. Use a significance level of 0.05, and assume that the data were collected from a random sample of students.

Step 1 ▶ Hypothesize

H_0: Humans are like random number generators and produce numbers in equal quantities.

H_A: ?

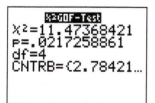

```
χ²GOF-Test
x²=11.47368421
p=.0217258861
df=4
CNTRB={2.78421...
```

TI-84 GOF output.

Step 2 ▶ Prepare

Choose chi-square goodness of fit (GOF). We have only one variable: *Integer Chosen*. Use a significance level of 0.05. We are assuming randomness. We must check to see that all the expected values are 5 or more. There were 38 students. Explain why all the expected values are 7.6.

Step 3 ▶ Compute to compare

$$\chi^2 = \frac{(3 - 7.6)^2}{7.6} + \frac{(5 - 7.6)^2}{7.6}$$
$$+ \underline{\quad} + \underline{\quad} + \underline{\quad} = \underline{\quad}$$

Complete the calculation of the chi-square statistic. Then check your calculated chi-square with the output. Obtain the p-value from the TI-84 output.

Step 4 ▶ Interpret and conclude

The p-value from the TI-84 output is _____.
Assuming that the null hypothesis is _____, the p-value means there is a _____ probability that another 38 students would give a result that is as extreme or more extreme than the current result of _____.

Reject or fail to reject the null hypothesis and pick a decision below.

i. These data suggest that humans have not been shown to be different from random number generators.

ii. These data suggest that humans have been shown to be different from random number generators.

10.35 Obesity and Marital Status

A study reported in the medical journal *Obesity* in 2009 analyzed data from the National Longitudinal Study of Adolescent Health. Obesity was defined as having a body mass index (BMI) of 30 or more. The research subjects were followed from adolescence to adulthood, with all individuals in the sample categorized in terms of whether or not they were obese and whether they were dating, cohabiting, or married.

	Dating	Cohabiting	Married
Obese	81	103	147
Not Obese	359	326	277

Question

Test the hypothesis that the variables *Relationship Status* and *Obesity* are related, using a significance level of 0.05. Also consider whether the study shows causality. The steps will guide you through the process. Minitab output is provided.

Step 1 ▶ Hypothesize

H_0: Relationship status and obesity are independent.

H_A: ?

```
Chi-Square Test: Dating, Cohabiting, Married
Expected counts are printed below observed counts

          Dating   Cohabiting   Married   Total
Obese        81          103       147     331
          112.64       109.82    108.54

Not         359          326       277     962
          327.36       319.18    315.46

Total       440          429       424    1293

Chi-Sq = 30.829, DF = 2, P-Value = 0.000
```

Step 2 ▶ Prepare

We choose the chi-square test of independence because the data were from *one* random sample in which the people were classified two different ways. We do not have a random sample or a random assignment, so we will test to see whether these results could easily have occurred by chance. Find the smallest expected value and report it. Is it more than 5?

Step 3 ▶ Compute to compare

Refer to the output given.

$\chi^2_{Obs} = $ _____

p-value = _____

Step 4 ▶ Interpret and conclude

Assuming that the null hypothesis is _____, the p-value means there is a _____ probability that another study like this would give a result that is as extreme or more extreme than the current result of _____.

Reject or fail to reject the null hypothesis, and state what that means.

Causality

Can we conclude from these data that living with someone is making some people obese and that marrying is making even more people obese? Can we conclude that obesity affects your relationship status? Explain why or why not.

Percentages

Find and compare the percentages of obese people in the three relationship statuses.

TECH TIPS

General Instructions for All Technology

🌐 **Example A (Chi-Square Test for Two-Way Tables): Perry Preschool and Graduation from High School**

In the 1960s an experiment was started in which a group of children were randomly assigned to attend preschool or not to attend preschool. They were studied for years, and whether they graduated from high school is shown in Table A.

We will show the chi-square test for two-way tables to see whether the factors are independent or not.

	Preschool	No Preschool
Grad HS	37	29
Not HS Grad	20	35

▲ **TABLE A** Two-way table for preschool and graduation from high school.

Discussion of Data

Much of technology is set up so that you can use the table summary (such as Table A) and find the calculated results. However, it is also possible to start with a spreadsheet containing the raw data. Table B shows the beginning of the raw data, for which there would be 121 rows for the 121 children.

Preschool	Graduate HS
Yes	No
Yes	Yes
No	Yes
No	Yes
Yes	Yes
No	No

▲ **TABLE B** Some raw data.

Example B Chi-Square for Goodness of Fit: Are Humans Like Random Number Generators?

One of the authors collected data from a class to see whether humans made selections randomly, as a random number generator would. Each of 38 students had to pick one of the integers one, two, three, four, or five. Table C summarizes the collected (*Observed*) data. If the students picked randomly, we would expect each number (one through five) to be chosen an equal number of times (uniform distribution). Because there were 38 students and 5 choices, each *Expected* value is $38 \times (1/5)$, or 7.6, as listed in Table C.

	One	Two	Three	Four	Five
Times *Observed* to Be Chosen	3	5	14	11	5
Times *Expected* to Be Chosen	7.6	7.6	7.6	7.6	7.6

▲ **TABLE C** Goodness-of-fit data.

TI-83/84

Chi-Square for Two-Way Tables

You will not put the data into the lists. You will use a matrix (table), and the data must be in the form of a summary such as Table A.

1. Press **2ND** and **MATRIX** (or **MATRX**).
2. Scroll over to **EDIT** and press **ENTER** when **1:** is highlighted.
3. See Figure 10A. Put in the dimensions. Because the table has two rows and two columns, press **2, ENTER, 2, ENTER**. (The first number is the number of rows, and the second number is the number of columns.)
4. Enter each of the four numbers in the table, as shown in Figure 10A. Press **ENTER** after typing each number.
5. Press **STAT**, and scroll over to **TESTS**.
6. Scroll down (or up) to **C: χ^2-Test** and press **ENTER**.
7. Leave the **Observed** as **A** and the **Expected** as **B**. Scroll down to **Calculate** and press **ENTER**.

   You should get the output shown in Figure 10B.

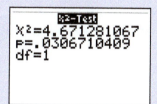

▲ **FIGURE 10A** TI-83/84 input for two-way table.

▲ **FIGURE 10B** TI-83/84 output for a chi-square test for two-way tables.

8. To see the expected values, click **2ND**, **MATRIX**, scroll over to **EDIT**, scroll down to **2: [B]**, and press **ENTER**. You may have to scroll to the right to see some of the numbers. They will be arranged in the same order as the table of observed values. Check these numbers for the required minimum value of 5.

Goodness-of-Fit Test Using a TI-84

(The TI-83 does not provide the goodness-of-fit test.)

1. Put the observed frequencies in one list, such as **L1**, and put the expected values in another list, such as **L2**, using the same order.
2. Then choose **Stat**, **Tests**, and **D: X²GOF-Test**.
3. Make sure the **Observed** list is the one in which you have the observed frequencies and that the **Expected** list is where you have the expected values. You will have to put in the value for **df**, which is the number of categories minus 1. In Example B there were five numbers to choose from, so df is 4 because $5 - 1 = 4$.
4. Then choose **Calculate** (or **Draw**).
5. The chi-square value comes out to be 11.47368, and the p-value is 0.0217258

MINITAB

Two-Way Tables

For Minitab you may have your data as a table summary (as shown in Table A) or as raw data (as shown in Table B).

Table Summary

1. Type a summary of your data into the columns.

C1	C2
37	29
20	35

   You may put labels above the numbers if you want to.

2. **Stat > Tables > Chi-square Test** for **Association > Summarized data in a two-way table**
3. Select both columns (by double clicking them) and click **OK**. Figure 10C shows the output.

```
Chi-Square Test: C1, C2
Expected counts are printed below observed counts
Chi-Square contributions are printed below expected counts

        C1    C2  Total
1       37    29     66
     31.09 34.91
     1.123 1.000

2       20    35     55
     25.91 29.09
     1.348 1.200

Total  57    64    121

Chi-Sq = 4.671, DF = 1, P-Value = 0.031
```

▲ **FIGURE 10C** Minitab output for chi-square test for two-way tables.

Raw Data

1. Make sure your raw data are in the columns. See Table B.
2. **Stat > Tables > Cross Tabulation and Chi-square**.
3. See Figure 10D. Click either C1 **For rows** and C2 **For columns** (or vice versa). Ignore **For layers**.

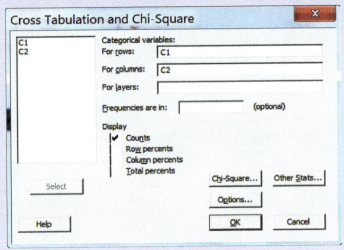

▲ FIGURE 10D Minitab input for cross tabulation and chi-square.

4. Click **Chi-Square**.

5. Select both **Chi-Square analysis** and **Expected cell counts**.

6. Click **OK** and click **OK**.

Goodness of Fit

1. Type your observed frequencies in one column, such as **C1**.

2. If you have expected values that are not equal, type them in another column, such as **C2**. (If all the expected values are the same, as in our Example B, they don't have to be typed in.)

3. **Stat > Tables > Chi-Square Goodness-of-Fit Test (One Variable)**

4. See Figure 10E. Click in the box next to **Observed Counts**, and then double click the column with the observed counts.

5. If there are **Equal proportions**, leave it. If you have a column of expected counts, click **Proportions specified by historical counts** and then choose the column containing the expected values.

Your results will show bar charts (as well as chi-square output) unless you click on **Graphs** and turn the graphs off.

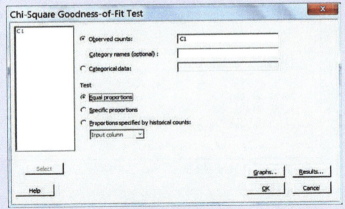

▲ FIGURE 10E Minitab goodness-of-fit options.

6. Click **OK**.

You should get a chi-square value of 11.4737 and a p-value of 0.022.

EXCEL

Two-Way Tables

1. Type a summary of your data into two (or more) columns, as shown in columns A and B in Figure 10F.

	A	B
1	37	29
2	20	35

▲ FIGURE 10F Excel input for two-way table.

2. To get the total of 66 (from 37 + 29), click in the box to the right of 29, and then click **fx**, double click **SUM**, and click **OK**. You can do the same thing for the other sums, each time starting from the cell in which you want to put the sum. Save the grand total for last. Your table with the totals should look like columns A, B, and C in Figure 10G. Alternatively, you could simply add to get the totals.

3. To get the expected values, you will be using the formula

$$\text{Expected value} = \frac{(\text{row marginal total}) \times (\text{column marginal total})}{(\text{grand total})}$$

To get the first expected value, 31.09091, click in the cell where you want the expected value to be placed (here, cell E1). (An empty column, such as column D in Figure 10G, improves the clarity.) Then type = and click on the **66** in the table, type ★ (for multiplication), click on the **57**, type / (for division), click on the **121**, and press **Enter**. Figure 10G shows part of the process for getting the expected value that goes below the 31.09. For each of the expected values, you start from the cell you want filled, and you click on the row total, ★ (for multiply), the column total, / (for divide), and the grand total and press **Enter**. Alternatively you could figure out the expected values by hand.

	A	B	C	D	E
1	37	29	66		31.09091
2	20	35	55		=A3*C1/C3
3	57	64	121		

▲ FIGURE 10G Excel, including totals and one expected value.

After you have all four expected values, make sure they are arranged in the same order as the original data.

4. Click **fx**.

5. Select a category: **Statistical** or **All**.

6. Choose **CHISQ.TEST**. For the **Actual_range**, highlight the table containing the observed frequencies, but do *not* include the row and column totals or the grand total. For the **Expected range**, highlight the table with the expected values.

You will see the p-value (0.030671). Press **OK** and it will show up in the active cell in the worksheet.

The preceding steps for Excel will give you the p-value but not the value for chi-square. If you want the numerical value for chi-square, continue with the steps that follow.

7. Click in an empty cell.

8. Click **fx**.

9. Select a category: **Statistical** or **All**.

10. Choose **CHISQ.INV.RT** (for inverse, right tail).

11. For the **Probability**, click on the cell from step 6 that shows the p-value of **0.030671**. For **Deg_freedom**, put in the degrees of freedom (df). For two-way tables,

$$df = (\text{number of rows} - 1)(\text{number of columns} - 1).$$

For Example A, df is 1. Click **OK**. You should get a chi-square of 4.67 for Example A.

Excel Goodness-of-Fit Test

1. Type your observed frequencies in one column and your expected frequencies in another column, in the same order.

2. Follow steps 4, 5, and 6 above.

   You will get a p-value of 0.021726.

   If you want the numerical value of chi-square, follow the instructions in steps 7–11 above. However, in step 11, for goodness of fit,

$$df = \text{number of categories} - 1$$

For Example B, the number of categories is 5, so df is 4. You will get a chi-square value of 11.47.

STATCRUNCH

Two-Way Tables

TABLE SUMMARY

1. Enter your data summary as shown in Figure 10H. Note that you can have column labels (Preschool or No Preschool) and also row labels (GradHS or NoGrad).

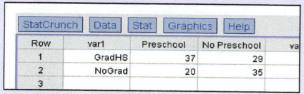

▲ **FIGURE 10H** StatCrunch input for two-way table.

2. **Stat > Tables > Contingency > with summary**

3. See Figure 10I. Select the columns that contain the summary frequencies, and select the column that contains the **Row labels**, here **var1**.

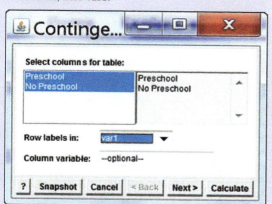

▲ **FIGURE 10I** StatCrunch two-way table options.

4. Click **Next** and click **Expected Count**.

5. Click **Calculate**.

   Figure 10J shows the well-labelled output.

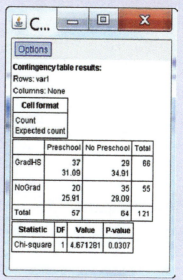

▲ **FIGURE 10J** StatCrunch output for two-way table.

Raw Data

1. Be sure you have raw data in the columns; see Table B.

2. **Stat > Tables > Contingency > with data**

3. Select both columns.

4. Click **Next** and check **Expected Count**.

5. Click **Calculate**.

Goodness-of-Fit Test

1. Enter the observed frequencies in one column and the expected frequencies in another column, in the same order.

2. **Stat > Goodness-of-fit > Chi-square test**

3. Select the column for **Observed**, and select the column for **Expected**.

4. Click **Calculate**.

   With the data on integer selection you should get a chi-square of 11.47 and a p-value of 0.0217.

SPSS

Two-Way Tables

TABLE SUMMARY

Unlike Minitab and Excel, SPSS will not allow us to simply enter the two-way table. Instead we have to create three columns: the first column will contain the different categories of the categorical variable, the second column will contain the different categories of the row variable, and the third column will contain the observed frequencies.

1. In the SPSS spreadsheet, select the **Variable View** tab (bottom left-hand corner).

2. Create three variables in the Variable View in the SPSS file: one for the row variable named *RowVar*, one for the column variable named *ColumnVar*, and the third for the observed frequencies named *Observed*. When you select the **Type** column, SPSS will ask you to indicate the type of data for the variable, and will provide you with a drop-down menu. For the *RowVar* and *ColumnVar*, select **String**, with a width of 15.

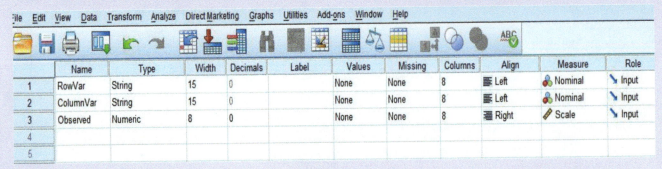

3. Select the **Data View** tab (bottom left-hand corner). Enter the data as it appears in the table below. Ensure you enter the data so that the observed frequencies in the Observed column match the row and column categories.

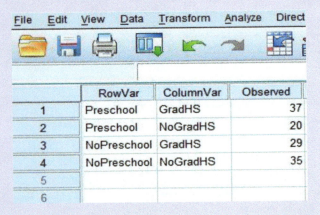

4. We now have to inform SPSS that the four observed values in the Observed column are not four data points, but data on 121 subjects. To do so, you will notice a **balancing-scale** icon below the **Add-ons** option on the menu bar.

5. Select [icon]. Select **Weight Cases by,** then move the *Observed* in the Frequency Variable field. Now press **OK**.

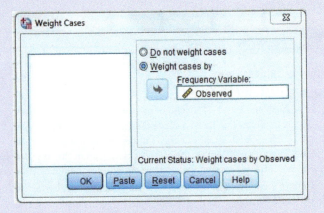

6. We have now entered the two-way table in SPSS. Now we need to do a test of independence. Select **Analyze > Descriptive Statistics > CrossTabs…**

7. Under the Row(s), select **RowVar**; under Column(s), select **ColumnVar**. In the Layer 1 of 1 field, select **Observed**. Check the box beside Display layer variables in table layers.

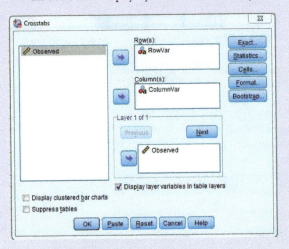

8. Select **Statistics** and then check the box beside **Chi-square**.

9. Select **Cells** and then check the box beside **Observed** and **Expected**. Select **Continue**.

10. Select **OK**. The observed value of the chi-square statistic is circled.

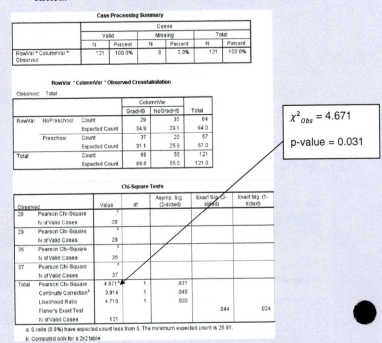

$\chi^2_{obs} = 4.671$

p-value = 0.031

RAW DATA

1. Two columns consist of categorical data. Select **Analyze > Tables > Custom Tables**.
2. Select the **Test Statistics** tab, then check the **Tests of independence (Chi-square)** box.
3. Select the **Table** tab. Drag the variable containing the columns of the two-way table to **Columns**, and the row variable of the two-way table to **Rows**. Select **OK**.

GOODNESS-OF-FIT TEST

1. In the SPSS spreadsheet, select **Variable View** and enter two variables. The first variable is the categorical variable Integer, the second represents the Observed frequency for each category of the Integer variable.

	Name	Type	Width	Decimals	Label	Values	Missing	Columns	Align	Measure	Role
1	Integer	Numeric	8	0		None	None	8	Right	Nominal	Input
2	Observed	Numeric	8	0		None	None	8	Right	Scale	Input

2. Select **Data View**. In the Integer column, enter 1 through 5. In the Observed column, enter the observed frequencies for the corresponding category.

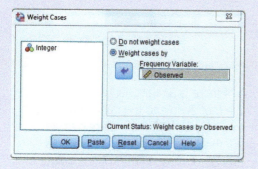

	Integer	Observed
1	1	3
2	2	5
3	3	14
4	4	11
5	5	5

3. Select **Data > Weight Cases**. Select **Weight cases by**. Select **Observed** and transfer this into the Frequency variable field. Select **OK**.

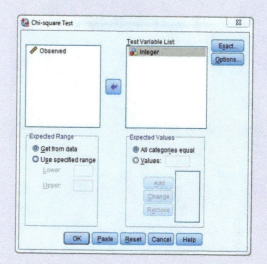

4. **Analyze > Nonparametric Tests > Legacy Dialogs > Chi-square**. Transfer the categorical variable column into the Test Variable List box by highlighting the Integer categorical variable and selecting the arrow. Select **All categories equal**. Select **OK**.

(Note: Should not all categories equal, then select **Values**. Enter the probability of each category according to the null hypothesis, then select **Add**. Repeat until you have accounted for all categories.)

5. The output.

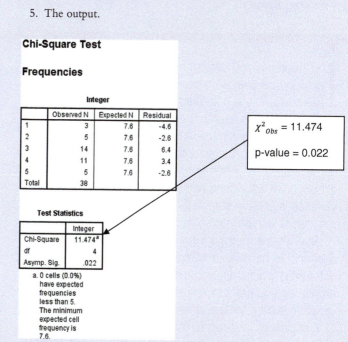

Chi-Square Test

Frequencies

Integer

	Observed N	Expected N	Residual
1	3	7.6	-4.6
2	5	7.6	-2.6
3	14	7.6	6.4
4	11	7.6	3.4
5	5	7.6	-2.6
Total	38		

Test Statistics

	Integer
Chi-Square	11.474[a]
df	4
Asymp. Sig.	.022

a. 0 cells (0.0%) have expected frequencies less than 5. The minimum expected cell frequency is 7.6.

$\chi^2_{Obs} = 11.474$

p-value = 0.022

11 Comparing Several Means: One-Way Analysis of Variance

rj lerich/Shutterstock

In Chapter 9, you learned how to compare the means of two populations using confidence intervals and hypothesis tests. There is nothing magical about the number two: we often need to compare three, four, or even more populations with each other. Analysis of variance, or ANOVA for short, is a method for doing just that. The name *analysis of variance* is slightly misleading, because although we will indeed use the variance (recall that the variance is just the standard deviation squared), it is really the *means* we are interested in.

ANOVA is a method for testing whether there is a relationship between a categorical variable that identifies different populations, and a numerical variable. For example, do you want to know which diet (the categorical variable) is best for losing weight (the numerical variable)? One approach is to randomly assign people to one of several diets and then compare the mean weight lost by each dieting type. If there is a relationship between the categorical variable *Diet Type* and the numerical variable *Weight Loss*, then it may be that the type of diet you choose determines the amount of weight you could lose. Is success in sports determined in part by the colour of the team uniform? To examine this question, we could compare the success rates of several different teams after grouping the teams by the categorical variable *Uniform Colour*.

In this chapter we will study some of the basic concepts of ANOVA. We will see how comparing the variation between the populations (or groups) and the variation within each of the populations (or groups) leads to a test statistic that can be used to compare the population means of several groups. We will also consider post-hoc tests, which allow us to identify which groups differ from which others once differences have been found to exist.

CASE STUDY

Seeing Red

Does the colour of your team uniform affect your performance? That's what researchers in England claimed, after studying data from 68 soccer teams over 56 seasons. On average, teams wearing red won 53% of their home games. Teams wearing blue won, on average, 51%, and teams wearing yellow/orange won only 50%. The researchers compared the performance of teams wearing four different colour groups (blue, orange or yellow, red, white) and found significant differences in performance, as measured by the percentage of home games won. (Teams wear their team colours only for home games.) Further investigation showed that teams wearing red did the best of all (Attrill et al. 2008).

You have seen two groups compared before, but how do we compare means across *four* different groups? This chapter covers techniques for doing so. Then we will return to this case study at the end of the chapter and see whether red is, statistically speaking, the "winningest" colour.

SECTION 11.1

Some General Principles of ANOVA

In earlier chapters, we compared two populations to each other, either with a *t*-test for comparing means, or with a confidence interval for the difference of two means. In this chapter we will examine situations that involve more than two populations. We will compare the means of these populations with a procedure called analysis of variance (or ANOVA). We will restrict our attention to **one-way analysis of variance**, which compares means of a numerical variable across populations that are distinguished by a single categorical variable, as described below. It is also possible to have two-way ANOVAs, which are used to compare means when there are two categorical variables and one numerical response variable, and even ANOVAs for more than two categorical variables. (These other methods will not be covered in this text.)

ANOVA is just another hypothesis test, so it follows the same four steps you have studied in earlier chapters. In this section we will give you an intuitive introduction to some of the fundamental concepts that are unique to ANOVA. In the next section we will examine the test statistic and its distribution in more detail.

Data and Assumptions

The data we will be working with have a very specific structure. The response variable is always numerical. Examples include the percentage of home games a soccer team wins, the number of kernels of corn that pop, the amount of weight a dieter loses, and the temperature of Earth in a given decade. We're comparing these numerical values across different populations, and these populations (or groups) are represented by a single categorical variable.

To illustrate, let us consider data from an experiment aimed at determining how to pop the perfect batch of popcorn (Kukuyeva et al. 2008). One of the factors the experimenters examined was the amount of oil used. They tried three different amounts of oil: none, ½ teaspoon, and 1 teaspoon. For our purposes, we call these groups None, Medium, and Maximum. They popped 36 bags using no oil, another 36 using a medium amount of oil, and another 36 using the maximum amount, with bags randomly assigned to each group. Each bag contained exactly 50 kernels. After 75 seconds, the bags were removed from a specific heat-setting, and the experimenters counted and recorded the number of kernels popped. Table 11.1 shows the first six rows of the results.

Details

Pronunciation
ANOVA is pronounced with the emphasis on the second syllable, an-**OH**-va.

Amount of Oil	Number of Kernels Popped
Maximum	8
Medium	26
Maximum	5
None	8
None	7
Medium	20

▲ TABLE 11.1 The first six lines of the popcorn data set.

The data set has two variables: a categorical variable (*Amount of Oil*) and a numerical variable (*Number of Kernels Popped*). We might summarize these data by showing the mean and standard deviation of the number of kernels popped in each group. Graphically, we can display boxplots to summarize the distributions of these data. Table 11.2 shows the summary statistics. Figure 11.1 shows boxplots of these data.

▶ **TABLE 11.2** The mean and standard deviation (in parentheses) for the number of kernels popped for each amount of oil.

Group:	None	Medium	Maximum
Mean (SD)	19.75 (11.76)	19.75 (11.83)	13.47 (9.30)

▶ **FIGURE 11.1** Boxplots showing the five-number summary of the distribution of number of kernels popped. The group in which the maximum amount of oil was used had a lower median number of good kernels than the other two groups.

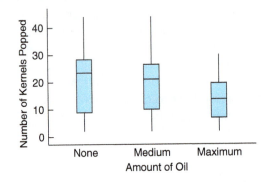

Does the amount of oil that is used affect the number of kernels that get popped? In order to answer this question using ANOVA, certain conditions must hold. For now we simply state the conditions. We will discuss how we can check these conditions and what to do when these conditions are not satisfied in Section 11.3.

Condition 1: *Random Samples.* Data in each group are a random sample from one population. This means that observations within each group are independent of each other.

Condition 2: *Independent Groups.* All samples are independent of each other.

Condition 3: *Same Variance.* The variance of the numerical variable (or if you prefer, the standard deviation) is the same for all populations being compared.

Condition 4: *Normal Distribution or Large Sample.* The population distributions of the numerical variable are approximately Normal or the sample size is large (at least 25 in each group).

Why Not Multiple *t*-Tests?

Figure 11.2 shows another perspective on the popcorn data. Each dot represents the number of popped kernels in one bag of popcorn. The mean number of popped kernels in each group is indicated by a red dot. We want to know whether the amount of oil affects the number of kernels popped. As you can see, this varies from bag to bag. But are the population means different? Or are observed differences of sample means due to chance? That is, if we were to pop a very large number of bags under these three different conditions, might the mean number of kernels popped all be the same?

▶ **FIGURE 11.2** Each dot represents a bag with 50 popcorn kernels in it. The bags were heated for 75 seconds, and the graph shows the number of kernels that had popped after this time. Different amounts of oil were used. The large red dots show the mean number of kernels popped.

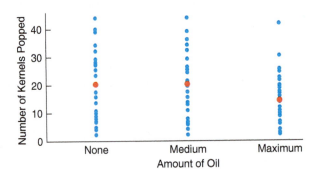

In Chapter 9, we would have answered these questions by doing a two-sample *t*-test. But as the name implies, two-sample *t*-tests are used for comparing only two populations. We need to compare three. We might try doing three separate two-sample *t*-tests. For example, we might test

Hypothesis 1
H_0: $\mu_{NoOil} = \mu_{MediumOil}$
H_A: $\mu_{NoOil} \neq \mu_{MediumOil}$

Hypothesis 2
H_0: $\mu_{NoOil} = \mu_{MaximumOil}$
H_A: $\mu_{NoOil} \neq \mu_{MaximumOil}$

Hypothesis 3
H_0: $\mu_{MediumOil} = \mu_{MaximumOil}$
H_A: $\mu_{MediumOil} \neq \mu_{MaximumOil}$

To compare all three populations, we need three different hypothesis tests. This is called a **multiple comparison**, because we are comparing multiple pairs of means. But this causes a problem.

To understand the problem, recall that whenever we do a significance test, there is a small probability that we will make the mistake of rejecting the null hypothesis when it is true. This probability is called the significance level, and we usually set it to be 0.05, or 5%.

The basic idea with multiple comparisons is that even though the probability of something going wrong on one occasion is small, if we keep repeating the experiment, eventually something *will* go wrong. By doing multiple tests, we are creating more opportunities to mistakenly reject the null hypothesis. The more tests we do, the greater the probability that we'll mistakenly reject the null hypothesis at least once.

The probability that we mistakenly reject the null hypothesis at least once after doing several hypothesis tests is called the **familywise error rate** (also known as *overall significance level*). Making "at least one" such mistake means that we make this error for one test, for two tests, or for all tests. When three hypothesis tests are performed, each with a significance level of 5%, the familywise error rate is $1-(0.95)^3 = 0.14$, or about 14%. In other words, the probability that we will conclude that at least one amount of oil is more effective than another, when the truth is that all amounts are equally effective, is 14%. This is not terribly high, but we were shooting for a 5% error rate, and 14% is quite a bit higher.

KEY POINT   The familywise error rate is the probability that you will mistakenly reject the null hypothesis (that is, reject the null hypothesis when it is true) in at least one of several hypothesis tests. The familywise error rate is always larger than the significance level for any one of the individual tests.

When we have only three populations (or groups) to compare, we need to make only three comparisons, and the familywise error rate goes from 5% (for one comparison) to 14%. But if we have more groups, the familywise error rate goes up dramatically. If we have four groups, then we need to make six comparisons. The overall significance level is now about 26%. If we have five groups, then we need to make ten comparisons, and there is about a 40% chance that we will mistakenly reject at least one of the ten null hypotheses.

Figure 11.3 shows how the familywise error rate increases as the number of groups increases. You can see that if you have ten groups, then the probability that you will mistakenly reject at least one null hypothesis is 90%. You are almost certain to make a mistake!

 Details

Familywise Error Rate
The event that "at least one test mistakenly rejects H_0" is the complement of "none of the tests mistakenly rejects H_0." The probability that out of three tests none mistakenly rejects H_0 is $(0.95)^3$. Therefore, the familywise error rate is $1 - (0.95)^3$.

 Details

Number of Pairwise Comparisons
The number of comparisons we need to make when comparing k groups by pairs is the same as the number of different ways in which you can select two objects from a set of k objects. This is given by
$$\frac{k(k-1)}{2},$$
where k is the number of groups you are comparing. We therefore need six comparisons when comparing four groups, ten comparisons when comparing five groups, and so on.

▶ **FIGURE 11.3** The familywise error rate—the probability that at least once we'll reject the null hypothesis when in fact it is true—increases dramatically as the number of groups increases. If there are ten groups and all of the means are equal, then the probability that we will mistakenly conclude that at least one is different from the others is about 90%.

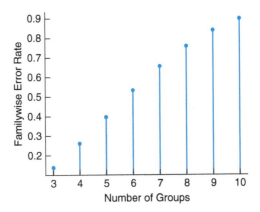

Looking Back

Power

Recall that, all other factors being equal, the *power* of a test (the probability of correctly rejecting the null hypothesis when it is false) decreases if the significance level goes down and increases if the significance level goes up.

Statisticians have worked out different ways of solving the problem of multiple comparisons. One straightforward solution is to reduce the significance level for each individual test, thereby achieving the desired familywise error rate (we will discuss this method at the end of Section 11.4). Unfortunately, reducing the significance level for every test leads to a loss of statistical power, meaning that there is a lower probability that we will correctly identify that two groups have different means. In contrast, the analysis of variance is a method that allows us to compare means from several groups simultaneously without any loss of power.

The Null and Alternative Hypotheses

The null and alternative hypotheses are the same for every ANOVA. If we are comparing k different groups (for example, $k = 3$ for the popcorn experiment), and if we call the population mean of the first group μ_1, the population mean of the second group μ_2, and so on, then the hypotheses are

H_0: $\mu_1 = \mu_2 = \cdots = \mu_k$

H_A: At least one of the population means is not equal to another, or H_0 is false.

Another way of stating these hypotheses is by considering the relationship between the two variables of interest. In those terms, the hypotheses are

H_0: There is no relationship between the categorical variable and the numerical variable.

H_A: There is some relationship: the population means differ among groups.

In the context of popping corn, the null hypothesis says that no matter what amount of oil you use (no oil, medium oil, or maximum oil), you'll always get the same mean number of kernels popped. The alternative hypothesis claims that the two variables are related, so that at least one mean is different from another. In other words, if the alternative hypothesis is true for this controlled experiment, then the amount of oil has an effect on the number of kernels popped: if you use different amounts of oil, you can expect a different mean number of kernels popped for at least one of the amounts of oil.

Rejecting the null hypothesis for an ANOVA is usually unfulfilling. We learn that at least one of the means is different from another, but we do not learn which one. We do not learn whether there is more than one mean that is different. We don't learn which is the biggest, which is the smallest, or really any information other than that the null hypothesis is not true. For this reason, an ANOVA test is often followed up with an exploration to look further at the relationship of the groups to one another. We'll give some approaches for this exploration, which is often called post-hoc analysis, in Section 11.4.

 KEY POINT One-way ANOVA tests whether a categorical variable is related to a numerical variable. This is the same as testing whether the mean value of a numerical variable is the same for all populations.

Visualizing ANOVA

ANOVA is based on comparing the different sources of variation that contribute to the overall variation in the data. There is variation *between* the data collected from each group, and there is variation in the data *within* each of the groups being compared. To help you understand what this means, let's think about our analysis visually.

As the name suggests, the analysis of variance determines whether the population means from the groups are the same or different by comparing the variances of the groups. Basically, if at least one of the means is very far away from another, we want to reject the null hypothesis. Here *very far* means "very far, relative to the amount of variation within the data."

Figure 11.4a shows a plot of means from four groups. (The data are simulated.) Do the means look similar or different to you?

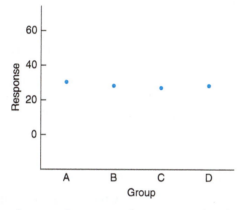

 Looking Back

Variance vs. Variation
Both *standard deviation* and *variance* have specific mathematical definitions. Standard deviation and variance are methods for measuring *variation*, which is itself a more general term and has no mathematical definition.

◄ **FIGURE 11.4a** The means of four different groups. The means are slightly different, but are they close enough together for the observed differences to be due to chance? Or are they so far apart that we conclude they're actually different?

Figure 11.4b shows the same four means, but now we also show the individual data points. You can see that the variation within each of the four groups appears to be the same, represented by the roughly equal vertical-spread of dots. This variation is much larger than the variation between the four means (the red dots), which are fairly close together. Therefore, the variation between means is small compared to the variation within groups, and we would expect our ANOVA to fail to reject the null hypothesis. There is not enough evidence to convince us that the means are different from each other. The small differences we see could easily be explained by chance.

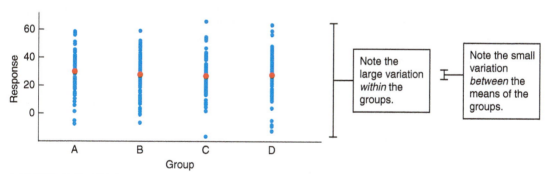

▲ **FIGURE 11.4b** With the actual data points displayed, we now see that the means are actually close together. The distances between means are much less than the distances between points within any of the groups.

In fact, the standard deviation of the four means is 1.38. The standard deviation within each of the groups is about 13.6. Thus the amount of variation between the means is much smaller than the amount of variation within each group.

Figure 11.4c on the next page shows another scenario. The means *are exactly the same as in Figures 11.4a and 11.4b*, but in this new data set, the variability is so small that the group means look very different from each other. The standard deviation between the group means is still 1.38. But now the standard deviation within each group is only 0.10.

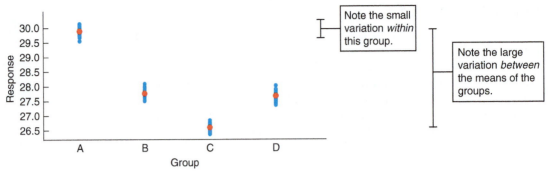

▲ **FIGURE 11.4c** These data have the same means as in Figures 11.4a and 11.4b, but there is more variation *between* the groups and less variation *within* each group. In this context, the means are very different from each other.

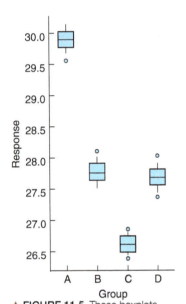

▲ **FIGURE 11.5** These boxplots show us mostly the same information as in Figure 11.4c. We see that the medians of the groups are very different with respect to the variation within each group. Because the distributions are assumed to be Normal, the medians (represented by the horizontal lines in the middle of the boxes) are very close to the means.

The amount of variation between the group means is much greater than the variation within each group, so the means are more different from each other. In this case, we would expect our ANOVA procedure to reject the null hypothesis.

Although ANOVA focuses on means, boxplots are a useful first step for visualizing ANOVA. This is true even though, as you'll recall, boxplots display the median, not the mean, of a sample of data. Under the condition of normality, the distribution is symmetric, so the mean and the median are the same. Therefore, boxplots help us see how different the means are. Figure 11.5 shows boxplots for the four groups in Figure 11.4c.

The Test Statistic and the ANOVA Table

To perform a hypothesis test, we need a test statistic. This means that these informal ideas—variation between groups and variation within groups—need to be converted into a number. The test statistic we use for ANOVA, called the *F*-statistic, does just that:

$$F = \frac{\text{Variation between groups}}{\text{Variation within groups}}$$

The *F*-statistic compares the variation between groups to the variation within groups. If the variation between groups is big relative to the variation within groups (as in Figure 11.4c), then *F* will tend to be a large number. If the variation between groups is small relative to that within groups (as in Figure 11.4b), then *F* will be a small number. We will reject the null hypothesis if *F* gets to be too big.

KEY POINT Large values of the *F*-statistic discredit the null hypothesis of equal population means for all groups, because a large value suggests that there is more variation between the groups than within each group.

EXAMPLE 1 Large and Small *F*-Values

We calculated the *F*-statistics for Figures 11.4b and 11.4c. One of these had an *F*-value of 1.03, and the other had an *F*-value of 17344.81.

QUESTION Which observed *F*-statistic belongs to which figure, and why?

CONCLUSION The null hypothesis is that the means are the same. Large values of the *F*-statistic discredit the null hypothesis. Although the means in Figures 11.4b and 11.4c have the same numerical value, the variation between groups is much greater in Figure 11.4c when compared to the variation within each group. For this reason, the large F-statistic of 17344.81 must belong to Figure 11.4c.

TRY THIS! Exercise 11.3

In the next section we will show you exactly how the *variation between groups* and the *variation within groups* are measured in order to calculate the F-statistic. The value of the F-statistic, together with the results of all calculations that lead to it, is often presented in what is called an **ANOVA table**. The table is usually obtained using statistical software.

EXAMPLE **2** Book Ratings

The website Goodreads (www.goodreads.com) invites visitors to list books they've read and to rate the books. Books are also "tagged" with keywords that identify the type of book. Figure 11.6 shows random samples of ratings for three different tags. Figure 11.7 shows the output from a one-way ANOVA analysis using StatCrunch.

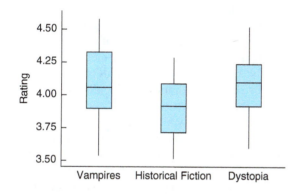

◀ **FIGURE 11.6** Ratings as posted by visitors to goodreads.com. The tags help identify the genre of the book.

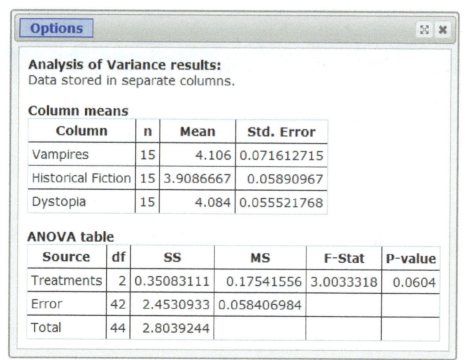

◀ **FIGURE 11.7** StatCrunch output for one-way ANOVA of the Goodreads data.

Analysis of Variance results:
Data stored in separate columns.

Column means

Column	n	Mean	Std. Error
Vampires	15	4.106	0.071612715
Historical Fiction	15	3.9086667	0.05890967
Dystopia	15	4.084	0.055521768

ANOVA table

Source	df	SS	MS	F-Stat	P-value
Treatments	2	0.35083111	0.17541556	3.0033318	0.0604
Error	42	2.4530933	0.058406984		
Total	44	2.8039244			

QUESTION State the null hypothesis and the alternative hypothesis. What is the value of the F-statistic?

CONCLUSION The null hypothesis is that the population mean ratings for all three tags (Vampires, Historical Fiction, and Dystopia) are equal. The alternative hypothesis is that at least one mean rating is different from another.

From the ANOVA table, we see that the F-statistic, given in the column labelled F-Stat, is 3.0033318, or about 3. You will see in Section 11.3 how the p-value appearing in the same table can be used to determine whether this value of F is large enough to reject the null hypothesis and thereby decide whether or not mean book ratings are the same for all three tags.

TRY THIS! Exercise 11.5

SECTION 11.2

Understanding the ANOVA Table

The ANOVA table displays the value of the F-statistic and the p-value required to carry out a complete test of hypothesis for comparing several means. It also presents the results of computations needed to calculate the value of the statistic. Those calculations are tedious, so they are rarely done by hand. However, since there is no better way of completely understanding ANOVA, we present the details of those calculations in this section. (This section may be skipped without loss of continuity.)

To provide a context for our discussion, we will consider the results of an experiment comparing weight loss for four types of diet. Researchers in nutrition randomly assigned four diets to 126 people (Dansinger et al. 2005). They weighed these people before the diet and again two months later. This allowed them to see how much weight each person lost. The data they obtained are summarized in Table 11.3 (for convenience, we have reported negative changes in weight as a positive weight loss). The ANOVA output for these data is shown in Figure 11.8.

▶ **TABLE 11.3** Means and standard deviations of weight loss (in kg) for each group of dieters and for all observations pooled together.

Diet	Number of Observations	Mean Weight Loss (kg)	Standard Deviation
Diet 1: Atkins	$n_1 = 31$	$\bar{x}_1 = 4.681$	$s_1 = 2.946$
Diet 2: Ornish	$n_2 = 29$	$\bar{x}_2 = 5.000$	$s_2 = 3.032$
Diet 3: Weight Watchers	$n_3 = 33$	$\bar{x}_3 = 4.200$	$s_3 = 3.834$
Diet 4: Zone	$n_4 = 33$	$\bar{x}_4 = 4.600$	$s_4 = 3.448$
All Observations	$N = 126$	$\bar{\bar{x}} = 4.607$	$s = 3.321$

Pay close attention to the notation we have used in Table 11.3. When observations are categorized by group, diet i has n_i observations with mean $\bar{x}_i$ and standard deviation s_i. When all observations are pooled together (the last row of the table), there are a total of N observations with mean $\bar{\bar{x}}$ (called the **grand mean**) and standard deviation s.

▶ **FIGURE 11.8** ANOVA Minitab output for weight loss of four groups of dieters.

One-way ANOVA: Weight Loss versus Diet

```
Source   DF      SS    MS     F      P
Diet      3    10.1   3.4  0.30  0.825
Error   122  1368.5  11.2
Total   125  1378.6
```

Explained Variation + Unexplained Variation = Total Variation

The amount of weight lost obviously varied from person to person. Why did different people lose different amounts of weight? One possible explanation—the one the researchers were interested in—is the type of diet. However, you can probably think of lots of other reasons why weight loss varied. Maybe gender matters. Maybe some people had more weight to lose. Maybe some people had different metabolisms, or some people exercised more than others. Maybe there are just unknown, immeasurable factors that influence how much weight a person will lose. All of these reasons except the first one (type of diet) are possibilities that were not being controlled by the researchers, so that any variation due to these possibilities is unexplained by the type of diet. Therefore, we can think of the **total variation** in the data obtained in this experiment as being either **explained variation** (explained by the type of diet) or **unexplained variation**.

ANOVA measures variation with sums of squares. Total variation, measured by the **Total Sum of Squares (SS_{total})**, is thus partitioned into explained and unexplained components, namely the **Sum of Squares Between Groups (SS_{between})** and the **Sum of Squares Within Groups (SS_{within})**. We can summarize this relationship with the following fundamental identity.

Formula 11.1: $SS_{\text{total}} = SS_{\text{between}} + SS_{\text{within}}$

KEY POINT Total variation as measured by the sum of squares can be broken into two pieces: explained variation (SS_{between}) and unexplained variation (SS_{within}). If the explained variation is large (compared to the unexplained), it indicates that the means of the groups are very different.

Total Sum of Squares

The Total Sum of Squares is given by the sum of squared deviations of all observations from the grand mean.

$$SS_{\text{total}} = \sum (x - \bar{\bar{x}})^2$$

This definition helps us understand why ANOVA is called the analysis of *variance*. This is simply the numerator in the formula for finding the variance when all observations are pooled together.

Recall that the variance is the square of the standard deviation:

$$s^2 = \frac{\sum (x - \bar{\bar{x}})^2}{N - 1} = \frac{\sum (\text{deviation})^2}{N - 1} = \frac{SS_{\text{total}}}{N - 1}$$

This means that we can find SS_{total} by multiplying the variance of all observations s^2 by the total sample size minus 1.

Formula 11.2: $SS_{\text{total}} = \sum (x - \bar{\bar{x}})^2 = (N - 1)s^2$

For our dieters example, we use the standard deviation $s = 3.321$ from Table 11.3, square it and multiply it by 125 (N is 126 and $126 - 1 = 125$) to get $SS_{\text{total}} = 125 (3.321)^2 = 1378.6$. In Figure 11.8, this value can be found in the row labelled Total under the column labelled SS.

Sum of Squares Between Groups

The Sum of Squares Between Groups measures the variability between the group means (the explained variation). Because there can be a different number of observations in each group, the squared deviation of each mean from the grand mean must take into account the group size.

$$SS_{\text{between}} = \sum n_i (\bar{x}_i - \bar{\bar{x}})^2$$

Using values from Table 11.3:

$$SS_{between} = 31(4.681 - 4.607)^2 + 29(5 - 4.607)^2 + 33(4.2 - 4.607)^2$$
$$+ 33(4.6 - 4.607)^2 = 10.1$$

In Figure 11.8, this value can be found in the row labelled Diet under the column labelled SS.

The variation between groups is sometimes called the **variation due to treatment** because it is the amount of variation that is explained by the treatment (in this case, the diet to which the subjects were assigned).

Sum of Squares within Groups

The Sum of Squares Within Groups measures the unexplained variation. It is also referred to as **variation due to error**, as in Figure 11.8, or as **residual variation**, because it is the variation that is "left over" after we have explained some of the variation with the treatment. It is given by the sum of squared deviations of each observation from its own group mean. We find it by adding the numerators of the variances in each group.

$$\textbf{Formula 11.3:} \ SS_{within} = \sum (n_i - 1)s_i^2$$

Using values from Table 11.3:

$$SS_{within} = 30(2.946)^2 + 28(3.032)^2 + 32(3.834)^2 + 32(3.448)^2 = 1368.6$$

In Figure 11.8, this value can be found in the row labelled Error under the column labelled SS.

Note that we could have obtained SS_{within} after knowing SS_{total} and $SS_{between}$ by using the identity in Formula 11.1. In general, if you know any of the two sums of squares, you can find the third one by addition or subtraction.

Mean Squares

Each sum of squares has a certain number of degrees of freedom (df) associated with it. These are found by counting the number of pieces of information contributing to that sum of squares and subtracting the number of independent pieces of information used to measure that variation. This is simpler than it sounds:

Diet: We have 4 different group means, compared with 1 grand mean, so df = 4 − 1 = 3
Error: We have 126 observations, compared with 4 group means, so df = 126 − 4 = 122
Total: We have 126 observations, compared with 1 grand mean, so df = 126 − 1 = 125

These values are found in the column labelled DF in Figure 11.8. In general, if the number of groups is k and the total number of observations is N, then

$$df_{between} = k - 1$$
$$df_{within} = N - k$$
$$df_{total} = df_{between} + df_{within} = N - 1$$

The column labelled MS in the ANOVA table contains the **mean squares**. These are simply the sums of squares divided by their corresponding df value. Dividing by the number of degrees of freedom adjusts the sums of squares by taking into account the fact that $SS_{between}$ gets bigger as the number of groups gets bigger and SS_{within} gets bigger as the number of observation gets bigger.

$$\textbf{Formula 11.4:} \ MS_{between} = \frac{SS_{between}}{k - 1} = \frac{\sum n_i (\bar{x}_i - \bar{\bar{x}})^2}{k - 1}$$

$$\textbf{Formula 11.5:} \ MS_{within} = \frac{SS_{within}}{N - k} = \frac{\sum (n_i - 1)s_i^2}{N - k}$$

Applying these formulas to the data in Table 11.3,

$$MS_{\text{between}} = MS_{\text{treatments}} = \frac{SS_{\text{between}}}{k-1} = \frac{10.1}{4-1} = 3.4$$

$$MS_{\text{within}} = MS_{\text{error}} = \frac{SS_{\text{error}}}{N-k} = \frac{1368.6}{126-4} = 11.2$$

These values appear under the column labelled MS in Figure 11.8.

When the null hypothesis is true and all means are the same, both mean squares approximate the shared population variance (remember that we assumed that the variance of all groups is the same). However, if the null hypothesis is not true, MS_{between} is influenced by the differences among the means whereas MS_{within} is not. Therefore, if the null hypothesis is true, both mean squares estimate the same quantity, and if the null hypothesis is not true, MS_{between} will tend to be larger than MS_{within}.

The *F*-Statistic

We compare the values of MS_{between} and MS_{within} using the *F*-statistic. It is calculated as the ratio of the two mean squares:

Formula 11.6: $F = \dfrac{\text{Variation between groups}}{\text{Variation within groups}} = \dfrac{MS_{\text{between}}}{MS_{\text{within}}}$

From what we said earlier, if the null hypothesis is true, *F* is approximately 1 and variations away from 1 occur only by chance. If the null hypothesis is not true, *F* will tend to be larger than 1. For our dieters example, $F = 3.4 / 11.2 = 0.30$, which is smaller than 1 and does not indicate a difference in means.

KEY POINT When the null hypothesis is true, both mean squares estimate the population variance and *F* is approximately 1. If the null hypothesis is not true, MS_{between} is influenced by the difference in means and MS_{within} is not, so MS_{between} is larger than MS_{within} and *F* is much larger than 1.

Table 11.4 shows the general form of an ANOVA table summarizing the required calculations. In this text, we will always rely on technology to find the p-value in the last column. We will discuss what this p-value represents later in this section when we talk about the sampling distribution of the *F*-statistic.

Source	df	SS	MS	F-Statistic	p-Value
Between/ Explained/ Treatment	$k-1$	$\sum n_i(\bar{x}_i - \bar{\bar{x}})^2$	$SS_{\text{between}}/(k-1)$	$MS_{\text{between}}/MS_{\text{within}}$	xxxx
Within/ Unexplained/ Error/Residual	$N-k$	$\sum (n_i - 1)s_i^2$	$SS_{\text{within}}/(N-k)$		
Total	$N-1$	$\sum (x - \bar{\bar{x}})^2$			

▲ **TABLE 11.4** The general form of an ANOVA table.

 Caution

Values of the *F*-statistic can never be negative. If you compute the value of the *F*-statistic and find that it is < 0, then check your calculation.

🌎 EXAMPLE 3 Mercury Concentration in Shorebird Eggs

Populations of some shorebird species are believed to be declining. One possible explanation for the decline is the harmful effect of contaminants such as methylmercury. To study this possibility, researchers at Environment Canada's National Wildlife Research Centre compared mercury contamination in eggs of four Canadian Arctic–breeding shorebird species: black-bellied plover, ruddy turnstone, semipalmated plover, and white-rumped sandpiper (the first two with declining populations and the latter two with stable or slightly increasing populations). The data they obtained are summarized in Table 11.5 (McCloskey et al. 2013).

▶ **TABLE 11.5** Mercury concentration in the eggs of four shorebird species.

Species	Black-Bellied Plover	Semipalmated Plover	Ruddy Turnstone	White-Rumped Sandpiper	All Observations
Mercury Concentration (mg/kg)	0.477 0.416 0.371 0.571 0.719	1.005 0.635 0.622 0.386 0.904	0.547 0.481 0.633 0.757 0.601	0.917 0.843 1.341 0.958 0.422	
Mean	$\bar{x}_1 = 0.5108$	$\bar{x}_2 = 0.7104$	$\bar{x}_3 = 0.6038$	$\bar{x}_4 = 0.8962$	$\bar{\bar{x}} = 0.6803$
Standard Deviation	$s_1 = 0.1384$	$s_2 = 0.2465$	$s_3 = 0.1032$	$s_4 = 0.3278$	$s = 0.2516$

QUESTION Construct the ANOVA table for this study. (The p-value is 0.076.)

SOLUTION To use the calculations summarized in Table 11.4, we identify $n_1 = n_2 = n_3 = n_4 = 5$, $k = 4$, and $N = 20$. Then

$$SS_{total} = (N - 1)s^2$$
$$= (20 - 1)(0.2516)^2 = 1.2027$$
$$SS_{within} = (n_1 - 1)s_1^2 + (n_2 - 1)s_2^2 + (n_3 - 1)s_3^2 + (n_4 - 1)s_4^2$$
$$= 4(0.1384)^2 + 4(0.2465)^2 + 4(0.1032)^2 + 4(0.3278)^2$$
$$= 0.7921$$
$$SS_{between} = SS_{total} - SS_{within} = 1.2027 - 0.7921 = 0.4106$$
$$df_{between} = k - 1 = 4 - 1 = 3$$
$$df_{within} = N - k = 20 - 4 = 16$$
$$df_{total} = N - 1 = 20 - 1 = 19$$
$$MS_{between} = 0.4106/3 = 0.1369$$
$$MS_{within} = 0.7921/16 = 0.0495$$
$$F = 0.1369/0.0495 = 2.77$$

CONCLUSION The results of our calculations are set out in Table 11.6. Note that if you obtain the same table using software, small differences are possible due to rounding.

▶ **TABLE 11.6** ANOVA table for mercury concentration in eggs of four shorebird species.

Source	df	SS	MS	F	p-Value
Between	3	0.4106	0.1369	2.77	0.076
Within	16	0.7921	0.0495		
Total	19	1.2027			

TRY THIS! Exercise 11.9

 EXAMPLE **4** Fuel Consumption

Does fuel consumption on the highway (measured in Canada in litres per 100 kilometres) vary by the number of cylinders in a car's engine? Data from Natural Resources Canada are used to perform an ANOVA for three types of cars: 4, 6, and 8 cylinders. Some entries in the ANOVA table are missing in Figure 11.9.

QUESTION Obtain the value of the F-statistic by finding all missing entries from the Minitab output.

```
One-way ANOVA: L/100K Highway versus Cylinders

Source      DF       SS       MS        F       P
Cylinders    ?   1860.44   ??????   ??????   0.000
Error      ???   ???????     1.33
Total      906   3064.37
```

◀ **FIGURE 11.9** Incomplete ANOVA table to test whether fuel consumption differs for three different types of cars.

SOLUTION

Degrees of freedom: There are three types of cars being considered (different numbers of cylinders), so $df_{cylinders}$ is $3 - 1 = 2$. Since $df_{total} = df_{cylinders} + df_{error}$, we find

$$df_{error} = df_{total} - df_{cylinders} = 906 - 2 = 904$$

Sums of Squares: Since $SS_{total} = SS_{cylinders} + SS_{error}$, we have (Formula 11.1)

$$SS_{error} = SS_{total} - SS_{cylinders} = 3064.37 - 1860.44 = 1203.93$$

Mean Squares (Formula 11.4):

$$MS_{cylinders} = \frac{SS_{cylinders}}{df_{cylinders}} = \frac{1860.44}{2} = 930.22$$

F-statistic (Formula 11.6):

$$F = \frac{MS_{cylinders}}{MS_{error}} = \frac{930.22}{1.33} = 699.4$$

CONCLUSION The value of the F-statistic is $F = 699.4$, meaning that variation between groups is nearly 700 times the variation within groups. This is much bigger than 1, so there is indication that mean fuel consumption is not the same for different numbers of cylinders. We will make this precise once we discuss the p-value.

TRY THIS! Exercise 11.13

The *F*-Statistic and Its Distribution

You've seen that if the null hypothesis is true and the population mean is the same for all groups, then the F-statistic will be approximately 1. Values of the F-statistic that are much larger than 1 discredit the null hypothesis. But how can we tell whether a particular F-value is large because the null hypothesis is wrong and the means are different, or whether it is large just because of chance?

The p-value measures our surprise at the outcome and is used to determine whether the F-statistic is "large." Recall that the p-value is the probability of getting a test statistic as extreme as or more extreme than the observed value, assuming the null hypothesis is true. For ANOVA, the p-value is the probability of getting a value of the F-statistic equal to or larger than the observed value, assuming that all the means are equal.

To find this probability, we need to know the distribution of the F-statistic. Under the ANOVA assumptions stated in Section 11.1, the F-statistic is a random variable that follows what is called the F-distribution (no surprise here). The shape of the F-distribution depends on two parameters: the number of degrees of freedom in the numerator and the number of degrees of freedom in the denominator. These are the degrees of freedom of the mean squares used to compute the F-statistic: $k - 1$ in the numerator (the df of $MS_{between}$) and $N - k$ in the denominator (the df of MS_{within}).

Figure 11.10 shows the *F*-distribution for several combinations of degrees of freedom. Note that negative values of *F* are not possible (after all, it is a ratio of mean *squares*). Also, the distributions are skewed to the right. However, as both numbers of degrees of freedom increase, the distribution is less skewed and concentrates more and more around 1.

▶ **FIGURE 11.10** Four *F*-distributions with different degrees of freedom. Note how the right-skewness decreases as both df increase. Also note that negative values are not possible.

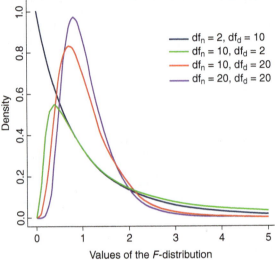

We will rely on p-values obtained by software, as those in the ANOVA tables in Figures 11.8 and 11.9. However, it is important to understand where the p-value comes from. For example, Figure 11.11 shows the *F*-distribution with 3 degrees of freedom in the numerator and 102 degrees of freedom in the denominator. This distribution is the one used to test the hypothesis that the four dieting groups all have the same mean weight loss. The shaded area (the area to the right of the observed *F*-value of 0.3005) represents the p-value, which is 0.8249.

▶ **FIGURE 11.11** The *F*-distribution with 3 degrees of freedom in the numerator and 102 degrees of freedom in the denominator. The shaded area is the probability that an *F*-statistic will be larger than 0.3005. This value is 0.8249, or about 82%. This is the p-value appearing in the ANOVA table in Figure 11.8 to test whether the diets differ in mean weight loss.

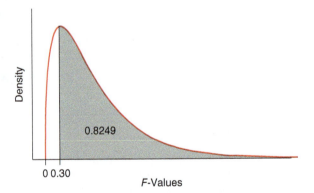

Clearly, this p-value is so large that we would not reject the null hypothesis. This shows that even though these diets use very different strategies for weight loss, they seem to have the same results on average. Although the amount of weight lost varies from person to person, this variation doesn't seem to have anything to do with the type of diet (at least after two months of dieting).

EXAMPLE **5** Mercury Concentration Revisited

The researchers who conducted the mercury concentration study concluded that there were no significant differences in mean egg mercury concentrations among the four shorebird species they considered (black–bellied plovers, ruddy turnstones, semipalmated plovers, and white-rumped sandpipers).

QUESTION Recall that the *F*-statistic obtained from the data was 2.77, with a p-value of 0.076. Use this information to justify the researchers' conclusion at a significance level of 5%. (Assume that the conditions for testing ANOVA hold.)

SOLUTION If the means are equal, then the probability of getting an *F*-statistic as large or larger than $F = 2.77$ is 0.076. Since this probability is larger than the significance level, the null hypothesis of equal means is not rejected.

CONCLUSION Because the null hypothesis was not rejected, the researchers are justified in concluding that there are no significant differences in mean egg mercury concentration.

TRY THIS! Exercise 11.15

The ANOVA Test

We are almost ready to incorporate everything we have learned so far about ANOVA into one complete hypothesis test. There is just one last issue left to discuss, and it has to do with assumptions.

Checking Conditions

The p-value from the ANOVA table measures the probability of getting an *F*-statistic equal to or larger than the observed value when the null hypothesis is true, but only when certain conditions hold. Remember that these are 1) random samples; 2) independent groups; 3) equal variance for all groups; and 4) either normality of observations or a large sample.

Of these four conditions, the first two are the most important, but also the hardest to check. Independence of the samples and independence of observations within samples are results of the data collection method. If you are collecting the data yourself, you can take measures to ensure randomness and independence. In other situations, you can get an idea of whether or not these conditions hold if the data collection method is well documented. Sometimes you just have to assume that they do, understanding that if in fact the assumptions do not hold, your results could be very wrong.

The first condition, random samples from each population so that observations within each sample are independent, is similar to the requirement for the one-sample *t*-test of Chapter 9. Having objects within a group that are related to each other violates this condition. For example, if we randomly sample family members within each group, then for many purposes these measurements would be related to each other, not independent.

The second condition, independent groups, would be violated if, say, the same objects were measured in each group. This is a fairly common data structure, particularly in medical research. For example, subjects might receive three different medications, one every six months. Researchers measure the subjects' reaction to the medications. The "groups" are the different medications, but because the same subjects appear in each group, the samples are not independent. A procedure called repeated measures ANOVA exists for analyzing data such as these, but it is beyond the scope of this book.

The third condition, that the variances or standard deviations of all the populations being compared be equal, is sometimes called the homoscedastic condition. **Homo-scedasticity** is a fancy word for "having the same variance." One general rule for checking this condition when all other conditions are met is that the largest standard deviation must be no more than twice the smallest.

For example, the standard deviations of the dieting groups are

Atkins	2.9 kg
Ornish	3.0 kg
Weight Watchers	3.8 kg
Zone	3.4 kg

The smallest SD is 2.9 kg, so as long as the largest SD is smaller than $2 \times 2.9 = 5.8$ kg, we may assume that this condition holds. Another way to see this is to divide the largest SD by the smallest: $3.8/2.9 = 1.3$, which is smaller than 2.

In other books, you may come across other general rules for checking this condition. The ANOVA procedure is fairly resistant to slight deviations from homoscedasticity, which is why some rules are slightly different.

The final condition is that the observations in each group be sampled from a population that follows a Normal distribution. This can be checked by examining a histogram for each group. However, unless the sample sizes are fairly large in each group, this can be hard to check because histograms from Normal populations don't always look Normal when the sample size is small. In these instances, it is best to display boxplots of the data. Another approach requires more work but gives better insight: subtract each observation from the average of its group. Then make a histogram of all these differences (called **residuals**). If these residuals look Normal, the condition holds. (In Section 13.5 we will discuss one more tool for checking normality: QQ plots.) The *F*-test is more sensitive to departures from Normality for small samples than other procedures we've studied up to this point, so some caution is needed.

What If Conditions Are Not Satisfied?

If either of the assumptions about independence is violated, then a one-way ANOVA is not the correct procedure to use. Other procedures exist for different situations, and these are usually covered in more advanced statistics courses.

If the same-variance condition is not satisfied, then transforming the data by replacing each value with either its square root or its logarithm will sometimes fix the problem. This transformation approach also sometimes works if the Normality condition fails. After replacing the data with their transformed values, you need to check the conditions again. If the conditions still fail, then you need a different procedure. In Chapter 13 we will discuss some procedures (called nonparametric procedures) that can sometimes be used in this situation, and we will demonstrate some transformations.

EXAMPLE 6 Checking Conditions

Atmospheric scientists often use anomaly temperatures to study global climate change. These temperatures are the difference between the readings at a particular location and the average global temperature for the entire twentieth century (1901–2000). A negative anomaly temperature is lower than the reference point, and a positive value means it is above that reference point. These are also called "residual" temperatures. All temperatures are measured in degrees Celsius (°C). The boxplots in Figure 11.12 on the next page show global surface temperatures grouped by "double decades" for the last century (that is, 1880–1899, 1900–1919, and so on). The data are global monthly averages—the average temperature on land around the world for a particular month. The temperatures are collected by a network of sensors at fixed locations around the planet. Figure 11.13 on the next page shows a histogram of the residuals from an ANOVA. It is tempting to do an ANOVA, because we have a numerical response variable (*Temperature Anomaly*) and a categorical predictor variable (*Double Decade*). However, the conditions do not hold.

QUESTION Which conditions are not satisfied for using ANOVA to test whether the mean global surface temperature is different for the given time periods?

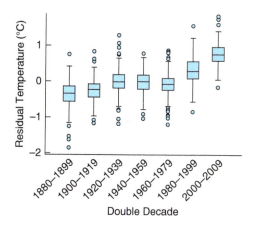

◀ **FIGURE 11.12** Mean global surface temperatures for each "double decade." Temperatures were measured relative to a reference temperature, which was the mean surface temperature for the twentieth century. Temperatures are in degrees Celsius.

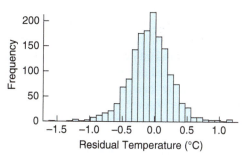

◀ **FIGURE 11.13** Residual temperatures. Each observation is the temperature minus the average temperature for its double decade.

CONCLUSION Judging on the basis of the boxplots, the amount of variation in each group seems about the same, so we would expect the standard deviations to be about the same. This means that the third condition—same variance—is met. The histogram of residuals looks roughly Normal, so the fourth condition is met. However, the first two conditions are not met. From month to month, temperatures are not independent. One unusually warm month is likely to be followed by another unusually warm month, so observations within groups might be dependent. Also, because the same objects were measured in each group, the groups are not independent. A method other than ANOVA must be used to decide whether differences in mean temperatures are due solely to chance variation.

TRY THIS! Exercise 11.17

Carrying Out an ANOVA Test

ANOVA is just another hypothesis test, like all the others we've covered. Example 7 shows you how to do a complete ANOVA by applying the same four-step procedure we've done for other hypothesis tests.

 EXAMPLE 7 Testing Popped Popcorn

Does the amount of oil used affect the number of kernels popped when one is making popcorn? Recall that researchers randomly assigned bags with 50 unpopped kernels to be popped with no oil, a medium amount of oil (1/2 tsp), or the maximum amount of oil (1 tsp) at a certain level of heat. Thirty-six bags were assigned to each group. After 75 seconds, the popped kernels were counted. A graphical summary of these data was provided in Figure 11.1.

QUESTION Using a significance level of 5%, carry out an ANOVA test, showing each of the four steps of a hypothesis test.

> **Looking Back**
>
> **Four Steps**
> The four steps of a hypothesis test are (1) hypothesize, (2) prepare, (3) compute to compare, and (4) interpret and conclude.

SOLUTION

Step 1: Hypothesize

$$H_0: \mu_{\text{NoOil}} = \mu_{\text{MediumOil}} = \mu_{\text{MaximumOil}}$$

H_A: The mean number of kernels popped is not the same for all amounts of oil used.

In words, the null hypothesis says that the mean number of kernels popped is not related to the amount of oil used, since the means are the same for all amounts of oil. The alternative hypothesis says that at least one of the means is different, or the null hypothesis is false.

Step 2: Prepare

In order for the F-statistic to follow the F-distribution, we need to check conditions. The first condition, independence between groups, holds because bags were randomly assigned to each group. You must assume that the second condition, independence within groups, holds. This condition would fail if, for example, the oven was still heating up while some bags in a group were tested. For the third condition, equal variances, refer to Figure 11.1 on page 514, which shows boxplots of the three groups. The interquartile ranges are about the same, so you can expect the standard deviations to be roughly equal as well. You can also see in Table 11.2 that the standard deviations can be assumed to be equal, since the largest standard deviation is no more than twice the smallest. The final condition, Normal distribution, is difficult to check with some statistical software packages. We note here that the response variable consists of counts, which are not Normally distributed because the Normal distribution has continuous, not discrete, values. However, because the counts have a large range (from 0 to 50), these distributions might be roughly Normal. You might not have the tools to check, so you'll have to make an assumption that the distributions are close enough to Normal for you to continue.

Step 3: Compute to compare

Figure 11.14 shows the ANOVA table from Minitab. We see that the observed value of the F-statistic is $F = 3.89$, meaning that the variation between groups (measured by MS_{Oil}) is almost four times greater than the variation within groups (measured by MS_{Error}). The p-value tells us that if the means are equal, then the probability of getting an F-statistic this large or larger is 0.023. At the 0.05 level of significance, this would be a surprising outcome if the null hypothesis were true.

▶ **FIGURE 11.14** ANOVA table (Minitab) for the popcorn experiment.

One-way ANOVA: kernels_popped versus oil

```
Source    DF      SS    MS      F      P
Oil        2     946   473   3.89  0.023
Error    105   12762   122
Total    107   13708
```

Step 4: Interpret and conclude

If there is no difference in the mean number of popped kernels between the three different groups, then the probability of observing an F-statistic that is at least as big as 3.89 is 0.023, or 2.3%. Because the p-value is small (smaller than our significance level of 0.05), we reject the null hypothesis and conclude that the mean amount of kernels popped is not the same for all amounts of oil used.

CONCLUSION Because we reject the null hypothesis, we conclude that the amount of oil used affects the number of kernels that get popped. We can make a causal conclusion here—that the amount of oil caused the differences we observed—because the bags were randomly assigned to the groups.

TRY THIS! Exercise 11.21

SNAPSHOT | ANALYSIS OF VARIANCE (ANOVA)

WHAT IS IT? ▶ ANOVA is a procedure for testing whether the means for several populations (or groups) are the same.

WHAT DOES IT DO? ▶ It compares the amount of variation between groups to the amount of variation within groups.

HOW DOES IT DO IT? ▶ If the population means of the groups are not all the same, the variation between groups will be larger than the variation within groups.

HOW IS IT USED? ▶ The F-statistic is the ratio of the variation between groups (measured with the mean square between groups) to the variation within groups (measured with the mean square within groups). If the F-statistic is large (evidenced by a p-value in the ANOVA table smaller than the significance level of the test), reject the null hypothesis and conclude that at least one mean is different from another.

WHEN IS IT USED? ▶ Observations must satisfy four conditions: (1) random samples; (2) independent groups; (3) equal variances; (4) normal distribution.

SECTION 11.4

Post-Hoc Procedures

As we noted earlier, rejecting the null hypothesis of an ANOVA can be anticlimactic. We learn that oil affects the results of popping popcorn, but we don't know which amount of oil works best. For this reason, after rejecting the null hypothesis of an ANOVA, we next do a **post-hoc analysis**. *Post-hoc* is Latin for "after this." The phrase reminds us that we do this analysis after we have looked at the data and determined (with a chance of making an error) that at least one of the means is too different from another to be convincingly explained by chance. If we do not reject the null hypothesis, then there is no need to do a post-hoc procedure, because we do not have enough evidence to conclude that the means differ.

The goal of a post-hoc analysis is to determine which groups have different means from the others, which groups have the highest means, which the lowest means, and so on. The spirit of post-hoc analysis is that we go into it knowing nothing other than that at least one of the means is different from another. As you saw in Section 11.1, we must be cautious when doing multiple comparisons of groups.

There are many procedures that can be used for post-hoc analysis. Here we present the Tukey Honestly Significant Difference (Tukey HSD) approach, which is based on computing simultaneous confidence intervals for differences between all pairs of means. Not only does the procedure allow us to find out which means are different from each other, it also gives us an estimate of how large the differences might be.

KEY POINT A post-hoc analysis is performed after rejecting the null hypothesis from an ANOVA and concluding that at least one of the group means is different from another. The goal is to determine *which* means are different by comparing all possible pairs of means. An appropriate correction must be made in order to keep the familywise error rate at a specified value.

Tukey Honestly Significant Difference Confidence Intervals

The **Tukey Honestly Significant Difference (HSD)** approach provides a set of **simultaneous confidence intervals** (at a given confidence level) for all differences of pairs of group means. Each interval that does not include 0 tells us that the corresponding means differ significantly.

The confidence level of the HSD intervals (say, 95%) does not refer to a particular interval, but instead refers to the entire set of intervals. This means that if the HSD approach were used to calculate intervals for many ANOVA data sets, then for approximately 95% of those data sets, *every* HSD interval would capture the true value of the difference in means, and only 5% of the time would *at least one* of the intervals fail to capture the true value of the difference. In other words, 0.05 is the familywise error rate for the collection of intervals, as we discussed at the beginning of this chapter.

Calculations for Tukey HSD intervals are straightforward. However, because they involve the use of tables for a new probability distribution, we will simply show you how to interpret intervals produced by statistical software.

As an example, let us examine Figure 11.15, which shows an extended ANOVA output for the popcorn experiment. The table with Tukey pairwise comparisons provides 95% confidence intervals for the following differences using the Tukey HSD approach:

- (Medium oil) minus (maximum oil), or $\mu_{MediumOil} - \mu_{MaximumOil}$

- (No oil) minus (maximum oil), or $\mu_{NoOil} - \mu_{MaximumOil}$

- (No oil) minus (medium oil), or $\mu_{NoOil} - \mu_{MediumOil}$

For example, the confidence interval for (medium minus maximum) is (0.10 to 12.45). Because this interval includes only positive numbers, we can be confident that the mean number of kernels popped is higher with the medium amount of oil than with the maximum amount of oil. The confidence interval for (no oil minus maximum) is also (0.10 to 12.45), so we make a similar conclusion: the mean number of kernels popped is higher with no oil than with the maximum amount of oil. On the other hand,

▶ **FIGURE 11.15** ANOVA table for popcorn data with Tukey HSD intervals included (Minitab).

TECH

```
One-way ANOVA: kernels_popped versus oil

Analysis of Variance

Source   DF   Adj SS   Adj MS   F-Value   P-Value
oil        2    945.9    472.9      3.89     0.023
Error    105  12762.5    121.5
Total    107  13708.3

Means

oil        N    Mean   StDev       95% CI
maximum   36   13.47    9.30   ( 9.83,  17.12)
medium    36   19.75   11.83   (16.11,  23.39)
none      36   19.75   11.76   (16.11,  23.39)

Pooled StDev = 11.0249
```

Tukey Pairwise Comparisons

```
Tukey Simultaneous Tests for Differences of Means

                        Difference    SE of                          Adjusted
Difference of Levels    of Means    Difference      95% CI     T-Value  P-Value
medium - maximum           6.28        2.60    ( 0.10, 12.45)    2.42    0.046
none - maximum             6.28        2.60    ( 0.10, 12.45)    2.42    0.046
none - medium              0.00        2.60    (-6.17,  6.17)    0.00    1.000

Individual confidence level = 98.07%
```

the confidence interval that compares using a medium amount of oil to using no oil does include 0. Therefore, no significant difference exists between using no oil and using the medium amount of oil. In summary, we conclude that using medium oil or no oil is better than using the maximum amount of oil, but it does not make any difference whether you use no oil or the medium amount of oil.

EXAMPLE 8 Seasonal Smog

In its yearly publication on air quality in Ontario, the Ontario Ministry of the Environment states that the typical smog season in that province occurs from May to September. To see whether there are indeed seasonal differences in air quality in Toronto, we randomly selected 35 dates between 2007 and 2013 within each of the following time frames: Early Spring (March 21 to April 30), Late Spring (May 1 to June 20), Summer (June 21 to September 20), Fall (September 21 to December 20), and Winter (December 21 to March 20). We then obtained data from airqualityontario. com on the Air Quality Index (AQI) for each of those dates at 4:00 p.m. in downtown Toronto. Assume that the conditions for ANOVA hold. Figure 11.16 shows a boxplot of the recorded AQI data by season. Note that air quality is considered very good for AQI readings between 1 and 15, good for readings between 16 and 31, moderate for readings between 32 and 49, poor between 50 and 99, and very poor for AQI readings of 100 or more.

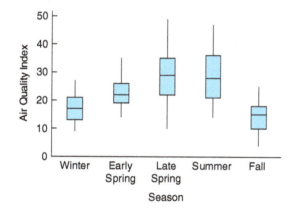

◀ **FIGURE 11.16** Air Quality Index in downtown Toronto for a random sample of dates between 2007 and 2013.

QUESTIONS

a. Figure 11.17 shows output from an ANOVA and post-hoc analysis. Carry out an ANOVA test.

b. If appropriate, carry out a post-hoc analysis to determine which groups are different from others. How are they different?

c. Do these data support seasonal differences in air quality in Toronto? If so, which seasons have the highest air quality readings?

SOLUTIONS

a. The null hypothesis is that mean AQI readings are the same for all time periods. The alternative hypothesis is that at least one time period has a mean AQI that is different from another's. We see from the value of the F-statistic in the ANOVA table that variation between groups, as measured by $MS_{treatments}$, is almost 32 times larger than variation within groups, as measured by MS_{error}. This would be quite a surprising result if the null hypothesis were true, as indicated by the extremely small p-value. We therefore reject the null hypothesis and conclude that the mean AQI reading varies between the different time periods.

▶ **FIGURE 11.17** Output from ANOVA analysis for AQI data (StatCrunch).

Options

Analysis of Variance results:
Data stored in separate columns.

Column means

Column	n	Mean	Std. dev	Std. Error
Fall	35	14.885714	5.1379295	0.86846859
EarlySpring	35	22.771429	5.3582576	0.90571084
LateSpring	35	28.914286	9.1759642	1.551021
Summer	35	28.571429	8.4793372	1.4332696
Winter	35	16.771429	4.6087239	0.77901653

ANOVA table

Source	df	SS	MS	F-Stat	P-value
Treatments	4	5908.1486	1477.0371	31.771474	<0.0001
Error	170	7903.2	46.489412		
Total	174	13811.349			

Tukey 95% Simultaneous Confidence Intervals:

Fall subtracted from

	Difference	Lower	Upper	P-value
EarlySpring	7.8857143	3.3916592	12.379769	<0.0001
LateSpring	14.028571	9.5345163	18.522627	<0.0001
Summer	13.685714	9.1916592	18.179769	<0.0001
Winter	1.8857143	-2.6083408	6.3797694	0.7757

EarlySpring subtracted from

	Difference	Lower	Upper	P-value
LateSpring	6.1428571	1.648802	10.636912	0.0021
Summer	5.8	1.3059449	10.294055	0.0044
Winter	-6	-10.494055	-1.5059449	0.0028

LateSpring subtracted from

	Difference	Lower	Upper	P-value
Summer	-0.34285714	-4.8369123	4.151198	0.9996
Winter	-12.142857	-16.636912	-7.648802	<0.0001

Summer subtracted from

	Difference	Lower	Upper	P-value
Winter	-11.8	-16.294055	-7.3059449	<0.0001

b. Because we rejected the null hypothesis, a post-hoc analysis is appropriate. The first table of Tukey HSD intervals shows us the mean AQI of each season minus the mean AQI for Fall. Positive values mean that AQI for that season is, on average, higher than for Fall. Therefore, we are confident that the mean AQI for Fall is *lower* than those for Early Spring, Late Spring, and Summer. The last interval includes 0, so mean AQI for Fall and Winter are the same.

The next table subtracts the mean AQI for Early Spring from the remaining seasons. The values for Late Spring and Summer are positive, so mean AQI for Early Spring is *lower* than mean AQI for Late Spring and Summer. The negative values of the last interval imply that mean AQI for Early Spring is *higher* than mean AQI for Winter.

The next table subtracts the mean AQI for Late Spring from the remaining seasons. The first interval contains 0, so there is no difference between Late Spring and Summer. The negative values of the second interval indicate that mean AQI for Late Spring is *higher* than mean AQI for Winter. Finally, from the negative values in the last comparison, we are confident that mean AQI for Summer is *higher* than that for Winter.

c. The time periods of Late Spring and Summer both have AQI means that are significantly higher than the mean AQI for the other time periods. Therefore, the time period with worst air quality in Toronto is between May and September (as stated by the Ontario Ministry of the Environment).

TRY THIS! Exercise 11.31

Visualizing Simultaneous Confidence Intervals

A useful trick for sorting out simultaneous confidence intervals like the Tukey HSD is first to write the names of the groups, from the group with the lowest sample mean on the left to the group with the highest sample mean on the right. (If sample means are equal, you can put them in any convenient order.) For example, the seasons sorted from lowest to highest sample mean AQI (refer to Figure 11.17) are

Fall   Winter   Early Spring   Late Spring   Summer

We draw lines underneath any groups whose confidence intervals include 0. (This tells us that their means are so close together that we can't tell the population means apart.)

<u>Fall   Winter</u>   Early Spring   <u>Summer   Late Spring</u>

This helps us see that Fall and Winter are about the same in mean AQI, that Early Spring is higher than Fall and Winter, and that Late Spring and Summer are about the same, higher than all the rest. Often this type of comparison is expressed in terms of the population means:

$$(\mu_{Fall} = \mu_{Winter}) < \mu_{EarlySpring} < (\mu_{LateSpring} = \mu_{Summer})$$

We can apply this technique to the popcorn experiment too:

Maximum Oil   <u>Medium Oil   No Oil</u>

and

$$\mu_{MaximumOil} < (\mu_{MediumOil} = \mu_{NoOil})$$

🌐 Bonferroni Intervals

For an extended, in-depth discussion of Bonferroni intervals, visit MyStatLab.

Final Thoughts on Post-Hoc Analyses

Different software packages provide very different options for performing the post-hoc analysis for an ANOVA. Most do some version of what we've presented: they give you simultaneous confidence intervals to compare pairs of means. A few, such as Minitab, default to showing you confidence intervals for *individual* groups, not for the *differences* between groups. We recommend that you ignore these individual intervals, because they fail to take into account the necessary post-hoc adjustments and because, unless you take great care, you can easily reach the wrong conclusion. Instead, ask the software to find simultaneous confidence intervals for *differences* between all pairs of means.

The post-hoc analyses we've discussed are intended to show us all possible comparisons between groups. This is most appropriate if, when you began the ANOVA, you did not know which groups would be bigger or smaller than the others. Sometimes, researchers have very definite hypotheses about the order of groups. (For example, for the air quality data, we were interested in finding out whether Late Spring and Summer had higher AQI than all other time periods.) It is possible to do more focused analyses that concentrate on comparing particular groups, not all pairs of groups. Those types of multiple comparisons are discussed in more advanced texts.

CASE STUDY REVISITED

The researchers were interested in understanding whether the colour of a soccer team's uniform affects its performance. They cited a history of research that suggests that some colours are more successful than others. Some researchers explain this by citing biological or evolutionary factors (many animals display red as a sign of dominance, and humans associate red with the emotions of anger and aggression). The researchers examined 55 years of soccer results in the United Kingdom. Part of their analysis focused on how the percentage of games won varied between colour groups. A boxplot of the data, Figure 11.18, shows that the median values differ and supports the hypothesis that teams with red jerseys are slightly more successful than other teams. The boxplot shows that while the same-variance requirement is satisfied, the number of outliers and a suggestion of skewness for certain groups suggest that the Normal condition might not be satisfied. Also, the data might not really be independent, because the teams play each other. (If one team wins a lot, the other teams must be winning less.) Because of these possible problems, the researchers decided to use a different approach, examples of which you'll see in Chapter 13. But it's instructive to first consider what we might learn from the ANOVA approach in this chapter. The output is shown in Figure 11.19 on the next page.

▶ **FIGURE 11.18** The percentages of home game wins for teams with jerseys of different colours: blue (B), red (R), white (W), and yellow or orange (YO). Teams wearing red shirts seem to have a slightly higher winning percentage than other teams, on average.

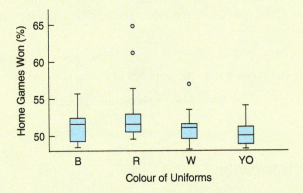

The p-value of 0.0361 means that, with a significance level of 5%, we reject the null hypothesis and conclude that the mean number of wins differs by colour of the team jersey.

We visualize the post-hoc analyses by writing the groups in order of their mean percentage of wins and underlining groups that have (statistically speaking) the same mean.

<u>YO   B   W</u>   R

This visualization shows us that the only confidence interval that does not include 0 is the one that compares red teams with yellow/orange teams. From this, we are confident that teams with red uniforms win a greater percentage of home games, on average, than teams with yellow/orange uniforms.

○ ○ ○   One Way ANOVA   Java Applet Window

Options

Analysis of Variance results:

Responses stored in percentwin.

Factors stored in colour.

Factor means

colour	n	Mean	Std. Error
B	23	51.239132	0.42154145
R	16	53.025	1.066634
W	11	51.29091	0.71343654
YO	18	50.283333	0.37593022

ANOVA table

Source	df	SS	MS	F-Stat	P-value
Treatments	3	65.40642	21.80214	3.0189104	0.0361
Error	64	462.19888	7.2218575		
Total	67	527.6053			

Tukey 95% Simultaneous Confidence Intervals

B subtracted from

	Lower	Upper
R	-0.5218412	4.0935802
W	-2.5468976	2.650455
YO	-3.186618	1.275024

R subtracted from

	Lower	Upper
W	-4.5105963	1.0424145
YO	-5.1773243	-0.30600926

W subtracted from

	Lower	Upper
YO	-3.7205107	1.7053592

◀ **FIGURE 11.19** Output from ANOVA to test whether teams with uniforms of different colours have different winning percentages, on average.

Although not all of the conditions for an ANOVA were satisfied, the conclusions are supported by more careful analyses that the authors of this study performed in addition to the basic ANOVA.

GOALS

The goal is to determine, using methods you have learned in this chapter, whether those who feel they are athletic have a better recovery heart rate.

MATERIALS

A clock or watch with a second hand is needed. The instructor can call out the starting and ending times.

ACTIVITY

To do this activity, you need to record your pulse in terms of beats per minute. To practise this, make sure you can find your pulse. Count how many beats you feel in 15 seconds, and multiply by 4.

Now stand up and sit down five times, and take your pulse immediately.

Sit and rest for one minute. Take your pulse.

Your recovery heart rate is the difference between the two pulse rates: the pulse after exercise (standing up and sitting down) minus the pulse rate after resting. Some physicians believe that the larger the difference, in general, the more fit you are.

Your instructor will collect your recovery pulse rate and also ask you to classify your general activity level.

To classify your activity level, think about how often you do an activity that raises your pulse rate for 20 minutes or more. If it is once a week or less, then you are in Group A. If it is twice a week to three times per week, you are in Group B. If it is four times a week or more, you are in Group C.

BEFORE THE ACTIVITY

1. Why can't we just use a *t*-test for the analysis of this data set?

2. What do you think will happen? Which group will have the highest mean recovery pulse rate?

AFTER THE ACTIVITY

Was your prediction about recovery rates correct?

CHAPTER REVIEW

Summary of Learning Objectives

1. **What is the difference between the significance level of a single test and the familywise error rate of multiple comparisons?** The significance level of a single test is the probability of rejecting the null hypothesis when it is true. When we perform multiple comparisons (several tests), the familywise error rate is the probability that we mistakenly reject the null hypothesis *at least once*. The familywise error rate is larger than the significance level of each test and, for a fixed significance level, it increases as the number of groups increases.

2. **What are the conditions for comparing means of groups using ANOVA?** (1) Random samples; (2) Independent groups; (3) Same variance in all groups; (4) Distribution of observations is Normal, or sample size is large.

3. **How are the elements of an ANOVA table calculated?** For the formulas below, N is the total number of observations; $\bar{\bar{x}}$ and s are the mean and standard deviation of all observations combined; n_i, $\bar{x}_i$, and s_i are the number of observations, the mean, and the standard deviation in group i.

Formula 11.1:

$$\text{Total Sum of Squares} = SS_{\text{total}} = SS_{\text{between}} + SS_{\text{within}}$$

Formula 11.2: $\text{Total Sum of Squares} = SS_{\text{total}} = (N - 1)s^2$

Formula 11.3:

$$\text{Sum of Squares Within Groups} = SS_{\text{within}} = \sum (n_i - 1)s_i^2$$

Formula 11.4:

$$\text{Mean Square Between} = MS_{\text{between}} = \frac{SS_{\text{between}}}{k - 1} = \frac{\sum n_i (\bar{x}_i - \bar{\bar{x}})^2}{k - 1}$$

Formula 11.5:

$$\text{Mean Square Within} = MS_{\text{within}} = \frac{SS_{\text{within}}}{N - k} = \frac{\sum (n_i - 1)s_i^2}{N - k}$$

Formula 11.6:

$$F\text{-statistic } F = \frac{\text{Variation between groups}}{\text{Variation within groups}} = \frac{MS_{\text{between}}}{MS_{\text{within}}}$$

4. **When do the value of the F-statistic and its p-value support rejecting the null hypothesis of equal means for all groups?** When the null hypothesis is not true, the variation between groups (measured by MS_{between}) is larger than the variation within groups (measured by MS_{within}). In that case, the value of the F-statistic will be large (much larger than 1) and the p-value will be small. When the p-value is smaller than the significance level, we reject the null hypothesis and conclude that at least one mean is different from another.

5. **When and how can I perform a post-hoc analysis?** When you reject the null hypothesis of ANOVA, you may go on to do a post-hoc analysis to identify which groups differ from which others. Obtain simultaneous confidence intervals for all possible differences of pairs of group means either by the Tukey HSD method or by using the Bonferroni Correction. The means of intervals that do not contain 0 can be considered significantly different.

Important Terms

One-way analysis
   of variance
   (ANOVA), *513*
Multiple comparisons, *515*
Familywise error rate, *515*
ANOVA table, *519*
Grand mean, *520*
Total variation, *521*

Explained variation (variation
   between groups, treatment
   variation), *521*
Unexplained variation
   (variation within groups,
   error variation, residual
   variation), *521*
Total Sum of Squares, *521*

Sum of Squares Between
   Groups, *521*
Sum of Squares Within
   Groups, *521*
Variation due to treatment, *522*
Variation due to error, *522*
Residual variation, *522*
Mean squares, *522*

Homoscedasticity, *527*
Residuals, *528*
Post-hoc analysis, *531*
Tukey Honestly Significant
   Difference (HSD), *532*
Simultaneous confidence
   intervals, *532*

Sources

Air Quality Ontario. http://www.airqualityontario.com (accessed March 5, 2014).

Attrill, M. J., K. A. Gresty, R. A. Hill, and R. A. Barton. 2008. Red shirt colour is associated with long-term team success in English football. *Journal of Sports Science* 26(6), 577–582.

Dansinger, M. L., J. A. Gleason, J. L. Griffith, H. P. Selker, and E. J. Schaefer. 2005. Comparison of the Atkins, Ornish, Weight Watchers, and Zone diets for weight loss and heart disease risk reduction. *Journal of the American Medical Association* 293(1), 43–53.

Kukuyeva, I. A., J. Wang, and Y. Yaglovskaya. 2008. Popcorn popping yield: An investigation. *JSM Proceedings.*

McCloskey, M., S. Robinson, P. A. Smith, and M. Forbes. 2013. Mercury concentration in the eggs of four Canadian Arctic-breeding shorebirds not predicted based on their population statuses. *Springer Plus* 2, 567.

Natural Resources Canada. Fuel 2013. *Fuel consumption guide.*

SECTION EXERCISES

SECTION 11.1

In Exercises 11.1 and 11.2, for each situation, choose the appropriate test: one-sample t-test, two-sample t-test, ANOVA, or chi-square test.

11.1 Choosing a Test

a. You wish to test whether a relationship exists between a categorical variable (such as rank of a professor at a university, assuming three ranks) and a numerical variable (such as yearly salary).

b. You wish to test whether the means of a numerical variable are different for two possible values of a categorical variable (such as yearly salary by gender).

11.2 Choosing a Test

a. You wish to test whether a relationship exists between two categorical variables.

b. You wish to test whether the sample mean of a numerical variable is not equal to a known population mean.

TRY **11.3 Comparing *F*-Values from Boxplots (Example 1)**
Refer to the figure. Assume that all distributions are Normal (therefore the sample mean and median are approximately equal) and that all the samples are the same size. Imagine carrying out two ANOVA tests. The first compares the means based on samples A, B, and C (above the horizontal line), and the second is based on samples L, M, and N (below the horizontal line). One of the calculated values of the *F*-statistic is 9.38, and the other is 150.00. Which value is which? Explain.

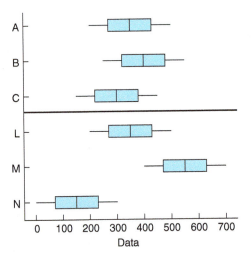

11.4 Comparing *F*-Values from Boxplots
Refer to the figure. Assume that all data sets are Normal and that all the samples are the same size. Imagine carrying out two ANOVA tests. The first compares the means based on samples A, B, and C (above the horizontal line), and the second is based on samples G, H, and K (below the horizontal line). One of the calculated values of the *F*-statistic is 9.38, and the other is 25.00. Which value is which? Explain.

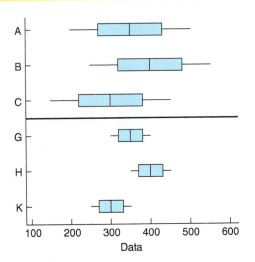

TRY **11.5 TV Watching and Education Level (Example 2)** Refer to the StatCrunch output for data from the General Social Survey, showing the effect of education level on the number of minutes per day spent watching TV (people who did not watch TV were not included in the sample). Assume that the population distributions are close enough to Normal to justify using ANOVA. (Source: Statistics Canada)

Options

Analysis of Variance results:
Responses in MinutesTV.
Factors in Education.

Factor means

Education	n	Mean	Std. dev	Std. Error
College/Trade Diploma	54	160.75926	98.939649	13.463981
HS diploma	29	193.41379	97.894447	18.178542
No HS Diploma	41	239.21951	149.32306	23.320344
Some postsecondary	25	155.72	88.858746	17.771749
University Degree	50	128.88	80.901966	11.441266

ANOVA table

Source	df	SS	MS	F-Stat	P-value
Treatments	4	304755.43	76188.857	6.7514305	<0.0001
Error	194	2189260.2	11284.847		
Total	198	2494015.7			

a. Write the null and alternative hypotheses for the effect of education level on the minutes spent watching TV per day.

b. Identify the value of the *F*-statistic from the StatCrunch output.

c. Which education-level group had the largest sample mean and which had the smallest sample mean?

d. Assuming that you did find a relationship between education level and the minutes spent watching TV per day, would this relationship mean that education level caused the differences in number of minutes watching TV per day? Can you think of a confounding variable?

11.6 Social Networks and Age Refer to the StatCrunch output for data from the General Social Survey, showing the effect of age on the number of minutes per day spent participating on social network sites such as Facebook or MySpace. (People who did not participate on social network sites were not included in the sample.) Assume that the population distributions are close enough to Normal to justify using ANOVA. (Source: Statistics Canada)

Options   ⌧ ✕

Analysis of Variance results:
Responses in SocialNetworkTime.
Factors in Age.

Factor means

Age	n	Mean	Std. dev	Std. Error
15 to 24	156	81.846154	79.987995	6.404165
25 to 34	79	75.708861	86.730965	9.7579959
35 to 44	73	64.972603	68.939783	8.0687913
45 to 54	60	88.566667	123.3951	15.930239
55 to 64	53	60.924528	70.002156	9.6155357

ANOVA table

Source	df	SS	MS	F-Stat	P-value
Treatments	4	35732.399	8933.0998	1.208981	0.3063
Error	416	3073803	7388.9495		
Total	420	3109535.4			

a. Write the null and alternative hypotheses for the effect of age on time spent participating on a social network.

b. Which age group had the largest sample mean and which had the smallest?

c. Identify the value of the *F*-statistic from the output.

11.7 Religious Participation and Volunteering Refer to the Minitab output for a random sample of respondents to the Canada Survey of Giving, Volunteering and Participating. The analysis shows the relationship between religious participation and yearly number of volunteer hours. Assume that the population distributions are close enough to Normal to justify using ANOVA. (Source: Statistics Canada)

One-way ANOVA: VolunteerHrs versus Religious Participation

```
Source                   DF      SS      MS     F     P
Religious Participation   4  1240761  310190  4.14  0.004
Error                   120  8985898   74882
Total                   124 10226659

S = 273.6   R-Sq = 12.13%   R-Sq(adj) = 9.20%

Level        N   Mean  StDev
1or2PerYear  25  161.3  195.9
3or4PerYear  25   99.5  144.7
Monthly      25  168.5  183.1
NotAtAll     25  173.9  267.6
Weekly       25  390.7  458.2
```

a. Write the null and alternative hypotheses for the relationship between religious participation and yearly number of volunteer hours.

b. Identify the value of the *F*-statistic from the Minitab output.

c. Which group had the largest sample mean and which had the smallest sample mean?

d. Assuming that you did find a relationship between religious participation and the yearly number of volunteer hours, would this relationship mean that religious participation caused the differences in the number of volunteer hours? Can you think of a confounding variable?

11.8 Marital Status and Volunteering Refer to the Minitab output for a random sample of respondents to Canada Survey of Giving, Volunteering and Participating. The output shows the relationship between marital status and yearly number of volunteer hours. Assume that the population distributions are close enough to Normal to justify using ANOVA. (Source: Statistics Canada)

One-way ANOVA: VolunteerHrs versus Marital

```
Source  DF      SS      MS     F      P
Marital  3  208000   69333  0.97  0.412
Error   96  6888678  71757
Total   99  7096678

S = 267.9   R-Sq = 2.93%   R-Sq(adj) = 0.00%

Level                 N    Mean   StDev
Married/CommonLaw     25  233.9   364.8
Single                25  153.9   217.4
Widowed               25  183.6   260.0
Separated/Divorced    25  108.4   197.7
```

a. Write the null and alternative hypotheses for the relationship between marital status and yearly number of volunteer hours.

b. Order the means from smallest to highest.

c. Identify the value of the *F*-statistic from the Minitab output.

d. Without referring to the p-value in the table, does the value of the *F*-statistic support rejection of the null hypothesis?

SECTION 11.2

In Exercises 11.9–11.12, use the given data to find $SS_{between}$, SS_{within}, SS_{total}, $df_{between}$, df_{within}, df_{total}, $MS_{between}$, and MS_{within}. Find the value of the F-statistic. Set out your results on a complete ANOVA table. For convenience, we have given you the overall mean $\bar{\bar{x}}$, the standard deviation of all observations s and the p-value. Assume the conditions for ANOVA are met.

TRY **11.9 Study Hours by Major (Example 3)** Three independent random samples of university students were asked how many hours per week they studied outside of class. Their responses and their majors are shown in the table. For these data, $\bar{\bar{x}} = 7.320$, $s = 3.775$, p-value $= 0.001$. See page 549 for guidance.

Math	SocSci	English	Math	SocSci	English
15	10	14	10	3	5
20	12	12	8	5	5
14	8	12	7	7	4
15	7	10	7	6	8
14	7	10	5	3	9
10	10	10	5	3	10
12	6	8	5	3	4
9	8	8	15	2	3
10	5	5	6	2	3
11	4	7	5	1	3
9	4	6	3	5	6
8	4	4	5	4	4
8	8	6			

11.10 Commuting Times A statistics professor recorded his commuting times (in seconds) using three different routes from home to work. The commuting times and the routes are shown in the table. For these data, $\bar{\bar{x}} = 732.7$, $s = 100.7$, p-value $= 0.572$.

Route 1	Route 2	Route 3
732	732	608
842	708	863
736	821	694
732	578	752
736	661	983
833	794	629
655	1029	605
688	674	628
727	552	717
721	657	748
695	869	679
707	652	637
843	745	767
852	648	765
789	869	620

11.11 Tomato Plants and Coloured Light Jennifer Brogan, a biology student who was taking a statistics class, exposed similar tomato plants to different colours of light. The average growth rates (in millimetres per week) are given in the table. For these data, $\bar{\bar{x}} = 6.784$, $s = 3.780$, p-value < 0.0001.

Blue	Red	Yellow	Green
5.34	13.67	4.61	2.72
7.45	13.04	6.63	1.08
7.15	10.16	5.29	3.97
5.53	13.12	5.29	2.66
6.34	11.06	4.76	3.69
7.16	11.43	5.57	1.96
7.77	13.98	6.57	3.38
5.09	13.49	5.25	1.87

11.12 Sleep and Age The table shows the number of minutes slept the night before the interview, by age, for a random sample of respondents to the 2010 General Social Survey. For these data, $\bar{\bar{x}} = 472.2$, $s = 140.3$, p-value $= 0.181$. (Source: Statistics Canada)

15 to 24	25 to 34	35 to 44	45 to 54
525	780	360	450
240	300	510	480
510	360	450	360
660	420	540	480
480	600	415	390
480	570	360	480
630	540	1195	495
510	390	285	510
540	420	240	360
420	270	270	420
480	480	510	465
435	600	435	420
540	390	330	420
480	600	600	480
600	1215	405	510
420	540	465	390
240	440	480	300
540	255	450	390
420	465	465	450
389	525	370	240
510	450	495	465
570	435	420	570
780	510	600	510
480	510	480	555
510	480	360	390
450	540	480	600
300	540	420	270
420	480	510	360
540	690	540	390
525	420	445	344

TRY 11.13 Paid Work and Education (Example 4) A random sample of respondents to the 2010 General Social Survey was taken. The number of minutes of paid work in one day and the highest level of education attained by the respondent (less than high school, high school, some university or college, diploma from college/trade, university degree) were recorded. People who did not work for pay were not included in the sample. The Minitab output for ANOVA from the data is shown. Find the missing entries. (Source: Statistics Canada)

One-way ANOVA: WorkHrs versus Education

```
Source      DF        SS      MS     F      P
Education    ?    ??????   ?????  ????  0.033
Error      ???   7866285   ?????
Total      249   8209496
```

11.14 Number of Televisions by Population-Centre Size A random sample of respondents to the 2012 Survey of Household Spending was taken. The number of televisions in the respondent's home and the population centre size (with three groups: 100,000 and over, less than 100,000, rural) were recorded. The Minitab output for ANOVA from the data is shown. Find the missing entries. (Source: Statistics Canada)

One-way ANOVA: TVs versus PopCentre

Source	DF	SS	MS	F	P
Population	?	????	????	????	0.903
Error	??	122.73	????		
Total	64	123.14			

TRY **11.15 Paid Work Revisited (Example 5)** Consider the p-value given in the ANOVA table provided in Exercise 11.13. Assuming that the conditions for ANOVA are met, use this p-value to test the hypothesis that the mean number of minutes of paid work varies by educational level. Use a 0.05 level of significance. State your conclusion in the context of the data.

11.16 Televisions Revisited Consider the p-value given in the ANOVA table provided in Exercise 11.14. Assuming that the conditions for ANOVA are met, use this p-value to test the hypothesis that the mean number of televisions in a home varies by population-centre size. Use a 0.05 level of significance. State your conclusion in the context of the data.

SECTION 11.3

TRY **11.17 Pulse Rates (Example 6)** Pulse rates were taken for five people each, in three different situations: sitting, after meditation, and after exercise. Explain why it would not be appropriate to use one-way ANOVA to test whether the population mean pulse rates were associated with activity.

Person	Sitting	Meditation	Exercise
A	84	72	96
B	76	72	84
C	68	64	76
D	68	68	76
E	76	84	80

11.18 Sports Television The Nielsen organization did a study of the relationship between the time men spent watching certain kinds of shows and age group. The data were measured in minutes per week. Minitab output for time watching sports television shows for two groups is provided. Is the same-variance condition for ANOVA satisfied? Is ANOVA appropriate? Explain.

One-way ANOVA: Sports versus Group

Source	DF	SS	MS	F	P
Group	1	3050	3050	3.47	0.079
Error	18	15842	880		
Total	19	18893			

S = 29.67   R-Sq = 16.15%   R-Sq(adj) = 11.49%

Level	N	Mean	StDev
Men18-34	10	346.10	40.25
Men55+	10	370.80	11.83

11.19 Comedy Television The Nielsen organization did a poll to determine whether men and women in different age groups watched different amounts of comedy television. Check the Minitab output to see whether the same-variance condition for ANOVA holds. Is ANOVA appropriate? Explain your answer.

One-way ANOVA: Men18-34, Men55+, wom18-34, wom55+

Source	DF	SS	MS	F	P
Factor	3	226818	75606	38.38	0.000
Error	36	70915	1970		
Total	39	297733			

S = 44.38   R-Sq = 76.18%   R-Sq(adj) = 74.20%

Level	N	Mean	StDev
Men18-34	10	287.30	65.05
Men55+	10	171.00	40.81
wom18-34	10	353.70	20.78
wom55	10	356.90	39.37

11.20 Music Survey The figure shows side-by-side boxplots of the number of hours per week that university students spent listening to music. Minitab output for ANOVA is also shown. Check whether the conditions for ANOVA hold. If not, state which ones fail and why.

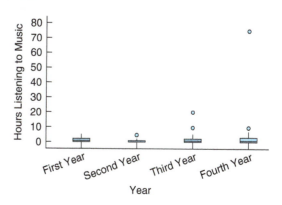

```
One-way ANOVA: Hours versus Year

Source    DF      SS     MS      F      P
YR         3   116.9   39.0   0.76  0.520
Error    117  6017.1   51.4
Total    120  6134.0


S = 7.171     R-Sq = 1.91%     R-Sq(adj) = 0.00%


Level        N    Mean    StDev
First Year   6   1.333    1.862
Second Year 20   0.900    1.165
Third Year  47   1.596    3.295
Fourth Year 48   3.333   10.793
```

TRY **11.21 Baseball Player Run-Times (Example 7)** Baseball-playing statistics students John Carlson and Paul McMurray collected data on baseball player run-times. Players were required to run 50 yards (45.72 metres) and were timed in seconds (pitchers did not have to run). Assume that the distribution of each population (outfielders, infielders, catchers) is close enough to Normal to satisfy the Normal condition for using ANOVA. Test the hypothesis that different positions have different mean run-times, using a significance level of 0.05. (Do not do post-hoc tests. Exercise 11.31 will ask for the post-hoc tests.) *See page 549 for guidance.*

11.22 Study Hours Revisited Refer to the data for Exercise 11.9. Test the hypothesis that the mean number of hours studying varies by major by reporting the *F*-statistic, the p-value, and the conclusion. Assume the conditions for ANOVA are met.

11.23 Ethics of Eating Meat A survey conducted by researchers Schwitzgebel and Rust asked subjects to choose a number from 1 to 9 to explain their feelings toward eating meat in response to the prompt: "Eating meat is . . . ."

Very Morally Bad	Some-what Morally Bad		Neutral		Some-what Morally Good		Very Morally Good
1	2	3	4	5	6	7	8	9

Three independent random samples of 30 ethics professors (Eth), 30 philosophy professors not specializing in ethics (Phil), and 30 professors in other disciplines (Other) were taken and the data are available at the text's website. Although the graphs are somewhat skewed, the sample sizes are large enough to satisfy the Normal condition for ANOVA. Test the hypothesis that the mean response is different for different groups of professors, reporting the value of the *F*-statistic, the p-value, and the conclusion in context. Use a significance level of 0.05. (Source: E. Schwitzgebel and J. Rust. 2009. The self-reported moral behavior of ethics professors. Unpublished manuscript. http://schwitzsplinters.blogspot.com/2009/05/do-ethicists-eat-less-meat.html)

11.24 Meat-Eating Behaviour The survey discussed in Exercise 11.23 (Schwitzgebel and Rust 2009) also asked people how many of their meals per week included meat. The data show three groups: ethicists (Eth), other philosophy professors who are not ethicists (Phil), and professors in other departments (Other). Determine whether you can reject the hypothesis that all the population means are equal at the 0.05 level. The data were obtained from three random samples. Assume that the distribution of each population is close enough to Normal to satisfy the Normal condition of an ANOVA. Do not do post-hoc tests.

11.25 Reaction Times for Athletes A random sample of people were asked whether they were athletic, moderately athletic (Mod), or not athletic (NotAth). Then they were tested for reaction speed. Reaction speed was measured indirectly, through reaction distance, as follows: a vertical metre stick was dropped and they caught it. The distance (in centimetres) that the stick fell is the reaction distance, and shorter distances correspond to faster reaction times. The data are shown in the accompanying table.

NotAth	Mod	Athletic
16.0	11.7	24.7
25.3	22.3	15.7
19.3	12.7	17.7
19.0	21.3	12.7
14.3	16.0	21.0
34.3	14.0	21.0
17.7	16.3	19.3
	28.3	25.0
	30.7	27.0
	15.0	10.3
	26.7	
	26.7	

a. Interpret the boxplots given. Compare the medians, interquartile ranges, and shapes, and mention any potential outliers.

b. Test the hypothesis that people with different levels of athletic ability (self-described) have different mean reaction distances, reporting the *F*-statistic, p-value, and conclusion. Assume that the distribution of each population is close enough to Normal to satisfy the Normal condition of an ANOVA and that the sample is randomly selected. Do not do post-hoc tests.

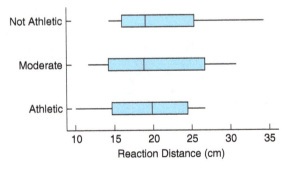

11.26 Tomato Plants Refer to the data for Exercise 11.11 on growth rate of tomato plants for different colours of light. The boxplots for the data are given below.

a. Interpret the boxplots given. Compare medians and interquartile ranges, and mention potential outliers.

b. Test the hypothesis that the colour of light affects growth rate—in other words, that the population mean growth rates differ by colour—reporting the value of the *F*-statistic, p-value, and conclusion. Assume that conditions for ANOVA are met. Use a significance level of 0.05. Do not do post-hoc tests.

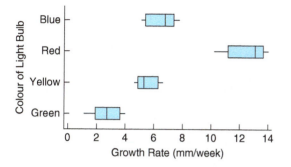

11.27 Work Hours Data were obtained from random samples of workers entering a hardware store who were asked how many hours of work they performed in the previous week. The workers were electricians (Elec), plumbers (Pb), and construction workers (Const).

a. Make side-by-side boxplots of the hours of work, and interpret the boxplots to determine whether the different professions work different numbers of hours.

b. Test the hypothesis that workers with different jobs have different mean number of hours of work, using the 0.05 level of significance. Assume that conditions for ANOVA are met. Show all four steps, numbered. (Do not do post-hoc tests.)

11.28 NHL "Goals For," by Division The National Hockey League (NHL) is divided into two conferences: the Eastern Conference and the Western Conference. Between 1998 and 2013, the Eastern Conference was further divided into the Atlantic (EA), the Northeast (EN), and the Southeast (ES) divisions, while the Western Conference was divided into the Central (WC), Northwest (WN), and Pacific (WP) divisions. (In 2013, each conference was reorganized into two divisions.) To test whether there were differences in scoring by division, we obtained a random sample of 17 "Goals For" totals in the regular season within that period independently for each division. (The 2012–2013 season was excluded from the sample because it was a short season.)

EA	EN	ES	WC	WN	WP
234	231	217	196	264	248
239	245	187	183	198	214
227	190	219	213	186	215
216	242	176	216	200	214
189	314	171	259	256	194
237	257	245	211	222	184
190	216	186	197	235	226
242	288	252	254	195	227

EA	EN	ES	WC	WN	WP
267	258	240	230	235	242
277	261	237	233	199	231
242	274	239	226	272	230
213	250	210	244	214	207
194	250	229	214	262	264
222	217	224	219	227	225
222	246	247	215	193	228
264	218	195	237	249	211
203	212	213	202	202	204

a. A histogram of residuals was obtained from these data. Does the Normality condition for ANOVA appear to hold?

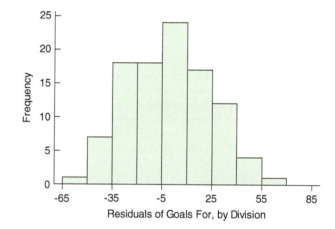

b. Obtain the standard deviation for each division. Does the condition of equal variances appear to hold?

c. Test whether the mean number of "Goals For" varied by division in the period between 1998 and 2012. Use a 5% significance level. (Do not do post-hoc tests.)

SECTION 11.4

11.29 House Prices The Tukey HSD confidence intervals (with a familywise error rate of 0.05) shown below were calculated for the mean prices of single detached homes in three Calgary neighbourhoods: Altadore, Hillhurst, and Richmond Park. Arrange the neighbourhoods from smallest sample mean on the left to largest on the right, underlining pairs for which the sample means are not significantly different. (The sample mean was largest for Altadore and smallest for Hillhurst.) Assume that conditions for ANOVA are met. Then write a sentence or two interpreting your results.

```
Altadore subtracted from:

               Lower   Center   Upper   --+---------+---------+---------+----
Hillhurst     -894.7   -538.8  -182.9   (--------*-------)
Richmond Park -725.9   -370.0   -14.2        (--------*--------)
                                        --+---------+---------+---------+----
                                        -800      -400        0       400

Hillhurst subtracted from:

               Lower   Center   Upper   --+---------+---------+---------+----
Richmond Park -187.1   168.8   524.6                 (--------*-------)
                                        --+---------+---------+---------+----
                                        -800      -400        0       400
```

11.30 House Prices The Tukey HSD confidence intervals (with a familywise error rate of 0.05) shown below were calculated for the mean prices of single detached homes in three Calgary neighbourhoods: Bankview, Killarney, and South Calgary. Arrange the neighbourhoods from smallest sample mean on the left to largest on the right, underlining pairs for which the sample means are not significantly different. (The sample mean was largest for South Calgary and smallest for Bankview.) Assume that conditions for ANOVA are met. Then write a sentence or two interpreting your results.

```
Bankview subtracted from:

               Lower  Center  Upper  -----+---------+---------+---------+----
Killarney      -63.0   202.3  467.5                (-------*------)
South Calgary  190.3   478.0  765.6                    (--------*-------)
                                      -----+---------+---------+---------+----
                                        -350        0       350      700

Killarney subtracted from:

               Lower  Center  Upper  -----+---------+---------+---------+----
South Calgary   10.5   275.7  540.9              (-------*------)
                                      -----+---------+---------+---------+----
                                        -350        0       350      700
```

For Exercises 11.31–11.36, refer to the exercise mentioned, and decide whether the p-value for ANOVA suggests that post-hoc tests should be done. For the post-hoc tests, use a familywise error rate of 0.05. Report confidence intervals for the difference between all possible pairs of means, and decide for each pair whether the null hypothesis of no difference can be rejected. (Note: You can compute 95% Tukey HSD confidence intervals, or 95% Bonferroni intervals, using 98.33% confidence for individual intervals for three comparisons.)

If there is at least one difference between means, list the groups from smallest mean on the left to largest mean on the right, underlining groups for which the sample means are not significantly different, and write sentences comparing means of the groups in the context of the data. If post-hoc tests are not appropriate, explain why.

TRY **11.31 Baseball Run-Times (Example 8)** Refer to Exercise 11.21, which showed the overall ANOVA test. Below is output for the post-hoc tests, which are appropriate because the null hypothesis (that all means are equal) was rejected. The mean times (in seconds) for running 50 yards (45.72 metres) were as follows: Outfielders 7.02, Infielders 7.13, Catchers 7.93. Follow the instructions given above.

```
Tukey 95% Simultaneous Confidence Intervals
All Pairwise Comparisons among Levels of Position
Individual confidence level = 98.01%


Position = Catchers subtracted from:


Position      Lower    Center    Upper
Infielders   -1.3948  -0.8020  -0.2091
Outfielders  -1.4890  -0.9050  -0.3210



Position = Infielders subtracted from:


Position      Lower    Center   Upper
Outfielders  -0.5906  -0.1030  0.3846
```

11.32 Study Hours Refer to Exercise 11.9.

11.33 Reaction Distances Refer to Exercise 11.25.

11.34 Tomato Plants Refer to Exercise 11.11. If using Bonferroni intervals, use 99.17% confidence intervals for six comparisons.

11.35 Hours of Work Refer to Exercise 11.27.

11.36 NHL "Goals For," by Division Refer to Exercise 11.28. Intervals based on the *t*-distribution would require 99.67% confidence intervals for 15 comparisons (not recommended).

11.37 House Prices (Example 9) The Bonferroni confidence intervals (with a familywise confidence level of 95%) shown below were calculated for the mean prices of single detached homes in three Calgary neighbourhoods: Altadore, Hillhurst, and Richmond Park. Arrange the neighbourhoods from smallest sample mean on the left to largest on the right, underlining pairs for which the sample means are not significantly different. (The sample mean was largest for Altadore and smallest for Hillhurst.) Assume that conditions for ANOVA are met. Then write a sentence or two interpreting your results.

```
Altadore subtracted from:

                      Lower    Upper
Hillhurst             -982      -96
Richmond Park         -748        8

Hillhurst subtracted from:

                      Lower    Upper
Richmond Park         -164      502
```

11.38 House Prices The Bonferroni confidence intervals (with a familywise confidence level of 95%) shown below were calculated for the mean prices of single detached homes in three Calgary neighbourhoods: Bankview, Killarney, and South Calgary. Arrange the neighbourhoods from smallest sample mean on the left to largest on the right, underlining pairs for which the sample means are not significantly different. (The sample mean was largest for South Calgary and smallest for Bankview.) Assume that conditions for ANOVA are met. Then write a sentence or two interpreting your results.

```
Bankview subtracted from:

                   Lower    Upper
Killarney          -46.1    450.6
South Calgary       125      831

Killarney subtracted from:

                   Lower    Upper
South Calgary       -14      566
```

CHAPTER REVIEW EXERCISES

11.39 Meat-Eating Ethics Refer to Exercise 11.23 and test the hypothesis that professors of different subjects have different mean beliefs about the ethics of eating meat. Use a 0.05 significance level. Report the p-value and conclusion from Exercise 11.23. Perform post-hoc tests, reporting confidence intervals for all pairs if appropriate; if they are not needed, explain why. As part of the post-hoc analysis, arrange the means from smallest on the left to largest on the right, underlining groups for which the sample means are not significantly different. Then explain the conclusion.

11.40 Meat-Eating Behaviour Refer to Exercise 11.24 and test the hypothesis that professors of different subjects have different mean numbers of meals containing meat in a week, using the 0.05 level of significance. Do post-hoc tests if appropriate; if they are not appropriate, explain why.

11.41 Marital Status and Body Mass Index A sample of respondents to the Canadian Community Health Survey was taken. The Minitab output relating marital status and body mass index (BMI) for those respondents is given. Verify that the constant-variance condition for ANOVA is met; assume that all other conditions are met. Test the hypothesis that BMI varies by marital status, using a 0.05 level of significance. Do not do post-hoc tests.

```
One-way ANOVA: BMI versus Marital Status

Source      DF       SS      MS      F      P
Marital      3    520.8   173.6   7.92  0.000
Error      596  13059.3    21.9
Total      599  13580.1

S = 4.681   R-Sq = 3.83%   R-Sq(adj) = 3.35%

Level                 N     Mean   StDev
Married/Common Law   348   27.138   4.619
Widowed              126   25.024   4.209
Divorced/Separated    80   25.856   5.105
Single                46   25.172   5.547
```

11.42 Video Game Playing and Age A sample of respondents to the 2010 General Social Survey was taken. The Minitab output relating number of minutes of video game playing in one day for four different age groups is given. People who did not play video games were not included in the sample. Verify that the constant-variance condition for ANOVA is met; assume that all other conditions are met. Test the hypothesis that video game playing time varies by age group, using a 0.05 level of significance. Do not do post-hoc tests.

```
One-way ANOVA: Video game minutes versus Age

Source   DF        SS      MS      F      P
Age       3     27702    9234   0.29  0.834
Error    96   3078643   32069
Total    99   3106345

S = 179.1   R-Sq = 0.89%   R-Sq(adj) = 0.00%

Level     N    Mean   StDev
15 to 24  25  166.0   120.3
25 to 34  25  170.7   215.6
35 to 44  25  127.9   146.1
45 to 54  25  157.3   214.4
```

11.43 Movies on Television The Nielsen organization did a study of the relationship between the time spent watching certain kinds of shows on television, measured in minutes per week, and age and gender groups. StatCrunch output for time watching movies on TV for four groups is given.

a. Test the hypothesis that different groups have different mean numbers of minutes watching movies, using the 0.05 level of significance. Assume that the conditions for ANOVA are met.

b. Using the output given for Tukey post-hoc tests, determine which sample means are significantly different from which others. Report and interpret all six confidence intervals for the differences in the means. Then arrange the groups from lowest mean on the left to highest on the right, with underlines connecting groups that do not have significantly different sample means. Then write a sentence or two explaining which group means are significantly different and how they differ.

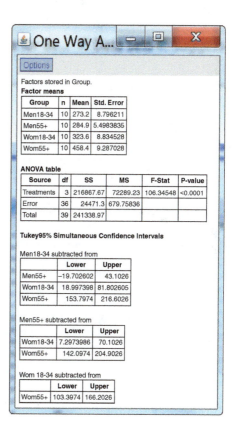

11.44 Hours of Television by Age Group The StatCrunch output shows the ANOVA results for testing whether there is a relationship between the number of hours of TV watched per week and age group: 50 and over, post-secondary students, grade school students.

a. Test the hypothesis that people in different age groups spend different amounts of time, on average, watching television. Use a significance level of 0.05. Assume that the conditions for ANOVA are met.

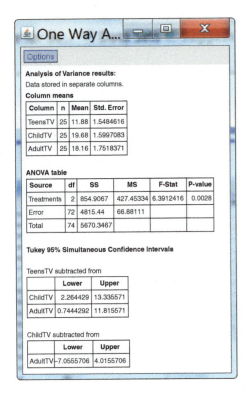

One Way A...

Options

Analysis of Variance results:

Data stored in separate columns.

Column means

Column	n	Mean	Std. Error
TeensTV	25	11.88	1.5484616
ChildTV	25	19.68	1.5997083
AdultTV	25	18.16	1.7518371

ANOVA table

Source	df	SS	MS	F-Stat	P-value
Treatments	2	854.9067	427.45334	6.3912416	0.0028
Error	72	4815.44	66.88111		
Total	74	5670.3467			

Tukey 95% Simultaneous Confidence Intervals

TeensTV subtracted from

	Lower	Upper
ChildTV	2.264429	13.335571
AdultTV	0.7444292	11.815571

ChildTV subtracted from

	Lower	Upper
AdultTV	-7.0555706	4.0155706

b. Using the output provided, determine which age group means are significantly different from each other. Report all the given confidence intervals for the difference between means, and tell what they show. Then arrange the groups from lowest mean on the left to highest on the right, with underlines connecting groups that do not have significantly different means. Finally, write a sentence or two explaining which group means are different and how they differ.

11.45 Sleep Time and Gender Using data from the General Social Survey, we performed an ANOVA to test whether gender is related to the length of time spent sleeping at night (in minutes). The ANOVA table and the output for a two-sample *t*-test with pooled variances are shown. In both cases, we are testing the hypothesis that the mean number of minutes spent sleeping at night for men and women are different. Assume that conditions for both tests have been met.

Compare the output by comparing p-values. Square the *t*-value and the pooled standard deviation to see what you get for comparison. Explain.

Source	DF	SS	MS	F	P
Gender	1	30443	30443	1.68	0.195
Error	398	7192082	18071		
Total	399	7222525			

```
Difference = mu (Male) - mu (Female)
Estimate for difference:  -17.9
95% CI for difference:  (-44.9, 9.2)
T-Test of difference = 0 (vs not =):
T-Value = -1.30  P-Value = 0.195  DF = 398
Both use Pooled StDev = 134.4268
```

11.46 Anchoring To test the effect of anchoring (see Exercise 2.54), students in a statistics class were randomly assigned a quantity, either 10% or 65%. The students were first asked whether they thought the percentage of member states of the United Nations that are in Africa was higher or lower than that quantity, and then they were asked to estimate the correct percentage. We analyzed data using one-way ANOVA and a two-sample *t*-test with pooled variances. In both cases we were testing the hypothesis that the mean estimates of the correct percentage were different for the two starting points. Compare the output of ANOVA and the two-sample *t*-test by looking at the *t*-statistics, *F*-statistics, and p-values.

Difference	Sample Diff.	Std. Err.	DF	T-Stat	P-value
$\mu_1 - \mu_2$	-24.377638	3.2625774	122	-7.4718957	<0.0001

ANOVA table

Source	df	SS	MS	F-Stat	P-value
Treatments	1	18302.534	18302.534	55.829225	<0.0001
Error	122	39995.346	327.8307		
Total	123	58297.88			

GUIDED EXERCISES

11.9 Study Hours by Major Three independent random samples of university students were asked how many hours per week they studied outside of class. Their responses and their majors are shown in the table. For these data, $\bar{\bar{x}} = 7.320$, $s = 3.775$, p-value $= 0.001$.

Math	SocSci	English		Math	SocSci	English
15	10	14		10	3	5
20	12	12		8	5	5
14	8	12		7	7	4
15	7	10		7	6	8
14	7	10		5	3	9
10	10	10		5	3	10
12	6	8		5	3	4
9	8	8		15	2	3
10	5	5		6	2	3
11	4	7		5	1	3
9	4	6		3	5	6
8	4	4		5	4	4
8	8	6				

Questions Use the data to find $SS_{between}$, SS_{within}, SS_{total}, $df_{between}$, df_{within}, df_{total}, $MS_{between}$, and MS_{within}. Find the value of the F-statistic. Set out your results on a complete ANOVA table. Assume that the conditions for ANOVA are met.

Step 1 ▶ Sample Sizes, Means, and Standard Deviations
Fill out the table, reporting the sample size in each group, the sample means, and the standard deviations.

	Sample Size	Mean	SD
English	25	7.040	3.164
Math	25	9.440	—
SocSci	—	—	—
All Observations	75	7.320	3.775

Step 2 ▶ Sums of Squares
Use Formula 11.2 to compute SS_{total}, Formula 11.3 to compute SS_{within}, and Formula 11.1 to find $SS_{between}$ by subtraction.

$$SS_{total} = (N-1)s^2 = (75-1) \times (3.775)^2 = ?$$

$$SS_{within} = \sum (n_i - 1)s_i^2 = (25-1) \times (0.634)^2 + ? = 855.4$$

$$SS_{between} = SS_{total} - SS_{within} = ?$$

Fill in the ANOVA Table as in Table 11.4 with the result of each one of your computations.

Step 3 ▶ Degrees of Freedom
Find the degrees of freedom with the formulas in Table 11.4, or reason as follows:
Between (Major): We have 3 group means, compared with 1 grand mean, so df $= 3 - 1 = 2$
Within (Error): We have 75 observations, compared with 3 group means, so df $= 75 - 3 = ?$
Total: We have ? observations, compared with 1 grand mean, so df $= ?$

Step 4 ▶ Mean Squares
Divide the sum of squares between groups and the sum of squares within groups by their corresponding number of degrees of freedom to obtain the mean squares:

$$MS_{between} = \frac{SS_{between}}{df_{between}} = ?$$

$$MS_{within} = \frac{SS_{within}}{df_{within}} = \frac{855.4}{72} = 11.9$$

Step 5 ▶ The F-Statistic
Find the value of the F-statistic by dividing $MS_{between}$ by MS_{within}. A large value of the F-statistic will be an indication that not all means are the same. Complete the table by including the p-value given to you.

	df	SS	MS	F	p-Value
Between (major)	2	—	—	—	0.001
Within (error)	72	855.4	11.9		
Total	—	—			

11.21 Baseball Player Run-Times (Example 7) Baseball-playing statistics students John Carlson and Paul McMurray collected data on baseball player run-times. Players were required to run 50 yards (45.72 m) and were timed in seconds (pitchers did not have to run). Assume that the distribution of each population is close enough to Normal to satisfy the Normal condition for using ANOVA.

Outfielders	Infielders	Catchers
6.70	7.62	7.90
6.75	7.20	7.82
7.13	6.37	7.92
7.42	7.12	7.64
7.05	7.04	8.82
6.32	7.15	7.47
7.13	6.89	
7.04	7.01	
7.47	8.54	
6.93	6.35	
7.01	7.10	
7.33		

QUESTION Test the hypothesis that different positions have different mean run-times, using a significance level of 0.05. In other words, is run-time independent of position played? (Do not do post-hoc tests.) Follow the steps given.

μ_{out} = population mean for outfielders

μ_{in} = population mean for infielders

μ_{cat} = population mean for catchers

Step 1 ► Hypothesize

H_o: $\mu_{out} = \mu_{in} = $?

H_A: At least one population mean is different from another.

Step 2 ► Prepare

Choose one-way ANOVA.
Conditions:

Random sample and observations independent of each other.

Independent groups.

Same variance: The ratio of largest standard deviation to smallest is $0.5916/0.3244 = 1.82$, which is less than 2.

Assume that the distribution of each population is close enough to Normal to satisfy the Normal condition for using ANOVA.

Step 3 ► Compute to Compare

$$F = ?$$
$$p\text{-value} = ?$$

Step 4 ► Interpret

Reject the null hypothesis if the p-value is less than or equal to 0.05. Explain in words what the conclusion implies about the three means.

TECH ♀ TIPS

General Instructions for Technology

All the technology will use the following data set.

🌍 **Example (Analysis of Variance)**
The two tables show the data we will use in two different forms. Table 11A consists of unstacked data, and Table 11B gives stacked data. Some technologies require one form and some the other form. The data were constructed for simplicity. To have context, imagine that each number represents the number of pets in a random sample of families with pets in fictitious communities C, E, and G.

C	G	E
1	11	2
2	13	3
1	12	2

▲ **TABLE 11A** Unstacked data.

n_{pets}	Community
1	C
2	C
1	C
11	G
13	G
12	G
2	E
2	E
3	E

▲ **TABLE 11B** Stacked data.

ANOVA

1. Press **STAT**, choose **EDIT**, and enter the unstacked numbers into **L1**, **L2**, and **L3**.

2. Press **STAT**, choose **TESTS**, then scroll up to **ANOVA** and press **ENTER**.

3. See Figure 11A. When you see **ANOVA(** enter the three lists' names separated from each other by commas (the comma button is above 7). To get **L1**, for example, press **2ND** and **1**.

   Enter: **L1 ꓹ L2 ꓹ L3)**

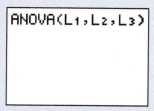

▲ **FIGURE 11A** TI-83/84 ANOVA input.

4. Press **ENTER**.

   You should get the output shown in Figure 11B. You will need to scroll down if you want to see all of the output.

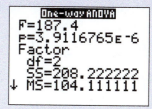

▲ **FIGURE 11B** TI-83/84 ANOVA output.

Post-Hoc Analysis

To carry out a post-hoc analysis, construct Bonferroni intervals. You will need to use two sample t-intervals, which are shown at the end of Chapter 9. Use **Pooled: Yes** if you previously performed ANOVA with the data. Remember to use 98.33% intervals for three groups (three comparisons), and 99.17% intervals for four groups (six comparisons).

With Minitab, it is possible to use either stacked data or unstacked data, but using stacked data is the preferred convention.

1. See Figure 11C. Enter the numbers in column 1 and the category values in column 2. (It is also allowable to use numerical codes instead of words for the category.) Be consistent with the category values. If you use C (capital C) for one, do not use c (lowercase c) for the other.

2. **Stat > ANOVA > One-Way**

↓	C1	C2-T
	Pets	Community
1	1	C
2	2	C
3	1	C
4	11	G
5	13	G
6	12	G
7	2	E
8	2	E
9	3	E
10		

▲ **FIGURE 11C** Minitab stacked data.

3. See Figure 11D. Be sure that the variable with the numbers (here, **C1 Pets**) goes in the **Response** box and that the variable with the code (here, **C2 Community**) goes in the **Factor** box. The

option **Response data are in one column for all factor levels** is what you need for stacked data.

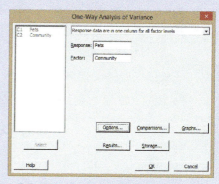

▲ **FIGURE 11D** Minitab ANOVA input.

4. For post-hoc Tukey intervals, click **Comparisons**. The **Error rate for comparisons** should be 5 for a familywise error rate of 0.05. Choose **Tukey** and make sure that the **Tests** option is selected.

5. Click **OK** and **OK** again.

   Part of the output is shown in Figure 11E.

One-way ANOVA: Pets versus Community

Source	DF	Adj SS	Adj MS	F-Value	P-Value
Community	2	208.222	104.111	187.40	0.000
Error	6	3.333	0.556		
Total	8	211.556			

▲ **FIGURE 11E** Minitab ANOVA output.

EXCEL

1. See Figure 11F. Enter unstacked data with or without labels into columns A, B, and C.

	A	B	C
1	C	G	E
2	1	11	2
3	2	13	2
4	1	12	3
5			

▲ **FIGURE 11F** Excel data.

2. Click **Data**, **Data Analysis** and choose **Anova: Single Factor**.

3. For **Input Range**, drag the cursor over all the numbers; do not include the labels.

4. Click **OK**.

Figure 11G shows part of the output.

ANOVA					
Source of Variation	*SS*	*df*	*MS*	*F*	*P-value*
Between Groups	208.2222	2	104.1111	187.4	3.91E-06
Within Groups	3.333333	6	0.555556		

▲ **FIGURE 11G** Excel ANOVA output.

To carry out a post-hoc analysis, you will need to perform *t*-tests for two samples, assuming equal variances (as shown at the end of Chapter 9), but using the Bonferroni Correction. Use **Alpha** as 0.017 for three groups (three comparisons), and 0.0083 for four groups (six comparisons).

STATCRUNCH

You may use stacked or unstacked data. We prefer stacked data.

1. See Figure 11H. Enter the numbers into one column and your code into another column. The code can be letters or numbers. Type the labels at the top, as shown.

2. **Stat > ANOVA > One Way**

3. See Figure 11I. Click **Values in a single column**. For **Responses in**, click the numerical variable (here, **Pets**). For **Factors in**, click the variable with the code (here, **Community**). (If you had unstacked data, you would click **Compare selected columns**.)

Row	Pets	Community
1	1	C
2	2	C
3	1	C
4	11	G
5	13	G
6	12	G
7	2	E
8	2	E
9	3	E

▲ **FIGURE 11H** StatCrunch stacked data.

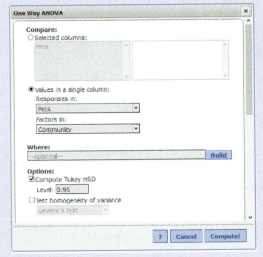

▲ **FIGURE 11I** StatCrunch ANOVA input.

4. To include post-hoc tests, click **Tukey HSD with confidence level** and leave **0.95** if alpha is 0.05.

5. Click **Compute!**

Part of the output is shown in Figure 11J.

ANOVA table					
Source	DF	SS	MS	F-Stat	P-value
Community	2	208.22222	104.11111	187.4	<0.0001
Error	6	3.3333333	0.55555556		
Total	8	211.55556			

▲ **FIGURE 11J** StatCrunch ANOVA output.

SPSS

1. Enter the data in stacked form, coding the grouping variable with numbers. See Figure 11K.

	Pets	Community
1	1.00	1.00
2	2.00	1.00
3	1.00	1.00
4	11.00	2.00
5	13.00	2.00
6	12.00	2.00
7	2.00	3.00
8	2.00	3.00
9	3.00	3.00

▲ **FIGURE 11K** Entering stacked data in SPSS. The categorical variable is coded with numbers.

2. Click on the **Variable View** tab at the bottom of the spreadsheet and then name your variables. To name the categories of your coded variable (in this case Community), click on its Values cell and add a label to every coded value. See Figure 11L.

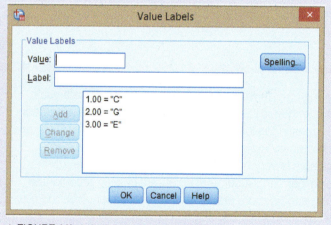

▲ **FIGURE 11L** Labelling categories in SPSS.

3. **Analyze > Compare Means > One-Way Anova**
4. See Figure 11M. Highlight the dependent variable and click the right arrow to move it to the **Dependent List** box.
5. Highlight the grouping variable and click the right arrow to move it to the **Factor** box.

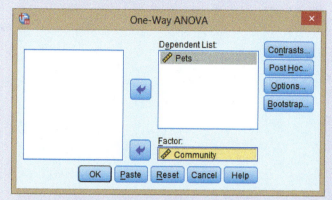

▲ **FIGURE 11M** SPSS ANOVA input.

6. To include post-hoc Tukey intervals, click on **Post Hoc** and select **Tukey**. Leave the **Significance Level** at 0.05 for a familywise error rate of 0.05.
7. Click **OK**.

Part of the output is shown in Figure 11N.

ANOVA					
Pets					
	Sum of Squares	df	Mean Square	F	Sig.
Between Groups	208.222	2	104.111	187.400	.000
Within Groups	3.333	6	.556		
Total	211.556	8			

▲ **FIGURE 11N** SPSS ANOVA output.

12 Design of Experiments and Sampling

David P. Lewis/Shutterstock

LEARNING OBJECTIVES

After completing this chapter, you should be able to:

1. Explain blocking and describe how it can help researchers control variation.
2. Define systematic sampling and identify situations where it can be useful for obtaining representative samples.
3. Define stratified sampling and identify situations where it can be useful for obtaining precise estimators.
4. Define cluster sampling and identify situations where it can be useful for obtaining precise estimators.
5. Evaluate published research papers critically.

We began our study of statistics in this textbook by talking about why and how we collect data. In Chapter 1, you saw that if the data are collected through a randomized, controlled experiment, then we can draw cause-and-effect conclusions whenever we observe significant differences between experimental groups. However, the differences between experimental groups can sometimes be subtle, and variability caused by factors other than the ones researchers are interested in will make those differences difficult to detect. In this chapter we will learn about different ways in which researchers control variation so as to increase the probability of detecting subtle differences.

In Chapter 7 we discussed simple random sampling as a method for obtaining a representative sample from a population. In many realistic situations—for example,

trying to determine the proportion of a province's youth that engages in harmful substance use, or the proportion of trees in the lodgepole pine forests of Western Canada affected by mountain pine beetle—a simple random sample is very difficult to collect. In this chapter we will also learn about some alternative sampling techniques that can be more practical and effective for obtaining representative samples.

The last section in this chapter (found in the course website) deals with reading and interpreting published scientific studies. Even if you do not carry out many experiments in your lifetime, you will often encounter results of experiments reported in the news, on blogs, and in newspapers. By knowing what questions to ask when evaluating published research, you will be able to make better judgments about the information you come across.

CASE STUDY

Does Stretching Improve Athletic Performance?

Traditionally, static stretching had always been considered an essential component of an athlete's warm-up, not only to prevent injuries and decrease muscle soreness, but also to improve performance. In recent years, however, there have been numerous studies showing that sustained static stretching can impair subsequent performance (Behm and Chaouachi 2011). As a result, many athletic teams and individuals have now incorporated dynamic stretching into their warm-up. Nevertheless, there are studies that discuss alternative ways in which static stretching can still be used in a warm-up to improve performance. For example, researchers at Memorial University of Newfoundland compared the effects of dynamic and static stretching within general and activity-specific warm-ups. The researchers found that athletes ran a 20-metre sprint faster and had increased sit-and-reach motion after an activity-specific warm-up that included static stretching (Samson et al. 2012).

What does this study tell us about preparing competitive athletes? What does it tell us about "weekend" athletes? Is this evidence that you should incorporate sport-specific exercises into your warm-up stretch if you plan on running a race? Are the results believable? Why was there no control group that did no stretches at all? Does it matter that all the subjects did all of the stretching regimens? In this chapter we examine the characteristics of controlled experiments so that we can understand whether we can generalize conclusions of studies to other groups. At the end of the chapter, we will return to this case study and consider the answers to these questions in light of what we have learned.

SECTION 12.1

Variation Out of Control

How can you do your best at your next midterm? Would taking a nap (before, not during, the exam) help? How could you find out? You could just try it, of course, but then if you did really well, you wouldn't know whether it was because of the nap or because it was just an easy exam for you. You could try it a few times, sometimes napping and sometimes not, but there's a lot of variability involved here. Sometimes your naps will be longer or your sleep deeper. Sometimes the exams will be harder or easier, and your level of preparation for the material will vary. And even if napping works for you, how could you know whether it would work for someone else? This natural variability, both between people and between contexts, will make it difficult to determine just what effect, if any, napping has on test performance.

For another example, consider the need to test the effectiveness of vaccines. Beginning in mid-2009, many people began to worry about the flu, as news of the H1N1 virus (also known as the "swine flu" virus) swept the world. Eventually, a vaccine was made available, but this raised more questions. Was the vaccine really effective? Were two doses required, or was one sufficient? Could the vaccine be inhaled, or was it better to have it injected? Certainly you could get the vaccine yourself and then see whether you got the flu, but if you remained healthy, it might be just because you weren't exposed to the virus. Or if you got sick, it might be just because, even with the vaccine, your body was susceptible to this particular virus. Again, natural variability makes it difficult to determine how effective a vaccine, or a particular vaccine regimen, is at preventing the flu.

Statisticians and researchers have developed several methods for controlling variability in order to find answers to important questions like these. In Chapter 1 we explained why these questions can be answered only with controlled experiments. In this chapter, we show you how it's done.

Review of Experimental Basics

Before getting to the heart of the chapter, let's review a few of the important concepts covered in Chapter 1.

The phrase *cause and effect* has a common English meaning, but nonetheless we need to be clear about its meaning in this context. For our purposes, we say that two variables X and Y have a cause-and-effect relationship if, whenever we change X for a person (or object), then Y typically changes in a predictable way. For example, if napping causes test scores to improve, then if you changed your test preparation from "no-nap" to "nap," you would see an increase in your test scores. If we gave you a flu vaccine, we would change your status from "not vaccinated" to "vaccinated," and we would hope to see your risk of getting the flu go down as a result.

We call the variable that we change—the "cause"—the **treatment variable**. The variable that we are interested in seeing changed—the "effect"—is called the **response variable**. The treatment variable records, for example, whether a subject received or did not receive the vaccine, and the response variable records whether or not that person later got the flu.

The trick is to determine whether changes that we see in the response variable are due to changes in the treatment variable; are due to changes in some other, unseen variables; or are due to chance. Unseen variables that might affect the response variable are called **confounding variables** (or confounders).

For example, a study examining the effectiveness of a company's test preparation courses for taking the Law School Admissions Test (LSAT—required by most Canadian law schools as part of their admission process) found that students who completed one of the company's LSAT preparation courses did better on the LSAT than students who did not. The treatment variable here records whether or not a student took a preparation course, and the response variable records the student's LSAT scores. One of the problems with this study is that preparation courses are expensive, and a student's decision to take a course depends on the student's ability to pay—a possible confounding variable.

To be a confounding variable, a variable must affect *both* the treatment *and* the response. The student's ability to pay meets this criterion, because it affects both the treatment (attend or not attend the LSAT preparation course) and the response (score on LSAT). A student's ability to pay for LSAT preparation affects the treatment variable because, on average, students who take the LSAT preparation class are better off financially than students in the group who do not take the class. And this ability to pay means that the students might, typically, have increased access to other resources that help them do better on the LSAT (for example, they might not need jobs and so would have more time to prepare); for this reason, the response variable is also affected.

Another possible confounding variable is motivation. Students who are motivated enough to spend money on a prep course, to go through the trouble of finding a prep course, and to put in the extra time attending the course might also be motivated enough to study in other ways. So even if the prep course is not effective, the students' extra motivation might be the reason for their higher LSAT scores.

Maybe you can think of other confounding variables as well. The presence of confounding variables means we cannot conclude that the prep course caused the higher LSAT scores. To be able to conclude that the prep course caused the change, we would have to eliminate all other explanations.

To eliminate other explanations, the experimenter must make sure that the subjects in the experiment are alike in every way except that they have different values for the treatment variable. To achieve this, experimenters can take control and assign subjects to a treatment group. When this is done, we call the experiment a **controlled experiment**.

Still, making sure that the subjects in the different treatment groups are all alike is difficult, because people (and animals and even some inanimate objects) are not all alike. This variability means that if we're not careful, some differences between the groups will arise that might be confounding variables and prevent us from concluding that the treatment caused any observed changes in the response variable.

Researchers use **random assignment** to ensure that different treatment groups are as similar as possible. To take a simple example, if we have two treatment groups, one getting a vaccine and the other a placebo, then by randomly assigning subjects to the two groups, we will have roughly equal proportions of men and women in both groups. In that way, gender cannot be a confounding factor, because both groups will have about the same numbers of each gender. Random assignment ensures that other variables, even some we don't know about, will be distributed in roughly equal proportions among the groups.

Observational studies are quite common, in part because it is not always possible to do a controlled experiment. How could researchers decide whether using a cell phone over many years causes brain cancer in a randomized study? First, such a study would be unethical. Second, even if they ignored ethical considerations, how could researchers make sure that subjects who were assigned to the treatment group used their phones often enough over many years? And how could they be sure that subjects in the control group did *not* use cell phones for many years?

A major drawback with observational studies is that they can establish only a relationship between the treatment and response variables; they cannot establish whether the relationship is the result of cause-and-effect. The news media often ignore this fact and report the results of observational studies as though they were controlled experiments. For example, the BBC News (2010) published this headline: "Happiness Wards Off Heart Disease, Study Suggests." The reported study must be an observational study, because how could researchers assign people to be happy for a long period of time? Therefore, we can't conclude that happiness causes a lower risk of heart disease, despite the claims of the headline.

Looking Back

Observational Studies and Confounding
Recall that in an observational study, we can never eliminate the possibility that a confounding variable exists. This means we cannot reach cause-and-effect conclusions on the basis of a single observational study.

> **KEY POINT** Random assignment to treatment groups ensures that the subjects in all groups are as similar as possible, so that the only real difference between groups is the treatment they receive.

EXAMPLE **1** Improving Memory

Which is better for improving memory: a short nap, caffeine, or nothing? In one study, researchers randomly assigned 61 subjects to one of three groups. All subjects took a basic memory test. Depending on which group they were assigned to, subjects then took a 30-minute nap, or had a moderate dose of caffeine, or did nothing. Afterward, subjects were again tested on their memory. Researchers found that the nappers improved more on the memory tests than either the caffeine takers or the placebo group (Mednick et al. 2008).

QUESTION For this controlled experiment, identify the treatment and response variables. Restate the conclusion of the study in terms of a cause-and-effect conclusion.

SOLUTION   The treatment variable here records the treatment group that each subject was assigned to: subjects napped, or had caffeine, or did neither. The response variable is the change in the subjects' memory test score. The conclusion could be stated as "Napping improves memory."

TRY THIS!   Exercise 12.9

Statistical Power

Random assignment helps researchers eliminate (or at least minimize) the effects of possible confounding variables. But there is always the possibility that observed changes in the response variable are simply due to chance rather than the treatment the subjects received.

Because statistical tests involve chance, even when the two groups we're comparing are truly different, there is a probability that we won't see this difference. On the other hand, there is a probability that we will correctly find that the groups are truly different. This probability, called the **power**, was introduced in Chapter 8. The power is the probability that, for a given value of the parameter, we will reject the null hypothesis. In other words, power measures the probability of detecting differences that really exist between groups.

Obviously, we want this probability to be big. Many researchers like to have a power of at least 80%. Higher is even better.

The power depends primarily on three things: the sample size, the size of the true difference between the groups, and the natural variability within the population. Of these three factors, researchers and statisticians have direct control only over sample size. Still, by identifying sources of natural variability in the population, researchers can design experiments that can improve the power by controlling for the variation.

Variability that exists within a population can arise from several different sources. One source is natural variability: the subjects (or objects) being studied naturally have variability. If we are comparing the weights of different groups of people, we should expect natural variability within these groups, because everyone's weight is slightly different. Another important source of variability is measurement error. This is the variability caused by the devices or methods used to measure something. For example, if you weigh yourself twice in a row, you don't always get exactly the same weight the second time. Figure 12.1 shows the distribution of weights of 2000 one-euro coins. You might expect that coins would weigh exactly the same, because heavier coins might be perceived as more valuable. Still, whether as a consequence of measurement error or of variations in the coin-minting process, we still see variability.

▶ **FIGURE 12.1** Even though the minting of coins is very carefully controlled, there is still variability, as this distribution of the weights of 2000 one-euro coins shows.

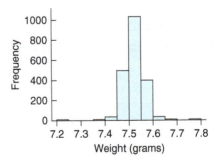

The best way to control for this variation when conducting a research study is to hold a variable fixed at a particular value. This is called **controlling for a variable**. If we are performing a study to see how naps affect memory, and we believe that caffeine intake affects naps, then we might control for caffeine amounts by requiring everyone to be caffeine-free. Or we might even give all the groups the same amount of caffeine, if we were interested in seeing how our conclusions were affected by caffeine.

Blocking

For factors that the researchers cannot control, they can apply blocking. **Blocking** is a technique in which researchers group similar objects into "blocks" and then assign treatments randomly within each block. Blocking helps achieve two purposes. It reduces bias (particularly useful when the sample sizes are small), and it increases statistical power.

In many medical studies, for example, different age groups respond differently to treatments. Researchers cannot control a person's age, but they can create blocks of subjects who are the same age (or nearly the same age) and in that way increase the statistical power of their study.

The basic idea is that once we've grouped similar subjects or objects together, we hope that subjects within a block will respond similarly to the treatment. If so, then we don't need to measure quite so many people, because there is less variability than we originally had.

 KEY POINT A block consists of subjects or objects that are similar on one or more variables. Objects *within* a block are then randomly assigned to treatment groups.

Creating Blocks

To create blocks, ask whether you know of any variables that might affect the outcome and cannot be controlled. If so, create the blocks by grouping together objects that are similar to one another on those variables.

Once you have created the blocks, you then randomly assign objects within each block either to the control group or to the treatment group (or to the many different treatment groups, if the study is considering several different treatments). Each block should have objects in all treatment and control groups.

For example, *The Globe and Mail* reported that writing about fears before tests can boost student grades (Taylor 2011). The report is based on a study about the effect that "expressive writing"—writing about emotions—can have in preventing students from "choking" on exams (Ramirez and Beilock 2011). Researchers recruited Grade 9 biology students at a large high school and evaluated students' attitudes toward their upcoming final exam. Some students were very anxious, but others were much less anxious. Because researchers suspected that one source of variation in the effects of the treatment might be the students' anxiety level, they created two blocks. One block consisted of students who were the most anxious about the final exam. The other block consisted of the least anxious students. Ten minutes before the exam, students in each block were randomly assigned to do one of two activities. Half of the students were told to write about their anxieties concerning the test; this expressive writing constituted the treatment. The other half of the students were told to write about any topic that was not covered by the exam; these students formed the control group. Figure 12.2 illustrates this blocking design.

At the end of the study, researchers found that the high-anxiety students who did the expressive writing outperformed the high-anxiety students in the control group. On the other hand, the low-anxiety students who did the expressive writing did not perform any differently from their control-group counterparts. The blocking structure of the experiment helped the researchers tease out some complex relations among anxiety, the treatment, and exam performance.

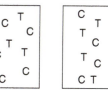

▲ **FIGURE 12.2** Each letter represents a student in the study. Students within each block are randomly assigned to either the Expressive Writing treatment (T) or the control group (C).

Control	EARLY
LATE1	LATE2
LATE2	Control
EARLY	LATE1

▲ **FIGURE 12.3** The layout of two blocks for the spruce seedling experiment. Four treatments are distributed at random among plots within blocks: (1) control, (2) EARLY, (3) LATE1, and (4) LATE2. Blocks group together seedlings in a similar environment.

Blocking is often used in agricultural and biological studies done "in the field." The reason is that when you are studying plants in the great outdoors, the amount of sunlight, water, and soil nutrients that a plant might receive can vary widely just a few metres in any direction. Figure 12.3 shows an illustration of two blocks for a study on the survival and growth of spruce seedlings. As an alternative to chemical herbicides for vegetation management in Quebec, large stock seedlings are produced in containers and planted the year after harvesting activities. After planting, the seedlings are mechanically released (MR) at varying ages, depending on light availability. Researchers were interested in studying the effect of delaying MR on the performance of the seedlings (Thiffault et al. 2013).

The experiment was conducted on 14 experimental sites, each one divided into five to eight blocks. In turn, each block was divided into four plots separated by buffers. Within each block, four release treatments were randomly distributed among plots: (1) control; (2) MR applied in July or August of the year during which light availability averaged 60% of full sunlight (EARLY); (3) MR applied at EARLY + one year (LATE1); and (4) MR applied at EARLY + two years (LATE2). By dividing the experimental site into blocks that group together seedlings in a similar environment and then randomizing within each block, the effect of differences in light, water, and soil on the seedlings was controlled.

EXAMPLE 2 Wash That Statistician Right Out of Your Hair

A cosmetics company has created a new dandruff shampoo, which it believes will work better than its older shampoo formula. Company investigators believe that the effects of the shampoo depend on hair colour. For this reason, they plan to block on hair colour. To do this, they create blocks that have people with blond hair, brown hair, black hair, red hair, and grey hair, respectively. They then randomly select three of the blocks to receive the new shampoo and the other two blocks to receive the old shampoo.

QUESTION Is this an effective design for the study? If not, describe an improvement.

SOLUTION No. The researchers randomly assigned entire blocks to treatment groups. Instead, they should randomize the treatments *within* blocks. If an entire block is assigned to the same treatment—for example, if all the black-hair subjects are assigned to the old shampoo—then researchers won't be able to determine whether the new shampoo works on black hair.

To conduct this study properly, they should randomly assign half of the blond-hair group to receive the new formula and half to receive the old. Then they should randomly assign half of the brown-hair subjects to receive the new formula and half to receive the old, and so on.

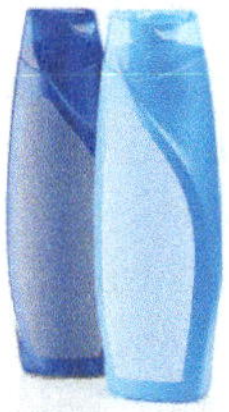

TRY THIS! Exercise 12.17

EXAMPLE 3 Baking Cookies

An amateur baker wants to experiment with two different cookie recipes. One recipe calls for margarine, the other for butter. The problem is that the oven the baker is using is a bit old and doesn't heat up consistently. If the oven is set to 350 degrees Fahrenheit (180 degrees Celsius), not every region in the oven will be exactly the same temperature. Through experience, the baker has some ideas about which areas are hotter and which are cooler, and these are shown in Figure 12.4. This figure also shows where each cookie will be placed.

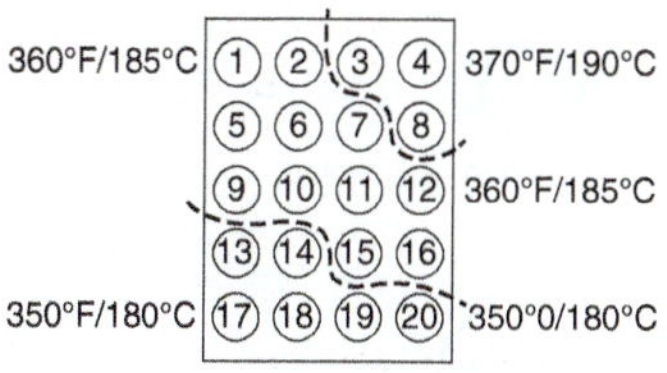

QUESTION Explain how to create blocks to test which cookie recipe tastes best.

SOLUTION The baker should create three blocks. The cookies within the 370°F/190°C zone (cookies 3, 4, and 8) should be in one block. The cookies within the 360°F/185°C zone (cookies 1, 2, 5, 6, 7, 9, 10, 11, 12, 15, and 16) are in another block, and the cookies in the 350°F/180°C zone (cookies 13, 14, 17, 18, 19, and 20) go in another block. Within each block, half of the spaces are randomly chosen to receive a margarine cookie, and the other half receive butter cookies. This can be done by putting the cookie numbers into three hats. One hat has the numbers for the 370°F/190°C block (numbers 3, 4, and 8), another hat has the numbers for the 360°F/185°C block, and the third hat has the numbers for the 350°F/180°C block. From each hat, half the numbers are drawn, and the selected numbers will be the margarine cookies. For blocks with an odd number of spaces, a coin flip can be used to determine whether the last space gets margarine (heads) or butter (tails).

TRY THIS! Exercise 12.19

▲ **FIGURE 12.4** The oven has three temperature regions, and baking conditions are similar within each region.

Blocking is useful because if you have correctly identified a variable that leads to different outcomes in your study, then by grouping subjects together on the basis of that variable, you have decreased the variability in the study—and decreasing the variability leads to greater statistical power.

Studies with small sample sizes can be greatly improved by blocking. Suppose that you wish to replicate the study about the effects of expressive writing on students in your own class. Imagine that there are 20 students, and most—say, 15 students—are not anxious. If you do not create blocks before you randomly assign 10 students to the treatment group and the other 10 to the control group, then it is possible that just by chance, all 5 of the anxious students will be in the control group. If this happens, then you will not be able to see the effect of the treatment, because the people who would be best helped by the treatment will not receive it.

Instead, if you created blocks, then one block would consist of the 5 anxious students and about half (2 or 3) would be guaranteed to be assigned to the treatment. Figure 12.5 compares one possible randomization with no blocks to a blocking design.

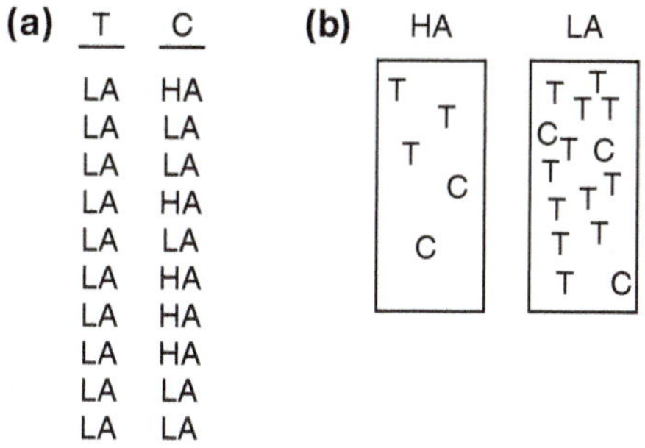

◀ **FIGURE 12.5 (a)** If there are no blocks, it is possible that all 5 of the high-anxiety students (HA) will be assigned to the control group. **(b)** Creating blocks based on anxiety level ensures that roughly half of the high-anxiety students (that is, 2 or 3 students) will be assigned to receive the treatment (T).

Blocking and Matching

As we have just discussed, blocking combines units that are similar in order to improve the power of an experiment. What unit can be more similar than matching a person with himself or herself? Researchers can sometimes exploit the fact that

Looking Back

Paired Samples

Paired samples are those in which each object in one group is associated with one particular object in the other group. They are also sometimes called dependent samples or dependent observations.

measuring the same person twice (usually before and then after applying a treatment) results in positively correlated values. Studies that use this structure illustrate the **matched-pairs design**. In Chapter 9 you saw examples of such paired samples, and you learned how to apply the paired t-test to test hypotheses about differences between two groups of paired data. Pairs of data are, in fact, a form of blocking.

For example, in a study seeking to evaluate the impact of a gambling awareness and prevention program on prison inmates' attitudes towards gambling (Nixon 2006), a group of men and women serving their sentences at the Lethbridge Correctional Centre in Alberta were screened before and after completing the program. In this study, each inmate is basically serving as his or her own control. The control group consists of the inmates before participating in the program. The treatment group consists of the *same* inmates as in the control group, but after they've completed the program. By pairing the pre- and postprogram screens, researchers were able to conclude that participants' attitudes toward gambling became significantly more negative after the program.

The next example illustrates how the use of matched pairs increases power by reducing variation, allowing us to detect differences due to a treatment.

EXAMPLE 4 Testing Diabetes Treatments

To combat diabetes, researchers compare two treatments designed to improve kidney functioning. One treatment uses both insulin and somatostatin (IS). The other uses insulin, somatosatin, and also glucagon (ISG). Patients receive each treatment (with some number of days between treatments so that the effects of the first can wear off). After each treatment, the amount of urea nitrogen in the urine over a 24-hour period is measured. Low levels suggest that the kidneys are not properly removing waste. The data are given in Table 12.1. Summary statistics are also provided. Assume that the subjects are randomly selected from a larger population and that the distribution of urea nitrogen levels in this population is approximately Normal.

▶ **TABLE 12.1** Outcome from the diabetes study. IS stands for "insulin with somatostatin"; ISG stands for "insulin with somatostatin and also glucagon." Urea nitrogen amounts are in units of grams detected in urine over a 24-hour period. (Source: Rasking and Unger, 1978)

Patient ID	IS (g/24 hr)	ISG (g/24 hr)	Difference
1	14	17	−3
2	6	8	−2
3	7	11	−4
4	6	9	−3
$\bar{x}$	8.25	11.25	−3.0
s	3.86	4.03	0.82

QUESTIONS

a. Perform a two-sample t-test (do not treat the data as paired data) to test whether the mean urea nitrogen levels are different under IS treatment and ISG. Assume that the patients are a random sample from a larger population. Use a 5% significance level.

b. Perform a paired t-test to test whether the mean urea nitrogen levels are different under IS treatment and under ISG treatment. Use a 5% significance level.

c. Which approach is better? Why are the conclusions different?

SOLUTIONS

a. We will quickly skip over the four steps of a hypothesis test so that we can emphasize the results of the two different procedures. Figure 12.6 shows the output from StatCrunch, which displays the null and alternative hypotheses, the observed value of the t-statistic, and the p-value.

◄ FIGURE 12.6 Output from two-sample *t*-test, no pairing.

Two sample T statistics with data

Options

Hypothesis test results:

μ_1 : mean of var2

μ_2 : mean of var3

$\mu_1 - \mu_2$: mean difference

$\mu_0 : \mu_1 - \mu_2 = 0$

$H_A : \mu_1 - \mu_2 \neq 0$

(without pooled variances)

Difference	Sample Mean	Std. Err.	DF	T-Stat	P-value
$\mu_1 - \mu_2$	−3	2.7913556	5.989039	−1.0747466	0.3239

From this we see that the value of the *t*-statistic is −1.07 and that the p-value is 0.3239. Because the p-value is bigger than 0.05, we do not reject the null hypothesis. Our conclusion is that there is no evidence of a difference in mean urea nitrogen levels between the two treatments.

b. Now we do a paired *t*-test. Figure 12.7 shows the StatCrunch output.

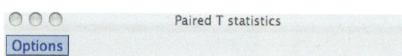

◄ FIGURE 12.7 Output from paired *t*-test.

Paired T statistics

Options

Hypothesis test results:

$\mu_1 - \mu_2$: mean of the paired difference between var2 and var3

$\mu_0 : \mu_1 - \mu_2 = 0$

$H_A : \mu_1 - \mu_2 \neq 0$

Difference	Sample Diff.	Std. Err.	DF	T-Stat	P-value
$\mu_1 - \mu_2$	−3	0.4082483	3	−7.3484693	0.0052

This time the *t*-statistic is very different: −7.3. And the p-value is much less than 0.05. This time, we reject the null hypothesis and conclude that the treatments have different effects on the mean urea nitrogen levels.

c. The data in this sample are paired; each patient contributes two data values to the sample. Because the values within pairs are positively correlated, the paired *t*-test has greater power than the two-sample *t*-test to detect differences in the population. The paired *t*-test is the more appropriate test for this situation. One clue as to why the paired *t*-test has greater power in this situation can be seen by comparing the standard deviation for the paired test statistic (identified as Std. Err. in the StatCrunch output) with that for the two-sample statistic. The standard deviation for the paired statistic is much smaller, because with this study design, correctly using the paired test statistic results in a much more precise estimator.

Note that in both part a and part b, the differences in the *sample* means are the same: −3.0. But our hypothesis is not about the sample, it is about the population. The paired *t*-test allowed us to see that the *population* means are different.

TRY THIS! Exercise 12.23

Another type of study that uses subjects as their own blocks is the **crossover design**. *Crossover design* is really just a more general term for the matched-pairs design. The difference is that sometimes there is more than one treatment, or more than one dosage of the same treatment. In a crossover design, researchers give all subjects the same set of treatments, but they usually randomly choose the order in which each subject receives the treatment.

In an effort to understand the relationship between consumption of insoluble fibre and reduced risk of obesity and diabetes, researchers at the University of Toronto used a crossover design to compare the effects of four caloric treatments on appetite, short-term food intake, and blood glucose before and after a meal 75 minutes later in healthy men. Four treatments were administered to young men after an overnight fast: high-fibre (HF) cereal, low-fibre (LF) cereal, white bread (WB), and water as control. All treatments were given with 250 mL milk and had equal calories, macronutrient content, volume, and weight. Subjects were randomly assigned to the *order* in which they received each treatment, but all subjects received all four treatments.

At 75 minutes after the start of the session (60 minutes after completing each treatment), subjects were given a pizza meal and were instructed to eat until comfortably full. By comparing measurements and answers to questionnaires for each subject before and after treatment, the researchers were able to conclude that the insoluble fibre found in the HF cereal suppressed appetite, lowered food intake, and improved glucose response to the meal consumed 75 minutes later.

SECTION 12.2

Sampling Techniques

In Chapter 7 we discussed simple random sampling (SRS), a basic method for selecting a sample so that every individual in the population has the same probability of being selected. In an SRS, we first create a list of all the individuals in our population. Then we randomly choose individuals without replacement to participate in our study.

This basic method creates a sample that, if large enough, is representative of the population. Because it is based on a random scheme, we can compute a margin of error that measures how far away our estimate is likely to be from the unknown value of the population parameter.

In practice, however, simple random sampling is often not the most convenient method for obtaining a representative sample. First, there are many situations where a list of persons or objects in the population is not available (for example, if the population of interest is all people living in Canada or all the trees in a large forest). Moreover, simple random samples can be very expensive due to travel and administrative costs when elements in the sample are far apart. In addition, simple random samples can be imprecise, giving large margins of error. In this section we provide an overview of other random sampling techniques that can be more convenient than simple random sampling. It is important to note that all the estimates discussed in this course assume that data were obtained from an SRS. If a different technique is used for obtaining a sample, a different technique must be used for obtaining estimates as well.

Review of Sampling Basics

Before talking about more complex sampling schemes, let's take a moment to review some of the basics we introduced in Chapter 7.

One goal of a survey is to estimate the value of a population parameter on the basis of a sample. *Parameters* are numbers that summarize a characteristic of a population. The proportion of Canadians who bought a new car in the last two years is a parameter, as is the mean weight of all Grade 8 students in your town. If we collect a representative sample from the population of interest, then a statistic from that sample can be used to estimate the parameter. A *statistic* is a number based on a sample of data. The average weight of 20 Grade 8 students chosen from your town is a statistic, as is the proportion of 100 people selected in Canada who say they bought a new car in the last two years.

Two features that measure the quality of an estimator are bias and precision. *Bias* measures how far away an estimator tends to be from the correct population value. If, on average, the estimator tends to get the value just right, then we say that the estimator is unbiased. *Precision* measures how the estimator varies from sample to sample. Different researchers using different random samples should get similar estimates when using a precise estimator. Precision is measured by the standard deviation the estimator would have if we were to repeat the survey many times. Ideally, an estimator is unbiased and has a small standard deviation.

Estimators can be biased for many different reasons. One common reason is that the sample is not representative of the population. For example, if we were to survey customers at a car dealership and ask whether they bought a new car in the last two years, these people would probably not be representative of the population as a whole. (They are probably less likely than the general population to have a new car at home if they're out shopping for a car.) Or consider a CTV.ca poll posted on the first day of the winter holiday season asking readers: "It's the busiest travel day of the year, are you heading anywhere today?" One hundred percent of respondents said "No." Clearly, this sample is not representative of the population, since it does not include any travellers. They were too busy travelling to be answering surveys.

One way in which a nonrepresentative sample often arises is in situations where the sample chooses itself by volunteering to participate. For example, in the summer of 2013, Macleans.ca conducted a poll on the legalization of marijuana. Interested readers could click on the link to answer this question: "Is it time to legalize marijuana?" About 60 percent respondents said "No." Is this representative of the entire Canadian population? Most probably not. Readers of Macleans.ca chose whether to click on the link, and this decision is quite likely to be based on the fact that they have strong opinions on the topic, which they wish to share.

This situation is similar to an observational study. People choose whether or not to participate in the poll, so we don't know whether our estimate of the population parameter is representative only of the sort of person who would read *Maclean's* and answer this poll, or is representative of the population as a whole. In contrast to the results of this self-selected sample, a random sampling of public opinion of 1189 Canadians conducted by Forum Research that same summer found that 69% of respondents favoured either legalization or decriminalization of marijuana.

The only way to collect data that avoids this potential bias is to select the sample randomly. A random sample has another advantage: it gives us a way to measure our confidence in the estimate. This measure takes the form of a confidence interval. For instance, a confidence interval enables us to say we're highly confident that the true population proportion is within, say, 3 percentage points of our estimate.

The precision of a survey estimator depends on the size of the sample and on the variability in the population. The good news is that the precision can always be improved by taking a larger sample (assuming you can afford to collect more data, that is). If everyone agrees and thinks the same way—in other words, if there is no variability—then the estimator will be extremely precise. When estimating a proportion, the worst-case scenario occurs when the population is evenly split. If the true proportion in the population is $p = 0.50$, then the precision will be as bad as it gets.

For example, if $p = 0.50$ and we take a simple random sample of 100, then the standard deviation of the estimator is

$$\sqrt{\frac{p(1-p)}{100}} = \sqrt{\frac{0.5 \times 0.5}{100}} = 0.05.$$

 Caution

Measurement Bias
Do not overlook the fact that estimates of population parameters can also be biased if the questions are poorly worded.

A population with less diversity, say $p = 0.90$, would produce more precise estimators because the standard deviation is smaller:

$$\sqrt{\frac{p(1 - p)}{100}} = \sqrt{\frac{0.9 \times 0.1}{100}} = 0.03.$$

Now that we have reviewed the basics of sampling, we can discuss several approaches to collecting samples that can be more convenient than simple random sampling.

Systematic Sampling

Systematic sampling is one technique that can be used, in some situations, to obtain a sample equivalent to an SRS. In a systematic sample, objects from the population are sampled at regular intervals, such as taking every fifth person after a random starting point. One of the most common examples of systematic sampling occurs in exit polls held during elections.

The purpose of an exit poll is to estimate the winner of an election before the votes are counted. They are called exit polls because people are surveyed as they exit the polling place. The pollsters—the people collecting the data—are instructed to stop people at specific intervals. For example, they might stop every fifth person (or every tenth person) throughout the day.

Systematic sampling works well when you have subjects coming at you in some sort of sequence and when you have good reason to believe that the population will be randomly mixed (relative to the variable being measured) during the time period when you collect that data. Exit polls would fail if, for example, pollsters collected data only first thing in the morning, or only in the middle of the afternoon. This is because it is possible that a certain type of voter goes to the polls before work, and if so, then a systematic sample taken only in the morning will be biased.

Systematic samples are used in quality control studies at manufacturing plants. Products come off an assembly line, and every tenth product after a random starting point might be inspected for defects. At the end of the day, this method yields a good estimate of the proportion of all products produced that day that have defects, as long as there is *no particular pattern* to the order in which defects arrive.

Stratified Sampling

Stratified sampling is a method for collecting data with increased precision. To perform stratified sampling, researchers first identify **strata**. Strata are like subpopulations; they are collections of individuals who are very similar to each other. Stratified sampling is based on a very simple principle: if we know that everyone in some group will answer the question the same way, then there's no need to ask everyone.

To create strata, a variable is chosen that identifies individuals who are similar in a way that is important for the response variable of interest. For example, suppose you were designing a survey to determine the proportion of adults who consider multiculturalism to be an important component of Canadian nationhood. According to a 2013 poll conducted by Leger Marketing (Boswell 2013), support for this idea depends on age: younger people are more likely to see multiculturalism as very important compared to older people. Thus, even though we could take a large sample of 1000 people to get an approximately 3-point margin of error for a 95% confidence interval, we could also stratify on age and take a smaller sample to get the same precision.

A stratified sample would divide the population into subpopulations, or strata, based on age group. One stratum (the singular form of *strata*) would consist of 18- to 24-year-olds, another of 25- to 44-year-olds, and so on. We would then randomly select people (using a simple random sample) within each stratum and ask their opinion.

Stratified sampling works because it creates "mini-populations" that have lower variability than the population as a whole. If the strata are chosen carefully, then within each stratum there will be less variability than in the population as a whole. This means that within each stratum, we can produce a more precise estimator.

The result is that we have mini-estimates from each of the mini-populations. These estimates are each very precise, because the strata were chosen to have low variability within them. We then combine the mini-estimates into one estimate for the entire population. We can show mathematically that in many cases, this combined estimator is more precise.

 KEY POINT Stratified sampling improves the precision of estimators by sampling from within strata. Each stratum is created in such a way that people (or objects) within the stratum are similar to one another.

Age is one variable commonly used for creating strata. Other commonly used variables include gender, educational level, geographic region, or a combination of variables such as these. For example, a study on bicycle ridership and bicycle helmet use among Canadian youth was based on data from the 2009/10 Health Behaviour in School-Aged Children survey (Davison 2013). The national sample was stratified by province/territory, type of school board (public vs. separate), urban–rural geographic status, school population size, and language of instruction (French vs. English). By using stratified data, researchers were able to obtain precise national estimates and to assess potential differences related to some of the population subgroups.

If the variable chosen to create the strata does not actually end up creating groups with similar-thinking members, then stratification will not offer any advantage over SRS. In fact, in some very unusual cases, it can make the precision worse! For this reason, it's important to choose the right stratification plan.

Cluster Sampling

Cluster sampling is a method that makes it easier to access large populations or populations where individuals occur naturally in groups, or **clusters**. To perform a cluster sample, researchers divide the population into clusters using some sort of natural or convenient distinction. Next, they select a simple random sample of clusters and measure every individual in the cluster. For example, the 2007–2008 Adult Inuit Health Survey (Saudny 2012), undertaken in 33 communities of the Canadian Inuit Nunangat (meaning "homeland"), used a simple random sample of households in each community, taken from lists of houses provided by the communities. Within each household, all Inuit adults aged 18 years or older (excluding pregnant women) were surveyed. Note that this is not the same as a simple random sample of Inuit adults, given that households (the clusters) are randomly selected, not people.

Clustering can happen over several stages. Randomly sampling, say, four provinces in Canada and surveying everyone in these four provinces is still a gigantic undertaking. Instead, after the provinces are selected, we might define a second stage of clusters consisting of cities, or maybe postal codes, regional districts, or the like. We would then take a random sample of these smaller clusters and survey everyone inside the clusters selected.

Researchers at the Canadian Forest Service have used cluster sampling to detect low-level infestation of mountain pine beetles in the lodgepole pine forests of western Canada. The epidemic is of great concern, since it is estimated that over 18 million hectares of forest had been affected by 2012. Being able to detect the proportion of damaged trees in areas in which there is not yet much damage is crucial to deterring their attack. By using satellite images, researchers can randomly select parcels of land to serve as clusters and

 Caution

Stratified Sampling and Blocking
Stratified sampling and blocking are similar. Both put subjects into groups (strata or blocks) so that subjects are similar within the group. However, stratified sampling is about ways of selecting subjects, and blocking is about a way of randomly assigning already selected subjects to treatment groups.

then investigate every tree within those parcels (Coggins et al. 2010). Cluster sampling is also used in humanitarian relief efforts to understand the extent to which people have been injured or killed by natural disasters. Researchers randomly select regions and then go door to door within them to collect damage reports.

Cluster sampling is sometimes confused with stratified sampling because both techniques break the population into groups. However, in some ways, cluster sampling is the opposite of stratified sampling. In stratified sampling, the strata contain people who are all as similar as possible (for example, all females in one stratum and all males in another). Cluster sampling, on the other hand, works best when each cluster by itself is representative of the entire population. This is rarely achieved, but when it *is* achieved, it ensures that estimates are as precise as possible.

 KEY POINT   Cluster sampling can be used to access populations where individuals occur naturally in groups, or clusters. To perform a cluster sample, we take a random sample of clusters and survey everyone within the selected clusters.

EXAMPLE **5** Student Drug Use Survey

Surveys that ask school-aged youth about their drinking, smoking, and illicit drug use are conducted on a regular basis across Canada. For example, for the New Brunswick Student Drug Use Survey, researchers enumerated every public school in the province with at least one class of any combination of Grades 7, 9, 10, and 12. They randomly selected schools from this list and then randomly selected classes from those grades in the selected schools. They surveyed all students in the selected classes and concluded that 48% of adolescent students in the province had consumed alcohol and about 28% had tried cannabis at least once during the previous year (Gupta 2012).

QUESTION Is this a systematic sample, a stratified sample, or a cluster sample?

SOLUTION This is a cluster sample. More precisely, this is a two-stage cluster sample. The clusters are schools at one stage and then classes at the second stage.

TRY THIS! Exercise 12.29

SECTION 12.3

Reading Research Papers

 Section 12.3 is available online, and can be found on MyStatLab.

At the beginning of this chapter, we reported on a study that found that athletes ran a 20-metre sprint faster and had increased sit-and-reach motion after an activity-specific warm-up that included static stretching. Here is the abstract:

The purpose of the study was to determine the effects of static and dynamic stretching protocols within general and activity specific warm-ups. Nine male and ten female subjects were tested under four warm-up conditions including a (1) general aerobic warm-up with static stretching, (2) general aerobic warm-up with dynamic stretching, (3) general and specific warm-up with static stretching and (4) general and specific warm-up with dynamic stretching. Following all conditions, subjects were tested for movement time (kicking movement of leg over 0.5 m distance), countermovement jump height, sit and reach flexibility and 6 repetitions of 20 metre sprints. Results indicated that when a sport specific warm-up was included, there was an 0.94% improvement ($p = 0.0013$) in 20 metre sprint time with both the dynamic and static stretch groups. No such difference in sprint performance between dynamic and static stretch groups existed in the absence of the sport specific warm-up. The static stretch condition increased sit and reach range of motion (ROM) by 2.8% more ($p = 0.0083$) than the dynamic condition. These results would support the use of static stretching within an activity specific warm-up to ensure maximal ROM along with an enhancement in sprint performance.

We can apply the six questions to help us determine how strong these results are.

1. What is the research question that these investigators are trying to answer?
2. What is their answer to the research question?
3. What were the methods they used to collect data?
4. Is the conclusion appropriate for the methods used to collect data?
5. To what population do the conclusions apply?
6. Have the results been replicated in other articles? Are the results consistent with what other researchers have suggested?

The answers follow.

- The research question is "Do static and dynamic stretching within general and activity-specific warm-ups have an effect on movement time, countermovement jump height, 20-metre sprint time or sit-and-reach range of motion (ROM)?

- They conclude that, when a sport specific warm-up is included, both dynamic and static stretching improve 20-metre sprint performance and increase reach range of motion (ROM). In the case of ROM, the increase is greater with static stretching. No change was found on movement time or on countermovement jump height.

- To collect these data, the researchers did not take a random sample. The researchers used a crossover design in which they blocked on athlete, and each athlete did every treatment. Although it does not say so in the abstract, the order in which an athlete did the treatments was randomly determined. The random assignment minimizes the effects of confounding factors, including the potential confounding factor caused by doing the routines in a particular order. The warm-ups were carefully controlled so that every athlete did precisely the same warm-up.

- The fact that random assignment was used (to determine the order of the warm-up conditions) means that the researchers are justified in making a cause-and-effect conclusion: we can conclude that, for these 19 athletes, the improvements in 20-metre sprint performance and ROM are caused by the warm-up condition that includes static stretching and a sport-specific warm-up.

- However, the athletes constituted a small sample that was not randomly selected. This means that we should not generalize these results to other athletes or to other sports. Note that the improvements in sprint time and ROM were very small (about 1% for sprint time and 3% for ROM). Although these slight improvements might be meaningful (clinically significant) to elite athletes, for most of us these differences are inconsequential.

We cannot tell from the abstract whether the results have been replicated elsewhere, nor do we know the extent to which the results are consistent with what other researchers have suggested. But we should keep in mind that one paper is not enough for us to believe in the results. We should try to find out whether other studies support the use of static stretching within an activity-specific warm-up to improve ROM and sprint performance.

EXPLORING STATISTICS

CLASS ACTIVITY

Reporting on Research Abstracts

GOALS	MATERIALS
To practise reading and interpreting scientific studies	Six questions provided below

BEFORE THE ACTIVITY

Find a reported study (either an experiment or an observational study) on the internet or in a magazine, journal, book, or newspaper in an area of interest to you. Print out or copy the abstract or summary. Good sources for medical studies include the *New England Journal of Medicine* archives (www.nejm.org/medical-articles/research) and the *Canadian Medical Association Journal* (www.cmaj.ca).

ACTIVITY

Write a report on your chosen abstract. Be sure to include the authors of the study; the title of the study; the journal, book, or magazine in which it was published; and the date of publication. In your report, answer these questions:

1. What is the research question that these investigators are trying to answer?

2. What is their answer to the research question?

3. What were the methods used to collect the data?

4. Is the conclusion appropriate for the methods? (For example, is the conclusion a cause-and-effect claim? Were the data collected in such a way as to support this claim?)

5. To what population do the conclusions apply?

6. Is any indication given that these results are consistent with what other researchers have suggested?

AFTER THE ACTIVITY

There is no follow-up to this activity.

CHAPTER REVIEW

Summary of Learning Objectives

1. **What is blocking and how can it help researchers control variation?** Blocking is the practice of creating groups of individuals who are similar, and then randomly assigning treatments within the groups. Blocking can control the effect of variables other than the ones of primary interest. It can help increase the power of a study (the probability of detecting true differences among the treatment groups).

2. **What is systematic sampling and when is it useful for obtaining representative samples?** Systematic sampling is done by regularly selecting every *n*th (such as every 10th) individual to appear in the sample. It results in a representative sample if the individuals appear in random order.

3. **What is stratified sampling and when is it useful for obtaining precise estimators?** Stratified sampling is done by creating strata (groups of individuals who are similar to one another), and then taking a random sample within each stratum.

It results in precise estimators if the variability within each stratum is smaller than the variability in the population.

4. **What is cluster sampling and when is it useful for obtaining precise estimators?** Cluster sampling is done by creating clusters (individuals who are grouped for convenience and who tend to be different from one another), obtaining a random sample of clusters, and measuring all individuals within those clusters. It is used for large populations or for populations where individuals occur naturally in groups. It results in precise estimators if clusters resemble the population.

5. **What are some of the questions I need to ask when evaluating published research papers?** How was randomness used? Have the results been replicated? Is the conclusion appropriate for the methods used to collect data? Remember that extraordinary results require extraordinary evidence.

Important Terms

Treatment variable, *556*
Response variable, *556*
Confounding variables, *556*
Controlled experiment, *557*

Random assignment, *557*
Observational study, *557*
Power, *558*
Controlling for a variable, *558*

Blocking, *559*
Matched-pairs design, *562*
Crossover design, *564*
Systematic sampling, *566*

Stratified sampling, *566*
Strata, *566*
Cluster sampling, *567*
Clusters, *567*

Sources

BBC News. February 18, 2010. http://news.bbc.co.uk (accessed May 13, 2010).

Behm, D. G., and A. Chaouachi. 2011. A review of the acute effects of static and dynamic stretching on performance. *European Journal of Applied Physiology* 111, 2633–2651.

Belluz, J. 2011. The truth about vitamin D. http://www2.macleans.ca/2011/10/12/the-truth-about-vitamin-d (accessed December 15, 2013).

Boswell, R. 2013. For younger Canadians, Tims beats monarchy on what shapes nationhood, poll finds. o.canada.com/news (accessed December 10, 2013).

Caldwell, B., and J. Crane. 2010. Randomized crossover trial of the acceptability of snus, nicotine gum, and Zonnic therapy for smoking reduction in heavy smokers. *Nicotine & Tobacco Research* 12(2), 179–183.

Coggins, S. B., N. C. Coops, and M. A. Wulder. 2010. Improvement of low level bark beetle damage estimates with adaptive cluster sampling. *Silva Fennica* 44(2), 289–301.

Davison, C. M., et al. 2013. Bicycle helmet use and bicycling-related injury among young Canadians: An equity analysis. *International Journal for Equity in Health* 12, 48.

Ferguson, C. J., and J. Kilburn. 2010. Much ado about nothing: The misestimation and overinterpretation of violent video game effects in Eastern and Western nations: Comment on Anderson et al. *Psychological Bulletin* 136(2), 174–178, discussion 182–187.

Gupta, N., H. Wang, M. Collette, and W. Pilgrim. 2012. New Brunswick Student Drug Survey Report. www.gnb.ca/health (accessed December 11, 2013).

Maclean's. 2013, June. Is it time to legalize marijuana? http://www2.macleans.ca/2013/06/14/is-it-time-to-legalize-marijuana (accessed December 18, 2013).

Mednick, S., D. Cai, J. Kanady, and S. Drummond. 2008. Comparing the benefits of caffeine, naps and placebo on verbal, motor and perceptual memory. *Behavioural Brain Research* 193, 79–86.

Neale, T. 2007. Even active video games not good enough for kids' fitness. MedPage Today. http://www.medpagetoday.com (accessed April 22, 2010).

Nixon, G., G. Leigh, and N. Nowatzki. 2006. Impacting attitudes towards gambling: A prison gambling awareness and prevention program. *Journal of Gambling Issues*, 17 (doi: 10.4309/jgi.2006.17.14).

Ramirez, G., and S. Beilock. 2011. Writing about testing worries boosts exam performance in the classroom. *Science* 331, 211.

Raskin, P., and R. Unger. 1978. Hyperglucagonemia and its suppression. *The New England Journal of Medicine* 299(9), 433–436.

Reid, R., et al. 2012. Randomized trial of an internet-based computer-tailored expert system for physical activity in patients with heart disease. *European Journal of Preventive Cardiology* 19, 1357–1364.

Samra, R. A., and G. H. Anderson. 2007. Insoluble cereal fiber reduces appetite and short-term food intake and glycemic response to food consumed 75 min later by healthy men. *American Journal of Clinical Nutrition* 86(4), 972–979.

Samson, M., et al. 2012. Effects of static and dynamic stretching within general and activity-specific warm-up protocols. *Journal of Sports Science and Medicine* 11(2), 279–285.

Saudny, H., D. Leggee, and G. Egeland. 2012. *International Journal of Circumpolar Health* 71, 19752.

Strayer, D. L., F. A. Drews, and D. J. Crouch. 2006. A comparison of the cell phone driver and the drunk driver. *Journal of the Human Factors and Ergonomics Society* 48(2), 381–391.

Taylor, P. 2011, January 13. Writing about fears before tests boosts student grades: Study. *The Globe and Mail.*

Thiffault, N., F. Hébert, L. Charette, and R. Jobidon. 2013. Large spruce seedling responses to the interacting effects of vegetation zone, competing vegetation dominance and year of mechanical release. *Forestry* (2014) 87 (1): 153–164. http://forestry.oxfordjournals.org/content/early/2013/11/27/forestry.cpt048.full (accessed December 13, 2013).

SECTION EXERCISES

SECTION 12.1

12.1 Happiness and Heart Disease These two headlines are on the same topic, but one has language that suggests a cause-and-effect relationship, and the other does not.

Headline A: "Happiness Wards Off Heart Disease, Study Says"

Headline B: "Happy People Have Healthier Hearts, Study Finds"

Which headline suggests a cause-and-effect relationship and which suggests only an association? (Source: news.bbc.co.uk, February 18, 2010. Accessed through Jonathan Mueller, http://jonathan.mueller.faculty.noctrl.edu)

12.2 Breastfeeding and IQ These two headlines are on the same topic, but one has language that suggests a cause-and-effect relationship, and the other does not.

Headline A: "Higher IQ Found in Breastfed Babies"

Headline B: "Breastfeeding Found to Boost Baby IQ"

State which headline claims a cause-and-effect relationship and which claims only an association. (Sources: http://www.iop.kcl.ac.uk/news and http://health.virginmedia.com)

12.3 Student Gambling and Proximity to a Casino

Researchers surveyed 1579 students in Canadian universities far from and close to a large casino regarding their gambling activities. It was found that students close to a casino manifested more serious gambling problems than students far from a casino. Was this a controlled experiment or an observational study? Explain. (Source: G. R. Adams et al. 2007. A study of differences in Canadian university students' gambling and proximity to a casino. *Journal of Gambling Issues* 19, 9–17)

12.4 Household Food Insecurity and Diabetes

Researchers analyzed data on household food insecurity (HFI) and diabetes from the Canadian Community Health Survey. They found that HFI (referring to the limited or uncertain access to food resulting from inadequate financial resources) was more prevalent among individuals with diabetes than among those without diabetes. Does this show that HFI causes diabetes? Why or why not? (Source: E. Gucciardi et al. 2009. Exploration of the relationship between household food insecurity and diabetes in Canada. *Diabetes Care* 32(12), 2218–2224)

12.5 Student Gambling and Proximity to a Casino

Using the information from Exercise 12.3, write two headlines announcing the results of the study. Make one of the headlines state or imply causality and one not imply causality. Explain which is which. Which headline is appropriate for these data, and why?

12.6 Household Food Insecurity and Diabetes

Using the information from Exercise 12.4, write two headlines announcing the results of the study. Make one of the headlines state or imply causality and one not imply causality. Explain which is which. Which headline is appropriate for these data, and why?

12.7 Premature Babies Some premature babies have trouble breathing. Researchers conducted a study to find out whether lowering the babies' body temperature increased their chance of survival. Is the study described in the following abstract excerpt an observational study or a controlled experiment? How can you tell?

"Methods: We performed a randomized trial of infants who were less than 6 hours of age and had a gestational age of at least 36 weeks. . . . We compared intensive care plus cooling of the body to 33.5°C for 72 hours and intensive care alone. The primary outcome was death or severe disability at 18 months of age."

"Conclusions: Induction of moderate hypothermia for 72 hours in infants who had perinatal asphyxia did not significantly reduce the combined rate of death or severe disability but resulted in improved neurologic outcomes in survivors."

(Source: D. V. Azzopardi et al. 2009. Moderate hypothermia to treat perinatal asphyxial encephalopathy. *New England Journal of Medicine* 361, 1340–1358)

12.8 Place of Residence and Postpartum Depression

Researchers conducted study to evaluate the relation between place of residence and risk of postpartum depression among Canadian women. Is the study described in the following abstract excerpt an observational study or a controlled experiment? Explain.

"Methods: Female postpartum respondents to the 2006 Canadian Maternity Experiences Survey ($n = 6126$) were classified as living in rural (< 1000 inhabitants or population density $< 400/km^2$), semirural (nonrural but $< 30,000$ inhabitants), semiurban (30,000–499,999 inhabitants) or urban ($\geq 500,000$ inhabitants) areas. We further subdivided women living in rural areas based on the social and occupational connectivity of their community to larger urban centres. We compared the prevalence of postpartum depression across these groups and adjusted for the effect of known risk factors for postpartum depression."

"Results: The prevalence of postpartum depression was higher among women living in urban areas than among those living in rural, semirural or semiurban areas. The difference between semiurban and urban areas could not be fully explained by other measured risk factors for postpartum depression."

(Source: S. N. Vigod et al. 2013. Relation between place of residence and postpartum depression. *Canadian Medical Association Journal.* 185 (13): 1129–1135)

TRY 12.9 Multiple Sclerosis Drugs (Example 1) Multiple sclerosis is a disease of the nervous system that causes severe weakness of the arms and legs, among many other damaging symptoms. Read the following excerpt from the abstract for this controlled experiment, and then:

a. Identify the treatment and response variables.

b. Restate the conclusion of the study in terms of a cause-and-effect conclusion.

"In this 12-month, double-blind . . . study we randomly assigned 1292 patients with relapsing–remitting multiple sclerosis who had a recent history of at least one relapse to receive either oral fingolimod at a daily dose of either 1.25 or 0.5 mg or intramuscular interferon beta-1a (an established therapy for multiple sclerosis) at a weekly dose of 30 μg.

The annualized relapse rate was significantly lower in both groups receiving fingolimod—0.20 (95% confidence interval [CI], 0.16 to 0.26) in the 1.25-mg group and 0.16 (95% CI, 0.12 to 0.21) in the 0.5-mg group—than in the interferon group (0.33; 95% CI, 0.26 to 0.42; P < 0.001 for both comparisons).

Conclusions: This trial showed the superior efficacy of oral fingolimod with respect to relapse rates and MRI outcomes in patients with multiple sclerosis, as compared with intramuscular interferon beta-1a."

(Source: J. A. Cohen et al. 2010. Oral fingolimod or intramuscular interferon for relapsing multiple sclerosis. *New England Journal of Medicine* 362, 402–415)

12.10 Antibacterial Scrub Read the excerpt from the following abstract from a controlled experiment, and then:

a. Identify the treatment and response variables.

b. Restate the conclusion of the study in terms of a cause-and-effect conclusion.

"We randomly assigned adults undergoing clean-contaminated surgery in six hospitals to preoperative skin preparation with either chlorhexidine–alcohol scrub or povidone–iodine scrub and paint. The primary outcome was any surgical-site infection within 30 days after surgery. Secondary outcomes included individual types of surgical-site infections.

The overall rate of surgical-site infection was significantly lower in the chlorhexidine–alcohol group than in the povidone–iodine group (9.5% vs. 16.1%; P = 0.004; relative risk, 0.59; 95% confidence interval, 0.41 to 0.85). Chlorhexidine–alcohol was significantly more protective than povidone–iodine against both superficial incisional infections (4.2% vs. 8.6%, P = 0.008) and deep incisional infections (1% vs. 3%, P = 0.05) but not against organ-space infections (4.4% vs. 4.5%).

Conclusions: Preoperative cleansing of the patient's skin with chlorhexidine–alcohol is superior to cleansing with povidone–iodine for preventing surgical-site infection after clean-contaminated surgery."

(Source: P. Daroui et al. 2010. Chlorhexidine–alcohol versus povidone–iodine for surgical-site antisepsis. *New England Journal of Medicine* 362, 18–26)

12.11 Mild Cognitive Impairment and Exercise Researchers at the University of British Columbia performed a controlled experiment to investigate the effect of exercise on memory performance in older adults with mild cognitive impairment. Read the following excerpt from the abstract of this experiment, and then:

a. Identify the treatment and response variable(s).

b. Restate the conclusions of the study in terms of cause-and-effect conclusions.

"We randomized 86 women aged 70–80 years with subjective memory complaints into one of three groups: resistance training, aerobic training, or balance and tone (control). All participants exercised twice per week for six months. We measured verbal memory and learning using the Rey Auditory Verbal Learning Test (RAVLT) and spatial memory using a computerized test, before and after trial completion. We found that the aerobic training group remembered significantly more items in the loss after interference condition of the RAVLT compared with the control group after six months of training. In addition, both experimental groups showed improved spatial memory performance in the most difficult condition where they were required to memorize the spatial location of three items, compared with the control group. Our results provide support for the prevailing notion that exercise can positively impact cognitive functioning and may represent an effective strategy to improve memory in those who have begun to experience cognitive decline."

(Source: L. S. Nagamatsu et al. 2013. Physical activity improves verbal and spatial memory in older adults with probable mild cognitive impairment: A 6-month randomized controlled trial. *Journal of Aging Research* 2013, 861893)

12.12 Childhood Exposure to Tobacco Smoke and Emphysema A December 2009 headline from esciencenews.com said, "Exposure to tobacco smoke in childhood home associated with early emphysema in adulthood."

a. Does this headline most likely refer to a controlled experiment or an observational study? Explain.

b. Can you think of a confounding factor that might cause emphysema and is not childhood exposure to smoking?

(Source: http://esciencenews.com)

12.13 Body Temperatures Two different simple random samples of body temperatures were taken from the same population of healthy adult men. One of the samples had 10 men and one had 30 men. Use the output provided to test the hypothesis that the mean temperature in the population of healthy adult men is not 37°C. Assume that the population distribution of temperatures is Normal and that we have random samples. Use a significance level of 0.05. The null hypothesis is that the population mean is 37°C, and the alternative hypothesis is that it is not 37°C.

a. Test the sample of 10 temperatures to decide whether you can reject the null hypothesis. Report the p-value and conclusion.

```
One-Sample T: 10men

Test of mu = 37 vs not = 37


Variable   N    Mean    StDev   SE Mean      95% CI          T     P
10men      10   36.761  0.438   0.139     (36.448, 37.075)  -1.72  0.119
```

b. Test the sample of 30 temperatures to decide whether you can reject the null hypothesis. Report the p-value and conclusion.

```
One-Sample T: 30men

Test of mu = 37 vs not = 37


Variable   N    Mean     StDev   SE Mean      95% CI          T     P
30men      30   36.7759  0.3811  0.0696    (36.6336, 36.9182)  -3.22  0.003
```

c. Explain the main reason for the different p-values and the different conclusions.

(Source: www.amstat.org/publications/jse/datasets/normtemp.dat.txt)

12.14 Gender and Use of Turn Signals Hector Porath, a statistics student, wanted to find out whether gender and the use of turn signals when driving are independent. He observed drivers when driving in his truck over a period of weeks, noting the drivers' gender and whether they used the turn signal when turning or changing lanes, as required by law. Use a significance level of 0.05.

	Men	Women
Turn Signal	585	452
No Signal	351	155
	936	607

a. In this sample, were men or women more likely to use their turn signals? Show both percentages.

b. Report the chi-square value and the p-value for a chi-square test of independence. Can you reject the null hypothesis that gender and use of turn signal are independent? If so, what do you conclude?

c. Now repeat your analysis using sample sizes that are about one-tenth the size of the real sample sizes:

	Men	Women
Turn Signal	59	45
No Signal	35	16
	94	61

d. Compare your answers to parts b and c, and explain what happened.

*12.15 Diet Pill and Power Imagine two studies of a diet pill that, manufacturers claim, will make people lose weight. The first study is based on a random sample of 100 men and women who have been taking the diet pill for 12 months. A hypothesis test is carried out to determine whether their mean weight change is negative. The second study was based on a random sample consisting solely of 100 men (no women) who had been taking the weight loss pill for 12 months. The same hypothesis test is carried out to determine whether their mean weight change is negative. Which study's hypothesis test will have greater power to detect whether the mean weight change is truly less than 0? Assume that the diet pill really does lower weight and that the effect of weight loss is larger on men than on women.

*12.16 LSAT Prep and Power Suppose an LSAT tutoring company really can improve LSAT scores by 10 points, on average. A competing company, however, uses a more intense tutoring approach and really can improve LSAT scores by 15 points, on average. Suppose you've been hired by both companies to test their claims that their tutoring improves LSAT scores. For both companies, you will collect a random sample of potential law school applicants to undergo tutoring. With both resulting samples, you

will test the hypothesis that the mean improvement is more than 0. Suppose it is important to keep the power of both studies at 80%. Will you use the same sample size for both studies? If so, explain why you can. If not, which study would require the largest sample size, and why? Assume that both samples of students will be drawn from the same population.

TRY **12.17 Brain Games (Example 2)** Researchers are interested in whether a video game that is designed to increase brain activity actually works. To test this, they plan to randomly assign subjects to either the treatment group (spend 15 minutes per day playing the game) or a control group (spend 15 minutes per day surfing the web). At the end of the study, the researchers will administer a test of "brain teasers" to see which group has the greater mental agility. Because they suspect that age might affect the outcome, the researchers will create blocks of ages: 18–25, 26–35, 36–45, and 46–55. To randomly assign subjects to treatment or control, they will place four tickets in a box. The tickets are labelled with the age groups. When an age group is selected, everyone in that age group will be assigned to the treatment group. They will select two age groups to go to treatment, and two to go to control. Is this an appropriate use of blocking? If so, explain why. If not, describe a better blocking plan.

12.18 A Smile a Day Smiling is a sign of a good mood, but can smiling improve a bad mood? Researchers plan to assign subjects to two groups. Subjects in both groups will rate their mood at the beginning of the study. Then subjects in the treatment group will be told to smile while they are asked to recount a pleasant memory. Subjects in the control group will also be asked to recount a pleasant memory, but they will not be told to smile. Both groups will again rate their moods, and researchers will determine whether the reported moods differ between the two groups. Because the initial, baseline mood rating might affect the outcome, after the first mood rating the subjects will be broken into two groups: one group with low ratings ("bad mood") and one with higher ratings ("good mood"). Patients in each group will then be randomly assigned to either the treatment group or the control group. Is this an appropriate use of blocking? If so, explain why. If not, describe a better blocking plan.

TRY ***12.19 Energy Return Running Shoes (Example 3)** Several sports brands have recently designed running shoes that they claim will ultimately have runners running farther and faster with less effort because of their effective "energy return." In order to test whether shoes with energy return are effective and compare them with regular running shoes, suppose that there are 40 long-distance runners: 20 of them are Olympic-level runners, and 20 are amateur runners. The designers will ask runners to run five kilometres as fast as possible. It is reasonable to assume that the effects of the running shoes might be different for the elite Olympic runners than for amateur runners.

a. Identify the treatment variable and the response variable.

b. Describe a simple randomized design (not blocked) to test whether the energy return shoes decrease race times. Explain in detail how you will assign runners to treatment groups. Your description should be detailed enough that a friend could carry out your instructions.

c. Describe a blocked design to test whether the energy return shoes decrease race times. Explain in detail how you will assign runners to treatment groups.

d. What advantage does the blocked design have?

e. Describe a way to use runners as their own controls to reduce variation.

*12.20 Flu Vaccines and Age Suppose you want to compare the effectiveness of the flu vaccine in preventing the flu using one of two different forms: nasal spray vs. injection. Suppose you have 60 subjects of different ages available, and you suspect that age might have an effect on the outcome. Assume there are 20 children from ages 2 to 15, 20 people from ages 16 to 30, and 20 people from ages 31 to 49.

a. Identify the treatment variable and the response variable.

b. Describe a simple randomized design (no blocking) to test whether the injection or the nasal spray is more effective. Explain in detail how to assign people to treatment groups.

c. Describe a blocked design (blocking by age) to test whether the injection or the nasal spray is more effective. Explain in detail how you will assign people to treatment groups.

d. What advantage does the blocked design have?

*12.21 Preventing Heart Attacks with Aspirin Suppose that you want to determine whether the use of one aspirin per day for people aged 50 and older reduces the chance of heart attack. You have 200 people available for the study, 100 men and 100 women. You suspect that aspirin might affect men and women differently. To ensure an appropriate comparison group, those who do not get aspirin should get a placebo.

a. Identify the treatment and response variables.

b. Describe in detail a simple randomized design (not blocked) to test whether aspirin lowers the risk of heart attack.

c. Describe a blocked design to test whether aspirin lowers the risk of heart attack; the blocking variable is gender.

d. Explain why researchers might prefer a blocked design.

*12.22 Tomato Plants and Fertilizer Suppose you grow tomato plants in a greenhouse and sell the tomatoes by weight, so that the amount of money you make depends on plants producing a large total weight of tomatoes.

You want to determine which of two fertilizers will produce a heavier harvest of tomatoes, fertilizer A or fertilizer B. There are two distinct regions in the greenhouse, one on the southern side that gets more light and one on the northern side that gets less light. There is room for 20 tomato plants on the southern side and 20 on the northern side. Assume that all the plants are beefsteak tomato plants.

a. Identify the treatment and response variables.

b. Describe a simple randomized design to test whether fertilizer A is better than fertilizer B.

c. Describe a blocked design to test which fertilizer produces a greater weight of tomatoes, blocking by southern side and northern side of the greenhouse. Explain why creating blocks based on whether plants are on the southern or northern side makes sense.

d. Explain why researchers might prefer a blocked design.

TRY **12.23 Used Textbooks (Example 4)** A random sample of textbooks at the University of Calgary Bookstore was obtained in 2013 and the used-textbook price of each textbook was observed. The used-textbook price of the same textbooks was also observed on Amazon.ca. Assume that the distribution of prices is sufficiently close to Normal for t-tests. We want to test the hypothesis that the mean price of a used textbook at the University of Calgary Bookstore is the same as the mean price of a used textbook on Amazon.ca. Assume that conditions for t-tests hold.

Price at Bookstore	Price at Amazon.ca
160.46	128.95
82.05	34.4
96.08	30.41
96.71	110.99
77.96	33.99
104.96	20
82.5	123.99
53.21	46.1
100.46	98.99
67.5	63.99
99.71	80
137.96	81.99
86.21	69.39
118.5	78.27
134.21	115

a. Use a two-sample t-test, and report the value of the observed test statistic and the p-value. Report whether you can reject the null hypothesis of no difference in prices at the 0.05 level.

b. Use a paired t-test, and report the observed value of the test statistic and the p-value. Report whether you can reject the null hypothesis of no difference in prices at the 0.05 level.

c. For these data, which is the appropriate test? Explain.

12.24 Textbook Prices A random sample of textbooks was obtained at a university in Ontario in 2013. The price of each book was observed on the Canada and United Kingdom Amazon websites (prices in the UK were obtained in pounds and changed to Canadian dollars). Determine whether the prices are significantly different, using a significance level of 0.05. Assume that the distribution of prices is sufficiently close to Normal for t-tests.

a. Use a two sample t-test; report the t-statistic and p-value, and report whether you can reject the null hypothesis of no difference in prices at the 0.05 level of significance.

b. Use a paired t-test; report the t-statistic and p-value, and report whether you can reject the null hypothesis of no difference in prices at the 0.05 level of significance.

c. Which is the appropriate test for this data set?

12.25 Reading Coloured Paper Some people believe that it is easier to read words printed on coloured paper than words printed on white paper. To test this theory, statistics student Paula Smith collected data. Subjects were timed as they read a passage printed in black ink on a sheet of salmon-coloured paper and also timed for reading the same passage printed with black ink on a sheet of white paper. Each person was randomly assigned to read material printed on either the white or the salmon paper first. The times in seconds are given in the table. We are assuming that smaller times (faster reading) imply that the reading is easier. Assume that these are a random sample of times and that the distribution of times is sufficiently close to Normal for t-tests.

Salmon	White
79	72
49	45
47	45
112	120
65	63
66	62
67	60
59	54

Salmon	White
140	160
64	57
67	61
73	72
64	48
126	122
67	73

a. Compare the sample means. Does your result fit with the theory given?

b. Use a two-sample *t*-test; report the *t*-statistic and p-value, and report whether you can reject the null hypothesis of no difference in times at the 0.05 level.

c. Use a paired *t*-test; report the *t*-statistic and p-value, and report whether you can reject the null hypothesis of no difference in times at the 0.05 level.

d. Which is the appropriate test for this data set?

e. Why is it essential that the researchers randomly assign the order so that some of the people read material on the salmon-coloured paper first and some read material on the white first?

 12.26 The Stroop Effect Suppose you had to identify the colour of ink for a series of printed words that spelled out a colour that did not match the ink colour. For example, what colour ink is used in the word RED? This might take longer than identifying the colour when the ink and printed word match (RED). This difference is an example of *interference* and is called the Stroop Effect, in reference to a famous study conducted by research psychologist J. R. Stroop (1897–1973).

Same	Different
32	66
12	31
17	40
16	25
25	36
18	15
18	39
24	35
20	32
24	30

The data in the table were collected to see whether interference was significant. Each of the 10 people studied identified colours of ink in two situations, and the time (in seconds) was recorded. There were 36 words in each trial. In column 1 (Same), the ink was the same colour as the meaning of the spelled-out word. In column 2 (Different) the colour of the ink was different from the meaning of the spelled-out word. Each person was randomly assigned to read the "same colour" or the "different colour" words first. Assume that all the conditions required for *t*-tests are satisfied.

a. Compare the sample means. Does the result fit with the theory given?

b. Use a two-sample *t*-test; report the *t*-statistic and p-value, and report whether you can reject the null hypothesis of no difference in times at the 0.05 level.

c. Use a paired *t*-test; report the *t*-statistic and p-value, and report whether you can reject the null hypothesis of no difference in times at the 0.05 level.

d. Which is the appropriate test for this data set?

e. Why is it appropriate to randomly assign the order so that some of the people read the "same colour" word first and some read the "different colour" word first?

12.27 Pulse Rates Suppose you want to test students' pulse rates in three different situations: after sitting in class, after exercise (standing up and sitting down five times), and after meditation (with eyes closed and counting silently and slowly from 1 to 5 repeatedly). To increase the power of your statistical tests, you plan to measure each student in all three situations. Why would you want to randomize the order so that some students start with sitting, some start with exercise, and some start with meditation?

12.28 Reading Coloured Paper Suppose you want to test students' reading with three different colours of paper to see whether the colour has an effect on reading speed. Assume that the same passage is written on three different colours of paper: light blue, yellow, and pink. Each student's reading speed will be tested on all three colours. Why would you want to randomize the order in which the different colours are presented?

SECTION 12.2

TRY **12.29 Student Records (Example 5)** Suppose a person with access to student records at your college or university has an alphabetical list of currently enrolled students. The person looks at the records of every 10th person (starting with a randomly selected person among the first 10) to see whether they have paid their latest tuition bill. What kind of sampling does this illustrate?

12.30 Student Records Suppose a person with access to student records at your college or university has a list of currently enrolled students. The person sorts the data to create two new lists. One contains all the male names, the other all the female names. The person then uses a random number generator to select 50 men and 50 women. What kind of sampling does this illustrate?

12.31 Pension Plan Suppose you wanted to collect opinions on how to improve the Canada Pension Plan. Describe the potential benefits of stratifying on age.

12.32 University Football Some Canadian universities have football programs that are expensive to run. Suppose you wanted to survey students at a certain university to find out whether they think funding for the football program at their school should be expanded or reduced. Why might you want to stratify your samples by gender?

12.33 Balancing the Books A national retail clothing chain suspects that individual stores throughout the country are making accounting mistakes when balancing their registers. The executive office staff suspect that the problem is worse in their large-volume stores, where there are many customers per day and, consequently, many possibilities for mistakes in the accounting. They divide all their stores into three groups: high volume, medium volume, and low volume. Within each of these groups, they take a random sample, without replacement, of 10 stores. Each store selected for the sample will have its accounts audited to look for accounting mistakes, and from this the executive office will estimate the proportion of all stores that have committed accounting errors. Is this an example of stratified random sampling, systematic sampling, or cluster sampling? Explain.

12.34 Grocery Shopping Patterns A certain university is interested in the grocery shopping patterns of married graduate students living in one of its family housing communities. The community consists of 139 two-bedroom townhomes, grouped into 12 different buildings. Because the survey is rather lengthy, the university does not want to survey all the families and decides to ask a sample of families instead. Three buildings are chosen at random and all the families in those three buildings are surveyed. Is this an example of stratified random sampling, systematic sampling, or cluster sampling?

🌍 SECTION 12.3

Section 12.3 Exercises are available online, and can be found on MyStatLab.

CHAPTER REVIEW EXERCISES

*12.49 Vaccinations for Diarrhea in Mexico Diarrhea can kill children and is often caused by rotavirus. Read the abstract below and answer the questions that follow.

> *"Methods:* We obtained data on deaths from diarrhea, regardless of cause, from January 2003 through May 2009 in Mexican children under five years of age. We compared diarrhea-related mortality in 2008 and during the 2008 and 2009 rotavirus seasons with the mortality at baseline (2003–2006), before the introduction of the rotavirus vaccine. Vaccine coverage was estimated from administrative data.
>
> *Results:* Diarrhea-related mortality fell from an annual median of 18.1 deaths per 100,000 children at baseline to 11.8 per 100,000 children in 2008 (rate reduction, 35%; 95% confidence interval [CI], 29 to 39; $P < 0.001$). . . . Mortality among unvaccinated children between the ages of 24 and 59 months was not significantly reduced. The reduction in the number of diarrhea-related deaths persisted through two full rotavirus seasons (2008 and 2009).
>
> *Conclusions:* After the introduction of a rotavirus vaccine, a significant decline in diarrhea-related deaths among Mexican children was observed, suggesting a potential benefit from rotavirus vaccination."

a. State the death rate before vaccine and the death rate after vaccine. What was the change in deaths per 100,000 children? From the given p-value, can you reject the null hypothesis of no change in death rate?

b. Would you conclude that the vaccine was effective? Why or why not?

(Source: R. Vesta et al. 2010. Effect of rotavirus vaccination on death from childhood diarrhea in Mexico. *New England Journal of Medicine* 62, 299–305)

12.50 Gestational Diabetes Comment on the following abstract, which discusses treatment of diabetes in pregnant women (gestational diabetes) and complications of childbirth.

> *"[Methods:]* We conducted a randomized clinical trial to determine whether treatment of women with gestational diabetes mellitus reduced the risk of perinatal [immediately before or after childbirth] complications. We randomly assigned women between 24 and 34 weeks' gestation who had gestational diabetes to receive dietary advice, blood glucose monitoring, and insulin therapy as needed (the intervention group) or routine care. Primary outcomes included serious perinatal complications (defined as death, shoulder dystocia, bone fracture, and nerve palsy), admission to the neonatal nursery, jaundice requiring phototherapy, induction of labour, cesarean birth, and maternal anxiety, depression, and health status.
>
> *[Results:]* The rate of serious perinatal complications was significantly lower among the infants of the 490 women in the intervention group than among the infants of the 510 women in the routine-care group (1 percent vs. 4 percent; . . . $P = 0.01$). . . .
>
> *Conclusions:* Treatment of gestational diabetes reduces serious perinatal morbidity. . . ."

a. Identify the treatment and the response variables.

b. Is the stated conclusion making a claim for cause and effect? If so, is this claim justified? Explain.

(Source: C. A. Crowther et al. 2005. Effect of treatment of gestational diabetes mellitus on pregnancy outcomes. *New England Journal of Medicine* 352, 2477–2486)

13 Inference Without Normality

outdoorsman/Shutterstock

LEARNING OBJECTIVES

After completing this chapter, you should be able to:

1. Determine when and how to apply the sign test to compare two dependent samples.
2. Determine when and how to apply the Mann-Whitney test to compare two independent samples.
3. Determine when and how to apply the Kruskal-Wallis test to compare three or more independent samples.
4. Determine when and how to apply a randomization test to compare two independent samples. 🌐
5. Interpret a QQ plot. 🌐
6. Determine when and how to use the geometric mean to estimate the centre of a distribution with confidence. 🌐

Many of the techniques you've learned for inference so far have relied on a single important mathematical idea: the Normal distribution. In many cases, when the population we're studying follows a Normal distribution, we can compute accurate confidence levels and compute p-values for our hypothesis tests. Confidence levels and p-values are important because they measure our level of uncertainty. Inference is an uncertain business and might seem completely useless if it were not for the fact that we can measure how far from the truth our estimates are likely to be.

However, not every variable has a distribution that is Normal. When the population is not Normal, the Central Limit Theorem tells us that if the sample size is large enough, the distribution of the sample mean or sample proportion is still approximately Normal. But what if we are not estimating a mean or proportion? The CLT doesn't help us if we want to estimate the population median, for example. In some contexts, such as skewed distributions, the median is a more natural measure of centre than is the mean. At other times, we might have too small a sample size to rely on the CLT. For example, biologists who study animals in the wild, as in the study of arctic foxes discussed below, sometimes work with small sample sizes and so cannot rely on the Central Limit Theorem to assure them that the Normal condition is satisfied.

Several approaches to inference will work regardless of whether the population follows the Normal distribution. The formal name for such approaches is **nonparametric inference**. This term covers a variety of techniques and procedures, and this chapter focuses on hypothesis tests that do not depend on the Normal distribution. Certain conditions need to be satisfied in order for these tests to provide valid inference, but generally these conditions are less strict than those that must be satisfied for the tests presented in earlier chapters.

CASE STUDY

How Arctic Foxes Find the Right Home

Understanding the factors that influence animals' habitat selection is an important aspect of animal ecology. To study how arctic foxes select a denning site among potential sites, and a breeding den among existing dens, researchers examined 83 arctic fox (*Alopex lagopus*) dens on Bylot Island, Nunavut (Szor et al. 2008). At each den, they measured landscape characteristics such as slope; distance to the closest coastline, lake, and stream; distance to a snow goose colony; and lemming availability. To determine whether arctic foxes *select* for particular environmental characteristics when establishing their den, researchers measured the same variables at random locations within the study area. Local characteristics such as snow cover and depth of loose soil were also measured at each den, as well as at a random potential denning site within 100 metres of the den. Finally, dens were classified as "nonbreeding" (no reproduction observed in several years), "natal" (cubs observed at the beginning of the breeding season), and "rearing" (movement of litter directly observed or cubs appeared only late in the breeding season).

Several of the variables measured did not appear to have a Normal distribution, so comparisons between them were made using nonparametric tests, the focus of this chapter. At the end of the chapter we will see how different tests were used for comparing different kinds of samples (two independent samples, two matched samples, or three independent samples).

The Sign Test for Paired Data

We begin our study of nonparametric techniques by discussing a test that is used when observations from two groups are paired (or dependent). Recall that paired samples occur when individuals from a single population are observed under two different settings (for example, measuring the same subject before and after receiving a treatment). Samples are also dependent when the individuals being measured are related somehow (as when we are comparing twins), or when individuals have been deliberately matched so as to have similar characteristics. In Chapter 9, we discussed using the paired *t*-test to compare the means of paired, or dependent, samples.

The **sign test** is a nonparametric test that can be used in place of the paired *t*-test. The sign test is particularly useful when the Normal condition of the paired *t*-test is not satisfied. Unlike the *t*-test, the sign test is based on the median of the population, not the mean. The sign test is similar to the paired *t*-test in that both are based on examining the differences between pairs of observations. Therefore, the first step in both tests is to subtract one observation from the other in each pair.

The sign test is useful for comparing two groups when these conditions are met:

1. The two groups are paired (sometimes called *matched*) so that every observation in one group is coupled with one particular observation in the other.

2. The pairs are independent of other pairs.

The sign test is a nonparametric test because it makes no assumptions about the distributions of the populations. Because it works whether or not the data come from a

Normal distribution, the sign test is helpful if you do not know whether your data are Normally distributed.

Interestingly, the sign test doesn't rely on the values of the differences in the pairs. As the name suggests, it relies only on the *signs* (negative or positive).

We'll begin with a brief overview and then show how to use the sign test with real data.

Overview of the Sign Test

The paired *t*-test and the sign test share the same first step: finding the differences within each pair. The differences between the paired observations in group 1 and group 2 are found by subtracting one value from the other in each pair. Figure 13.1 shows the first few rows of data from a study examining whether the sense of smell is different when we're sitting and when we're lying down (Lundstrom et al. 2006). Each row is a person, and the person's sense of smell was measured under two settings: once sitting up and once lying down. The *difference* variable records the value when sitting minus the value when lying down. For the first subject, the computed difference is $13.5 - 13.25 = 0.25$. (Recall from Example 11 in Chapter 9 that bigger numbers indicate a better ability to detect odours.)

▶ **FIGURE 13.1** Measures of the sense of smell for the first 16 people in the data table. The *difference* variable measures the difference "Sitting Up minus Lying Down."

StatCrunch	Edit	Data	Stat	Graphics	Help
Row	**Sitting Up**	**Lying Down**	**Sex**	**Difference**	
1	13.5	13.25	woman	0.25	
2	13.5	13	woman	0.5	
3	12.75	11.5	woman	1.25	
4	12.5	12.5	man	0	
5	9.25	10	man	-0.75	
6	12.5	13	woman	-0.5	
7	14	11	woman	3	
8	5	2.75	man	2.25	
9	12.75	11.5	woman	1.25	
10	13.75	13.5	woman	0.25	
11	8.75	8.75	man	0	
12	12.75	13.75	man	-1	
13	9	10.75	man	-1.75	
14	10	3.75	woman	6.25	
15	7.5	9	man	-1.5	
16	12.25	9.75	woman	2.5	

Stating Hypotheses

We treat the computed differences as a random sample from a population of differences, and state our hypotheses in terms of the median of that population.

$$H_0: \text{The median difference} = 0.$$

$$H_A: \text{The median difference} \neq 0.$$

Because the median is the value with half of the observations above it and half below it, if we select an observation at random, then there is a 50% chance that it will be bigger than the median and a 50% chance that it will be smaller. Therefore, the null hypothesis is saying that in the population, half of the differences are positive and half are negative.

We have shown a two-tailed alternative hypothesis, but the test can be modified easily enough to perform it with a one-tailed alternative.

Calculating the Test Statistic

The test statistic is quite simple: count the number of positive signs in the computed differences. Ignore any computed differences of 0. We will call this test statistic S (for "sign"). For example, Figure 13.1 shows nine positive signs, five negative signs, and two values of 0 for the variable *difference*. So we find that $S = 9$. You also need to know the number of nonzero differences; we call this number n. Here $n = 14$.

If the null hypothesis is correct and the median is 0, then half of the values should be above 0 and half below. In other words, we should see about half of the pairs, $n/2$, with positive signs. If we see too many positive signs, or too few, then we suspect that the null hypothesis is not true.

Finding the p-Value

After finding S, we need to know whether the observed value of S is unusually large or unusually small. The p-value is then the probability of getting a value of S as far or farther from $n/2$ as the observed value, assuming the true median is 0.

As we said earlier, when the null hypothesis is correct and the true median is 0, then about half of the observations will be bigger than 0 and the probability that a randomly selected observation is positive will be 0.5. Let's consider the sign of a computed difference a success when it is positive. Then we can interpret the test statistic S as counting the number of successes in n independent trials with the probability of success $p = 0.5$. This means that we can apply the binomial model and can compute the exact p-value by using the binomial distribution.

Applying the Sign Test

Let's examine some examples to illustrate how to use the sign test.

EXAMPLE 1 Testing Sense of Smell

Does our sense of smell vary on the basis of whether we are sitting or lying down? Thirty-six subjects had their sense of smell measured in both positions (which position was measured first was determined randomly). The first 16 rows of data are shown in Figure 13.1. The computed difference for three of the subjects was 0, so these observations will not be used. The StatCrunch output for a sign test is provided in Figure 13.2.

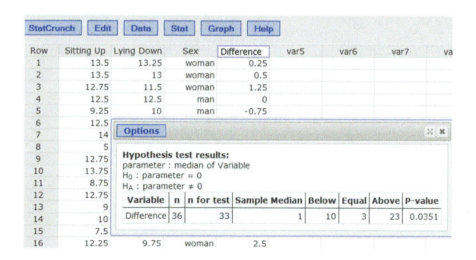

> **Details**
>
> **A Positive Spin**
> There is nothing special about counting positive signs. You could also base the test on the number of negative signs.

> **Looking Back**
>
> **The Binomial Model**
> The binomial model (Section 6.3) provides probabilities for random experiments in which you are counting the number of successes and these three characteristics hold:
> 1. There is a fixed number of trials, n (the number of pairs for which the difference is not 0).
> 2. The only two possible outcomes are success and failure (positive sign and negative sign).
> 3. The trials are independent (pairs are independent of each other), so the probability of success p is the same for all trials ($p = 0.5$ for the sign test).

TECH

◀ **FIGURE 13.2** StatCrunch output for a sign test of the data on sense of smell.

QUESTION Is one's sense of smell different when one is lying down and when one is sitting? Use the provided StatCrunch output to perform a sign test. Follow the four-step procedure for hypothesis tests.

SOLUTION Most of the heavy lifting was done by the software. However, it is your responsibility to make sure the test was appropriate for these data and to interpret the output in a meaningful context.

Step 1: Hypothesize

H_0: The median difference in smelling ability is 0.
H_A: The median difference in smelling ability is not 0.

Step 2: Prepare
The data are clearly paired, because each subject was measured under two settings. We assume that each pair is independent of every other.

Step 3: Compute to compare
The value of the test statistic is $S = 23$. This is found in StatCrunch under the Above column. "Above" means the number of observations that were above, or greater than, the null hypothesis value of 0. The sample size n is 33. (There were 36 observations, but three had differences of 0 and so were discarded.)

If the null hypothesis is true, then about half, or 16 to 17, of the observations should be positive. We instead saw 23. Is this surprising?

The reported p-value is 0.0351. This is a two-tailed p-value, as we can see in the output in Figure 13.2, where the alternative hypothesis is given.

The exact computation of the p-value is illustrated in Figure 13.3, which shows the sampling distribution of S obtained with the binomial calculator in StatCrunch (with $n = 33$ and $p = 0.5$). The statistic S will be "as extreme or more extreme" than 23 when it is as far or farther above the mean value of $33/2 = 16.5$ than 23 is (that is, 6.5 counts or more above the mean), or as far or farther below 16.5 than 10 is (that is, 6.5 counts or more below the mean). The probability of these extreme values is indicated in black in the figure. The p-value is thus $1 - 0.9649 = 0.0351$, as reported in Figure 13.2.

► **FIGURE 13.3** The sampling distribution of S. The probability of getting 23 or more, or 10 or fewer, positive signs in 33 pairs is indicated in black.

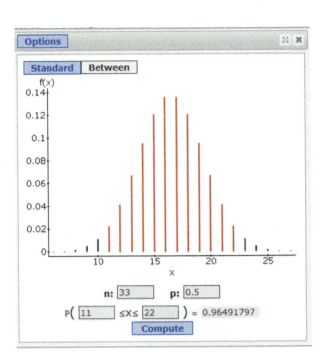

Step 4: Interpret and conclude
Using a significance level of 5%, we reject the null hypothesis because the p-value is less than 0.05. We conclude that the median difference in smelling ability is not 0 and one's sense of smell is in fact different when one is lying down and when one is sitting up.

TRY THIS! Exercise 13.1

The sign test is very useful and can even be used for one-sample tests of the median (see Exercises 13.54 and 13.55). The sign test suffers from low power compared to the paired *t*-test. Recall that power is the probability that you will correctly reject the null hypothesis. If you know that the population distribution is Normal, or if your sample size is large, then the paired *t*-test is the best choice because you'll have a higher probability of correctly rejecting the null hypothesis. However, if you're not sure whether the sample size is large enough, or you know that it's not large enough, then the sign test is a more reliable test than the paired *t*-test.

SNAPSHOT THE SIGN TEST

WHAT IS IT? ▶	A hypothesis test of whether the median difference among paired data is 0.
WHAT DOES IT DO? ▶	It compares the number of pairs that have positive differences with what is expected when the null hypothesis is true, which is that half of the differences should be positive.
HOW DOES IT DO IT? ▶	It uses the binomial model to calculate the p-value of the number of positive differences observed.
HOW IS IT USED? ▶	If many more than half, or many fewer, are positive (evidenced by a p-value smaller than the significance level), we reject the null hypothesis of the median being 0.
WHEN IS IT USED? ▶	It can be used whenever the paired *t*-test is used, but in particular when the sample size is too small to apply the paired *t*-test or when the distribution is known to be non-Normal.

SECTION 13.2

Mann-Whitney Test for Two Independent Groups

The **Mann-Whitney test** can be used wherever you can use a *t*-test for two independent groups (see Section 9.4). It can also be used in many situations in which you can't use the *t*-test—for example, when the population distributions appear not to be Normal or when the sample sizes are too small for the Central Limit Theorem to provide a useful approximate result.

In order for us to use the Mann-Whitney, the following conditions must be satisfied.

1. There are two independent groups.

2. The response variable is numerical and continuous.

3. Each group is a random sample from some population.

4. The observations are independent of one another.

5. The population distribution of each group has the same shape.

In practice, the Mann-Whitney test also works for noncontinuous (that is, discrete) response variables, as long as the values can be ordered. Thus, the Mann-Whitney test is often applied to ranks—such as first place, second place, and so on—in competitions, and to ordinal data (for example, see Exercise 13.15).

Even though the Mann-Whitney test requires that the two population distributions have the same shape, we don't care what this shape is. In other words, we don't care whether both groups come from a Normal distribution, a uniform distribution, or *any* particular distribution. We care only that they both come from a distribution with the same shape.

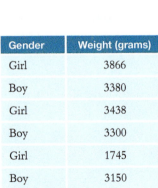

Details

Mann-Whitney Test
The Mann-Whitney test is also called the Mann-Whitney-Wilcoxon test and the Wilcoxon Rank Sum test.

Overview of the Mann-Whitney Test

The Mann-Whitney test requires some pre-processing before you begin. Rather than using the actual data values, the Mann-Whitney is based on the **ranks** of the values once the observations of both groups have been combined. This means that the smallest value in the entire data set gets the rank of 1, the next smallest is ranked 2, and so on.

Stating Hypotheses

Like the two-sample t-test, the Mann-Whitney test is used to compare the centres of two distributions. Unlike the t-test, the Mann-Whitney compares the medians of the population distributions, not the means. This is a particularly compelling approach when comparing skewed distributions; in this context, the median is a more natural measure of centre than the mean.

H_0: The median of population 1 is equal to the median of population 2.
H_A: The medians are not equal.

We can also have one-tailed alternatives.

> **KEY POINT** The Mann-Whitney test is based on the ranks of the observations, not on their actual values.

If the medians of the populations are equal, then the ranks of the combined observations should be randomly mixed between the two groups. If all the low ranks fall into one group in your sample, and all the high ranks into another, then the null hypothesis might not be true.

Finding the Test Statistic

The first step is to compute the rank of each observation. When doing this, you ignore which group the observations belong to. To illustrate, let's compare the weights of newborn boys and girls, using the very small data set shown in Table 13.1. (In fact, the Mann-Whitney does not work well with such very small data sets, but the small size makes it easier to understand how the test works.) The full data set consists of all babies born at a hospital in Brisbane, Australia, in one 24-hour period (Dunn 1999), and Table 13.1 shows a random sample of six of these babies. Do the weights differ by gender?

The easiest way to rank the observations is to sort them from smallest to largest, ignoring whether the weight belongs to a boy or a girl, and then assign the first the rank of 1, the second the rank of 2, and so on. Table 13.2 shows the result of this ranking of the original data.

The test statistic, represented by the letter W, is simply the sum of the ranks of one of the groups. Technically, it doesn't matter which group you choose, because if you know the sum of the ranks of one group, it is possible to determine the sum of

Gender	Weight (grams)
Girl	3866
Boy	3380
Girl	3438
Boy	3300
Girl	1745
Boy	3150

▲ **TABLE 13.1** Weights of six randomly selected babies all born on the same day at the same hospital.

the others (because the ranks must always sum to the same value). Most packages assume you used the group that produced the smallest sum, but other packages will give you results for both groups. For example, when we add up the ranks of the girls, we get $W = 6 + 5 + 1 = 12$.

The intuition behind the Mann-Whitney W-statistic is this: if all of the heaviest babies were girls, then they would get the top three ranks: 4, 5, 6. In that case, $W = 4 + 5 + 6 = 15$. At the other extreme, if the lightest babies were all girls, they would get the lowest ranks: 1, 2, 3. Then $W = 1 + 2 + 3 = 6$.

However, if the null hypothesis is true and both groups are really the same, then it will be as though the ranks were randomly assigned to groups. So we would expect each group to have a mix of low and high ranks. This means that if the null hypothesis is true, then W should be somewhere close to the midpoint between 6 and 15: about 10 or 11.

In this case, we observed $W = 12$, which is very slightly larger than what the null hypothesis might lead us to expect. We now ask how likely a value of 12 or larger is, if the ranks were really just distributed by chance.

Gender	Weight	Rank
Girl	3866	6
Boy	3380	4
Girl	3438	5
Boy	3300	3
Girl	1745	1
Boy	3150	2

▲ **TABLE 13.2** Ranks based on baby weights. The smallest is assigned the rank 1.

Finding the p-Value

The distribution of W does not have a simple formula that allows us to compute probabilities, so we rely heavily on statistical software to compute p-values. For large sample sizes, and particularly when there are values that are tied (in other words, several values are the same and get the same rank), approximate probabilities are calculated by statistical software.

Figure 13.4 shows output from StatCrunch that gives the p-value as 0.70. Because the sample size was not large and there were no ties, an exact p-value was computed. (StatCrunch, like some other statistical packages, automatically decides whether to compute an exact p-value or an approximation.)

TECH

Hypothesis test results:

m1 = median of weight where gender="girl"

m2 = median of weight where gender="boy"

Parameter : m1 – m2

H_0 : Parameter = 0

H_A : Parameter ≠ 0

Difference	n1	n2	Diff. Est.	Test Stat.	P-value	Method
m1 – m2	3	3	138	12	0.7	Exact

◄ **FIGURE 13.4** Output from the Mann-Whitney test on StatCrunch. The test statistic is $W = 12$, and the p-value for a two-tailed alternative is 0.7.

Applying the Mann-Whitney Test

Many statisticians prefer to use the Mann-Whitney test, rather than the t-test, for many situations. This is because the Mann-Whitney is more robust (it doesn't require that we know whether the populations are Normally distributed or whether the sample size is "large enough").

To see how to apply the Mann-Whitney, let's consider the full sample of 26 boys and 18 girls born in one 24-hour period at a hospital in Brisbane, Australia.

EXAMPLE 2 Weights of Boy and Girl Babies

Figure 13.5 shows StatCrunch output from a Mann–Whitney test to determine whether boy babies tend to have different weights from girl babies. A preliminary check of histograms (not shown) for the boy and girl weights show that both distributions are roughly symmetric, although both have an outlier on the low end.

▶ **FIGURE 13.5** StatCrunch output from a Mann-Whitney test to compare the typical weight of baby boys with that of baby girls. Girls are coded with gender = 1.

○ ○ ○   Mann-Whitney   **Java Applet Window ⚠**

Options

Hypothesis test results:
m1 = median of weight where gender=1
m2 = median of weight where gender=2
Parameter : m1 – m2
H_0 : Parameter = 0
H_A : Parameter ≠ 0

Difference	n1	n2	Diff. Est.	Test Stat.	P-value	Method
m1 – m2	18	26	–124.5	365.5	0.3519	Norm. Approx.

QUESTION Do boy babies weigh a different amount, typically, than girl babies? Perform a Mann–Whitney test, using the computer output provided. Use a 5% significance level.

SOLUTION

Step 1: Hypothesize

H_0: The median weight of boys equals the median weight of girls.
H_A: The median weight of boys does not equal the median weight of girls.

Step 2: Prepare
The Mann–Whitney test is appropriate because:

1. The samples are independent (this would not be true if there were boy and girl twin siblings in the sample).

2. The variable measured (weight) is numerical (and continuous).

3. Although the babies are not a random sample, we shall think of the babies born this day as representative of all babies born.

4. We assume that the distributions of boys' and girls' weights have the same shape.

Step 3: Compute to compare
We read from the output that the test statistic has the value 365.5, with a p-value (for a two-tailed alternative) of 0.3519.

Step 4: Interpret and conclude
If the median weight of boys and girls is the same, the probability of observing a more surprising outcome than 365.5 is 0.3519. Because the p-value is larger than 0.05, we cannot reject the null hypothesis and find insufficient evidence that median weights differ between baby boys and girls.

TRY THIS! Exercise 13.9

Sample Size and the Mann-Whitney Test

The Mann-Whitney test has relatively low power. This means that even if the alternative hypothesis is true (the groups really are different), the Mann-Whitney test can be less likely than other tests to reject the null hypothesis. For example, suppose that the three heaviest weights in our small sample of six babies all belonged to the girls. In other words, the girls had the ranks 4, 5, and 6, and the boys had the three lower ranks. Even in this extreme case, the p-value for the two-tailed alternative is 0.10, and we would not reject the null hypothesis. When the sample size is very small (under 10 for total number of both groups), be aware that it might not be possible to reject the null hypothesis, even if the null is not true.

For larger sample sizes, the *W*-statistic follows, approximately, a Normal distribution. For this reason, some software packages automatically produce an approximate p-value using the Normal distribution, rather than an exact p-value, because this makes the computation faster. The StatCrunch display in Figure 13.5 tells us that the method used was "Norm. Approx"; that is, StatCrunch made the decision to use the Normal approximation for this sample size.

What Can Go Wrong?

Although it is true that you don't have to worry about whether the data follow the Normal distribution, you still need to check the conditions carefully. In Section 13.1 we noted that if you do not have independent groups, then you need to use the sign test. You might also have a few other things to worry about.

Ties in the Data. In theory, if the response variable is continuous, as in the case of baby weights, then it is impossible for two babies to weigh exactly the same amount. In practice, however, we can weigh objects only to a certain level of precision. Because we must round these numbers, it is possible to get ties—two or more babies who weigh the same. There were no ties in our data set of 44 babies, but it's not hard to imagine that there would be ties in a data set of, say, 44,000 babies.

When ties occur, it is not possible to give each observation its own rank. Instead, several observations share the same rank. One approach is to give tied observations their average rank. For example, if we saw the data

$$15.5, \ 16.0, \ 16.0, \ 16.0, \ 18.2$$

we would assign them the ranks

$$1, \ 3, \ 3, \ 3, \ 5$$

because the three values of 16.0 were assigned the ranks 2, 3, 4, and the average of these ranks is 3.

Doing this averaging leads to "conservative" p-values: p-values that tend to be too high. Most statistical software packages apply an adjustment that gives a more accurate p-value. Some software packages display a warning that says something like "adjusted for ties." If your software gives you a choice of different p-values, use the one that has been adjusted for ties.

Different-Shaped Distributions. The Mann-Whitney test requires that the shapes of the two population distributions be the same because if they are different (such as one being symmetric and the other left-skewed), then the Mann-Whitney test might reject the null hypothesis even when the medians are the same. In practice, any difference between the two distributions in shape, centre, or spread between the two distributions can lead to rejecting the null hypothesis. Most statistical software packages treat the Mann-Whitney as a test based on the median values, and this is how we presented it. However, this interpretation is valid only when the shapes and spreads of the distributions are the same.

SNAPSHOT   THE MANN-WHITNEY TEST

WHAT IS IT? ▶ A hypothesis test to compare the centres of two independent numerical variables.

WHAT DOES IT DO? ▶ It tests the hypothesis that the medians of two populations are the same.

HOW DOES IT DO IT? ▶ The original observations are combined and ranked from smallest to largest. If the null hypothesis is true, the ranks should be randomly mixed between the two groups and the sums of ranks should be roughly the same.

HOW IS IT USED? ▶ If the sum of ranks of one group is much larger than the other (evidenced by a p-value smaller than the significance level), we reject the null hypothesis of equal medians.

WHEN IS IT USED? ▶ It can be used whenever the t-test for two independent samples is used, and when the Normal condition of the t-test is not met.

t-Test or Mann-Whitney Test?

How do you decide whether to use the two-sample t-test for independent samples or the Mann–Whitney test? To some extent, it is a matter of preference. There are a few things to consider, though.

Because the Mann–Whitney test can be used to compare medians, it is preferred in situations where the distributions are skewed or outliers are present.

If you don't know whether the distributions of the populations are Normal, and are not willing to assume that they are, then the Mann–Whitney is useful. If your sample sizes are large, then the Mann–Whitney and two-sample t-tests should lead you to the same conclusion. But when the sample sizes are too small for the Central Limit Theorem to apply (less than 25 in most cases, larger if the distributions are severely skewed), then the Mann–Whitney will produce more reliable results.

Even though one condition of the tests is that the data be continuous, the Mann–Whitney also works when the data are ordinal (can be ordered) but not necessarily continuous. The most common example is when the data are ranks to begin with. This is often the situation when data from contests are examined. For example, a panel of judges might rank 12 wines using the numbers 1 (best) to 12 (worst), and we might want to compare judges to see whether they tend to give the same ranks. The t-test would not be good for these data, which are very non-Normal. The Mann–Whitney would be a more suitable test.

Many statisticians feel that for most situations, the Mann–Whitney test can be used instead of the two-sample t-test.

SECTION 13.3

Kruskal–Wallis Test for Comparing Several Groups

As we learned in Chapter 11, ANOVA is a powerful procedure that allows us to compare the means of three, four, or even more groups with each other. The **Kruskal–Wallis test** is a nonparametric test that can be used instead of one-way ANOVA whenever the Normality assumption of ANOVA is not satisfied.

The Kruskal-Wallis test is valid under conditions similar to those of the Mann-Whitney test, except that they must be satisfied by several groups, not just two. These conditions are:

1. All groups are independent.
2. The response variable is numerical and continuous.
3. Each group is a random sample from some population.
4. The observations are independent of one another.
5. The population distribution of each group has the same shape.

Once again, we require that all population distributions have the same shape, with no restrictions on what that shape should be.

Overview of the Kruskal-Wallis Test

The Kruskal-Wallis test is a simple generalization of the Mann-Whitney test to more than two groups. As such, it is a test that compares medians by using ranks.

Stating Hypotheses

The Kruskal-Wallis test compares the medians of three or more population distributions. It is therefore very useful when comparing skewed distributions.

H_0: The median is the same for all groups.
H_A: At least one median is different from another.

If the null hypothesis is true, the ranks of the combined observations should be randomly mixed between all groups. If, however, some groups consist mainly of observations with small ranks and some others consist mainly of observations with large ranks, then this might be evidence that the null hypothesis is not true.

> **KEY POINT** The Kruskal-Wallis test for comparing medians of several groups is based on the ranks of the combined observations, not on their actual values.

The Test Statistic and Its p-Value

The steps for conducting the Kruskal-Wallis test are similar to those for conducting the Mann-Whitney test. The first step is to combine all observations and rank them from smallest to largest. Then the ranks are summed within each group, and the sums are used to calculate the test statistic, represented in this case by the letter H. The test statistic measures the amount that the observed rank averages differ from the common value expected under the null hypothesis. Large values of H come from large deviations and are an indication that ranks are not randomly mixed between groups. We will not provide the exact formula for calculating H because we'll always rely on statistical software to perform the Kruskal-Wallis test.

For very small sample sizes, the distribution of H can be obtained exactly, and statistical software will provide an exact p-value. For large sample sizes and for samples with ties, the p-values provided by software are approximate probabilities (based on the chi-square distribution).

Applying the Kruskal-Wallis Test

To see how to apply the Kruskal-Wallis test, let's revisit the mercury concentration data that we examined in Section 11.2.

EXAMPLE 3 Mercury Concentration in Shorebird Eggs

Researchers at Environment Canada's National Wildlife Research Centre compared mercury contamination in the eggs of four Canadian Arctic–breeding shorebird species: black-bellied plover, ruddy turnstone, semipalmated plover, and white-rumped sandpiper (see Table 11.5). As we saw in Examples 3 and 5 in Chapter 11, the researchers used ANOVA to compare the mean egg mercury concentrations among the four species. However, ANOVA assumes that the population distributions are Normal. If researchers had not been willing to assume that the populations are Normal (based on only five observations per sample), mercury concentrations could have been compared using the Kruskal-Wallis test instead. Figure 13.6 shows the output from the Kruskal-Wallis test applied to the mercury concentration data.

▶ **FIGURE 13.6** Minitab output from a Kruskal-Wallis test to compare the typical mercury concentration in the eggs of four shorebird species.

```
Kruskal-Wallis Test: Hg versus Species

Kruskal-Wallis Test on Hg

Species    N   Median   Ave Rank       Z
BBPL       5   0.4768        6.0   -1.96
RUTU       5   0.6007        9.4   -0.48
SEPL       5   0.6353       11.8    0.57
WRSA       5   0.9174       14.8    1.88
Overall   20                10.5

H = 5.95  DF = 3  P = 0.114
```

QUESTION Is the typical amount of mercury concentration the same for the eggs of all four shorebird species? Perform a Kruskal-Wallis test, using the computer output provided. Use a 5% level of significance.

SOLUTION

Step 1: Hypothesize

H_0: The median mercury concentration is the same for eggs in all four groups.
H_A: At least one median is different from another.

Step 2: Prepare
The experts had reason to believe that all assumptions of ANOVA were valid. The only condition that we are not assuming here is Normality, so that the Kruskal-Wallis test is appropriate.

Step 3: Compute to compare
We read from the output that the value of the H statistic is 5.95, with a p-value of 0.114.

Step 4: Interpret and conclude
If the median mercury concentration is the same for eggs in all four groups, there is a 0.114 probability of observing an outcome that is more surprising than 5.95. The p-value is larger than the significance level of 0.05. Therefore, we cannot reject the null hypothesis and conclude that the typical mercury concentration is the same for all four species of shorebirds. (This is the same conclusion as the one obtained with ANOVA.)

TRY THIS! Exercise 13.17

Note that because the Kruskal-Wallis test is an extension of the Mann-Whitney test, the remarks we made about sample size, ties, groups with different shapes, and ordinal data also apply to the Kruskal-Wallis test. Note too that when the Kruskal-Wallis test rejects the null hypothesis, you can conclude that the medians are not all the same, but this does not tell you which pairs are significantly different. For that you must perform a post-hoc analysis. For example, one way to do the analysis is based on the Mann-Whitney test and the Bonferroni Correction. However, we will not discuss that topic here.

SNAPSHOT THE KRUSKAL-WALLIS TEST

WHAT IS IT? ▶ A hypothesis test to compare the centre of three or more groups of numerical variables.

WHAT DOES IT DO? ▶ It tests the hypothesis that the medians of three or more populations are the same.

HOW DOES IT DO IT? ▶ The original observations are combined and ranked from smallest to largest. If the null hypothesis is true, the ranks should be randomly mixed between all groups and the average rank in all groups should be roughly the same.

HOW IS IT USED? ▶ If the value of the test statistic is large (evidenced by a p-value smaller than the significance level), we reject the null hypothesis of equal medians.

WHEN IS IT USED? ▶ It can be used whenever one-way ANOVA can be used, but it can also be used if the Normality condition of ANOVA is not met.

SECTION 13.4

Randomization Tests

 Section 13.4 is available online, and can be found on MyStatLab.

SECTION 13.5

Transforming Data

 Section 13.5 is available online, and can be found on MyStatLab.

CASE STUDY REVISITED

What particular environmental characteristics influence arctic foxes when selecting their denning sites? Researchers measured different landscape, local, and reproductive characteristics of 83 observed dens in Bylot Island, Nunavut. Since the variables of interest did not appear to be Normally distributed, the nonparametric tests of this chapter were used to make comparisons. The level of significance used was 0.05.

First, researchers compared the landscape characteristics of the 83 observed dens with those of randomly selected locations within the study area. These two samples are independent, so the Mann-Whitney test is appropriate to compare the medians of both groups. For instance, it was found that dens were located on steeper slopes than random sites (p-value < 0.001), and were closer to streams than random sites (p-value = 0.032). No differences were observed in distance to the closest lake (p-value = 0.154) or lemming availability (p-value = 0.526).

Second, the biologists compared the local characteristics of the dens with those of a randomly selected potential denning site (in natural ridges and/or in slopes of 10° or more) close to each den. These two samples are matched, so the sign test is appropriate for comparing the medians of both groups. The sign test revealed that median percentage of snow cover was lower on dens than on other potential sites (p-value = 0.009), that median ground temperature was higher at dens (p-value < 0.001), and that there was no difference in the median height of mounds (p-value = 0.124).

Finally, researchers compared environmental characteristics of dens when classified by reproductive type (20 natal, 7 rearing, and 56 non-breeding). Because we have three independent samples, comparisons were made using the Kruskal-Wallis test. Some of the findings were that rearing dens were closer to a stream than non-breeding dens (p-value = 0.018), and that both natal and rearing dens were located in areas of higher lemming availability than non-breeding dens (p-value < 0.001). Moreover, the number of dens in a five-kilometre radius was lower around natal dens than around non-breeding ones (p-value = 0.002). It seems that foxes select areas that have sufficient food resources and that are far enough away from other dens for reproductive purposes.

EXPLORING STATISTICS

CLASS ACTIVITY

Balancing on One Foot

GOALS	MATERIALS
To understand how the p-value for the sign test is calculated.	• A timer capable of timing to the nearest second. • A coin for each pair of students.

ACTIVITY

Pair up. Use a coin flip to determine which leg you stand on first. (Heads, start by standing on dominant foot.) With your partner, take turns recording how long each of you can stand on this foot with your eyes closed. If your partner is still balancing after 3 minutes, stop him or her and record this as 180 seconds, with an asterisk (*) to indicate that the true time was even longer. Repeat with the other foot. (Each person will have two measurements: one with the dominant foot and one with the nondominant foot.) Be sure to record which time belongs to the dominant foot and which to the nondominant foot.

Use the sign test to determine whether the students in the class do a better job (have longer times) using the dominant foot. If a student stands indeterminately long on one foot but not on the other, his or her data can still be included. If a student stands indeterminately long on *both* feet, we recommend that you exclude the observation.

BEFORE THE ACTIVITY

1. How should you choose which foot is used first? Does it matter?

2. When measuring the times, what do you think the shape of a histogram of the data of standing times for the dominant foot will be and why?

3. Are the time for a student's dominant foot and the time for that student's nondominant foot dependent or independent? Why?

AFTER THE ACTIVITY

To answer the question of whether students can balance longer on the dominant foot, gather the data for all the students in the following table.

Number of Students with Dominant Foot Time Greater Than Nondominant	Number of Students with Dominant Foot Time Less Than Nondominant	Number of Students with Both Times the Same

Carry out a hypothesis test to see whether students can typically stand longer on their dominant foot than on their nondominant foot. Is a paired *t*-test appropriate? If it is, carry this out and then compare the results to those of a sign test. If it's not, explain why not, and explain why a sign test is appropriate. Then carry out the sign test.

CHAPTER REVIEW

Summary of Learning Objectives

1. **When and how can I apply the sign test to compare two dependent samples?** You can apply the sign test whenever the paired *t*-test can be used, and when the Normality assumption of that test does not hold. The test is based on counting the number of positive differences in the data set.

2. **When and how can I apply the Mann-Whitney test to compare two independent samples?** You can apply the Mann-Whitney test whenever the *t*-test for independent samples can be used, and when the Normality assumption of that test does not hold. The test is based on ranking all observations together and summing the ranks in each group.

3. **When and how can I apply the Kruskal-Wallis test to compare several independent samples?** You can apply the Kruskal-Wallis test whenever ANOVA can be used, and when the Normality assumption of that test does not hold. The test is based on ranking all observations together and calculating a statistic based on the sums of ranks in each group.

4. **When and how can I apply the randomization test to compare to dependent samples?** You can apply the randomization test to compare any statistic in two independent groups without needing to know the population distributions. A chance model is created by randomly assigning the observed values to two groups, computing the test statistic, and repeating many times.

5. **How do I interpret a QQ plot?** A QQ plot supports Normality when the points in the plot fall approximately along a straight line.

6. **When and how can I use the geometric mean to estimate the centre of a distribution?** You can use the geometric mean if all values are greater than 0, if the distribution of data is right-skewed, and if the log-transformed data are approximately Normal. Find a confidence interval for the transformed data and then back transform.

Important Terms

Nonparametric inference, *580*   Mann-Whitney test, *585*   Rank, *586*   Kruskal-Wallis test, *590*
Sign test, *581*

Sources

Canadian Home Builders' Association Pulse Survey. 2013. www.chba.ca/uploads/pulse_survey_results/main_report2103.pdf (accessed January 15, 2014).

CBC News. August 22, 2014. http://www.cbc.ca/news/canada/calgary/alberta-s-cloud-seeding-pilots-see-2nd-busiest-year-in-20-years-1.2744786 (accessed September 2, 2015).

Dunn, P. 1999. Time of birth, sex and birth weight of 44 babies. *Journal of Statistics Education* 7(3). http://www.amstat.org/publications/jse/jse_2001/jse_data_archive.html (viewed April 25, 2010).

Lowe, C. G., R. N. Bray, and D. R. Nelson. 1994. Feeding and associated electrical behavior of the Pacific electric ray *Torpedo californica* in the field. *Marine Biology* 120, 161–169.

Lundstrom, J., J. Boyle, and M. Jones-Gotman. 2006. Sit up and smell the roses better: Olfactory sensitivity to phenyl ethyl alcohol is dependent on body position. *Chemical Senses* 31, 249–252.

McCloskey, M., et al. 2013. Mercury concentration in the eggs of four Canadian Arctic-breeding shorebirds not predicted based on their population statuses. *Springer Plus* 2, 567.

Simpson, J., A. Olsen, and J. C. Eden. 1975. A Bayesian analysis of a multiplicative treatment effect in weather modification. *Technometrics* 17, 161–166. Used in J. M. Chambers, W. S. Cleveland, B. Keliner, and P. A. Tukey. 1983. *Graphical methods for data analysis*. lib.stat.cmu.edu/DASL/Datafiles/Clouds.html (viewed April 25, 2010).

Szor, G., D. Berteaux, and G. Gauthier. 2008. Finding the right home: Distribution of food resources and terrain characteristics influence selection of denning sites and reproductive dens in arctic foxes. *Polar Biology* 31, 351–362.

SECTION EXERCISES

SECTION 13.1

TRY **13.1 Lead Exposure (Example 1)** Excessive lead levels can negatively affect brain functions; lead poisoning is particularly dangerous to children. A study was conducted to find out whether children of battery factory workers had higher levels of lead in their blood than a matched group of children. Each child in the experimental group was matched with a child in the control group of the same age living in the same neighbourhood. Although these were not a random sample of children, we can test the hypothesis that the difference is too large to occur by chance if the child from the control group was randomly chosen. The figure shows a histogram of the differences in lead level.

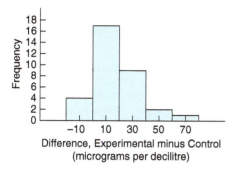

Difference, Experimental minus Control
(micrograms per decilitre)

The differences were found by calculating "factory child's lead level minus matched control child's lead level." Lead levels were concentrations in the blood, measured in micrograms per decilitre. A positive difference means the child of a factory worker has a higher lead concentration than the child in the control group. The data consisted of 1 tie (the same value for the child and the matching child), 28 pairs in which the factory worker's child had a higher level of lead, and 4 pairs in which the factory worker's child had a lower level.

Carry out a sign test to determine whether children whose parents are exposed to lead at work have a higher lead level than children whose parents are not exposed to lead at work. Use a significance level of 0.05 to see whether the experimental group had higher levels of lead.

(Source: Data appeared in B. Trumbo. 2001. *Learning Statistics with Real Data.* North Scituate, Massachusetts: Duxbury Press)

13.2 Cost of Living Index The data in the table were collected for a random sample of Canadian cities from Numbeo.com, a website that provides information on living conditions in cities and countries worldwide using data contributed by users. Both indices provided are calculated relative to prices in New York City: the Groceries Index is used to compare grocery prices (a Groceries Index of 108.16 means that grocery prices are 8.16% more expensive than in New York City), and the Local Purchasing Power Index is used to compare purchasing power in buying goods and services with an average salary (a Local Purchasing Power Index of 94.56 means that it is possible to buy 5.44% less goods and services with an average salary than in New York City).

City	Groceries Index	Local Purchasing Power Index
Regina, SK	108.16	94.56
Calgary, AB	102.15	118.80
Abbotsford, BC	97.04	116.70
Barrie, ON	104.65	92.77
Ottawa, ON	92.28	131.88
Toronto, ON	91.27	101.75
Montreal, QC	93.09	100.23
Surrey, BC	94.41	102.13
Winnipeg, MB	90.22	77.40
London, ON	88.24	87.06
Kelowna, BC	90.17	90.97
Quebec City, QC	98.91	105.17
Lethbridge, AB	80.00	38.66
Red Deer, AB	92.35	135.49
Kitchener, ON	96.75	139.51
Saskatoon, SK	95.45	87.12

a. Compare the medians for both indices.

b. Perform a sign test to determine whether the Groceries Index differs from the Local Purchasing Power Index for Canadian cities (as calculated by Numbeo.com). Use a significance level of 0.05.

(Source: www.Numbeo.com, accessed January 23, 2014)

13.3 The Stroop Effect Suppose you had to identify the colour of ink for a series of printed words, but the printed word appeared in a colour of ink that did not match the name of the colour. For example, if you were shown "RED" then you should say "Blue," but you might incorrectly say "Red" because that is what the word spells. It might take longer to correctly identify a colour when it was used to print a word whose meaning did not match that colour than to identify the colour when the ink colour and printed word matched. This difference in times is an example of something psychologists call *interference* and is called the Stroop effect, after research psychologist J. R. Stroop (1897–1973).

Same	Diff	Same	Diff
32	66	18	15
12	31	18	39
17	40	24	35
16	25	20	32
25	36	24	30

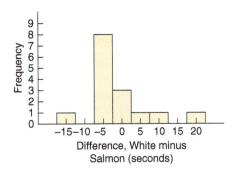

The data in the table were collected by a student conducting research on the Stroop effect. Each of 10 subjects identified colours of ink in two different situations, and the time (in seconds) was recorded. There were 36 words in each trial. In column 1, the ink was the same colour as the word. In column 2, the ink and the words were different colours. Whether the subject started with the colour matching the word or different was randomly determined. Treat the data as though they came from a random sample.

a. Write a sentence comparing the median time to identify the colour for the two groups. Did the task tend to take longer when the colours were different?

b. Perform a sign test to test whether those who see the ink in the "wrong" colour tend to take longer to identify the colour. Use a significance level of 0.05.

13.4 Reading Material on Coloured Paper In the past, some people believed it was easier to read words printed on coloured paper than on white paper, while other people believed it was easier to read words printed on white paper. To test these theories, researchers asked a sample of 15 subjects to read a passage printed in black ink twice: once on salmon-coloured paper and once on white paper. The time it took to read each passage, in seconds, is given in the table. Whether the person read the salmon-coloured paper first or the white paper first was determined randomly. A histogram of the differences is also shown.

Salmon	White
79	72
49	45
47	45
112	120
65	63
66	62
67	60
59	54
140	160
64	57
67	61
73	72
64	48
126	122
67	73

a. Compare the typical values for the two groups.

b. Refer to the histogram of differences. Why is the *t*-test potentially not appropriate for these data?

c. Carry out an appropriate hypothesis test that the typical reading time is not the same for words printed on salmon-coloured paper (at least for this passage). Use a significance level of 0.05 (with a two-tailed alternative) and interpret your results.

13.5 Males' Pulse Rates Students in a statistics class were asked to measure their resting pulse rates. After that, the instructor unexpectedly screamed and ran from one side of the class to the other. Students again measured their pulse rates. The pulse rates (in beats per minute) were recorded before and after the scream for the male students in the class. Perform a sign test to see whether the median pulse rate went up significantly, using a significance level of 0.05 and treating the sample as random. The data can be found in Exercise 9.62 on page 447.

13.6 Females' Pulse Rates Refer to Exercise 13.5. This time, the data (beats per minute) came from female students before and after the scream. Perform a sign test to see whether the median pulse rate went up significantly, using a significance level of 0.05 and treating the sample as random. The data can be found in Exercise 9.61 on page 447.

13.7 Ages of Brides and Grooms A random sample of the ages of 14 brides and their grooms showed that in 10 of the pairs the grooms were older, in 1 pair they were the same age, and in 3 pairs the bride was older. Perform a sign test with a significance level of 0.05 to test the hypothesis that grooms tend to be older than their brides.

13.8 Textbook Prices A random sample of textbooks at the University of Calgary (U of C) Bookstore was obtained in 2013. The price of a new textbook was recorded and then compared to the price of the same new textbook on Amazon.ca. Perform a sign test with a significance level of 0.05 to test the hypothesis that new books at the U of C Bookstore tend to be more expensive than on Amazon.ca. For 10 of the books the prices were higher at U of C, and for 5 of the books they were higher at Amazon.ca. There were no ties.

SECTION 13.2

TRY 13.9 Meat-Eating Behaviour (Example 2) A researcher was interested in the ethics of eating meat, so he studied and compared ethicists (philosophy professors who taught ethics) with professors who taught other subjects to find out whether ethicists eat less meat. The subjects were asked how many meals they eat per week that include meat. The data provided are a random sample from the full study. Vegetarians (who eat no meat) were excluded. Assume that the shapes and spreads of the distributions are the same.

a. Refer to the output given. Compare the sample medians. What do they tell us about the research question?

b. Refer to the output to perform a Mann-Whitney test using a significance level of 0.05.

```
Mann-Whitney Test and CI
              N    Median
Ethicists    16    4.500
Control      12    6.500


Point estimate for ETA1-ETA2 is -2.000
95.2 Percent CI for ETA1-ETA2 is (-3.999, 0.001)
W = 198.0
Test of ETA1 = ETA2 vs ETA1 < ETA2 is significant at 0.0599
The test is significant at 0.0582 (adjusted for ties)
```

(Source: E. Schwitzgebel and J. Rust. 2009. The self-reported moral behavior of ethics professors. Unpublished manuscript. http://schwitzsplinters.blogspot.com)

13.10 Credit Card Debt A statistics student who was interested in credit card debt asked a random sample of students for the total amount of their credit card debt. We eliminated the two women and the one man who had a debt of 0, which left 18 women and 19 men.

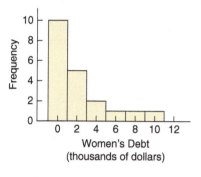

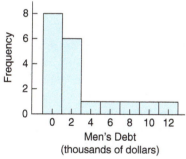

a. By looking at the histograms of the data, determine whether it would be appropriate to perform a two-sample *t*-test using this data set. Explain.

b. Refer to the Minitab output. Which group had a higher median debt in this sample?

c. Refer to the Minitab output to test whether the typical credit card debt (as measured by the median) is different for men and women, using a significance level of 0.05.

```
Mann-Whitney Test and CI: Women, Men
             N    Median
Women       18    725.0
Men         19   1250.0


Point estimate for ETA1-ETA2 is -212.0
95.3 Percent CI for ETA1-ETA2 is (-1100.0, 700.1)
W = 322.5
The test is significant at 0.5635 level
```

13.11 Cleaning Archeological Artifacts Archeologists who work in a "dig" often unearth dirty objects, such as those made of ceramic, metal, glass, and other substances. The traditional method of cleaning these objects has been to brush them gently with a soft brush, which takes a long time. Therefore, archeologists have been looking for other cleaning methods that take less time, do a good job, and do not damage the artifacts. A substance called Calgon (sodium hexametaphosphate) can be used; the objects are soaked in it, and no brushing is required. It has been determined that Calgon does not damage the objects. In order to determine whether it cleans as well as brushing does, investigators measured the weights of the objects (in grams) before and after cleaning. We have reported some of the differences in weights (dirty weight minus clean weight, in grams) and also the method of treatment (b is for brushing and c is for Calgon); you should use the complete data set from the website. Use a Mann-Whitney test with a significance level of 0.05 to determine whether the two methods result in significantly different changes in median weight. Assume that the shapes and spreads of the two distributions are the same.

Diff	Method
1.3	b
1.9	b
1.2	b
0.5	c
0.1	c

(Source: Neumann, T. W., and R. M. Sanford. 1998. Cleaning artifacts with Calgon. *American Antiquity* 63(1), 157–160)

13.12 Body Temperatures Body temperatures for 65 healthy females and 65 healthy males were collected. The samples suggest that the body temperatures are Normally distributed for both men and women. Assume that the standard deviations of the populations are roughly equal.

a. Use the following output to test the hypothesis that the means are not equal, using a significance level of 0.05. Report the p-value and conclusion or explain why the test should not be done.

(a)

```
Two-Sample T-Test and CI: tempF, tempM

        N    Mean   StDev   SE Mean
tempF  65  36.725   0.388    0.048
tempM  65  36.885   0.413    0.051


T-Test of difference = 0 (vs not =):
T-Value = -2.29
P-Value = 0.024
```

b. Use the following output to test the hypothesis that population *medians* are the same using a significance level of 0.05.

(b)

```
Mann-Whitney Test and CI: tempF, tempM

        N  Median
tempF  65  36.722
tempM  65  36.889


W = 3782.0
Test of ETA1 = ETA2 vs ETA1 not = ETA2
is significant at 0.0270
The test is significant at 0.0268
 (adjusted for ties)
```

13.13 Tobogganing Students Heathyr Francis and Colin Hoag performed an experiment in which they measured the time they took to reach the bottom of Armour Hill in Peterborough, Ontario, when tobogganing on cafeteria trays that had not been waxed and on cafeteria trays that had been waxed. They hypothesized that tobogganing on waxed trays would be faster. Assume that the shapes and spreads of the distributions of times for both types of trays are the same.

a. Refer to the Minitab output given. Compare the sample medians. What do they tell us about the students' hypothesis?

b. Refer to the Minitab output to perform a Mann-Whitney test using a significance level of 0.05.

```
Mann-Whitney Test and CI: Waxed, Not Waxed

            N  Median
Waxed      13  4.8800
Not Waxed  13  5.5500


Point estimate for ETA1-ETA2 is -0.7500
95.4 Percent CI for ETA1-ETA2 is (-1.1600,-0.3801)
W = 108.0
Test of ETA1 = ETA2 vs ETA1 < ETA2 is significant at 0.0003
```

13.14 Weights of Athletes The table shows a selection of *some* of the weights for a random sample of Ontario University Athletics (OUA) players: 20 male hockey players (H) and 20 male soccer players (S). Refer to the Mann-Whitney output. Assume that the shapes and spreads of the two distributions are the same.

Weight	Sport
82	S
70	S
68	S
77	H
91	H
86	H

```
Mann-Whitney Test and CI: soccer, hockey

         N  Median
soccer  20  77.000
hockey  20  86.000

Point estimate for ETA1-ETA2 is -10.000
95.0 Percent CI for ETA1-ETA2 is (-13.998,-6.000)
W = 261.0
Test of ETA1 = ETA2 vs ETA1 not = ETA2 is significant at 0.0001
The test is significant at 0.0001 (adjusted for ties)
```

a. Which group tends to weigh more in this sample? Compare the median weights by referring to the output.

b. Are these data paired or independent? Explain.

c. Test the hypothesis that the median weights of OUA soccer players and hockey players are different. Use a 0.05 significance level, and use the Mann-Whitney test.

13.15 Shifts in Polar Bear Diet In a study aimed at understanding how the terrestrial diet of polar bears (that is, what they consume during the ice-free season) has changed because of climate change, researchers evaluated the contents of passively sampled polar bear scat in western Hudson Bay and compared it to observations from a similar study conducted 40 years earlier. Among the many tests they conducted, they used a Mann-Whitney test to evaluate whether the rank order of the observed frequencies of food items is derived from the same diet. The null and alternative hypotheses in this case are:

H_0: The rank order of food items is the same for both diets.
H_A: The rank order of food items is not the same for both diets.

Perform a Mann-Whitney test using the computer output provided. Use a significance level of 0.05 and assume that all conditions for the Mann-Whitney test for ordinal data are valid.

```
Mann-Whitney Test and CI: Current Diet, Previous Diet

                         N  Median
Frequency Current Diet  29  0.00264
Frequency Previous Diet 15  0.02935


Point estimate for η1 - η2 is -0.01389
95.2 Percent CI for η1 - η2 is (-0.04712,-0.00320)
W = 553.0
Test of η1 = η2 vs η1 ≠ η2 is significant at 0.0142
The test is significant at 0.0138 (adjusted for ties)
```

(Source: Gormezano, L. J., and R. F. Rockwell. 2013. What to eat now? Shifts in polar bear diet during the ice-free season in western Hudson Bay. *Ecology and Evolution* 10, 3509–3523)

13.16 Traditional Foods in the Yukon In a study on food security in Yukon First Nations communities, 33 members of Tlingit households in Teslin were interviewed. Their responses regarding the consumption of traditional foods were compared with data from 1992. For instance, it was found that the median annual frequency of consumption of chinook salmon was 24 times per year in 1992, and 4 times per year in 2008. The medians were compared using a Mann-Whitney test, with p-value < 0.01. Is there a difference in median frequency of consumption of chinook salmon for the two points in time? Use a 0.05 level of significance.

(Source: Schuster, R. C., et al. 2011. Importance of traditional foods for the food security of two First Nations Communities in the Yukon, Canada. *International Journal of Circumpolar Health* 70(3), 286–300)

SECTION 13.3

TRY 13.17 Sodium in Breakfast Cereals (Example 3) A random sample from three types of breakfast cereals was taken: gluten-free, children's, and general. The sodium content per serving was recorded from the cereals' Nutrition Facts labels. Is the typical amount of sodium per serving the same for all three types of cereal? Perform a

Kruskal-Wallis test using the computer output provided. Assume that the shapes and spreads of the three distributions are all the same. Use a 5% level of significance.

```
Kruskal-Wallis Test: Sodium versus Cereal Type

Kruskal-Wallis Test on Sodium

Cereal Type   N   Median   Ave Rank      Z
Children      5    150.0        8.2    0.12
Gluten-free   5    120.0        5.1   -1.78
Regular       5    190.0       10.7    1.65
Overall      15                 8.0

H = 3.93  DF = 2  P = 0.140
H = 3.94  DF = 2  P = 0.139  (adjusted for ties)
```

13.18 Weight of Athletes A random sample of Ontario University Athletics (OUA) male athletes was obtained: 20 hockey players, 20 soccer players, and 20 male basketball players. Perform a Kruskal-Wallis test to compare the median weight of the three groups using the computer output provided. Use a 5% level of significance. Assume that the shapes and spreads of the three distributions are all the same.

```
Kruskal-Wallis Test: Weight versus Sport

Kruskal-Wallis Test on Weight

Sport        N   Median   Ave Rank      Z
basketball  20    87.00       37.9    2.32
hockey      20    86.00       37.8    2.28
soccer      20    77.00       15.8   -4.60
Overall     60               30.5

H = 21.18  DF = 2  P = 0.000
H = 21.33  DF = 2  P = 0.000  (adjusted for ties)
```

13.19 Highway Fuel Consumption Does fuel consumption on the highway (measured in Canada in litres per 100 kilometres) vary by the number of cylinders in a car's engine? A random sample of car models with 4, 6, and 8 cylinders was taken. Data on their fuel consumption on the highway were obtained from Natural Resources Canada. Assume that the shapes and spreads of the three distributions are all the same. Test the hypothesis that median highway fuel consumption of car models with 4, 6, and 8 cylinders is the same, using the Kruskal-Wallis test and a significance level of 0.05.

13.20 City Fuel Consumption Does fuel consumption in the city (measured in Canada in litres per 100 kilometres) vary by the number of cylinders in a car's engine? A random sample of car models with 4, 6, and 8 cylinders was taken. Data on their fuel consumption in the city were obtained from Natural Resources Canada. Assume that the shapes and spreads of the three distributions are all the same. Test the hypothesis that median city fuel consumption of car models with 4, 6, and 8 cylinders is the same, using the Kruskal-Wallis test and a significance level of 0.05.

13.21 Marital Status and Body Mass Index A sample of respondents to the Canadian Community Health Survey was taken. The Minitab output relating marital status and body mass index (BMI) for those respondents is given. Use the Kruskal-Wallis test to test the hypothesis that BMI varies by marital status, using a 0.05 level of significance. Assume that the shape and spread of the distributions of BMI are the same for all four groups.

```
Kruskal-Wallis Test: BMI versus MaritalStatus

Kruskal-Wallis Test on BMI20

Status     N   Median   Ave Rank      Z
Divorced  20    26.04       37.6   -0.65
Married   20    27.29       46.0    1.23
Single    20    28.95       51.7    2.48
Widowed   20    23.73       26.7   -3.06
Overall   80                40.5

H = 13.10  DF = 3  P = 0.004
H = 13.10  DF = 3  P = 0.004  (adjusted for ties)
```

13.22 Number of Televisions by Population-Centre Size A random sample of respondents to the 2012 Survey of Household Spending was taken. The number of televisions in the respondent's home and the population-centre size were recorded (1 is 100,000 and over, 2 is less than 100,000, 3 is rural). The Minitab output for a Kruskal-Wallis test is shown below. Use the output to test the hypothesis that the median number of televisions in a home varies by population-centre size. Use a 0.05 level of significance. Assume that all conditions for using the Kruskal-Wallis test with ordinal data are met. (Source: Statistics Canada)

```
Kruskal-Wallis Test: TVs versus PopCentre

Kruskal-Wallis Test on tv

PopCentre    N   Median   Ave Rank      Z
1           26    2.000       32.6   -0.13
2           21    2.000       34.3    0.37
3           18    2.000       32.1   -0.24
Overall     65                33.0

H = 0.15  DF = 2  P = 0.929
H = 0.15  DF = 2  P = 0.926  (adjusted for ties)
```

13.23 Number of Phones by Population-Centre Size A random sample of respondents to the 2012 Survey of Household Spending was taken. The number of telephones connected to a landline in the respondent's home and the population-centre size were recorded (1 is 100,000 and over, 2 is less than 100,000, 3 is rural). The Minitab output for a Kruskal-Wallis test is shown on the next page. Use the output to test the hypothesis that the median number of telephones connected to a landline in a home varies by population-centre size. Use a 0.05 level of significance. Assume that all conditions for using the Kruskal-Wallis test with ordinal data are met. (Source: Statistics Canada)

```
Kruskal-Wallis Test: Phones versus PopCentre

Kruskal-Wallis Test on Phones

PopCentre    N   Median  Ave Rank      Z
1            50   2.000     75.5    -0.00
2            50   2.000     77.7     0.44
3            50   2.000     73.3    -0.43
Overall     150             75.5

H = 0.25  DF = 2  P = 0.881
H = 0.27  DF = 2  P = 0.875  (adjusted for ties)
```

13.24 Sleep and Age A random sample of respondents to the 2010 General Social Survey was taken, stratified by age group. The age group of the respondent and the number of minutes slept the night before the interview were recorded. Test the hypothesis that the median number of minutes slept is the same for all age groups. Use a 0.05 significance level, and use the Kruskal-Wallis test.

13.25 Body Shape Perceptions A study was conducted with the purpose of comparing body shape perceptions and preferences between urban and rural Aboriginal and non-Aboriginal girls and women. Samples of female students in Grade 8 and their mothers were obtained from four schools: two in Winnipeg (suburb and inner city) and two in southern Manitoba (rural and First Nations communities). A series of nine line drawings of female body shapes (presented from thin to heavy in an ordinal scale, so that the thinnest drawing was 1 and the heaviest was 9) was used to assess participants' perceptions.

In one question, participants were asked to select the drawing that looked most like their body shape. The women's median responses and the p-value for a Kruskal-Wallis test for comparing women's perceptions by location were:

Suburban	Rural	Urban Aboriginal	First Nations Community	P-value
5	5	6	6	0.04

Using a level of significance of 0.05, is there enough evidence to reject the null hypothesis that the median perceived body shape is the same for all four locations?

(Source: Marchessault, G. 2004. Body shape perceptions of aboriginal and non-aboriginal girls and women in southern Manitoba, Canada. *Canadian Journal of Diabetes* 28(4), 369-379)

13.26 Body Shape Preferences Refer to Exercise 13.25. In another question, participants were asked to select the drawing that looked more like the body shape they would most like to resemble. The women's median responses and the p-value for a Kruskal-Wallis test for comparing women's perceptions by location were:

Suburban	Rural	Urban Aboriginal	First Nations Community	P-value
4	5	5	5	0.10

Using a level of significance of 0.05, is there enough evidence to reject the null hypothesis that the median desired body shape is the same for all four locations?

SECTION 13.4

Section 13.4 Exercises are available online, and can be found on MyStatLab.

SECTION 13.5

Section 13.5 Exercises are available online, and can be found on MyStatLab.

CHAPTER REVIEW EXERCISES

For Exercises 13.49 through 13.53, choose from the following tests, as appropriate: paired t-test, sign test, two-sample t-test, Mann-Whitney test, ANOVA, and Kruskal-Wallis test. There may be two acceptable choices.

13.49 Ages of Married Couples You have data on the ages of both partners in a random sample of married couples and want to find out whether husbands tend to be older than their wives. There are 15 married couples in your sample. Which test(s) can you use? Answer for each circumstance.

  a. Assume that the distributions of ages are Normal.

  b. Assume that the distributions of ages for both men and women are not Normal, and assume that the distribution of differences in age for each couple is not Normal.

  c. Assume the distributions of ages are not Normal for both men and women, but assume that the distribution of differences in age is Normal.

13.50 Comparing Cumulative Averages You know the cumulative grade averages of a random sample of 10 university men and a random sample of 10 university women, and you want to test the hypothesis that the typical cumulative averages are different. Which test(s) should you choose for each situation?

  a. Suppose your preliminary investigations lead you to conclude that both the distribution of cumulative averages for men and the distribution of cumulative averages for women are approximately Normal.

  b. Suppose your preliminary investigations lead you to conclude that the distributions of both variables are not Normal.

13.51 Voicemail Suppose you are interested in the length of recorded outgoing voicemail messages for professors at your school. You call 10 randomly selected male professors and 10 randomly selected female professors over the weekend and time their outgoing messages. You want to see whether women tend to have longer outgoing messages than men. Which test(s) should you choose for each situation?

  a. Assume that the length of messages is Normally distributed both for men and for women.

  b. Assume that one or both distributions are strongly right-skewed.

13.52 Pulse Rates Suppose you want to determine whether meditation can cause a decrease in pulse rate. You randomly select 15 students, teach them a meditation technique, and then measure their pulse rates before and after meditation. Which test(s) should you choose for each situation?

a. Assume that your analysis shows that the differences in pulse rates are Normally distributed.

b. Assume that the differences in pulse rates are strongly skewed.

13.53 Employee Training Suppose a manager wants to determine whether the typical time an employee requires to complete a certain task differs depending on the level of training of the employee (Beginner, Intermediate, and Advanced). She randomly selects 10 employees for each of the three levels of training and measures the time each one of them takes to complete the task. If testing the hypothesis that the typical time is the same for all three training levels, which test(s) should she choose for each situation?

a. Assume that the time to complete the task is Normally distributed for all three groups.

b. Assume that the distributions of time to complete the task are right skewed.

 13.54 Average Body Temperatures Many people believe that healthy people typically have a body temperature of 37°C. We took a random sample of 10 healthy people and found the following temperatures:

36.9, 37.1, 37.1, 37.1, 37, 36.2, 36.9, 36.7, 36.8, 36.7

Use the sign test to test the hypothesis that the median is not 37°C. Refer to Exercise 13.53 for guidance.

g **13.55 Smarties** A box of Smarties is supposed to have, on average, 56 Smarties. A random sample of five boxes was taken and the number of Smarties in each box was counted. Here are the results:

55, 61, 54, 52, and 52

Carry out a sign test to determine whether the median number of Smarties per box is 56. Use a significance level of 0.05. Also, why is the sign test a more appropriate choice than the one-sample *t*-test? *See the steps below for guidance.*

GUIDED EXERCISES

13.55 Smarties A box of Smarties typically has 56 Smarties. A random sample of five boxes was taken and the number of Smarties in each box was counted. Here are the results:

55, 61, 54, 52, and 52

Carry out a sign test to determine whether the median number of Smarties per box is 56. Use a significance level of 0.05. Also, why is the sign test a more appropriate choice than the one-sample *t*-test?

Step 0 ▶ Fill in the missing numbers to find the difference between the observed value and the value we would expect if the hypothesis were true.

Obs	Null Value	Difference
55	56	−1
61	56	
54		−2
52		
52	56	−4

Step 1 ▶ H_0: _____

H_A: The median number of Smarties per box is different from 56 (or the median difference is not 0).

Step 2 ▶ Choose the sign test as instructed. What assumptions should be checked?

Step 3 ▶ Find the p-value. You may use a computer to do a sign test of whether the median difference is different from 0. Or you may use binomial probabilities, because the p-value is equivalent to the probability of getting one or fewer, or four or more heads in five tosses of a fair coin.

Step 4 ▶ Can you reject the null hypothesis that the median is 56 Smarties per box?

Why Use the Sign Test? Why is the sign test more appropriate than the one-sample *t*-test for this data set?

TECH TIPS

General Instructions for All Technology

The TI-83/84 is not programmed to do nonparametric tests.

🌐 **Example A: Sign Test** Suppose that eight people go on a diet, and the following weights show what happened. Determine whether you can reject the hypothesis of no weight change.

Person	Weight Before	Weight After	Change in Weight
1	85	83	2
2	102	102	0
3	92	91	1
4	70	68	2
5	64	66	−2
6	107	104	3
7	169	166	3
8	127	125	2

Example B: Mann-Whitney Test Suppose you have a random sample of cumulative grade averages for three men and three women, and you want to use a nonparametric test (the Mann-Whitney test) to determine whether you can reject the hypothesis of no difference.

Men	Women
62	83
86	78
74	76

Example C: Kruskal-Wallis Test Suppose you have a random sample of families with pets in the fictitious communities C, E, and G, and you count the number of pets in each family. You want to use the Kruskal-Wallis test to determine whether you can reject the hypothesis of no difference in medians between communities.

npets	Community
1	C
2	C
1	C
11	G
13	G
12	G
2	E
2	E
3	E

Example A: Sign Test

Minitab uses the column of differences for the sign test. Start with either step 1 or step 2.

1. Enter the differences into one column and go to step 3.
2. If you have entered two columns of data (labelled **Before** and **After**) and want to use Minitab to calculate the differences first, click **Calc** and **Calculator**. Figure 13A shows what to do if you want column 3 to be the differences where column 1 has the weight before and column 2 has the weight after. Click **OK**. The differences will appear in column 3, with the variable name "Difference."

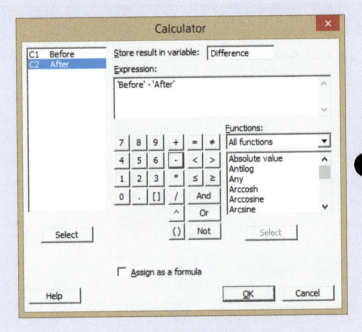

▲ **FIGURE 13A** Minitab input for calculating differences.

3. **Stat > Nonparametrics > 1-Sample Sign**
4. See Figure 13B. Double click on **Differences** to place it in the **Variables** box (or wherever the differences are). Choose **Test median** and leave the default at **0.0**. If you wanted to use a one-tailed alternative expecting weight loss, you would change the **Alternative** to **greater than** because when we did the subtraction, those with a weight loss resulted in a positive number.
5. Click **OK**.

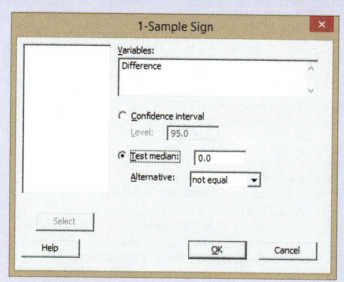

▲ **FIGURE 13B** Minitab one-sample sign input.

▲ **FIGURE 13D** Minitab Mann-Whitney input.

The output for a two-tailed alternative is shown in Figure 13C.

```
Sign Test for Median: Difference

Sign test of median =  0.00000 versus ≠ 0.00000

             N  Below  Equal  Above     P   Median
Difference   8    1      1      6   0.1250  2.000
```

▲ **FIGURE 13C** Minitab one-sample sign output.

Example B: Mann-Whitney Test

1. Enter the six cumulative averages unstacked (as given previously) into columns 1 and 2. Add labels (**Men** and **Women**) above the columns.
2. **Stat > Nonparametrics > Mann-Whitney**
3. Refer to Figure 13D. Double click one of the columns for the **First Sample**, and double click the other column for the **Second Sample**. You may change the **Alternative** if you want it to be one-tailed.

4. Click **OK**.

The p-value comes out to be **0.6625**.

Example C: Kruskal-Wallis Test

For this test, Minitab requires stacked data.

1. Enter the numbers in column 1 and the category values in column 2. Be consistent with the category values.
2. **Stat > Nonparametrics > Kruskal-Wallis**
3. The variable with the numbers (here **C1 npets**) goes in the **Response** box and the categorical variable (here **C2 Community**) goes in the **Factor** box.

The output is shown in Figure 13E.

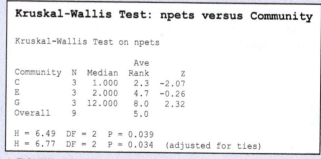

```
Kruskal-Wallis Test: npets versus Community

Kruskal-Wallis Test on npets

                          Ave
Community  N  Median  Rank      Z
C          3   1.000   2.3  -2.07
E          3   2.000   4.7  -0.26
G          3  12.000   8.0   2.32
Overall    9           5.0

H = 6.49  DF = 2  P = 0.039
H = 6.77  DF = 2  P = 0.034  (adjusted for ties)
```

▲ **FIGURE 13E** Minitab Kruskal-Wallis output.

EXCEL

Example A: Sign Test

1. Enter "**Before**" and the list of before weights in column A. Enter "**After**" and the list of after weights in column B. You should include the labels at the top of each column.

2. **Add-ins > XLSTAT > Nonparametric tests > Comparison of two samples (Wilcoxon, Mann-Whitney, . . .)**

3. See Figure 13F. Click in the **Sample 1:** box to make it active, and then select the data in column A, including the label "Before." Click in the **Sample 2:** box to make it active, and then select the data in column B, including the label "After." For **Data Format:** select **Paired samples**. Select **Sign test**. Click **OK**.

4. Click **Continue** and then **OK**, if needed. The two-tailed p-value is shown in the output to be 0.125.

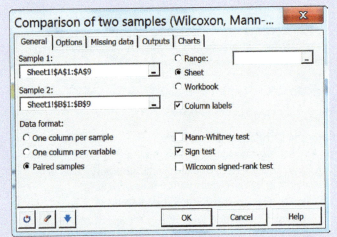

▲ FIGURE 13F XLSTAT sign test input.

Example B: Mann-Whitney Test

1. Enter the cumulative averages into columns A and B, including the headings "Men" and "Women" at the top.

2. **Add-ins > XLSTAT > Nonparametric tests > Comparison of two samples (Wilcoxon, Mann-Whitney, . . .)**

3. Click in the **Sample 1:** box to make it active, and then select column A, including the label "**Men.**" Click in the **Sample 2:** box to make it active, and then select column B, including the label "**Women.**" For **Data Format**, it is *different from* Figure 13F to the left: select **One column per sample**. Select **Mann-Whitney test**. Click **OK**.

4. Click **Continue** and then **OK** if needed. The p-value (two-tailed) is shown to be 0.663.

Example C: Kruskal-Wallis Test

1. Enter the stacked data in the first two columns.

2. **Add-ins > XLSTAT > Test a hypothesis > Nonparametric Tests > Comparison of k samples**

3. See Figure 13G. Click on **One Column per Variable** and check the **Column labels** and the **Kruskal-Wallis test** options. Click in the **Data:** box to make it active and select the column containing the numerical data. Click in the **Sample identifiers:** box and select the column containing the categorical data.

4. Click **OK**.

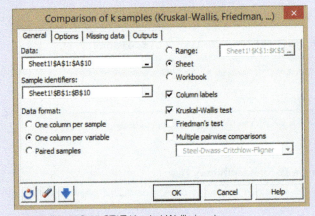

▲ FIGURE 13G XLSTAT Kruskal-Wallis input.

STATCRUNCH

Example A: Sign Test

You may start with step 1 or step 2.

1. Enter the differences in one column and then go to step 5.

2. Enter in the two columns of data given in Example A (weight before and weight after).

To calculate the difference:

3. **Data > Compute expression**

4. See Figure 13H. For **Y:** choose one of the columns (such as **var1**) and for **X:** choose the other column (**var2**). Then choose **Y-X** in the **Functions box**, and click **Set Expression** and **Compute**. There will be a column of differences added to your spreadsheet.

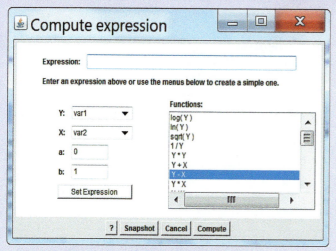

▲ FIGURE 13H StatCrunch input for finding differences.

5. **Stat > Nonparametrics > Sign Test**

6. Click the column of differences. Click **Next** if you want to change your alternative to be one-tailed.

7. Click **Calculate**.

Figure 13I shows the output for a two-tailed alternative.

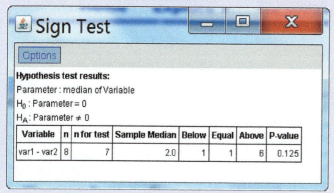

▲ FIGURE 13I StatCrunch sign test output.

Example B: Mann-Whitney Test (unstacked data)

1. Enter the cumulative averages unstacked (as shown previously) into **var1** and **var2**. You can put labels above the columns if you want.

2. **Stat > Nonparametrics > Mann-Whitney**

3. For **Sample 1: Values in:** select one of the columns, and for **Sample 2: Values in:** select the other column.

4. If you want to change the alternative to one-tailed, click **Next** and do it.

5. Click **Calculate**.

Figure 13J shows the output.

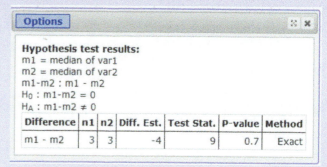

▲ FIGURE 13J StatCrunch Mann-Whitney output.

Example B: Mann-Whitney Test (stacked data)

1. Enter the cumulative averages stacked (as shown in Figure 13K), including the headings (here CumAvge and Gender).

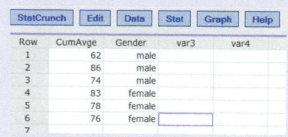

▲ FIGURE 13K StatCrunch cumulative average data.

2. **Stat > Nonparametrics > Mann-Whitney**

3. See Figure 13L. For **Sample 1: Values in:** select **CumAvge**, and in the box for **Where:** enter **Gender="male."** Be very careful with your typing. Typing "Male" instead of "male" will cause trouble.

4. For **Sample 2: Values in:** select **CumAvge**, and in the box for **Where:** enter **Gender="female."**

5. Select the appropriate hypothesis test.

6. Click **Compute!**

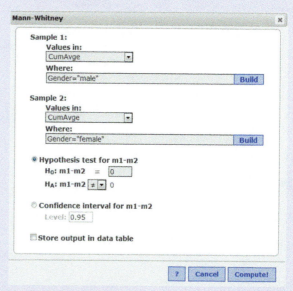

▲ FIGURE 13L StatCrunch input for Mann-Whitney for stacked data.

You will get a p-value of **0.7.**

Example C: Kruskal-Wallis Test

1. Enter the number of pets stacked, with categories in the variable **Community**.
2. **Stat > Nonparametrics > Kruskal-Wallis**
3. See Figure 13M. Click **Values in a single column** for stacked data. For **Responses in:** select the numerical variable (here **npets**), and for **Factors in:** select the categorical variable (here **Community**). Make sure that **Adjust for ties** is selected.
4. Click **Compute!**

You will get a p-value of **0.0339**.

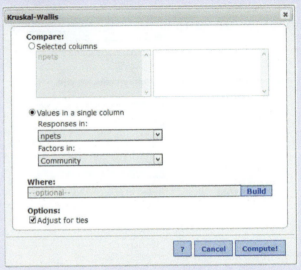

▲ **FIGURE 13M** StatCrunch input for Kruskal-Wallis for stacked data.

SPSS

Example A: Sign Test

1. Enter the data in two columns, and use the **Data View** to name them (here, **Before** and **After**) and to set their **Measure** as **Scale**.
2. **Analyze > Nonparametric tests > Related samples**
3. In the **Fields** tab, move the two variables to the **Test Fields:** box.
4. See Figure 13N. In the **Settings** tab, select **Customize tests** and then **Sign test (2 samples)**.

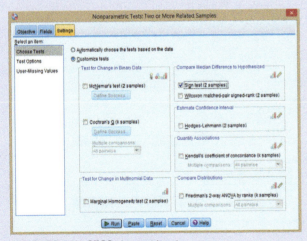

▲ **FIGURE 13N** SPSS sign test input.

5. Click **Run.**

The output is shown in Figure 13O.

Hypothesis Test Summary

	Null Hypothesis	Test	Sig.	Decision
1	The median of differences between Before and After equals 0.	Related-Samples Sign Test	.125[1]	Retain the null hypothesis.

Asymptotic significances are displayed. The significance level is .05.

[1]Exact significance is displayed for this test.

▲ **FIGURE 13O** SPSS sign test output.

Example B: Mann-Whitney Test

1. Enter the stacked data in two columns, and use the **Variable view** to name them (here **CumAvge** and **Gender**) and to set their **Measure** as **Scale** for the numerical variable and as **Nominal** for the categorical one.
2. **Analyze > Nonparametric statistics > Independent samples**
3. In the **Fields** tab, move the numerical variable to the **Test fields:** box and the categorical variable to the **Groups:** box.
4. In the **Settings** tab, select **Customize tests** and **Mann-Whitney U (2 samples)**.
5. Click **Run.**

The output can be seen in Figure 13P.

Hypothesis Test Summary

	Null Hypothesis	Test	Sig.	Decision
1	The distribution of CumAvge is the same across categories of Gender.	Independent-Samples Mann-Whitney U Test	.700[1]	Retain the null hypothesis.

Asymptotic significances are displayed. The significance level is .05.

[1] Exact significance is displayed for this test.

▲ **FIGURE 13P** SPSS output for Mann-Whitney test.

Example C: Kruskal–Wallis Test

1. Enter the stacked data in two columns, and use the **Variable view** to name them (here **npets** and **Community**) and to set their **Measure** as **Scale** for the numerical variable and as **Nominal** for the categorical one.

2. **Analyze > Nonparametric statistics > Independent samples**

3. In the **Fields** tab, move the numerical variable to the **Test fields:** box and the categorical variable to the **Groups:** box.

4. See Figure 13Q. In the **Settings** tab, select **Customize tests** and **Kruskal–Wallis 1-way ANOVA (k samples)**. Under **Multiple comparisons**, choose **None**.

5. Click **Run**.

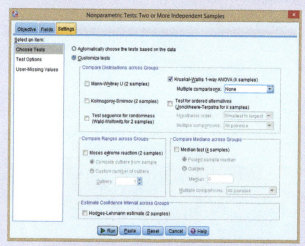

▲ **FIGURE 13Q** SPSS input for Kruskal-Wallis test.

14 Inference for Regression

LEARNING OBJECTIVES

After completing this chapter, you should be able to:

1. State the conditions under which a linear model can be used.

2. Check each of these conditions, and be aware of the statistical consequences when these conditions do not hold.

3. Build upon knowledge obtained from Chapter 4 to obtain and interpret regression analysis output.

4. Use regression analysis output to perform hypothesis tests and find a confidence interval for the *y*-intercept term of the model.

5. Use the same regression analysis output to conduct a hypothesis test to determine whether the two variables are related and find a confidence interval for the slope.

6. For a given *x*-value, employ the regression model to predict the value of *y* using a confidence interval or a prediction interval.

David Carillet/123RF

This chapter builds on our knowledge of bivariate data acquired in Chapter 4. There, we explained how linear regression can be used to understand the relationship between two numerical variables, and how we can take this understanding to build a model that allows us to predict one variable based on the value of the other variable. Since then, you've learned about samples and populations, and how the knowledge of a sample can be projected to the understanding of the population through the process of statistical inference. In this chapter we bring these two concepts together to show how inferences about a population can be made with regression.

We examine two types of inference. The first involves the slope of the linear model. This is important because if there is no linear relationship between the two variables,

then the slope of the model will be 0. For example, suppose a medical clinic has a new way of triaging patients which they believe will reduce the amount of time a patient waits to receive medical attention. If the slope of the regression line between the waiting times using the new diagnosing method and before the new diagnosing method is 0, then there is no relationship between the new waiting times and the old waiting times, suggesting that the new method of triaging patients doesn't work.

The other type of inference is to make predictions. You saw several examples of this in Chapter 4, such as how you can predict the value of a vehicle based on its age in years. We're now ready to present the techniques that will enable you to describe the certainty in these types of predictions, and to add to these predictions a margin of error.

CASE STUDY

Identifying Ballot Flaws in an Important Election

The U.S. Presidential Election of 2000—November 7, 2000—was one of the closest in history. Early exit polls conducted by television networks projected that Bush was to win Florida (and hence the 2000 Presidential election), so Gore called Bush to concede. While Gore was on his way to make his concession speech, updated exit polls inferred that Gore might win Florida, so Gore retracted his concession. A vote recount later took place and determined that Bush received the most votes in the State of Florida.

Angry Democratic voters in Palm Beach County complained that a confusing "butterfly" lay-out ballot caused them to accidently vote for the Reform Party candidate—Pat Buchanan—instead of Gore. By this chapter's end, you'll see how regression can be used to determine if there is statistical evidence supporting the claim of upset Democratic voters, or if it is nothing more than sour-grapes.

SECTION 14.1

The Linear Regression Model

When we think of models, we may think of many things—airplane models, architecture models, maybe even weather models. These models are representations, or imitations, of what will happen in real life. The architect of a skyscraper will build a small-scale model to imitate what it will look like after it is built, and weather forecasters will use various models to make important weather predictions. For example, predictions on snowfall amounts can be very useful for airport authorities and road maintenance crews.

Here we will encounter a **statistical model**. Like other models, a statistical model intends to imitate "real-life" data. The closer a model imitates real life, the better the model is. An important statistical skill, then, is to determine how well the statistical model fits the real-life data. If the model does not fit the data well, the model is not a good imitator of real life and should not be used.

Components of the Model

In Chapter 4 you learned that the regression line is a statistical method used to summarize the linear relationship between two numerical variables. This was the only condition needed—that the nature of their relationship be linear. If the relationship is not linear, then our predictions will be wrong, in some cases severely wrong.

We will now go beyond the expression of the linear relationship between two variables. Specifically, we want to measure how certain—or uncertain—our predictions from the regression line are so that we may make inferences about a population when the regression line is based on a random sample of data. Through the provision of a statistical model that has such uncertainty built into it, we can quantify this uncertainty by calculating the margins of error for confidence intervals and finding the p-values for hypothesis tests.

The statistical model imitates how the real data were generated. There are two components of the data generation:

1. For a given value of the predictor variable, a linear equation determines what the value of the response variable is *expected* to be.

 Looking Back

Describing Relationships
In Chapter 4 you learned that you should examine the trend (positive, negative, nonexistent), strength (strong trends have little vertical scatter), and shape (linear or nonlinear trend) and report them in the context of the data.

2. Randomness happens! This is incorporated into the model by allowing the *observed* value of the response variable to be either larger than (above) or smaller than (below) what is *expected*.

Point 1 is called the **deterministic component** of the model. The statistical model we will use is linear, and therefore determines the nature of the relationship between the two variables.

Point 2 is called the **random component**. This allows for the response variable to vary for a particular value of the predictor variable. It is this random component that creates the uncertainty in the inferences we wish to make.

To show how the model generates data, we selected four books of different lengths. We know the total number of pages in each book exactly, because we can just open the book and look at the final page number. These numbers are 203, 317, 409, and 765. We will exploit what we learned in Chapter 4 about the relationship between page numbers and width of books.

1. The regression line from Chapter 4, based on a sample of 24 books, says that the width of a book (in millimetres) should be

$$\text{Predicted Width} = 6.22 + 0.0366 \text{ Pages}$$

This is the deterministic component of our model. The deterministic component tells us that our 203-page book is *expected* to be $6.22 + 0.0366 \times 203 = 13.6498$ mm wide. For our four books, the expected widths are shown in the accompanying table.

Number of Pages	Width According to Straight-Line Model (mm)
203	13.6
317	17.8
409	21.2
765	34.2

These points are shown in Figure 14.1a, along with the linear equation that tells us where other books are *expected* to appear.

2. There is a discrepancy between statistics determining what is *expected* to happen and what really happens (or is *observed* to happen)—similar to our life-experiences. The random component of the model builds in such a discrepancy by allowing for the scattering of points around the linear model. Instead of a book with a width of 13.6 mm, we see 13.6 mm plus or minus some random amount. We could simulate this plus-or-minus amount with a random number generator or on a computer. We would instruct the computer to pick a number from a Normal distribution with a mean of 0 and a standard deviation of, say, 5 mm. The value we observe is the value we expect (the deterministic part of the model) plus or minus this random amount. If the random amount is positive, the book is wider than we expected and the observation is above the regression line. If negative, the book is thinner than we expected and the observed width is below the regression line.

In real life, where does this randomness come from? When we measured the books, randomness pushed its way into our study. Different books with the same number of pages have different widths because of the type of paper used, the way the book is bound, the type of cover on the book (hard or soft), just to mention a few possible reasons. We also introduced some measurement error. Measurement error occurs because measurements vary from measure to measure, so if we measured the width of a book the next day, we might get a slightly different value. Thus, measurements of the same object vary but are centred on the true value. The results of adding this random component are shown in Figure 14.1b.

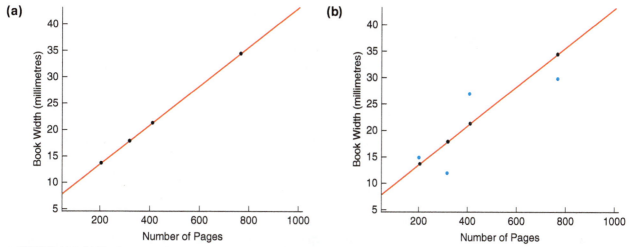

▲ **FIGURE 14.1** **(a)** The first step of the model is to determine the book widths so that the points fall on the straight line that they *expect* to follow. **(b)** The second step is to add the random component, which moves each point slightly above or below the line by an amount randomly sampled from a Normal distribution.

EXAMPLE **1** Model of Mercury Level in Fresh Water

Biologists studying the relationship between the mercury levels in freshwater lakes and the mercury levels of fish living in those lakes believe that the deterministic component of the relationship is a straight line. A scatterplot (not shown) shows that even though the general trend is linear, the points do not fall exactly on a straight line.

QUESTION What factors might account for the random component of this regression model?

SOLUTION Variability might appear in the instruments used to measure mercury levels. The size of a fish might also affect the amount of mercury in its system. Different breeds of fish might process mercury differently, and this might affect the amount of mercury found.

TRY THIS! Exercise 14.1

Table 14.1 lists, for each book in our sample, the width we expected to see (if the widths were completely determined by the straight line), the width we actually saw, and the deviation of the observed width from the straight-line, or expected, width.

Pages	Straight-Line Width	Observed Width	Deviation
203	13.6	15.0	1.4
317	17.8	12	−5.8
409	21.2	27	5.8
765	34.2	30	−4.2

◀ **TABLE 14.1** Each row represents one book, and we list the number of pages, the width the book would have if all the points perfectly followed the linear model, the observed width, and the deviation (observed width minus straight-line width).

The deviations from the straight line have a technical name: **residuals**. *Residual* means "what's left over after something is taken away" or "remainder." The idea here is that the residual is the extra that doesn't fit on the line. Sometimes it's referred to as the error, because it represents how far away the observed value is from what is expected (according to the linear model). The typical deviation is measured by the standard deviation, σ (sigma). You can think of σ as measuring how small or large the random component of the model is.

> **KEY POINT** A residual is the difference between the observed y-value and the predicted (or expected) y-value that lies on the line. By looking at all the residuals, we can understand the difference between the predictions of our statistical model and the real-life data.

Up to now, we've described the concept of the linear model. To be more precise, we'll visit the conditions that must be satisfied for the linear statistical model to be a valid imitator of the data.

1. Linearity: The response variable y is to depend linearly on the predictor variable x.

2. Normality: The residuals follow a Normal distribution with a mean of 0 and a standard deviation represented by σ. In shorthand, the residuals are $N(0, \sigma)$.

3. Constant standard deviation, or SD: The standard deviation σ is the same for all values of the predictor variable x. This will be explained in more detail very soon. (For example, see Figure 14.7.)

4. Independence: The residuals are independent of each other. Knowing that one y-value is, say, above the regression line does not affect the location of another y-value with respect to the line.

Checking the Conditions of the Model

A very useful tool for checking conditions 1 and 3 of the model is the **residual plot**. A residual plot is a scatterplot that has the residuals on the vertical axis and the original x-values on the horizontal axis. Residual plots are like magnifying glasses, in that they zoom in on potential problems in the model and make deviations from the linearity condition and the constant standard deviation condition easier to spot.

Most statistical software packages either produce residual plots automatically as part of the regression analysis or will produce them upon request. Figure 14.2 shows the residual plot for our four books.

▶ **FIGURE 14.2** A residual plot for the four data points in Table 14.1. The vertical axis indicates the residuals (the observed width minus the width if it fell exactly on the straight line), and the horizontal axis marks the values of the predictor variable (the number of pages).

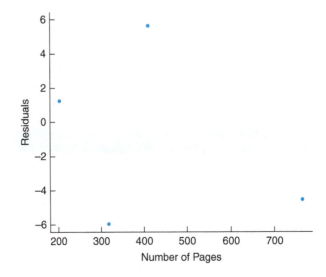

Figure 14.3a shows a scatterplot of the cost of a plane trip versus the distance travelled for five trips. The regression line is included on the scatterplot. The coloured vertical lines represent the residuals. The value of the residual is the length of the vertical line, which is the distance between the point and the regression line. If the point is above the line, then the residual has a positive value. If the point is below the line, then the residual has a negative value.

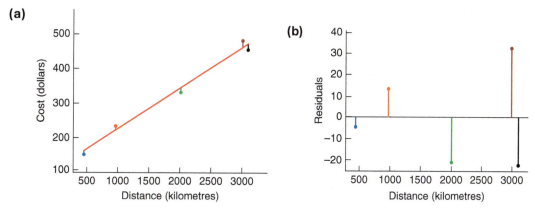

▲ **FIGURE 14.3** **(a)** The original scatterplot with the regression line. **(b)** The resulting residual plot.

Figure 14.3b shows these residuals plotted on the vertical axis. It illustrates that the residual plot magnifies the residuals so that they can be seen more clearly. The coloured vertical lines have the same lengths as they did in Figure 14.3a, but the scale of the plot in Figure 14.3b makes them easier to see.

Checking Linearity

If the trend in the original data is linear, then the residual plot should have *no* slope. In other words, the residual plot should have a flat trend. For example, Figure 14.4a shows a scatterplot for the larger collection of books; width is plotted against length, measured in terms of number of pages. The regression line has been added to help you see that the trend is linear. Figure 14.4b shows the residual plot. The residual plot has no trend. This is good, because it indicates that the first condition of the linear model is satisfied.

TECH

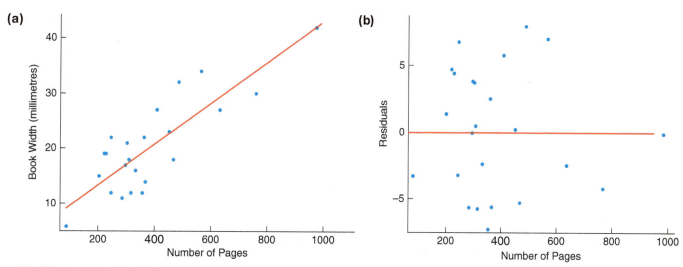

▲ **FIGURE 14.4** **(a)** The width of books versus the number of pages. The trend is linear. **(b)** The residual plot for the regression line in Figure 14.4a. The lack of a trend suggests that the first condition of the model, that *pages* and *width* have a linear trend, is satisfied.

When the trend is nonlinear, as it is for the relationship between age of a mother at childbirth and age-specific birthrate (number of live births per 1000 women) in Canada shown in Figure 14.5a, the residual plot will display some sort of trend. You can see this trend clearly in Figure 14.5b.

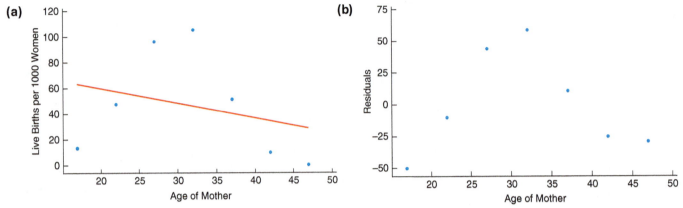

▲ FIGURE 14.5 (a) The relationship between age of a mother at childbirth and the number of live births per 1000 women. The line does not fit the data's nonlinear trend. It appears to be a close fit for women near the ages of 25 and 35. (b) The residual plot shows the presence of a trend in the residuals, confirming that the relationship between age and the age-specific number of live births per 1000 women is nonlinear.

> **KEY POINT** If the first condition of the model is satisfied and the shape of the relationship is linear, then the residual plot (a scatterplot of residuals versus *x*-values) will show no trend.

🌎 EXAMPLE **2** To Life!

In Chapter 4 we examined a scatterplot showing the relationship between the life expectancy of people living in a country and their wine consumption per person (in litres). Figure 14.6 shows the residual plot that results from fitting a linear regression model attempting to predict a country's life expectancy as a function of its per-person annual wine consumption.

▶ FIGURE 14.6 Residuals from a linear regression that predicts life expectancy of a country based on per-person wine consumption.

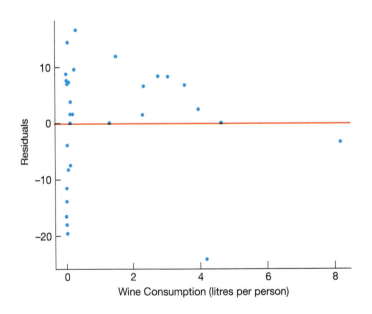

QUESTION   Does the residual plot suggest that a country's life expectancy is a linear function of its per-person wine consumption?

SOLUTION The residual plot shows a trend: moving from left to right, the residuals increase sharply and then drop gradually as the *x*-variable—wine consumption per person—increases. The presence of this trend means that the statistical model is nonlinear, and that the first condition of the model is not valid.

TRY THIS! Exercise 14.3

Checking the Constant Standard Deviation (SD) Condition

The constant SD condition of the linear model says that the standard deviation in the *y*-values must be the same for all values of the predictor variable. Essentially, this means that the amount of vertical spread about the line is the same across the entire line. This is easier to explain with a picture of what happens when the condition fails.

To illustrate how the lack of common standard deviation can occur, Figure 14.7a shows the linear relationship between the daily maximum temperature and the Air Quality Index (AQI) in downtown Toronto for a random sample of 209 days. Higher AQI values mean higher levels of air pollution, which lead to more respiratory problems. Here the daily maximum temperature will be the predictor, or *x*-variable, and the AQI will be the response, or *y*-variable. As you can see, the relationship between these two variables shows a larger and larger spread as the daily maximum temperature increases (as we move from left to right), with increased scattering of points around the line. Within this relationship, there isn't a common standard deviation in the AQI variable for all values of maximum temperature. This means that if we attempt to predict the AQI based on its linear relationship with the daily maximum temperature, the prediction would be good for small daily maximum temperatures, since the observed data are close to what we expect. However, the prediction would worsen as the daily maximum temperatures increase. The observed data are farther and farther away from what we expect.

Figure 14.7b is the residual plot created from the linear regression model. You will notice that it has the shape of a wedge of pizza. This wedge shape, whether it gets wider and wider or narrower and narrower going from left to right, is the sign that the condition of constant standard deviation is not satisfied. This wedge shape appears, to a lesser extent, in the original scatterplot. It is much more obvious in the residual plot. In general, a residual plot will help us check whether the constant SD condition holds. A residual plot that supports a constant SD for all values of the *x*-variable will not show a wedge shape; it will look like a rectangular band centred around the residual value 0.

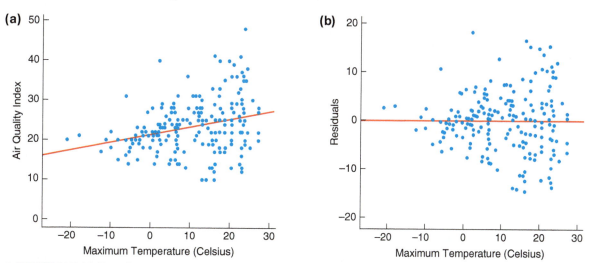

▲ **FIGURE 14.7** **(a)** Air quality data showing a nonconstant standard deviation. This violates one of the conditions that must hold for the linear model to be a valid description of the data. **(b)** Residual plot for Figure 14.7a. The increasing wedge shape is a sure sign that the condition requiring constant standard deviation for all values of *x* has been violated. The residual plot clearly shows little vertical variation for values of *x* between −20 and −10. However, there is quite a bit of variation for larger values of *x* (where residuals range from about −15 to +20).

🌐 EXAMPLE 3 Predicting the Median Monthly Selling Price of Homes in a City

What is the relationship between the median selling price of a house in a city and the number of homes for sale in any given month? One of the authors used simple random sampling to randomly pick 30 months. For each month, the total number of homes that were for sale during the month and the median selling price of all homes sold in the same month were recorded. The regression line that predicted the median monthly house price from the total number of homes available for sale in the month was found. Figure 14.8 shows the residual plot from this regression line.

▶ **FIGURE 14.8** Residual plot for a regression that predicts the median monthly selling price of a home in a large city based on the number of homes for sale in the same month.

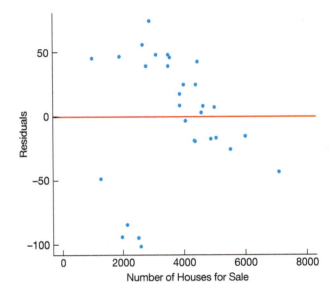

QUESTION Evaluate the residual plot to determine whether the conditions of the linear regression model hold. If not, which conditions don't hold? Why?

SOLUTION The residual plot shows a decreasing trend. This means that the relationship between these two variables is nonlinear. Second, the residual plot indicates that there is not a constant standard deviation in the median monthly selling price because of the lack of a rectangular band centred about the horizontal line 0.

TRY THIS! Exercise 14.5

KEY POINT
A residual plot with no structure is a good thing: it indicates that the linearity and constant SD conditions are satisfied. A wedge shape in a residual plot indicates that the constant SD condition does not hold. A trend in the residual plot indicates that the linearity condition does not hold.

Checking Normality

To check the second condition of the linear model, that the residuals follow a Normal distribution, we look at the distribution of the residuals. This can be done either through a histogram of the residuals or a QQ plot, although the QQ plot is more useful in most situations. Figure 14.9a shows a QQ plot for the residuals from the data in

Example 3. The QQ plot is not a straight line, which suggests that these residuals are not Normal. Figure 14.9b shows an accompanying histogram of the residuals.

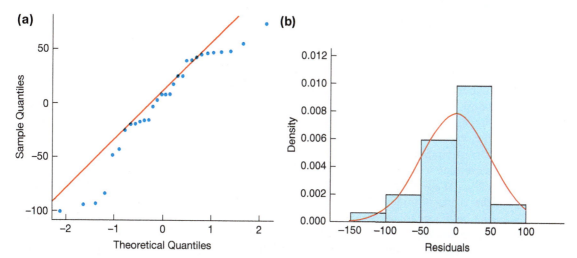

▲ **FIGURE 14.9 (a)** The QQ plot for the residuals shown in Figure 14.8 (from the median monthly price of homes sold in a city, given the number of houses for sale in the same month) indicates that these residuals do not follow a Normal distribution. **(b)** The histogram of the residuals shows a left-skewed distribution.

EXAMPLE 4 Book Widths

Figure 14.10a shows the residual plot from predicting the width of a book on the basis of the length of the book (measured in terms of number of pages). Figure 14.10b is a QQ plot of these residuals. The residual plot has no features: no trend and no wedge shape. This suggests that two of the conditions of the statistical model—linearity and constant standard deviation—are satisfied.

QUESTION Is the Normality condition of the linear regression model satisfied?

> **Looking Back**
>
> **Checking Normality**
> Recall from Chapter 13 that the QQ plot is used to check whether a sample distribution is approximately Normal. If the points follow (more or less) a straight line, then the sample distribution is approximately Normal.

TECH

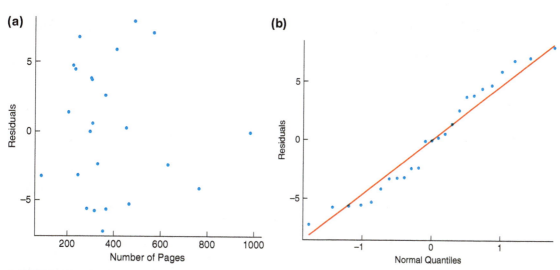

▲ **FIGURE 14.10 (a)** Residual plot for predicting the width of a book on the basis of the number of pages in the book. **(b)** The QQ plot for residuals that comes from predicting the width of a book on the basis of the number of pages in the book, using a straight line.

SOLUTION Yes. Because the points of the QQ plot generally follow a straight line, we can conclude that the residuals are approximately Normally distributed.

TRY THIS! Exercise 14.7

Checking the Independence Condition

The independence condition usually cannot be checked by looking at the data. If you know that the data were collected in a particular order, then you might try plotting the data against the order in which they were collected. If you see a trend, it indicates that the observations might not be independent. However, you generally do not have this information. Sometimes, those who collected the data can give you enough information to determine whether this condition might be violated. For example, if you're studying the effects of a weekly music class on math scores for students in a school, you might suspect that scores of students who are in the same classroom with the same math teacher might not be independent, because if one student does very well in math, it might indicate that others in that class did very well in math, too.

In most situations, however, you will have to assume that this condition holds and be prepared to accept that your conclusions might not be sound if it is later discovered that the data are not independent.

KEY POINT You should always check that the conditions of the linear regression model hold before interpreting the regression line.

1. Linearity: Use a residual plot. If it has no trend, the linearity condition is satisfied.
2. Constant standard deviation: Use a residual plot. If it lacks a wedge shape, then the constant SD condition is satisfied.
3. Normality: Make a QQ plot of the residuals. If it (mostly) follows a straight line, the Normality condition is satisfied.
4. Independence: Review any information you have about how the data were collected to decide whether the independence condition is satisfied.

SECTION 14.2

Using the Linear Model

What influences the value of the Canadian dollar? Our economy is very strongly tied to the U.S. economy. After all, the United States is Canada's largest trading partner: Statistics Canada reports that 76% of Canada's exports went to the United States in 2014, while 67% of all goods imported into Canada were from the United States. In addition, about 75% of Canadians live within 160 kilometres from the border shared with the United States.

Historically, the Canadian dollar (CAD) has fluctuated in value—in some instances wildly—compared to the U.S. dollar (USD). In the mid 1950s, the CAD was worth more than the USD, meaning that it took less than $1CAD to buy a $1USD. The value of the CAD relative to the USD dropped significantly in the early 1960s, and because of this volatility the CAD was fixed to be worth $0.925 USD in the mid 1960s. It stayed this way until 1970. This fixed exchange rate was abandoned after 1970, and how many CADs it took to buy $1USD was allowed to "float" as a means to combat high inflation in the early 1970s. This action caused the CAD to again be worth more than the USD.

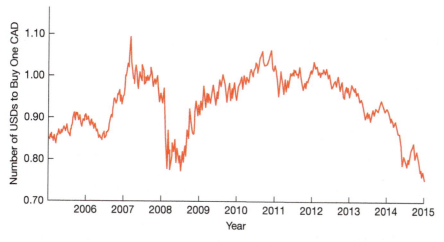

◀ **FIGURE 14.11** Fluctuations in how much one CAD equals in USD from 2005 to early 2015. (Source: xe.com)

In the 1990s and the early 2000s, the CAD declined significantly relative to the USD, the low point being in late January 2002, where $1CAD was worth $0.617USD. After 2008, the value of the Canadian dollar rose significantly, to the point where the CAD stayed close in value to the USD (with slight fluctuations) for a few years. Since 2014, the value of the CAD has experienced a sharp decline. See Figure 14.11.

What is the reason behind the behaviour of the CAD? The changes in value of the CAD relative to the USD are in part due to the fact that the Canadian economy relies heavily on natural resources, among them crude oil and natural gas. The largest U.S. imports from Canada are in crude oil and natural gas, which totalled about 109 billion USD in 2013 (ustr.gov/countries-regions/americas/Canada).

This back-story on the Canadian economy's dependence on the United States brings up an interesting question: Can the value of the CAD relative to the USD—that is, how many CADs it takes to buy one USD—be linearly dependent on the price of oil? Perhaps this is of particular interest to many of us, particularly Canadians who plan vacations or shopping trips to the United States, or simply participate in online-shopping from U.S. internet sites.

We can answer this question through the use of statistical inference. Our regression model will allow us to perform hypothesis tests on the y-intercept and slope so that we can reject (or fail to reject) the idea that we can predict values of the y-variable based on its linear dependence on the x-variable.

Estimators for the Intercept and Slope

We must now be careful to distinguish between the *population* model and the *estimate* of the model. The population model is the model we would have if we had all the y-values and their corresponding x-values for *all* objects in the population. The linear population model looks like this:

$$y = \beta_0 + \beta_1 x + e$$

Here we have followed customary statistical practice and used Greek letters to represent population parameters (just like using μ to represent the population mean). There are two parameters in the population model:

β_0 represents the y-intercept term of the population model.

β_1 represents the slope term of the population model.

(The e term simply represents the random component of the model.)

The method we use for estimating these population parameters is the same as the one we encountered in Chapter 4 but with different notation. The "hat" over each character now tells us that the symbol represents a statistic; it is computed from the data and is used to estimate the corresponding parameter.

$\hat{\beta}_0$ represents the estimator of the y-intercept in the population model.

$\hat{\beta}_1$ represents the estimator of the slope term in the population model.

In addition,

$\hat{y}$ represents the predicted value of the y-variable for a given value, x, of the x-variable. The formulas from Chapter 4 used to compute these estimators are then

$$\hat{\beta}_1 = r\frac{s_y}{s_x} \quad \text{and} \quad \hat{\beta}_0 = \bar{y} - \hat{\beta}_1\bar{x}$$

We can now write the estimate of the population model as

$$\hat{y} = \hat{\beta}_0 + \hat{\beta}_1 x \qquad \text{(Note that there is no } e \text{ term.)}$$

As in Chapter 4, we expect that you will use these formulas only on rare occasions. Most of the time, your software will compute them for you. Your responsibility is to interpret the output correctly and evaluate whether the conditions of the regression model hold sufficiently well for you to learn anything from the computer output.

If the conditions of the linear model appear to be satisfied, then there are two facts to know about the estimators $\hat{\beta}_0$ and $\hat{\beta}_1$:

1. Each estimator is a statistic whose distribution is Normal.

2. Each estimator is unbiased.

Even if the Normality condition is violated so that the errors are not Normal, the Central Limit Theorem comes to the rescue. Because of the CLT, if the sample sizes are large enough, the distributions of both the y-intercept and slope will be approximately Normal, and this approximation is better for larger sample sizes.

The fact that the estimators are unbiased means that our calculated values for the y-intercept and slope, based on our data, will typically be about the same as the population values. This means that if each of a large number of researchers drew a random sample of the two variables from the same population and found the regression line, then the mean of all their y-intercepts and slopes would be the population values.

How close *our* estimates of the slope and intercept are likely to be to the true population values depends on how much these estimates vary from sample to sample. This variability is measured by the standard deviation. The estimated standard deviations for these estimators will be provided to you by the software package you use.

 KEY POINT The estimators for the y-intercept and the slope of a regression line are unbiased. If the Normality condition holds, then the distribution of each of these estimators is Normal. If the Normality condition does not hold, then the distributions are approximately Normal (and the larger the sample size, the better).

Hypothesis Tests for Intercept and Slope

The test statistics for both the intercept and the slope have a familiar form, which was introduced in Chapter 8 for the one-proportion z-test and was also used in Chapter 9 for the one-sample t-test:

$$t = \frac{\text{estimator} - \text{null value}}{SD}$$

where SD stands for the estimated standard deviation of the estimator.

For the y-intercept,

$$t = \frac{\hat{\beta}_0 - \text{null value}}{SD_{\hat{\beta}_0}}$$

For the slope,

$$t = \frac{\hat{\beta}_1 - \text{null value}}{SD_{\hat{\beta}_1}}$$

 **Looking Back**

The *t*-Test
The test statistic for the one-sample t-test (Formula 9.2) is

$$t = \frac{\bar{x} - \mu_0}{SD_{\text{est}}}$$

The value for the estimated standard deviation is given in the software output. If the conditions for the linear regression model hold, then both of these test statistics follow a t-distribution with $n - 2$ degrees of freedom (n is the number of observations).

Most statistical software is designed to automatically produce a test of a very specific hypothesis about the slope:

> H_0: The slope of the model is 0.
>
> H_A: The slope of the model does not equal 0.

Or, in the notation of the population model,

> H_0: $\beta_1 = 0$
>
> H_A: $\beta_1 \neq 0$

This is a very important test. If the y-variable can't be predicted as a linear function of the x-variable, then the slope of the population linear model *must be* zero. Hence, this test could be reworded as

> H_0: The y-variable cannot be expressed as a linear function of the x-variable.
>
> H_A: The y-variable can be expressed as a linear function of the x-variable.

Or as

> H_0: The correlation is 0.
>
> H_A: The correlation is not 0.

The next example will show you how to find the information you need to do a test on the slope from the output provided.

EXAMPLE 5 Mario Kart Auction

Suppose you want to buy a game on eBay, the online auction site. You make a bid, and if the next person to come along wants the item, he or she can bid more than you did. At the end of the scheduled time, the person who has made the highest bid gets to purchase the item. Suppose you want to buy a Mario Kart Wii game on eBay. (This is a popular video game that runs on the Wii system.) You might suspect that the more people who are bidding, the more expensive the item will be. David Diez, a statistician, collected data from a sample of auctions for Mario Kart on eBay in the fall of 2009.

QUESTION Can the final cost of the item be expressed as a linear model that depends on the number of people who bid for the item? Use Figure 14.12 on the next page, which shows the results from running a regression where the total price for a Mario Kart is the response variable and the number of bids for that item is the predictor variable. State the hypotheses, the observed value of the test statistic, and the p-value. State your conclusion using a 5% significance level. Assume that the conditions of the linear model are satisfied.

SOLUTION To test whether the final cost of the item can be expressed as a linear model depending on the number of people who bid for the item, we will *assume that it can't*. This means that the slope of the linear population model is 0. Usually, we would create a scatterplot of the data to verify visually that the trend is linear and to ensure that there are no unusual observations in the scatterplot. We won't do that here, because we are told to assume that all the conditions of the linear model hold. We proceed accordingly:

H_0: $\beta_1 = 0$. Price can't be expressed as a linear model that depends on the number of bids.

H_A: $\beta_1 \neq 0$. Price can be expressed as a linear model that depends on the number of bids.

Looking Back

Standard Deviation of Sample Means

The standard deviation of the distribution of the sample mean is

$$SD = \frac{\sigma}{\sqrt{n}}$$

where σ is the population standard deviation. Because n is bigger than 1, the standard deviation of the sample mean is always smaller than the population standard deviation.

▶ **FIGURE 14.12** StatCrunch output from a regression model that predicts the price (totalPr), in dollars, for a Mario Kart game on an eBay auction for a given number of bids (nBids).

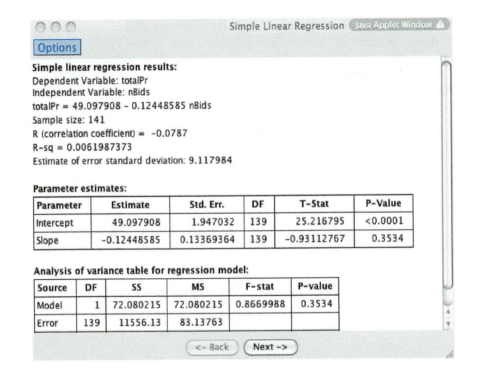

Simple Linear Regression Java Applet Window ▲

Options

Simple linear regression results:
Dependent Variable: totalPr
Independent Variable: nBids
totalPr = 49.097908 - 0.12448585 nBids
Sample size: 141
R (correlation coefficient) = -0.0787
R-sq = 0.0061987373
Estimate of error standard deviation: 9.117984

Parameter estimates:

Parameter	Estimate	Std. Err.	DF	T–Stat	P–Value
Intercept	49.097908	1.947032	139	25.216795	<0.0001
Slope	-0.12448585	0.13369364	139	-0.93112767	0.3534

Analysis of variance table for regression model:

Source	DF	SS	MS	F–stat	P–value
Model	1	72.080215	72.080215	0.8669988	0.3534
Error	139	11556.13	83.13763		

<– Back   Next –>

The observed value of the *t*-statistic is given at the intersection of the column labelled T-Stat and the row labelled Slope:

$$t = -0.9311$$

The p-value is found immediately to the right of the value of the *t*-statistic, and is given as 0.3534.

This means that if a similar data set were collected and a regression model were obtained trying to express the final cost of the item as a linear function of the number of people who bid for the item, the probability of observing greater evidence against the null than the observed evidence of $t = -0.9311$ is 0.3534. Since the p-value is bigger than 0.05, we fail to reject the null hypothesis.

CONCLUSION There is a 0.3535 probability of observing a more surprising outcome, if the null hypothesis of a zero-slope is true. Do not reject the null hypothesis. The data indicate that the final price of the item can't be expressed as a linear model that depends on the number of bids.

TRY THIS! Exercise 14.9

If you wish to test a value other than 0 in the null hypothesis, you need to do so by hand. The same is true of tests of the intercept; the software tests that the intercept is 0, so if you wish to test another value in your null hypothesis, you need to do the test by hand. Example 6 provides us with one such example.

🌍 EXAMPLE 6 Value of the Canadian Dollar and the Price of Oil: *y*-Intercept of the Model

One of the authors took a simple random sample of 20 trading days from 2000 to 2013. For each day chosen, the number of CADs needed to buy one USD and the price of a barrel of oil (West Texas Intermediate, WTI) were both observed. The scatterplot is shown in Figure 14.13. Output from a regression that expresses the value of the CAD as a linear model that depends on the price of oil is shown in Figure 14.14.

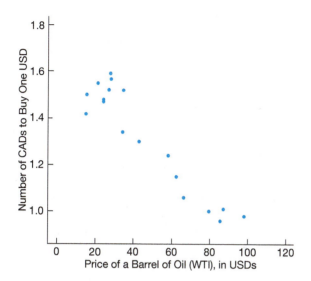

◄ FIGURE 14.13 Scatter plot of data on the value of the CAD relative to the USD and the price of oil.

```
Regression Analysis: CAD to USD versus Price Oil/Barre
The regression equation is
CAD to USD = 1.68 - 0.00799 Price oil/Barrel

Predictor               Coef     SE Coef        T        P
Constant             1.68225     0.03439    48.92    0.000
Price Oil/Barrel  -0.0079902   0.0006685   -11.95    0.000

S = 0.0766841    R-Sq = 88.8%    R-Sq(adj) = 88.2%

Analysis of Variance
Source           DF        SS        MS         F        P
Regression        1   0.84003   0.84003    142.85    0.000
Residual Error   18   0.10588   0.00588
Total            19   0.94588
```

◄ FIGURE 14.14 Minitab regression analysis output, using the price of oil to predict the value of the CAD relative to the value of the USD.

QUESTION Looking at the scatterplot, it appears as if a straight line can be drawn through the y-axis somewhere around 1.7. Use this regression output to test the hypothesis that if the price of oil were \$0 per barrel, it would take 1.70 CADs to buy one USD. Be sure to carefully state the null and alternative hypotheses, and to state your conclusion using the 5% level of significance.

SOLUTION From the output in Figure 14.14, we see that $\hat{\beta}_0 = 1.68225$ and $\hat{\beta}_1 = 0.00799$. The estimate of the population model that states the value of the CAD relative to the USD as a linear function of the price of oil (WTI) is then

$$\hat{y} = 1.68225 + (-0.00799)x$$

or, rounding to three decimals and rewriting this in the context of the data, the regression line is

$$\text{Predicted Value of CAD} = 1.682 - 0.008 \text{ Price of Oil}$$

The computer output provided assumes that we are testing whether the y-intercept is equal to 0, which would mean that the regression line would pass through the origin of the scatterplot. We can see that this is not the case, since the y-intercept appears to be in the area of 1.70. However, for the sake of practice, let's complete the test that the value of the y-intercept in the population model is 0. We would test the following:

$$H_0: \beta_0 = 0$$
$$H_A: \beta_0 \neq 0$$

The observed value of the t-statistic can be obtained directly from the output: $t = 48.92$. This value is computed by

$$t = \frac{\hat{\beta}_0 - \text{null value}}{SD_{\hat{\beta}_0}} = \frac{1.682 - 0}{0.03439} \approx 48.92$$

The estimate of the standard deviation of $\hat{\beta}_0$ is provided in the computer output in the column labelled "SE Coef" in the Constant row. The p-value is very small, less than 0.0001. Because it is less than 0.05, we reject the null hypothesis and conclude from these data that the y-intercept of the model is indeed not 0.

Now consider the proposed value of the y-intercept, a value of 1.70. This means that it would take 1.70 CADs to buy one USD and that the y-intercept of the population model would be equal to 1.70, or $\beta_0 = 1.70$, if the price of oil were \$0. The observed value of the estimate of the y-intercept, 1.682, is not the same as the proposed value. But is this due to chance? We test the following:

$$H_0: \beta_0 = 1.70$$
$$H_A: \beta_0 \neq 1.70$$

Here we have to compute the value of the t-statistic because we are not testing whether it is equal to 0 or not. The null value is 1.70. We find

$$t = \frac{\hat{\beta}_0 - \text{null value}}{SD_{\hat{\beta}_0}} = \frac{1.682 - 1.70}{0.03439} = -0.52$$

The p-value is the probability of observing a t-statistic that is as extreme or more extreme than the observed t-value of -0.52. The DF column for the Residual Error row tells us that the statistic has a t-distribution with 18 degrees of freedom ($n - 2 = 20 - 2 = 18$). We could look up this probability in a table, but it is much better to use technology. Figure 14.15 shows the output from StatCrunch's calculator

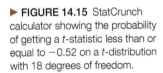 **FIGURE 14.15** StatCrunch calculator showing the probability of getting a t-statistic less than or equal to -0.52 on a t-distribution with 18 degrees of freedom.

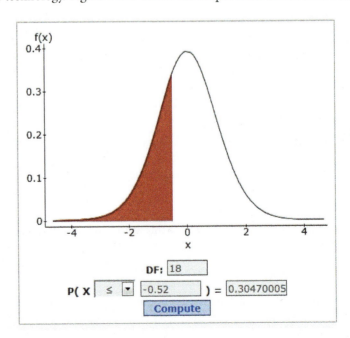

feature. This tells us that the probability of getting a t-statistic equal to or less than -0.52 is 0.305.

This is only half of the required probability. Since our alternative hypothesis is two-tailed, we also need the probability of getting a t-statistic equal to or bigger than 0.52. Because of the perfect symmetry of the t-distribution, the p-value is simply twice 0.305; that is, p-value $= 0.61$. There is a 61% chance that running the regression on another sample of 20 data values will produce greater evidence against the null hypothesis than the current data.

CONCLUSION There is a 0.61 probability of observing a more surprising outcome, if the null hypothesis is true. Because 0.61 is not less than the significance level of 0.05, we fail to reject the null hypothesis. We can infer from these data that the y-intercept term of the population model is 1.70.

TRY THIS! Exercise 14.11

EXAMPLE 7 Value of the Canadian Dollar and the Price of Oil: Slope of the Model

QUESTION Returning to Example 6, can we say that the value of the Canadian dollar relative to the U.S. dollar depends linearly on the price of oil (WTI)? And if this is the case, can we say that an increase in the price of oil by one USD will mean that you need $0.01 (one cent) less to convert a CAD to a USD? Test using a level of significance of 0.05. Be sure to carefully state the null and alternative hypotheses and your conclusion.

SOLUTION First, if the value of the CAD doesn't linearly depend on the price of oil, then the correlation between these two variables is zero. This means that the value of the slope in the population model is 0. We can test the following:

$$H_0: \beta_1 = 0$$
$$H_A: \beta_1 \neq 0$$

The output in Figure 14.14 does provide the necessary t-statistic. In the T column and the PriceOil/Barrel row, $t = -11.95$. To the right of this value, the p-value $= 0.000$. The p-value is *really not* 0, but it is very, very small. Because it is less than 0.05, the null hypothesis is rejected and we can conclude from these data that the slope of the linear population model is not zero. Even more, we can say that yes, the value of the CAD relative to the USD depends linearly on the price of a barrel of oil.

Second, by how much does the Canadian dollar become more valuable if the price of oil rises? The scatterplot in Figure 14.13 shows that a negative linear relationship exists. As the price of oil increases, the number of CADs needed to buy one USD decreases—meaning that the CAD becomes more valuable relative to the USD. In other words, the slope is negative. But can the value of this slope be -0.01?

Specifically, if the price of a barrel of oil increases by one USD, does this mean that it takes $0.01 less CAD to buy one USD? We test to see whether the slope of the population linear model is -0.01:

$$H_0: \beta_1 = -0.01$$
$$H_A: \beta_1 \neq -0.01$$

We can't use the software output in Figure 14.14. We compute the *t*-statistic using

$$t = \frac{\hat{\beta}_1 - \text{null value}}{SD_{\hat{\beta}_1}}$$

The estimated value of the standard deviation in the estimate of the slope term is obtained from the software output and found in the column labelled "SE Coef" in the PriceOil/Barrel row. This value is $SD_{\hat{\beta}_1} = 0.0007$. Since null value is -0.01, we find the *t*-statistic to be

$$t = \frac{\hat{\beta}_1 - \text{null value}}{SD_{\hat{\beta}_1}} = \frac{-0.008 - (-0.01)}{0.0007} = \frac{0.002}{0.0007} \approx 2.86$$

To find the p-value, we need to find the probability of observing a *t*-statistic that is 2.86 or more on the *t*-distribution with 18 degrees of freedom, then multiply this probability by 2 (remember that the test is two-tailed). Figure 14.16 shows the area to the right of 2.86 to be 0.005. Multiplying this by 2 gives a p-value of 0.01.

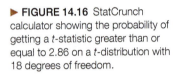

► **FIGURE 14.16** StatCrunch calculator showing the probability of getting a *t*-statistic greater than or equal to 2.86 on a *t*-distribution with 18 degrees of freedom.

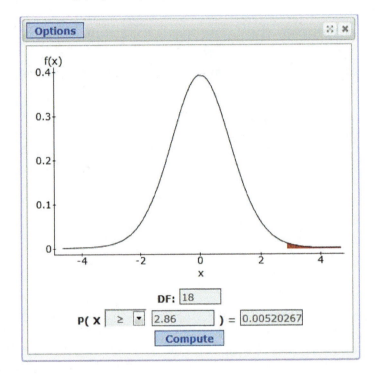

CONCLUSION There is a 0.01 probability of observing a more surprising outcome, if the null hypothesis is true. Because this p-value is less than the significance level of 0.05, reject the null hypothesis that the slope of the population model is equal to -0.01. We can infer from these data that the slope term of the population model is not negative 0.01—or, that as the price of oil increases by one USD, the amount of CAD needed to buy one USD does not decrease by \$0.01.

TRY THIS! Exercise 14.15

Confidence Intervals for Intercept and Slope

Confidence intervals for the intercept and slope follow a familiar form:

$$\text{estimate} \pm t^* SD_{\text{est}}$$

This is the same form for all the confidence intervals we've presented. The constant t^* is chosen from a t-distribution so that we get an interval with the desired confidence level. (You'll almost always use a 95% confidence level.) The estimate here can be either the intercept or the slope. The SD_{est} is the standard deviation and is obtained from the regression output.

For instance, to predict the price of a Mario Kart Wii game (totalPr) from the number of bids (nBids), we found this regression line from the output in Figure 14.17:

$$\text{Predicted totalPr} = 49.1 - 0.12 \text{ nBids}$$

The standard deviation for the slope is 0.134 (after rounding) and is found in the StatCrunch output column labelled Std. Err.

The best way to find the confidence intervals for the intercept and slope is to read them from the output. Most software packages provide confidence intervals for both parameters. Figure 14.17 shows the StatCrunch output for the linear regression to predict the total price of the Mario Kart on the basis of the number of bids.

► FIGURE 14.17 Regression output including confidence intervals for predicting the price of the Mario Kart on the basis of the number of bids received in an eBay auction. A 95% confidence level for the intercept is 45.2 to 52.9. A 95% confidence interval for the slope is −0.39 to 0.14.

TECH

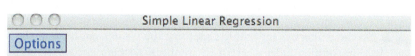

Simple Linear Regression

Options

Simple linear regression results:
Dependent Variable: totalPr
Independent Variable: nBids
totalPr = 49.097908 – 0.12448585 nBids
Sample size: 141
R (correlation coefficient) = −0.0787
R-sq = 0.0061987373
Estimate of error standard deviation: 9.117984

Parameter estimates:

Parameter	Estimate	Std. Err.	DF	95% L. Limit	95% U. Limit
Intercept	49.097908	1.947032	139	45.24828	52.947536
Slope	-0.12448585	0.13369364	139	-0.38882193	0.13985023

The lower and upper bounds of the confidence intervals are taken directly from the output. For example, we are 95% confident that the true intercept (the value of the intercept that we would get if we saw all eBay auctions and not just our small sample) is between 45.2 and 52.9. Perhaps more interestingly, we are 95% confident that the true slope is between −0.39 and 0.14. Because this interval includes 0, we cannot rule out the possibility that the true slope is 0. In other words, we cannot rule out the possibility that there is no linear relationship between the number of bids the Mario Kart receives at auction and the price that is finally paid.

Interpreting Confidence Intervals for Regression

The interpretation of the confidence intervals for the intercept and slope of a regression equation is exactly the same as the interpretation of the confidence intervals of other parameters. The confidence interval gives us a range of plausible population values. We can use this to test hypotheses, as the next example shows.

EXAMPLE 8 Value of the Canadian Dollar Confidence Intervals

The output in Figure 14.18 shows the StatCrunch output that repeats the regression for predicting the value of the CAD relative to the USD, linearly dependent on the price of a barrel of oil (WTI). This time, the software was asked to provide confidence intervals for both the y-intercept and the slope of the linear population model.

▶ **FIGURE 14.18** StatCrunch output to predict the value of CAD, given the price of oil.

Simple linear regression results:
Dependent Variable: CADtoUSD
Independent Variable: PriceOil/Barrel
CADtoUSD = 1.682253 - 0.007990155 PriceOil/Barrel
Sample size: 20
R (correlation coefficient) = -0.94238832
R-sq = 0.88809575
Estimate of error standard deviation: 0.076684054

Parameter estimates:

Parameter	Estimate	Std. Err.	DF	95% L. Limit	95% U. Limit
Intercept	1.682253	0.034387049	18	1.6100085	1.7544976
Slope	-0.007990155	0.00066851685	18	-0.0093946568	-0.0065856533

QUESTION Do these intervals support the idea that the y-intercept term of the model is 1.70 and the slope of the model is -0.01? State the 95% confidence intervals for the intercept and the slope, and explain whether these support the values proposed in the preceding statement.

SOLUTION The 95% confidence interval for the y-intercept term, β_0, is 1.61 to 1.74. The 95% confidence interval for the slope, β_1, is -0.009 to -0.007.

CONCLUSION Because the confidence interval for the y-intercept captures 1.70, we have no reason to believe that the y-intercept term of the model is not 1.70. Notice how this finding coincides with the conclusion of the hypothesis test about the y-intercept term presented in Example 6.

The confidence interval for the slope term does not include -0.01, since this is below the lower bound of -0.009. We have a statistical reason to believe that the slope is not -0.01. In fact, the true value of the slope of the linear population model is somewhere between -0.009 and -0.007. This means that as the price of a barrel of oil (WTI) increases by 1 USD, it will take anywhere from 0.007 to 0.009 fewer CAD to buy one USD.

TRY THIS! Exercise 14.16

SECTION 14.3

Predicting Values and Estimating Means

The regression line is also useful for making predictions about future observations, as we saw in Chapter 4. But there are two different types of questions we can ask of a regression line, and it is important to be able to tell these two types of questions apart.

One type of question involves all objects in the population and is concerned with the mean value of the response variable, or y-variable, for a given x-value of the predictor variable. The other type of question involves a single object from the population and deals with the value of the response variable for this object given its x-value of the predictor variable. Even though these two questions use the same x-value, their answers are different due to the difference in variation associated with each case.

Figure 14.19 shows a regression line that can be used to predict the amount of mercury found in largemouth bass (a freshwater fish) on the basis of the pH of the lake where they are caught. pH measures the acidity of the water. A value of 7 is neutral, a

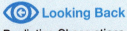

Looking Back

Predicting Observations
Review Example 3 in Chapter 4 to see how we predicted the width of a book on the basis of the number of pages.

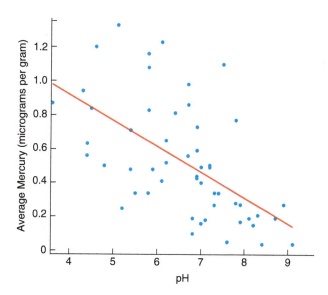

◄ **FIGURE 14.19** Mercury levels found in largemouth bass as a function of the pH of the water where they are caught. Mercury is measured in micrograms of mercury per gram of fish.

value of 0 represents the highest level of acidity, and a value of 14 represents the lowest level of acidity (the most basic or alkaline reading). The data are based on samples of fish caught in 53 lakes in Florida (Lange et al. 1993).

Evidence exists that humans can get mercury poisoning from eating fish with mercury in their tissue. For this reason, it is important to understand and predict the mercury content of fish that swim in these lakes.

The equation of the regression line shown is

$$\text{Predicted mercury level} = 1.53 - 0.152 \text{ pH}$$

There are two questions we might ask:

1. If the acidity of a lake measures pH 7, what is the mean level of mercury found in all fish in the lake?

2. I've just caught a fish from a lake that measures pH 7. What mercury level will that fish have?

The answer to both these questions uses the same value of the predictor variable, $x = 7$, and it starts with the regression line:

$$\text{Predicted mercury} = 1.53 - 0.152 \times 7 = 0.466$$

However, Question 2 has greater uncertainty because it is asking about an individual fish as opposed to a collection of fish. Recall from Chapter 7 that there is more variation in one observation randomly chosen from a population than there is in the mean of many observations. The same idea applies here.

The answer to Question 1 is a confidence interval for the mean value. For a given confidence level, we are estimating the *mean of all y*-values of a population that consists of all objects that have a specific *x*-value.

The answer to Question 2 has the same form as a confidence interval. However, we call it a **prediction interval** because we are attempting to capture a *single y*-value for a specific *x*-value for a given level of confidence. The prediction interval for a single *y*-value will always be wider than the confidence interval for the mean *y*-value because there is less variation in the mean of a group of observations than there is for a single observation.

Figure 14.20 shows output from StatCrunch. Most statistical software will either show you both a prediction and a confidence interval or ask you to choose which of these you want. StatCrunch shows you both (and allows you to input any value for *x* that you want). The information you are looking for is given last, after the summary information about the regression model.

► **FIGURE 14.20** StatCrunch regression output for predicting mercury level in fish based on the water's pH. The last table shows a confidence interval (C.I.) for estimating the mean mercury content of fish caught in a lake with pH = 7, and the prediction interval (P.I.) for an individual fish caught in a lake with pH = 7.

○ ○ ○   Simple Linear Regression

Options

Simple linear regression results:
Dependent Variable: Avg_Mercury
Independent Variable: pH
Avg_Mercury = 1.5309187 − 0.15230086 pH
Sample size: 53
R (correlation coefficient) = −0.5754
R-sq = 0.3310853
Estimate of error standard deviation: 0.2816448

Parameter estimates:

Parameter	Estimate	Std. Err.	DF	T-Stat	P-Value
Intercept	1.5309187	0.20349288	51	7.5232058	<0.0001
Slope	−0.15230086	0.030313263	51	−5.024232	<0.0001

Analysis of variance table for regression model:

Source	DF	SS	MS	F-stat	P-value
Model	1	2.0023627	2.0023627	25.242905	<0.0001
Error	51	4.0455127	0.07932378		
Total	52	6.0478754			

Predicted values:

X value	Pred. Y	s.e.(Pred. y)	95% C.I.	95% P.I.
7	0.46481267	0.040628992	(0.38324657, 0.5463788)	(−0.106465735, 1.0360911)

Note that the confidence interval is much narrower than the prediction interval. In fact, the prediction interval is so wide that it includes negative values, even though negative mercury levels are impossible. This suggests that there might be too much variability in the data for us to make a useful prediction of how much mercury an individual bass might contain, although we can get a possibly useful estimate of the mean mercury level of all bass in the lake.

KEY POINT   Prediction intervals are used to express the uncertainty in predicting an individual observation. They are interpreted the same way as confidence intervals. A 95% prediction interval of (−0.11, 1.04) means we are 95% confident that the amount of mercury found in a single fish caught from a lake with pH = 7 will be in this interval.

EXAMPLE 9 Frozen Dinners

A consumer group plots the number of calories advertised by the manufacturer for frozen dinners (single portion) against the actual caloric content based on laboratory testing. The group's regression line predicts that a frozen dinner advertised to have 1000 calories actually has, on average, 1100 calories.

QUESTION   Which of the two questions that follow can be answered with a confidence interval? Which can be answered with a prediction interval?

    A. For all frozen dinners, what is the mean calorie content if the advertised content is 1000 calories?

    B. The Frozen Man TV Dinner advertises that it contains 1000 calories. What is the actual calorie content of one dinner?

SOLUTION Question A requires a confidence interval, because we are making an estimation of the mean of a large group of frozen dinners. Question B requires a prediction interval, because we are predicting the true calorie content for an individual product.

TRY THIS! Exercise 14.19

EXAMPLE 10 One More Book

A professor wants to buy a book from an online bookseller, but he has only 40 millimetres of space left on his bookshelf. If the book won't fit, he doesn't want to buy it. From the online listing, he knows that the book has 598 pages. On the basis of statistics student Edwin Onega's sample of books, he performs a regression to predict the width of a book (in mm) from the number of pages it contains. The output is shown in Figure 14.21. Assume that the conditions of the linear regression model hold.

Simple linear regression results:
Dependent Variable: width
Independent Variable: pages
width = 6.2208385 + 0.036551695 pages
Sample size: 25
R (correlation coefficient) = 0.8468
R-sq = 0.71699643
Estimate of error standard deviation: 4.707955

Parameter estimates:

Parameter	Estimate	Std. Err.	DF	T-Stat	P-Value
Intercept	6.2208385	2.0173435	23	3.0836785	0.0052
Slope	0.036551695	0.0047882963	23	7.6335487	<0.0001

Analysis of variance table for regression model:

Source	DF	SS	MS	F-stat	P-value
Model	1	1291.5687	1291.5687	58.27107	<0.0001
Error	23	509.79126	22.164837		
Total	24	1801.36			

Predicted values:

X value	Pred. Y	s.e.(Pred. y)	95% C.I.	95% P.I.
598	28.078753	1.432286	(25.115843, 31.04166)	(17.89888, 38.258625)

◀ **FIGURE 14.21** Regression output for predicting the width of a book on the basis of its number of pages. The output is based on a random sample of books.

QUESTION How wide should the professor expect the book to be? Should he use a prediction interval or a confidence interval to decide whether the book will fit on his shelf? Should he buy the book?

SOLUTION The book is expected to be about 28.1 mm wide. Because the professor is predicting the width of a single book, he should use a prediction interval. This tells us that he can be highly confident that the width of the book could be as small as 17.9 mm or as great as 38.3 mm. Because he has 40 mm of space, he can be confident that the book will fit. He should buy the book.

TRY THIS! Exercise 14.23

What Can Go Wrong?

What happens if the conditions are not satisfied? Sometimes, disaster. Other times, not so much.

If the Linearity Condition Is Not Satisfied

Disaster. Estimates of slope and intercept may be biased. Predicted values and estimated means will be biased. Confidence intervals and prediction intervals are not reliable.

An option is to transform the data. Sometimes taking the log of all the values for either *x* or *y*, or both, will "straighten out" a nonlinear trend. Figure 14.22a repeats the scatterplot given in Example 2. It shows a nonlinear relationship between the life expectancy of people in a country and the country's per-person wine consumption. Figure 14.22b shows the same data after a log transform, plotting the log of the per-person wine consumption to the log of the life expectancy.

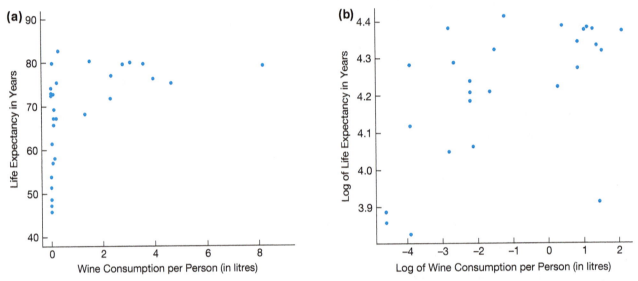

▲ **FIGURE 14.22** **(a)** The relationship between per-person annual wine consumption in a country and the life expectancy is nonlinear (www.who.int). **(b)** The relationship between the log of the annual wine consumption of a country and the log of the country's life expectancy could be considered linear (with a possible outlier); an attempt could be made to fit a regression line to this scatterplot.

Transforming the variables can make interpretation of the output tricky. We will not get into details here, but we advise you to consult a statistician if you find yourself in this situation.

If the Errors Are Not Normal

If the errors are not Normal, all is not lost. Assuming that the other conditions hold, you will still get unbiased estimates of the slope and intercept and of predicted values of *y* (or mean values of *y*) for a given value of *x*.

Because of the Central Limit Theorem, the p-values for hypothesis tests of the slope and intercept will be approximately correct. If the sample size is large, then this approximation can be quite good. Confidence intervals for the mean value of *y* at any given *x*-value will also be approximately correct. However, prediction intervals may not be accurate.

In some situations, the distribution of the residuals is so far from Normal that the Central Limit Theorem doesn't rescue us. In many of these situations, more advanced techniques exist that can provide better p-values and confidence intervals than we can get simply by relying on the Central Limit Theorem. For example, if the response variable has only two values, 0 (failure) and 1 (success), the population model will not be linear and the linear model is to be abandoned.

If the Standard Deviation Is Not the Same for All Values of x

You will still have unbiased estimates of the slope and intercept, and unbiased estimates of means and predicted values. However, the confidence intervals, prediction intervals, and p-values will not be accurate. Statisticians have other techniques for dealing with this situation. Transformations sometimes fix this problem, but sometimes they do not.

If the Errors Are Not Independent of Each Other

Disaster. If the errors are not independent, then the regression model is not appropriate. One common situation in which errors are not independent is when dealing with time-series data. **Time-series data** occur when the predictor variable is time. For example, we might plot daily maximum temperature against the date, intending to predict tomorrow's temperature. The linear regression model will fail for several reasons, but one is that the errors are not independent. If it is hotter than usual on one day (so the error is positive), there is more likely to be a hotter-than-usual temperature the next day. That is, if one day has a positive error, the next day is more likely to have a positive error as well.

Influential Points

You should also be aware that regression models can be greatly influenced by outliers. Not all outliers, but outliers that appear at the extremes of the x-variable's distribution, can have strong effect on the estimated slope. Beware of very low or very high x-values that also do not follow the linear trend. Don't delete these observations, but be aware that if they were not in the data set, or if they had different y-values, then your conclusions could change. Investigate these points to see whether you can learn anything about why they are exceptional. Perhaps they are mistaken entries; if so, you can delete them. Or perhaps they are evidence that an exception to the rule requires that you reconsider your model.

In general, it is good practice to take influential points out, find the regression line, and determine whether your conclusions are greatly affected by comparing your results with and without the influential point.

Interpreting r-Squared

Recall from Chapter 4 that the square of the correlation coefficient, r-squared or r^2 (also called the coefficient of determination), is used to measure "goodness of fit." Roughly speaking, goodness of fit is a number that tells us how close the points come to our model. In order for us to interpret r-squared, the linearity condition of the linear regression model must be satisfied. A common mistake is to think that a high r-squared value means that the conditions are satisfied. In fact, you should check the conditions using the methods discussed in this chapter before you even *look* at the r-squared value.

The coefficient of determination ranges from 0% to 100% and represents the amount of variability in y that we have "explained" with our regression line. The higher the value, the better. How do we know whether r-squared is high enough?

Surprisingly, this is a question that shouldn't concern you. After you've checked that the conditions of the model are satisfied, the most important thing to check in the model is whether the slope is 0 or not. Look at the hypothesis test for whether the slope is 0. If you reject the null hypothesis and conclude that the slope is not 0, then congratulations! You have discovered that you can express the response variable in a model that linearly depends on the predictor variable. The value of r-squared is not sufficient for deciding whether the linear relationship is strong enough. We can decide whether the relationship is strong enough (and hence r-squared is high enough) by determining whether the regression line is useful for our purposes.

Recall that r-squared tells us how closely the points are clustered about the line. When you have a high value for r-squared, it means that your estimates and predictions will be more precise. But you shouldn't trust r-squared to tell you whether you should find prediction intervals or confidence intervals. Go ahead and compute them, and decide for yourself whether they are useful. If the intervals are too wide, then your r-squared is too low.

Looking Back

Coefficient of Determination
The correlation coefficient squared (r-squared) is called the coefficient of determination. In Section 4.4, you learned that r-squared measures how much of the variation in the response variable is explained by the explanatory variable.

Details

r-Squared

The coefficient of determination is actually not too useful in many situations. Knowing the value of the slope and knowing whether it is "statistically significant" (has a p-value ≤ 0.05) provide much more useful information than knowing r-squared.

For example, suppose an admissions officer at a large university uses applicants' Grade 12 average marks to determine how successful they would be if admitted to the school. She has a large sample of data from current students that includes their Grade 12 averages and their first-year GPAs. She carries out a regression to predict GPA on the basis of one's Grade 12 average mark. After confirming that the conditions of the linear model are satisfied, she finds a regression line

$$\text{Predicted GPA} = 1.108 + 0.02518 \text{ (one's Grade 12 average mark)}$$

with r-squared = 0.104 (or 10.4%). From the output, she sees that the p-value for the hypothesis test for the slope is 0.02.

Now, this r-squared value seems low, but she can still learn quite a bit from the data. The output tells her to reject the null hypothesis that the slope is 0. She then concludes that the first-year GPA can be stated to depend linearly on the average mark in Grade 12. Now she's interested in what the mean GPA will be for all first-year students who had a Grade 12 average mark of 78%.

The 95% confidence interval for the mean GPA of all students with an average Grade 12 mark of 78% is (2.7, 2.9). This is useful information for her, because it tells her that these students will, on average, have a GPA of about C+ at the end of their first year. Even though the r-squared value was low, it still yielded useful information: (1) there is a real relationship between Grade 12 average marks and GPA, and (2) we can find useful confidence intervals for mean GPAs for groups of students.

On the other hand, suppose a worried parent calls the university. The parent's son got a 78% average in Grade 12. What will his first-year GPA be? The same regression line provides a 95% prediction interval of 1.7 to 3.6. In other words, we are confident that this student will end his first year with a GPA somewhere between a D+ and an A. Well, we didn't really need a regression analysis to tell us that. There is too much variability in the data to make predictions for individual students.

CASE STUDY REVISITED

Recall the case study at the beginning of this chapter. Were Democrat voters justified in their anger? Did the butterfly ballot cause some to accidentally vote for Pat Buchanan rather than Al Gore, who was the candidate they intended to vote for?

Let's assume that the voters who supported the Democratic presidential candidate, Al Gore, are not correct and that the layout of the butterfly ballot, pictured in Figure 14.23, of Palm Beach County did not cause those intending to vote for Gore to vote for Buchanan.

▶ **FIGURE 14.23** The butterfly ballot of Palm Beach County, Florida.

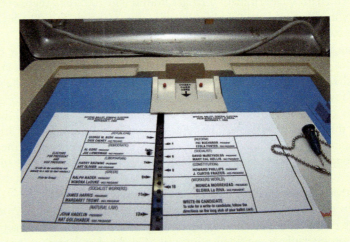

Figure 14.24 shows the scatterplot of the relationship between the number of votes Bush received in a county in Florida and the number of votes Buchanan received in

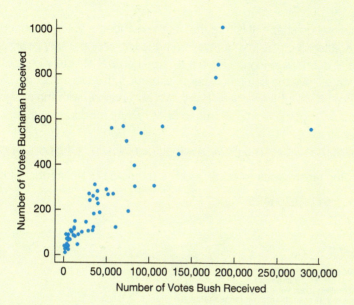

the same county, for all counties in Florida *excluding* Palm Beach County. The number of votes Bush received will be treated as the predictor variable *x*, and the number of votes Buchanan received in the same county is the response variable *y*. The relationship appears to be linear: as the number of votes Bush received increases, so does the number of votes Buchanan received. It also appears as if the points are closely scattered around a line, which would mean that the *r*-squared value might be high. In addition, there appears to be an influential point at the pair of values $x = 289{,}456$, and $y = 561$. We should not be too concerned about this data point, as these are votes for Dade County, which includes the city of Miami (where there are a lot of voters).

From the scatterplot, let's see if we can create a statistical model that will predict the number of votes Buchanan received in a county as a linear function of the number of votes Bush received. Figures 14.25a and 14.25b show that the conditions that allow us to attempt to create this model hold. We see no trend in the residual plot,

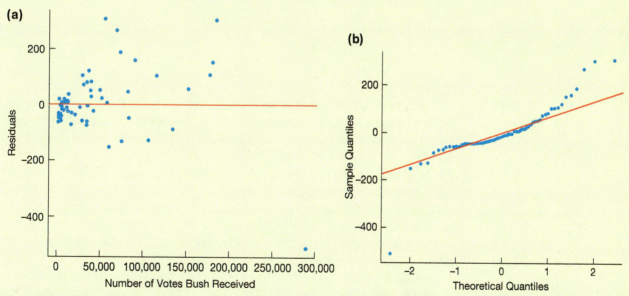

▲ **FIGURE 14.25** **(a)** Residual plot for predicting the number of votes Buchanan received for a given number of votes Bush received. The lack of trend means that the linearity condition holds. The rectangular band—or lack of a wedge shape—means that the constant standard deviation condition is also satisfied. **(b)** The QQ plot of the residuals does not deviate from a Normal distribution. There appear to be differences from a Normal distribution at the upper end, but these are due to the different sized counties being used in the regression.

and no definite wedge shape. It is true that as the number of votes Bush received increases, the scattering of the points away from the regression line appears to increase. However, not all counties in Florida have the same number of voters because not all counties in Florida have the same number of citizens. If this were true, we would probably see a more prevalent rectangular band. We will continue with the analysis because the scattering of the points seems to be very tight for counties that appear to be similar in voter size.

From the output in Figure 14.26, we see that the estimate of the population model is

Predicted Number of Buchanan Votes = 65.503332 + 0.0034817744 Number of Bush Votes

and that *r*-squared is 0.75348377 (or 75%).

▶ **FIGURE 14.26** StatCrunch output from a linear regression model predicting the number of votes Buchanan would get in a Florida county.

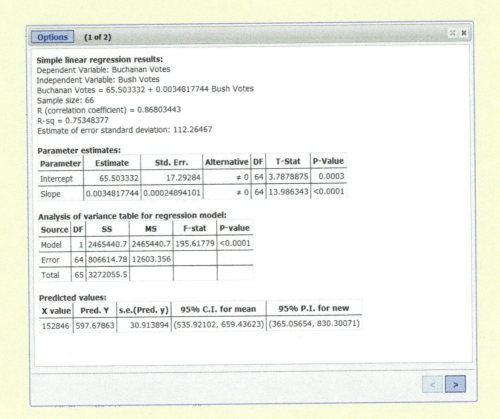

The p-value for the test of whether the *y*-intercept is 0 is 0.0003. This is less than 0.05, so we reject the null hypothesis that the intercept of the population model is 0 ($H_0: \beta_0 = 0$). This tells us that the *y*-intercept is not zero. This finding is substantiated by a 95% C.I. for the *y*-intercept: (30.95, 100.05).

The p-value for the test of whether the slope is 0 is less than 0.0001. We reject the null hypothesis that the model is not linear ($H_0: \beta_1 = 0$), and can conclude that the number of votes Buchanan received in a county is linearly dependent on the number of votes Bush received in the same county. A 95% confidence interval for the slope is (0.003, 0.004)—which means that for every additional 1000 votes Bush received in a county, Buchanan received an extra 3 to 4 votes.

We use the linear model to obtain a 95% prediction interval for the number of votes Buchanan should have received in Palm Beach County, where Bush received 152,846 votes. The regression model predicts that Buchanan would have received somewhere between 365 and 830 votes. The actual number of votes Buchanan received in Palm Beach County was 3407!

To see how rare the observation from Palm Beach County is, note that the common standard deviation of errors is estimated to be 112.26. The observed y-value of 3407 is about 25 standard deviations away from what we would expect it to be. Figure 14.27 shows the scatterplot with the regression line, and includes the Palm Beach County votes for Bush and Buchanan.

As it turns out, the difference between the number of votes Buchanan got in Palm Beach County and the number of votes the model predicted is $3407 - 830 = 2577$ votes. George W. Bush won the state of Florida, and therefore won the U.S. presidential election.

In total, Bush received 2,912,790 votes and Gore received 2,912,253, a difference of 537 votes. Perhaps a different ballot in Palm Beach County would have produced a different American president in 2000.

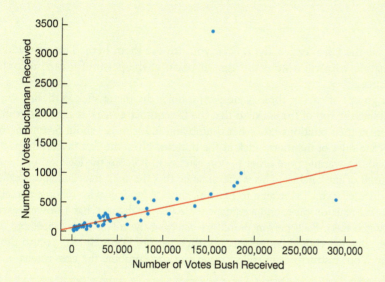

◀ FIGURE 14.27 Figure 14.24, including the regression model and the voting data for Palm Beach County.

EXPLORING STATISTICS

CLASS ACTIVITY

Older and Slower?

GOALS	MATERIALS
To use a collection of data to test whether two variables are related.	Metre stick or yard stick.

ACTIVITY

If you still have the Chapter 3 activity data, you can use them here. The only additional information you will need is the age (in years) of the person for each recorded reaction distance.

Work in groups of two or three. One person holds the metre stick vertically, with one hand holding the top of the stick, so that the 0-centimetre mark is at the bottom. The other person then positions his or her thumb and index finger about 5 centimetres apart on opposite sides of the metre stick at the bottom. Now the first person drops the metre stick without warning; the other person catches it. Record the location of the middle of the thumb of the catcher. This is the distance that the stick travelled and is called the reaction distance, which is related to reaction time. A student who records a small distance has a fast reaction time, and a student with a larger distance has a slower reaction time. Now switch tasks. Each person should try catching the metre stick twice, and the better (shorter) distance should be reported for each person. For each trial, record the age of the catcher. Your instructor will collect your data and combine the class results.

BEFORE THE ACTIVITY

1. If there is no relationship between age and reaction distance, what will a scatterplot look like?

2. If there is a relationship, do you expect it to be positive or negative? This will be your theory, which you will test with the activity.

3. What reasons other than age might explain why a catcher's reaction distances vary?

AFTER THE ACTIVITY

Report the regression line to predict reaction distance from age. Do the conditions of the linear regression model hold? If not, which ones fail?

Regardless of whether the conditions hold, find 95% confidence intervals to test whether your theory (from question 2 in the section Before the Activity) is supported by the data.

You can use the data in the table below, and merge your class data with these observations, if your class doesn't have much variety in ages.

Age	ReacDist(cm)	Age	ReacDist(cm)	Age	ReacDist(cm)	Age	ReacDist(cm)	Age	ReacDist(cm)
21	12	21	16	51	13	18	16	51	27
45	22	50	18	37	16	24	28	53	34
33	16	23	13	68	19	78	31	51	27
41	25	43	21	22	14	50	25	58	27
63	25	28	19	22	14	61	15	29	10

CHAPTER REVIEW

Summary of Learning Objectives

1. **What are the conditions that must hold in order to make statistical inferences about a linear regression model?** In order to make statistical generalizations about the linear model that expresses the response variable y as a linear function of the predictor variable x, the following conditions must hold: (1) the relationship between the two variables is linear; (2) the residuals are approximately Normally distributed; (3) the standard deviation of the residuals is the same for each value of the x-variable (common standard deviation); and (4) residuals are independent of each other.

2. **How are the conditions of the model checked?** The conditions are checked by creating two graphs: a residual plot and a QQ plot. A residual plot graphs each observed value of the x-variable with its residual. If the residual has no trend, the condition of linearity holds. In addition, if the residual plot has a rectangular band centred about zero, the common standard deviation condition holds. Alternatively, a wedge-shaped residual plot means that the common standard deviation condition *does not* hold. The QQ plot is used to see whether the residuals are Normally distributed. A roughly straight line means that the Normality condition holds. The condition of independence is difficult to verify, but beware of time series (regressions where time is the x-variable), because observations there are often not independent. If any of these conditions do not appear to be satisfied, the linear model cannot be estimated from the observed data.

3. **How are the statistics in a regression analysis of the data computed?** It is best to use technology, such as a standard statistical analysis software, to generate the statistics that are used to estimate the value of the y-intercept and the slope of the model. These statistics can be computed by hand with formulas obtained in Chapter 4, but they usually involve long calculations.

4. **How can I test whether the y-intercept term of the model, β_0, is statistically important to the model?** You

can test whether the y-intercept is statistically important to the model using the following hypotheses:

$$H_0: \beta_0 = 0$$
$$H_A: \beta_0 \neq 0$$

The t-statistic and p-value are obtained from the regression output to determine whether the null hypothesis is to be rejected or not. A confidence interval for β_0 can also be obtained from the regression output. If this confidence interval captures the value of 0, then β_0 is not statistically important to the model.

5. **How can I tell whether the response variable y depends linearly on the predictor variable x?** If there is no relationship between the two variables, then the slope will be equal to 0. The hypotheses about the slope term β_1 are the following:

$$H_0: \beta_1 = 0$$
$$H_A: \beta_1 \neq 0$$

The t-statistic and p-value are obtained from the regression output. If the p-value is less than the significance level, then the null hypothesis is rejected, meaning that the response variable y does depend linearly on the predictor variable x. A confidence interval for β_1 can be found in the same regression output. If this confidence interval does not include 0, then one can infer that the slope of the model is not 0.

6. **For a given value of the predictor variable x, what will the value of the y-variable be?** This depends. A confidence interval can be used to estimate the mean y-value of a group of persons or objects that all have a specific x-value. A prediction interval is used to predict a single y-value for a single person or object having a specific x-value. Prediction intervals are wider than confidence intervals because there is more uncertainty in predicting an individual outcome than an average outcome. Both of these intervals can, and should, be computed with the help of computer software.

Important Terms

Statistical model, *611*	Random component, *612*	Residual plot, *614*	Time series data, *635*
Deterministic component, *612*	Residuals, *614*	Prediction interval, *631*	

Sources

Calgary Real Estate Board. www.creb.com (accessed October 10, 2013).

Florida 2000. http://americanhistory.si.edu/vote/florida.html.

Hastie, T. J., and R. J. Tibshirani. 1990. *Generalized additive models.* Boca Raton, FL: Chapman & Hall/CRC.

Lange, T. L., H. E. Royals, and L. L. Connor. 1993. Influence of water chemistry on mercury concentration in largemouth bass from Florida lakes. *Transactions of the American Fisheries Society* 122, 74–84. http://wiki.stat.ucla.edu/socr/index.php/NISER_081107_ID_Data (accessed April 19, 2010).

Lee, D., R. Lane, and G. Chang. 2001. Three-dimension reconstruction for high-speed volume measurement. *Proceedings of the International Society for*

Optical Engineering, Machine Vision and Three-Dimensional Imaging Systems for Inspection and Metrology 4189, 258–267.

Leger, A., A. Cochrane, and F. Moore. 1979. Factors associated with cardiac mortality in developed countries with particular reference to the consumption of wine. *The Lancet* 313(8124), 1017–1020.

Onega, E. 2005. Book width data. UCLA Statistics 120A class project.

Ontario Ministry of the Environment. www.airqualityontario.com/reports (accessed October 21, 2013).

World Health Statistics. 2013. http://www.who.int/gho/publications/world_health_statistics/EN_WHS2013_Full.pdf (accessed October 10, 2013).

SECTION EXERCISES

SECTION 14.1

TRY **14.1 Predicting Exam Marks (Example 1)** A statistics professor tells his students in a class—similar to this one—that he knows their final exam mark without students writing the final exam. He tells them that their final exam mark can be predicted from their going-into-the-final-exam mark, or term mark, with this equation:

$$PredictedFinalExamMark = 2.808 + 0.912(TermMark)$$

This tells us that the deterministic part of the model that predicts a student's final exam mark based on their term mark is linear. What factors might contribute to the random component? In other words, why might a student's final exam mark not be exactly what the professor's model predicts?

14.2 Used Car Values A student wishes to buy a used car. He finds a consumer website that says the price of a used car is determined by its age according to the following formula:

Predicted price in thousands of dollars $= 17 - 0.8$ (age in years)

This is the deterministic part of a population model for predicting the price of a used car as being linearly dependent on the car's age. What factors might contribute to the random component? In other words, why might the price of a car he buys not be exactly what is predicted by this model?

TRY **14.3 Used BMWs (Example 2)** Figure (a) shows a scatterplot of the price and age of a random sample of used BMW cars and includes the regression line. Figure (b) shows a residual plot based on the regression line.

   a. Is the linear model appropriate for these data? Explain.

   b. How old is the car that is farthest from the regression line?

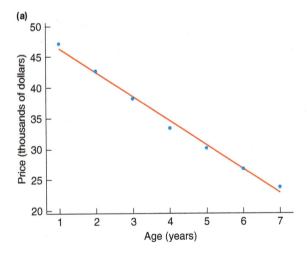

(a)

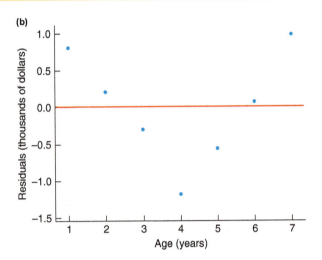

(b)

14.4 Pulse Rates Figure (a) shows a scatterplot with the regression line for pulse rates for a large number of students in a statistics class before and after running in place for two minutes. Figure (b) shows the residual plot of the data. Figure (c) shows a QQ plot of the residuals. Does a model that tries to predict the pulse rates *after* a run based on its linear dependence on the pulse rate *before* the run seem appropriate, based on these data? Why or why not? Assume that the observations are independently measured.

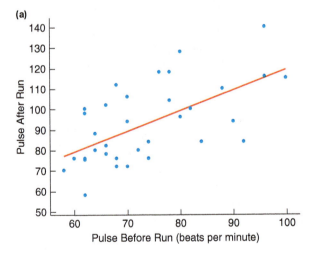

(a)

(b)

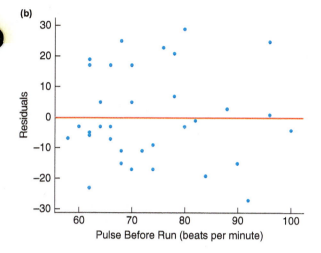

(a)

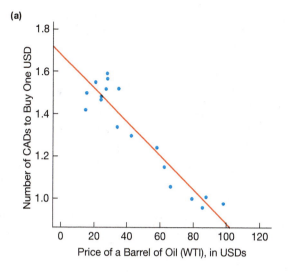

(c)

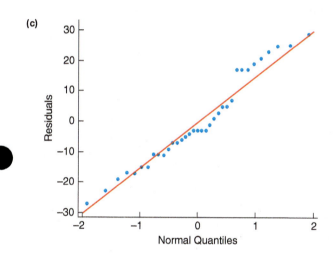

(b)

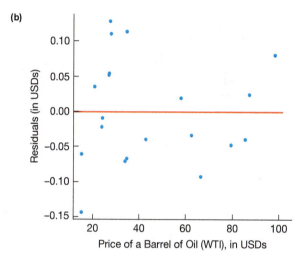

* **14.6 Canadian Population** Figure (a) shows a scatterplot for the Canadian population (in millions) from 1945 to 2015. Figure (b) shows a residual plot of the same data. Can you predict that the Canadian population will linearly depend on the year? Why or why not? (Source: www.statcan.gc.ca)

(a)

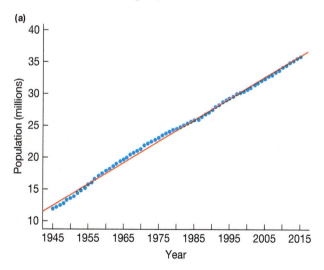

TRY **14.5 Value of the Canadian Dollar and the Price of Oil (Example 3)** Figure (a) shows a scatterplot of the price of a barrel of oil (West Texas Intermediate) and how many Canadian dollars it takes to buy one American dollar. Figure (b) shows a residual plot of the same data. Does a model that tries to predict how many CAD it takes to buy one USD based on its linear dependence on the price of oil seem appropriate, based on these data? Why or why not? Assume that the observations are independently measured.

(b)

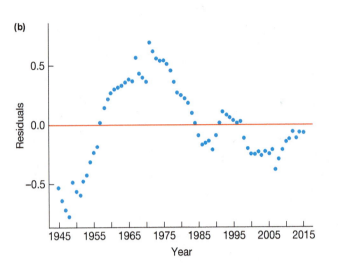

(c)

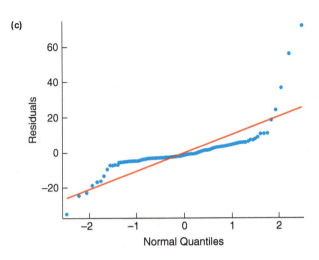

TRY 14.7 Wages of Twins (Example 4) Figure (a) shows a scatterplot of wages of twins (in dollars per hour) for a group of 183 pairs of twins. Figure (b) shows a residual plot of the same data. Figure (c) shows a QQ plot of these residuals. Is the linear regression model appropriate for these data? Why or why not? Assume that the observations are independently measured.

(a)

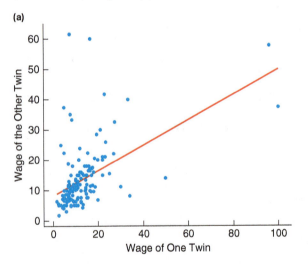

(b)

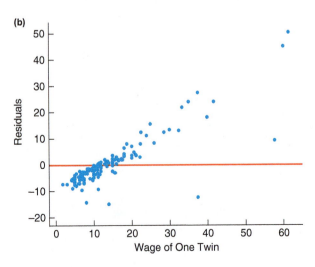

14.8 Simulated Data Figure (a) shows a scatterplot of some simulated data, and Figure (b) shows a residual plot of the same data. Is the linear regression model appropriate for these data? Why or why not? Assume that the observations are independently measured.

(a)

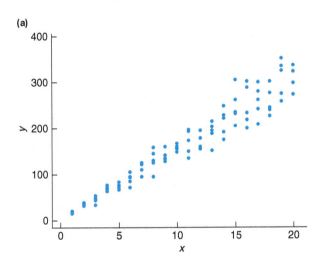

(b)

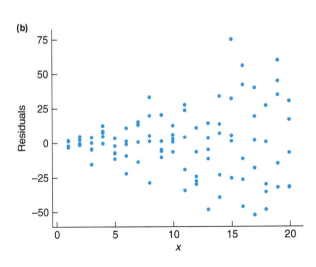

SECTION 14.2

14.9 Age and Weight (Example 5) Do older students tend to weigh more than younger students? Our data are ages and weights for a random sample of 76 students. A scatterplot (not shown here) shows that the relationship between age (years) and weight (pounds) is linear. Refer to the Minitab output given.

```
Regression Analysis: Weight versus Age
The regression equation is
Weight = 129 + 0.843 Age

76 cases used, 7 cases contain missing values

Predictor   Coef    SE Coef   T     P
Constant    129.10  15.19     8.50  0.000
Age         0.8429  0.5884    1.43  0.156

S = 37.5072   R-Sq = 2.7%   R-Sq(adj) = 1.4%
```

a. According to the equation for weight, do weights tend to be larger or smaller for older students than for younger students in this sample? Explain.

b. Use the Minitab output to test the hypothesis that the slope is zero in this population using a significance level of 0.05. Show all four steps of the hypothesis test, and explain your conclusion. Assume that all the required conditions are satisfied and that the sample is representative of the population of all students. The statistics for the test that the slope is 0 are in the row labelled "Age."

c. Consider the decision you made in part b. Would you expect the 95% confidence interval for the slope term to contain zero? Why or why not?

d. By hand, compute a 95% confidence interval for the slope term and interpret its meaning.

14.10 NHL Team Payroll and Regular Season Points

Does having a higher team payroll in the NHL result in a better team, and therefore a better regular-season performance? Data on the amount of money paid to a team's players and its regular-season points total were collected from the 2011–12 season. A scatterplot is shown below along with Minitab output. Assume independence.
(Source: *USA Today*. http://content.usatoday.com/sportsdata/hockey/nhl/salaries, accessed October 17, 2013)

a. As an NHL team pays its players more, what seems to happen to its regular-season points total? Use the scatterplot to explain your answer.

b. Use the Minitab output to test the hypothesis that an NHL team's regular-season points total linearly depends on how much the team pays all its players, using a significance level of 0.05. Assume that all the necessary conditions are satisfied.

c. Use the Minitab output to test the hypothesis that the y-intercept term of the population model is 0, using a significance level of 0.05.

d. Do you think that a 95% confidence interval for the slope will capture the value of zero? By hand, compute a 95% confidence interval for the slope term and interpret its meaning in the context of this data.

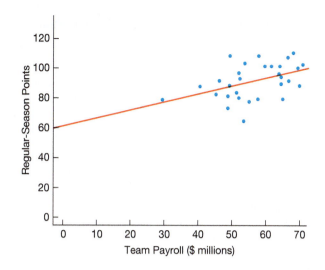

```
Regression Analysis: PTS versus Payroll

The regression equation is

PTS = 61.5 + 0.538 Payroll


Predictor   Coef    SE Coef   T      P

Constant    61.47   11.67     5.27   0.000

Payroll     0.5382  0.2031    2.65   0.013
```

14.11 Education of Parents (Example 6) Each of 29 randomly sampled university students reported the number of years of formal education completed by his or her mother and father. For example, a value of 12 means that the parent completed high school but had no further education. (The numbers ranged from 0 to 18.) The regression equation shown in the output is for predicting years of education for the father on the basis of years of education for the mother. Assume that all the required conditions for regression are fulfilled.

a. Identify the estimate of the y-intercept of this model. Explain what it would mean if this were 0.

b. Use the output given to test the hypothesis that the y-intercept is zero, showing all the steps. Use a level of significance of 0.05. The statistics for the test that the intercept is 0 can be found in the row labelled "Constant."

c. Using a significance level of 0.05, test the hypothesis that years of education for the father linearly depends on years of education for the mother. Assume that all the necessary conditions are satisfied.

d. By hand, compute a 95% confidence interval for the slope term and interpret its meaning in the context of these data.

```
Regression Analysis: FatherEd versus MotherEd

The regression equation is
FatherEd = 2.78 + 0.637 MotherEd

Predictor   Coef   SE Coef   T    P
Constant   2.785   1.396   2.00  0.056
MotherEd   0.6370  0.1483  4.30  0.000

S = 3.63005   R-Sq = 40.6%   R-Sq(adj) = 38.4
```

14.12 Education of Parents Refer to Exercise 14.11 and the output given.

a. What would it mean for the slope term of the model to be 1?

b. Test the hypothesis that the slope term of the model is 1 using a significance level of 0.05.

Use the table here to decide whether the p-value is less than 0.01, between 0.01 and 0.05, or more than 0.05 for part b. The df is 27.

alpha	0.05	0.01
tails	2	2
df		
26	2.056	2.779
27	2.052	2.771
28	2.048	2.763

* 14.13 A random sample of 50 first-year university students was taken from a population of all first-year students who had a part-time job while studying. The students were asked their grade point average (GPA) and how many hours they worked at their part-time job per week. The sample was taken after all students had completed their first term. The Minitab output of a regression analysis that predicts GPA as a linear function of the number of hours worked per week at the part-time job is shown. Assume that all the conditions needed are satisfied, and use a significance level of 0.05 for any tests.

a. What is the value of the y-intercept of the regression line? Interpret its meaning here.

b. What is the value of the slope of the regression line? Interpret its meaning here.

c. Test the hypothesis that the slope of the population model is 0 (significance level is 0.05), and explain what your answer means.

```
Regression Analysis: GPA versus HrsPTWork
The regression equation is
GPA = 3.32 - 0.0176 HrsPTWork

Predictor       Coef     SE Coef     T      P
Constant       3.3213    0.1286    25.82  0.000
HrsPTWork     -0.017630  0.009094  -1.94  0.058

S = 0.357702   R-Sq = 7.1%   R-Sq(adj) = 5.2%
```

14.14 Trash The weight of trash (in pounds) produced by a household and the number of people living in the household were obtained for 13 houses. Refer to the Minitab regression output. Assume that all the conditions necessary for regression analysis are met.

```
Regression Analysis: Trash versus People
The regression equation is
Trash = 2.34 + 11.3 People

Predictor   Coef   SE Coef   T     P
Constant   2.340   6.869   0.34  0.740
People    11.300   1.867   6.05  0.000

S = 11.8519   R-Sq = 76.9%   R-Sq(adj) = 74.8%
```

a. What is the value of the y-intercept?

b. What would it mean if the y-intercept were 0?

c. Test the hypothesis that the y-intercept is 0 using a significance level of 0.05.

TRY *** 14.15 Predicting Exam Marks (Example 7)** Exercise 14.1 gave the estimate of the population model that predicts a student's final exam mark based on its linear dependence on their term mark. The StatCrunch output of a regression analysis is based on a random sample of 211 students. Assume that all the necessary conditions hold.

a. According to the regression line, what's the mean final exam mark of a student who has a term mark of 0%?

b. Give the estimate of the slope of the population model. Think about, but do not write down, the interpretation of its meaning in the context of these data.

c. State the 95% confidence interval for the slope. Interpret its meaning.

d. A student who has not done well in the course claims that he's going to "ace the final," reasoning that there is "no relationship" between how students do on the final and how they did in the course. Given what you know about these data, what would you advise this student? Use your finding in part c.

Options	(1 of 2)

Simple linear regression results:
Dependent Variable: Final Exam (%)
Independent Variable: Current Term Mark (without fina
Final Exam (%) = 2.8081699 + 0.91204966 Current Term Mark (without fina
Sample size: 211
R (correlation coefficient) = 0.74519098
R-sq = 0.5553096
Estimate of error standard deviation: 10.880612

Parameter estimates:

Parameter	Estimate	Std. Err.	DF	95% L. Limit	95% U. Limit
Intercept	2.8081699	4.0326599	209	-5.1417329	10.758073
Slope	0.91204966	0.056455549	209	0.80075435	1.023345

TRY **14.16 Home Price and Inventory (Example 8)** The output shows the results of a regression analysis that tried to predict the median monthly selling price of a home in a large Canadian city (in $1000s) on the basis of the number of homes for sale in the same month. This is based on a random sample of 30 months of real estate activity in this city. Assume that all conditions necessary are satisfied.

    a. According to the supply-and-demand theory, as the number of homes for sale increases, homes prices will fall, and therefore the median price of homes sold in the month will fall. If this were true, would the slope of a population model that predicts the median selling price of a home in a month as linearly dependent on the number of homes for sale be positive, negative, or 0?

    b. From the output, state the 95% confidence interval for the slope and interpret its meaning in the context of the data.

    c. Consider the slope value of 0.02. Interpret the meaning of this slope value in the context of the data.

    d. Using a significance level of 0.05, test the hypothesis that the slope of the population model that predicts the median selling price of a home in a month to be linearly dependent on the number of homes for sale is 0.02.

Options   (1 of 2)

Simple linear regression results:
Dependent Variable: MedianPrice
Independent Variable: Inventory
MedianPrice = 286.0614 + 0.024791684 Inventory
Sample size: 30
R (correlation coefficient) = 0.58160113
R-sq = 0.33825987
Estimate of error standard deviation: 49.26176

Parameter estimates:

Parameter	Estimate	Std. Err.	DF	95% L. Limit	95% U. Limit
Intercept	286.0614	25.940232	28	232.92524	339.19755
Slope	0.024791684	0.0065530807	28	0.011368307	0.038215062

Regression Analysis: Median(1000s) versus Inventory
The regression equation is
MedianSample(1000s) = 286 + 0.0248 InventorySample

Predictor	Coef	SE Coef	T	P
Constant	286.06	25.94	11.03	0.000
InventorySample	0.024792	0.006553	3.78	0.001

S = 49.2618   R-Sq = 33.8%   R-Sq(adj) = 31.5%

14.17 Trash and Confidence Intervals The output provided for Exercise 14.14 provides a regression line to predict the amount of trash produced by a household on the basis of the number of people living in the household. Suppose you found a 95% confidence interval for the y-intercept of the regression line. Would that confidence interval include 0? (Refer to the output in Exercise 14.14.)

14.18 NHL Team Payroll and Regular-Season Points In Exercise 14.10, you examined the linear relationship between an NHL hockey team's regular-season points total and its team payroll (in $ millions). Would a 95% confidence interval for the slope, based on the same data, include 0? Explain.

SECTION 14.3

TRY **14.19 Predicting GPA (Example 9)** A student has been accepted by two universities and wants to estimate what GPA she might get at each of the two schools. Fortunately, she has data on recent graduates from each school. Specifically, the data consist of their GPAs and the average of their Grade 12 marks. She aims to take these data to build a population model that will predict her GPA at each school, based on the average of her Grade 12 marks. Should she use a confidence interval or a prediction interval for the prediction of her own GPA? Explain.

14.20 Used BMWs A used-car dealer is purchasing 50 used BMWs from one dealer in order to sell them for a profit. Working with collected data, the dealer has found a regression model to predict the selling price on the basis of the car's age. He wants to predict the total amount he will get for these 50 cars in order to make sure he does not lose money. All 50 cars are three years old (they were turned in after their leases expired). Should he use a confidence interval or a prediction interval for the mean selling price of these 50 cars? Explain.

14.21 Loggers A logging company has the diameter of each of a large number of trees and wants to estimate the mean value of usable cubic metres of wood the company will get if it cuts the trees down. Working with a sample of trees, company planners find the regression line that predicts the volume of lumber (in cubic metres) on the basis of the diameter of the tree. Should they use a prediction interval or a confidence interval? Explain.

14.22 Regular-Season Points—How Much? Exercise 14.10 used regression to estimate the population model that allows you to predict how many regular-season points an NHL team will get as a linear function of the team's payroll (in $ millions). Suppose that at the start of an NHL season you search the internet for the payroll of your favourite NHL team in order to predict its regular-season points total. Would you use a prediction interval or a confidence interval to predict this value? Explain.

TRY **14.23 House Prices (Example 10)** Figure (a) contains the selling price (in dollars) and floor area (in square feet) of 81 recently sold homes in a region where a buyer wants to purchase a home.

    a. Use the equation to predict the price of a home with 2500 square feet.

(a)

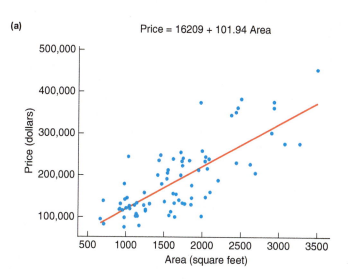

Price = 16209 + 101.94 Area

(b)

```
Predicted Values for New Observations

New
Obs   Fit SE Fit      95% CI            95% PI
  1 271056  10085 (250975, 291138) (160581, 381532)


Values of Predictors for New Observations

New
Obs   Area
  1   2500
```

b. The buyer wants to know the uncertainty in the prices he might pay for a home with 2500 square feet in this region. Should he use a prediction interval or a confidence interval? Explain.

c. Report the correct 95% interval, confidence or prediction as determined in part b, for the predicted price. See Figure (b).

d. The buyer has prequalified for a loan up to $400,000. Is he likely to be able to afford a house in this area with 2500 square feet?

14.24 Figure (a) contains the price and the percentage of pages that are full-page advertisements for a random sample of eight magazines chosen by one of the authors.

(a)

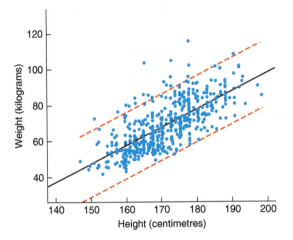

Price = 9.40 − 0.072 Per Ads

a. Use the provided regression line to predict the price of a magazine that has 55% of its pages devoted to full-page advertisements.

b. You want to know the uncertainty in the answer you obtained in part a. Should you use a prediction interval or a confidence interval? Explain.

c. Report the correct 95% interval, confidence or prediction as determined in part b, for the predicted price of the magazine. See Figure (b).

d. Suppose you have a stack of magazines, with each one having 40% of its pages devoted to full-page advertisements. You want to predict the average price paid for all these magazines. Should you use a prediction interval or a confidence interval? Select and report the interval, interpreting its meaning. See Figure (c).

(b)

```
Predicted Values for New Observations

New Obs    Fit  SE Fit      95% CI         95% PI
     1   5.428   0.310  (4.670, 6.186)  (3.367, 7.488)

Values of Predictors for New Observations
New Obs  PercentageOfPagesAds
     1              55.0
```

(c)

```
Predicted Values for New Observations

New Obs    Fit  SE Fit      95% CI         95% PI
     1   6.508   0.314  (5.740, 7.277)  (4.444, 8.573)

Values of Predictors for New Observations
New Obs  PercentageOfPagesAds
     1              40.0
```

14.25 Height and Weight A scatterplot of the heights and weights of 507 people is shown below, along with the regression line that predicts a person's height as being linearly dependent on a person's weight. This scatterplot also shows the 95% prediction intervals. Using the graph, estimate the lower and upper bounds resulting from predicting the weight of someone who is 175 centimetres tall.

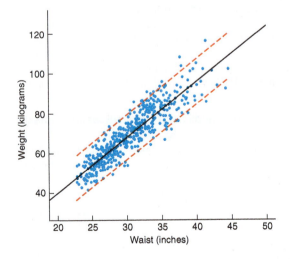

14.26 Waist Size and Weight The scatterplot below shows the waist sizes (in inches) and weights of the same 507 people mentioned in Exercise 14.25, along with the regression line that predicts a person's weight as being linearly dependent on their waist size. This scatterplot also shows the 95% prediction intervals. Using the graph, estimate the lower and upper bounds resulting from predicting the weight of someone who has a waist size of 32 inches.

14.27 Height and Weight The accompanying scatterplot shows two sets of intervals for the 507 people in Exercise 14.25. For a given height, one is the prediction interval and the other is a confidence interval. Which is which? Explain how you can tell.

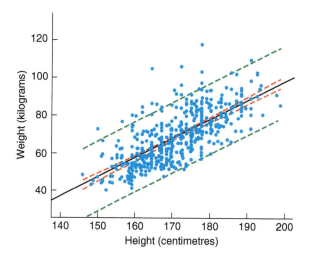

14.28 Waist Size and Weight The accompanying scatterplot shows two sets of intervals for the 507 people in Exercise 14.26. For a given waist size, one is the prediction interval and the other a confidence interval. Which is which? Explain how you can tell.

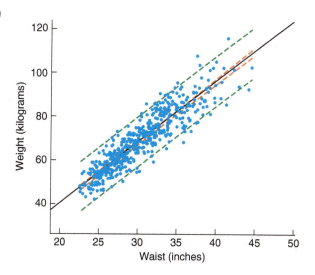

14.29 NHL Team Payroll and Regular-Season Points

Figure (a) shows a scatterplot with the estimate of the population model that predicts the regular-season points of an NHL team based on its payroll (in $ millions). Figure (b) gives a prediction (Fit), a prediction interval, and a confidence interval for the regular-season points for a given team payroll of $x = 65$ million.

a. Identify which interval is which and explain why one of the intervals is wider than the other.

b. Interpret the confidence interval in the context of the data.

c. Interpret the prediction interval in the context of the data.

(a)

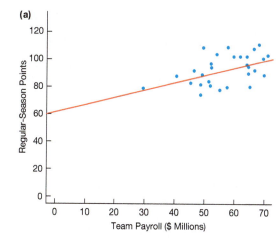

(b)

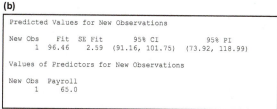

```
Predicted Values for New Observations

New Obs    Fit   SE Fit      95% CI          95% PI
   1     96.46   2.59   (91.16, 101.75)  (73.92, 118.99)

Values of Predictors for New Observations

New Obs  Payroll
   1       65.0
```

14.30 Predicting Education Figure (a) shows a scatterplot with the regression line for predicting the father's education from the mother's education for a random sample of 29 students. Figure (b) shows the confidence interval and the prediction interval for the father for a new observation when the mother has 10 years of education.

(a)

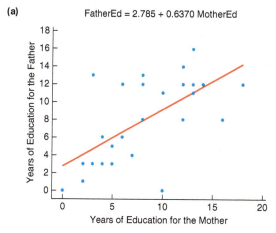

$$\text{FatherEd} = 2.785 + 0.6370\ \text{MotherEd}$$

(b)

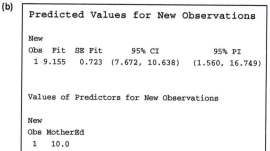

```
Predicted Values for New Observations

New
Obs  Fit  SE Fit      95% CI          95% PI
 1  9.155  0.723  (7.672, 10.638)  (1.560, 16.749)


Values of Predictors for New Observations

New
Obs MotherEd
 1   10.0
```

a. Identify which interval is which. Explain what they show and why one interval is wider than the other.

b. Interpret the confidence interval.

c. Interpret the prediction interval.

CHAPTER REVIEW EXERCISES

* 14.31 Life Expectancy and Gestation Periods for Animals

Data were collected showing the gestation period (in days) and the average longevity (in years) for 32 animals. Assume that all conditions of the linear regression model hold. This set of data can be found in Exercise 2.28 on page 63.

a. Make a scatterplot with gestation period as the x-variable and longevity as the y-variable, and insert the correct regression line. Report the regression equation.

b. One animal lives much longer than we would expect, given its gestation period. Identify this animal.

c. From the data, find a confidence interval for the mean longevity of animals with a gestation period of 266 days.

d. Humans have a gestation period of about 266 days. Does the confidence interval for the average life span for humans seem to fit what you know about humans' life spans? Explain.

* 14.32 Predicting Exam Marks
Exercise 14.1 gave the estimate of the population model that predicts a student's final exam mark based on its linear dependence on their term mark, in an introductory statistics course similar to this one. The StatCrunch output provided is based on a regression analysis of 211 students. Assume that all the conditions of the linear regression model hold.

a. Write the estimate of the population model that predicts a student's final exam mark as being linearly dependent on their term mark.

b. From these data, can you conclude that a student's final exam mark is linearly dependent on their term mark? Use a significance level of 5%.

c. Using the output in Figure (b), provide a 95% confidence interval for the slope term of the population model. Interpret its meaning in the context of the data.

d. Using a 95% confidence interval, what is the mean final exam mark of all students who have a term mark of 75%?

e. Using a 95% confidence interval, what is the final exam mark of a student who has a term mark of 75%?

(a)

Options (1 of 2)

Simple linear regression results:
Dependent Variable: FinalExamMark
Independent Variable: TermMark
FinalExamMark = 2.8081699 + 0.91204966 TermMark
Sample size: 211
R (correlation coefficient) = 0.74519098
R-sq = 0.5553096
Estimate of error standard deviation: 10.880612

Parameter estimates:

Parameter	Estimate	Std. Err.	Alternative	DF	T-Stat	P-Value
Intercept	2.8081699	4.0326599	≠ 0	209	0.69635674	0.487
Slope	0.91204966	0.056455549	≠ 0	209	16.155182	<0.0001

Analysis of variance table for regression model:

Source	DF	SS	MS	F-stat	P-value
Model	1	30897.999	30897.999	260.9899	<0.0001
Error	209	24743.033	118.38772		
Total	210	55641.033			

Predicted values:

X value	Pred. Y	s.e.(Pred. y)	95% C.I. for mean	95% P.I. for new
75	71.211895	0.79680068	(69.641098, 72.782691)	(49.704641, 92.719148)

(b)

Parameter estimates:

Parameter	Estimate	Std. Err.	DF	95% L. Limit	95% U. Limit
Intercept	2.8081699	4.0326599	209	-5.1417329	10.758073
Slope	0.91204966	0.056455549	209	0.80075435	1.023345

* 14.33 Is an Athlete Using Performance Enhancing Drugs?

Barry Bonds was a professional baseball player and currently holds the record for most home runs in a season. During the 2001 regular season Bonds hit 73 home runs, beating the previous record of 70, which was held by Mark McGwire, who admitted after his retirement that he used performance enhancing drugs (PEDs). Barry Bonds has been accused of using PEDs. But what do the data say?

Below is a chart listing his season playing major league baseball and his home run to at-bat ratio. The latter is used because as Bonds started to hit more and more home runs, pitchers would intentionally walk him. An intentional walk is not counted as an "at bat."

Bonds's Season	Home Run to At-Bat Ratio
1	0.0454
2	0.0446
3	0.0328
4	0.0654
5	0.0490
6	0.0719
7	0.0853
8	0.0946
9	0.0652
10	0.0812
11	0.0752
12	0.0670
13	0.0957
14*	0.1021
15**	0.1534*

The double asterisk marking his 15th season signals that he hit 73 home runs that season. His alleged PED usage was brought up in his 14th season (marked by the single asterisk). Treat Bonds's season—how many seasons he is into his major league baseball career—as the predictor variable x and the home run to at-bat ratio as the response variable y.

a. Using statistical software, make a scatterplot of these data up to and including season 14; do not include season 15. Also, estimate the population model that will predict Bonds's home run to at-bat ratio based on its linear dependence on the number of seasons he has played.

b. Assume that all the conditions of the model hold. Can you predict Bonds's home run to at-bat ratio based on its linear dependence on how many seasons he has played? Test using a significance level of 0.05.

c. From your software output, find a 95% confidence interval for the slope of the linear model you estimated in part a. Interpret its meaning in the context of the data.

d. The 2001 season was Barry Bonds's 15th, or $x = 15$. Find a 95% prediction interval for his home run to at-bat ratio in 2001. Interpret the meaning of this interval.

e. During the 2001 season, Barry Bonds had 476 at bats. Multiply the lower and upper bounds of the interval found in part d by 476. What does this new interval give?

f. Compare the observed number of home runs in 2001, 73, with how many you would have predicted with 95% confidence. What is your conclusion about Bonds's PED usage? Explain.

General Instructions for All Technology

The basic steps for estimating the linear population model that will express the response variable y as a function of the predictor variable x and making a scatterplot were shown in Chapter 4.

🌐 Example

The table shows years of education and annual income (in $1000s) for a random sample of eight people. Note that 16 years means that a person has completed Grade 12 and four years of post-secondary education.

YearsEdu	Income
11	63.0
6	54.2
7	24.2
17	92.3
11	34.2
13	79.1
16	67.8
16	91.0

TI-83/84

The only confidence interval available for regression is for the slope, and it is available only on the TI-84. To find it, press **STAT**, choose **TESTS**, and choose **LinRegTint**. For the slope of the eight years of education and incomes given in the example, the 95% confidence interval comes out to be (1.1774, 9.9765).

Residual Plot

1. Press **STAT** and choose **EDIT** and enter years of education in **L1** and incomes in **L2**.
2. Press **STAT** and choose **CALC, 8: LinReg (a + bx)**.
3. Press **2ND L1 ، 2ND L2 ENTER**. Remember that the predictor—here, it's years of education—must go in before the response and that the comma must be entered (it's the button above the 7 button on the keypad). You will see the numbers for the regression equation.
4. Now, to create the residual plot, use Plot2 (assuming that you might have used Plot1 for the scatterplot). Choose **2ND STATPLOT**, and turn **Plot1 Off**. Choose **2ND STATPLOT**, **Plot2, On, Type:** scatterplot (first choice, in the upper left corner), **Xlist: L1, Ylist: RESID**. (Do this by pressing **2ND LIST, RESID**. You might have to scroll down to see **RESID**.)
5. To make the graph, press **ZOOM** and **9**.
6. Press **Trace** to see the numbers, and use the arrows on the keypad to move to other points.
7. Figure 14A shows a residual plot of the six points.

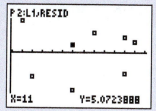

▲ **FIGURE 14A** TI-83/84 residual plot.

Hypothesis Test

With the data set, you can test the hypothesis that the population slope, β is 0. This is equivalent to testing that the population correlation, ρ is 0. (See β and ρ in Figure 14B.)

▲ **FIGURE 14B** TI-83/84 input for a regression test.

1. Press **STAT**, choose **EDIT**, and enter the years of education into **L1** and the incomes into **L2**.
2. Press **STAT**, choose **TESTS**, and choose **LinRegTTest**.
3. See Figure 14B. Be sure the predictor (**L1** in our example) is the **XList** and that the response (**L2** in our example) is the **YList**. Here we are testing the hypothesis that the slope is greater than 0. You can use $\neq$ if you want a two-tailed hypothesis.
4. Scroll down to **Calculate** and press **ENTER**.

Figure 14C shows the output.

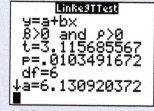

▲ **FIGURE 14C** TI/84 output for a regression test.

MINITAB

Residual Plot

1. Enter the years of education and annual income into columns **C1** and **C2**. Add the labels **YearsEdu** and **Income** in the label area above the data.
2. **Stat > Regression > Fitted Line Plot**
3. Be sure to put the dependent variable (here, **YearsEdu**) in the **Response (Y)** box and the independent variable (here, **Income**) in the **Predictor (X)** box.
4. Click **Graphs.**
5. See Figure 14D. In the **Fitted Line Plot – Graphs** leave the default **Regular**, and in the **Residuals versus the variables** box put the independent variable, here **YearsEdu**. Click **OK** and **OK** again.

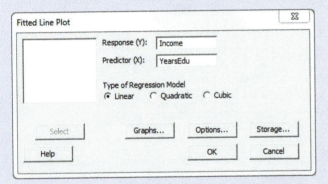

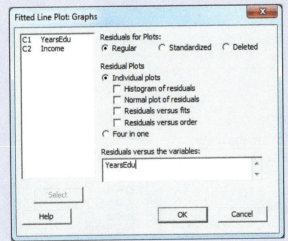

▲ **FIGURE 14D** Minitab input for a residual plot.

You will get a scatterplot with the regression line and also a residual plot like Figure 14E. You may have to click **Window** and **3** or **4** below **Window** to see the other graph.

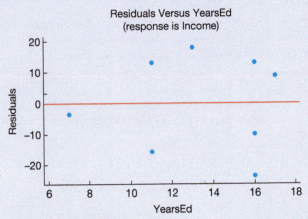

▲ **FIGURE 14E** Minitab residual plot.

A Scatterplot with the Regression Line with Prediction and Confidence Intervals

1. The years of education should be in column **C1** and the incomes in column **C2**, with the labels **YearsEdu** and **Income** at the top.
2. **Stat > Regression > Fitted Line Plot**
3. After entering the **Response** (**Income**) and the **Predictor** (**YearsEdu**), click **Options**.
4. Click **Display confidence intervals** or **Display prediction intervals**, or both, as we have shown in Figure 14F. Click **OK**, and click **OK** again for the next screen. You may have to click **Window** and select an option below **Window** to see it.

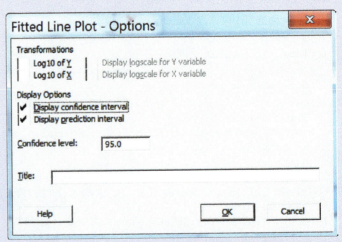

▲ **FIGURE 14F** Minitab input for prediction and confidence intervals.

Figure 14G shows the result.

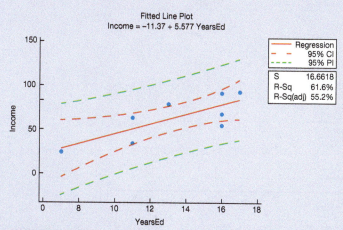

▲ FIGURE 14G Minitab prediction and confidence intervals.

Regression Summary and Numerical Confidence and Prediction Intervals

1. Your data should be in columns **C1** and **C1**, labelled **YearsEd** and **Income**.

2. **Stat > Regression > Regression**

3. In the **Response** box put Y, here **Income**. In the **Predictors** box put X, here **YearsEd**.

4. Click **Options**. In the box below **Prediction intervals for new observation**, enter the years of education for a new person; here we used 16 years.

5. Click **OK** and **OK** again.

The output is shown in Figure 14H and includes the prediction and confidence intervals at the bottom. These are for prediction of

ranges with 95% confidence from a new person's income who has 16 years of education. The output in Figure 14H can also be used to decide whether the null hypothesis that the slope is 0 can be rejected. Because the p-value is 0.021, you can reject the hypothesis that the slope is 0. This output can also be used to test whether the intercept is 0; because the p-value is 0.662, you fail to reject the hypothesis that the intercept is 0.

```
The regression equation is
Income = - 11.4 + 5.58 YearsEd

Predictor     Coef   SECoef      T      P
Constant    -11.37    24.76  -0.46  0.662
YearsEd       5.577    1.798   3.10  0.021

S = 16.6618   R-Sq = 61.6%   R-Sq(adj) = 55.2%

Analysis of Variance

Source          DF      SS      MS      F      P
Regression       1  2671.0  2671.0   9.62  0.021
Residual Error   6  1665.7   277.6
Total            7  4336.7


Predicted Values for New Observations

New ObsFit   SE Fit      95% CI            95% PI
1   77.86     7.55   (59.39, 96.33)  (33.11, 122.62)

Values of Predictors for New Observations

New ObsYearsEd
    1      16.0
```

▲ FIGURE 14H Minitab output for regression, including intervals.

Minitab does not supply output reporting confidence intervals for the slope or intercept.

EXCEL

Excel can give regression output and residual plots simultaneously.

1. Enter the years of education into column **A** and the incomes into column **B**.

2. Click **Data**, click **Data Analysis**, and double click **Regression**.

3. See Figure 14I. For **Input Y Range**, highlight the data for the incomes (without the label Income), and for **Input X Range**, highlight the data for the years of education (without the label YearsEd); then click **Residual Plots** and **OK**.

In a new spreadsheet, you will get numerical output like that shown in Figure 14J and a residual plot like that shown in Figure 14K. To see the numerical output, you may have to click **Home**, **Format** (in the **Cells** group), and **AutoFit Column Width**. Note in Figure 14J that confidence intervals are given for the intercept (−71.9509, 49.2161) and for the slope (1.1775, 9.9765). These can be used to test hypotheses about the slope and intercept.

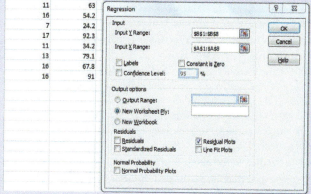

▲ FIGURE 14I Excel input for regression and residual plots.

SUMMARY OUTPUT

Regression Statistics	
Multiple R	0.784795847
R Square	0.615904521
Adjusted R Square	0.551888608
Standard Error	16.66178051
Observations	8

ANOVA

	df	SS	MS	F	Significance F
Regression	1	2670.965422	2670.965	9.621116	0.021068231
Residual	6	1665.689578	277.6149		
Total	7	4336.655			

	Coefficients	Standard Error	t Stat	P-value	Lower 95%	Upper 95%	Lower 95.0%	Upper 95.0%
Intercept	-11.3673945	24.7591557	-0.45912	0.662312	-71.95086585	49.21607691	-71.95086585	49.21607691
X Variable 1	5.577001456	1.797993155	3.101792	0.021068	1.177470705	9.976532206	1.177470705	9.976532206

▲ FIGURE 14J Excel regression output.

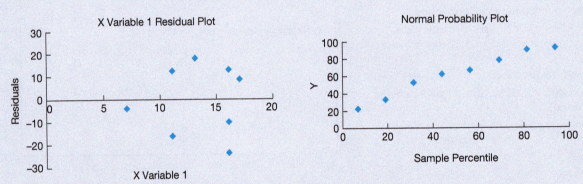

▲ FIGURE 14K Excel residual plot.

1. Enter the years of education into **var1** and the incomes into **var2**. Label var1 as **YearsEd** and var2 as **Income**.
2. **Stat > Regression > Simple Linear**
3. For the **X-Variable**, pick **YearsEd** from the drop-down list. Pick **Income** for the **Y-Variable**.
4. Click **Confidence Intervals**, leaving the default level at 0.95. This instructs StatCrunch to compute 95% confidence intervals for both the y-intercept and the slope term of the population model. If you choose **Hypothesis tests**, StatCrunch will provide the output for hypothesis tests with a y-intercept of 0 and slope of 0.
5. Click **Predict Y for X=**, and type in **16.**
6. You may now click on **Fitting line plot** or **Residuals vs. X-values,** then **Compute!** You may have to drag the left edge of the output window to the left as the output may not be completely visible. The output is shown in Figure 14L and the residual plot in Figure 14M. Note that the confidence intervals for the y-intercept and slope terms are given, as well as a confidence interval for the mean income of all people having 16 years of education: **95% C.I. for mean**, and a prediction interval containing the income of a person having 16 years of education: **95% P.I. for new**.

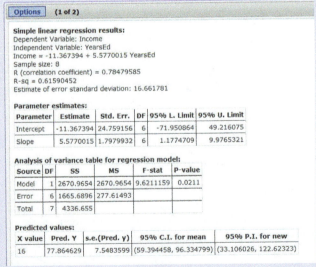

▲ FIGURE 14L StatCrunch regression output.

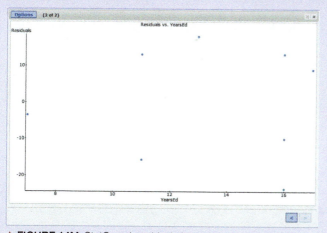

▲ **FIGURE 14M** StatCrunch residual plot.

SPSS

1. Enter the years of education into the first column **var00001** and the incomes into the second column **var00002**. Click the Variable View tab at the bottom, and type **YearsEd** in the first-row and first-column cell, and **Income** in the first-column and second-row cell. Under the Decimals column, enter 0 for **YearsEd** and leave as 2 for **Income**. Select **Data View**.

2. **Analyze > Regression > Linear**

3. With the arrow, transfer **Income** into the **Dependent** field; move **YearsEd** into the **Independent(s)** field. To obtain a residual plot, click **Plots**. Transfer ***ZRESID** into the **Y-field** and ***ZPRED** into the **X-field**, as shown in Figure 14N. Click **Continue**. (Note: This residual plot standardized the residual terms and the values of the y-variable, but the form of the residual plot will be the same as if the residuals were on the y-axis and YearsEd on the x-axis.)

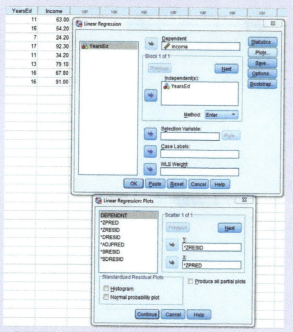

▲ **FIGURE 14N** SPSS input for regression output.

4. Select **Statistics . . .** Check the boxes beside **Estimates** and **Confidence intervals**. Leave the **Level (%)** at 95. This instructs SPSS to create confidence intervals for the y-intercept and slope of the population model. Select **Continue**. Press **OK**.

5. Select **Save . . .** In the Residuals portion on the top right-hand side, check the box next to **Unstandardized**. Select the boxes next to **Mean** and **Prediction** in the Prediction Intervals portion. See Figure 14O. Now select **Continue**, then **OK**.

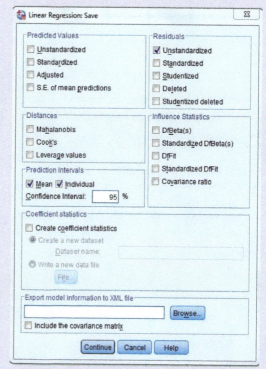

▲ **FIGURE 14O** SPSS input for confidence and prediction intervals.

6. The relevant SPSS output is in Figure 14P, along with the residual plot in Figure 14Q.

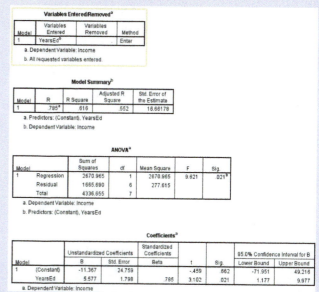

▲ **FIGURE 14P** Partial SPSS regression output.

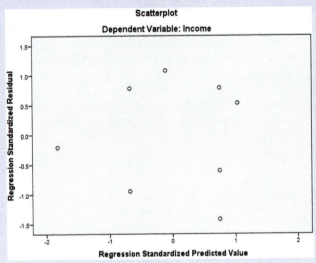

▲ FIGURE 14Q SPSS residual plot.

Confidence and Prediction Intervals

Refer to the Data View shown in Figure 14R. Column 3 contains the residuals; columns 4 and 5 provide the lower and upper limits of the confidence interval for the mean Income value for a given value

in the YearsEd column and the value in the row; and columns 6 and 7 provide the prediction intervals for the Income value for a given value in YearsEd column and the value in the row. A 95% confidence interval for the mean income of all people having 16 years of education has a lower bound of **59.3944** and an upper bound of **96.3348**. A 95% prediction interval has a lower bound of **33.1060** and an upper bound of **122.6232**. See Figure 14R.

YearsEd	Income	RES_1	LMCI_1	UMCI_1	LICI_1	UICI_1
11	63.00	13.02038	32.17646	67.78278	5.49212	94.46712
16	54.20	-23.66463	59.39446	96.33480	33.10602	122.62323
7	24.20	-3.47162	-3.86262	59.20585	-23.87053	79.21377
17	92.30	8.85837	61.94462	104.93864	37.35143	129.53163
11	34.20	-15.77962	32.17646	67.78278	5.49212	94.46712
13	79.10	17.96638	46.62518	75.64207	17.85915	104.40810
16	67.80	-10.06463	59.39446	96.33480	33.10602	122.62323
16	91.00	13.13537	59.39446	96.33480	33.10602	122.62323

▲ FIGURE 14R SPSS output showing confidence and prediction intervals for a given predictor variable value.

Note: SPSS does not supply confidence intervals and prediction intervals for any *x*-value that is not in the data.

Appendix A: Tables

Table 1: Random Numbers

Line						
01	21033	32522	19305	90633	80873	19167
02	17516	69328	88389	19770	33197	27336
03	26427	40650	70251	84413	30896	21490
04	45506	44716	02498	15327	79149	28409
05	55185	74834	81172	89281	48134	71185
06	87964	43751	80971	50613	81441	30505
07	09106	73117	57952	04393	93402	50753
08	88797	07440	69213	33593	42134	24168
09	34685	46775	32139	22787	28783	39481
10	07104	43091	14311	69671	01536	02673
11	27583	01866	58250	38103	35825	94513
12	60801	04439	58621	09840	35119	60372
13	62708	04888	37221	49537	96024	24004
14	21169	14082	65865	29690	00280	35738
15	13893	00626	11773	14897	37119	29729
16	19872	41310	65041	61105	31028	80297
17	29331	36997	05601	09785	18100	44164
18	76846	74048	08496	22599	29379	11114
19	11848	80809	25818	38857	23811	80902
20	85757	33963	93076	39950	29658	07530
21	71141	00618	48403	46083	40368	33990
22	47371	36443	41894	62134	86876	18548
23	46633	10669	95848	69055	49044	75595
24	79118	21098	63279	26834	43443	38267
25	91874	87217	11503	47925	13289	42106
26	85337	08882	68429	61767	18930	37688
27	88513	05437	22776	17562	03820	44785
28	31498	85304	22393	21634	34560	77404
29	93074	27086	62559	86590	18420	33290
30	90549	53094	76282	53105	45531	90061
31	11373	96871	38157	98368	39536	08079
32	52022	59093	30647	33241	16027	70336
33	14709	93220	89547	95320	39134	07646
34	57584	28114	91168	16320	81609	60807
35	31867	85872	91430	45554	21567	15082
36	07033	75250	34546	75298	33893	64487
37	02779	72645	32699	86009	73729	44206
38	24512	01116	49826	50882	44086	87757
39	52463	30164	80073	55917	60995	38655
40	82588	59267	13570	56434	66413	99518
41	20999	05039	87835	63010	82980	66193
42	09084	98948	09541	80623	15915	71042

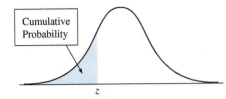

Cumulative Probability

Cumulative probability for z is the area under the standard normal curve to the left of z.

Table 2: Standard Normal Cumulative Probabilities

z	.00
−5.0	.000000287
−4.5	.00000340
−4.0	.0000317
−3.5	.000233

z	.00	.01	.02	.03	.04	.05	.06	.07	.08	.09
−3.4	.0003	.0003	.0003	.0003	.0003	.0003	.0003	.0003	.0003	.0002
−3.3	.0005	.0005	.0005	.0004	.0004	.0004	.0004	.0004	.0004	.0003
−3.2	.0007	.0007	.0006	.0006	.0006	.0006	.0006	.0005	.0005	.0005
−3.1	.0010	.0009	.0009	.0009	.0008	.0008	.0008	.0008	.0007	.0007
−3.0	.0013	.0013	.0013	.0012	.0012	.0011	.0011	.0011	.0010	.0010
−2.9	.0019	.0018	.0018	.0017	.0016	.0016	.0015	.0015	.0014	.0014
−2.8	.0026	.0025	.0024	.0023	.0023	.0022	.0021	.0021	.0020	.0019
−2.7	.0035	.0034	.0033	.0032	.0031	.0030	.0029	.0028	.0027	.0026
−2.6	.0047	.0045	.0044	.0043	.0041	.0040	.0039	.0038	.0037	.0036
−2.5	.0062	.0060	.0059	.0057	.0055	.0054	.0052	.0051	.0049	.0048
−2.4	.0082	.0080	.0078	.0075	.0073	.0071	.0069	.0068	.0066	.0064
−2.3	.0107	.0104	.0102	.0099	.0096	.0094	.0091	.0089	.0087	.0084
−2.2	.0139	.0136	.0132	.0129	.0125	.0122	.0119	.0116	.0113	.0110
−2.1	.0179	.0174	.0170	.0166	.0162	.0158	.0154	.0150	.0146	.0143
−2.0	.0228	.0222	.0217	.0212	.0207	.0202	.0197	.0192	.0188	.0183
−1.9	.0287	.0281	.0274	.0268	.0262	.0256	.0250	.0244	.0239	.0233
−1.8	.0359	.0351	.0344	.0336	.0329	.0322	.0314	.0307	.0301	.0294
−1.7	.0446	.0436	.0427	.0418	.0409	.0401	.0392	.0384	.0375	.0367
−1.6	.0548	.0537	.0526	.0516	.0505	.0495	.0485	.0475	.0465	.0455
−1.5	.0668	.0655	.0643	.0630	.0618	.0606	.0594	.0582	.0571	.0559
−1.4	.0808	.0793	.0778	.0764	.0749	.0735	.0721	.0708	.0694	.0681
−1.3	.0968	.0951	.0934	.0918	.0901	.0885	.0869	.0853	.0838	.0823
−1.2	.1151	.1131	.1112	.1093	.1075	.1056	.1038	.1020	.1003	.0985
−1.1	.1357	.1335	.1314	.1292	.1271	.1251	.1230	.1210	.1190	.1170
−1.0	.1587	.1562	.1539	.1515	.1492	.1469	.1446	.1423	.1401	.1379
−0.9	.1841	.1814	.1788	.1762	.1736	.1711	.1685	.1660	.1635	.1611
−0.8	.2119	.2090	.2061	.2033	.2005	.1977	.1949	.1922	.1894	.1867
−0.7	.2420	.2389	.2358	.2327	.2296	.2266	.2236	.2206	.2177	.2148
−0.6	.2743	.2709	.2676	.2643	.2611	.2578	.2546	.2514	.2483	.2451
−0.5	.3085	.3050	.3015	.2981	.2946	.2912	.2877	.2843	.2810	.2776
−0.4	.3446	.3409	.3372	.3336	.3300	.3264	.3228	.3192	.3156	.3121
−0.3	.3821	.3783	.3745	.3707	.3669	.3632	.3594	.3557	.3520	.3483
−0.2	.4207	.4168	.4129	.4090	.4052	.4013	.3974	.3936	.3897	.3859
−0.1	.4602	.4562	.4522	.4483	.4443	.4404	.4364	.4325	.4286	.4247
−0.0	.5000	.4960	.4920	.4880	.4840	.4801	.4761	.4721	.4681	.4641

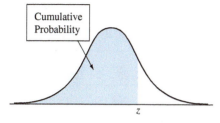

Cumulative probability for z is the area under the standard normal curve to the left of z.

Table 2: Standard Normal Cumulative Probabilities (*continued*)

z	.00	.01	.02	.03	.04	.05	.06	.07	.08	.09
0.0	.5000	.5040	.5080	.5120	.5160	.5199	.5239	.5279	.5319	.5359
0.1	.5398	.5438	.5478	.5517	.5557	.5596	.5636	.5675	.5714	.5753
0.2	.5793	.5832	.5871	.5910	.5948	.5987	.6026	.6064	.6103	.6141
0.3	.6179	.6217	.6255	.6293	.6331	.6368	.6406	.6443	.6480	.6517
0.4	.6554	.6591	.6628	.6664	.6700	.6736	.6772	.6808	.6844	.6879
0.5	.6915	.6950	.6985	.7019	.7054	.7088	.7123	.7157	.7190	.7224
0.6	.7257	.7291	.7324	.7357	.7389	.7422	.7454	.7486	.7517	.7549
0.7	.7580	.7611	.7642	.7673	.7704	.7734	.7764	.7794	.7823	.7852
0.8	.7881	.7910	.7939	.7967	.7995	.8023	.8051	.8078	.8106	.8133
0.9	.8159	.8186	.8212	.8238	.8264	.8289	.8315	.8340	.8365	.8389
1.0	.8413	.8438	.8461	.8485	.8508	.8531	.8554	.8577	.8599	.8621
1.1	.8643	.8665	.8686	.8708	.8729	.8749	.8770	.8790	.8810	.8830
1.2	.8849	.8869	.8888	.8907	.8925	.8944	.8962	.8980	.8997	.9015
1.3	.9032	.9049	.9066	.9082	.9099	.9115	.9131	.9147	.9162	.9177
1.4	.9192	.9207	.9222	.9236	.9251	.9265	.9279	.9292	.9306	.9319
1.5	.9332	.9345	.9357	.9370	.9382	.9394	.9406	.9418	.9429	.9441
1.6	.9452	.9463	.9474	.9484	.9495	.9505	.9515	.9525	.9535	.9545
1.7	.9554	.9564	.9573	.9582	.9591	.9599	.9608	.9616	.9625	.9633
1.8	.9641	.9649	.9656	.9664	.9671	.9678	.9686	.9693	.9699	.9706
1.9	.9713	.9719	.9726	.9732	.9738	.9744	.9750	.9756	.9761	.9767
2.0	.9772	.9778	.9783	.9788	.9793	.9798	.9803	.9808	.9812	.9817
2.1	.9821	.9826	.9830	.9834	.9838	.9842	.9846	.9850	.9854	.9857
2.2	.9861	.9864	.9868	.9871	.9875	.9878	.9881	.9884	.9887	.9890
2.3	.9893	.9896	.9898	.9901	.9904	.9906	.9909	.9911	.9913	.9916
2.4	.9918	.9920	.9922	.9925	.9927	.9929	.9931	.9932	.9934	.9936
2.5	.9938	.9940	.9941	.9943	.9945	.9946	.9948	.9949	.9951	.9952
2.6	.9953	.9955	.9956	.9957	.9959	.9960	.9961	.9962	.9963	.9964
2.7	.9965	.9966	.9967	.9968	.9969	.9970	.9971	.9972	.9973	.9974
2.8	.9974	.9975	.9976	.9977	.9977	.9978	.9979	.9979	.9980	.9981
2.9	.9981	.9982	.9982	.9983	.9984	.9984	.9985	.9985	.9986	.9986
3.0	.9987	.9987	.9987	.9988	.9988	.9989	.9989	.9989	.9990	.9990
3.1	.9990	.9991	.9991	.9991	.9992	.9992	.9992	.9992	.9993	.9993
3.2	.9993	.9993	.9994	.9994	.9994	.9994	.9994	.9995	.9995	.9995
3.3	.9995	.9995	.9995	.9996	.9996	.9996	.9996	.9996	.9996	.9997
3.4	.9997	.9997	.9997	.9997	.9997	.9997	.9997	.9997	.9997	.9998

z	.00
3.5	.999767
4.0	.9999683
4.5	.9999966
5.0	.999999713

Table 3: Binomial Probabilities

Table entries represent $b(n,p,x)$, or the probability of observing x successes in n independent trials with fixed probability of success p.

n	x	.01	.05	.10	.20	.30	.40	.50	.60	.70	.80	.90	.95	.99	x
2	0	.980	.902	.810	.640	.490	.360	.250	.160	.090	.040	.010	.002	0+	0
	1	.020	.095	.180	.320	.420	.480	.500	.480	.420	.320	.180	.095	.020	1
	2	0+	.002	.010	.040	.090	.160	.250	.360	.490	.640	.810	.902	.980	2
3	0	.970	.857	.729	.512	.343	.216	.125	.064	.027	.008	.001	0+	0+	0
	1	.029	.135	.243	.384	.441	.432	.375	.288	.189	.096	.027	.007	0+	1
	2	0+	.007	.027	.096	.189	.288	.375	.432	.441	.384	.243	.135	.029	2
	3	0+	0+	.001	.008	.027	.064	.125	.216	.343	.512	.729	.857	.970	3
4	0	.961	.815	.656	.410	.240	.130	.062	.026	.008	.002	0+	0+	0+	0
	1	.039	.171	.292	.410	.412	.346	.250	.154	.076	.026	.004	0+	0+	1
	2	.001	.014	.049	.154	.265	.346	.375	.346	.265	.154	.049	.014	.001	2
	3	0+	0+	.004	.026	.076	.154	.250	.346	.412	.410	.292	.171	.039	3
	4	0+	0+	0+	.002	.008	.026	.062	.130	.240	.410	.656	.815	.961	4
5	0	.951	.774	.590	.328	.168	.078	.031	.010	.002	0+	0+	0+	0+	0
	1	.048	.204	.328	.410	.360	.259	.156	.077	.028	.006	0+	0+	0+	1
	2	.001	.021	.073	.205	.309	.346	.312	.230	.132	.051	.008	.001	0+	2
	3	0+	.001	.008	.051	.132	.230	.312	.346	.309	.205	.073	.021	.001	3
	4	0+	0+	0+	.006	.028	.077	.156	.259	.360	.410	.328	.204	.048	4
	5	0+	0+	0+	0+	.002	.010	.031	.078	.168	.328	.590	.774	.951	5
6	0	.941	.735	.531	.262	.118	.047	.016	.004	.001	0+	0+	0+	0+	0
	1	.057	.232	.354	.393	.303	.187	.094	.037	.010	.002	0+	0+	0+	1
	2	.001	.031	.098	.246	.324	.311	.234	.138	.060	.015	.001	0+	0+	2
	3	0+	.002	.015	.082	.185	.276	.312	.276	.185	.082	.015	.002	0+	3
	4	0+	0+	.001	.015	.060	.138	.234	.311	.324	.246	.098	.031	.001	4
	5	0+	0+	0+	.002	.010	.037	.094	.187	.303	.393	.354	.232	.057	5
	6	0+	0+	0+	0+	.001	.004	.016	.047	.118	.262	.531	.735	.941	6
7	0	.932	.698	.478	.210	.082	.028	.008	.002	0+	0+	0+	0+	0+	0
	1	.066	.257	.372	.367	.247	.131	.055	.017	.004	0+	0+	0+	0+	1
	2	.002	.041	.124	.275	.318	.261	.164	.077	.025	.004	0+	0+	0+	2
	3	0+	.004	.023	.115	.227	.290	.273	.194	.097	.029	.003	0+	0+	3
	4	0+	0+	.003	.029	.097	.194	.273	.290	.227	.115	.023	.004	0+	4
	5	0+	0+	0+	.004	.025	.077	.164	.261	.318	.275	.124	.041	.002	5
	6	0+	0+	0+	0+	.004	.017	.055	.131	.247	.367	.372	.257	.066	6
	7	0+	0+	0+	0+	0+	.002	.008	.028	.082	.210	.478	.698	.932	7
8	0	.923	.663	.430	.168	.058	.017	.004	.001	0+	0+	0+	0+	0+	0
	1	.075	.279	.383	.336	.198	.090	.031	.008	.001	0+	0+	0+	0+	1
	2	.003	.051	.149	.294	.296	.209	.109	.041	.010	.001	0+	0+	0+	2
	3	0+	.005	.033	.147	.254	.279	.219	.124	.047	.009	0+	0+	0+	3
	4	0+	0+	.005	.046	.136	.232	.273	.232	.136	.046	.005	0+	0+	4
	5	0+	0+	0+	.009	.047	.124	.219	.279	.254	.147	.033	.005	0+	5
	6	0+	0+	0+	.001	.010	.041	.109	.209	.296	.294	.149	.051	.003	6
	7	0+	0+	0+	0+	.001	.008	.031	.090	.198	.336	.383	.279	.075	7
	8	0+	0+	0+	0+	0+	.001	.004	.017	.058	.168	.430	.663	.923	8

NOTE: 0+ represents a probability less than 0.0005.

Table 3: Binomial Probabilities (*continued*)

n	x							p							x
		.01	.05	.10	.20	.30	.40	.50	.60	.70	.80	.90	.95	.99	
9	0	.914	.630	.387	.134	.040	.010	.002	0+	0+	0+	0+	0+	0+	0
	1	.083	.299	.387	.302	.156	.060	.018	.004	0+	0+	0+	0+	0+	1
	2	.003	.063	.172	.302	.267	.161	.070	.021	.004	0+	0+	0+	0+	2
	3	0+	.008	.045	.176	.267	.251	.164	.074	.021	.003	0+	0+	0+	3
	4	0+	.001	.007	.066	.172	.251	.246	.167	.074	.017	.001	0+	0+	4
	5	0+	0+	.001	.017	.074	.167	.246	.251	.172	.066	.007	.001	0+	5
	6	0+	0+	0+	.003	.021	.074	.164	.251	.267	.176	.045	.008	0+	6
	7	0+	0+	0+	0+	.004	.021	.070	.161	.267	.302	.172	.063	.003	7
	8	0+	0+	0+	0+	0+	.004	.018	.060	.156	.302	.387	.299	.083	8
	9	0+	0+	0+	0+	0+	0+	.002	.010	.040	.134	.387	.630	.914	9
10	0	.904	.599	.349	.107	.028	.006	.001	0+	0+	0+	0+	0+	0+	0
	1	.091	.315	.387	.268	.121	.040	.010	.002	0+	0+	0+	0+	0+	1
	2	.004	.075	.194	.302	.233	.121	.044	.011	.001	0+	0+	0+	0+	2
	3	0+	.010	.057	.201	.267	.215	.117	.042	.009	.001	0+	0+	0+	3
	4	0+	.001	.011	.088	.200	.251	.205	.111	.037	.006	0+	0+	0+	4
	5	0+	0+	.001	.026	.103	.201	.246	.201	.103	.026	.001	0+	0+	5
	6	0+	0+	0+	.006	.037	.111	.205	.251	.200	.088	.011	.001	0+	6
	7	0+	0+	0+	.001	.009	.042	.117	.215	.267	.201	.057	.010	0+	7
	8	0+	0+	0+	0+	.001	.011	.044	.121	.233	.302	.194	.075	.004	8
	9	0+	0+	0+	0+	0+	.002	.010	.040	.121	.268	.387	.315	.091	9
	10	0+	0+	0+	0+	0+	0+	.001	.006	.028	.107	.349	.599	.904	10
11	0	.895	.569	.314	.086	.020	.004	0+	0+	0+	0+	0+	0+	0+	0
	1	.099	.329	.384	.236	.093	.027	.005	.001	0+	0+	0+	0+	0+	1
	2	.005	.087	.213	.295	.200	.089	.027	.005	.001	0+	0+	0+	0+	2
	3	0+	.014	.071	.221	.257	.177	.081	.023	.004	0+	0+	0+	0+	3
	4	0+	.001	.016	.111	.220	.236	.161	.070	.017	.002	0+	0+	0+	4
	5	0+	0+	.002	.039	.132	.221	.226	.147	.057	.010	0+	0+	0+	5
	6	0+	0+	0+	.010	.057	.147	.226	.221	.132	.039	.002	0+	0+	6
	7	0+	0+	0+	.002	.017	.070	.161	.236	.220	.111	.016	.001	0+	7
	8	0+	0+	0+	0+	.004	.023	.081	.177	.257	.221	.071	.014	0+	8
	9	0+	0+	0+	0+	.001	.005	.027	.089	.200	.295	.213	.087	.005	9
	10	0+	0+	0+	0+	0+	.001	.005	.027	.093	.236	.384	.329	.099	10
	11	0+	0+	0+	0+	0+	0+	0+	.004	.020	.086	.314	.569	.895	11
12	0	.886	.540	.282	.069	.014	.002	0+	0+	0+	0+	0+	0+	0+	0
	1	.107	.341	.377	.206	.071	.017	.003	0+	0+	0+	0+	0+	0+	1
	2	.006	.099	.230	.283	.168	.064	.016	.002	0+	0+	0+	0+	0+	2
	3	0+	.017	.085	.236	.240	.142	.054	.012	.001	0+	0+	0+	0+	3
	4	0+	.002	.021	.133	.231	.213	.121	.042	.008	.001	0+	0+	0+	4
	5	0+	0+	.004	.053	.158	.227	.193	.101	.029	.003	0+	0+	0+	5
	6	0+	0+	0+	.016	.079	.177	.226	.177	.079	.016	0+	0+	0+	6
	7	0+	0+	0+	.003	.029	.101	.193	.227	.158	.053	.004	0+	0+	7
	8	0+	0+	0+	.001	.008	.042	.121	.213	.231	.133	.021	.002	0+	8
	9	0+	0+	0+	0+	.001	.012	.054	.142	.240	.236	.085	.017	0+	9
	10	0+	0+	0+	0+	0+	.002	.016	.064	.168	.283	.230	.099	.006	10
	11	0+	0+	0+	0+	0+	0+	.003	.017	.071	.206	.377	.341	.107	11
	12	0+	0+	0+	0+	0+	0+	0+	.002	.014	.069	.282	.540	.886	12

NOTE: 0+ represents a probability less than 0.0005.

(*continued*)

Table 3: Binomial Probabilities (*continued*)

n	x	.01	.05	.10	.20	.30	.40	.50	.60	.70	.80	.90	.95	.99	x
13	0	.878	.513	.254	.055	.010	.001	0+	0+	0+	0+	0+	0+	0+	0
	1	.115	.351	.367	.179	.054	.011	.002	0+	0+	0+	0+	0+	0+	1
	2	.007	.111	.245	.268	.139	.045	.010	.001	0+	0+	0+	0+	0+	2
	3	0+	.021	.100	.246	.218	.111	.035	.006	.001	0+	0+	0+	0+	3
	4	0+	.003	.028	.154	.234	.184	.087	.024	.003	0+	0+	0+	0+	4
	5	0+	0+	.006	.069	.180	.221	.157	.066	.014	.001	0+	0+	0+	5
	6	0+	0+	.001	.023	.103	.197	.209	.131	.044	.006	0+	0+	0+	6
	7	0+	0+	0+	.006	.044	.131	.209	.197	.103	.023	.001	0+	0+	7
	8	0+	0+	0+	.001	.014	.066	.157	.221	.180	.069	.006	0+	0+	8
	9	0+	0+	0+	0+	.003	.024	.087	.184	.234	.154	.028	.003	0+	9
	10	0+	0+	0+	0+	.001	.006	.035	.111	.218	.246	.100	.021	0+	10
	11	0+	0+	0+	0+	0+	.001	.010	.045	.139	.268	.245	.111	.007	11
	12	0+	0+	0+	0+	0+	0+	.002	.011	.054	.179	.367	.351	.115	12
	13	0+	0+	0+	0+	0+	0+	0+	.001	.010	.055	.254	.513	.878	13
14	0	.869	.488	.229	.044	.007	.001	0+	0+	0+	0+	0+	0+	0+	0
	1	.123	.359	.356	.154	.041	.007	.001	0+	0+	0+	0+	0+	0+	1
	2	.008	.123	.257	.250	.113	.032	.006	.001	0+	0+	0+	0+	0+	2
	3	0+	.026	.114	.250	.194	.085	.022	.003	0+	0+	0+	0+	0+	3
	4	0+	.004	.035	.172	.229	.155	.061	.014	.001	0+	0+	0+	0+	4
	5	0+	0+	.008	.086	.196	.207	.122	.041	.007	0+	0+	0+	0+	5
	6	0+	0+	.001	.032	.126	.207	.183	.092	.023	.002	0+	0+	0+	6
	7	0+	0+	0+	.009	.062	.157	.209	.157	.062	.009	0+	0+	0+	7
	8	0+	0+	0+	.002	.023	.092	.183	.207	.126	.032	.001	0+	0+	8
	9	0+	0+	0+	0+	.007	.041	.122	.207	.196	.086	.008	0+	0+	9
	10	0+	0+	0+	0+	.001	.014	.061	.155	.229	.172	.035	.004	0+	10
	11	0+	0+	0+	0+	0+	.003	.022	.085	.194	.250	.114	.026	0+	11
	12	0+	0+	0+	0+	0+	.001	.006	.032	.113	.250	.257	.123	.008	12
	13	0+	0+	0+	0+	0+	0+	.001	.007	.041	.154	.356	.359	.123	13
	14	0+	0+	0+	0+	0+	0+	0+	.001	.007	.044	.229	.488	.869	14
15	0	.860	.463	.206	.035	.005	0+	0+	0+	0+	0+	0+	0+	0+	0
	1	.130	.366	.343	.132	.031	.005	0+	0+	0+	0+	0+	0+	0+	1
	2	.009	.135	.267	.231	.092	.022	.003	0+	0+	0+	0+	0+	0+	2
	3	0+	.031	.129	.250	.170	.063	.014	.002	0+	0+	0+	0+	0+	3
	4	0+	.005	.043	.188	.219	.127	.042	.007	.001	0+	0+	0+	0+	4
	5	0+	.001	.010	.103	.206	.186	.092	.024	.003	0+	0+	0+	0+	5
	6	0+	0+	.002	.043	.147	.207	.153	.061	.012	.001	0+	0+	0+	6
	7	0+	0+	0+	.014	.081	.177	.196	.118	.035	.003	0+	0+	0+	7
	8	0+	0+	0+	.003	.035	.118	.196	.177	.081	.014	0+	0+	0+	8
	9	0+	0+	0+	.001	.012	.061	.153	.207	.147	.043	.002	0+	0+	9
	10	0+	0+	0+	0+	.003	.024	.092	.186	.206	.103	.010	.001	0+	10
	11	0+	0+	0+	0+	.001	.007	.042	.127	.219	.188	.043	.005	0+	11
	12	0+	0+	0+	0+	0+	.002	.014	.063	.170	.250	.129	.031	0+	12
	13	0+	0+	0+	0+	0+	0+	.003	.022	.092	.231	.267	.135	.009	13
	14	0+	0+	0+	0+	0+	0+	0+	.005	.031	.132	.343	.366	.130	14
	15	0+	0+	0+	0+	0+	0+	0+	0+	.005	.035	.206	.463	.860	15

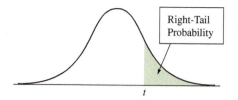

Table 4: *t*-Distribution Critical Values

	Confidence Level					
	80%	90%	95%	98%	99%	99.8%
	Right-Tail Probability					
df	0.100	0.050	0.025	0.010	0.005	0.001
1	3.078	6.314	12.706	31.821	63.656	318.289
2	1.886	2.920	4.303	6.965	9.925	22.328
3	1.638	2.353	3.182	4.541	5.841	10.214
4	1.533	2.132	2.776	3.747	4.604	7.173
5	1.476	2.015	2.571	3.365	4.032	5.894
6	1.440	1.943	2.447	3.143	3.707	5.208
7	1.415	1.895	2.365	2.998	3.499	4.785
8	1.397	1.860	2.306	2.896	3.355	4.501
9	1.383	1.833	2.262	2.821	3.250	4.297
10	1.372	1.812	2.228	2.764	3.169	4.144
11	1.363	1.796	2.201	2.718	3.106	4.025
12	1.356	1.782	2.179	2.681	3.055	3.930
13	1.350	1.771	2.160	2.650	3.012	3.852
14	1.345	1.761	2.145	2.624	2.977	3.787
15	1.341	1.753	2.131	2.602	2.947	3.733
16	1.337	1.746	2.120	2.583	2.921	3.686
17	1.333	1.740	2.110	2.567	2.898	3.646
18	1.330	1.734	2.101	2.552	2.878	3.611
19	1.328	1.729	2.093	2.539	2.861	3.579
20	1.325	1.725	2.086	2.528	2.845	3.552
21	1.323	1.721	2.080	2.518	2.831	3.527
22	1.321	1.717	2.074	2.508	2.819	3.505
23	1.319	1.714	2.069	2.500	2.807	3.485
24	1.318	1.711	2.064	2.492	2.797	3.467
25	1.316	1.708	2.060	2.485	2.787	3.450
26	1.315	1.706	2.056	2.479	2.779	3.435
27	1.314	1.703	2.052	2.473	2.771	3.421
28	1.313	1.701	2.048	2.467	2.763	3.408
29	1.311	1.699	2.045	2.462	2.756	3.396
30	1.310	1.697	2.042	2.457	2.750	3.385
40	1.303	1.684	2.021	2.423	2.704	3.307
50	1.299	1.676	2.009	2.403	2.678	3.261
60	1.296	1.671	2.000	2.390	2.660	3.232
80	1.292	1.664	1.990	2.374	2.639	3.195
100	1.290	1.660	1.984	2.364	2.626	3.174
∞	1.282	1.645	1.960	2.326	2.576	3.091

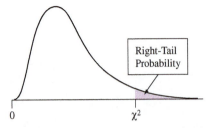

Table 5: Chi-Squared Distribution for Values of Various Right-Tail Probabilities

	Right-Tail Probability						
df	0.250	0.100	0.050	0.025	0.010	0.005	0.001
1	1.32	2.71	3.84	5.02	6.63	7.88	10.83
2	2.77	4.61	5.99	7.38	9.21	10.60	13.82
3	4.11	6.25	7.81	9.35	11.34	12.84	16.27
4	5.39	7.78	9.49	11.14	13.28	14.86	18.47
5	6.63	9.24	11.07	12.83	15.09	16.75	20.52
6	7.84	10.64	12.59	14.45	16.81	18.55	22.46
7	9.04	12.02	14.07	16.01	18.48	20.28	24.32
8	10.22	13.36	15.51	17.53	20.09	21.96	26.12
9	11.39	14.68	16.92	19.02	21.67	23.59	27.88
10	12.55	15.99	18.31	20.48	23.21	25.19	29.59
11	13.70	17.28	19.68	21.92	24.72	26.76	31.26
12	14.85	18.55	21.03	23.34	26.22	28.30	32.91
13	15.98	19.81	22.36	24.74	27.69	29.82	34.53
14	17.12	21.06	23.68	26.12	29.14	31.32	36.12
15	18.25	22.31	25.00	27.49	30.58	32.80	37.70
16	19.37	23.54	26.30	28.85	32.00	34.27	39.25
17	20.49	24.77	27.59	30.19	33.41	35.72	40.79
18	21.60	25.99	28.87	31.53	34.81	37.16	42.31
19	22.72	27.20	30.14	32.85	36.19	38.58	43.82
20	23.83	28.41	31.41	34.17	37.57	40.00	45.32
25	29.34	34.38	37.65	40.65	44.31	46.93	52.62
30	34.80	40.26	43.77	46.98	50.89	53.67	59.70
40	45.62	51.80	55.76	59.34	63.69	66.77	73.40
50	56.33	63.17	67.50	71.42	76.15	79.49	86.66
60	66.98	74.40	79.08	83.30	88.38	91.95	99.61
70	77.58	85.53	90.53	95.02	100.43	104.21	112.32
80	88.13	96.58	101.88	106.63	112.33	116.32	124.84
90	98.65	107.57	113.15	118.14	124.12	128.30	137.21
100	109.14	118.50	124.34	129.56	135.81	140.17	149.45

Appendix B:
Answers to Odd-Numbered Exercises

CHAPTER 1

Section 1.2

1.1 a. Handedness: categorical **b.** Age: numerical

1.3 Male is categorical with two categories. The 1's represent males, and the 0's represent females. If you added the numbers, you would get the number of males, so it makes sense here.

1.5 a. Stacked **b.** 1 means smoker, and 0 means nonsmoker.

c.

Smoker	Nonsmoker
15	18
14	23
13	19
23	21
	18
	15

Section 1.3

1.7 a. $189/29{,}617 = 0.64\%$ changes **b.** $124/14{,}513 = 0.85\%$ changes **c.** The higher percentage of change was in the class told to change their answers, so the instruction did seem to have a small effect.

1.9 a. $15/38 = 39.5\%$ of the class were male **b.** $0.641(234) = 149.994$, or 150 men in the class

c. $0.40(x) = 20$
$x = 20/0.4 = 50$ people in the class

1.11 The frequency of women is 7, the proportion is $7/11$, and the percentage is 63.6%.

1.13 $0.2543x = 13{,}386{,}000$
$x = 52{,}638{,}616$ or a rounded version of this

1.15 Steps 1–3 are shown in the accompanying table.

Province	Persons with Diabetes	Population	Rank by Cases	Diabetes/ Population	Diabetes per 1000 Population	Rank by Rate
Ontario	770,410	11,498,657	1	0.067	67	2
Quebec	448,122	6,894,185	2	0.065	65	3
British Columbia	224,775	3,943,421	3	0.057	57	6
Alberta	195,440	3,203,934	4	0.061	61	5
Nova Scotia	69,721	810,698	5	0.086	86	1
Manitoba	62,058	1,000,935	6	0.062	62	4

4: The ranks are not the same. Nova Scotia is fifth in number of cases but has the highest rate among these provinces.

5: Among these six provinces, you would be most likely to meet someone with diabetes if you were in Nova Scotia and least likely if you were in British Columbia.

1.17 2003: 10.6%, 2005: 8.8%, 2007: 7.4%, 2009: 6.2%, 2011: 5.5%
The percentage of people exposed to second-hand smoke is decreasing over time.

1.19 We don't know the total number of students in the two classes. The larger number of women at 8 a.m. may just result from a larger number of students at 8 a.m.

Section 1.4

1.21 Observational study

1.23 Controlled experiment

1.25 Controlled experiment

1.27 Observational study

1.29 This was an observational study, and from it you cannot conclude that the tutoring raises the grades. Possible confounders (answers may vary): 1. It may be the more highly motivated who attend the tutoring, and this motivation is what causes the grades to go up. 2. It could be that those with more time attend the tutoring, and it is the increased time studying that causes the grades to go up.

1.31 It was an observational study. There was no random assignment. They simply looked at records. We cannot say that CABG causes better results, because there may have been confounding variables.

1.33 The students should have been randomly assigned to the treatment. Half of the students should have been given a placebo. Also, ideally the person to whom the subjects report their results should not know whether they are taking vitamin C or a placebo, making the study double-blind.

1.35 Because this was not a randomized experiment (no one assigned people to be happy), we should not infer causation. It is possible that healthier people tend to be happier, and it was the health of those people that caused them not to catch a cold. If we cannot infer causation, then you should not believe that a change in happiness would change the likelihood of catching a cold.

1.37 Ask whether the patients were randomly assigned the full or the half dose. Without randomization there could be bias, and we cannot infer causation. With randomization we can infer causation.

1.39 This was an observational study. We cannot conclude cause and effect from observational studies.

1.41 a. LD: 8% tumours; LL: 28% tumours **b.** A controlled experiment. You can tell by the random assignment. **c.** Yes, we can conclude cause and effect because it was a controlled experiment, and random assignment will balance out potential confounding variables.

Chapter Review Exercises

1.43 a. Recent immigrants: $20/143 = 14\%$ **b.** Non-recent immigrants: $183/769 = 23.8\%$ **c.** Canadian-born: $520/1496 = 34.8\%$ **d.** Canadian-born participants have the highest rate of panic attacks. Because this is not a controlled experiment, we cannot conclude that a person's immigrant status directly affects that person's likelihood of having panic attacks. One confounding variable could be age. Other confounding variables are possible.

1.45 a. The two-way table follows.

	Boy	Girl
Concerned	11	12
Not Concerned	8	7

b. Concerned boys: $11/19 = 57.9\%$, concerned girls: $12/19 = 63.2\%$ **c.** In this sample, girls are more likely than boys to be concerned about potential environmental contaminants.

1.47 Answers will vary but should include randomization, placebo, control, and blinds.

1.49 This was an observational study, not a controlled experiment. From observational studies you cannot conclude cause and effect. Therefore, offering to participate in clinical trials would probably have very little effect on one's chance of surviving. Possible confounders will vary. For example, the people who are willing to participate in clinical trials may tend to follow the advice of doctors more, and it may be the practice of following advice that raises their chances of survival.

1.51 No, we cannot conclude causation. There appears to be no control group for comparison.

CHAPTER 2

Sections 2.1 and 2.2

2.1 a. 24 would be classified as obese. **b.** 24/146 is about 16%, which is much less than 25%.

2.3 New vertical axis labels: 0, 0.04, 0.08, 0.12, 0.16, 0.20, 0.24, 0.28, 0.32, and 0.36. Note that 0.04 comes from 1/25.

2.5 a. 1 (or 2) have no TVs. **b.** 9 TVs **c.** 27 **d.** 6 homes **e.** 6/90, or 0.0667

2.7 a. Calgary **b.** Winnipeg **c.** Calgary

2.9 It should be right-skewed.

2.11 It would be bimodal because men and women tend to have different heights and therefore different armspans.

2.13 About 56 years (between 52 and 60)

2.15 Riding the bus shows a larger typical value and also more variation.

2.17 a. Unimodal (mode at 12 years of elementary and high school education completed) and left-skewed **b.** Approximately 12,900 respondents **c.** 12,900/20,134 = 64%

2.19 Most of the observations for waxed trays take less time than the observations for trays without wax. The distribution of time for trays without wax is right-skewed, with some observations that took a long time in comparison to the rest. The histograms suggest that waxing cafeteria trays before tobogganing makes the trays go faster.

2.21 1. b **2.** c **3.** a

2.23 1. See the dotplots. Histograms would also be good for visualizing the distributions. Stemplots would not work with these data sets because all the observed values have only one digit.

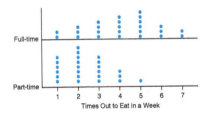

2. Full-time is a bit left-skewed, and part-time is a bit right-skewed.

3. Those with full-time jobs go out to eat more than those with part-time jobs.

4. The full-time workers have a distribution that is more spread out; full-time distribution goes from 1 to 7, whereas part-time goes only from 1 to 5.

5. There are no outliers—that is, no dots detached from the main group with an empty space between.

6. For the full-time workers the distribution is a little left-skewed, and for the part-time workers it is a little right-skewed. The full-time workers tend to go out to eat more, and their distribution is more spread out.

2.25 See histogram.

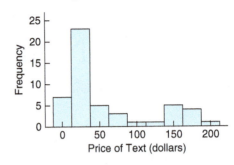

The histogram is bimodal, with modes at about $25 and about $150.

2.27 See histogram. The histogram is right-skewed. The typical value is around 12 (between 10 and 15) years, and there are three outliers: Asian elephant (40), African elephant (35), and hippo (41). Humans (75 years) would be way off to the right; they live much longer than other mammals.

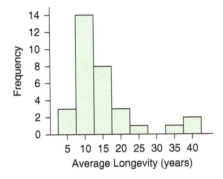

2.29 1. b **2.** a **3.** c

Sections 2.3 and 2.4

2.31 No, the largest category is Wrong to Right, which suggests that changes tend to make the answers more likely to be right.

2.33 a. The mode for 2011 is Feature Phone, whereas for 2012 and 2013 it is Smartphone. The percentage of mobile subscribers who use a smartphone has increased every year from 2011 to 2013. **b.** There was more variation in the data in 2011.

2.35 a. College or technical diploma. It is easier to determine this from the bar chart because it is not easy to determine which slice in the pie chart is larger when slices are so similar in size. **b.** Bachelor's degree or higher.

2.37 a. In 2040, it is projected that fewer adults will be between the ages of 25 and 64 and more will be over 65 years old than in 2020. The category of persons aged 24 and below is predicted to stay relatively the same size during this time frame. **b.** With a greater number of retired persons and fewer working adults, less money will be available for a larger number of eligible retired persons. It will be difficult to continue operating the Canada Pension Plan as it is now.

2.39 A bar chart and a pie chart are both appropriate. We construct a Pareto chart. The mode is natural gas and variation is not very high.

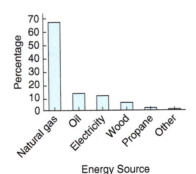

Chapter Review Exercises

2.41 Histograms: One for the males and one for the females would be appropriate. Dotplots or stemplots would also work for this numerical data set.

2.43 a. The diseases with higher rates for HRT were heart attack, stroke, pulmonary embolism, and breast cancer. The diseases with lower rates for HRT were endometrial cancer, colorectal cancer, and hip fracture. **b.** Comparing the rates makes more sense than comparing just the numbers, in case there were more women in one group than in the other.

2.45 The vertical axis does not start at zero and thus exaggerates the differences. Make a graph for which the vertical axis starts at zero.

2.47 a. Pie chart **b.** Histogram

2.49 The shapes are very similar; the later period is warmer, and with slightly more variability. This is consistent with theories on global warming.

2.51 Dotplots will vary.

2.53 Graphs will vary. Histograms, dotplots, or stemplots are all appropriate. The prices in Vancouver's West Side tend to be higher and more varied than the prices in East Vancouver.

2.55 The data set should be right-skewed with some unusually high numbers.

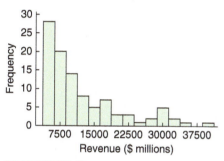

CHAPTER 3

Section 3.1

3.1 c

3.3 The typical age of business people in this group is roughly between 52 and 60 (or about 56 years). (The distribution is symmetric, so the mean should be roughly in the middle.)

3.5 a. The typical number of vacation days is about 17.2, the mean. One could also say that number of vacation days tends to be about 17.2, on average. **b.** The standard deviation of paid vacation days for the six countries is 10.4. **c.** The United States, at 0, is farthest from the mean and contributes most to the standard deviation.

3.7 a. 60.8, Older: 60.8 (the mean age for the first six prime ministers) is more than 52.7 for the most recent six prime ministers. **b.** Greater: 11.7 (the standard deviation of ages for the first six prime ministers) is greater than the 8.3 for the most recent six prime ministers.

3.9 a. 3.6, 2.3, Alberta **b.** 1.96, 2.50, Saskatchewan **c.** Alberta

3.11 a. Kitchen waste: 53.8%. Yard waste: 76.6%. In a typical CMA, households tend to compost more yard waste than they do kitchen waste. **b.** Kitchen waste: 20.0%. Yard waste: 11.6%. There is more variation in the percentage of households composting kitchen waste than there is in the percentage of households composting yard waste.

3.13 The rental prices in Quebec City (Figure a) have a larger standard deviation than the prices in Ottawa.

3.15 a. Top: 3462 + 500 = 3962
Bottom: 3462 − 500 = 2962
b. Yes, a birth weight of 2800 grams is more than one SD below the mean because it is less than 2962.

3.17 a. The mean is 3 years. **b.** Larger: The mean is 23 years of age. When 20 is added to each number, the mean increases by 20. **c.** The standard deviation is 1.4 years. **d.** The same. The standard deviation in 20 years is still 1.4. Adding 20 to each number does not affect the standard deviation. Standard deviation does not depend on the size of the numbers, only on how far apart they are.

3.19 SD for the 100-metre event would be smaller. All the runners come to the finish line within a few seconds of each other. In the marathon, the runners can be quite widely spread after running that long distance.

Section 3.2

3.21 Answers correspond to the guided steps.
1: 95% (See the accompanying curve.)
2: 1382 is from 1094 + 288, because it is one standard deviation above the mean.
3: As shown on the curve, A is 518, B is 806, and C is 1670.
4: Answer a. About 95% between 518 and 1670.
5: Answer b: About 68% between 806 and 1382.
6: Answer c: Most would not consider 1383 unusual because it is between 1382 and 1670.
7: Answer d: 380 is unusually small, because it is less than 518, which means it is more than two standard deviations below the mean, and so less than 2.5% of the population have values lower than this.

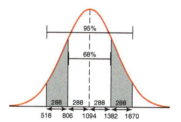

3.23 $z = \dfrac{2622 - 3514}{892} = \dfrac{-892}{892} = -1$

a. About 68% according to the Empirical Rule, because the z-scores are −1 and 1. **b.** About 95% according to the Empirical Rule. **c.** Nearly all the data should be within three standard deviations of the mean. Three standard deviations above the mean is

$$3514 + 3(892) = 6190$$

Because 9000 is quite a bit above 6190, a property crime rate of 9000 is inconsistent with the data.

3.25 a. −2 **b.** 167.5 cm

3.27 The z-score for a temperature of −30°C in Winnipeg in January is −2.5, and the z-score for a temperature of 37°C in Kelowna in July is 1.94. The temperature in Winnipeg is more unusual.

3.29 a. $z = \dfrac{2500 - 3462}{500} = \dfrac{-962}{500} = -1.92$

b. $z = \dfrac{2500 - 2622}{500} = \dfrac{-122}{500} = -0.24$

c. A birth rate of 2500 grams is more common (the z-score is closer to 0) for babies born one month early. In other words, there are higher percentages of babies with low birth weight among those born one month early. This makes sense because babies gain weight during gestation, and babies born one month early have had less time to gain weight.

3.31 70 + 1.5(10) = 85

Section 3.3

3.33 Two measures of centre are the mean and the median. The median is preferred for data that are strongly skewed or have outliers. If the data are relatively symmetric, the mean is preferred but the median can also be used.

3.35

224	237	244	246	256		261	268	293	340	415
		Q1			median			Q3		

a. The median of $258.5 million is the typical income for the 10 top-grossing Pixar animated movies. **b.** IQR = 293 − 244 = 49 million. This is the range of the middle 50% of the sorted incomes in the 10 top-grossing Pixar animated movies.

3.37

| 28.2 | 29.0 | 29.5 | | 31.4 | 32.6 | 37.1 |
| | Q1 | | median | | Q3 | |

a. 30.45 cents per litre **b.** IQR = Q3 − Q1 = 32.6 − 29.0 = 3.6 cents per litre

3.39 a. 3, 2, Alberta **b.** 3, 2, Alberta (Answers for interquartile range may vary with technology.)

Section 3.4

3.41 a. Outliers are observed values that are far from the main group of data. In a histogram they are separated from the others by space. If they are mistakes, they should be removed. If they are not mistakes, outliers must be investigated further. **b.** The median is more resistant, which implies that it changes less than the mean (when comparing the data with and without outliers).

3.43 The corrected value will give a different mean but not a different median. Medians are not as affected by the size of extreme scores, but the mean is affected.

3.45 a. The shape is right-skewed, the median is 20, and the interquartile range is 35 − 19 = 16. There is an outlier at 66. **b.** The mean is 27.3 (it should be marked in the second bin) and the median is 20 (it should be marked in the first bin). The mean is much larger because of the outlier, 66.

3.47 a. Both data sets are right-skewed and have outliers that represent large numbers of hours of study, so the medians (and interquartile ranges) should be compared. **b.** The median of 7 was larger for the women; the men's median was only 4. The interquartile range was 4.5 for the women and 3 for the men, so the IQR was larger for the women. Both data sets are right-skewed with outliers at around 15 or 20 hours. Summary: The women tended to study more and had more variation as measured by the interquartile range.

Section 3.5

3.49 a. Africa, Oceania, Asia, America, Europe **b.** Africa has the largest IQR. **c.** America has the smallest IQR. **d.** Africa and America have potential outliers. **e.** 62 is an outlier in America because the difference between that value and the first quartile is more than 1.5 times the IQR of that group (the box is small). However, because life expectancy tends to be lower in Asia than in America, and there is more variability (the box is larger), the difference between a life expectancy of 60.5 and the first quartile of that group is still less than 1.5 times the IQR of that group.

3.51 Answers will vary: Winnipeg and Vancouver are the warmest cities in terms of median temperature, while St. John's has the lowest median temperature. Winnipeg has the lowest temperature recorded, and the highest variation in temperature, while Vancouver has the lowest variation in temperatures.

The choice of favourite city will vary.

3.53 a. Histogram 1 goes with boxplot c.
Histogram 2 goes with boxplot b.
Histogram 3 goes with boxplot a.
Reasoning: A boxplot with a whisker (or potential outliers) on the far right corresponds to a histogram that is right-skewed. A boxplot that is centred approximately symmetrically corresponds to a histogram that is not very skewed.
b. Histogram 1 is strongly right-skewed, histogram 2 is left-skewed, and histogram 3 is relatively symmetric.
Histogram 1 would have a mean larger than the median.
Histogram 2 would have a mean smaller than the median.
Histogram 3 would have about the same mean and median.

3.55 a. The median is 7. Q1 is 6.1 and Q3 is 10.4, so the IQR is 4.3. There are no potential outliers.

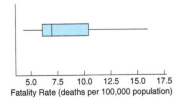
Fatality Rate (deaths per 100,000 population)

b. A low population relative to the number of deaths is another way of seeing a high death rate.

Chapter Review Exercises

3.57 Both data sets are slightly right-skewed because of the potential outliers. The men tend to be faster than the women, as shown by the lower values of all quantities in the five-number summary. The interquartile range is slightly larger for the women, as shown by the larger box.

3.59 a. The median is 651 km². The typical province or territory has an area of about 651 km². **b.** IQR = 1211 − 239 = 972 km² **c.** The mean area is 768 km². **d.** The mean is much larger than the median because the area of Nunavut is much larger than the area of the other regions, thereby increasing the value of the mean. The median is unaffected by this extreme observation. **e.** It is appropriate to report the median when there are outliers, as in this case.

3.61 The answers given follow the steps in the Guided Exercises.
1:

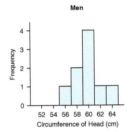
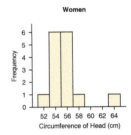

2: The men's histogram is roughly symmetric (bell-shaped). The women's histogram is bell-shaped except for the high-end outlier, so it may be called right-skewed.
3: Compare the medians and interquartile ranges because of the outlier for the women.
4: median. men: 59.5 cm, women: 55 cm
5: Men's IQR = 3.75. Women's IQR = 2.5. IQR may vary with different technology.
6: The measurement of 63 for the women was an outlier.
7: Both data sets are unimodal and roughly symmetric except for one large outlier for the women. The men tended to have larger heads with more variation in size than the women. However, there was a large outlier (63 cm) for the women.

3.63 Summary statistics are shown below. The 5 p.m. class did better, typically; both the mean and the median are higher. Also, the spread (as reflected in both the standard deviation and the IQR) is larger for the 11 a.m. class, so the 5 p.m. class has less variation.

The visual comparison is shown by the boxplots. Both distributions are slightly left-skewed. Therefore, you can compare the means and standard deviations *or* the medians and IQRs.

```
Minitab Statistics
Variable  N    Mean    Median  StDev  Min    Max    Q1   Q3
11am      15   70.73   72.5    19.84  39     100    53   86
5pm       19   84.78   86.5    11.95  64.5   104.5  73   94
```

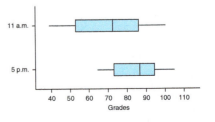

3.65 The graph is bimodal, with modes around 165 centimetres and around 175 centimetres. There are two modes because men tend to be taller than women.

3.67 a. The approximate mean student fee is around 580 dollars.
b. The approximate standard deviation is about 240, from $(1460 - 20)/6$.
c. The data set is unimodal and roughly symmetric, and so all (or nearly all) of the data should be within three standard deviations of the mean. Thus, one boundary is up 3SD and one is down 3SD, which is a difference of 6SD.

3.69 and 3.71 Constructed numbers will vary.

3.73 and 3.75 Answers will vary but should include graphs and comparison of centres and variation.

CHAPTER 4

Section 4.1

4.1 a. The number of acres has a stronger relationship with the value of the land, as shown by the fact that the points are less scattered in a vertical direction. **b.** Acreage. The relationship is stronger between the value of land and acreage than with the number of fireplaces because the vertical spread is less.

4.3 Very little trend.

4.5 The more people weigh, the more weight they tend to want to lose.

4.7 Metropolitan areas that issue a large number of non-residential building permits also tend to issue a large number of residential building permits.

4.9 The trend is positive. The higher the percentage of adults who smoke, the higher the percentage of youth aged 12 to 19 who smoke.

4.11 Linear regression is not appropriate because the trend is not linear, it is curved.

4.13 Linear regression is not appropriate because the trend is not linear, it is curved.

4.15 The correlation between age and average grade would be near zero.

4.17.   0.767 a
 0.299 b
 −0.980 c

4.19 a. 0.907 **b.** The correlation remains the same ($r = 0.907$) if you multiply by a constant. **c.** The correlation remains the same ($r = 0.907$) if you add a constant.

Section 4.2

4.21 a. Between \$17 and \$23 (Answers will vary.) **b.** \$21.25

4.23 a. Predicted Armspan $= 18.62 + 0.87$ Height
b. (Differences with the calculator output are due to rounding.)
$b_1 = 0.9496 (8.097/8.793) = 0.874$ **c.** $b_0 = 159.86 - 0.874(161.55) = 18.67$
d. Armspan $= 18.62 + 0.87(163) = 160.43$, or about 160 cm

4.25 a. Refer to the scatterplot. **b.** The trend is not linear.

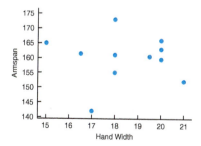

4.27 a. Predicted Armspan $= 13.1 + 0.948$ Height (Rounding may vary.)
b. Minitab: slope $= 0.948$, intercept $= 13.1$
StatCrunch: slope $= 0.94847838$, intercept $= 13.093566$
Excel: slope $= 0.948478$, intercept $= 13.09357$
TI-83/84: slope $= 0.9484783769$, intercept $= 13.09356647$
SPSS: slope $= 0.948$, intercept $= 13.094$

4.29 The horizontal axis starts at 0. To zoom in on the data, the horizontal axis should have started at about 160. This would have rescaled the graph, making it easier to interpret.

4.31 The relationship for the women is stronger because the correlation is closer to 1.

4.33 a. The slope would be near 0. **b.** r is about 0. **c.** Last two digits of Social Insurance Number is not related to age.

4.35 Explanations will vary.

	x	y
a.	litres of gas	kilometres driven
b.	laying date	clutch size
c.	weight	belt size

4.37 a. The negative trend shows that countries with higher contraceptive prevalence rates tend to have lower fertility rates. **b.** $5.39 - 4.79(0.70) = 2.04$, or about 2 births per woman

4.39 a. The graph shows that young drivers and old drivers have more fatalities and that the safest drivers are between about 40 and 60 years of age. **b.** It would not be appropriate for linear regression because the trend is not linear.

4.41. The answers are given in the order shown in the Guidance section.

1: The regression line is shown with the scatterplot.

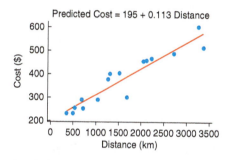

2: Is the linear model appropriate?

Given: In this case the answer is yes, because there is a linear trend. It is hard to see with so few points, but a strong curvature is not present and the cost tends to increase as the kilometres increase.

3: Predicted Cost $= 195 + 0.113$ Distance

4: Put in the correct regression line (shown in Step 1).

5: Interpret the slope and intercept in context.

For the slope: For every additional kilometre, on average, the price goes up by 0.113 dollars (or about 11 cents).

For the intercept: A trip of 0 kilometres is predicted to cost about 195 dollars on average. Beware of extrapolation. The linear trend might not continue near 0 kilometres and so this prediction could be very different from truth.

6: Final answer: For the hypothetical flight of 566 kilometres, you would expect to pay

$$195 + 0.113 \times 566 = 258.96, \text{ or about 259 dollars}$$

4.43 a.

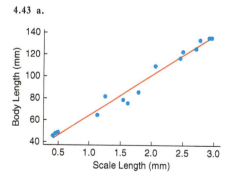

b. 0.987 **c.** Predicted Body Length $= 27.4 + 36.4$ Scale Length **d.** The slope is 36.4. Pumpkinseed fish whose scale lengths differ by 1 mm have body lengths that differ by approximately 36.4 mm. **e.** 27.4 mm

4.45 a. The correlation should be positive. Food items that contain a high amount of fat tend to have a lot of calories. **b.** See graph. **c.** 0.855 **d.** Equation and line are shown on plot. **e.** The difference in average number of calories for Tim Hortons breakfast items whose fat content differs by 1 gram is about 12 calories.

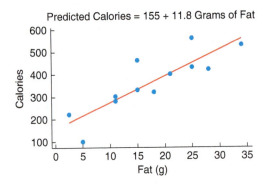

Predicted Calories = 155 + 11.8 Grams of Fat

Section 4.3

4.47 a. An influential point is a point that changes the regression equation in a significant way. **b.** Going to church may not cause lower blood pressure; just because two variables are related does not show that one caused the other. It could be that healthy people are more likely to go to church, or there could be other confounding factors.

4.49 Older children have larger shoes and have studied math longer. Large shoes do not cause higher grades. Both are affected by age.

4.51 Square 0.67 and you get 0.4489, so the coefficient of determination is about 45%. Therefore, 45% of the variation in weight can be explained by the regression line.

4.53 The cholesterol going down might be partly caused by regression toward the mean.

4.55 a. The salary is $2.099 thousand less for each year later that the person was hired, or $2.099 thousand more for each year earlier. **b.** The intercept ($4,255,000) would be the salary for a person who started in the year 0, which does not make sense.

4.57 a. See graph.

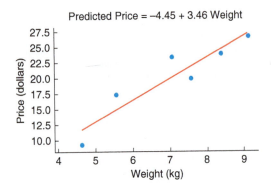

Predicted Price = −4.45 + 3.46 Weight

b. $r = 0.933$
A positive correlation suggests that larger turkeys tend to have a higher price. **c.** Predicted Price = −4.45 + 3.46 Weight **d.** The line is on the graph. **e.** The slope: For each additional kilogram, the price goes up by $3.46. The interpretation of the intercept is inappropriate, because it is not possible to have a turkey that weighs 0 kilograms.
f. The 14-kilogram free turkey changes the correlation to −0.397 and changes the equation to

$$\text{Predicted Price} = 27.1 - 1.24 \text{ Weight}$$

This implies that the bigger the turkey, the less it costs! The 14-kilogram free turkey was an influential point, which really changed the results.

4.59 a. Positive correlation **b.** The difference in expenditure per student for provinces whose educators' pay differs by 1 dollar is about 6 cents ($0.06). **c.** It does not make sense to interpret the intercept, which would predict that for an average pay of $0, expenditure per student would be $6427.

4.61 a. Correlation is negative. **b.** The difference in grades for students whose hours of paid work differ by one hour is almost half a point, with students who work less getting better grades. **c.** A student who did not work would expect to get a score of about 87 on average.

4.63 a. Predicted Mother's Education = 3.12 + 0.637 Father's Education; Predicted Mother's Education = 3.12 + 0.637 (12) = 10.76; Predicted Mother's Education = 3.12 + 0.637 (4.0) = 5.67
b. Predicted Father's Education = 2.78 + 0.637 (Mother's Education);

Predicted Father's Education = 2.78 + 0.637 (12) = 10.42;

Predicted Father's Education = 2.78 + 0.637 (4) = 5.33
c. Regression toward the mean: Values for the predictor variable that are far from the mean lead to responses that are closer to the mean.

4.65 1: i. Slope: $b_1 = r\dfrac{s_y}{s_x} = 0.7\dfrac{10}{10} = 0.7$

ii. Intercept: $b_0 = \bar{y} - b_1\bar{x}$

$$b_0 = 75 - 0.7(75) = 22.5$$

iii. Equation: Predicted Final = 22.5 + 0.7 Midterm

2: Predicted Final = 22.5 + 0.7 Midterm

$$= 22.5 + 0.7(95)$$

$$= 89$$

3: The score of 89 is lower than 95 because of regression toward the mean.

Chapter Review Exercises

4.67 a. $r = 0.941$

Predicted Weight = −245 + 5.80 Height

b.

Height	Weight
60(2.54) = 152.4 cm	105/2.205 = 47.6190 kg
66(2.54) = 167.64 cm	140/2.205 = 63.4921 kg
72(2.54) = 182.88 cm	185/2.205 = 83.9002 kg
70(2.54) = 177.8 cm	145/2.205 = 65.7596 kg
63(2.54) = 160.02 cm	120/2.205 = 54.4218 kg

c. The correlation between height and weight is 0.941. It does not matter whether you use inches and pounds or centimetres and kilograms. A change of units does not affect the correlation.
d. The equations are different.

Predicted Weight Pounds = −245 + 5.80 Height (in inches)

Predicted Weight Kilograms = −111 + 1.03 Height (in centimetres)

4.69 a. Choose $r = +0.84$ **b.** Price = −11.3 + 0.209 Square Feet

The slope is 0.209. It says that the difference in average price for homes that differ in size by one square foot is about 209 dollars. The intercept of −11.3 represents the price of a home with 0 square feet, which does not make sense.
c. 2000 sq ft: about $407 thousand **d.** $0.84^2 = 0.7056$
About 71% of the variation in price can be explained by the regression line.

4.71 a. See graph.

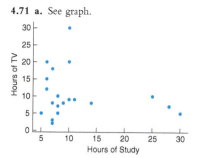

b. The trend is not linear. **c.** The correlation is near zero.

4.73 a. r is the square root of 0.057, which is 0.24. It is positive because the slope is positive. **b.** Predicted Weight = 49.4 + 0.413(35) = 63.86, or about 64 kilograms. **c.** The difference in average weight for females whose age differs by one year is 0.413 kilograms. **d.** It is not appropriate to interpret the intercept because no woman is 0 years of age.

4.75 The trend is positive. In general, if one twin has a higher-than-average level of education, so does the other twin. The point that shows one twin with 1 year of education and the other twin with 12 years is an outlier. (The point showing one twin with 15 years and the other with 8 years could also be considered unusual.)

4.77 There is a positive trend, and the relationship is very strong (97.5% of variation explained by the regression line). The slope of 0.998 is approximately 1, so for every beat per minute more on the first measurement, there is a beat per minute more on the second one. The intercept cannot be interpreted. The regression implies that both measurements are about the same.

4.79 Correlation table:

	Diameter	Height
Height	0.519	
Volume	0.967	0.598

The diameter is a better predictor of volume than the height because there is a larger correlation between diameter and volume than between height and volume.

4.81 There appears to be a positive trend: movies that have larger budgets bring in more income. However, there are two very influential points (*Avatar* and *Titanic*). If we ignore those points, the rest of the points do not seem to follow a linear trend, so it is debatable whether or not linear regression should be performed. The regression equation is Predicted Gross Income = 585 + 3.50 Budget, which indicates that for each additional million dollars budgeted, gross income tends to increase by $3.5 M. The intercept here cannot be interpreted.

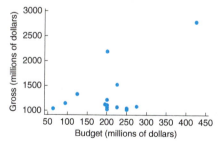

4.83 and 4.85 Answers will vary.

CHAPTER 5

Section 5.1

5.1 a. 2 6 4 2 7   4 0 6 5 0
b. TTTTH   TTTHT
c. No. We got 2 heads.

5.3 True value of the probability; it is not based on an experiment.

5.5 Estimated probability; it is based on an experiment.

Section 5.2

5.7 a. The nine equally likely outcomes are Beasley, Blackett, Coffee, Craft, Fowlkes, Higgs, Lammey, Skahan, Ward. **b.** The outcomes that make up event A are Blackett and Skahan. **c.** 2/9, or about 22.2% **d.** Beasley, Coffee, Craft, Fowlkes, Higgs, Lammey, Ward.

5.9 1.3 could not be a probability because it is larger than 1. 150% could not be a probability because it is larger than 100%. −0.50 could not be a probability because it is negative (less than 0).

5.11 a. A heart: 13/52 or 1/4 **b.** A red card: 26/52 or 1/2 **c.** An ace: 4/52 or 1/13 **d.** A face card: 12/52 or 3/13 **e.** A three: 4/52 or 1/13 Answers may also be in decimal or percentage form.

5.13 a. P(guessing correctly) = 1/2 **b.** P(guessing incorrectly) = 1/2

5.15

	Number of Girls	Probability
a.	0	1/16
b.	1	4/16 = 1/4
c.	2	6/16 = 3/8
d.	3	4/16 = 1/4
e.	4	1/16

5.17 The probability of being born on a Friday OR Saturday OR Sunday is 3/7, or 42.86%.

5.19 a. 1037/1948 = 53.2% **b.** 375/1948 = 19.3%

5.21 224/1948 = 11.5%

5.23 (474 + 740)/1948 = 62.3%

5.25 The answers follow the guided steps.

1. P(female) = 1037/1948

2. P(NDP) = 375/1948

3. They are not mutually exclusive because there are people who are female AND identify with the NDP.

4. P(female AND NDP) = 224/1948

5. If you don't subtract the probability of being female AND identifying with the NDP, you will be counting those people twice, once when you count the females and once when you count those who identify with the NDP.

6. $\frac{1037}{1948} + \frac{375}{1948} - \frac{224}{1948} = \frac{1188}{1948} = 61\%$

7. The probability of being female OR identifying with the NDP is 61%.

5.27 a. Mutually exclusive **b.** Not mutually exclusive

5.29 Answers will vary. Choose any two categories that do not "overlap." For example, two events that are mutually exclusive are identifying with the NDP and identifying with the Conservative Party.

5.31 a. You don't know what percentage of households have at least one cat AND at least one dog. You cannot simply add the percentages, because the events are not mutually exclusive and you would count households with at least one cat AND at least one dog twice. **b.** P(at least one cat OR at least one dog) = 0.30, or 30%.

5.33 a. 4/6, or 66.7% **b.** 3/6 = 1/2, or 50%

5.35 a. A OR B: 0.18 + 0.25 = 0.43 **b.** A OR B OR C: 0.18 + 0.25 + 0.37 = 0.80 **c.** Lower than a C: 1 − 0.80 = 0.20

5.37 a. Most: Category 3: married OR have children **b.** Fewest: Category 4: married AND have children

5.39 a. 0 heads: 1/4 (Decimals and percentages are also acceptable.) **b.** 1 head: 1/2 (from 2/4) **c.** 2 heads: 1/4 **d.** At least 1 head: 3/4 **e.** Not more than 2 heads (which means 2 or fewer heads): 1 (from 4/4)

5.41 The total is 34,483 thousand.
a. More than 20 and at most 40: 9460/34,483, or 27.4% **b.** Over 60: (5634 + 1378)/34,483, or 20.3% **c.** More than 20 and less than 40 OR over 60: 9460/34,483 + 7012/34,483 = 16,472/34,483 or about 47.8%. Since the two age categories of "more than 20 and at most 40" and "over 60" are mutually exclusive, it is enough to simply add the probabilities corresponding to these events.

5.43 a. More than 8 mistakes: $1 - 0.48 - 0.30 = 0.22$ **b.** 3 or more mistakes: $0.30 + 0.22 = 0.52$ **c.** At most 8 mistakes: $0.48 + 0.30 = 0.78$ **d.** The events in parts a and c are complementary because "at most 8 mistakes" means from 0 mistakes up to 8 mistakes. "More than 8 mistakes" means 9, 10, up to 12 mistakes. Together, these mutually exclusive events form the entire sample space.

5.45 a. Male: 48/108, or 44.4% **b.** At least 20 hrs on Facebook: 3/108, or 2.8% **c.** Male OR at least 20 hrs on Facebook: 48/108, or 44.4% **d.** Female OR at least 20 hrs on Facebook: 63/108, or 58.3%

Section 5.3

5.47 a. NDP | female **b. i.** female | NDP: 224/375, or 59.7% **ii.** NDP | female: 224/1037, or 21.6% **iii.** 224/1948, or 11.5%

5.49 a. 261/1037 = 25.2% **b.** 213/911 = 23.4% **c.** Women

5.51 Because men are more likely to be left-handed than women, gender and handedness are related.

5.53 a. Hair colour and age are independent because hair colour does not change in this age range (assuming that this age range is not susceptible to premature greying of their hair). **b.** Hair colour and eye colour are not independent, because people with dark eyes are more likely to have dark hair.

5.55 Nationality and opinion on same-sex marriage are not independent; they are related. Canadians were more likely to support same-sex marriage.

5.57 They are not independent because females are more likely than males to identify with the NDP.

5.59 The answers follow the format for the Guided Exercises.

	M	W	Total
Right	18	42	60
Left	12	28	40
Total	30	70	100

Step 1: See table.

Step 2: 60/100, or 60%

Step 3: 18/30 = 60%

Step 4: The variables are independent because the probability of having the right thumb on top given a person is a man is equal to the probability that a person has the right thumb on top (for the whole data set).

5.61 a. See table.

	Used Marijuana	Not Used Marijuana	Total
Male	11	37	48
Female	9	51	60
Total	20	88	108

b. Marijuana: 20/108; Marijuana | Male: 11/48. Because these two probabilities are not the same, the events male and marijuana use in the past six months are not independent.

5.63 a. 1/8 **b.** 1/8

5.65 They are the same. Both probabilities are $\left(\frac{1}{6}\right)^5$ or $\frac{1}{7776}$.

5.67 a. Neither graduated with debt: $0.40(0.40) = 0.16$ **b.** At least one graduated with debt: $1 - 0.16 = 0.84$

5.69 P(have C AND test positive) = P(have C) P(test positive | have C)
$$= 0.00008(0.84)$$
$$= 0.000067$$

5.71
a. $\text{P(C | test positive)} = \dfrac{(0.00008 \times 0.84)}{(0.00008 \times 0.84) + (0.99992 \times 0.03)} = 0.0022$

b. $\text{P(No C | test positive)} = \dfrac{(0.99992 \times 0.03)}{(0.00008 \times 0.84) + (0.99992 \times 0.03)} = 0.9978$

5.73 a. i. P(test positive | PC) **b. i.** P(test positive | no PC)
c. $\text{P(PC | test positive)} = \dfrac{(0.143 \times 0.75)}{(0.143 \times 0.75) + (0.857 \times 0.03)} = 0.8066$

d. $\text{P(PC | test negative)} = \dfrac{(0.143 \times 0.25)}{(0.143 \times 0.25) + (0.857 \times 0.97)} = 0.0412$

5.75
a. $\text{P(M | not complete)} = \dfrac{(0.7 \times 0.05)}{(0.7 \times 0.05) + (0.3 \times 0.1)} = 0.538$

b. $\text{P(C | complete)} = \dfrac{(0.3 \times 0.9)}{(0.3 \times 0.9) + (0.7 \times 0.95)} = 0.2888$

Section 5.4

5.77 a. Use only eight of the digits 0 through 9, say 1–8, and ignore 0 and 9. Count how many times a 1 appears. **b.** The estimated probability is 1/5 and the true probability is 1/8.

5.79 The estimated probabilities are 8/20, 20/100, and 167/1000. The true probability is 1/6. As the number of rolls increases, the estimated probability approaches the true probability.

5.81 a. 0.5 **b.** About 200 rolls (answers will vary) **c.** Law of Large Numbers **d.** H

5.83 a. You could use the numbers 1, 2, 3, 4, 5, and 6 to represent the outcomes and ignore 0 and 7–9, but answers to this will vary. **b.** The estimated probability will vary. The true probability is 1/6.

Chapter Review Exercises

5.85 The estimated probability is 377/1300, or 29%.

5.87 a. Independent: the flip of one coin has no bearing on the flip of the following coin. **b.** Related: certain breeds tend to be quite large while others are small.

5.89 a. $(0.38)^4 = 0.0209$ **b.** $1 - 0.0209 = 0.9791$

5.91 a. $(0.80)^2 = 0.64$ **b.** The probability will be different because the events are not independent.

5.93 a. Both used marijuana: $(0.20)^2 = 0.04$ **b.** One OR the other used marijuana: $0.20 + 0.20 - 0.04 = 0.36$ **c.** One OR the other used marijuana, but not both: $0.20 + 0.20 - 2 \times 0.04 = 0.32$

5.95 a. 800 **b.** 1200

5.97 a. P(test pos) = $(0.1 \times 0.95) + (0.90 \times 0.02) = 0.1130$
b. $\text{P(steroid use | test positive)} = \dfrac{(0.1 \times 0.95)}{(0.1 \times 0.95) + (0.9 \times 0.02)} = 0.8407$

c. $\text{P(steroid use | test negative)} = \dfrac{(0.1 \times 0.05)}{(0.1 \times 0.05) + (0.9 \times 0.98)} = 0.0056$

5.99 a. P(ban) = $(0.24 \times 0.67) + (0.38 \times 0.61) + (0.07 \times 0.57) + (0.13 \times 0.55) + (0.18 \times 0.51) = 0.5958$ **b.** P(Prai | ban) = $(0.18 \times 0.51)/0.5958 = 0.1541$ **c.** P(Que | no ban) = $(0.24 \times 0.33)/(1 - 0.5958) = 0.1959$

5.101 Answers will vary. Example: red die is 1, blue die is 2.

5.103 Answers will vary.

5.105 Answers will vary.

5.107 Smaller sample sizes typically have more variability than larger sample sizes. Therefore, the player is more likely to perform poorly (or exceedingly well) in games during which the player plays less.

5.109 a. A single trial consists of filling six bottles. **b.** One way (of many) to represent the status of each bottle would be to let the digits 0 and 1 represent an underfilled bottle and the remaining eight digits 2 through 9 represent a correctly filled bottle. **c.** The response variable is how many of the bottles in a six-pack are underfilled. **d.** The event of interest is whether three or more bottles in a six-pack are underfilled. **e. and f.** Answers will vary depending on the assignment of part b.

CHAPTER 6

Answers may vary slightly due to rounding or type of technology used.

Section 6.1

6.1 a. Discrete **b.** Continuous

6.3 a. Discrete **b.** Continuous

6.5

Outcome	1	2	3	4	5	6
Probability	0.1	0.2	0.2	0.2	0.2	0.1

6.7 a. See table.

Win	Prob
$3	1/6
$0	1/2
−$4	1/3

b. See graph.

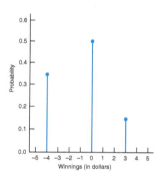

6.9 a. See table.

Win	Prob
−$400	0.45
$400	0.55

b. See graph.

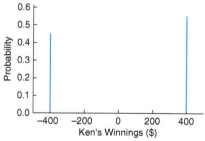

c. If you were Billy, it would not be in your favour to go second; you would want to be in Ken's position and go first.

6.11 $(15 − 7)(0.05) = 0.4$, or 40%, and the area between 7 and 15 should be shaded.

Section 6.2

6.13 a. ii., 95% **b.** i., almost all **c.** iii., 68% **d.** iv., 50% **e.** ii., 13.5%

6.15 a. iii., 50% **b.** iii., 68% **c.** v., about 0% **d.** v., about 0% **e.** i., 95% **f.** iv., 13.5%

6.17 Figure (b), about 0.63

6.19 a. 0.8461, or about 85% **b.** $1 − 0.8461 = 0.1539$, or about 15%

6.21 a. 0.9608, or about 96% **b.** $1 − 0.9608 = 0.0392$, or about 4% **c.** $0.1515 − 0.0968 = 0.0547$, or about 5%

6.23 a, b, and **c** are all 0.000. **d.** The proportion to the right of 4.00 would be the largest of the three, and the proportion to the right of 50.00 would be the smallest. **e.** below −10.00

6.25 The answers use the steps given in the Guided Exercises.

1. $z = \dfrac{x − \mu}{\sigma} = \dfrac{80 − 63}{10} = \dfrac{17}{10} = 1.7$

2. 63 is the mean, and it belongs right below 0 because 0 is the mean of the standard Normal or the mean z-score.

3. and 4. are shown in the sketch.

5. 0.9554

6. $1 − 0.9554 = 0.0446$

7. The percentage of female students writing the PAT in math who scored 80% or more is about 4.46%.

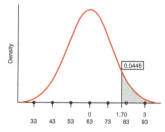

6.27 0.8413, or about 84%

6.29 0.6827, or about 68% (Empirical Rule)

6.31 a. 0.2912, or about 29% **b.** 0.0485, or about 5% **c.** $0.29(0.29) = 0.084$, or about 8% **d.** 29% of 750, or about 218

6.33 0.3707

6.35 a. 0.2420, or about 24% **b.** 0.0968, or about 9.7%

6.37 About 0.6% of the days in January have maximum temperatures of −30°C or less.

6.39 a. 0.4168, or about 42% **b.** about 51 **c.** 63 **d.** Answers will vary.

6.41 Part a asks for a probability, and part b asks for an originating value.

6.43 $z = −1.28$

6.45 a. $z = 0.56$ **b.** $z = −1.00$

6.47 The answers follow the guided steps.

1. The test score will be above the mean, because 96% of female students score worse, so it must be a very high grade.

2. See the figure.

3. $z = 1.75$

4. See the figure.

5. $63 + 1.75(10) = 63 + 17.5 = 80.5$

6. See the figure.

7. The PAT score for female Grade 12 students at the 96th percentile is 80.5.

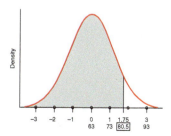

6.49 37.2°C

6.51 155 cm

6.53 a. The Wechsler IQ at the 75th percentile is 110. **b.** The interquartile range (IQR) is 110 − 90, or 20. **c.** The interquartile range (20) is larger than the standard deviation (15).

6.55 a. 76th percentile **b.** About 177.8 cm

Section 6.3

6.57 Conditions

Two complementary outcomes: boy or girl

Fixed number of trials: 4 children

Same probability of success on each trial: 1/2 probability of a boy

All trials independent: Because there are no twins, the gender of each child is independent of the gender of the others.

6.59 There is not a fixed number of trials, because the students flip the coins *until* the class is over.

6.61 It is not a binomial experiment, because the two people (married to each other) are not independent with respect to getting a divorce. If one gets a divorce, then the other one gets a divorce.

6.63 $b(n, p, x)$ **a.** $b(100, 0.38, 44)$ **b.** $b(10, 0.90, 9)$ **c.** $b(10, 0.25, 6)$ **d.** $b(20, 0.30, 8)$

6.65 $b(6, 0.40, 2) = 0.311$

6.67 a. $b(10, 0.08, 2 \text{ or fewer}) = 0.9599$, or about 96% **b.** $b(10, 0.08, 3 \text{ or more}) = 1 − b(10, 0.08, 2 \text{ or fewer}) = 0.0401$, or about 4% **c.** $b(10, 0.08, \text{from 1 to 3}) = 0.5598$, or about 56%

6.69 a. $(0.5)(0.5) = 0.25$, or 25% **b.** $(0.5)(0.5)(0.5) = 0.125$, or about 13% **c.** $1 − 0.125 = 0.875$, or about 88% **d.** Yes, the more children she has, the more likely she will be to have at least one boy.

6.71 a. $0.8(0.8)(0.8) = 0.512$ **b.** At least one being late is the complement of all being on time:

$$1 − 0.512 = 0.488$$

c. The flights might not be independent, because the weather could be bad and that might cause most of the flights to be late. Thus if one flight is late, the others are more likely to be late.

6.73 a. $0.25(20) = 5$; expect 5 **b.** $b(20, 0.25, 7) = 0.1124$ **c.** $b(20, 0.25, 7 \text{ or fewer}) = 0.8982$

6.75 a. YY YN NY NN

   b. YY 0.0676
   YN 0.1924
   NY 0.1924
   NN 0.5476

c. Neither has only cell: 0.5476 **d.** Exactly one has only cell: 0.3848

e. Both have only cell: 0.0676

6.77 a. In 50 flips, expect 25 heads, because np is 50 times 1/2.

   b. $\sigma = \sqrt{np(1 − p)} = \sqrt{50(0.5)(1 − 0.5)} = \sqrt{12.5} = 3.54$, or about 4 **c.** You should expect between 21 and 29 heads.

6.79 We expect 50 out of 200 people to have participated in online dating, give or take $\sqrt{200\,(0.25)\,(0.75)} = 6.12$.

6.81 a. Expect 11.

b. $\sigma = \sqrt{np(1 − p)} = \sqrt{100(0.11)(0.89)} = \sqrt{9.79} = 3.12$, or about 3, so the range of likely values is from 8 to 14.

c. Yes, because 25 is outside the range in part b.

Chapter Review Exercises

6.83 0.0409, or about 4%

6.85 a. 0.5987, or about 60% **b.** 37.2°C

6.87 Answers will vary. However, the probability that the next flip will be a head is 50%, because coin flips are independent.

6.89 a. $\mu = np = 200(0.32) = 64$ give or take about 7, because $\sigma = \sqrt{np(1 − p)} = \sqrt{200(0.32)(1 − 0.32)} = \sqrt{43.52} = 6.597$, or about 7 **b.** Yes, because 110 is outside the range in part a.

6.91 a. 189, give or take about 8 **b.** No, because 185 is inside the range in part a.

CHAPTER 7

Answers may vary slightly due to rounding or type of technology used.

Section 7.1

7.1 A parameter summarizes a characteristic of the population, and a statistic summarizes a characteristic of a sample.

7.3 a. $\bar{x}$ is a statistic, and μ is a parameter. **b.** $\bar{x}$

7.5 If you knew the ages of all Canadian prime ministers when they first became prime minister, you should not make inferences because you have the population, not a sample from the population.

7.7 You want to test a sample of batteries. If you tested them all until they burned out, no usable batteries would be left.

7.9 First, all 10 cards are put in a bowl. Then one is drawn out and noted.
   "With replacement": The card that is selected is replaced in the bowl, and a second draw is done. It is possible that the same student could be picked twice.
   "Without replacement": After the first card is drawn out, it is not replaced, and the second draw must be a different card.

7.11 Chosen: 7, 3, 5, 2

7.13 Billy took a convenience sample. The students polled are not likely to be a representation of the entire student population, so the inference is incorrect.

7.15 The population is all readers of *Time* magazine on the internet. The *Time* internet poll used a voluntary-response sample. It could be that only people who were really angry with the United States took time to submit their answers. The poll may have shown bias because of that fact.

7.17 The administrator could dismiss the negative findings by saying the results could be biased because the small percentage who chose to return the survey might be very different from the majority who did not return the survey.

7.19 No, the people you met would not be a random sample but a convenience sample.

7.21

	With Persuasion	Without Persuasion
Support Differential Fees	21 + 20	8 + 12
Oppose Differential Fees	4 + 4	17 + 12

a. With persuasion 8/49 = 16.3%
b. Without persuasion 29/49 = 59.2%
c. Yes, the results were as expected, since those who heard the student's persuasive statement were less opposed (16.3%) than those who did not hear it (59.2%).

Section 7.2

7.23 a. The sketch should show bullet holes consistently to the left of the target and close to each other. If the bullets go consistently to the left, then there is bias, not lack of precision. **b.** The sketch should show bullet holes that are all near the centre of the target.

7.25 The small mean might have occurred by chance.

7.27 a. $17/30$, or about 56.7%, odd digits **b.** $17/30$ is $\hat{p}$ (p-hat), the sample proportion. **c.** The error is $17/30$ minus $15/30$ (or $2/30$) or about 6.7%

7.29 a. We should expect 0.18, or 18%, blue candies.

b. $\sqrt{\dfrac{p(1 − p)}{n}} = \sqrt{\dfrac{0.18 \times (1 − 0.18)}{100}} = \sqrt{\dfrac{0.1476}{100}} = \sqrt{0.001476} = 0.0384$

or about 3.84%.

c. We expect 18% blue candies, give or take 3.84%.

7.31 a. 50% seniors **b.** 0% seniors **c.** 50% seniors **d.** 100% seniors

Repetition	p (pop prop of seniors)	$\hat{p}$ (sample prop of seniors)	Error: $\hat{p} - p$
1 (from part a)	$2/5 = 0.4$	$1/2 = 0.5$	$0.5 - 0.4 = 0.1$
2 (from part b)	$2/5 = 0.4$	$0/2 = 0.0$	$0.0 - 0.4 = -0.4$
3 (from part c)	$2/5 = 0.4$	$1/2 = 0.5$	$0.5 - 0.4 = 0.1$
4 (from part d)	$2/5 = 0.4$	$2/2 = 1.0$	$1.0 - 0.4 = 0.6$

Section 7.3

7.33 $z = \dfrac{0.24 - 0.18}{0.0384} = 1.56$

The area to the right of 1.56 is 0.0594.

The probability that the percentage of blue candies will be 24% or more is 0.0594.

7.35 Because the sampling distribution of the sample proportion is approximately Normal, we know the probability that the proportion of available First Nations jurors will fall within two standard deviations is about 0.95. Therefore, the probability of falling more than two standard deviations away from the mean of 0.10 is about 0.05.

7.37 Answers are given in the order shown in the Guided Exercises.

Step 1: $p = 0.15$

Step 2: $np = 70(0.15) = 10.5$ which is more than 10

$n(1 - p) = 70(0.85) = 59.5$ which is more than 10

The other assumptions were given.

Step 3:

$$SD = \sqrt{\frac{p(1 - p)}{n}} = \sqrt{\frac{0.15(1 - 0.15)}{70}} = \sqrt{\frac{0.1275}{70}} = \sqrt{0.00182} = 0.0427$$

$$z = \frac{0.12 - 0.15}{0.0427} = -0.70$$

The area to the right of a z-value of -0.70 is 0.7580.

Step 4: The probability is represented by the area to the right of -0.70, because the question asks for the probability that the sample proportion will be "at least" 0.12, which translates to a z-value of -0.70. The means we are asked to find the probability that the z-value will be -0.70 or greater.

Step 5: The probability that at least 12% of 70 will not find an articling position is 0.7580, or about 76%.

7.39 a. Expect 0.08. **b.** The approximately probability is 0.122. It should be shown in a Normal curve. **c.** 0.0099 or 1%, and 360 chairs **d.** The answer to part c is smaller because 9% is farther out in the right tail than 8.5%, and it is the tail area that gives the probability we want.

7.41 a. 0.5 **b.** 0.5 **c.** 0.103 **d.** Lower, because the probability of guessing correctly on each question is lower when there are four options.

Section 7.4

7.43 (0.0463, 0.0599)

7.45 a. 920/2000, or 46.0%, believe there will good times financially. **b.** (43.82%, 48.18%)

7.47 a. We are 95% confident that the population percentage of voters supporting Candidate X is between 53% and 57%. **b.** There is no evidence that Candidate X could lose, because the interval is entirely above 50%. **c.** A sample from Toronto would not be representative of the entire country and would thus be worthless in this context.

7.49 a. 17/30, or 0.5667 **b.** SD_{est} given as 0.090 $m = 1.96 \times 0.090 = 0.1764$ **c.** 95% CI (0.390, 0.743) **d.** $m = 1.28 \times 0.090 = 0.115$ 80% CI (0.452, 0.682) **e.** 99% CI (0.335, 0.799) **f.** The 99% confidence interval is widest, and the 80% interval is narrowest. A greater confidence level requires a larger $z^{\star}$.

7.51 a. $SD_{est} \sqrt{\frac{0.9(1 - 0.90)}{1500}} = 0.0077$, or 0.77% **b.** 1.5% **c.** (88.50%, 91.5%) **d.** The confidence interval found in c would support this claim, as the lower bound is greater than 85%, and we are confident that the current percentage is higher than 85%.

7.53 a. 92/113, or 81.4%, reported dreaming in colour. **b.** (0.742, 0.886) **c.** The interval does not capture 29.24%. The results in 2003 were significantly different from the results in 1942.

7.55 a. Each student should find 15, because 15 is half of 30. **b.** You would expect about 4 out of 40 not to capture 50%, because with a 90% confidence interval about 10% should not capture, and 10% of 40 is 4.

7.57 The proportion 78/308 is the population proportion, not a sample proportion. You should not find a confidence interval unless you have a sample and are making statements about the population from which the sample has been drawn.

7.59 a. 84/561 = 14.97% **b.** 95% CI (0.120, 0.179) **c.** 90% CI (0.1249, 0.1745) **d.** The 95% interval is wider and the 90% interval is narrower. To get a higher degree of confidence, we need to widen the interval.

7.61 a. 525/1009 = 52% **b.** 95% CI (0.489, 0.551) **c.** A 99% CI would be wider.

7.63 a. 74/1438 = 5.15% **b.** 95% CI (0.0401, 0.0629) **c.** 5% is plausible because it is inside the interval.

Section 7.5

7.65 a. $n = \dfrac{1}{m^2} = \dfrac{1}{0.015^2} = \dfrac{1}{0.000225} = 4444.4$

They should poll 4445 people.

b. A 1% margin of error would require a larger sample than a 1.5% margin of error. **c.** 90% would require a smaller sample size.

7.67 $n = \dfrac{1}{m^2} = \dfrac{1}{0.03^2} = \dfrac{1}{0.0009} = 1111.1$: Requires 1112.

$n = \dfrac{1}{m^2} = \dfrac{1}{0.015^2} = \dfrac{1}{0.000225} = 4444.4$: Requires 4445.

4445/1112 is 4.

To get half the margin of error, you must multiply the sample size by 4.

Chapter Review Exercises

7.69 a. 515/691, or 74.5%, had been exposed to traffic. **b.** 95% CI (0.713, 0.778) **c.** No. Without random assignment, you cannot draw conclusions about cause and effect.

7.71 $n = 1101$

$n = \dfrac{1}{m^2}$

and so $m = \dfrac{1}{\sqrt{n}} = \dfrac{1}{\sqrt{1101}} = \dfrac{1}{33.1813} = 0.0301$, or about 3%

7.73 a. 838/1101 is 76%. **b.** We are 95% confident that the proportion of Canadians who support being able to purchase private health insurance is between 73.58% and 78.6%. **c.** Yes, as the lower bound of the interval in part b is greater than 2/3. **d.** The percentage is the same. With a small sample size the interval would be wider.

7.75 a. 307/363 is 84.6%. **b.** We are 95% confident that the proportion of Ontario residents who support being able to purchase private health insurance is between 80.89% and 88.31%. **c.** Yes, as the lower bound of the interval in part b is greater than 70% in British Columbia.

7.77 95% confidence interval (52%, 60%) or (0.52, 0.60)
This suggests that a majority of adults believe the feeding tube should have been removed, because the interval is entirely above 50%.

CHAPTER 8

Answers may vary slightly due to type of technology or rounding.

Section 8.1

8.1 population parameter

8.3 Small.

8.5 ii $p = 0.50$

8.7 a. iv **b.** alternative

8.9 a. i **b.** ii

8.11 iii

8.13 does not, 0.05

8.15 $z = -0.82$

8.17 a. $z = -2.12$ **b.** The p-value tells us that if the true proportion of teenagers who use their cell phone while driving is 0.25, then there is a 0.017 probability that one would get a sample proportion that is 0.12 or smaller.

Section 8.2

8.19 In Figure (a), the shaded area could be a p-value because it includes tail areas only; it would be for a two-tailed alternative because both tails are shaded. In Figure (b) the shaded area would not be a p-value because it is the area between two z-values.

8.21 $z = 3.00$. It is farthest from 0 and therefore has the smallest tail area.

8.23 He has not demonstrated ESP; 10 right out of 20 is only 50% right, which you should expect from guessing.

Section 8.3

8.25 H_0: The death rate after starting hand washing is still 9.9%, or $p = 0.099$ (p is the proportion of all deaths at the clinic).

H_A: The death rate after starting hand washing is less than 9.9%, or $p < 0.099$.

8.27 a. H_0: The proportion of Canadians who have driven at least once while impaired has not changed since 2010, or $p = 0.27$. H_A: The proportion of Canadians who have driven at least once while impaired has changed since 2010, or $p \neq 0.27$. **b.** two-tailed

8.29 *Step 1:* H_0: $p = 0.50$, H_A: $p < 0.50$, where p is the proportion of Canadians living in Alberta, Saskatchewan, and Manitoba who favour stronger gun laws. *Step 2:* One proportion z-test (given), sample size is large (247 times 0.5 equals 123.5 which is more than 10), sample is taken randomly, and the population is large. *Step 3:* $\hat{p} = 44/247 = 0.1781$, $SD = 0.0318$, $z = -10.12$, p-value < 0.0001. *Step 4:* If the null is true, we are unlikely to observe a more surprising result. Reject H_0. Choose conclusion ii.

8.31 Random sample was mentioned.

Large sample: $np_0 = 113(0.29) = 32.77 > 10$ and $n(1 - p_0) = 113(0.71) = 80.23 > 10$.

Large population: There are more than 1130 people in the population of dreamers.

So the conditions are met.

8.33 $z = 2.56$, p-value $= 0.005$.

8.35 *Step 3:* $z = 2.83$, p-value $= 0.002$. *Step 4:* Reject H_0. The probability of doing this well by chance alone is so small that we must conclude that the student is not guessing.

8.37 Pick the graph shown in Figure (a). The observed value of 13 right out of 20 is more than half, so the z-statistic will be bigger than 0. The right tail area corresponds to the p-value.

8.39 a. *Step 1:* H_A: $p > 0.50$, where p is the population proportion of people who believe that schools should ban sugary foods. *Step 2:* One-proportion z-test, the sampling is random, the sample size large, and the population large. *Step 3:* $z = 1.26$, $p = 0.103$ (one-tailed). *Step 4:* Do not reject the null hypothesis.

b. Pick ii.

8.41 a. $\hat{p} = 532/1005$, or 0.5299. **b.** *Step 1:* H_0: $p = 0.45$, H_A: $p \neq 0.45$, where p is the proportion of Canadians who believe global warming is

fact. *Step 2:* One proportion z-test (given), the sample size is large (1005 times 0.45 equals 450, which is more than 10), the sample is taken randomly, and the population is large. *Step 3:* $SD = 0.0318$, $z = 5.09$, p-value < 0.0001. **c.** *Step 4:* If the null is true, it is unlikely to observe a more surprising result. Reject H_0. **d.** Choose ii.

8.43 *Step 1:* H_0: $p = 0.25$, H_A: $p \neq 0.25$, where p is the proportion of fish with levels of mercury that are unsafe to eat. *Step 2:* One proportion z-test (given), the sample size is large (250 times 0.25 equals 62.5, which is more than 10), the sample is taken randomly, and the population is large. *Step 3:* $SD = 0.0274$, $z = 1.83$, p-value $= 0.0672$. *Step 4:* If the null is true, we are unlikely to observe a more surprising result. Do not reject H_0. We are not saying that the percentage is 25%; rather we are only saying we cannot reject the claim that it is 25%.

8.45 *Step 1:* H_A: $p \neq 0.09$, where p is the population proportion of T's in the English language. *Step 2:* One-proportion z-test, the sample is random and large enough, and the population is large. *Step 3:* $z = -0.86$, p-value $= 0.392$. *Step 4:* Do not reject H_0. We cannot reject 9% as the current proportion of T's.

Section 8.4

8.47

0: Vioxx percentage heart attack $= 3.5\%$

Placebo percentage heart attack $= 1.9\%$

So the risk of heart attack in the sample was greater for those taking Vioxx.

1: H_0: $p_V = p_p$, where p_V is the population proportion of heart attacks for those who could use Vioxx and p_p is the population proportion of heart attacks for those who could use the placebo.

H_A: $p_V > p_p$

2: We don't have a random sample, but we do have random assignment.

$n_1 \times \hat{p} = 1287(0.027069) = 34.84$, which is more than 10

$n_1 \times (1 - \hat{p}) = 1287(0.972931) = 1252.16$, which is more than 10

$n_2 \times \hat{p} = 1299(0.027069) = 35.16$, which is more than 10

$n_2 \times (1 - \hat{p}) \geq 1299(0.027069) = 35.16$, which is more than 10

3: $z = 2.46$ (or -2.46)

p-value $= 0.007$

4: Reject H_0 and choose ii. Do not generalize because you do not have a random sample.

Causality: Yes, you can conclude cause and effect for this group of patients because of the format of the study, including random assignment to groups. Vioxx caused a significantly increased rate of heart attacks.

8.49 a. Vaccine: 1.9% got the virus. Placebo: 4.9% got the virus. So the vaccine group got the virus at a lower rate, which is what was hoped for. **b.** *Step 3:* $z = 5.85$ (or -5.85), p-value < 0.001. *Step 4:* Reject H_0. The vaccine causes a significantly lower chance of getting the virus, but don't generalize.

8.51 a. For nicotine gum, the proportion quitting was 0.106. For the placebo, it was 0.040. This was what was hoped for—that the drug was helpful compared to the placebo. **b.** $z = 7.23$ (or -7.23) **c.** p-value < 0.0001. If the null hypothesis is true, the probability that another placebo-controlled experiment would produce an outcome that is just as surprising as this outcome is less than 0.0001. **d.** Reject H_0. The proportion of smokers who quit using nicotine gum is significantly higher than the proportion of smokers who quit using a placebo. We can't generalize because we do not have a random sample.

8.53 a. Men: 46.2% smiling. Women: 51.1% smiling. **b.** *Step 1:* H_A: $p_{men} \neq p_{women}$ (where p is the proportion smiling). *Step 2:* Two-proportion z-test, large sample size, assume random sample, population large. *Step 3:* $z = 6.13$ (or -6.13), p-value < 0.001. *Step 4:* Reject H_0. There is a significant difference in rate of smiling for men and women. **c.** The difference is significant because of the large sample size.

Section 8.5

8.55 No; we don't use "prove" because we cannot be 100% sure of conclusions based on chance processes.

8.57 It is a null hypothesis.

8.59 Interpretations b and d are valid. Interpretations a and c are both "accepting" the null hypothesis claim, which is an incorrect way of expressing the outcome.

8.61 Far apart. Assuming the standard deviations are the same, the farther apart the two proportions are, the larger the absolute value of the numerator of z, and therefore the larger the absolute value of z and the smaller the p-value.

8.63 a. $0.43 \times 400 = 172$ Ontarians and $0.35 \times 400 = 140$ Albertans supported a plastic bag ban. **b.** *Step 1:* H_0: $p_{Ont} = p_{Alta}$, H_A: $p_{Ont} \neq p_{Alta}$. Use the two-proportion z-test, and compute $\hat{p} = \frac{172 + 140}{400 + 400} = 0.39$. The sample sizes are large enough, as $400 \times 0.39 = 156$ and $400 \times 0.61 = 244$ are greater than 10. The sample sizes are equal, so this is only checked once. The samples are random, and the populations both large. *Step 3:* $z = 2.32$, p-value $= 0.02$. *Step 4:* If the null is true, the probability of observing a result that is just as or more surprising is 0.01. Reject H_0. From the data, there is a difference in the population proportions. **c.** Repeat b, $\hat{p} = \frac{172 + 70}{400 + 200} = 0.4033$, $z = 1.88$, p-value $= 0.06$. Fail to reject H_0. From the data, there is no difference in the population proportions. **d.** Decreasing the sample size changed the result because the p-value increased from 2% to 6%.

8.65 Interpretation iii.

8.67 a. One-proportion z-test. The population is all the riding's voters. **b.** Two-proportion z-test. One population is all men at the university, and the other population is all women at that university.

8.69 a. p = the population proportion of correct answers
　H_0: $p = 0.50$ (he is just guessing), H_A: $p > 0.50$ (he is not just guessing). One-proportion z-test. **b.** p_a is the population proportion of athletes who can balance for at least 10 seconds. p_n is the population proportion of non-athletes who can balance for at least 10 seconds.
　H_0: $p_a = p_n$
　H_A: $p_a \neq p_n$
Two-proportion z-test.

Chapter Review Exercises

8.71 6 right out of 20 is less than half, so he cannot tell the difference.
(Or: H_A: $p > 0.50$, $z = -1.79$, p-value $= 0.963$, do not reject H_0.)

8.73 *Step 1:* H_0: $p = 0.306$, H_A: $p < 0.306$, where p is the proportion of Canadians who vote NDP. *Step 2:* One proportion z-test (given), sample size is large (1202 times 0.306 equals 367.8, which is more than 10), sample is taken randomly, and the population is large. *Step 3:* $\hat{p} = \frac{361}{1202} = 0.3003$, $z = -0.43$, p-value $= 0.335$. *Step 4:* If the null is true, there is a 0.335 probability of observing a more surprising result. Do not reject H_0. We can conclude from the data that the proportion of NDP voters has not declined.

8.75 *Step 1:* H_0: $p = 0.50$, H_A: $p > 0.50$, where p is the proportion of Canadians who wish for same-sex marriage to remain legal. *Step 2:* One proportion z-test (given), sample size is large (1003 times 0.50 equals 501.5, which is more than 10), sample is taken randomly, and the population is large. *Step 3:* $\hat{p} = \frac{612}{1003} = 0.6102$, $z = 6.98$, p-value < 0.0001. *Step 4:* If the null is true, there is a probability of less than 0.0001 that we'll observe a more surprising result. Reject H_0. We can conclude from the data that the proportion of Canadians who wish for same-sex marriage to remain legal is the majority.

8.77 The p-value is the area to the right of $z = 1$ and the area to the left of $z = -1$. Approximately 68% of z-scores lie within one standard deviation of the mean. Therefore, 32% of z-scores lie outside this region. The p-value is then about 32%.

8.79 About 2 or 3, since 5% of 50 is 2.5. This means that a coin would be declared biased, when in fact it is not, about 2 or 3 times, or 5% of the time.

8.81 It would be inappropriate to perform a two-proportion z-test because the percentages given are population parameters and not sample statistics.

8.83 *Step 1:* H_0: $p_{Can} = p_{US}$, H_A: $p_{Can} > p_{US}$. Use the two-proportion z-test, and compute $\hat{p} = \frac{829 + 504}{1626 + 1028} = 0.5023$. The sample sizes are large enough, as $1626 \times 0.5023 = 817$, $1626 \times 0.4977 = 809$,

$1028 \times 0.5023 = 516$, $1028 \times 0.4977 = 512$ are greater than 10. The samples are random, and the populations both large. *Step 3:* $z = 0.98$, p-value $= 0.163$. *Step 4:* If the null is true, the probability of observing a result that is just as or more surprising is 0.163. Fail to reject H_0. From the data, there is no difference in the population proportions.

8.85 a. Number of men who support $= (1012/2)(0.74) = 374$, number of women who support $= (1012/2)(0.47) = 238$.

	Men	Women	Total
Support	374	238	612
Do not support	132	268	400
Total	506	506	1012

b. *Step 1:* H_0: $p_M = p_W$, H_A: $p_M > p_W$. Use the two-proportion z-test, and compute $\hat{p} = \frac{374 + 238}{506 + 506} = 0.605$. The sample sizes are large enough, as $506 \times 0.605 = 306.13$, $506 \times 0.395 = 199.77$ are greater than 10, for both samples. The samples are random, and the populations both large. *Step 3:* $z = 8.74$, p-value < 0.0001. *Step 4:* If the null is true, the probability of observing a result that is just as or more surprising is less than 0.0001. Reject H_0. From the data, there is a difference in the population proportions.

8.87 a. *Step 1:* H_0: $p_M = p_p$, H_A: $p_M < p_p$. Use the two-proportion z-test, and compute $\hat{p} = \frac{30 + 57}{104 + 105} = 0.416$. All the conditions necessary for the two-proportion z-test hold. *Step 3:* $z = -3.73$, p-value < 0.0001. *Step 4:* If the null is true, the probability of observing a result that is just as or more surprising is less than 0.0001. Reject H_0. From the data, $p_M < p_p$.

CHAPTER 9

Answers may vary due to rounding or type of technology used.

Section 9.1

9.1 a. Parameters: 54.4 years, 15.5 years **b.** Statistics: 50.2 years, 18.0 years

9.3 a. See the accompanying figure.

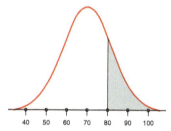

b. 16% (By the Empirical Rule, 68% of the observed values are between 60 and 80, which leaves 32% outside of those boundaries. But we want only the right half.)

9.5 The sample mean is based on a random sample, so different samples will have different means. Having an "unbiased" estimator does not mean that the sample mean will be equal to the population mean. Instead, it means that if we took all possible samples of bats, the mean of all the sample means would be the same as the population mean.

9.7 The histogram would be a display of the data resulting from the random sample, and therefore the histogram would be of the distribution of the sample.

9.9 a. The histogram would be a display of the data resulting from many random samples, each producing a mean. Therefore, the histogram would be a sampling distribution of the mean. **b.** A histogram of the waiting times for one of these samples would give the distribution of the sample.

9.11 a. About 58 kilograms because the sample mean is unbiased.

b. $\dfrac{9}{\sqrt{100}} = 0.9$ kg

Section 9.2

9.13 a. It is large enough because the sample size of 100 is larger than 25.
b. The mean is 58 kilograms and the standard deviation is

$$SD = \frac{\sigma}{\sqrt{n}} = \frac{9}{\sqrt{100}} = 0.9 \text{ kg}$$

c. $2 \times 0.13326 = 0.26652$, or 0.2665

9.15 (a): Calls. (b): Means: has a smaller standard deviation (narrower) and is more Normal (less right-skewed).

9.17 a. 4.21 and 0.82 are parameters; 4.10 and 0.89 are statistics.
b. $\mu = 4.21$, $\sigma = 0.82$, $\bar{x} = 4.10$, $s = 0.89$
c. The conditions are satisfied. The sample is random, and the sample size of 40 is greater than 25. The distribution shape would be Normal.

Section 9.3

9.19 a. i. is correct: (76.75, 85.75); ii. and iii. are both incorrect. **b.** It tells us a range of plausible values for the population mean cumulative average, where the population is all statistics students at the school. Yes, reject 72 because it is not in the interval. We are confident that the statistics students have a higher population mean than 72.

9.21 a. i. is correct: (50.35, 59.65). Both ii. and iii. are incorrect. **b.** No, it does not capture 10. Do not reject the claim of 56 Smarties because 56 is in the interval.

9.23 a. C-level **b.** C-interval

9.25 a. 1.699 **b.** Wider because t^* is bigger (2.045), which makes the margin of error bigger:

$$\text{Margin of error} = t^* \frac{s}{\sqrt{n}}$$

9.27 a. $m = t^* \frac{s}{\sqrt{n}} = 2.093 \frac{5.51}{\sqrt{20}} = 2.5787$, or about 2.58

160.8 ± 2.58 95% CI (158.2 to 163.4). I am 95% confident that the population mean height is between 158.2 and 163.4 centimetres.

b. $m = t^* \frac{s}{\sqrt{n}} = 2.861 \frac{5.51}{\sqrt{20}} = 3.52$, or about 1.4

160.8 ± 3.52 99% CI (157.3, 164.3). I am 99% confident the that population mean height is between 157.3 and 164.3 centimetres.

c. The 99% interval is wider because it has a greater confidence level, and therefore we use a bigger value of t^*, which creates a wider interval.

9.29 a. Wider **b.** Narrower **c.** Wider

9.31 *Step 1:* H_0: $\mu = 37$, H_A: $\mu \neq 37$. *Step 2:* One-sample t-test, random sample, population of values is Normally distributed, use 0.05. *Step 3:* $t = -1.63$, p-value = 0.1384. *Step 4:* If the null is true, there is a 0.1384 probability of observing a t-value that is just as extreme or more than -1.63. Do not reject H_0.

9.33 a. *Step 1:* H_0: $\mu = 30,000$, H_A: $\mu > 30,000$. *Step 2:* One-sample t-test, random sample, not strongly skewed, use 0.05. *Step 3:* $t = 1.20$, p-value = 0.1221. *Step 4:* If the null is true, there is a 0.1221 probability of observing a t-value that is just as extreme or more than 1.20. Do not reject H_0. Conclude that in-province tuition of MBA programs in the country is not greater than $30,000. **b.** *Step 3:* $t = 1.47$, p-value = 0.076. *Step 4:* If the null is true, there is a 0.076 probability of observing a t-value that is just as extreme or more than 1.47. Do not reject H_0. Conclude that in-province tuition of MBA programs in the country is not greater than $30,000.
c. Different t-values are a result of the different sample sizes.

9.35 a. $\bar{x} = 64.17$ **b.** $s = 17.24$ **c.** *Step 1:* H_0: $\mu = 70$, H_A: $\mu < 70$.
Step 2: One-sample t-test, random sample, not strongly skewed, use 0.05.
Step 3: $t = -1.85$, p-value = 0.037. *Step 4:* If the null is true, there is a 0.037 probability of observing a t-value that is just as extreme or more than -1.85. Reject H_0. Conclude that the mean score is less than 70%.

9.37 *Step 1:* H_0: $\mu_{\text{before}} = \mu_{\text{after}}$ [or $\mu_{\text{difference}} = 0$]; H_A: $\mu_{\text{before}} > \mu_{\text{after}}$ [or $\mu_{\text{difference}} > 0$]. *Step 2:* One-sample t-test, assume conditions are met (given). *Step 3:* $t = 1.39$, p-value = 0.098. *Step 4:* Do not reject H_0. Meditation does not lower pulse rates significantly.

9.39 $t = 1.70$ for all three.
a. H_A: $\mu \neq 9$, p-value = 0.188. Do not reject H_0.
b. H_A: $\mu < 9$, p-value = 0.906. Do not reject H_0.
c. H_A: $\mu > 9$, p-value = 0.094. Do not reject H_0.

9.41 a

9.43 Expect $0.95(200) = 190$ to capture and 10 to miss.

9.45 It should not be interpreted. The data are not a random sample, and so inference based on a confidence interval is not possible.

Section 9.4

9.47 a. Independent **b.** Paired (or dependent)

9.49 *Step 1:* H_A: $\mu_{\text{oc}} \neq \mu_{\text{mc}}$ where μ is the population mean number of TVs. *Step 2:* Two-sample t-test, samples large ($n = 30$), independent, and random, use 0.05. *Step 3:* $t = 0.95$, p-value = 0.345. *Step 4:* There is a 0.345 probability of observing a more surprising result, if the null is true. Do not reject H_0. Choose i. Confidence interval: $(-0.404, 1.138)$. Because the interval for the difference captures 0, we cannot reject the hypothesis that the mean difference in number of TVs is 0.

9.51 a. The men's sample mean triglyceride level of 139.5 was higher than the women's sample mean of 84.4. **b.** *Step 1:* H_A: $\mu_{\text{men}} > \mu_{\text{women}}$ where μ is the population mean triglyceride level. *Step 2:* Two-sample t-test, assume the conditions are met. *Step 3:* $t = 4.02$ or -4.02, p-value < 0.001. *Step 4:* There is a less than 0.001 probability of observing a more surprising result, if the null is true. Reject H_0. The mean triglyceride level is significantly higher for men than for women. Choose output B: Difference = $\mu_{\text{female}} - \mu_{\text{male}}$, which tests whether this difference is less than 0, which is the one-tailed hypothesis that we want.

9.53 $(-82.5, -27.7)$. Because the difference of 0 is not captured, it shows there is a significant difference. Also, the difference $\mu_{\text{female}} - \mu_{\text{male}}$ is negative, which shows that the men's mean (triglyceride level) is significantly higher than the women's mean.

9.55 *Step 1:* H_A: $\mu_{\text{men}} \neq \mu_{\text{women}}$ where μ is the population mean clothing expense for one month. *Step 2:* Two-sample t-test, assume Normal and random. *Step 3:* $t = 1.42$ or -1.42, p-value = 0.171. *Step 4:* There is a 0.171 probability of observing a more surprising result, if the null is true. Do not reject H_0. The mean clothing expense is not significantly different for men and women.

9.57 a. The 95% interval would capture 0, because we could not reject the hypothesis that the mean amounts spent on clothing are the same. **b.** A 99% interval would also capture 0, because it is wider than the 95% interval and centred at the same place. **c.** $(-18.4, 97.7)$. Because the interval captures 0, we cannot reject the hypothesis that the mean difference in spending on clothing is 0, which shows we cannot reject the hypothesis that the means are the same.

9.59 *Step 1:* H_A: $\mu_{\text{letter}} < \mu_{\text{no letter}}$ where μ is the population mean rate of crime. *Step 2:* Two-sample t-test, large sample sizes, not random samples, so don't generalize to a larger population; random assignment allows us to assume causality. *Step 3:* $t = 1.77$ or -1.77, p-value = 0.041 (one-tailed). *Step 4:* There is a 0.041 probability of observing a more surprising result, if the null is true. Reject H_0. The police letter reduced the number of crimes reported for these properties, but we cannot generalize to other properties.

9.61 *Step 1:* H_A: $\mu_{\text{before}} < \mu_{\text{after}}$ where μ is the population mean pulse rate. *Step 2:* Paired t-test, each woman is measured twice (repeated measures), so a measurement in the first column is coupled with a measurement of the same person in the second column, assume random and Normal, use 0.05.
Step 3: $t = 4.90$ or -4.90, p-value < 0.001. *Step 4:* There is less than a 0.001 probability of observing a more surprising result, if the null is true. Reject H_0. The sample mean before was 74.8 and the sample mean after was 83.7. The pulse rates of women go up significantly after a scream.

9.63 a. $\bar{x}_{\text{UCBOOK}} = 99.90$, $\bar{x}_{\text{AMAZON}} = 74.43$. The sample mean from the UC bookstore is larger. **b.** *Step 1:* H_0: $\mu_{\text{UCBOOK}} = \mu_{\text{AMAZON}}$, or $\mu_{\text{difference}} = 0$, H_A: $\mu_{\text{UCBOOK}} \neq \mu_{\text{AMAZON}}$, or $\mu_{\text{difference}} \neq 0$.
Step 2: Paired t-test, matched samples, assume random and Normal (given), use 0.05. *Step 3:* $t = 3.04$, p-value = 0.009. *Step 4:* If the null is true, there is a 0.009 probability of observing a t-value that is just as extreme or more than 3.04. Reject H_0. The means are significantly different.

9.65 a. $\bar{x}_{\text{groom}} = 27.3$ was larger ($\bar{x}_{\text{bride}} = 25.9$).

b. *Step 1:* H_A: $\mu_{\text{bride}} \neq \mu_{\text{groom}}$ where μ is the population mean age at marriage. *Step 2:* Paired *t*-test, random, and large samples. *Step 3:* $t = 2.24$ or -2.24, p-value $= 0.033$. *Step 4:* There is a 0.033 probability of observing a more surprising result, if the null is true. Reject H_0. The mean ages of brides and grooms are significantly different. **c.** H_A: $\mu_{\text{bride}} < \mu_{\text{groom}}$. The new p-value would be half of 0.033, or about 0.017.

9.67 a. 95% CI $(-1.44, 0.25)$ captures 0, so the hypothesis that the means are equal cannot be rejected. **b.** *Step 1:* H_A: $\mu_{\text{measured}} \neq \mu_{\text{reported(converted to cm)}}$ where μ is the population mean height of men. *Step 2:* Paired *t*-test, each person is the source of two numbers, assume conditions for *t*-tests hold (given). *Step 3:* $t = 1.50$ or -1.50, p-value $= 0.155$. *Step 4:* There is a 0.155 probability of observing a more surprising result, if the null is true. Do not reject H_0. The mean measured and reported heights are not significantly different for men, or there's not enough evidence to support the claim that the typical self-reported height differs from the typical measured height for men.

9.69 a. $\bar{x}_{10\%} = 15.1$, $\bar{x}_{65\%} = 39.5$. The sample mean is lower for students starting at the lower point of 10%. **b.** *Step 1:* H_0: $\mu_{10\%} = \mu_{65\%}$, H_A: $\mu_{10\%} < \mu_{65\%}$. *Step 2:* Two sample *t*-test, independent samples, assume random and Normal (given), use 0.05. *Step 3:* $t = -7.71$, p-value < 0.001. *Step 4:* If the null is true, there is less than a 0.001 probability of observing a *t*-value that is just as extreme or more than -7.71. Reject H_0. The means are significantly different.

Chapter Review Exercises

9.71 a. Paired *t* **b.** Two-sample *t* **c.** Two-sample *t*

9.73 a. *Step 1:* H_0: $\mu_f = \mu_m$, H_A: $\mu_f > \mu_m$. *Step 2:* Two sample *t*-test, independent samples, assume random and Normal (given), use 0.05. *Step 3:* $t = 11.35$, p-value < 0.0001. *Step 4:* If the null is true, there is less than a 0.0001 probability of observing a *t*-value that is just as extreme or more than 11.35. Reject H_0. The mean running time for men is smaller than for women. **b.** We are 95% confident that the true mean running time for men is between 1343 seconds and 1904 seconds less than the true mean running time for women.

9.75 *Step 1:* H_A: $\mu_{\text{before}} < \mu_{\text{after}}$ where μ is the population mean pulse rate (before and after coffee). *Step 2:* Paired *t*-test (repeated measures), assume conditions hold (given). *Step 3:* $t = -2.96$, p-value $= 0.005$. *Step 4:* There is a 0.005 probability of observing a more surprising outcome, if the null is true. Reject H_0. Heart rates increase significantly after coffee. (The average rate before coffee was 82.4, and the average rate after coffee was 87.5.)

9.77 The typical number of hours was a little higher for the boys and the variation was almost the same. $\bar{x}_{\text{girls}} = 9.8$ and $\bar{x}_{\text{boys}} = 10.3$. $s_{\text{girls}} = 5.4$ and $s_{\text{boys}} = 5.5$. See the histograms.

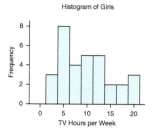

Histogram of Girls

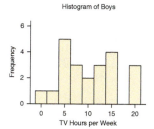

Histogram of Boys

Step 1: H_A: $\mu_{\text{girls}} \neq \mu_{\text{boys}}$ where μ is the population mean number of TV viewing hours. *Step 2:* Two-sample *t*-test, random samples, assume the sample sizes of 32 girls and 22 boys is large enough that slight non-Normality is not a problem. *Step 3:* $t = -0.38$ or 0.38, p-value $= 0.706$. *Step 4:* There is a probability of 0.706 of observing a more surprising result, if the null is true. You cannot reject the null hypothesis. There is not enough evidence to conclude that boys and girls differ in the typical hours of TV watched.

9.79 a. Choose (a), the two-sample t-test; the data are not paired. *Step 1:* H_A: $\mu_{\text{men}} \neq \mu_{\text{women}}$ where μ is the population mean number of work hours. *Step 2:* Two sample *t*-test, random, $n = 50 > 25$. *Step 3:* $t = 4.09$, p-value < 0.001. *Step 4:* There is a probability of less than 0.001 of observing a more surprising result, if the null is true. Reject H_0. The mean number of work hours for men and women are significantly different. **b.** 95% CI for difference in work hours, $\mu_{\text{men}} - \mu_{\text{women}}$: (6.18, 17.86). Because it does not capture 0, we can reject the hypothesis of no difference. Because the interval contains only positive values, we know that the mean number of work hours is greater for men than for women.

9.81 Wish to test $\mu_{15-24} > \mu_{25-34}$, so we choose output (b) because $\mu_1 > \mu_2$, *Step 1:* H_0: $\mu_{15-24} = \mu_{25-34}$, H_A: $\mu_{15-24} > \mu_{25-34}$. *Step 2:* Two-sample *t*-test, independent samples, assume random and Normal (given), use 0.05. *Step 3:* $t = -0.525$, p-value 0.6991. *Step 4:* If the null is true, there is a 0.6991 probability of observing a *t*-value that is just as extreme or more than 0.525. Do not reject H_0. The means are the same.

9.83 The table shows the results. The average of s^2 in the table is 2.8889 (or about 2.89), and if you take the square root, you get about 1.6997 (or about 1.70), which is the value for sigma (σ) given in the TI-83/84 output shown

Sample	s	s^2
1, 1	0	0
1, 2	0.7071	0.5
1, 5	2.8284	8.0
2, 1	0.7071	0.5
2, 2	0	0
2, 5	2.1213	4.5
5, 1	2.8284	8.0
5, 2	2.1213	4.5
5, 5	0	0
	$26/9 = 2.8889$	Sum 26.0

in the exercise. This demonstrates that s^2 is an unbiased estimator of σ^2.

9.85 Answers will vary.

CHAPTER 10

Answers may vary slightly due to type of technology or rounding.

Section 10.1

10.1 a. Proportions are used for categorical data. **b.** Chi-square tests are used for categorical data.

10.3

	Boy	Girl
Concerned	11	12
Not Concerned	8	7

10.5 *Mean GPA*: numerical and continuous. *Field of Study*: categorical.

10.7 a. $\dfrac{84}{100} = 0.84$ **b.** 84 **c.** Expect $0.83 \times 100 = 83$ households to have internet access.

10.9 a.

	High TV Violence	Low TV Violence	Total
Yes, Physical Abuse	13	27	40
No Physical Abuse	18	95	113
Total	31	122	153

b. $40/153 = 26.1\%$ **c.** $0.261438(31) = 8.10$
d. Expected values are shown in the table.

	High TV Violence	Low TV Violence	Total
Yes, Physical Abuse	8.10	31.90	40
No Physical Abuse	22.90	90.10	113
Total	31	122	153

10.11 a. 29% of 16 is 4.64, so 4.64 should have artery disease and 11.36 should not.

b. $\chi^2_{Obs} = \dfrac{(9 - 4.64)^2}{4.64} + \dfrac{(7 - 11.36)^2}{11.36} = \dfrac{19.0096}{4.64} + \dfrac{19.0096}{11.36}$
$= 4.097 + 1.673 = 5.770$

10.13 a. One-fifth of 152 is 30.4 (expected correct), and four-fifths of 152 is 121.6 (expected incorrect).

b. $\chi^2_{Obs} = \dfrac{(39 - 30.4)^2}{30.4} + \dfrac{(113 - 121.6)^2}{121.6} = \dfrac{73.96}{30.4} + \dfrac{73.96}{121.6}$
$= 2.433 + 0.608 = 3.041$

10.15

$\chi^2_{Obs} = \dfrac{(13 - 8.10)^2}{8.1} + \dfrac{(27 - 31.90)^2}{31.9} + \dfrac{(18 - 22.90)^2}{22.9} + \dfrac{(95 - 90.10)^2}{90.1}$
$= 2.964 + 0.753 + 1.048 + 0.266 = 5.03$

From technology to avoid rounding: Chi-square = 5.02

10.17 Observed (expected) frequencies. Red: 4 (11.48) Purple: 10 (14.09) Green: 7 (10.53) Blue: 17 (10.09) Orange: 14 (12.62) Yellow: 17 (10.18) Brown: 14 (9.31) Pink: 4 (8.70)

$\chi^2_{Obs} = \dfrac{(4 - 11.48)^2}{11.48} + \dfrac{(10 - 14.09)^2}{14.09} + \dfrac{(7 - 10.53)^2}{10.53} + \dfrac{(17 - 10.09)^2}{10.09}$
$+ \dfrac{(14 - 12.62)^2}{12.62} + \dfrac{(17 - 10.18)^2}{10.18} + \dfrac{(14 - 9.31)^2}{9.31} + \dfrac{(4 - 8.70)^2}{8.70}$
$= 21.598$

Section 10.2

10.19 One categorical variable.

10.21

1: H_A: Humans are not like random number generators and are not equally likely to pick all the integers.

2: If the integers are equally likely to be picked and there are 5 integers, then $38/5 = 7.6$, so the expected value counts for each value are all 7.6, which is larger than 5.

3: $\chi^2_{Obs} = \dfrac{(3 - 7.6)^2}{7.6} + \dfrac{(5 - 7.6)^2}{7.6} + \dfrac{(14 - 7.6)^2}{7.6} + \dfrac{(11 - 7.6)^2}{7.6}$
$+ \dfrac{(5 - 7.6)^2}{7.6} = 11.47$
11.47 is the same in the output. p-value $= 0.022$.

4: There is a 0.022 probability of observing a more surprising outcome, if the null is true. Reject the null hypothesis and pick option ii.

10.23 *Step 1:* H_A: $p(\text{heads}) \neq 0.50$, or the coin is biased. *Step 2:* Chi-square GOF, both expected values are $25 > 5$. *Step 3:* $\chi^2_{Obs} = 8.00$, p-value $= 0.005$. *Step 4:* There is a probability of 0.005 of observing a more surprising outcome, if the null is true. Reject H_0. The coin is biased.

10.25 *Step 1:* H_A: The die is *not* fair and does not produce proportions of $1/6$ for each possible outcome. *Step 2:* Chi-square GOF, expected values all $1/6$ of 120 or $20 > 5$, assume random sample. *Step 3:* $\chi^2_{Obs} = 9.20$, p-value $= 0.101$. *Step 4:* There is a 0.101 probability of observing a more surprising result, if the null is true. We cannot reject H_0. The die has not been shown to be unfair.

10.27 a. *Step 1:* H_A: $p \neq 0.20$, where p is the probability that an expert correctly identifies a Stradivarius violin. *Step 2:* Chi-square GOF, we assume independent identifications (although sample is not random) expected values are large enough. *Step 3:* $\chi^2_{Obs} = 3.04$, p-value $= 0.081$. *Step 4:* There is a 0.081 probability of observing a more surprising outcome, if the null is true. Because the p-value is 0.081, which is more than 0.05, we conclude that the results are not significantly different from guessing, which would produce about 20% correct identifications. **b.** *Step 1:* H_A: $p > 0.20$, where p is the probability that an expert correctly identifies a Stradivarius violin. *Step 2:* One-proportion z-test, expected numbers of success and failure both more than 10, we assume independent identifications (although sample is not random). *Step 3:* $z = 1.74$, p-value $= 0.041$. *Step 4:* There is a 0.041 probability of observing a more surprising outcome, if the null is true. Because the p-value is 0.041, we can reject H_0 and conclude that the probability of correct identification is significantly higher than 20%. **c.** The one-tailed hypothesis has a p-value that is half that of the two-tailed hypothesis, and we can therefore reject H_0 with the one-tailed hypothesis.

Section 10.3

10.29 Independence: one sample.

10.31 Homogeneity: random assignment (to four groups).

10.33 The data are for the entire population (not a sample), and therefore there is no need for inference. The data are given as rates (percentages), not frequencies (counts), and there is not enough information for us to convert these percentages to counts.

10.35

Step 1: H_A: The variables *Relationship Status* and *Obesity* are not independent (are related).

Step 2: Chi-square test of independence (given). The smallest expected value is 108.54, which is much more than 5.

Step 3: $\chi^2_{Obs} = 30.83$, p-value < 0.001.

Step 4: There is a less than 0.001 probability of observing a more surprising outcome, if the null is true. Reject H_0. There is a connection between obesity and marital status; they are not independent. However, we should not generalize.
Causality? No, it is an observational study.
Percentage Obese: Dating: $81/440 = 18.4\%$ Cohabiting: $103/429 = 24.0\%$ Married: $147/424 = 34.7\%$

10.37 *Step 1:* H_A: For men, watching violent TV is not independent of abusiveness. *Step 2:* Chi-square test of independence (one sample), expected values all more than 5, sample not random. *Step 3:* $\chi^2_{Obs} = 5.02$, p-value $= 0.025$. *Step 4:* There is a 0.025 probability of observing a more surprising outcome, if the null is true. Reject H_0. High TV violence viewing as a child is related to abusiveness as an adult in men, but don't generalize to all males and don't conclude causality.

10.39 a. Independence: one sample with two variables. **b.** *Step 1:* H_0: Level of education and travel for vacation are independent. H_A: Level of education and travel for vacation are related. *Step 2:* Chi-square test of independence (one sample), random sample, minimum expected count is greater than 5. *Step 3:* $\chi^2_{Obs} = 29.228$, p-value < 0.0001. *Step 4:* There is a less than 0.0001 probability of observing an outcome more surprising than what is observed, if the null is true. Reject H_0; level of education and travelling for vacation are related.

10.41 a. HS Grad rate for no preschool: $29/64$, or 45.3%. The preschool kids had a higher graduation rate. **b.** *Step 1:* H_A: Graduation and preschool are not independent (they are related). *Step 2:* Chi-square test of homogeneity, random assignment, not a random sample, the smallest expected value is $25.91 > 5$. *Step 3:* $\chi^2_{Obs} = 4.67$, p-value $= 0.031$. *Step 4:* There is a 0.031 probability of observing a more surprising outcome, if the null is true. Reject H_0. Graduation and preschool are related: causality, yes, generalization, no.

10.43 a. For preschool, 50% graduated, and for no preschool, $21/39 = 53.8\%$ graduated. It is surprising to see that the boys who did not go to preschool had a bit higher graduation rate. **b.** *Step 1:* H_A: For the boys, graduation and preschool are related. *Step 2:* Chi-square test for homogeneity, random assignment, not a random sample, the smallest expected value $15.32 > 5$. *Step 3:* $\chi^2_{Obs} = 0.10$, p-value $= 0.747$. *Step 4:* Do not reject H_0. For the boys, there is no evidence that attending preschool is related to graduating from high school. **c.** The results do not generalize to other groups of boys and girls, but what evidence we have suggests that although preschool might be effective for girls, it may not be for boys, at least with regard to graduation from high school.

10.45 a. Surgery: $22/29 = 75.9\%$ free from diabetes. No surgery: $4/26 = 15.4\%$ free from diabetes. The surgery patients were much more likely to be free from diabetes. **b.** Although there is an observed value that is less than 5, there is no expected value less than 5, so you can use chi-square. **c.** *Step 1:* H_A: Surgery and recovery from diabetes are not independent. *Step 2:* Chi-square test of homogeneity, random assignment, not a random sample, there are no expected values less than 5. *Step 3:* $\chi^2_{Obs} = 20.12$, p-value < 0.001. *Step 4:* There is less than 0.001 probability of observing a more surprising outcome, if the null is true. Reject H_0. The surgery significantly affects the chance of recovery from diabetes, but don't generalize.

10.47 a. With no confederate, $6/18$ (33.3%) followed the directions and took the stairs. With a compliant confederate, $16/18$ (88.9%) followed directions. With a noncompliant confederate, $5/18$ (27.8%) followed directions. Thus, the subject was influenced to tend to do the same thing as the confederate. **b.** A p-value can never be larger than 1. The p-value is about 2.7 times 10 to the negative fourth power or 0.00027, which is less than 0.001. **c.** *Step 1:* H_A: Treatment and compliance are not independent. *Step 2:* Chi-square test of homogeneity, random assignment, not a random sample, expected values are all $9 > 5$. *Step 3:* $\chi^2_{Obs} = 16.44$, p-value < 0.001. *Step 4:* There is less than a 0.001 probability of observing a more surprising outcome, if the null is true. Reject H_0. There is a significant effect: causality: yes, generalization: no.

10.49 a. LD: $4/50 = 8\%$ tumour; LL $15/50 = 30\%$ tumour. Thus, there is a higher rate of tumours in the mice that were exposed to light 24 hours a day.
b.

	LD	LL
Mice with Tumour(s)	4	15
Mice without Tumour(s)	46	35

10.51 *Step 1:* H_0: Gender and transportation method are independent. H_A: Gender and transportation method are related. *Step 2:* Chi-square test of independence (one sample), random sample, minimum expected count is greater than 5. *Step 3:* $\chi^2_{Obs} = 1.770$, p-value $= 0.413$. *Step 4:* There is a 0.413 probability of observing an outcome more surprising than what is observed, if the null is true. Do not reject H_0. Gender and transportation method are independent.

10.53 a. The minimum expected frequency is $4.78 < 5$. The table, without combining categories, could not be used to perform a Chi-square test of independence.

b.

	ProtEvanChr	Catholic	OtherChr	Other	None
Yes	439	492	126	105	326
No	63	65	18	11	26
Don't Know	34	36	18	6	18
Total	536	593	162	122	369

c. $\frac{326}{369} = 0.8835$, or 88.07%. $\frac{1162}{1411} = 0.8235$, or 82.35% **d.** *Step 1:* H_0: Religion and view on climate change are independent. H_A: Religion and view on climate change are related. *Step 2:* Chi-square test of independence (one sample), random sample, minimum expected count is greater than 5. *Step 3:* $\chi^2_{Obs} = 14.874$, p-value $= 0.062$. *Step 4:* There is a 0.062 probability of observing an outcome more surprising than what is observed, if the null is true. Do not reject H_0. Religion and view on climate change are independent.

10.55 a. You would get a smaller p-value, because it is more extreme in the direction of the antivenom working. **b.** You would get a larger p-value, because the results are less extreme. **c.** The p-value for the test in part a is 0.0002 (both one-tailed and two-tailed); yes, it is smaller. The p-value for the test in part b is 0.1002 (one-tailed) and 0.1319 (two-tailed); yes, it is larger.

Chapter Review Exercises

10.57 a. 13.8% of those attending preschool had a least one felony arrest, 47.7% of those not attending preschool had at least one felony arrest.
b.

	Preschool	No Preschool
Arrest	8	31
No Arrest	50	34

Step 1: H_0: Preschool attendance and arrest rate are independent. H_A: Preschool attendance and arrest rate are related. *Step 2:* Chi-square test of independence (one sample), random sample, minimum expected count is greater than 5. *Step 3:* $\chi^2_{Obs} = 16.266$, p-value < 0.001. *Step 4:* There is less than a 0.001 probability of observing an outcome more surprising than what is observed, if the null is true. Reject H_0. Preschool attendance and arrest rate are related. **c.** H_0: $p_{Preschool} = p_{NoPreschool}$, H_A: $p_{Preschool} < p_{NoPreschool}$, $z = 4.03$, p-value < 0.0001. There is less than a 0.0001 probability of observing a more surprising outcome, if the null is true. Reject H_0. The felony crime rates are lower for those who attended preschool. **d.** A two-proportion z-test has the advantage of allowing one-tailed or two-tailed alternatives.

10.59 a. Android (0.404), Apple (0.369), BlackBerry (0.201), Windows (0.017), Other (0.009). **b.** Expected frequencies: Android (43% of 1000 is 430), Apple (35% of 1000 is 350), BlackBerry (19% of 1000 is 19), Windows (2% of 1000 is 20), and Other (1% of 1000 is 10). **c.** *Step 1:* H_0: The market share of smartphones has not changed. H_A: The market share of smartphones has changed. *Step 2:* Chi-square goodness-of-fit test to see if the sample data follow a proposed distribution. Random sample, minimum expected count is greater than 5. *Step 3:* $\chi^2_{Obs} = 5.124$, p-value 0.2748. *Step 4:* There is a 0.2748 probability of observing an outcome more surprising than what is observed, if the null is true. Do not reject H_0. The smartphone market share has not changed.

10.61 a.

	Drug	Placebo
Clots	34	60
No Clots	8867	8841

b. Blood clot percentage for those receiving the drug, 0.38%. For those getting the placebo, 0.67%. **c.** *Step 1:* H_0: Treatment type and blood clots are independent. H_A: Treatment type and blood clots are related. *Step 2:* Chi-square test of independence (one sample), random sample, minimum expected count is greater than 5. *Step 3:* $\chi^2_{Obs} = 7.230$, p-value = 0.007. *Step 4:* There is a 0.007 probability of observing an outcome more surprising than what is observed, if the null is true. Reject H_0. Treatment type is related to getting blood clots. **d.** Yes, participants were randomly assigned to the treatment or the control (placebo) group.

10.63 *Step 1:* H_0: Education level and opinion are independent. H_A: Education level and opinion are related. *Step 2:* Chi-square test of independence (one sample), random sample, minimum expected count is greater than 5. *Step 3:* $\chi^2_{Obs} = 1.221$, p-value = 0.976. *Step 4:* There is a 0.976 probability of observing an outcome more surprising than what is observed, if the null is true. Do not reject H_0. Education level and opinion are independent.

10.65 a. *Step 1:* H_A: The presence or absence of robots is not independent of grouping. *Step 2:* Chi-square test for homogeneity, random (given), two expected values are 5, which is on the low side for this approximation. *Step 3:* $\chi^2_{Obs} = 4.32$, p-value = 0.038. *Step 4:* There is a 0.038 probability of observing a more surprising outcome, if the null is true. Reject H_0. The proportions are not the same. The robots have a significant effect. **b.** With Fisher's Exact Test, using a two-tailed alternative, the p-value is 0.080. You cannot reject H_0. The robots do not have a significant effect. **c.** For chi-square, the p-value was 0.038, and with Fisher's Exact Test, the p-value was 0.080. Fisher's Exact Test is accurate, and the chi-square test is a large-sample approximation. The approximation is not very good with two expected values of 5, and that is why the two p-values are so different. The p-value of 0.080 is the accurate value.

CHAPTER 11

Correct answers may vary slightly due to rounding and type of technology used. All *t*-statistics are reported as positive values, although the sign of your *t*-statistics (positive or negative) must be consistent with which group you chose for group 1.

Section 11.1

11.1 a. ANOVA **b.** Two-sample *t*-test

11.3 The *F*-value of 9.38 goes with A, B, and C, and the *F*-value of 150.00 goes with L, M, and N. The reason for the difference is that the variation between groups (the separation between means) is larger for L, M, and N relative to the variation within groups (which is the same in all groups).

$$F = \frac{\text{Variation between Groups}}{\text{Variation within Groups}}$$

11.5 a. H_0: The mean time spent watching TV is the same for all education levels. H_A: At least one mean is different from another. **b.** 6.75 **c.** The No High School Diploma group had the largest sample mean, while the University Degree group had the lowest. **d.** No (this is an observational study). One possible confounding variable is age.

11.7 a. H_0: The mean time spent volunteering is the same for all religious participation groups. H_A: At least one mean is different from another. **b.** 4.14 **c.** The group that participated weekly had the largest sample mean, while the group that participated 3 or 4 times per year had the lowest. **d.** No (this is an observational study). One possible confounding variable is age.

Section 11.2

11.9

Source	df	SS	MS	F	p-value
Between (major)	2	199	99.5	8.4	0.001
Within (error)	72	855.4	11.9		
Total	74	1054.5			

11.11

Source	df	SS	MS	F	p-value
Between (colour)	3	442.9	32.4	118	<0.0001
Within (error)	28	32.4	1.16		
Total	31	442.9			

11.13

Source	DF	SS	MS	F	p-value
Education	4	343211	85803	2.67	0.033
Error	245	7866285	32107		
Total	249	8209496			

11.15 p-value = 0.033 < 0.05, so we reject H_0. Evidence suggests that the mean number of minutes of paid work is not the same for all education levels.

Section 11.3

11.17 The pulse rates are not in three independent groups, so the condition of independent groups fails.

11.19 $65.05/20.78 = 3.13$, which is more than 2. The same-variance condition fails. ANOVA is not appropriate.

11.21 *Step 1:* H_0: $\mu_{out} = \mu_{in} = \mu_{cat}$ H_A: At least one population mean is different from another. *Step 2:* Choose one-way ANOVA. Conditions are checked in the question statement. *Step 3:* $F = 8.00$, p-value = 0.002. *Step 4:* Reject H_0. The population means for the groups are not all equal.

11.23 $F = 4.85$, p-value = 0.010. Reject H_0. Feelings about the ethics of eating meat vary across the disciplines.

11.25 a. The medians and interquartile ranges are all similar, although the median for the athletes was a little larger (slower!) than the others, and the inter-quartile range was a bit larger for the moderate group. Also, the shapes are not strongly skewed. There are no potential outliers. **b.** $F = 0.10$, p-value = 0.903. The sample means were not significantly different, and we conclude that we cannot reject the hypothesis that the population means are the same.

11.27 a. The median number of hours worked looks lowest for electricians. The medians for construction workers and plumbers are very similar. The interquartile ranges are all similar, and there are no potential outliers.

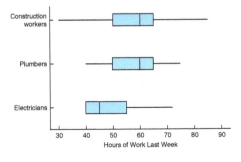

b. *Step 1:* H_0: All population means are equal. H_A: The population means are not all equal. *Step 2:* One-way ANOVA; assume conditions met (given in the problem statement). *Step 3:* $F = 7.48$, p-value = 0.001. *Step 4:* Reject H_0. The population means for number of hours of work are not all equal.

Section 11.4

All calculations for post-hoc tests were done with pooled variances.

11.29 The only CI that captures zero is the one comparing Hillhurst and Richmond Park, so that is the only difference that is not statistically significant.

<u>Hillhurst   Richmond Park</u>   Altadore

We may conclude that the mean home price in Altadore is significantly higher than that of Hillhurst and Richmond Park. The latter two have means that are not significantly different.

11.31 Infielders minus catchers; 95% CI $(-1.39, -0.21)$: Because both boundaries are negative, we can reject the hypothesis of equality and say that catchers take more time. Outfielders minus catchers; 95% CI $(-1.49$ to $-0.32)$: Because both boundaries are negative, we can reject the hypothesis of equality and say that catchers take more time. Outfielders minus infielders: 95% CI $(-0.59, 0.38)$: Because 0 is captured between the negative and positive endpoints, we cannot reject the null hypothesis of no difference.

<u>Outfielders   Infielders</u>   Catchers

Catchers have a statistically significantly higher mean run-time than do either infielders or outfielders; the mean run-times of infielders and outfielders are not statistically different.

11.33 The p-value for ANOVA was 0.903. We cannot reject the null hypothesis of no differences in population mean reaction distances, and so you should not do post-hoc tests. In other words, the sample means are not significantly different.

11.35 Pb is plumber, Const is construction worker, and Elec is electrician For the TI-83/84, 98.33% confidence intervals were obtained, and Pooled Yes was chosen.

Comparison	Tukey CI	TI-83/84 CI	Reject H_0?
Pb minus Const	$(-4.83, 8.81)$	$(-5.39, 9.38)$	No
Elec minus Const	$(-15.31, -1.67)$	$(-16.04, -0.93)$	Yes
Elec minus Pb	$(-17.37, -3.59)$	$(-16.72, -4.24)$	Yes

<u>Electrician   Construction   Plumber</u>

Electricians have a mean that is less than the means for the others. There was insufficient evidence to conclude that there is a difference between the mean hours of construction workers and the mean hours of plumbers.

11.37 The only CI that does not capture zero is the one comparing Hillhurst and Altadore, so this is the only difference that is statistically significant.

<u>Hillhurst   Richmond Park</u>   Altadore

The mean home price in Altadore is significantly higher than that of Hillhurst. There is no difference in means between Altadore and Richmond Park and between Hillhurst and Richmond Park.

Chapter Review Exercises

11.39 The p-value for the ANOVA test was 0.01. Because the overall significance level is 0.05, we can reject the null hypothesis that all the population means are the same and therefore should perform post-hoc tests. For the TI-83/84 intervals, the confidence level was 98.33%, and Pooled Yes was chosen.

Comparison	Tukey CI	TI-83/84 CI	Reject H_0?
Phil minus Eth	$(-1.12, 0.26)$	$(-1.21, 0.34)$	No
Other minus Eth	$(-0.22, 1.16)$	$(-0.13, 1.06)$	No
Other minus Phil	$(0.21, 1.59)$	$(0.15, 1.66)$	Yes

<u>Philosophy Professors   Ethicists</u>   Other professors

Remember that smaller numbers correspond to a worse opinion about the ethics of eating meat. The mean opinion of eating meat is worse for philosophy professors than for other professors. The other two differences are too small to be significant.

11.41 The ratio of the smallest standard deviation to the largest is 5.547/4.209, or about 1.32, which is less than 2, so the same-variance condition is satisfied. The hypothesis that the population mean BMI (for different marital statuses) are all the same is rejected, because the p-value is 0.000. At least one mean BMI is different from another.

11.43 a. There are significant differences. **b.** OM is older men, YM is younger men, OW is older women, and YW is younger women.

Comparison	CI	Reject H_0?
OM minus YM	$(-19.70, 43.10)$	No
YW minus YM	$(19.00, 81.80)$	Yes
OW minus YM	$(153.80, 216.60)$	Yes
YW minus OM	$(7.30, 70.10)$	Yes
OW minus OM	$(142.10, 204.90)$	Yes
OW minus YW	$(103.40, 166.20)$	Yes

<u>Younger men   Older men</u>   Younger women   Older women

The population mean for older women is larger than all the others. The population mean for younger women is larger than those for both older men and younger men. There is insufficient evidence to conclude that the population mean for younger men and the mean for older men are different.

11.45 The p-values are the same. The F-statistic is the square of the t-statistic. You get the same conclusion either way: Do not reject the null hypothesis of equal population mean number of minutes slept at night for men and women.

CHAPTER 12

Section 12.1

12.1 Headline A suggests a cause-and-effect relationship, because it tells us that happiness prevents ("wards off") heart diseases. Headline B merely claims an association: People who are happier tend to have less heart disease.

12.3 It was an observational study. Subjects in the study themselves chose where to attend university.

12.5 Answers may vary, but "Increased casino proximity leads to increased prevalence of problem gambling" is incorrect because the study is observational, not a randomized experiment. "Increased casino proximity is related to increased prevalence of problem gambling" is okay because it does not imply causality.

12.7 It is a controlled experiment. We can tell because it was a "randomized" trial, and therefore researchers randomly assigned subjects to treatment groups.

12.9 a. The treatment variable is the drug administered: fingolimod or interferon. The response variable is whether or not the patient relapses. **b.** Conclusion: The drug fingolimod causes a decrease in the relapse rate of multiple sclerosis compared to interferon.

12.11 a. The treatment variable is the type of exercise routine. Two response variables were measured: score in the verbal memory RAVLT test and score in a computerized spatial memory test. **b.** "Aerobic training improves verbal memory performance. Resistance training and aerobic training improve spatial memory performance."

12.13 Both use the one-sample t-test.
a. $p = 0.144$, do not reject H_0. **b.** $p = 0.001$, reject H_0. **c.** The larger sample size results in a smaller standard deviation of the sample mean, which,

in turn, results in a *t*-statistic value farther from 0 and a p-value that is smaller. (The sample means are very similar, and the standard deviations are also very similar.)

12.15 The second study will have greater power. The fact that the effect of the pill differs for men and women means that there is more variability in the population that combines men and women (study 1) than in the population with only men (study 2). Thus, although the results of the studies are generalized to different populations, the second study is drawing a sample from a population with less variability (and a larger weight loss) and therefore more power.

12.17 This is not an appropriate use of blocking. In this design, the researchers randomized the blocks, not the subjects. Randomization should happen within blocks. For this study, each patient in a block should be assigned a number, and these numbers should be put into a bowl, mixed up. There will be four bowls, one for each age group. From each bowl (each block), half of the subjects' numbers are chosen, and these people will receive the treatment.

12.19 a. The treatment variable is the type of running shoe (energy return or regular). The response variable is the race time for running five kilometres. **b.** Answers will vary. Pool all 40 runners. Choose 20 at random for the treatment group (energy return shoes) by assigning a unique number 1–40 to each runner and then randomly selecting 20 of those numbers. The 20 remaining runners are then assigned to the control group (regular running shoes). Record their times. **c.** Separate the 20 Olympic-level runners from the amateurs. Assign a unique number 1–20 to the 20 runners in each group. Then choose at random 10 of the 20 numbered runners in each group for the treatment group (energy return shoes); the remaining 10 of each group are assigned to the control group (regular running shoes). Then record their times. **d.** The blocked design ensures that an equal number of each type of runner is chosen for the treatment and control groups. Also, variability within each group is reduced, so the power of the study increases. **e.** Have each participant race twice: once using each type (energy return or regular) of running shoes. Select the order in which shoes are worn randomly.

12.21 a. The treatment variable records whether subjects get aspirin or placebo. The response variable is whether the person has a heart attack. **b.** You could put 100 slips of paper marked A and 100 slips of paper marked B in a bag. Each person would draw out a slip of paper. Those who got A would get the aspirin, and those who got B would get the placebo. Then observe the subjects for a given time interval to see whether they have a heart attack, and compare the percentages with heart attacks for the two groups. **c.** Randomly assign half of the men and half of the women to use the aspirin and the rest to use a placebo. You could use two separate bags, one for the men and one for the women. Each bag would have 100 slips of paper: 50 marked A and 50 marked B. Each woman draws randomly from the women's bag, and each man draws randomly from the men's bag. Then observe the subjects for a given time interval to see whether they have a heart attack, and determine the percentage of aspirin-taking men who had a heart attack, the percentage of placebo-taking men who had a heart attack, the percentage of aspirin-taking women who had a heart attack, and the percentage of placebo-taking women who had a heart attack. **d.** The blocked design improves statistical power, in part by preventing an uneven distribution of men and women in the two groups. With the blocked design, we have a higher probability of determining whether aspirin reduces the risk of heart attack, if it actually does so.

12.23 a. *t*-statistic = 2.15, p-value = 0.041. Reject H_0. **b.** *t*-statistic = 3.04, p-value = 0.009. Reject H_0. **c.** The paired *t*-test is appropriate because the items are matched.

12.25 a. The mean for white paper was smaller (the means were 74.3 and 76.3). This contradicts the idea that reading material written on coloured paper is easier to read. **b.** Two-sample *t*-test: *t*-statistic = 0.19, p-value = 0.854. Do not reject H_0. **c.** Paired *t*-test: *t*-statistic = 0.97, p-value = 0.349. Do not reject H_0. **d.** The paired *t*-test is appropriate because each person is tested twice, so the numbers are coupled. **e.** People might get faster if they had read the passage previously, and you don't want the order of reading to affect the answer.

12.27 The order might have an effect. For example, after exercise the pulse might stay elevated for a while, and if there was not a long waiting time between the two sets of observations, the higher pulse after exercise might affect the next situation. Randomizing the order ensures that effects such as these are balanced out in the total analysis.

Section 12.2

12.29 Systematic sampling

12.31 The opinions on how to improve the Canada Pension Plan might vary widely from age group to age group, but they might be fairly similar within an age group. Stratified sampling would allow us to compare answers in different age groups and improve the precision of our estimates.

12.33 This is an example of stratified sampling. The strata consist of high-volume, medium-volume, and low-volume stores. These strata were chosen because stores within a stratum are seen as similar. A random sample is then taken from within each stratum.

Section 12.3

12.35 a. No, we cannot generalize, because this was not a random sample. **b.** Yes, we can infer causality because of random assignment.

12.37 a. You can generalize to other people admitted to this hospital who would have been assigned a standard ward room because of the random sampling from that group. **b.** Yes, you can infer causality because of the random assignment.

12.39 Because a random sample was not used (or we do not know whether one was used), we cannot generalize to the larger public. Because patients were randomly assigned to treatment groups (full dose or reduced dose), we can conclude cause-and-effect. However, it might appear that both full dose and reduced dose have the same effect only because researchers did not have a large enough sample to detect a difference. We *can* say that among persons 60 years of age or older, the intradermal injection causes a less vigorous antibody response.

12.41 a. It does not matter which treatment is chosen; the treatments are not significantly different. **b.** Report one interval. The first interval given (−6.8% to 6.7%) represents the difference in survival rates for patients receiving the two treatments. The fact that the interval includes 0 means we cannot rule out the possibility that the survival rate is the same for both treatments. The other interval (−0.5, 7.90) also does not show a significant difference because it captures 0.

12.43 a. Take a nonrandom sample of students and randomly assign some to the reception and some to attend a "control group" meeting where they do something else (such as learn the history of the university). **b.** Take a random sample of students and offer them the choice of attending the reception or attending a "control group" meeting where they do something else. **c.** Take a random sample of students. Then randomly assign some of the students in this sample to the reception and some to the "control group" meeting.

12.45

1. They want to know whether low-dose vaccine is as effective as the regular dose.

2. It appears to be effective in people aged 18 to 60 but not for those above 60.

3. You cannot tell whether random assignment was used, because it was not mentioned in this excerpt.

4. Because we do not know the methods, we do not know whether the conclusion was appropriate.

5. Because there was no random sampling and we cannot tell whether there was random assignment, we cannot generalize beyond these subjects.

6. No other studies are mentioned, so this might be the first study of its kind.

12.47

1. Which method of teaching bioethics to surgical patients is more effective: a standardized patient (SP)–based seminar or a traditional seminar?

2. A traditional seminar is superior to an SP seminar.

3. Subjects were randomly assigned to attend one or the other of the two seminars. It does not appear that students were initially chosen at random.

4. Since random assignment was used, researchers may infer cause-and-effect.

5. Since it does not seem that participants were chosen at random, we cannot generalize the results beyond this group of students.

6. We cannot tell from the excerpt.

Chapter Review Exercises

12.49 a. The death rate before the vaccine was 18.1 deaths per 100,000 children. After the vaccine, the death rate fell to 11.8 deaths per 100,000 children. The difference is 6.3 fewer deaths per 100,000 children after the vaccine was introduced. The small p-value (less than 0.001) means we can reject the null hypothesis that the death rate was unchanged and conclude that the death rate decreased. **b.** Although there are many indications that the vaccine is successful, this was not a randomized study. We cannot rule out the possibility that a confounding variable, not the vaccine, caused the decrease in death rates. (For example, because the comparison was done using different years, there might have been a difference in weather that contributed to the difference in disease rates.)

CHAPTER 13

Section 13.1

13.1 *Step 1:* H_0: The median levels of lead in the blood are the same. H_A: The median level of lead in the blood is larger for the experimental group (one-tailed). *Step 2:* Sign test (paired). *Step 3:* $S = 28$ or $S = 4$, p-value < 0.001. *Step 4:* Reject H_0. The median level of lead in the blood was larger for the children in the experimental group.

13.3 a. The medians were 19 (for same) and 33.50 (for different). Yes, it tended to take longer for the different colours. **b.** *Step 1:* H_0: The medians are equal. H_A: Median time for same $<$ median time for different. *Step 2:* Sign test (paired). *Step 3:* $S = 1$ or 9, p-value $= 0.011$. *Step 4:* Reject H_0. The difference is significant.

13.5 *Step 1:* H_0: The medians are equal. H_A: The median pulse rate goes up (one-tailed). *Step 2:* Sign test (paired). *Step 3:* $S = 4$ or 5, p-value $= 0.500$. *Step 4:* Do not reject H_0. The median pulse rate did not go up significantly for men.

13.7 *Step 1:* H_0: The medians are equal. H_A: Median age for grooms $>$ median age for brides. *Step 2:* Sign test (paired). *Step 3:* $S = 10$ or 3, p-value $= 0.046$ from $b(13, 0.5, 3$ or fewer$)$. *Step 4:* Reject H_0. The median age for the grooms is significantly higher than the median age for the brides.

Section 13.2

13.9 a. The median for the ethicists was 4.5 meals per week, which is lower than the median for the control group (6.5). Typically, ethicists eat fewer meals with meat per week than nonethicists. **b.** *Step 1:* H_A: Median meals of meat per week of ethicists $<$ median of the control group. *Step 2:* Mann-Whitney test (independent). *Step 3:* $W = 198$, p-value $= 0.058$. *Step 4:* Do not reject H_0. We have not found a significant difference in behaviour.

13.11 *Step 1:* H_A: Median weight change for brushing $\neq$ median weight change for Calgon. *Step 2:* Mann-Whitney test (independent). *Step 3:* $W = 45$, p-value $= 0.541$. *Step 4:* The difference is not significant. We have not shown a difference between brushing and Calgon.

13.13 a. The sample median for waxed trays is smaller (faster descent) than the sample median for non-waxed trays. The results appear to support the students' hypothesis. **b.** *Step 1:* H_A: Median time for waxed trays $<$ median for non-waxed trays. *Step 2:* Mann-Whitney (assume it is valid). *Step 3:* $W = 108$, and p-value $= 0.0003$. *Step 4:* Reject H_0. The median time to reach the bottom of the hill is less with waxed trays than with non-waxed trays.

13.15 Steps 1 and 2 are given. *Step 3:* $W = 553$, and p-value $= 0.0138$. *Step 4:* Reject H_0. The rank order of food items is not the same for both diets.

Section 13.3

13.17 *Step 1:* H_A: The median sodium content is not the same for all three types of cereal. *Step 2:* We have random samples, independent observations of a numerical and continuous variable. We are told that the shapes and spreads of the three distributions are the same. Kruskal-Wallis is appropriate. *Step 3:* $H = 3.94$, and p-value $= 0.139$. *Step 4:* We fail to reject H_0. There is insufficient evidence to conclude that the median sodium content is not the same for all three types of cereal.

13.19 *Step 1:* H_A: The median highway fuel consumption is not the same for all three groups. *Step 2:* We have random samples from three independent groups (4, 6, and 8 cylinders), and the response variable is numerical and continuous; we are told to assume that the shapes of the distributions are the same. *Step 3:* $H = 20.69$, and p-value < 0.0001. *Step 4:* Reject H_0. There is sufficient evidence that the population median highway fuel consumption for cars with 4, 6, and 8 cylinders are not all the same.

13.21 *Step 1:* H_A: The median BMI is not the same for all four marital-status groups. *Step 2:* We have random samples from four independent groups, and the response variable is numerical and continuous; we are told to assume that the shapes of the distributions are the same. *Step 3:* $H = 13.10$, and p-value $= 0.004$. *Step 4:* Reject H_0. There is sufficient evidence that the population median BMI is not the same for all four marital-status groups.

13.23 *Step 1:* H_A: The median number of telephones is not the same for all population-centre sizes. *Step 2:* We are told to assume that the conditions required in order to perform a Kruskal-Wallis test for ordinal data are satisfied. *Step 3:* $H = 0.27$, and p-value $= 0.875$. *Step 4:* We fail to reject H_0. There is insufficient evidence to conclude that the median number of telephones is not the same for all population-centre sizes.

13.25 The p-value of 0.04 is lower than 0.05, so there is enough evidence to reject the null hypothesis that the median perceived body shape is the same for all four locations.

Section 13.4

13.27 a. The red line looks like it is pretty far out in the tail of the data and suggests visually that there is a real difference in extraversion between the sporty and the nonsporty students. **b.** The p-value is 0.012. **c.** We reject the null hypothesis and conclude that "sporty" students typically have a higher level of extraversion than "nonsporty" students. **d.** We could get an approximate p-value using the histogram, by finding the (approximate) proportion of observations to the right of the red vertical line.

13.29 a. The distributions are right-skewed, and the median is often a better choice for skewed data than the mean. **b.** 525 is not far out in the right-tail, so it is not unusually large. **c.** The one-tailed p-value is larger than 0.05, so the two-tailed p-value will be even larger. Do not reject H_0. The population median for the men has not been shown to be different from the population median for the women.

13.31 Choose 0.025 by looking at the graph, knowing the observed number is 368.9 acre-feet. Reject the null hypothesis. The mean rainfall is greater for the seeded clouds.

13.33 Explanation a

Section 13.5

13.35 You should have a random sample from the population.

13.37 The data should be drawn from Normal distributions, or the sample sizes should be large (typically at least 25 from each population). Observations must be independent of each other. The groups must be independent of each other.

13.39 a. Histogram 1 goes with (b), and 2 goes with (a). **b.** 1 is roughly bell-shaped (Normal), and 2 is right-skewed. **c.** Use a log transform on the data that are shown in histogram 2.

13.41 a. 1, 1.30, 2, 2.74, 3 **b.** 10 (because $10^1 = 10$), 31.62, 100, 1000, 1584.89

13.43 Don't worry if your numbers are a bit different because of rounding. **a.** 1, 2.447, 2.778, 4.176 **b.** 2.600 **c.** 398.11 **d.** Mean is 3972.5, median is 440.

Geometric Mean	Median	Mean
398	440	3972.5

13.45 a. We are 95% confident that the population mean of cash carried is between $6.28 and $19.66. **b.** (4.31, 11.83). We are 95% confident that the population geometric mean is between $4.31 and $11.83. The confidence interval for the geometric mean (from the logs) is narrower. **d.** The confidence interval for the geometric mean is more appropriate, because the distribution of the log-transformed data is more symmetric, and so the confidence level for the geometric mean will be more accurate. Also, we can get a more precise (smaller margin of error) estimate for the geometric mean than for the mean, based on this sample.

13.47 a. Right-skewed **b.** (4.04, 6.31) **c.** It is closer to Normal than the distribution of untransformed data. **d.** (0.515, 0.7025) **e.** (3.27, 5.04). We are 95% confident that the population geometric mean number of hours of exercise per week for all students at this college is between 3.27 hours and 5.04 hours. **f.** Answers may vary. The interval for the geometric mean is more precise (smaller margin of error), which suggests that the geometric mean might be a better measure of centre. On the other hand, the sample size is large, so both confidence intervals are valid and the population mean could also be used.

Chapter Review Exercises

13.49 a. Paired t-test or sign test **b.** Sign test **c.** Paired t-test or sign test

13.51 a. Two-sample t-test or Mann-Whitney test **b.** Mann-Whitney test

13.53 a. ANOVA or Kruskal-Wallis test **b.** Kruskal-Wallis test (if distributions have the same shape)

13.55 Step 0:

Obs	Null Value	Difference
55	56	−1
61	56	5
54	56	−2
52	56	−4
52	56	−4

1: H_0: The median number of Smarties is 56 (or the median difference is 0). H_A: The median number of Smarties is not 56 (or the median difference is not 0).

2: Use the one-sample sign test. The sample of Smarties boxes was random, so all pairs of observations are independent.

3: p-value = 0.375

4: Fail to reject H_0. There is insufficient evidence that the population median number of Smarties per box is not 56.

Why? We have a small sample and do not know whether the distribution is Normal or not.

CHAPTER 14

Section 14.1

14.1 Answers will vary. Some possibilities: the amount of time the student could study, the amount of sleep the student got the night before, the particular choice of questions on the exam, the noise level in the room, the health of the student.

14.3 a. The residual plot shows that the trend is not a straight line, so the linear condition fails. The linear model is not appropriate. **b.** The car that is four years old is the farthest from the regression line because its residual is the biggest (in absolute value).

14.5 The residual plot shows no clear trend and has no wedge shape. This would indicate that the constant standard deviation condition does hold and the linear model seems appropriate, so inferences (including confidence intervals and prediction intervals) would be appropriate.

14.7 The residual plot shows an increasing trend, and the QQ plot does not follow a straight line. Linear regression is inappropriate for this data set, because the linearity condition and the Normality condition fail.

Section 14.2

14.9 a. The slope (0.843) is positive, showing that the older people *in the sample* tended to weigh a bit more. **b.** *Step 1:* H_0: Slope = 0, H_A: Slope ≠ 0. *Step 2:* t-test for slope. *Step 3:* $t = 1.43$, p-value = 0.156. *Step 4:* There is a 0.156 probability of observing a more surprising outcome, if the null is true. Do not reject H_0. We do not have enough evidence to reject the hypothesis that the slope is 0. There is not a linear relationship between age and weight. **c.** We would expect the 95% CI for the slope to include zero. **d.** 95% CI for the slope is (−0.33, 2.02), which does capture 0.

14.11 a. The intercept is 2.78. If the intercept were 0, it would mean that if a mother had 0 years of education, then the father would be predicted also to have 0 years of education. **b.** *Step 1:* H_0: Intercept = 0, H_A: Intercept ≠ 0. *Step 2:* t-test for intercept. The conditions are assumed met. *Step 3:* $t = 2.00$, p-value = 0.056. *Step 4:* There is a 0.056 probability of observing a more surprising outcome, if the null is true. We cannot reject H_0. There is not enough evidence to reject an intercept of 0. **c.** *Step 1:* H_0: Slope = 0, H_A: Slope ≠ 0. *Step 2:* t-test for slope. The conditions are met. *Step 3:* $t = 4.30$, p-value < 0.0001. Reject H_0. *Step 4:* There is less than a 0.0001 probability of observing a more surprising outcome, if the null is true. Reject H_0. One can predict the years of education of the father based on the years of education of the mother. **d.** 95% CI for the slope is (0.333, 0.941).

14.13 a. 3.32. On average, a student who works zero hours per week at a part-time job will have a GPA of 3.32. **b.** The slope is −0.0176. On average, for each additional hour a student works at their part-time job, their GPA will decrease by 0.0176, in this sample. **c.** *Step 1:* H_0: Slope = 0. H_A: Slope ≠ 0. *Step 2:* We proceed with a t-test for the slope since all the conditions hold. *Step 3:* $t = -1.94$, p-value = 0.058. *Step 4:* There is a 0.058 probability of observing a more surprising outcome, if the null is true. Do not reject H_0. One cannot predict a student's first-year GPA based on the number of hours they work per week at a part-time job.

14.15 a. This is the y-intercept. A term mark of zero will result in an average final mark of 2.808. **b.** The estimated value of the slope is 0.9124. **c.** (0.801, 1.023). An increase in the term mark of 1% will result in an increase in the final exam mark by an average of somewhere between 0.801% and 1.023%. **d.** If the student's claim was true, the slope of the model would be 0 and the 95% CI for the slope would capture 0. From c, the lower bound is 0.801 and the upper bound is 1.023. The student's claim is not statistically supported.

14.17 a. Yes. The output shows that we cannot reject the null hypothesis that the intercept is 0 (because the p-value is 0.740, which is larger than 0.05). This means that the confidence interval will include 0 pounds of trash.

Section 14.3

14.19 A prediction interval, since she is estimating a single value of the response variable y, not a mean value.

14.21 A confidence interval, since they are estimating a mean value of the response variable y, not a single value.

14.23 a. $271,059 **b.** Prediction interval, because we are predicting the value for one house, not for the mean of a group of houses. **c.** ($160,581, $381,532) **d.** Yes, he can afford a house because he has access to enough money to pay for the price at the top of the 95% interval.

14.25 (About 57, about 87)

14.27 The green lines are prediction intervals (for individuals), and the red lines are confidence intervals (for means). Means tend to be more stable than individual measurements and give more precise results, which is why their intervals are narrower.

14.29 a. 95% PI (73.92, 118.99) or about (74, 119), and the 95% CI for the mean is (91.16, 101.75). The confidence interval for the mean is narrower because there is less variation in the prediction of the mean compared to the prediction of a single value. **b.** For all teams with a $65 million payroll, we can be 95% confident that the mean number of regular-season points is somewhere between 91.16 and 101.75. **c.** For one team with a $65 million payroll, we can be 95% confident that their regular-season point total will be somewhere between 73.92 and 118.99.

Chapter Review Exercises

14.31 a. See graph. The equation is

Longevity = 7.84 + 0.0327 Gestation

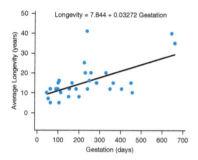

Longevity = 7.844 + 0.03272 Gestation

b. The hippopotamus is predicted to live about 10 years but lives over 40 years, on average.

c. CI is 13.92 to 19.18 years.

d. Humans do not fit into this pattern and are not included in the data set. The average human life expectancy is much more than the top of the confidence interval, which is 19.18 years.

14.33 a. The estimate of the model is HRtoAtBatRatio = 0.0395 + 0.004013Season.

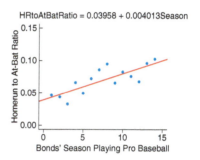

HRtoAtBatRatio = 0.03958 + 0.004013Season

b. Test if the slope of the model is zero. *Step 1:* H$_0$: Slope = 0. H$_A$: Slope ≠ 0. *Step 2:* We proceed with a *t*-test for the slope since all the conditions hold. *Step 3:* t = 4.52, p-value = 0.001. *Step 4:* There is a 0.001 probability of observing a more surprising outcome, if the null is true. Reject H$_0$. One can predict Bonds's home run to at-bat ratio based on the number of seasons he has played. **c.** 95% CI for the slope is (0.002, 0.006). For each additional season played, his home run to at-bat ratio will increase, on average, from 0.002 to 0.006. **d.** 95% PI is (0.06628, 0.13326). From this data we would predict Bonds' home run to at-bat ratio for the 2001 season to be somewhere between 0.06628 and 0.13326. **e.** (0.06628 × 476 = 31.55, 0.13326 × 476 = 63.43) **f.** Answers will vary.

Index

Clusters, 567–568
Cluster sampling, 567–568, 572
Coefficient of determination. See r^2
Comparison group, 13
Complement, probabilities and, 197
Conditional probabilities, 210–215
  finding, 212–213
  formula for, 213
  "given that" vs. AND, 211
Confidence intervals, 392, 432–435,
    652–656
  calculating, 411–413
  confidence level and, 322–323
  estimates for, 406–414, 422–425
  estimators and, 411
  finding when population proportion is
    not known, 324–325
  for independent samples, 422–425, 437
  interpretation of, 326
  for linear model, 628–630
  margin of error and, 321, 323–324
  one-sample t-test and, 454–455, 456, 458
  paired t-test and, 455, 458
  for population means, 406–414, 437
  for population parameters, 408, 412
  for population proportion, 321–328, 331,
    342–343
  prediction intervals and, 632
  sample size and, 328–329
  for slope, 628–630
  t-statistic and, 405
  two-sample t-test and, 455, 456, 458
  two-tailed alternative hypothesis and, 432
  for y-intercept, 628–630
Confidence level, 322–323, 407, 409–411
  margin of error and, 323, 411
  Normal distribution and, 423, 580
  random sample and, 423
Confounding variables, 15, 23, 556, 557
Constant, estimators for, 621–622
Context, 5–6
  correlation coefficient in, 137–139
  IQR in, 97–98
  mean in, 80
  median in, 94–95
  regression line in, 145–146
  SD in, 85–86
  z-scores in, 91–92
Continuous random variables, 244–245, 271
  areas under curves and, 247–252
  Normal probability model for, 249–262
Control group, 13, 16–17, 371, 562
Controlled experiments, 16–18
  blocking in, 559–564
  design of, 554–579
  extending results for, 19
  power in, 558–559
  sampling for, 554–579
  treatment groups in, 481
Controlling for a variable, 558

Convenience sample, 304
Correlation, 158–159, 187, 188, 189, 190, 191
Correlation coefficient
  calculation of, 139, 167
  causality and, 138–139, 158
  in context, 137–139
  linearity and, 142
  regression line slope and, 155
  scatterplots for, 136, 137
  for strength, 136–143
  trend and, 142
Crossover design, 564
Cumulative probabilities, 271

D

Data, 5–7
  for ANOVA, 513–520
  categorical variables and, 463, 492
  defined, 4
  graphs for, 32–75
  interactive displays for, 55
  stacked, 8, 9, 83–85
  statistics and, 2–31, 565
  storage of, 8–9
  transformation of, 13:6–14, 593
  unstacked data, 8
Data collection, 481
  causality and, 13–21
  surveys for, 4
Data dredging, 12:5–6
Data sets, 5, 9, 33–34
Degrees of freedom (df), 526
  chi-square distribution and, 469–470, 479
  for F-distribution, 526
  for t-distribution, 405–406, 411, 416, 430
Dependent observations, 562
Dependent samples, 421, 437, 562
Dependent variable, 151
Descriptive statistics, 5
Deterministic component, of statistical
    model, 612–613
Deviation, 86
df. See Degrees of freedom
Diaconnis, Persi, 195
Discrete random variables, 244–247,
    262–278
Distribution of data sets, 33–34
Distributions. See also specific types
  of binomial probability model, 265–266
  boxplots for, 104–106
  centre of, 39
  comparing with different-shapes, 103–104
  description of, 47
  F-statistic and, 525–527
  histograms of, 41, 43
  of sample, 33–34, 58
  shape of, 40–41, 100–101
  spread of, 40
  symmetric, 40, 78–83

typical value of, 40
  variability of, 39, 45–46
Dotplots, 34–35, 94
Double-blind studies, 17, 371

E

Empirical Rule, 88–90, 260–261, 319
Errors. See also Margin of error
  familywise error rate, 515–516
  variation due to, 522
Estimates
  bias and, 396
  for confidence intervals, 406–414, 422–425
  for mean differences, 422–425
  of population parameters, 304, 307, 395
  in surveys, 300, 307
Estimators, 621–622. See also Unbiased
    estimators
  bias and, 565
  confidence intervals and, 411
  population and, 565
  precision of, 565, 567
  SD of, 423, 565, 622
  simulations for, 308–313
  stratified sampling and, 567
  in surveys, 300, 307, 308–313, 565
Events. See also Independent events; Random
    events
  AND and, 200–201
  OR and, 202–203
  mutually exclusive, 203–205
  probabilities and, 197–226
  related, 215–226
  simulations of, 5:1–6
  tree diagrams for, 221–223
Excel
  for ANOVA, 552
  for bar chart, 73
  for binomial probability model, 294
  for boxplots, 127
  for chi-square test, 508–509
  for confidence interval of population
    proportion, 342
  for correlation, 189
  for descriptive statistics, 127
  for dotplot, 73
  entering data in, 73
  for geometric mean, 13:24
  for goodness-of-fit, 509
  for histogram, 73
  for inverse Normal values, 293–294
  for Kruskal-Wallis test, 606
  for log transform, 13:24
  for Mann-Whitney test, 606
  for Normal probability model, 293
  for one-proportion z-test, 391
  for one-sample t-test, 456
  for paired t-test, 456
  for QQ plots, 13:24

U

Unbiased estimators, 397, 565
  for *y*-intercept, 622
Unexplained variation, for ANOVA table, 521
Unimodal distribution, 42
  boxplots for, 107
  Empirical Rule for, 260, 261
Unstacked data, 8

V

Variability. *See also* Interquartile range; Range;
    Standard deviation; Variance; Variation
  of categorical distribution, 51–52
  of distributions, 39
  IQR and, 96–100
  of numerical distributions, 45–46
  range and, 100
  scatterplots for, 131–136
Variables. *See also specific types*
  categorical, 7
  confounding, 15
  continuous random, 244–245
  correlation coefficient for, 136–143
  in data sets, 5
  discrete random, 244–245
  numerical, 7, 244–245
  outcome, 13
  regression analysis for, 130–191
  response, 13
  in statistics, 5
  treatment, 13
  types of, 6–7

Variance. *See also* Analysis of variance
  calculation of, 78, 111
  Empirical Rule and, 88–90
  SD and, 87–88
Variation
  numerical summaries of, 76–129
  probabilities and, 192–241
  SD and, 83–88
  in statistics, 3
Variation due to error, 522
Variation due to treatment, 522
Venn diagram
  AND in, 200
  OR in, 202
  for conditional probabilities, 211
  for mutually exclusive events,
    203–204

W

Whiskers, 104, 105
Without Normal distribution, statistical
    inference, 580–609
Without replacement, 200, 276, 305,
    308–317, 354

X

x-variable
  regression line and, 151
  regression line slope and, 155
  SD and, 635
  y-variable and, 623

Y

y-intercept
  confidence intervals for, 628–630
  estimators for, 621–622
  hypothesis testing for, 622–628, 641
  linearity and, 634
  for regression line, 144, 146, 147,
    157, 167
  unbiased estimator for, 622
y-variable
  estimators for, 622
  regression line and, 151
  regression line slope and, 155
  residuals and, 614
  x-variable and, 623

Z

z-scores
  calculation of, 92, 111
  in context, 91
  percentiles and, 260
  probability distributions and, 255–256
  SD and, 91–93, 255–256, 260
  standard Normal model and, 255–256
z-test. *See also* One-proportion *z*-test
  independent samples and, 480
z-test statistic, 349–350. *See also* Two-
    proportion *z*-test
  one-proportion, 364, 377
  one-sample *t*-test and, 415
  two-proportion, 366, 370, 377